Safety Symbols

These symbols appear in laboratory activities. They warn of possible dangers in the laboratory and remind you to work carefully.

 Safety Goggles Wear safety goggles to protect your eyes in any activity involving chemicals, flames or heating, or glassware.

 Lab Apron Wear a laboratory apron to protect your skin and clothing from damage.

 Breakage Handle breakable materials, such as glassware, with care. Do not touch broken glassware.

 Heat-Resistant Gloves Use an oven mitt or other hand protection when handling hot materials such as hot plates or hot glassware.

 Plastic Gloves Wear disposable plastic gloves when working with harmful chemicals and organisms. Keep your hands away from your face, and dispose of the gloves according to your teacher's instructions.

 Heating Use a clamp or tongs to pick up hot glassware. Do not touch hot objects with your bare hands.

 Flames Before you work with flames, tie back loose hair and clothing. Follow instructions from your teacher about lighting and extinguishing flames.

 No Flames When using flammable materials, make sure there are no flames, sparks, or other exposed heat sources present.

 Corrosive Chemical Avoid getting acid or other corrosive chemicals on your skin or clothing or in your eyes. Do not inhale the vapors. Wash your hands after the activity.

 Poison Do not let any poisonous chemical come into contact with your skin, and do not inhale its vapors. Wash your hands when you are finished with the activity.

 Fumes Work in a ventilated area when harmful vapors may be involved. Avoid inhaling vapors directly. Only test an odor when directed to do so by your teacher, and use a wafting motion to direct the vapor toward your nose.

 Sharp Object Scissors, scalpels, knives, needles, pins, and tacks can cut your skin. Always direct a sharp edge or point away from yourself and others.

 Animal Safety Treat live or preserved animals or animal parts with care to avoid harming the animals or yourself. Wash your hands when you are finished with the activity.

 Plant Safety Handle plants only as directed by your teacher. If you are allergic to certain plants, tell your teacher; do not do an activity involving those plants. Avoid touching harmful plants such as poison ivy. Wash your hands when you are finished with the activity.

 Electric Shock To avoid electric shock, never use electrical equipment around water, or when the equipment is wet or your hands are wet. Be sure cords are untangled and cannot trip anyone. Unplug equipment not in use.

 Physical Safety When an experiment involves physical activity, avoid injuring yourself or others. Alert your teacher if there is any reason you should not participate.

 Disposal Dispose of chemicals and other laboratory materials safely. Follow the instructions from your teacher.

 Hand Washing Wash your hands thoroughly when finished with the activity. Use antibacterial soap and warm water. Rinse well.

 General Safety Awareness When this symbol appears, follow the instructions provided. When you are asked to develop your own procedure in a lab, have your teacher approve your plan before you go further.

PRENTICE HALL Science Explorer

Indiana Grade 7

PEARSON

Prentice
Hall

Upper Saddle River, New Jersey
Needham, Massachusetts

PRENTICE HALL Science Explorer
Grade 7

Grade-Specific Resources
Indiana Student Edition
Indiana Interactive Textbook
Indiana Teacher's Edition
Indiana All-in-One Teaching Resources
Indiana Guided Reading and Study Workbook
Indiana Student Edition on Audio CD
Indiana Laboratory Manual
Progress-Monitoring Assessment Blackline Masters
Test Practice Student Workbook
Discovery Channel Video
Lab Activity Video
Consumable and Nonconsumable Materials Kits

Program Print Resources
Integrated Science Laboratory Manual
Computer Microscope Lab Manual
Inquiry Skills Activity Books
Test-Taking Tips With Transparencies
Teacher's ELL Handbook
Reading in the Content Area

Program Technology Resources
Indiana Teacher Express™ CD-ROM
Indiana Interactive Textbook
Indiana ExamView®, Computer Test Bank CD-ROM
Presentation Pro CD-ROM
Lab zone™ Easy Planner CD-ROM
Student Edition Worksheet Library CD-ROM
Probeware Lab Manual With CD-ROM
Computer Microscope and Lab Manual
Materials Ordering CD-ROM
Discovery Channel DVD Library
Lab Activity DVD Library
Web Site at PHSchool.com

Acknowledgments appear on p. 862, which constitutes an extension of this copyright page.

Cover
Top: Indiana Dunes National Lakeshore, Lake Michigan
Bottom: Competitive kayaker

PEARSON
Prentice Hall

ISBN 0-13-125990-3
1 2 3 4 5 6 7 8 9 10   07 06 05 04

INDIANA

Indiana Program Advisors

Teachers from around the State of Indiana gave Prentice Hall feedback on how to shape our science programs for your success! Your teacher's colleagues are listed below.

Middle School Program Advisors

Paul Boyle
Science Teacher
Perry Heights Middle School
Evansville, Indiana

Deborah Garrett
Middle School Curriculum Chair
Scribner Middle School
New Albany, Indiana

J.D. Hartshorn Jr.
Science Teacher
John Marshall Middle School
Indianapolis, Indiana

Sugar Keedy
Science Department Chair
Eastwood Middle School
Indianapolis, Indiana

Rosana Pape
Science Teacher
Blackhawk Middle School
Fort Wayne, Indiana

Leslie Rector
Science Department Chair
Fall Creek Valley Middle School
Indianapolis, Indiana

Janet Sharp
Science Teacher
Shortridge Middle School
Indianapolis, Indiana

Elizabeth Swayze
Science Teacher
Belzer Middle School
Indianapolis, Indiana

High School Program Advisors

Franklin Bynum
Science Department Chair
Warren Central High School
Indianapolis, Indiana

Roy Connor
Science Department Chair
Muncie Central High School
Muncie, Indiana

Loyce Fandrei
Science Department Chair
Gavit High School
Hammond, Indiana

Michael E. Lankert
Science Department Chair
New Albany High School
New Albany, Indiana

Kevin Leineweber
Science Teacher
Tippecanoe School Corporation
Lafayette, Indiana

Timothy Ricker
Science Department Chair
Broad Ripple High School
Indianapolis, Indiana

Jean Schick
Science Department Chair
Blomington High School North
Bloomington, Indiana

Elvia Solis
Science Department Chair
Arlington High School
Indianapolis, Indiana

Bryan Trippeer
Science Teacher
Crown Point High School
Crown Point, Indiana

Program Authors

Michael J. Padilla, Ph.D.
Professor of Science Education
University of Georgia
Athens, Georgia

Michael Padilla is a leader in middle school science education. He has served as an author and elected officer for the National Science Teachers Association and as a writer of the National Science Education Standards. As lead author of Science Explorer, Mike has inspired the team in developing a program that meets the needs of middle grades students, promotes science inquiry, and is aligned with the National Science Education Standards.

Ioannis Miaoulis, Ph.D.
President
Museum of Science
Boston, Massachusetts

Originally trained as a mechanical engineer, Ioannis Miaoulis is in the forefront of the national movement to increase technological literacy. As dean of the Tufts University School of Engineering, Dr. Miaoulis spearheaded the introduction of engineering into the Massachusetts curriculum. Currently he is working with school systems across the country to engage students in engineering activities and to foster discussions on the impact of science and technology on society.

Martha Cyr, Ph.D.
Director of K–12 Outreach
Worcester Polytechnic Institute
Worcester, Massachusetts

Martha Cyr is a noted expert in engineering outreach. She has over nine years of experience with programs and activities that emphasize the use of engineering principles, through hands-on projects, to excite and motivate students and teachers of mathematics and science in grades K–12. Her goal is to stimulate a continued interest in science and mathematics through engineering.

Book Authors

Andrew C. Kemp, Ph.D.
Assistant Professor of Education
University of Louisville
Louisville, Kentucky

John G. Little
Science Teacher
St. Mary's High School
Stockton, California

Beth Miaoulis
Technology Writer
Sherborn, Massachusetts

Steve Miller
Science Writer
State College, Pennsylvania

Jay M. Pasachoff, Ph.D.
Professor of Astronomy
Williams College
Williamstown, Massachusetts

Carole Garbuny Vogel
Science Writer
Lexington, Massachusetts

Thomas Wellnitz
Science Instructor
The Paideia School
Atlanta, Georgia

Consultants

Reading Consultant

Nancy Romance, Ph.D.
Professor of Science
  Education
Florida Atlantic University
Fort Lauderdale, Florida

Mathematics Consultant

William Tate, Ph.D.
Professor of Education and
  American Culture Studies
Washington University
St. Louis, Missouri

Tufts University Content Reviewers

Faculty from Tufts University in Medford, Massachusetts, participated in the development of *Science Explorer* chapter projects, reviewed the student books for content accuracy, and helped coordinate field testing.

Astier M. Almedom, Ph.D.
Department of Biology

Wayne Chudyk, Ph.D.
Department of Civil and Environmental Engineering

John Durant, Ph.D.
Department of Civil and Environmental Engineering

George S. Ellmore, Ph.D.
Department of Biology

David Kaplan
Department of Chemical Engineering

Samuel Kounaves, Ph.D.
Department of Chemistry

David H. Lee, Ph.D.
Department of Chemistry

Doug Matson, Ph.D.
Department of Mechanical Engineering

Karen Panetta, Ph.D.
Department of Electrical Engineering and Computer Science

John C. Ridge, Ph.D.
Department of Geology

William Waller, Ph.D.
Department of Astronomy

Content Reviewers

Jeff Bodart, Ph.D.
Chipola Junior College
Marianna, Florida

Michael Castellani, Ph.D.
Department of Chemistry
Marshall University
Huntington, West Virginia

Eugene Chiang, Ph.D.
Department of Astronomy
University of California–Berkeley
Berkeley, California

Charles C. Curtis, Ph.D.
Department of Physics
University of Arizona
Tucson, Arizona

Daniel Kirk-Davidoff, Ph.D.
Department of Meteorology
University of Maryland
College Park, Maryland

Diane Doser, Ph.D.
Department of Geological Sciences
University of Texas at El Paso
El Paso, Texas

Richard Duhrkopf, Ph.D.
Department of Biology
Baylor University
Waco, Texas

Michael Hacker
Co-director, Center for Technological Literacy
Hofstra University
Hempstead, New York

Michael W. Hamburger, Ph.D.
Department of Geological Sciences
Indiana University
Bloomington, Indiana

Alice Hankla, Ph.D.
The Galloway School
Atlanta, Georgia

Donald Jackson, Ph.D.
Department of Molecular Pharmacology, Physiology, & Biotechnology
Brown University
Providence, Rhode Island

Jeremiah Jarrett, Ph.D.
Department of Biological Sciences
Central Connecticut State University
New Britain, Connecticut

Becky Mansfield, Ph.D.
Department of Geography
Columbus, Ohio

Joe McCullough, Ph.D.
Department of Natural and Applied Sciences
Cabrillo College
Aptos, California

Robert J. Mellors, Ph.D.
Department of Geological Sciences
San Diego State University
San Diego, California

Joseph M. Moran, Ph.D.
American Meteorological Society
Washington, D.C.

David J. Morrissey, Ph.D.
Department of Chemistry
Michigan State University
East Lansing, Michigan

Philip A. Reed, Ph.D.
Department of Occupational & Technical Studies
Old Dominion University
Norfolk, Virginia

Scott M. Rochette, Ph.D.
Department of Earth Sciences
State University of New York, College at Brockport
Brockport, New York

Laurence D. Rosenheim, Ph.D.
Department of Chemistry
Indiana State University
Terre Haute, Indiana

Ronald Sass, Ph.D.
Department of Ecology & Evolutionary Biology
Rice University
Houston, Texas

George Schatz, Ph.D.
Department of Chemistry
Northwestern University
Evanston, Illinois

Sara Seager, Ph.D.
Carnegie Institution of Washington
Washington, D.C.

John R. Villarreal, Ph.D.
College of Science and Engineering
The University of Texas–Pan American
Edinburg, Texas

Kenneth Welty, Ph.D.
School of Education
University of Wisconsin–Stout
Stout, Wisconsin

Edward J. Zalisko, Ph.D.
Department of Biology
Blackburn College
Carlinville, Illinois

Contents

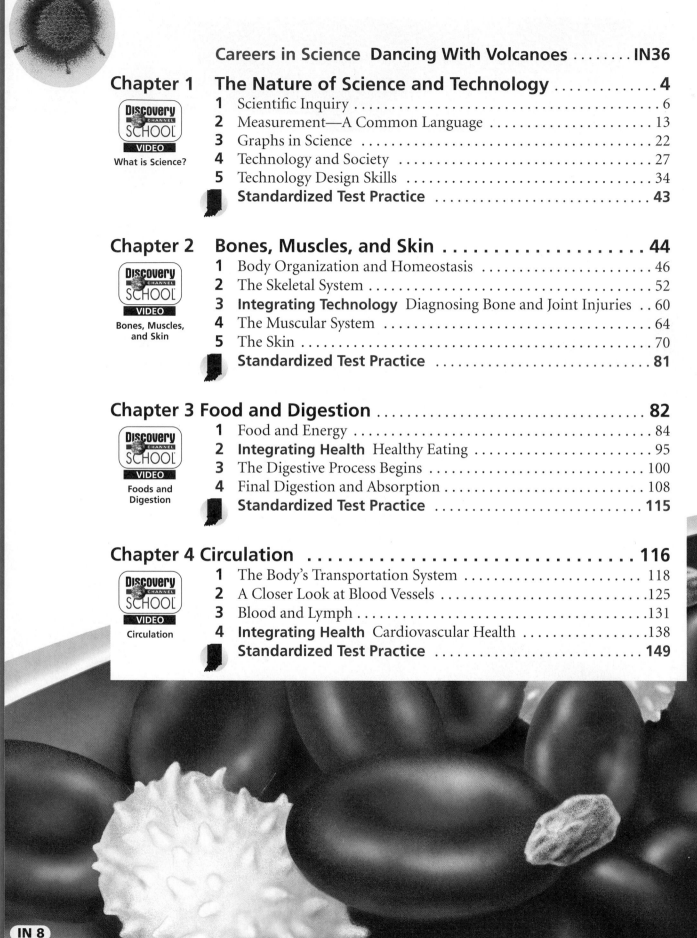

Contents

INDIANA

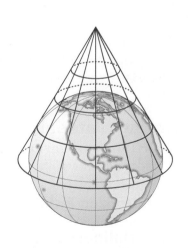

Contents

VIDEO

Enhance understanding through dynamic video.

Preview Get motivated with this introduction to the chapter content.

Field Trip Explore a real-world story related to the chapter content.

Assessment Review content and take an assessment.

Web Links

Get connected to exciting Web resources in every lesson.

SciLINKS® Find Web links on topics relating to every section.

Active Art Interact with selected visuals from every chapter online.

Planet Diary® Explore news and natural phenomena through weekly reports.

Science News® Keep up to date with the latest science discoveries.

Interactive Textbook

Experience the complete textbook online and on CD-ROM.

Activities Practice skills and learn content.

Videos Explore content and learn important lab skills.

Audio Support Hear key terms spoken and defined.

Self-Assessment Use instant feedback to help you track your progress.

Activities

Lab zone Try This **Activity** IN Standard 2 Scientific Thinking

Lab zone Skills **Activity** IN Standard 5 The Mathematical World

Activities

Lab zone At-Home **Activity** — IN Standard 1 The Nature of Science and Technology

• Tech & Design • — IN Standard 1 The Nature of Science and Technology

active art ▶ Illustrations come alive online

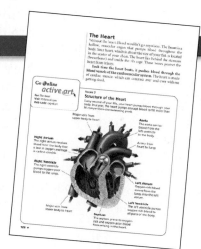

Activities

Indiana Academic Standards

Indiana organizes the science information you will learn into seven standards. Following you'll find this information summarized for you. Each standard is further divided into several numbered statements, or indicators, that give more detail. Use the Standards Checkpoints that follow to check your mastery of the standards.

INDIANA CONNECTION

The Indiana Department of Environmental Management (IDEM) uses many tools to protect people and the environment from the toxic materials in contaminated land. IDEM scientists may test samples from contaminated sites, make maps and computer models of how these sites, or perform experiments to test ways of cleaning up or sealing off the toxic materials.

Standard 1 The Nature of Science and Technology

Students learn more about the natural world through labs, projects, classroom activities, and readings. Students use different scientific methods to solve practical problems.

7.1.1 Recognize that when similar experiments give different results, more research may be needed.

7.1.2 Explain that what people expect to observe often affects what they do observe.

7.1.3 Explain the importance of keeping honest, clear, and accurate records.

7.1.4 Describe how further study can help scientists choose among different explanations for the same evidence.

7.1.5 Identify important contributions to science, mathematics, and technology by people of different cultures and times.

7.1.6 Provide examples of people who overcame adversity to excel in the fields of science.

7.1.7 Explain how people use science to solve practical problems in design and technology.

7.1.8 Describe some benefits and drawbacks to technology, such as a technology that helps some organisms but hurts others.

7.1.9 Explain how societies influence what types of technology are developed and used.

7.1.10 Identify ways that technology influences the course of history.

7.1.11 Illustrate how numbers can be represented by sequences of only two symbols and how that affects the storage of information.

Where You Will Find It
Chapter 1; Chapter 3, Section 1; Chapter 7, Section 3; Chapter 9, Section 2; Chapter 17; Section 4

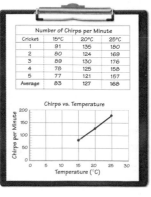

Standard 2 Scientific Thinking

Students use various tools for measuring and calculating. They use math and numbers to draw conclusions from their data whenever possible. Students discuss and debate how data should be interpreted and understand that there may be more than one reasonable way to interpret the same data.

7.2.1 Find what percentage one number is of another. Find any percentage of any number.
7.2.2 Use formulas to calculate the circumference, area, and volume of various shapes.
7.2.3 Use the precision of original data to determine the precision and significant digits of a calculated value.
7.2.4 Express numbers such as 10, 100, and 1,000 as powers of 10.
7.2.5 Estimate probabilities of outcomes based on experience or the number of possible outcomes.
7.2.6 Measure length, volume, weight, elapsed time, rates, or temperatures, and choose appropriate units.
7.2.7 Use graphs, diagrams, and symbols in writing to provide evidence for conclusions.
7.2.8 Question claims based on statements that are vague or made by people speaking outside their area of expertise.

Where You Will Find It

Chapter 2, Section 3; Chapter 7, Section 1 and 3; Chapter 10; Chapter 12, Section 3; Chapter 16; Chapter 17, Sections 2 and 4

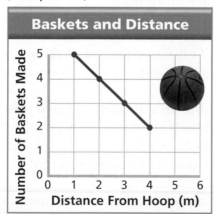

Baskets and Distance

Number of Baskets Made — Distance From Hoop (m)

Standard 3 The Physical Setting

Students collect and organize data. They use these data to identify relationships between physical objects, events, and processes. Students think logically about their data and question their ideas about the natural world.

7.3.1 Recognize that the sun is a star located near the edge of a galaxy. The universe contains billions of galaxies. Each galaxy contains billions of stars.
7.3.2 Recognize that the sun is much closer to Earth than any other star. Sunlight reaches Earth much sooner than the light of other stars.

7.3.3 Describe how changes in Earth's crust sometimes changed climates abruptly.

7.3.4 Explain how heat flow and movement within Earth cause earthquakes and volcanic eruptions and create mountains and ocean basins.

7.3.5 Explain how heat carried by ocean currents influences climate.

7.3.6 Describe how gas and dust from volcanoes change the atmosphere.

7.3.7 Give examples of abrupt and very slow changes in Earth's surface.

7.3.8 Describe how sediments are buried and bonded together by dissolved minerals to form solid rock.

7.3.9 Explain that pressure and heat can change deeply buried sedimentary rock. These rock layers may become land surface, and subsequently erode.

7.3.10 Explain how layers of sedimentary rock can show the history of the Earth's surface and life forms. The youngest layers are not always found on top.

7.3.11 Explain that the sun loses energy by giving off light. A small part of that light reaches Earth with a wide range of wavelengths.

7.3.12 Investigate how the temperature and acidity of a solution influence reaction rates.

7.3.13 Explain that many substances dissolve in water. These substances can affect the rates of reactions in the water.

7.3.14 Explain that heat is almost always one of the products of an energy transformation.

7.3.15 Describe various ways that electrical energy can be produced and transformed into other forms of energy.

7.3.16 Recognize that different ways of obtaining, transforming, and distributing energy have different impacts on the environment.

7.3.17 Investigate how an unbalanced force affects an object's speed and path. If the force always acts toward the same point, the object's path may curve into an orbit.

7.3.18 Describe that waves move at different speeds in different materials.

7.3.19 Explain that human eyes see a narrow part of the electromagnetic spectrum.

7.3.20 Describe that seeing occurs when light waves enter the eye, just as sound is heard when sound waves enter the ear.

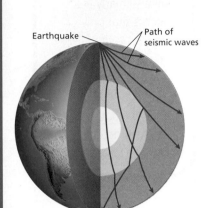

Earthquake — Path of seismic waves

Where You Will Find It

Standard 4 The Living Environment

Students describe how matter and energy flow through ecosystems. They recognize how differences between plant and animal cells are responsible for the main differences between plants and animals. Students use differences in structure and function to tell species apart. They use microscopes to observe cells and recognize that the cells of all organisms function in similar ways.

7.4.1 Explain that similarities among organisms in anatomy and at the cellular level are used to classify organisms.

7.4.2 Describe that all organisms are part of and depend on the ocean food web or the land food web.

7.4.3 Describe how a fertilized egg carries genetic information from each parent and forms a new organism.

7.4.4 Explain that cells constantly divide to make more cells for growth and repair. Various organs and tissues provide cells with food, air, and waste removal.

7.4.5 Explain that the basic functions of all organisms occur in similar ways within cells.

7.4.6 Explain how food provides fuel and the building material for all organisms.

7.4.7 Describe how plants make their own food.

7.4.8 Describe how plant-eating organisms break down plant structures to obtain the materials and energy that they need. These organisms are consumed by other organisms.

7.4.9 Understand that one or more environmental factors control population growth.

7.4.10 Describe how technologies used in food production, sanitation, and disease prevention have changed how people live and the growth of human population.

7.4.11 Explain that the amount of food energy a person needs depends on weight, age, sex, activity, and efficiency. Exercise is important to health.

7.4.12 Explain that parasites can cause disease. A person can catch a cold many times because there are many different cold viruses.

7.4.13 Explain that white blood cells fight invaders. Antibodies produced by white blood cells can fight off subsequent invaders of the same kind.

7.4.14 Explain that the environment may contain dangerous levels of harmful substances. Public health requires monitoring of soil, air, and water quality.

Where You Will Find It
Chapter 12 Interdisciplinary Exploration; Chapter 15; Chapter 16; Chapter 17; Chapter 19, Sections 1 and 2

INDIANA CONNECTION

Dairy farmers in north-western Indiana grow corn and soybean plants to feed to their cattle. These plants capture and store energy form sunlight, and absorb nutrients from the soil. Cows obtain energy and nutrients by eating the plants and give up energy and nutrients in the form of milk. The farmers send part of the milk to a factory in Fair Oaks to be made into cheese. People who eat the cheese receive energy that the plants captured from sunlight, and nutrients that these plants absorbed from soil.

Companies in Indianapolis, Mishiwaka, and Richmond produce gears and other metal parts that are used in cars, aircraft, and medical instruments. Poorly made parts do not fit together well, and can endanger passengers and patients. Quality-control workers calculate the average sizes of parts and the risk that a part will be too big or small. The workers compare this risk to the cost of measuring the parts to decide what percentage of the parts the workers need to measure.

Standard 5 The Mathematical World
Students use math to describe and analyze data.

7.5.1 Demonstrate how negative numbers are shown and used on a number line.

7.5.2 Illustrate parallel, perpendicular, or oblique lines.

7.5.3 Demonstrate how the scale of a graph or drawing affects its interpretation.

7.5.4 Describe that large, well-chosen samples can accurately represent the whole.

Where You Will Find It
Chapter 1, Sections 1 and 3; Skills Handbook

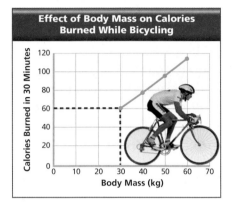

INDIANA CONNECTION

Before 1977, scientists divided living things into two main groups— bacteria and all other living things. In 1977, scientist Carl Woese proposed a third group. Many scientists rejected Woese's conclusions because he used a new kind of experiment. Scientists at Indiana University in Bloomington performed experiments that helped to confirm Woese's ideas.

Standard 6 Historical Perspectives
Students learn how science works through historical examples. By studying these examples, they learn that new ideas depend on the time and place in which they occur. New scientific ideas are often rejected by scientists and sometimes come from unexpected observations. Ideas grow or change slowly as many scientists discuss the ideas and perform experiments to test them.

7.6.1 Describe old explanations for disease and the discovery that diseases are caused by microorganisms.

7.6.2 Explain how Louis Pasteur discovered that microorganisms can spoil food or cause diseases. Microorganisms can also be useful. Specific kinds of germs cause specific diseases.

7.6.3 Explain that Louis Pasteur found that infection causes immunity to future infection by the same organism, and that a vaccine can provide immunity without causing disease.

7.6.4 Describe how the germ theory of disease led to sanitation, pasteurization of milk, quarantine, clean surgery, vaccination, and antibiotics.

Where You Will Find It
Chapter 6

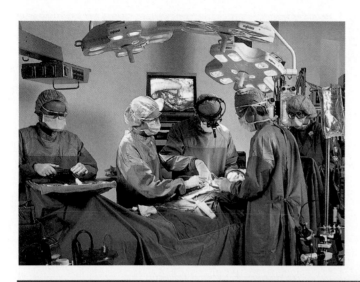

Standard 7 Common Themes

Students analyze how systems keep themselves in balance. They investigate how different models can represent the same data, and make graphs to show how changes in one thing cause changes in another.

7.7.1 Explain that the output from one part of a system can become the input to other parts, and that this can control the whole system.
7.7.2 Use different models to represent the same thing, noting that the model's type and complexity depend on its purpose.
7.7.3 Describe how systems usually change until they reach equilibrium, and remain that way unless their surroundings change.
7.7.4 Use equations to show a change over time or in response to changes in other variables.

Where You Will Find It
Chapter 4; Chapter 5; Chapter 6, Section 4; Chapter 15, Section 1; Chapter 18, Section 3; Chapter 20, Section 3

INDIANA CONNECTION

Building heaters made in LaPorte and the electric power plant in Schererville each have automatic controls to keep them working smoothly. Heaters have thermostats that turn the heater on and off to keep the temperature in the comfortable range. Power plants have systems that measure and adjust how much power the plant produces to match the needs of users.

Standards Checkpoint 1

Use after Chapter 4.
For help, go to the section in red.

1 The Nature of Science and Technology

1. **Which of the following is true of scientific theories? (Chapter 1)**

   A They are always true.

   B They are unchangeable.

   C They are unchallenged.

   D They are open to revision.

2. **Which statement can NOT be tested in a scientific way? (Chapter 1)**

   A Animal research to study cancer is immoral.

   B Animal research can help study cancer.

   C Experiments with animals can help find new medicines.

   D Experiments with animals have found causes for diseases.

3. **Describe how a person from a different culture has contributed to scientific knowledge. (Chapter 1)**

2 Scientific Thinking

Use the information below to answer questions 4 through 6.

Jeff wanted to find out whether the type of food given to fish affected their growth. He obtained two different tanks and placed one fish in each tank. He measured the growth after one month. Below is a table that contains his results:

Tank	Type of Fish	Volume of tank (L)	Food Type	Fish Growth (cm)
A	Goldfish	50	Shrimp	0.9
B	Beta	100	Algae	2.1

4. **Which variables were different in tanks A and B? (Chapter 2, Section 3)**

5. **What were the variables in Jeff's experiment? (Chapter 2, Section 3)**

6. **Jeff concluded that fish that are fed algae grow faster than fish that are fed shrimp. Do you think Jeff's conclusion is valid? Use facts about Jeff's experiment to support your answer. (Chapter 2, Section 3)**

5 The Mathematical World

7. Graphs of data can be used to _____. (Chapter 1, Section 1)

A replace missing data

B detect patterns in data

C prove a hypothesis correct

D plan the experiment

8. A sample for an experiment on a group of animals should include _____. (Chapter 1, Section 1)

A all the animals in the group

B a certain number of the animals

C one typical animal

D a certain percentage of the animals

9. Use the example of temperature to explain how it is possible for a measurement to be a negative number. (Chapter 1, Section 1)

7 Common Themes

Use the information below to answer questions 10 and 11.

The graph below shows how average blood pressure, measured when the ventricles contract, changes as men and women grow older.

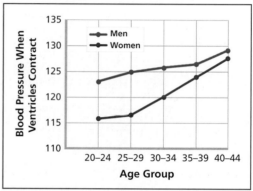

Changes in Blood Pressure

10. What does the graph indicate about the effect of age on people's blood pressure? (Chapter 2, Sections 3 and 4)

A Blood pressure increases as people get older.

B Blood pressure decreases as people get older

C Blood pressure increases and then decreases as people get older.

D Blood pressure does not change as people get older.

11. What factors does the graph indicate have important effects on blood pressure? (Chapter 2, Sections 3 and 4)

A age and sex

B age only

C sex only

D neither age nor sex

12. Describe how your heartbeat is regulated. (Chapter 4, Section 1)

3 The Physical Setting

1. Describe and explain how seeing occurs when light waves enter the eye. (Chapter 7, Section 3; Chapter 8, Section 3)

Use the information below to answer question 2.

The diagram below shows two plates of the Earth's crust colliding.

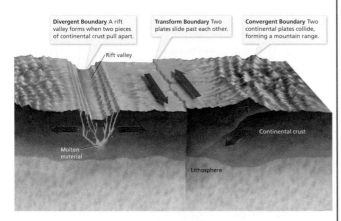

Divergent Boundary A rift valley forms when two pieces of continental crust pull apart.

Transform Boundary Two plates slide past each other.

Convergent Boundary Two continental plates collide, forming a mountain range.

Rift valley

Continental crust

Molten material

Lithosphere

2. Describe the process illustrated above. (Chapter 8, Section 3)

  A A mountain range is being formed at a convergent boundary.

  B A mountain range is being formed at a transform boundary.

  C A volcano is being formed at a divergent boundary.

  D A volcano is being formed at a transform boundary.

3. Which of the following changes is caused by sea-floor spreading? (Chapter 7, Section 3; Chapter 8, Section 3)

  A erosion

  B continental drift

  C global warming

  D rift valley formation

4 The Living Environment

4. Which of the following may infect the body and cause a disease? (Chapter 6, Sections 1, 2, and 3)

  A bacteria, fungi, vaccines, and antibiotics

  B viruses, parasites, lymphocytes, and B cells

  C viruses, bacteria, fungi, and parasites

  D lymphocytes, phagocytes, B cells, and T cells

5. Imagine that you are hiking with a friend. You come across a creek and your friend wants to fill his canteen with some of the creek's water. Explain to your friend why it is not safe to drink water from the creek. (Chapter 6, Sections 1, 2, and 3)

Use the diagram below to answer question 6.

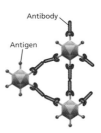

Antigen

Virus

Antibody

Antigen

6. In the figure above, which structure is a protein produced by a B cell? (Chapter 6, Sections 1, 2, and 3)

  A the virus

  B the antigen

  C the antibody

  D none of the above

7. **Why did most geologists initially reject Alfred Wegener's theory of continental drift? (Chapter 8, Section 5)**

   A He did not give evidence of how climates changed.

   B He could not explain how continents drifted.

   C He could not explain the distribution of fossils.

   D He did not give evidence of land features on different continents.

8. **Which would spoil faster, a bottle of milk in the refrigerator or a bottle of milk left on the counter? Explain your answer. (Chapter 6, Section 1)**

9. **Which of the following scientists discovered that killing the microorganisms that caused a certain kind of disease could prevent the spread of that disease? (Chapter 6, Section 1)**

   A Louis Pasteur

   B Robert Koch

   C Joseph Lister

   D John Snow

Use the information below to answer question 10.

The graph below shows the average daily water loss in humans.

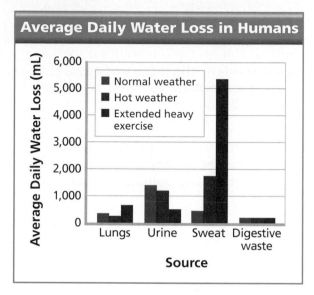

10. **What is the relationship between sweat and urine? (Chapter 5, Section 3)**

    A As a person sweats more, they urinate less.

    B As a person sweats less, they urinate less.

    C A person only sweats in hot weather.

    D There is no relationship between sweat and urine.

11. **Explain how the excretory system changes until it reaches equilibrium, and remains that way until the equilibrium is disturbed. (Chapter 5, Section 3)**

Standards Checkpoint 3

Use after Chapter 12
For help, go to the section in red.

1 The Nature of Science and Technology

1. Describe briefly the history of advancements in metal technology. (Chapter 10, Section 3; Chapter 12, Section 2)

2. Which of the following properties of minerals can be determined by first finding a mineral's mass and volume? (Chapter 10, Section 1)

   A hardness

   B luster

   C streak

   D density

3. Miami, Florida is located at latitude 25° 46 min. N and longitude 80° 12 min. W. What would a reasonable coordinate be for Seattle, Washington? (Chapter 12, Section 2)

   A 47° 37 min N, 65° 18 min W

   B 47° 37 min S, 122° 20 min E

   C 47° 37 min N, 122° 20 min W

   D 18° 25 min N, 122° 20 min W

2 Scientific Thinking

4. The appropriate unit for measuring volume is_____. (Chapter 10, Sections 1 and 3)

   A cm

   B cm^2

   C cm^3

   D gm

5. A graduated cylinder contains a quartz crystal immersed in 85 mL of water. The meniscus of the water above the crystal reads 110 mL. What is the volume of the quartz crystal? (Chapter 10, Sections 1 and 3)

   A 20 mL   C 30 mL

   B 25 mL   D 50 mL

6. Calculate the density of an apatite crystal that has a volume of 24 cm^3 and a mass of 15 g. (Chapter 10, Sections 1 and 3)

3 The Physical Setting

Use the information below to answer questions 7 and 8.

The diagram below illustrates one of the types of stresses that occur in the Earth's crust.

7. **Examine the diagram above. What form of stress is illustrated? (Chapter 9, Section 1)**

   A compression   C shearing

   B tension   D folding

8. **The form of stress shown above typically leads to _____. (Chapter 9, Sections 1 and 2)**

   A earthquakes

   B volcanic eruptions

   C mountain range formation

   D compression

9. **Describe how sediments of sand and smaller particles are buried and are bonded together by dissolved minerals to form solid rock again. (Chapter 11, Sections 3 and 6)**

7 Common Themes

Use the information below to answer question 10.

The diagram below illustrates two of the types of waves that occur during earthquakes.

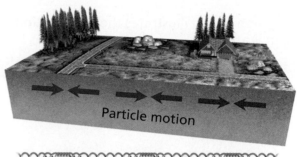

Particle motion

Direction of waves ⟶

10. **What kind of wave is modeled in the diagram? (Chapter 9, Section 2)**

    A P wave   C Both P and S waves

    B S wave   D Neither P nor S waves

11. **A plate traveled 2 million years at a speed of 6.0×10^{-5} km/yr. How far did it travel? (Chapter 9, Section 4)**

    A 120 km   C 12 km

    B 300 km   D 3 km

12. **Explain the difference between the Richter scale and the Mercalli scale. (Chapter 9, Section 3)**

Standards Checkpoint 4

Use after Chapter 16

For help, go to the section in red.

2 Scientific Thinking

1. How is weathering related to surface area? (Chapter 13, Section 1l; Chapter 15, Section 3)

Use the information below to answer questions 2 and 3.

The graph below illustrates the composition of ocean water.

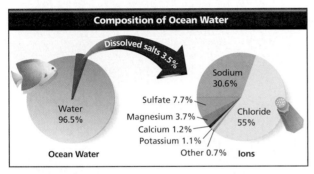

Composition of Ocean Water

Dissolved salts 3.5%

Water 96.5%

Ocean Water

Sulfate 7.7%
Magnesium 3.7%
Calcium 1.2%
Potassium 1.1%
Other 0.7%

Sodium 30.6%
Chloride 55%

Ions

2. What percentage of ocean water is composed of salts? (Chapter 13, Section 1l; Chapter 15, Section 3)

A 3.5%

B 3.7%

C 55%

D 96.5%

3. Approximately what percentage of ocean water is composed of chloride ions? (Chapter 13, Section 1; Chapter 15, Section 3)

A 1.9%

B 3.5%

C 30.6%

D 55%

3 The Physical Setting

4. Describe the process of soil formation. (Chapter 14, Section 2; Chapter 15, Section 4; Chapter 16, Sections 2 and 3)

5. The most important way that ocean surface currents affect climate is by influencing_____. (Chapter 15, Section 4)

A humidity

B temperature

C altitude

D winds

6. Explain how the sun loses energy by giving off light. (Chapter 16, Sections 2 and 3)

7. Which of the following forces causes the planets to orbit around the sun? (Chapter 14, Section 2; Chapter 15, Section 4; Chapter 16, Sections 2 and 3)

A gravity

B magnetism

C electrical charge

D thermal energy

5 The Mathematical World

8. Illustrate a pair of parallel lines and a pair of perpendicular lines. (Chapter 16, Section 5)

Use the information below to answer questions 9-11.

The table below gives some facts about the outer planets.

9. Donna is making a scale model of the outer planets. She is going to build her model using a scale of 1 cm to every 10,000 kilometers. What will the diameter of her model of Uranus be? (Chapter 16, Section 5)

   A 0.511 cm

   B 5.11 cm

   C 51.1 cm

   D 511 cm

10. If Donna built a model of the whole solar system using the same scale, how far would Pluto be from the sun in her model? (Chapter 16, Section 5)

    A 5,870,000,000 km

    B 587, 000 cm

    C 5,870 km

    D 5,870 cm

11. How many times does Saturn revolve around the sun in 174 Earth years? (Chapter 16, Section 5)

    A 1 time

    B 6 times

    C 29 times

    D 174 times

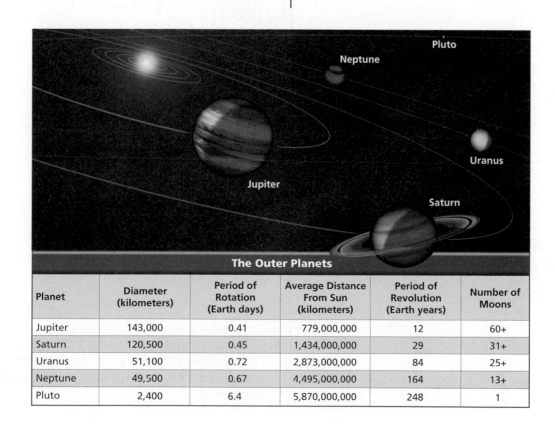

The Outer Planets

Planet	Diameter (kilometers)	Period of Rotation (Earth days)	Average Distance From Sun (kilometers)	Period of Revolution (Earth years)	Number of Moons
Jupiter	143,000	0.41	779,000,000	12	60+
Saturn	120,500	0.45	1,434,000,000	29	31+
Uranus	51,100	0.72	2,873,000,000	84	25+
Neptune	49,500	0.67	4,495,000,000	164	13+
Pluto	2,400	6.4	5,870,000,000	248	1

Standards Checkpoint 5

Use after Chapter 20
For help, go to the section in red.

1 The Nature of Science and Technology

1. **Which scientist proposed the atom was a positively charged sphere with electrons embedded in it? (Chapter 19, Section 1)**

   A John Dalton   C Ernest Rutherford

   B J. J. Thomson   D Niels Bohr

2. **Describe the present modern model of the atom. (Chapter 19, Section 1)**

3. **The sun is 150,000,000 km from Earth. How is this number written in scientific notation? (Chapter 17, Section 4)**

   A 150×10^6 C 1.5×10^6

   B 15×10^7 D 1.5×10^8

2 Scientific Thinking

Use the information below to answer questions 4 and 5.

The information below is an excerpt of the periodic table of elements.

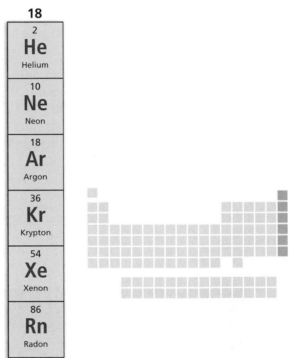

4. **What is the atomic number of xenon? (Chapter 19, Section 2)**

   A 2   C 4.0026

   B 54   D 131.30

5. **What group of elements is shown above? (Chapter 19, Section 2)**

   A halogen family   C noble gases

   B metalloids   D oxygen family

6. **A gas exerts a force of 50 N over a surface. The surface has an area of 2 m². What is the pressure on the surface in N/m²? (Chapter 18, Section 3)**

3 The Physical Setting

Use the information below to answer question 7.

The diagram below illustrates the electromagnetic spectrum.

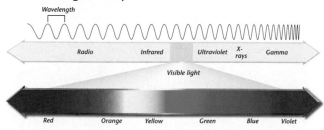

7. Which portion of the electromagnetic spectrum can be seen by the human eye? (Chapter 17, Section 1)

   A infrared waves and visible light waves

   B visible light waves only

   C infrared waves and ultraviolet waves

   D ultraviolet waves only

8. Which of the following choices orders the structures of the universe from smallest to largest? (Chapter 17, Section 4)

   A galaxy, galaxy cluster, solar system, star

   B solar system, galaxy, star, galaxy cluster

   C solar system, star, galaxy, galaxy cluster

   D star, solar system, galaxy, galaxy cluster

9. In which galaxy is our sun located? Describe the sun's relative position in its galaxy. (Chapter 17, Section 4)

7 Common Themes

10. What two variables affect the pressure being exerted on an object? (Chapter 18, Sections 3 and 4)

   A force and area

   B newtons and pascals

   C mass and temperature

   D volume and weight

11. What is the relationship between volume and pressure in a gas? (Chapter 18, Sections 3 and 4)

   A As volume increases, pressure increases.

   B As volume increases, pressure decreases.

   C As volume increases, pressure fluctuates.

   D As volume decreases, pressure decreases.

Use the information below to answer question 12.

The table below illustrates the relationship between temperature and pressure in gases.

Temperature (°C)	Pressure (kPa)
0	8
5	11
10	14
15	17
20	20
25	23

12. Examine the table and explain the relationship between temperature and pressure. (Chapter 18, Sections 3 and 4)

Dancing With Volcanoes

A helicopter moves toward the top of an erupting volcano. With care and speed, a team of scientists gets out to do their work.

"I've been out there sometimes when lava is shooting out of the ground 100 meters high," says volcanologist Margaret Mangan. "The main thing you're struck with is the sound. It's like the roaring of many jet engines. Then there's the smell of sulfur, which is choking. The wind can blow particles from the lava fountain over you, little bits of congealed lava. It feels like a hot sandstorm."

Other times, the eruption is gentler. Lava flows out of the ground in a single channel. "You can walk right up to the channel, just like you'd walk up to a river's edge. We wear what's like a ski mask to keep our faces from getting burnt by the radiant heat. We wear fire-retardant cloth and thick shoes and gloves, to keep our clothes from catching fire. It's hot and sweaty, but you're too excited about what you're doing to think about it."

As a helicopter hovers nearby, lava oozes down Mount Kilauea, a volcano on the island of Hawaii.

Margaret Mangan grew up in Washington, D.C., and received a Ph.D. from Johns Hopkins University in Baltimore, Maryland. She is a geologist with the Volcano Hazards Team of the U.S. Geological Survey in Menlo Park, California. Formerly, she was the scientist-in-charge of the Hawaiian Volcano Observatory. Maggie has two daughters. She enjoys giving talks and hands-on workshops for middle school science students.

Dr. Margaret Mangan studies lava samples.

Talking With
Dr. Margaret Mangan

? How did you get interested in science?

When I was little, I had no interest in science. I wanted to be a dancer. But I did have a good teacher in high school who taught earth science. He was amazingly interesting and funny. In the back of my mind, that stuck with me. After high school, I worked and studied dance. Then I decided to go to college. Because of that earth science course, I took geology and really liked it. But I had to catch up. I had never taken chemistry, physics, or precalculus in high school. So I did some "quick study" work and got up to speed.

? How did you choose volcanology?

When I became a graduate student in geology, I studied crystals and mineral science. It appealed to the artist in me because the study of crystals has a lot to do with symmetry and structure—how things are put together. When I needed to support myself, I got a job with the U.S. Geological Survey. I worked as an assistant to a volcanologist in an area of Oregon and Washington called the Columbia River flood basalts.

Layers of basalt lava

Layers of lava formed these flood basalts in Columbia Gorge, Washington.

? What are flood basalts?

Beneath Earth's crust, molten rock, or magma, collects in pockets called magma chambers. On top of magma chambers, cracks can open in the ground. We call them fissures. The underground magma is so hot and so fluid that it runs out as a flood of lava, eventually forming a flood basalt. Millions of years ago in the part of Washington where I was working, fissures opened up and lava began to flow west. Our research was to find out how big the lava flows were and how far they traveled.

We hiked into beautiful canyons, which look like birthday cakes with layers of basalt lava stacked one on top of another, hundreds of meters deep. I loved being outside in the middle of canyons and rolling hills. In the midst of that amazing outpouring of volcanism, I learned I wanted to do science outdoors and to study volcanoes.

I kept working for the U.S. Geological Survey, but also started my Ph.D. thesis research on magma chambers. After completing my degree, I hopped on a plane with my husband and daughters to live and work in Hawaii.

? What was your work like in Hawaii?

I had two main jobs. One was to keep track of the eruption that's gone on at Kilauea volcano since 1983. We wanted to make sure that people coming to the volcano and living near the volcano were safe. We observed the volcano closely and then passed information to the local government and the National Park Service.

I also started a research project related to the Kilauea eruption. I wanted to know why some explosions are bigger than others. You start with the same volcano, the same type of magma underneath. But sometimes it'll come oozing out of the ground and other times it'll erupt in big explosions. My research, which I'm still doing here in California, takes me back and forth between the real volcanoes and the laboratory. I try to simulate or model a volcanic eruption by making a very small magma chamber right in the lab.

In the laboratory, I put a small piece of lava and some water inside a capsule about as big as my index finger. Then I subject it to the temperature and pressures that would be underneath a volcano. After a few days, I lower the temperature and pressure. This simulates the way the pressure lessens and the magma starts to cool as it rises to the surface of a volcano. Finally, I put the capsule in contact with ice. This stops the process in its tracks, and simulates how magma suddenly cools when it comes out of a vent into the atmosphere.

? What are you learning from your research?

I'm looking for what affects how explosive an eruption is. Right now, the research is very much focused on the "soda can model." You take a soda can, shake it a tad, open it, and the soda kind of wells over your hand. But if you shake it a lot, then open it, it flies up to the ceiling. There's no difference in the carbonation. The percentage of CO_2 gas is the same in both cans. What is different is the rate of degassing—the rate at which the bubbles of gas form. That's what makes the "eruption" strong or gentle.

Maggie collects lava samples from Mount Kilauea.

? Isn't studying volcanoes dangerous?

Well, the danger is a drawback. There's always a concern for safety, even in the lab work. When I do field work, I ask myself: What are the conditions I'm approaching? There's a level of danger, but I'm very careful to think it through and act in ways that keep me safe. Once you make a decision to do something, you move in, you do it. You can't let the fear affect your actions, because then you get clumsy. You have to be controlled and organized.

Writing in Science

Career Link Maggie says her training as a dancer gave her a sense of discipline. She feels that learning about practice, self-control, and organization have helped her be a better scientist. What interests, experiences, or parts of your personality might make you a good scientist? Why do you think so?

Go Online
PHSchool.com

For: More on this career
Visit: PHSchool.com
Web Code: cfb-1000

The Nature of Science and Technology

Academic Standards

This chapter addresses these Indiana standards.

The Nature of Science and Technology

7.1.4 Describe how further study can help scientists choose among different explanations for the same evidence.

7.1.7 Explain how people use science to solve practical problems in design and technology.

7.1.8 Describe some benefits and drawbacks to technology, such as a technology that helps some organisms but hurts others.

7.1.9 Explain how societies influence what types of technology are developed and used.

7.1.10 Identify ways that technology influences the course of history.

The Mathematical World

7.5.4 Describe that large, well-chosen samples can accurately represent the whole.

interactive Textbook

This scientist studies young bearded seals ▶ that live in subzero waters near Norway.

Lab zone Chapter **Project**

Design and Build a Scale Model

How do scientists study something as large as the solar system or as tiny as an atom? One tool they use is a model. Models help scientists picture things that are difficult to see or understand. In this chapter project, you will create a three-dimensional model of a building or room.

Your Goal To create a three-dimensional model that shows the size relationships among the different parts of the model

To complete this project, you must

● measure or find the actual dimensions of the structure to be modeled

● sketch your model on graph paper and calculate the size of each part you will include

● construct your three-dimensional model

● follow the safety guidelines in Appendix A

Plan It! Choose a room in your house or school, or a familiar building to model. Think about how you could construct a smaller replica of that room or building. Preview the chapter to find out how scientists make measurements. Then write a brief plan detailing how you will proceed with this project. Make sure your plan includes a sketch and a list of the materials you will use. After your teacher approves your plan, start working on your model.

Scientific Inquiry

Reading Preview

Key Concepts
- What is scientific inquiry?
- What makes a hypothesis testable?
- How do scientific theories differ from scientific laws?
- What is scientific literacy and how is it important?

Key Terms
- scientific inquiry
- hypothesis • variable
- controlled experiment
- manipulated variable
- responding variable
- operational definition • data
- communicating
- scientific theory • scientific law
- scientific literacy

Target Reading Skill
Building Vocabulary A definition states the meaning of a word or phrase by telling about its most important feature or function. After you read this section, reread the paragraphs that contain definitions of Key Terms. Use all the information you have learned to write a definition of each Key Term in your own words.

▼ A snowy tree cricket

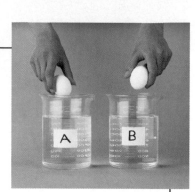

Lab zone Discover **Activity**

What's Happening?
1. Your teacher will give you two eggs and two beakers filled with water.
2. Put one egg in each beaker. Observe what happens.

Think It Over
Posing Questions Write down three questions you have about your observations. How could you find out the answer?

"Chirp, chirp, chirp." It is one of the hottest nights of summer and your bedroom windows are wide open. On most nights, the quiet chirping of crickets gently lulls you to sleep, but not tonight. The noise from the crickets is almost deafening!

Why do all the crickets in your neighborhood seem determined to keep you awake tonight? Could the crickets be chirping more because of the heat? How could you find out?

As you lie awake, you are probably not thinking much about science. But, in fact, you are thinking just as a scientist would. You made observations—you heard the loud chirping of the crickets and felt the heat of the summer night. Your observations led you to infer that heat might cause increased chirping. You might even make a prediction: "If it's cooler tomorrow night, the crickets will be quieter."

The Scientific Process

Although you might not know it, your thinking and questioning is the start of the **scientific inquiry** process. **Scientific inquiry refers to the diverse ways in which scientists study the natural world and propose explanations based on the evidence they gather.** If you have ever tried to figure out why your CD player has stopped working, then you have used scientific inquiry. Similarly, you could use scientific inquiry to find out whether there is a relationship between the air temperature and crickets' chirping.

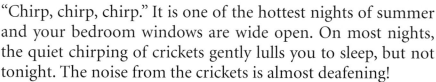

Posing Questions Scientific inquiry often begins with a problem or question about an observation. In the case of the crickets, your question might be: Does the air temperature affect the chirping of crickets? Of course, questions don't just come to you from nowhere. Instead, questions come from experiences that you have and from observations and inferences that you make. Curiosity plays a large role as well. Think of a time that you observed something unusual or unexpected. Chances are good that your curiosity sparked a number of questions.

Some questions cannot be investigated by scientific inquiry. Think about the difference between the two questions below.

• Why has my CD player stopped working?

• What kind of music should I listen to on my CD player?

The first question is a scientific question because it can be answered by making observations and gathering evidence. For example, you could change the batteries in your CD player and observe whether it begins to work. In contrast, the second question has to do with personal opinions or values. Scientific inquiry cannot answer questions about personal tastes or judgments.

Developing a Hypothesis How could you explain your observation of noisy crickets on that summer night? "Perhaps crickets chirp more when the temperature is higher," you think. In trying to answer the question, you are in fact developing a hypothesis. A **hypothesis** (plural: *hypotheses*) is a possible explanation for a set of observations or answer to a scientific question. In this case, your hypothesis would be that cricket chirping increases at higher air temperatures.

In science, a hypothesis must be testable. This means that researchers must be able to carry out investigations and gather evidence that will either support or disprove the hypothesis. Many trials will be needed before a hypothesis can be accepted as true.

✓ **Reading Checkpoint** What is a hypothesis?

Discovery CHANNEL SCHOOL

The Work of Scientists

Video Preview
▶ Video Field Trip
Video Assessment

Perhaps crickets chirp more when the temperature is higher.

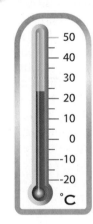

FIGURE 1
Developing Hypotheses
A hypothesis is one possible way to explain a set of observations. A hypothesis must be testable—scientists must be able to carry out investigations to test the hypothesis.
Developing Hypotheses
Propose another hypothesis that could account for this boy's observations.

FIGURE 2

A Controlled Experiment
In their controlled experiment, these students are using the same kind of containers, thermometers, leaves, and crickets. The manipulated variable in this experiment is temperature. The responding variable is the number of cricket chirps per minute at each temperature.
Controlling Variables *What other variables must the students keep constant in this experiment?*

Designing an Experiment To test your hypothesis, you will need to observe crickets at different air temperatures. All other **variables,** or factors that can change in an experiment, must be exactly the same. Other variables include the kind of crickets, the type of container you test them in, and the type of thermometer you use. By keeping all of these variables the same, you will know that any difference in cricket chirping must be due to temperature alone.

An experiment in which only one variable is manipulated at a time is called a **controlled experiment.** The one variable that is purposely changed to test a hypothesis is called the **manipulated variable** (also called the independent variable). In your cricket experiment, the manipulated variable is the air temperature. The factor that may change in response to the manipulated variable is called the **responding variable** (also called the dependent variable). The responding variable here is the number of cricket chirps.

One other important aspect of a well-designed experiment is having clear operational definitions. An **operational definition** is a statement that describes how to measure a particular variable or define a particular term. For example, in this experiment you would need to determine what sounds will count as a single "chirp."

Collecting and Interpreting Data Before you begin your experiment, you should create a data table in which to record your data. **Data** are the facts, figures, and other evidence gathered through observations. A data table provides you with an organized way to collect and record your observations.

Graphing Your Results After all the data have been collected, they need to be interpreted. One useful tool that can help you interpret data is a graph. Graphs can reveal patterns or trends in data. You will learn more about graphs in Section 3.

Drawing Conclusions A conclusion is a summary of what you have learned from an experiment. In drawing your conclusion, you should ask yourself whether the data supports the hypothesis. You also need to consider whether you collected enough data and whether anything happened during the experiment that might have affected the results. After reviewing the data, you decide that the evidence supports your original hypothesis. You conclude that cricket chirping does increase with temperature. It's no wonder that you have trouble sleeping on those warm summer nights!

Scientific inquiry usually doesn't end once a set of experiments is done. Often, a scientific inquiry raises new questions. These new questions can lead to new hypotheses and new experiments.

In this cricket experiment, you decided to test your hypothesis in one particular way. Your friend may do it another way. Furthermore, different questions may require different approaches to finding answers. For example, a scientist studying the moon may rely more on observations rather than controlled experiments to test a hypothesis.

Scientific inquiry is a process with many paths, not a rigid sequence of steps. Often, a surprising observation or accidental discovery leads into inquiry. New information springs up, then a scientist's path takes a different turn. Work may go forward—or even backward—when testing a hunch or fitting a new idea with existing ones.

Reading Checkpoint Why doesn't the scientific inquiry process follow a rigid set of steps?

Pose Questions

Form a Hypothesis

Communicate

Design an Experiment

Draw Conclusions

Collect and Interpret Data

FIGURE 3
The Nature of Inquiry
There is no set path that a scientific inquiry must follow. Observations at each stage of the process may lead you to modify your hypothesis or experiment. Conclusions from one experiment often lead to new questions and experiments.

Go Online
active art

For: The Nature of Inquiry activity
Visit: PHSchool.com
Web Code: cgp-6012

Communicating An important part of the scientific inquiry process is communicating your results. **Communicating** is the sharing of ideas and experimental findings with others through writing and speaking. Scientists share their ideas in many ways. For example, they give talks at scientific meetings, exchange information on the Internet, or publish articles in scientific journals. When scientists communicate their research, they describe their procedures in full detail so that others can repeat their experiments.

 **Reading Checkpoint** Why is communicating important to scientists?

Scientific Theories and Laws

As a body of knowledge, science is built up cautiously. Scientists do not accept a new hypothesis after just one successful experiment. Rather, a hypothesis is tested repeatedly as many different scientists try to apply it to their own work.

Scientific Theories Sometimes, a large set of related observations can be connected by a single explanation. This can lead to the development of a scientific theory. A **scientific theory** is a well-tested explanation for a wide range of observations or experimental results.

Scientists accept a theory only when there is a large body of evidence that supports it. However, future testing can still prove an accepted theory to be incorrect. If that happens, scientists may modify the theory, or discard it altogether.

Scientific Laws When scientists repeatedly observe the same result in specific circumstances, they may arrive at a scientific law. A **scientific law** is a statement that describes what scientists expect to happen every time under a particular set of conditions. **Unlike a theory, a scientific law describes an observed pattern in nature without attempting to explain it.** You can think of a scientific law as a rule of nature.

 **Reading Checkpoint** What does a scientific law describe?

FIGURE 4
A Scientific Theory
Based on observations of sunsets and sunrises, ancient people theorized that the sun revolved around Earth. New evidence led scientists to abandon that ancient theory. Today, scientists know that Earth, along with the other planets in the solar system, revolves around the sun.

Scientific Literacy

You may be wondering how the methods used by scientists apply to you. Not everyone is going to be a scientist. Why should you study science? How could anyone possibly learn everything there is to know about science?

Of course, it is not possible to become an expert in every field of science. Nor is it possible to test everything scientifically by yourself. Instead, you need to have scientific literacy. Having **scientific literacy** means that you understand basic scientific terms and principles well enough that you can evaluate information, make personal decisions, and take part in public affairs. **By having scientific literacy, you will be able to identify good sources of scientific information, evaluate them for accuracy, and apply the knowledge to questions or problems in your life.** You will also be able to keep up with the latest scientific trends and be well qualified for jobs.

So, why should you study science? The real question is, why wouldn't you?

 **Reading Checkpoint** Why is a good understanding of scientific terms and principles important?

FIGURE 5
Sources of Scientific Information
Scientists often give lectures to other scientists and to members of the general public.

Section 1 Assessment

⊙ Target Reading Skill Building Vocabulary Use your definitions to help you answer the questions below.

Reviewing Key Concepts

1. **a. Defining** Define the term *scientific inquiry*.
   b. Explaining A friend claims that ceiling fans are better than air conditioning because they cool the air faster than air conditioners do. Could you investigate this through scientific inquiry? Explain.
   c. Problem Solving What kind of data would you need to collect to carry out this experiment?

2. **a. Reviewing** What is meant by saying that a hypothesis must be testable?
   b. Developing Hypotheses Every time you and your friend study for an exam while listening to classical music, both of you do well on the exam. What testable hypothesis can you develop from your observations?

3. **a. Defining** What is a scientific theory? What is a scientific law?
   b. Comparing and Contrasting How do scientific theories differ from scientific laws?
   c. Classifying The students who conducted the cricket experiment concluded that their results supported their hypothesis. Can their supported hypothesis be called a theory? Why or why not?

4. **a. Defining** What is scientific literacy?

Writing in Science

Summary Suppose you will be traveling to a convention of cricket scientists from around the world. Write a paragraph describing the results of your cricket experiment. Include questions you'd like to ask other cricket scientists while at the conference.

Piecing Information Together

Problem

How do the skills of observing and inferring help scientists piece together information?

Skills Focus

observing, inferring, predicting

Materials

- paperback book, cut into sections and stapled together
- paper
- pencil

Procedure

1. Examine the small section of the book your teacher gives you. Use your observation skills to list any facts you can state confidently about the book, including its characters, setting, or events.

2. Based on your observations, what can you infer the book is about? Write one or two sentences describing the book's storyline.

3. Get together with a partner and share your book sections, observations, inferences, and story descriptions.

4. Together, write a new one- or two-sentence story description based on your shared observations and information.

5. Get together with another pair of students. Repeat Steps 3 and 4.

6. After you have written your description of the story as a group of four, look back over all your story descriptions. Note how they have changed over time.

Analyze and Conclude

1. **Observing** Look over the list of observations you made in Step 1. Were any of the observations really inferences? If so, explain why.

2. **Inferring** How confident did you feel about the inference you made about the storyline in Step 2? How did your confidence level change when your observations included additional sections of the book?

3. **Predicting** How do you think your level of confidence would change if you observed more and more sections of the book? Explain your reasoning.

4. **Communicating** Write a paragraph explaining how this activity resembles the work of scientists. How do the observations and inferences you made relate to those that scientists make? What do your story descriptions represent?

More to Explore

Choose a scientific article from a newspaper or magazine. Read the article and identify three observations and three inferences that the scientists made.

Measurement—A Common Language

Reading Preview

Key Concepts
- Why do scientists use a standard measurement system?
- What are the SI units of measure for length, mass, volume, density, time, and temperature?
- How are conversion factors useful?

Key Terms
- metric system • SI • mass
- weight • volume • meniscus
- density

Target Reading Skill

Comparing and Contrasting
As you read, compare and contrast different types of measurement by completing a table like the one below.

Measurement

Characteristic	Length	Mass
Definition		
SI unit		
Measuring tool		

Discover Activity

How Many Shoes?
1. Trace an outline of your shoe onto a piece of paper. Cut out your pattern.
2. Use your pattern to measure the length of your classroom in "shoes."
3. Compare your measurement to those of three classmates. Did you all measure the same number of "shoes"?

Think It Over
Inferring Why do you think it is important that people use standard units of measurement?

Did you ever ask a relative for an old family recipe? If so, the answer might have been, "Use just the right amount of flour and water. Add a spoonful of oil and a pinch of salt. Bake it for awhile until it looks just right."

Instructions like these would be difficult to follow. How much flour is "just the right amount"? How big is a spoonful or a pinch? It would be impossible for you to know what your relative had in mind. You could end up with disastrous results.

In tasks such as cooking, ▶ measurements can be critical!

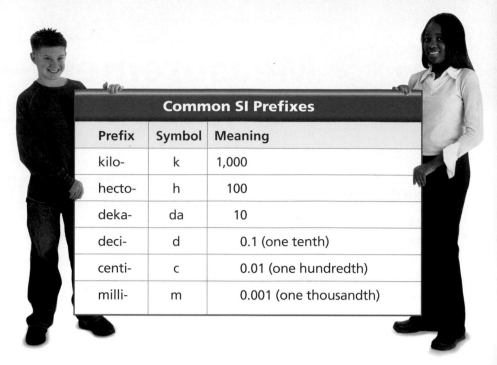

Common SI Prefixes		
Prefix	**Symbol**	**Meaning**
kilo-	k	1,000
hecto-	h	100
deka-	da	10
deci-	d	0.1 (one tenth)
centi-	c	0.01 (one hundredth)
milli-	m	0.001 (one thousandth)

A Standard Measurement System

The recipe example illustrates the importance of using a standard system of measurement. This is especially true in science. Using the same system of measurement minimizes confusion among scientists all over the world.

The Metric System More than 200 years ago, most countries used their own measurement systems. Sometimes two or more different systems were used in the same country. In the 1790s, scientists in France developed a universal system of measurement called the metric system. The **metric system** is a system of measurement based on the number 10.

The International System of Units (SI) Modern scientists use a version of the metric system called the International System of Units, abbreviated as **SI** (for the French, *Système International d'Unités*). Scientists all over the world use SI units to measure length, volume, mass, density, temperature, and time. **Using SI as the standard system of measurement allows scientists to compare data and communicate with each other about their results.** In this book and others in the *Science Explorer* program, you will use both SI and other metric units.

Figure 6 lists the prefixes used to name the most common SI units. Because they are based on multiples of 10, SI units are easy to use. Each unit is ten times larger than the next smallest unit and one tenth the size of the next largest unit. This is similar to our money system, in which a dime is worth ten times more than a penny, but one tenth as much as a dollar.

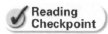 **Reading Checkpoint** SI units are based on multiples of what number?

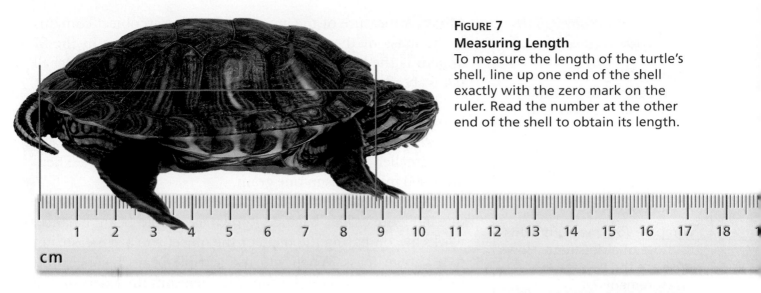

FIGURE 7
Measuring Length
To measure the length of the turtle's shell, line up one end of the shell exactly with the zero mark on the ruler. Read the number at the other end of the shell to obtain its length.

cm

Units of Measurement

Suppose your friend says, "I can throw a softball 15!" That doesn't tell you much. You need to know what unit was used to measure the throw. A throw of 15 centimeters isn't very impressive. A throw of 15 kilometers is impossible.

Length The distance from one point to another is length. **The basic unit of length in the SI system is the meter (m).** One meter is about the distance from the floor to a doorknob. A softball throw would be measured in meters. So would your height. Most students your age are between 1.5 and 2 meters tall.

To measure a long distance, scientists use a unit known as the kilometer (km). The prefix *kilo-* means one thousand. There are 1,000 meters in a kilometer.

To measure objects smaller than a meter, scientists use units called the centimeter (cm) or the millimeter (mm). The prefix *centi-* means "one-hundredth," while the prefix *milli-* means one-thousandth. One meter, then, is equal to 100 centimeters or 1,000 millimeters.

A very common tool used to measure length is the metric ruler. As you can see in Figure 7, a metric ruler is divided into centimeters. The centimeter markings are the longer lines numbered 1, 2, 3, and so on. Each centimeter is then divided into 10 millimeters, which are marked by the shorter lines.

To use a metric ruler, line one end of the object up exactly with the zero mark. Then read the number at the other end of the object. The shell of the turtle in Figure 7 is 8.8 centimeters, or 88 millimeters, long.

Common Conversions for Length	
1 km	= 1,000 m
1 m	= 100 cm
1 m	= 1,000 mm
1 cm	= 10 mm

✓ **Reading Checkpoint** One centimeter is divided into how many millimeters?

Measuring

Use a balance to determine the mass of the following objects.

- a CD
- a crumpled sheet of note-book paper
- this textbook

Compare your measurements to those of a classmate. How close are the two sets of measurements?

Mass A measure of the amount of matter an object contains is the **mass** of the object. **The basic unit of mass in the SI system is the kilogram (kg).** The mass of a wooden baseball bat is about 1 kilogram.

To measure the mass of smaller objects, you will use a unit known as the gram (g). As you can guess, there are 1,000 grams in a kilogram. A large paper clip has a mass of about 1 gram. Even smaller masses are measured in milligrams (mg). There are 1,000 milligrams in one gram.

To find the mass of an object, you may use a balance like the one in Figure 8. This balance, known as a triple-beam balance, works by comparing the mass of the object you are measuring to a known mass. When you use a triple-beam balance, you first place the object on the pan. You then shift the riders on the beams until they balance the mass of the object. You can find step-by-step instructions for using a triple-beam balance in Appendix C.

Mass is often confused with weight. But weight is not the same thing as mass. **Weight** is a measure of the force of gravity acting on an object. This force can change from place to place. For example, you would weigh less on the moon because the force of gravity is much weaker on the moon than on Earth. But how would your mass compare? Because mass measures the amount of matter an object contains, it remains constant wherever an object may be. Your mass on the moon is the same as your mass on Earth.

Volume The amount of space an object takes up is its **volume.** To measure the volume of a liquid, scientists use a unit known as the liter (L). You can measure smaller liquid volumes using milliliters (mL). There are 1,000 milliliters in a liter.

FIGURE 8
Measuring Mass
You can use a triple-beam balance to find the mass of small objects. To measure mass, place the object on the pan and shift the riders on each beam until the pointer stops at zero. **Observing** *What is the mass of this turtle?*

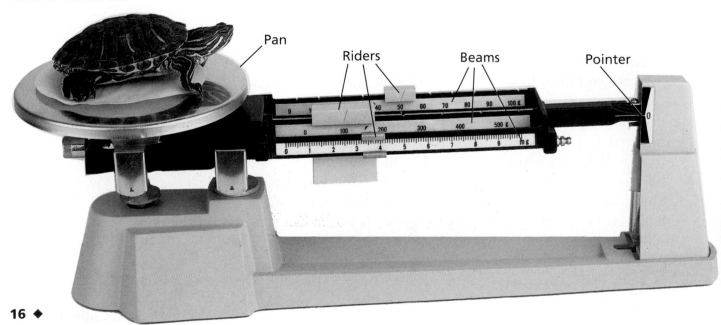

Pan   Riders   Beams   Pointer

To measure the volume of a liquid, scientists commonly use a graduated cylinder. The graduated cylinder in Figure 9 is marked off in 1-milliliter segments. Notice that the top surface of the water in the graduated cylinder is curved. This curve is called the **meniscus.** To determine the volume of water, you should read the milliliter marking at the bottom of the curve.

Density Two objects of the same size can have very different masses. This is because different materials have different densities. **Density** is a measure of how much mass is contained in a given volume. To calculate the density of an object, divide its mass by its volume.

$$\text{Density} = \frac{\text{Mass}}{\text{Volume}}$$

Because density is actually made up of two other measurements—mass and volume—an object's density is expressed as a combination of two units. Two common units of density are grams per cubic centimeter (g/cm^3) and grams per milliliter (g/mL). In each case, the numerator is a measure of mass while the denominator is a measure of volume.

Time **The second (s) is the SI unit used to measure time.** Your heart beats about once per second—when you are not running, that is! The second can easily be divided by multiples of 10, like the other SI units. For example, a millisecond (ms) is one-thousandth of a second. Longer periods of time are expressed in minutes or hours. There are 60 seconds in a minute, and 60 minutes in an hour.

Clocks and watches are used to measure time. Some clocks are more accurate than others. Some digital stopwatches, which are used to time races, can measure time accurately to one hundredth of a second.

✓ **Reading Checkpoint** How many milliseconds are in one second?

FIGURE 9
Measuring Volume
To measure the volume of a regular solid use the formula: Volume = Length × Width × Height. To measure the volume of an irregular solid, immerse the solid in water, and measure how much the water level rises.
Observing *What is the proper way to read a meniscus?*

25 cm

20 cm

6 cm

FIGURE 10
Measuring Time
A stopwatch can be used to measure time.

Common Conversions for Time	
1 s	= 1,000 ms
1 min	= 60 s
1 h	= 60 min

Common Conversions for Temperature		
0°C	=	273 K
100°C	=	373 K

Celsius (°C)   **Kelvin (K)**

Boiling Point of Water   **100**   **373**

Freezing Point of Water   **0**   **273**

Absolute Zero   **−273**   **0**

FIGURE 11
Measuring Temperature
Scientists use the Celsius and Kelvin scales to measure temperature. Units on both scales are the same size. **Observing** *At what temperature on the Kelvin scale does water boil?*

Temperature As you head out the door each morning, one of the first things you might notice is the temperature. Is it cold out this morning? How high will the temperature rise?

Scientists commonly use the Celsius temperature scale. On the Celsius scale, water freezes at 0°C and boils at 100°C. There are exactly 100 degrees between the freezing point and boiling point of water. Normal human body temperature is about 37°C.

In addition to the Celsius scale, scientists sometimes use another temperature scale, called the Kelvin scale. In fact, the kelvin (K) is the official SI unit for temperature. Units on the Kelvin scale are the same size as those on the Celsius scale. Figure 11 compares these two temperature scales.

Zero on the Kelvin scale (0 K) is the temperature that scientists consider to be the coldest possible temperature. Nothing can get colder than this temperature, called absolute zero. Absolute zero is equal to −273°C on the Celsius scale. The Kelvin scale is useful because it does not have negative numbers to complicate calculations.

You can measure temperature using a thermometer. When you first place the thermometer in a substance, the liquid inside the thermometer will begin to move up or down. Wait until the level of the liquid stops changing. Then read the number next to the top of the liquid in the thermometer.

 **Reading Checkpoint**   What is the official SI unit for temperature?

Converting Between Units

Do you have a jar where you keep all your pennies? Suppose you counted your penny collection and discovered that you had 236 pennies. How many dollars does that equal? With only a little thought, you could probably answer, "$2.36."

Just like converting between dollars and cents, it is often necessary to convert from one unit of measurement to another. **To convert one measurement to another, you need to know the appropriate conversion factor. A conversion factor is an equation that shows how two units of measurement are related.** For conversion factors, refer to the conversion tables included throughout this section.

Suppose you walk 1.5 kilometers to a friend's house. How many meters have you walked? To convert 1.5 kilometers to meters, follow these steps:

❶ Begin by writing down the measurement you want to convert.

❷ Find a conversion factor that relates the two units you are converting.

❸ Write the conversion factor as a fraction. Make sure to place the units you are converting from in the denominator.

❹ Multiply the measurement you are converting from by the fraction. When you do this, the units in the measurement will cancel out with the units in the denominator of the fraction. Your answer will then be in the units you are converting to.

By converting between units, you now know that you walked 1,500 meters to your friend's house.

 **Reading Checkpoint** What is a conversion factor?

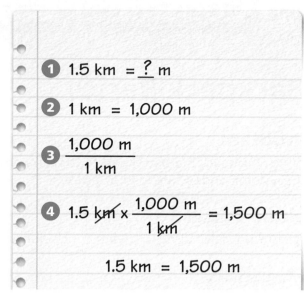

FIGURE 12
Converting Between Units
Using the appropriate conversion factor, you can easily convert one unit of measurement to another. This example shows how to convert 1.5 kilometers to meters.

Section 2 Assessment

Target Reading Skill

Comparing and Contrasting Use the information in your table about the different types of measurement to answer Question 2.

Reviewing Key Concepts

1. a. **Identifying** What is the standard measurement system used by scientists around the world?
   b. **Predicting** Suppose that two scientists use different measurement systems in their work. What problems might arise if they shared their data?
2. a. **Listing** What SI unit would you use to measure the length of a baseball bat? What SI unit would you use to measure the mass of a baseball?
   b. **Estimating** Estimate the length of a baseball bat and mass of a baseball. Be sure to use the appropriate SI units in your predictions. How could you determine how close your estimates are?

3. a. **Reviewing** What is a conversion factor?
   b. **Identifying** What conversion factor would you use to convert between liters and milliliters?
   c. **Calculating** Your cat's bowl holds 0.25 liters of liquid. How many milliliters of water can you pour into the bowl?

Math Practice

4. **Volume** How many mililiters of water are there in a 1.2 liter bottle of water?
5. **Converting Units** The temperature is 293 K. What is the temperature in degrees Celsius?

Backpack Basics

Problem

Which backpack is a better choice for carrying the recommended safe load of books?

Skills Focus

measuring, calculating, drawing conclusions

Materials

- balance • 5–6 textbooks • meter stick
- 2 backpacks (one large and one small)

Procedure

PART 1 Determining Your Maximum Safe Load

1. To prevent back problems, experts recommend that the mass of the backpack you carry should be no greater than 15 percent of your body mass. Use the table below to find your "maximum safe load."

Determining Maximum Safe Load	
Body Mass kg (lbs)	**Maximum Safe Load (kg)**
30 (66)	4.5
35 (77)	5.3
40 (88)	6.0
45 (99)	6.8
50 (110)	7.5
55 (121)	8.3
60 (132)	9.0
65 (143)	9.8
70 (154)	10.5
75 (165)	11.3
80 (176)	12.0
85 (187)	12.8

2. To determine how many textbooks equal your maximum safe load, use a balance to find the mass of one textbook. Next, divide your maximum safe load by the mass of the textbook. Your answer is the number of textbooks (of that size) you can safely carry in a backpack.

PART 2 Comparing Backpacks

3. Your teacher will give you two backpacks—one large and one small. Load each backpack with the number of textbooks you calculated in Step 2. Carry each backpack on your back for one minute and note how it feels. Also, observe how empty or full each backpack is.

4. Using a meter stick, measure the length, width, and height in centimeters of each backpack. Your partner should stretch out the backpacks fully as you measure them. Record the dimensions in a data table like the one at the top of the next page.

5. Calculate the volume of each backpack using this formula:

$$\text{Volume} = \text{Length} \times \text{Width} \times \text{Height}$$

Record the volumes in your data table.

6. Calculate the approximate volume of the textbook you used in Part 1. Measure its length, width, and height in centimeters, and then multiply these measurements together.

Data Table						
Backpack	Length (cm)	Width (cm)	Height (cm)	Volume (cm³)	Total Number of Textbooks	Total Mass of Textbooks (kg)
1						
2						

7. Calculate the total number of textbooks that could fit into each backpack by dividing the volume of each backpack (from Step 5) by the volume of one textbook (from Step 6). Record the results for each backpack in your data table.

8. Calculate the total mass of textbooks that could fit into each backpack by multiplying the mass of one textbook (from Step 2) by the total number of textbooks that fit into each (from Step 7). Record the results in your data table.

Analyze and Conclude

1. **Observing** Is each backpack large enough to carry your maximum safe load? What differences did you notice between the two backpacks when carrying this load of books?

2. **Measuring** How do the two backpacks compare in volume? What is the total mass of books that each backpack could carry?

3. **Calculating** Calculate how many times your maximum safe load each backpack could carry. (*Hint:* Divide the total mass of books from Step 8 by your maximum safe load in Step 1.)

4. **Drawing Conclusions** Based on the calculations and observations you made in this lab, what are some of the pros and cons of each backpack?

5. **Communicating** Choose one of the backpacks and write an advertisement for it. In your advertisement, be sure to explain why it would be the best choice for students.

More to Explore

For a week, record the actual mass of the backpack you carry to school each day. Then calculate the average (mean) mass of your backpack. How does this compare to your recommended maximum safe load?

Graphs in Science

Reading Preview

Key Concepts
- What type of data can line graphs display?
- How do you determine a line of best fit or the slope of a graph?
- Why are line graphs powerful tools in science?

Key Terms
- graph • horizontal axis
- vertical axis • origin
- coordinate • data point
- line of best fit • linear graph
- slope • nonlinear graph

Target Reading Skill
Building Vocabulary A definition states the meaning of a word or phrase by telling about its most important feature or function. After you read this section, reread the paragraphs that contain definitions of Key Terms. Use all the information you have learned to write a definition of each Key Term in your own words.

What's in a Picture?
1. Read over the information written below.
2. At 4 months, Jay's dog Kuma was was 17 cm tall at the shoulders. By the time he turned 8 months, Kuma had grown 9 cm. By 12 months, he was 34 cm tall.
3. Look at the "picture" below.

Think It Over
Inferring What are the advantages of showing information in a visual way, rather than with words in paragraph form?

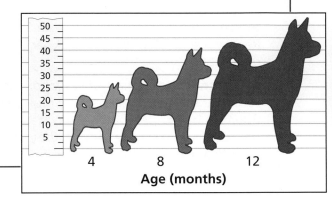

It's another hot summer evening and you're listening to the crickets again. The sound reminds you of the experiment you did to discover whether the rate of the crickets' chirping was related to temperature. You collected a lot of data during that experiment. Then you organized the data into a data table like the one in Figure 13 and studied it to figure out the results.

Now you're ready to write up your experiment and communicate the results with other students. Is there a better way to show the relationship of chirping and temperature than a data table? You'd like to present the results so that the relationship can been seen right away.

The Importance of Graphs

Creating a data table is one way to organize experimental data. Another way to show data is in the form of a graph. You can think of a **graph** as a "picture" of your data. This section focuses specifically on line graphs—what they are used for and how to interpret the patterns they reveal.

Using Line Graphs The data table in Figure 13 shows how many chirps were counted for five crickets at three temperatures. From the data table, you can tell that as the temperature increases, the number of chirps increases as well. But a line graph could reveal more clearly how these variables are related.

Line graphs are used to display data to show how one variable (the responding variable) changes in response to another variable (the manipulated variable). In the cricket experiment, the responding variable is the number of chirps per minute. The manipulated variable is the temperature of the air.

Plotting a Line Graph A line graph has several parts, which are shown in Figure 14.

- **A horizontal axis (or *x*-axis) and a vertical axis (or *y*-axis)·** The **horizontal axis** or x-axis, is the graph line that runs left to right. The **vertical axis,** or y-axis, is the graph line that runs up and down. The point where they cross is the **origin.**

- **Labels for the axes** The horizontal axis shows the manipulated variable. The vertical axis shows the responding variable. The scale of each axis is designed to span from the smallest value to the largest that will be shown.

- **A point on the graph for each piece of data.** A **coordinate** is a pair of numbers used to determine the position of a **data point** on a graph.

- **A line connecting the data points** The line shows the trend of the data.

- **A title** The title explains what the graph shows.

Reading Checkpoint What is a data point?

Number of Chirps per Minute			
Cricket	15°C	20°C	25°C
1	91	135	180
2	80	124	169
3	89	130	176
4	78	125	158
5	77	121	157
Average	83	127	168

FIGURE 13
Collecting Data
The results of the cricket chirping experiment were collected in this data table.
Interpreting Data *Did each cricket chirp more as the temperature rose? Did you have to examine the data in the table closely to answer the question?*

FIGURE 14
Displaying Data in a Line Graph
The line graph shows how the average number of chirps rises as the temperature rises.
Inferring *Why might a line graph be more useful than a data table?*

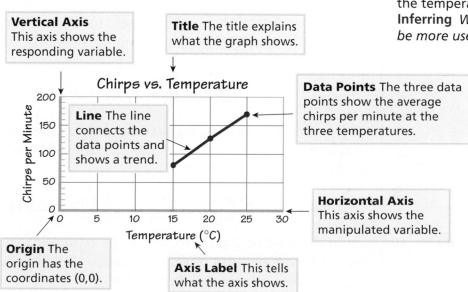

Vertical Axis
This axis shows the responding variable.

Title The title explains what the graph shows.

Line The line connects the data points and shows a trend.

Data Points The three data points show the average chirps per minute at the three temperatures.

Horizontal Axis
This axis shows the manipulated variable.

Origin The origin has the coordinates (0,0).

Axis Label This tells what the axis shows.

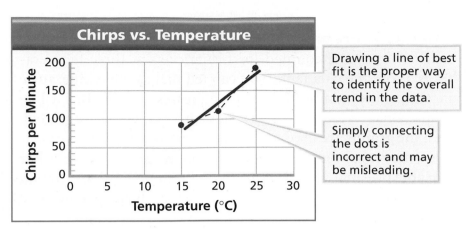

Chirps vs. Temperature

Drawing a line of best fit is the proper way to identify the overall trend in the data.

Simply connecting the dots is incorrect and may be misleading.

FIGURE 15

Drawing a Line of Best Fit
For this graph, a line going upwards from left to right reflects the data more accuratly than a zig-zag line does. **Relating Cause and Effect** *What factors might explain why the data points don't fall perfectly along a straight line?*

Line of Best Fit Sometimes the data points from experimental results don't line up in a straight line. That's because whenever data is collected, small measurement errors and inaccuracies can be introduced. Suppose your friend does the same cricket experiment as you did and plots the graph shown in Figure 15.

Your friend's graph shows the points going upwards from left to right. However, if your friend simply connects the dots, the line would be zigzag, rather than straight. Instead, she draws a straight line between the data points to reflect the general pattern. This graph line, called the **line of best fit,** may touch very few or none of the points. **A line of best fit emphasizes the overall trend shown by all the data taken as a whole.** Notice that the resulting line of best fit for this graph is a straight line. A line graph in which the data points yield a straight line is called a **linear graph.**

Slope

When a line graph is linear, you can determine a value called slope. One way to define **slope** is the steepness of the graph line. **The slope of a graph line tells you how much y changes for every change in x.** Thus, another definition of slope is the ratio of the vertical change (the "rise") to the horizontal change (the "run"). Slope is calculated using this formula:

$$\textbf{Slope} = \frac{\textbf{Rise}}{\textbf{Run}} = \frac{Y_2 - Y_1}{X_2 - X_1}$$

To calculate slope, pick any two points on the line and write down the coordinates. In Figure 16, suppose you chose the points (20, 10) and (50, 25).

$$\textbf{Slope} = \frac{25 \text{ km} - 10 \text{ km}}{50 \text{ min} - 20 \text{ min}} = \frac{15 \text{ km}}{30 \text{ min}} = 0.5 \text{ km/min}$$

In the case of Figure 16, the slope represents the distance the car travels per unit of time, or its speed. A slope of 0.5 tells you that the car has a speed of 0.5 km/min.

FIGURE 16

Slope
The slope of a line indicates how much y changes for every change in x. **Calculating** *What is the slope of this line?*

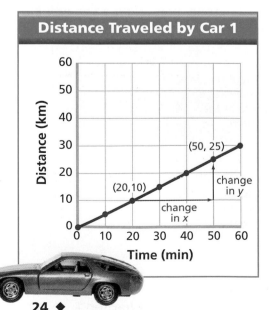

Distance Traveled by Car 1

(50, 25)

(20,10)

change in y

change in x

Car Travel

The graph shows the distance a car travels in a one-hour period. Use the graph to answer the questions below.

1. **Reading Graphs** What variable is plotted on the horizontal axis? What variable is plotted on the vertical axis?

2. **Interpreting Data** How far does the car travel in the first 10 minutes? In 40 minutes?

3. **Predicting** Use the graph to predict how far the car would travel in 120 minutes. Assume the car continues to travel at the same speed.

4. **Calculating** Calculate the slope of the graph. What information does the slope provide about the speed of Car 2?

5. **Drawing Conclusions** Compare this graph to the one for Car 1 in Figure 16. What is the relationship between the steepness of the graph lines and the speed of the cars?

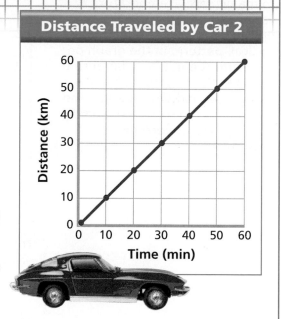

Distance Traveled by Car 2

Using Graphs to Identify Trends

Your data won't always give you a graph with a straight line. A line graph in which the data points do not fall along a straight line is called a **nonlinear graph.**

Whether a graph is linear or nonlinear, the information it contains is very useful. **Line graphs are powerful tools in science because they allow you to identify trends and make predictions.** Line graphs show several types of trends.

Linear Trends When a graph is linear, you can easily see how two variables are related. The graphs in Figure 14 on page 23, Figure 15, and Figure 16 all show linear trends. You can use linear graphs to make predictions or estimate values between data points. Look back at Figure 14. How many chirps per minute would you expect to count at 17°C?

Nonlinear Trends In some nonlinear graphs, the trend rises and then levels off. In other nonlinear graphs, data points fall along a curve. Figure 17 shows such a graph. In each time interval, the truck moves a greater distance. This trend shows that the truck's speed is increasing.

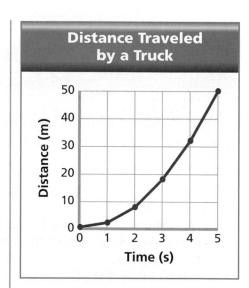

Distance Traveled by a Truck

FIGURE 17
Nonlinear Graph
In this nonlinear graph, the data points fall along a curve. Instead of moving at a steady rate, the truck is increasing its speed.

FIGURE 18
Looking for Trends
In many places, temperature varies with the seasons. The graph on the left shows a repeating, or cyclical, pattern. In the graph on the right, there is no relationship between the number of hits these players get and their masses. The data points are scattered, and the graph shows no recognizable pattern.

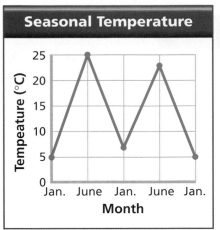

Seasonal Temperature

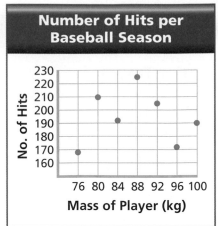

Number of Hits per Baseball Season

In some nonlinear graphs, the data points show a changing trend. In the graph on the left in Figure 18, there is a repeating pattern. From this graph you can infer that the location where the data were collected has very warm summers and cool winters.

No Trend Sometimes when you plot data points you cannot find a trend. In the graph on the right in Figure 18, the data points are scattered in no recognizable pattern. This tells you that the mass of a baseball player has no effect on the number of hits recorded in a season.

 **Reading Checkpoint** What is a nonlinear graph?

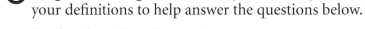

Section 3 Assessment

Target Reading Skill Building Vocabulary Use your definitions to help answer the questions below.

Reviewing Key Concepts

1. a. **Reviewing** What can graphs reveal that data tables cannot?
   b. **Describing** What can a line graph tell you about the relationship between the variables in an experiment?
   c. **Interpreting Data** Could you use a line graph to show data about how the population of mice (the responding variable) changes with the food supply (the manipulated variable)? Explain.

2. a. **Defining** What is a line of best fit?
   b. **Explaining** Why is a line of best fit more appropriate for graphing experimental results than simply connecting the data points?

   c. **Comparing and Contrasting** How does a graph line with a steeper slope compare to one with a shallower slope?

3. a. **Listing** List two things that line graphs allow scientists to do.
   b. **Reading Graphs** Describe how the graph on the left in Figure 18 allows scientists to do these two things.

Lab zone At-Home **Activity**

Graphs and Weather Look for local weather data in your newspaper or on the Internet. What types of graphs, if any, do you find? If there are no graphs, what data on the page might be made into a graph?

Reading Preview

Key Concepts
- What is the goal of technology?
- What are the components of a technological system?
- How does technology have both a good and a bad impact on society?
- Why is it important to analyze both the risks and benefits of a technology?

Key Terms
- technology • obsolete
- system • goal • input
- process • output • feedback
- risk-benefit analysis

Target Reading Skill
Relating Cause and Effect As you read, identify one positive and one negative effect of each technology discussed in this section. Write the information in a graphic organizer like the one below.

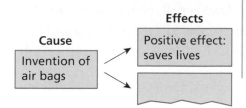

Discover **Activity**

What Are Some Examples of Technology?
1. Look at the objects in the photographs.
2. With a partner, discuss whether or not each object is an example of technology. Write your reasons for each decision.

Think It Over
Forming Operational Definitions On what basis did you and your partner decide whether an object was an example of technology? What is your definition of *technology*?

The year is 1900, and you are going to visit your aunt and uncle in a distant city. You awaken before dawn and get dressed by the flickering light of an oil lamp. Then you and your family hurry to the train station. The train ride is quite an experience. You never imagined anything could move so fast.

Your aunt and uncle greet you with hot soup prepared on their shiny, black, coal-burning stove. After the meal, you help with the cleanup. As you wash the bowls and spoons, you are amazed by the water faucet. To get water at home, you must go outside and pump it by hand.

FIGURE 19
Technology in the Early 1900s
The products shown in these ads are examples of technology. Although they may seem outdated, they were sensations in their time!

Lab zone Skills Activity

Classifying

Look around you. Write down one example of each of the six areas of technology. Compare your list with a classmate's. Discuss any items on your lists that you classified differently.

What Is Technology?

Trains, coal-burning stoves, and oil lamps all made life easier for people living in 1900. All of these items are examples of technology. Modern devices such as computers and CD players are examples of technology, too. In addition to things that people make, technology can also refer to the knowledge and processes needed to produce those objects. **Technology** is how people change the world around them to meet their needs or to solve practical problems.

The goal of technology is to improve the way people live. Medicines help you recover from sickness. Eyeglasses and binoculars extend your ability to see. The Internet makes it easier for you to obtain information.

Technology changes over time. A product may become **obsolete**, or no longer used. Oil lamps became obsolete when electric lighting was invented. Electric lighting is an example of current technology, which means it is in use at this time. Incandescent, fluorescent, and halogen bulbs are commonly used today. Technologies that are in use at the same time are called coexisting technologies.

New, or emerging, technologies may lead to improvements in products. Perhaps in the future, light bulbs will be as small and bright as halogen bulbs and use as little energy as fluorescent bulbs.

The products of technology can be classified into six major areas shown in Figure 20. Think about all the technologies involved in bringing a box of cereal to your breakfast table. Trains (transportation) carry grain from farms to factories (construction). There, vitamins and minerals (biological and chemical) are added to the grain. The cereal is baked in an oven (energy and power) and then packaged (manufacturing). The cereal company advertises the product on TV (communication).

 **Reading Checkpoint** What is an example of transportation technology?

FIGURE 20

Areas of Technology
Technology can be classified into six major areas. Almost everything you do involves products from the different areas of technology.

The Six Areas of Technology	
Area of Technology	**Examples**
Communication	Cellphones, Televisions
Transportation	Automobiles, Airplanes, Bicycles, Trains
Manufacturing	Clothing, Furniture
Energy and power	Heating, Lighting
Biological and chemical	Fertilizers, Detergents
Construction	Houses, Schools, Roads

Technology as a System

When you hear the word *system*, what comes to mind? Maybe you think of your school system or the circulatory system in your body. All **systems** have one thing in common: They are made of parts that work together. The parts of your school system include buildings, books, and teachers. All of these parts are involved in educating the students in your community.

Technology products can be thought of as systems, too. **A technological system includes a goal, inputs, processes, outputs, and, in some cases, feedback.** Figure 21 describes these components in one familiar technological system—an oven.

Technological systems are designed to achieve a particular **goal**, or purpose. An **input** is something that is put into a system in order to reach that goal. The **process** is a sequence of actions that the system undergoes. An **output** is a result or product. If the system works correctly, the output should match the goal. Some technological systems have an additional component, called feedback. **Feedback** is information a system uses to monitor the input, process, and output so that the system can adjust itself to meet the goal.

 **Reading Checkpoint** What do all systems have in common?

FIGURE 21

The Oven as a System
An oven is a technological system. Input, process, output, and feedback are all involved in achieving the goal of cooking food—such as tasty cookies!

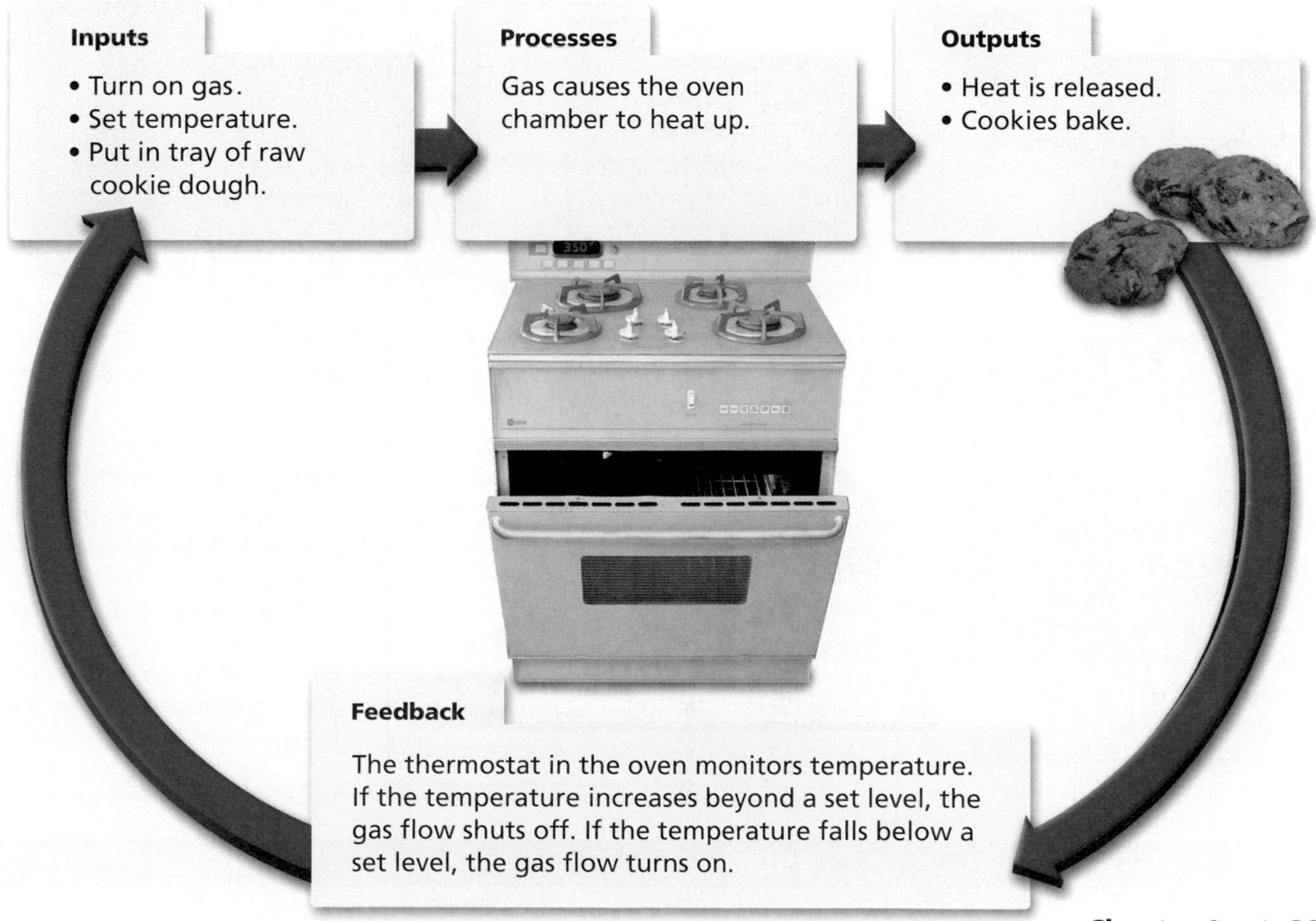

Goal

Bake a tray of chocolate chip cookies.

Inputs

- Turn on gas.
- Set temperature.
- Put in tray of raw cookie dough.

Processes

Gas causes the oven chamber to heat up.

Outputs

- Heat is released.
- Cookies bake.

Feedback

The thermostat in the oven monitors temperature. If the temperature increases beyond a set level, the gas flow shuts off. If the temperature falls below a set level, the gas flow turns on.

Technology's Impact on Society

In the early 1800s, many skilled weavers in England worked at home, weaving cloth by hand on looms. Then the steam-powered loom was invented, and weaving could be done by unskilled workers in factories. Some weavers rebelled against the power looms. They invaded factories and smashed the machinery.

The situation of the English weavers is an example of how technology can affect society. The term *society* refers to a group of people who live together in an area and have certain things in common, such as a form of government. In every age of history, technology has had a large impact on society. During the Stone Age, for example, people could communicate only by speaking directly to each other. Today, in the Information Age, computers allow people to share information quickly around the world.

Science and **History**

Wireless Communication
Since the late 1800s, many developments in communication have turned our world into a global village.

1901
First Transatlantic Signals
On December 12, the first transatlantic radio signal was sent from Poldhu Cove, Cornwall, England, to Signal Hill, Newfoundland. The coded radio waves traveled more than 3,000 km through the air.

1895
First Wireless Transmission
Italian engineer and inventor Guglielmo Marconi successfully used radio waves to send a coded wireless signal a distance of more than 2 km.

1888
Electromagnetic Waves
German scientist Heinrich Hertz proved that radio waves exist. Hertz demonstrated that the waves could be reflected, refracted, diffracted, and polarized just like light waves.

1923
Ship-to-Ship Communication
For the first time, people on one ship could talk to people on another. The signals were sent as electromagnetic waves, received by an antenna, and converted into sound.

| 1880 | 1900 | 1920 |

Technological advances like plumbing, cars, telephones, and computers have done much to move societies forward through the centuries. **However, it is important to keep in mind that technology has both good and bad impacts on society.** Often, many of the bad consequences are unintentional and are not recognized until after the technology has been put to use.

Many technological products are designed to improve people's safety. For example, chemicals called pesticides protect crops from insects, so farmers can produce more food. However, pesticides also can harm people and animals that eat foods containing these chemicals.

Reading Checkpoint) **What is a society?**

Writing in Science

Research and Write Use library or Internet resources to find out more about Guglielmo Marconi. Imagine that you were hired as his assistant. Write a short letter to a friend that describes your new job.

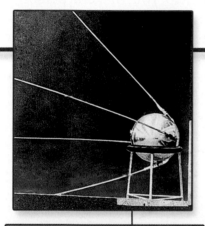

1957
Sputnik I
On October 4, the Soviet Union became the first country to successfully launch an artificial satellite into orbit. This development led to a new era in communications. Since then, more than 5,000 artificial satellites have been placed in orbit.

1963
Geosynchronous Orbit
Communications satellites are launched into orbits at altitudes of about 35,000 km. At this altitude, a satellite orbits Earth at the same rate as Earth rotates.

1979
Cellular Phone Network
In Japan, the world's first cellular phone network allowed people to make wireless phone calls. Today, cellular phone towers like the one above are common.

1960   **1980**   **2000**

Analyzing Risks and Benefits

If technology can create problems, how then can people decide whether or not to use a new technology? And how do governments determine whether a new technology should be regulated, or limited by laws?

In deciding whether to use a particular technology—or how to use it—people must analyze its possible risks and benefits. The process of **risk-benefit analysis** involves evaluating the possible problems, or risks, of a technology compared to the expected advantages, or benefits. This analysis requires logical thinking and common sense. Different people may make different decisions about whether—and how—a technology should be used.

Identifying the Risks and Benefits Look at Figure 22 to see how risk-benefit analysis can help you make a personal decision, such as whether or not to use headphones. Risk-benefit analysis also helps governments establish regulations about new technology products. For example, suppose a company has developed a new bicycle helmet made of a lightweight material. The helmet provides less protection than older, heavier helmets, but it is much more comfortable and stylish.

FIGURE 22
The Risks and Benefits of Using Headphones
Should you use headphones? Evaluating the risks and benefits can help you decide.
Problem Solving *What decision would you makes, and why?*

Benefit
Able to listen to your own music without disturbing others

Benefit
Can tune out loud noises and other distractions in environment

Benefit
Can be easily carried

Risk
Can damage hearing at high volumes

Risk
Can prevent you from hearing oncoming traffic, horns, and sirens

Risk
Can be easily lost

Identifying the Risks and Benefits In determining whether the new helmet is acceptable safety gear, a government agency first identifies both its risks and its benefits. The main risk of the new helmet is the greater possibility of injury than with heavier helmets. But since the new helmet is more comfortable and looks better, more people may wear it. The benefit of the new helmet, then, is that more people would have some form of head protection, rather than no protection at all.

Often, in evaluating a technology's risks and benefits, individuals and societies must consider human values. A value is something that a person or society regards as important, such as health, honesty, convenience, and personal freedom.

Difficulties can arise when different values conflict—when one value favors a technology while another value cautions against it. In the case of the new helmets, the conflicting values could be safety versus people's freedom of choice. When values conflict, a decision involves trade-offs—exchanging one benefit for another. For example, by choosing the lightweight helmet, people trade safety for style.

 **Reading Checkpoint** What is meant by a value?

For: Links on technology and society
Visit: www.SciLinks.org
Web Code: scn-1633

Section 4 Assessment

 **Target Reading Skill** Relating Cause and Effect Refer to your graphic organizer about the effects of technology to help you answer Question 3 below.

Reviewing Key Concepts

1. a. Reviewing What is technology?
   b. Applying Concepts How does a telephone fulfill the definition of technology?
2. a. Reviewing What four components do all technological systems include? What fifth component do some systems also have?
   b. Applying Concepts An alarm clock is a technological system. Identify each component in this system.
3. a. Explaining Explain this statement: Technology does not provide perfect solutions to the problems it helps solve.
   b. Applying Concepts Suppose a robot that cooks meals in minutes has been invented. What positive impacts might it have?

   c. Relating Cause and Effect What negative impacts might the robot have over time on jobs, the pace of life, and other things?
4. a. Defining What is a risk-benefit analysis?
   b. Problem Solving What risks and benefits should be considered when deciding whether or not to buy an insect repellent?
   c. Making Judgments Do you think that government agencies should perform risk-benefit analyses on all insect repellents? Explain your reasoning.

Writing in Science

Summary Suppose you are a curator of a history museum. You are organizing an exhibit featuring inventions that have had dramatic impacts on society. Choose one invention that changed people's lives after it was invented. Write a summary about the invention to be posted at the exhibit.

Reading Preview

Key Concepts
- What are the steps in the technology design process, and what is involved in each step?
- What are patents?

Key Terms
- engineer • brainstorming
- constraint • trade-off
- prototype • troubleshooting
- patent

Target Reading Skill

Sequencing A sequence is the order in which a series of events occurs. As you read, make a flowchart that shows the steps in the technology design process. Put the steps of the process in separate boxes in the flowchart in the order in which they typically occur.

The Technology Design Process

| Identify the need. |
| Research the problem. |

Discover Activity

Identifying a Need

1. With a team of three or four classmates, make a list of foods that people commonly heat in a microwave oven.
2. Discuss with your group the quality of these foods. Could any of them be improved? Think about convenience, cooking time, and packaging as well as the taste and texture of the actual food.
3. As a group, decide which improvement is most important.

Think It Over
Communicating You work for a company that produces foods for microwave ovens. Write a memo to the design team, explaining the improvement you want made in the product.

You watch the timer count down as you wait for the sound. Pop! It's starting. Pop, pop, pop! It's getting faster. You watch the bag inflate as the popping gets more intense. Now you can smell it. Just a few seconds to go, and the popping slows down. Beep! Your popcorn is ready. Be careful as you take it out of the microwave oven—the bag is hot!

Have you ever wondered about the microwave oven—what it is made of and how its parts function together? The design of the microwave oven is the key to its success as a technology.

A microwave oven cooks food by exposing it to high-energy waves called microwaves. Inside the oven, a device called a magnetron shown in Figure 23 produces microwaves. The water in food absorbs the microwaves. Any microwaves that "miss" the food hit the inside of the oven and bounce around until they hit the food and are absorbed.

When the water in food absorbs the microwaves, the energy raises the temperature of the food. When the water inside a kernel of popcorn gets hot enough, it expands and the kernel pops.

How a Microwave Oven Works

A microwave oven produces microwaves and scatters them throughout the oven to reach the food to be cooked.

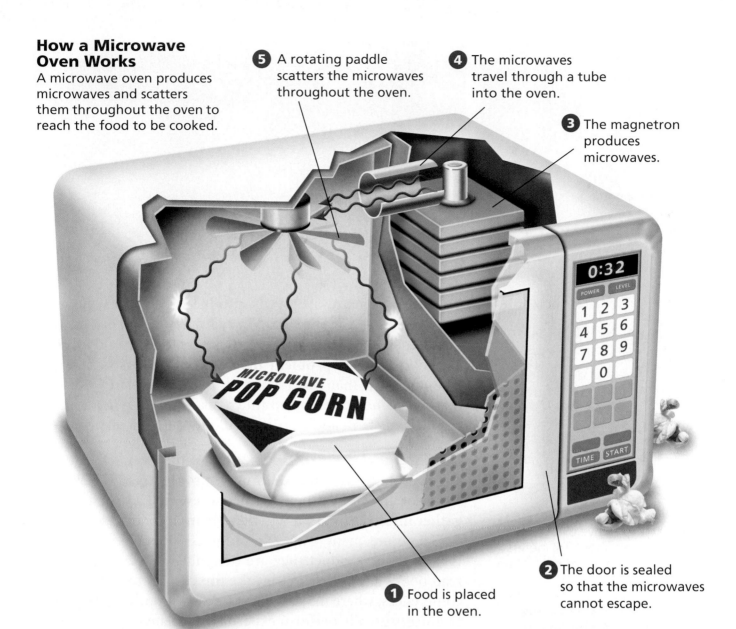

5 A rotating paddle scatters the microwaves throughout the oven.

4 The microwaves travel through a tube into the oven.

3 The magnetron produces microwaves.

1 Food is placed in the oven.

2 The door is sealed so that the microwaves cannot escape.

The Technology Design Process

The microwave oven was the result of a technology design process. The technology design process is a method by which an idea for a new technology is developed into a final product. This process is sometimes called the engineering design process because it often involves the work of engineers. An **engineer** is a person who is trained to use both technological and scientific knowledge to solve practical problems.

Identifying a Need Microwaves were used for radar long before they were used for cooking. The ability of microwave energy to heat matter was noticed in the 1940s. However, the main focus of research at the time was on radar technology. It took more than 20 years to go from the discovery that microwaves could heat matter to a countertop microwave oven.

FIGURE 23
Microwave Oven
A microwave oven produces microwaves and scatters them throughout the oven to reach the food to be cooked.

For: More on microwave ovens
Visit: PHSchool.com
Web Code: cgh-5030

The first microwave ovens, produced in 1947, were large, expensive, and complicated to install. They would not fit easily into someone's kitchen. **When engineers identify a need, they clearly define the problem they are trying to solve.** In this case, the need that was identified was for a microwave oven that would not take up too much space in a kitchen and not cost too much. In addition, it should be safe and easy to use.

Researching the Problem What is the next stage for the engineering team? **After defining a problem, engineers need to research it fully. When engineers research a problem, they gather information that will help them in their tasks.**

There are many ways that engineers obtain information related to the product they are designing. The engineers may read books and articles about the topic. They may also attend conferences, where they can share ideas with other researchers. Engineers usually perform experiments related to the technology they are designing. In addition, engineers often talk to people like you to find out what customers want.

Engineers have to think about details that the people who use the product may take for granted. For example, when engineers work on designs for microwave ovens, one of the considerations is the size. The microwave oven must fit into a reasonable amount of space on a kitchen counter or under a cabinet. But it has to have enough space inside to hold a plate or bowl of food.

Designing a Solution Once a team has a clear understanding of the problem, it is time to start thinking about solutions. **The solution stage involves coming up with ideas, or thinking about different ways to solve the problem. Engineers weigh many possible solutions and choose the best one.** The best design is the one that meets the needs and has the fewest negative characteristics.

FIGURE 24
Identifying a Need
The first microwave oven was very large. It stood about 1.7 meters tall and had a mass of more than 340 kilograms!
Comparing and Contrasting *How is the modern microwave oven shown here different from the first model?*

An important activity that helps generate ideas is called brainstorming. **Brainstorming** is a process in which group members freely suggest any creative solutions that come to mind. After brainstorming, engineers may refine their ideas by making sketches or constructing models.

Engineers must evaluate the constraints of each possible design. A **constraint** is any factor that limits or restricts a design. For example, the microwave oven must have metal walls so that the microwaves bounce around inside instead of escaping.

Another physical constraint that engineers must consider is the strength of the materials they use. Additional constraints might relate to how much money the finished product can cost and the overall size and appearance of the product. The amount of time needed to manufacture a product can be an additional constraint that engineers must consider.

A team must sometimes make trade-offs on some features of the design. A **trade-off** is an exchange in which one benefit is given up in order to obtain another. For example, people want to be able to see inside the microwave oven. A microwave oven cannot have a light bulb within the oven because the microwaves would overheat the bulb's filament, causing the light bulb to burn out. The light in a microwave oven is behind a metal grid. This design protects the light bulb, but it does reduce the amount of light inside the oven.

 Reading Checkpoint **What is brainstorming?**

FIGURE 25
Design Features
The circular object at the top of this microwave oven rotates to distribute the microwaves evenly throughout the oven. The light is behind a metal grid so that the microwaves cannot overheat the bulb.

Building a Prototype A **prototype** is a working model used to test a design. Prototypes are generally full size and made of the materials proposed for the final product. Many prototypes today, however, are completely "virtual," or computer generated.

Prototypes are used to test the operation of a product, including how well it works, how long it lasts, and how safe it is to use. One of the important tests for a microwave oven is the fit of the door. If the door does not seal correctly, microwaves will leak out. A microwave detector held near the door will indicate if there is leakage. In addition to wasting energy, leakage is a safety hazard.

Troubleshooting and Redesigning The next stage in the design process is to identify the causes of any problems and to redesign the product to address the problems. The process of analyzing a design problem and finding a way to fix it is called **troubleshooting**.

If the leakage test shows that the door becomes loose over time, the engineers have to change the design. Then the new door has to be tested to make sure that the change has solved the problem.

Communicating the Solution Engineers must communicate to consumers how a product meets their needs. They must also communicate with those involved in bringing the product to consumers. For example, engineers need to explain the design to manufacturers who will produce the product. The engineers must also describe their ideas to marketing people, who will advertise the product.

✓ **Reading Checkpoint** What is a prototype?

FIGURE 26
Communicating With Consumers
Companies use advertisements to tell customers about their products. This ad is for the first countertop microwave oven.

LIVE THE CAREFREE ELECTRIC WAY.
Make the greatest cooking discovery since fire.
It sizzles a hamburger in 60 seconds, does a 5-pound roast in 37½ minutes, cuts most cooking times 75%—the flameless electric way.

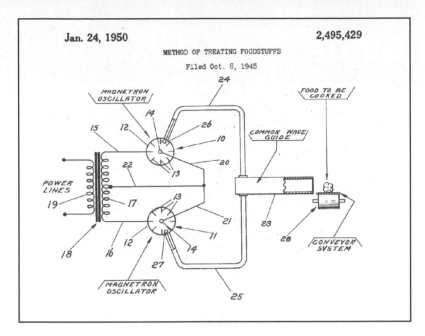

Jan. 24, 1950   2,495,429

METHOD OF TREATING FOODSTUFFS
Filed Oct. 8, 1945

FIGURE 27
Patent
The application for a patent must include diagrams that show how the device works. This diagram is from the first patent issued for a microwave oven.

Patents

Because new products may bring fame or wealth to an inventor or company, **patents** are usually obtained to protect the inventions. **A patent is a legal document issued by a government that gives the inventor exclusive rights to make, use, or sell the invention for a limited time.** If others want to use the invention, they must obtain the patent owner's permission. After the patent's time runs out, however, anyone can make or sell the invention. An inventor may begin a patent application while the design is still in progress.

Section 5 Assessment

Target Reading Skill Sequencing Refer to your flowchart about the technology design process as you answer Question 1.

Reviewing Key Concepts

1. a. Listing List the stages in the technology design process. Describe each stage in a sentence.
   b. Explaining What are design constraints? Give two examples of constraints that should be considered when designing a bicycle frame.
   c. Making Judgments A team working on new packaging for microwaveable french toast has developed a design that will make the french toast crisper. It will also add to the cost of the product and make the package larger. Which trade-off would you make? Explain.

2. a. Defining What is a patent?
   b. Explaining Creativity is a key part of the design process. Explain how patents help reward creativity.
   c. Inferring Why do you think patents remain in effect only for a limited time, rather than forever?

Lab zone At-Home **Activity**

Instructional Manual With a family member, review the instruction manual for a device in your home. Possibilities include kitchen appliances, DVD players, cameras, and hair dryers. Think about the importance of communication between the manufacturer and the user. What would you do to make the manual clearer or easier to use?

Study Guide

1 Scientific Inquiry

Key Concepts

- Scientific inquiry refers to the ways in which scientists study the natural world and propose explanations based on the evidence they gather.

- In science, a hypothesis must be testable. Researchers carry out investigations that will either support or disprove the hypothesis.

- Unlike a theory, a scientific law describes an observed pattern in nature without explaining it.

- By having scientific literacy, you will be able to evaluate scientific information for accuracy.

Key Terms

- scientific inquiry • hypothesis • variable
- controlled experiment • manipulated variable
- responding variable • operational definition
- data • communicating • scientific theory
- scientific law • scientific literacy

2 Measurement—A Common Language

Key Concepts

- Using SI as the standard system of measurement allows scientists to compare data and communicate with each other about their results.

- The basic unit of length in the SI system is the meter (m) and the basic unit of mass is the kilogram (kg).

- Because density is actually made up of two other measurements—mass and volume—an object's density is expressed as a combination of two units.

- The second (s) is the SI unit used to measure time and the kelvin (K) is the unit for temperature.

- A conversion factor is an equation that shows how two units of measurement are related.

Key Terms

- metric system • SI • mass • weight
- volume • meniscus • density

3 Graphs in Science

Key Concepts

- Line graphs are used to show how one variable changes in response to another variable.

- A line of best fit emphasizes the overall trend shown by all the data taken as a whole.

- Line graphs allow you to identify trends and make predictions.

Key Terms

- graph • horizontal axis • vertical axis • origin
- coordinate • data point • line of best fit
- linear graph • slope • nonlinear graph

4 Technology and Society

Key Concepts

- The goal of technology is to improve the way people live.

- A technological system includes a goal, inputs, processes, outputs, and feedback.

- In addition to positive effects, technology can have negative consequences.

- In deciding whether to use a particular technology people analyze its risks and benefits.

Key Terms

- technology • obsolete • system • goal
- input • process • output • feedback
- risk-benefit analysis

5 Technology Design Skills

Key Concepts

- When engineers identify a need, they define the problem they are trying to solve. They gather information and find ways to solve the problem.

- Prototypes are used to test the operation of a product. Then engineers identify the causes of any problems and to redesign the product.

- A patent is issued by a government and gives the inventor exclusive rights to make, use, or sell the invention for a limited time.

Key Terms

- engineer • brainstorming • constraint
- trade-off • prototype • troubleshooting • patent

Review and Assessment

Organizing Information

Identifying Main Ideas Copy the graphic organizer about technological systems onto a separate sheet of paper. Then complete it and add a title. (For more on Identifying Main Ideas, see the Skills Handbook.)

Main Idea

A technological system includes a goal, inputs, processes, outputs, and in some cases, feedback.

Detail	Detail	Detail	Detail	Detail
a. ___?___	b. ___?___	c. ___?___	d. ___?___	e. ___?___

Reviewing Key Terms

Choose the letter of the best answer.

1. The facts, figures, and other evidence gathered through observations are called
   a. predictions.
   b. hypotheses.
   c. conclusions.
   d. data.

2. Being able to understand basic scientific terms and principles well enough to apply them to your life is called
   a. classifying.
   b. scientific inquiry.
   c. scientific literacy.
   d. controlling variables.

3. The curved surface of the water in a graduated cylinder is called a
   a. slope.　　　　b. prototype.
   c. meniscus.　　d. variable.

4. To emphasize the overall trend shown by the data in a line graph, you should draw a
   a. line of best fit.　b. slope.
   c. y-axis.　　　　d. data point.

5. The process of evaluating the possible problems of a technology compared to its expected advantages is called
   a. feedback.
   b. risk-benefit analysis.
   c. brainstorming.
   d. prototyping.

If the statement is true, write *true*. If it is false, change the underlined word or words to make the statement true.

6. A <u>hypothesis</u> is a factor that can change in an experiment.

7. A <u>scientific theory</u> is a well-tested explanation for a wide range of observations.

8. A common unit of <u>volume</u> is g/cm^3.

9. The horizontal axis on a graph is also known as the <u>x-axis</u>.

10. A <u>constraint</u> is any factor that limits or restricts a technological design.

Writing in Science

Interview You are a sports reporter interviewing an Olympic swimmer who lost the silver medal by a few hundreths of a second. Write a one page interview in which you discuss the meaning of time and the advanced instruments used to measure time.

The Work of Scientists

Video Preview
Video Field Trip
▶ Video Assessment

Review and Assessment

Checking Concepts

11. What are some ways scientists communicate with one another?

12. Why is it important to have clear operational definitions in an experiment?

13. In your own words, describe the difference between mass and weight.

14. Give an example of an obsolete technology and an emerging technology.

15. Do you think that technology affected the lives of people living in your great-grandparents' generation? Explain.

16. What steps might engineers take to research a design problem fully?

Thinking Critically

17. Making Judgments You read an ad claiming that scientific studies prove that frozen fruit is more nutritious than canned vegetables. What questions would you want answered before you accept this claim?

18. Inferring Suppose you are doing an experiment and recording your results. When would a line graph be more useful than a data table? When would a data table be more useful than a line graph?

19. Relating Cause and Effect The keyboard is the most common input device in a computer system. What might cause keyboards to become obsolete?

20. Problem Solving Suppose you came home to the scene below. How might you change the tank's design so that the cat couldn't get into it and air could circulate?

Math Practice

21. Calculating Density An ice cube with a volume of 9 cm³ has a mass of 8.1 g. What is its density?

22. Converting Units You just agreed to take part in a 2,500-m race to raise money for a good cause. How many kilometers will you be running?

Applying Skills

Use the data table below to answer Questions 23–24.

Three students conducted a controlled experiment to find out how walking and running affected their heart rates.

Effect of Activity on Heart Rate (in beats per minute)			
Student	Heart Rate (at rest)	Heart Rate (walking)	Heart Rate (running)
1	70	90	115
2	72	80	100
3	80	100	120

23. Controlling Variables What is the manipulated variable in this experiment? What is the responding variable?

24. Designing Experiments Design a controlled experiment to determine which activity has more of an effect on a person's heart rate— jumping rope or doing push-ups.

Lab zone Chapter **Project**

Performance Assessment Display your model and explain how you chose its scale. What was the most difficult thing about creating your model to scale? How could you improve your model?

🔵 Standardized Test Practice

Choose the letter of the best answer.

1. What would be the best way to measure the mass of a small object like a rock?
   A using a graduated cylinder
   B using a bathroom scale
   C using a triple-beam balance
   D using a meter stick

2. Engineers have designed a car with a new engine and body design. Which of the following trade-offs would have a negative impact on public safety?
   A choosing lower-cost materials over good results in crash tests
   B choosing the appearance of the car seats over their comfort
   C choosing to install a more powerful music system over a better air conditioning system
   D choosing a more powerful engine over better gas mileage

3. A new sunscreen that has to be applied only once a week has been developed. The sunscreen is an example of
   A energy and power technology
   B communication technology
   C construction technology
   D biological and chemical technology

The graph compares how well two different brands of insulated mugs retained heat. Use the graph to answer question 4.

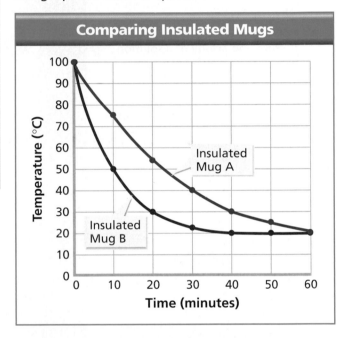

Comparing Insulated Mugs

4. What was the manipulated variable in this experiment?
   A the temperature of the water
   B location of the travel mug
   C brand of travel mug
   D how long the water was allowed to cool

Open-Ended Question

5. Suppose a newly designed robot automatically scans products at checkout lines in supermarkets. The robot can perform no other function. The cost to install a robot at a cash register is less than the cost of hiring a cashier. Describe some of the positive and negative impacts that this new technology might have on society.

Chapter 2

Bones, Muscles, and Skin

Academic Standards

This chapter addresses these Indiana standards.

The Physical Setting

7.3.12 Investigate how the temperature and acidity of a solution influence reaction rates.

The Living Environment

7.4.4 Explain that cells constantly divide to make more cells for growth and repair. Various organs and tissues provide cells with food, air, and waste removal.

7.4.5 Explain that the basic functions of all organisms occur in similar ways within cells.

Common Themes

7.7.2 Use different models to represent the same thing, noting that the model's type and complexity depend on its purpose.

7.7.3 Describe how systems usually change until they reach equilibrium, and remain that way unless their surroundings change.

No matter your age or ability level, playing sports is fun and healthful. ▶

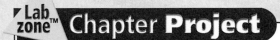

Chapter **Project**

Design and Build a Hand Prosthesis

A prosthesis is an artificial device that replaces a human body part. Designing artificial replacements, such as prosthetic hands, can be a challenging task. This is because even a simple act, such as picking up a pen, involves a complex interaction of body parts.

Your Goal To design, build, and test a replacement for a human hand

Your prosthesis must

● grasp and lift a variety of objects
● be activated by pulling a cord or string
● spring back when the cord is released
● be built following the safety guidelines in Appendix A

Plan It! Before you design your prosthetic hand, study the human hand. Watch how the fingers move to pick up objects. Make a list of devices that mimic the ability of the hand to pick up objects. Examples include tongs, tweezers, pliers, and chopsticks. Then, choose materials for your hand and sketch your design. When your teacher has approved your design, build and test your prosthetic hand.

Body Organization and Homeostasis

Reading Preview

Key Concepts
- What are the levels of organization in the body?
- What is homeostasis?

Key Terms
- cell • cell membrane
- nucleus • cytoplasm
- tissue • muscle tissue
- nervous tissue
- connective tissue
- epithelial tissue
- organ • organ system
- homeostasis • stress

Target Reading Skill

Outlining An outline shows the relationship between main ideas and supporting ideas. As you read, make an outline about body organization and homeostasis. Use the red headings for the main ideas and the blue headings for the supporting ideas.

Body Organization and Homeostasis

I. Cells
   A. Structures of cells
   B.
II. Tissues

Lab zone · Discover **Activity**

How Does Your Body Respond?

1. Stack one book on top of another one.
2. Lift the two stacked books in front of you so the lowest book is about level with your shoulders. Hold the books in this position for 30 seconds. While you are performing this activity, note how your body responds. For example, how do your arms feel at the beginning and toward the end of the 30 seconds?
3. Balance one book on the top of your head. Walk a few steps with the book on your head.

Think It Over
Inferring List all the parts of your body that worked together as you performed the activities in Steps 1 through 3.

The bell rings—lunchtime! You hurry down the noisy halls to the cafeteria. The unmistakable aroma of hot pizza makes your mouth water. At last, you balance your tray of pizza and salad while you pay the cashier. You look around the cafeteria for your friends. Then, you walk to the table, sit down, and begin to eat.

Think about how many parts of your body were involved in the simple act of getting and eating your lunch. Every minute of the day, whether you are eating, studying, walking, or even sleeping, your body is busily at work. Each part of the body has a specific job to do. And all the different parts of your body usually work together so smoothly that you don't even notice them.

This smooth functioning is due partly to the way in which the body is organized. **The levels of organization in the human body consist of cells, tissues, organs, and organ systems.** The smallest unit of organization is the cell. The next largest unit is tissue; then, organs. Finally, the organ system is the largest unit of organization.

Cells

A **cell** is the basic unit of structure and function in a living thing. Complex organisms are composed of many cells in the same way a brick building is composed of many bricks. The human body contains about 100 trillion cells. Cells are quite tiny, and most cannot be seen without a microscope.

Structures of Cells Most animal cells, including those in the human body, have a structure similar to the cell in Figure 1. The **cell membrane** forms the outside boundary of the cell. Inside the cell membrane is a large structure called the nucleus. The **nucleus** is the control center that directs the cell's activities and contains the information that determines the cell's form and function. When the cell divides, or reproduces, this information is passed along to the newly formed cells. The material within a cell apart from the nucleus is called the **cytoplasm** (SYT uh plaz um). The cytoplasm is made of a clear, jellylike substance containing many cell structures called organelles.

Functions of Cells Cells carry on the processes that keep organisms alive. Inside cells, for example, molecules from digested food undergo chemical reactions that release energy for the body's activities. Cells also grow and reproduce. And they get rid of waste products that result from these activities.

 **Reading Checkpoint** What is the function of the nucleus?

Lab zone Try This **Activity**

How Is a Book Organized?

In this activity, you will analyze the levels of organization in a book.

1. Examine this textbook to see how it is subdivided—into chapters, sections, and so on.

2. Make a concept map that shows this pattern of organization. Place the largest subdivision at the top of the map and the smallest at the bottom.

3. Compare the levels of organization in this textbook to those in the human body.

Making Models Which level of organization in the textbook represents cells? Which represents tissues? Organs? Organ systems?

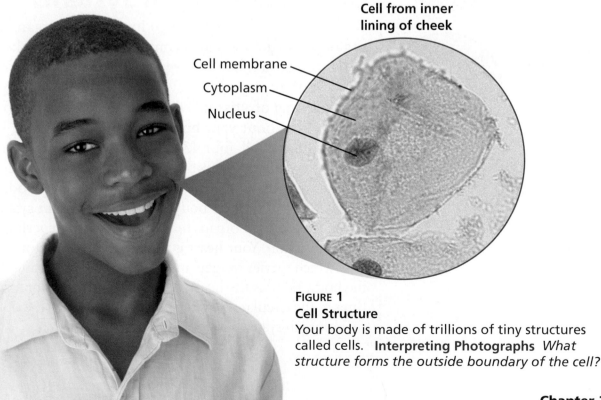

Cell from inner lining of cheek

Cell membrane
Cytoplasm
Nucleus

FIGURE 1
Cell Structure
Your body is made of trillions of tiny structures called cells. **Interpreting Photographs** *What structure forms the outside boundary of the cell?*

FIGURE 2
Types of Tissues

Your body contains four kinds of tissues: muscle, nervous, connective, and epithelial.

Comparing and Contrasting *How is the function of nervous tissue different from that of epithelial tissue?*

Muscle Tissue
Every movement you make depends on muscle tissue. The muscle tissue shown here allows your body to move.

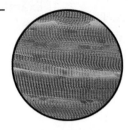

Nervous Tissue
Nervous tissue, such as the brain cells shown here, enables you to see, hear, and think.

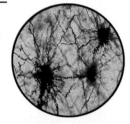

Connective Tissue
Connective tissue, such as the bone shown here, connects and supports parts of your body.

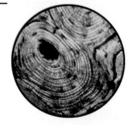

Epithelial Tissue
Epithelial tissue, such as the skin cells shown here, covers the surfaces of your body and lines your internal organs.

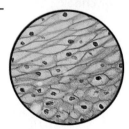

Tissues

The next largest unit of organization in your body is a tissue. A **tissue** is a group of similar cells that perform the same function. The human body contains four basic types of tissue: muscle tissue, nervous tissue, connective tissue, and epithelial tissue. To see examples of each of these tissues, look at Figure 2.

Like the muscle cells that form it, **muscle tissue** can contract, or shorten. By doing this, muscle tissue makes parts of your body move. While muscle tissue carries out movement, **nervous tissue** directs and controls the process. Nervous tissue carries electrical messages back and forth between the brain and other parts of the body. Another type of tissue, **connective tissue,** provides support for your body and connects all its parts. Bone tissue and fat are connective tissues.

The surfaces of your body, inside and out, are covered by **epithelial tissue** (ep uh THEE lee ul). Some epithelial tissue, such as your skin, protects the delicate structures that lie beneath it. The lining of your digestive system consists of epithelial tissue that allows you to digest and absorb the nutrients in your food.

 **Reading Checkpoint** **What is the job of muscle tissue?**

Organs and Organ Systems

Your stomach, heart, brain, and lungs are all organs. An **organ** is a structure that is composed of different kinds of tissue. Like a tissue, an organ performs a specific job. The job of an organ, however, is generally more complex than that of a tissue. The heart, for example, pumps blood throughout your body, over and over again. The heart contains all four kinds of tissue—muscle, nervous, connective, and epithelial. Each type of tissue contributes to the organ's overall job of pumping blood.

Each organ in your body is part of an **organ system,** which is a group of organs that work together to perform a major function. Your heart is part of your circulatory system, which carries oxygen and other materials throughout the body. Besides the heart, blood vessels are major structures in the circulatory system. Figure 3 shows some of the major organ systems in the human body.

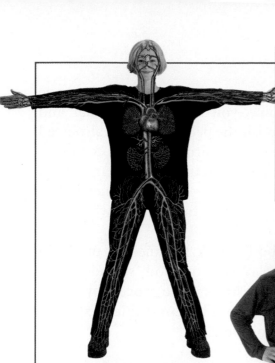

FIGURE 3

Organ Systems

The human body is made up of eleven organ systems. Eight of the systems are shown here.
Interpreting Diagrams *Which two systems work together to get oxygen to your cells?*

Skeletal System
Supports and protects the body.

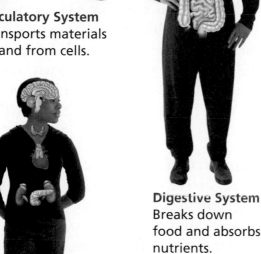

Circulatory System
Transports materials to and from cells.

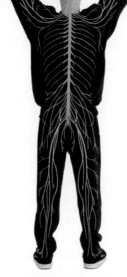

Digestive System
Breaks down food and absorbs nutrients.

Nervous System
Detects information from the environment and controls body functions.

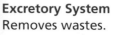

Respiratory System
Takes in oxygen and eliminates carbon dioxide.

Endocrine System
Controls many body processes by means of chemicals.

Muscular System
Enables movement of the body and internal organs.

Excretory System
Removes wastes.

Go Online
SciLINKS NSTA

For: Links on body systems
Visit: www.SciLinks.org
Web Code: scn-0411

Homeostasis

The different organ systems work together and depend on one another. When you ride a bike, you use your muscular and skeletal systems to steer and push the pedals. But you also need your nervous system to direct your arms and legs to move. Your respiratory, digestive, and circulatory systems work together to fuel your muscles with the energy they need. And your excretory system removes the wastes produced while your muscles are hard at work.

All the systems of the body work together to maintain **homeostasis** (hoh mee oh STAY sis), the body's tendency to keep an internal balance. **Homeostasis is the process by which an organism's internal environment is kept stable in spite of changes in the external environment.**

Homeostasis in Action To see homeostasis in action, all you have to do is take your temperature when the air is cold. Then, take it again in an overheated room. No matter what the temperature of the air around you, your internal body temperature will be close to 37°C. Of course, if you become sick, your body temperature may rise. But when you are well again, it returns to 37°C.

Maintaining Homeostasis Your body has various ways of maintaining homeostasis. For example, when you are too warm, you sweat. Sweating helps to cool your body. On the other hand, when you are cold, you shiver. Shivering occurs when your muscles rapidly contract and relax. This action produces heat that helps keep you warm. Both of these processes help your body maintain homeostasis by regulating your temperature.

FIGURE 4
Maintaining Homeostasis
Regardless of the surrounding temperature, your body temperature remains fairly constant at about 37°C. Sweating (left) and shivering (right) help regulate your body temperature.
Applying Concepts *What is the term for the body's tendency to maintain a stable internal environment?*

Stress and Homeostasis Sometimes, things can happen to throw off homeostasis. As a result, your heart may beat more rapidly or your breathing may increase. These reactions of your circulatory and respiratory systems are signs of stress. **Stress** is the reaction of your body to potentially threatening, challenging, or disturbing events.

Think about what happens when you leave the starting line in a bike race. As you pedal, your heart beats faster and your breathing increases. What is happening in your body? First, your endocrine system releases a chemical called adrenaline into your bloodstream. Adrenaline gives you a burst of energy and prepares your body to take action. As you pedal, your muscles work harder and require more oxygen. Oxygen is carried by the circulatory system, so your heart beats even faster to move more blood to your muscles. Your breath comes faster and faster, too, so that more oxygen can get into your body. Your body is experiencing stress.

If stress is over quickly, your body soon returns to its normal state. Think about the bike race again. After you cross the finish line, you continue to breathe hard for the next few minutes. Soon, however, your breathing and heart rate return to normal. The level of adrenaline in your blood returns to normal. Thus, homeostasis is restored after just a few minutes of rest.

 **What is stress?**

FIGURE 5
Stress
Your body reacts to stress, such as the start of a bike race, by releasing adrenaline and carrying more oxygen to body cells.

Section 1 Assessment

Target Reading Skill Outlining Use the information in your outline to help you answer the questions below.

Reviewing Key Concepts

1. a. Identifying List the four levels of organization in the human body from smallest to largest. Give an example of each level.
  b. Comparing and Contrasting What is the difference between tissues and organs?
  c. Applying Concepts What systems of the body are involved when you prepare a sandwich and then eat it?

2. a. Defining What is homeostasis?
  b. Explaining How does stress affect homeostasis?
  c. Relating Cause and Effect Describe what happens inside your body as you give an oral report in front of your class.

Writing in Science

Summary Write a paragraph that explains what body systems are involved when you sit down to do your homework. Be sure to begin your paragraph with a topic sentence and include supporting details.

The Skeletal System

Reading Preview

Key Concepts
- What are the functions of the skeleton?
- What role do joints play in the body?
- What are the characteristics of bone, and how can you keep your bones strong and healthy?

Key Terms
- skeleton • vertebra • joint
- ligament • cartilage
- compact bone • spongy bone
- marrow • osteoporosis

Target Reading Skill
Asking Questions Before you read, preview the red headings. In a graphic organizer like the one below, ask a *what* or *how* question for each heading. As you read, answer your questions.

The Skeletal System

Question	Answer
What does the skeleton do?	The skeletal system provides shape . . .

Lab zone Discover **Activity**

Hard as a Rock?

1. Your teacher will give you a rock and a leg bone from a cooked turkey or chicken.
2. Use a hand lens to examine both the rock and the bone.
3. Gently tap both the rock and the bone on a hard surface.
4. Pick up each object to feel how heavy it is.
5. Wash your hands. Then make notes of your observations.

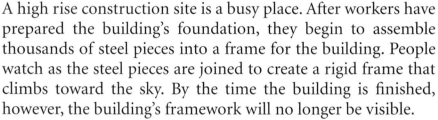

Think It Over
Observing Based on your observations, why do you think bones are sometimes compared to rocks? List some ways in which bones and rocks are similar and different.

A high rise construction site is a busy place. After workers have prepared the building's foundation, they begin to assemble thousands of steel pieces into a frame for the building. People watch as the steel pieces are joined to create a rigid frame that climbs toward the sky. By the time the building is finished, however, the building's framework will no longer be visible.

Like a building, you also have an inner framework, but it isn't made up of steel. Your framework, or **skeleton,** is made up of all the bones in your body. The number of bones in your skeleton, or skeletal system, depends on your age. A newborn has about 275 bones. An adult, however, has about 206 bones. As a baby grows, some of the bones in the body fuse together. For example, as you grew, some of the bones in your skull fused together.

What the Skeletal System Does

Just as a building could not stand without its frame, you would collapse without your skeleton. **Your skeleton has five major functions. It provides shape and support, enables you to move, protects your organs, produces blood cells, and stores minerals and other materials until your body needs them.**

Shape and Support Your skeleton determines the shape of your body, much as a steel frame determines the shape of a building. The backbone, or vertebral column, is the center of the skeleton. Locate the backbone in Figure 6. Notice that the bones in the skeleton are in some way connected to this column. If you move your fingers down the center of your back, you can feel the 26 small bones, or **vertebrae** (VUR tuh bray) (singular: *vertebra*), that make up your backbone. Bend forward at the waist and feel the bones adjust as you move. You can think of each individual vertebra as a bead on a string. Just as a beaded necklace is flexible and able to bend, so too is your vertebral column. If your backbone were just one bone, you would not be able to bend or twist.

 **Reading Checkpoint** Why is the vertebral column considered the center of the skeleton?

FIGURE 6

The Skeleton

The skeleton provides a framework that supports and protects many other body parts. **Comparing and Contrasting** *In what ways is the skeleton like the steel framework of a building? In what ways is it different?*

Skull

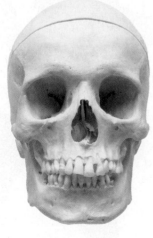

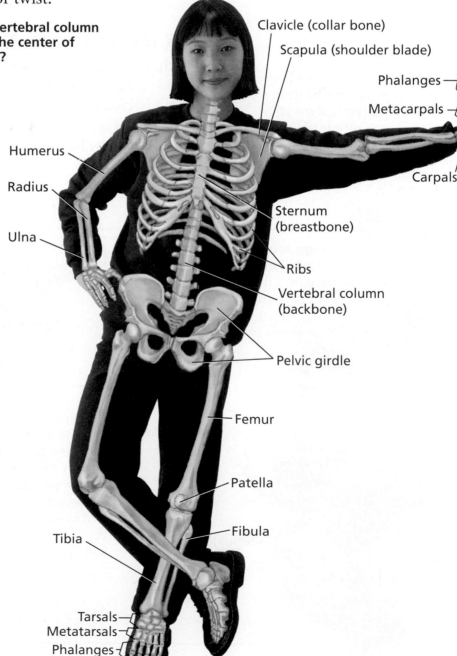

Clavicle (collar bone)
Scapula (shoulder blade)
Phalanges
Metacarpals
Humerus
Radius
Carpals
Ulna
Sternum (breastbone)
Ribs
Vertebral column (backbone)
Pelvic girdle
Femur
Patella
Fibula
Tibia
Tarsals
Metatarsals
Phalanges

Movement and Protection Your skeleton allows you to move. Most of the body's bones are associated with muscles. The muscles pull on the bones to make the body move. Bones also protect many of the organs in your body. For example, your skull protects your brain, and your breastbone and ribs form a protective cage around your heart and lungs.

Production and Storage of Substances Some of your bones produce substances that your body needs. You can think of the long bones of your arms and legs as factories that make certain blood cells. Bones also store minerals such as calcium and phosphorus. When the body needs these minerals, the bones release small amounts of them into the blood.

Joints of the Skeleton

Suppose that a single long bone ran the length of your leg. How would you get out of bed or run for the school bus? Luckily, your body contains many small bones rather than fewer large ones. A **joint** is a place in the body where two bones come together. **Joints allow bones to move in different ways.** There are two kinds of joints—immovable joints and movable joints.

Go Online
active art

For: Movable Joints activity
Visit: PHSchool.com
Web Code: cep-4012

FIGURE 7
Movable Joints
Without movable joints, your body would be as stiff as a board. The different kinds of joints allow your body to move in a variety of ways. **Comparing and Contrasting** *How is the movement of a hinge joint different from that of a ball-and-socket joint?*

Hinge Joint
A hinge joint allows forward or backward motion. Your knee is a hinge joint that allows you to bend and straighten your leg. Your elbow is also a hinge joint.

Ball-and-Socket Joint
Ball-and-socket joints allow the greatest range of motion. The ball-and-socket joint in your shoulder allows you to swing your arm freely in a circle. Your hips also have ball-and-socket joints.

Immovable Joints Some joints in the body connect bones in a way that allows little or no movement. These joints are called immovable joints. The bones of the skull are held together by immovable joints.

Movable Joints Most of the joints in the body are movable joints. Movable joints allow the body to make a wide range of movements. Look at Figure 7 to see the variety of movements that these joints make possible.

The bones in movable joints are held together by strong connective tissues called **ligaments.** Most joints have a second type of connective tissue, called **cartilage** (KAHR tuh lij), which is more flexible than bone. Cartilage covers the ends of the bones and keeps them from rubbing against each other. For example, in the knee, cartilage acts as a cushion that keeps your femur (thighbone) from rubbing against the bones of your lower leg. In addition, a fluid lubricates the ends of the bones, allowing them to move smoothly over each other.

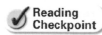 **Reading Checkpoint** How are movable joints held together?

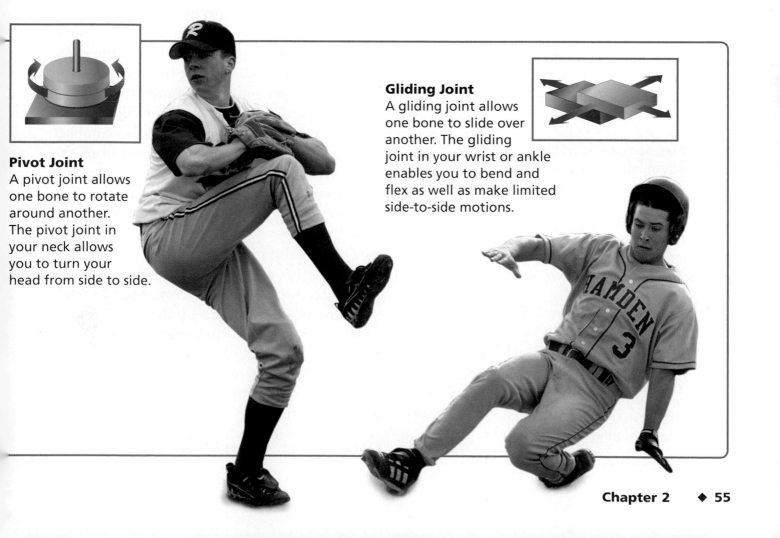

Pivot Joint
A pivot joint allows one bone to rotate around another. The pivot joint in your neck allows you to turn your head from side to side.

Gliding Joint
A gliding joint allows one bone to slide over another. The gliding joint in your wrist or ankle enables you to bend and flex as well as make limited side-to-side motions.

FIGURE 8

Bone Structure

The most obvious feature of a long bone, such as the femur, is its long shaft. Running through the compact bone tissue within the shaft is a system of canals. The canals bring materials to the living bone cells.
Interpreting Diagrams *What different tissues make up the femur?*

Femur

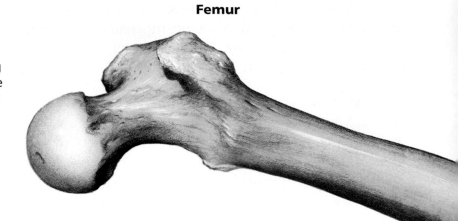

Bones—Strong and Living

When you think of a skeleton, you may think of the paper cut-outs that are used as decorations at Halloween. Many people connect skeletons with death. The ancient Greeks did, too. The word *skeleton* actually comes from a Greek word meaning "a dried body." The bones of your skeleton, however, are not dead at all. **Bones are complex living structures that undergo growth and development.**

Bone Structure Figure 8 shows the structure of the femur, or thighbone. The femur, which is the body's longest bone, connects the pelvic bones to the lower leg bones. Notice that a thin, tough membrane covers all of the bone except the ends. Blood vessels and nerves enter and leave the bone through the membrane. Beneath the bone's outer membrane is a layer of **compact bone,** which is hard and dense, but not solid. As you can see in Figure 8, small canals run through the compact bone. These canals carry blood vessels and nerves from the bone's surface to the living cells within the bone.

Just inside the femur's compact bone is a layer of spongy bone. Like a sponge, **spongy bone** has many small spaces within it. This structure makes spongy bone tissue lightweight but strong. Spongy bone is also found at the ends of the bone.

The spaces in many bones contain a soft, connective tissue called **marrow.** There are two types of marrow—red and yellow. Red bone marrow produces some of the body's blood cells. As a child, most of your bones contained red bone marrow. As a teenager, only the ends of your femurs, skull, hip bones, and sternum (breastbone) contain red marrow. Your other bones contain yellow marrow. This marrow stores fat that can serve as an energy reserve.

 **Reading Checkpoint** **What are the two types of bone marrow?**

Lab zone **Try This Activity**

Soft Bones?

In this activity, you will explore the role that calcium plays in bones.

1. Put on protective gloves. Soak one clean chicken bone in a jar filled with water. Soak a second clean chicken bone in a jar filled with vinegar. (Vinegar causes calcium to dissolve out of bone.)

2. After one week, put on protective gloves and remove the bones from the jars.

3. Compare how the two bones look and feel. Note any differences between the two bones.

Drawing Conclusions Based on your results, explain why it is important to consume a diet that is high in calcium.

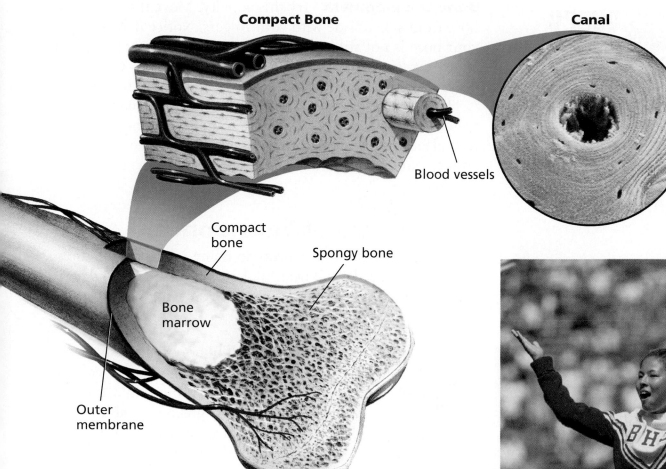

Compact Bone

Canal

Blood vessels

Compact bone

Spongy bone

Bone marrow

Outer membrane

Bone Strength The structure of bone makes it both strong and lightweight. In fact, bones are so strong that they can absorb more force without breaking than can concrete or granite rock. Yet, bones are much lighter than these materials. In fact, only about 20 percent of an average adult's body weight is bone.

Have you ever heard the phrase "as hard as a rock"? Most rock is hard because it is made up of minerals that are packed tightly together. In a similar way, bones are hard because they contain minerals—primarily phosphorus and calcium.

Bone Growth Bones are alive—they contain cells and tissues, such as blood and nerves. Because they are alive, bones also form new bone tissue as you grow. Even after you are grown, however, bone tissue continues to form within your bones. For example, every time you play soccer or basketball, some of your bones absorb the force of your weight. They respond by making new bone tissue.

Sometimes, new bone tissue forms after an accident. If you break a bone, for example, new bone tissue forms to fill the gap between the broken ends of the bone. In fact, the healed region of new bone may be stronger than the original bone!

FIGURE 9
Bone Strength
You can jump up and down or turn cartwheels without breaking bones.

Discovery
CHANNEL
SCHOOL

Bones, Muscle, and Skin

Video Preview
▶ Video Field Trip
Video Assessment

Bone Development Try this activity: Move the tip of your nose from side to side with your fingers. Notice that the tip of your nose is not stiff. That is because it contains cartilage. As an infant, much of your skeleton was cartilage. Over time, most of the cartilage was replaced with hard bone tissue.

The replacement of cartilage by bone tissue usually is complete by the time you stop growing. You've seen, however, that not all of your body's cartilage is replaced by bone. Even in adults, many joints contain cartilage that protects the ends of the bones.

Taking Care of Your Bones

Because your skeleton performs so many necessary functions, it is important to keep it healthy. **A combination of a balanced diet and regular exercise are important for a lifetime of healthy bones.**

Diet One way to help ensure healthy bones is to eat a well-balanced diet. A well-balanced diet includes enough calcium and phosphorus to keep your bones strong while they are growing. Meats, whole grains, and leafy green vegetables are all good sources of both calcium and phosphorus. Dairy products, including yogurt, are good sources of calcium.

Exercise Another way to build and maintain strong bones is to get plenty of exercise. During activities such as running, skating, or dancing, your bones support the weight of your entire body. These weight-bearing activities help your bones grow stronger and denser. To prevent injuries while exercising, be sure to wear appropriate safety equipment, such as a helmet and pads.

 **Reading Checkpoint** **What are two ways to keep your bones healthy?**

FIGURE 10
Caring for Your Bones
Exercising regularly and eating a balanced diet help to keep your bones strong and healthy.

Healthy Spine   **Spine with Osteoporosis**

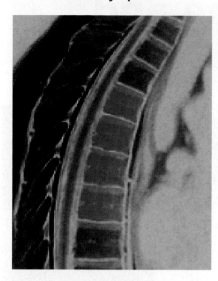 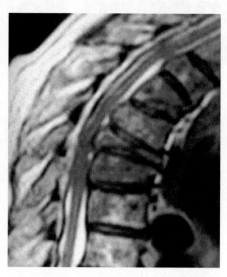

FIGURE 11
Osteoporosis
Without enough calcium in the diet, a person's bones weaken. These photos show how the shape and structure of vertebrae in a healthy spine compare with those in a person with osteoporosis.
Relating Cause and Effect *What can you do to prevent osteoporosis?*

Osteoporosis As people become older, their bones begin to lose some of the minerals they contain. Mineral loss can lead to **osteoporosis** (ahs tee oh puh ROH sis), a condition in which the body's bones become weak and break easily. You can see the effect of osteoporosis in Figure 11. Osteoporosis is more common in women than in men. Evidence indicates that regular exercise throughout life can help prevent osteoporosis. A diet with enough calcium can also help prevent osteoporosis. If you eat enough calcium-rich foods now, during your teenage years, you may help prevent osteoporosis later in life.

Section 2 Assessment

Target Reading Skill Asking Questions Work with a partner to check the answers in your graphic organizer.

Reviewing Key Concepts

1. **a. Listing** What are five functions of the skeleton?
   b. Explaining How does the skeleton protect the body?
   c. Predicting How would your life be different if your backbone consisted of just one long bone?
2. **a. Naming** What are four types of movable joints?
   b. Comparing and Contrasting Compare immovable joints with movable joints.
   c. Classifying Which of your movable joints are ball-and-socket joints?
3. **a. Identifying** What are three types of tissue in bone?
   b. Relating Cause and Effect How does the structure of bones make them both strong and lightweight?
   c. Applying Concepts How do a well-balanced diet and weight-bearing exercise help keep bones strong?

Lab zone **At-Home Activity**

Model Joints Choose two examples of movable joints from Figure 7. Ask a family member to perform separate movements that involve one joint and then the other. Make drawings to represent the joints and bones involved in each movement. Use the drawings to explain to your family how the motions of the two joints differ.

Diagnosing Bone and Joint Injuries

Reading Preview

Key Concepts
- What are some injuries of the skeletal system, and how can they be identified?
- How can bone and joint injuries be treated?

Key Terms
- fracture • dislocation
- sprain • X-ray
- magnetic resonance imaging
- arthritis • arthroscope

🎯 Target Reading Skill
Comparing and Contrasting
When you compare and contrast things, you explain how they are alike and different. As you read, compare and contrast X-rays and MRIs by completing a table like the one below.

Procedure	X-Rays	MRI
Effect on body cells		
Types of injuries identified		

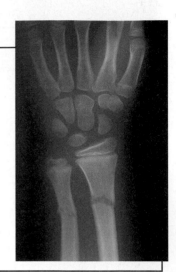

Lab zone **Discover Activity**

What Do X-ray Images Show?
1. Examine the photo of an X-ray image.
2. Try to identify what part of the human body the X-ray shows.
3. Locate the break in a bone.

Think It Over
Observing What types of structures are seen clearly in the X-ray? What types of structures cannot be seen?

You're walking home from school on a winter day. It's cold outside, and the ground is icy. Suddenly, you slip. As you lose your balance, you put out your arms to break your fall. The next thing you know, you're on the ground. Your hands sting, and you notice they are scraped. One wrist is starting to swell, and it hurts! If you try to move your wrist, it hurts even more. You need to get to a doctor—and fast.

Common Skeletal System Injuries

On the way to the doctor, you might be wondering, "Is my wrist broken?" Your swollen wrist could be broken, or it could be injured in some other way. **Three common skeletal system injuries are fractures, dislocations, and sprains.**

Fracture A **fracture,** or a break in a bone, can occur when you fall in such a way that all of your weight is placed on only a few bones. There are two kinds of fractures—simple and compound. In a simple fracture, the bone may be cracked or completely broken into two or more pieces. In a compound fracture, the broken ends of the bone stick out through the skin.

Dislocation A second injury of the skeletal system is a dislocation. A **dislocation** occurs when the end of a bone comes out of its joint. Sometimes a doctor can put back a dislocated bone without surgery. Other times surgery is needed.

Sprain A **sprain** occurs when ligaments are stretched too far and tear in places. If you have ever stumbled and turned an ankle, you may have felt a sharp pain. The pain probably occurred because the ligaments on the outside of your ankle stretched too far and partially tore. Sprains, especially of the ankle, are the most common joint injuries. Both sprains and fractures can cause swelling around the injured area.

 **Reading Checkpoint** What is the difference between a simple fracture and a compound fracture?

 Go Online
SciLINKS™ NSTA

For: Links on medical technology
Visit: www.SciLinks.org
Web Code: scn-0413

Identifying Injuries

When you see the doctor, she looks at your wrist and decides she needs to look inside your wrist to determine what's wrong. **Two ways to identify injuries of the skeletal system are X-rays and magnetic resonance imaging.**

X-rays X-ray images can determine whether bones have been broken. **X-rays** are a form of energy that travels in waves, like the light that your eyes can see.

Before an X-ray image is taken, a lead apron is placed on your body to protect you from unnecessary exposure to X-rays. Photographic film is placed under the area to be viewed. Then, a machine that emits a beam of X-rays is aimed at the area. The X-rays pass through soft tissue but not through bone. The X-rays absorbed by the bone do not reach the film. After the film is developed, it shows bones as clearly defined white areas.

One limitation of X-rays is that they cannot be used directly to view injuries to soft tissues, such as muscle and internal organs. In addition, the energy in X-rays can damage your body cells. This is why you should not have unnecessary X-ray images taken.

FIGURE 12
X-ray Diagnosis
X-rays can be used to determine whether or not you have broken a bone or dislocated a joint. **Applying Concepts** *What are some limitations of X-rays?*

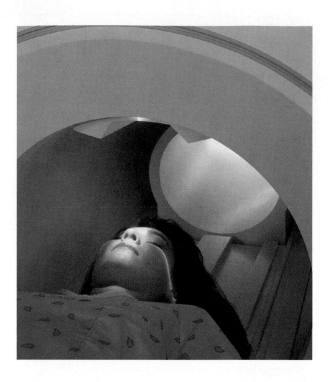

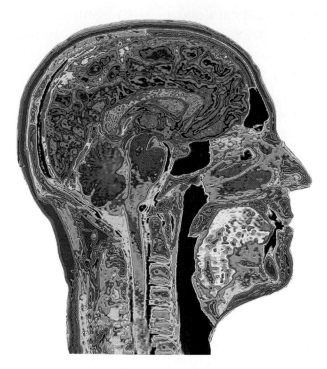

FIGURE 13
Magnetic Resonance Imaging
Magnetic resonance imaging can produce images of muscles and other soft tissues in the body. The image on the right was produced using magnetic resonance imaging.

Magnetic Resonance Imaging A method for taking clear images of both the bones and soft tissues of the body is called **magnetic resonance imaging,** or MRI. An MRI scanner is a large machine that contains electromagnets. The person is placed on a platform that is inside the field of the magnet. The person is then exposed to short bursts of magnetic energy. This magnetic energy causes atoms within the body to vibrate, or resonate. A computer then analyzes the vibration patterns and produces an image of the area.

MRI images are amazingly sharp and clear. MRI can produce images of body tissues at any angle. In addition, MRI can show a clear image of muscles and other soft tissues that an X-ray image cannot show. Another advantage of MRI is that there is no evidence that it can damage cells. Because MRI machines are very expensive to buy and use, this technique is not commonly used to identify possible broken bones.

 **Reading Checkpoint** What is one advantage that MRI has over an X-ray?

Treating Injuries

The doctor determines that your wrist is broken and puts a cast on it. You must wear the cast for six weeks until the bone heals. **In addition to wearing a cast, two other ways to treat skeletal system injuries include surgical procedures such as joint replacement and arthroscopy.**

Joint Replacement Not all injuries to the skeleton involve broken bones. Sometimes, the joints are injured or diseased and require treatment. This is often true for people who have arthritis. **Arthritis** is a disease of the joints that makes movement painful. When movement becomes extremely painful or impossible, the joint may need to be replaced with an artificial one made of metals or plastics. Doctors can replace knees, hips, shoulders, fingers, and wrists. During surgery, the natural joint is removed and an artificial one is cemented in its place.

Arthroscopy Joint injuries can also be treated by arthroscopic surgery. Doctors make a small incision and insert a slim, tube-shaped instrument called an **arthroscope** (AHR thruh skohp) into the joint. Attached to the arthroscope is a camera that projects the image from inside the joint onto a monitor. This allows doctors to look inside the joint to see what is wrong. After the problem is diagnosed, tiny instruments are inserted through one or more additional small incisions to make the necessary repairs. The arthroscope has helped to diagnose and repair many joint problems.

 **Reading Checkpoint** What is arthritis?

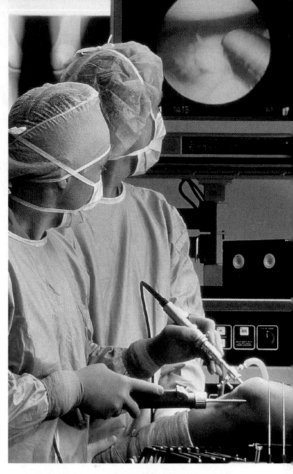

FIGURE 14
Arthroscopic Surgery
To diagnose and treat a knee injury, this surgeon has inserted an arthroscope into the patient's knee.

Section 3 Assessment

Target Reading Skill Comparing and Contrasting Use the information in your table about X-rays and MRI to help you answer Question 1 below.

Reviewing Key Concepts

1. a. **Listing** What are three common skeletal system injuries?
   b. **Comparing and Contrasting** How might each of the different skeletal system injuries be diagnosed?
   c. **Applying Concepts** Suppose that an X-ray of your injured wrist did not show a fracture. But, after a month, your wrist is still painful and stiff. Why might your doctor order an MRI?
2. a. **Identifying** What are two ways to treat bone and joint injuries surgically?
   b. **Summarizing** Which joints can be replaced surgically and how is it done?
   c. **Making Judgments** How has arthroscopic surgery improved the methods for treating skeletal injuries?

Lab zone At-Home Activity

Safety First List the types of exercise you and your family members do. With your family, brainstorm a list of safety gear and precautions to use for each activity in order to prevent skeletal system injuries. (For example, for bicycling, you might list wearing a helmet, stretching before riding, and avoiding busy streets and nighttime riding.) How can you put these safety measures into practice?

The Muscular System

Reading Preview

Key Concepts
- What types of muscles are found in the body?
- Why do skeletal muscles work in pairs?

Key Terms
- involuntary muscle
- voluntary muscle
- skeletal muscle
- tendon
- striated muscle
- smooth muscle
- cardiac muscle

Target Reading Skill
Previewing Visuals When you preview, you look ahead at the material to be read. Preview Figure 15. Then, in a graphic organizer like the one below, write two questions that you have about the diagram. As you read, answer your questions.

Types of Muscle

Q.	How does skeletal muscle help my body move?
A.	
Q.	

Lab zone Discover **Activity**

How Do Muscles Work?

1. Grip a spring-type clothespin with the thumb and index finger of your writing hand. Squeeze the clothespin open and shut as quickly as possible for two minutes. Count how many times you can squeeze the clothespin before your muscles tire.

2. Rest for one minute. Then, repeat Step 1.

Think It Over
Predicting What do you think would happen if you repeated Steps 1 and 2 with your other hand? Give a reason for your prediction. Then, test your prediction.

A rabbit becomes still when it senses danger. The rabbit sits so still that it doesn't seem to move a muscle. Could you sit without moving any muscles? Saliva builds up in your mouth. You swallow. You need to breathe. Your chest expands to let air in. All of these actions involve muscles. It is impossible to sit absolutely still without muscle movement.

There are about 600 muscles in your body. Muscles have many functions. For example, they keep your heart beating, pull your mouth into a smile, and move the bones of your skeleton. The girl doing karate on the next page uses many of her muscles to move her arms, legs, hands, feet, and head. Other muscles expand and contract her chest and allow her to breathe.

Types of Muscle

Some of your body's movements, such as smiling, are easy to control. Other movements, such as the beating of your heart, are impossible to control completely. That is because some of your muscles are not under your conscious control. Those muscles are called **involuntary muscles.** Involuntary muscles are responsible for such essential activities as breathing and digesting food.

The muscles that are under your conscious control are called **voluntary muscles.** Smiling, turning a page in a book, and getting out of your chair when the bell rings are all actions controlled by voluntary muscles.

Your body has three types of muscle tissue—skeletal muscle, smooth muscle, and cardiac muscle. Some of these muscle tissues are involuntary, and some are voluntary. In Figure 15, you see a magnified view of each type of muscle in the body. Both skeletal and smooth muscles are found in many places in the body. Cardiac muscle is found only in the heart. Each muscle type performs specific functions in the body.

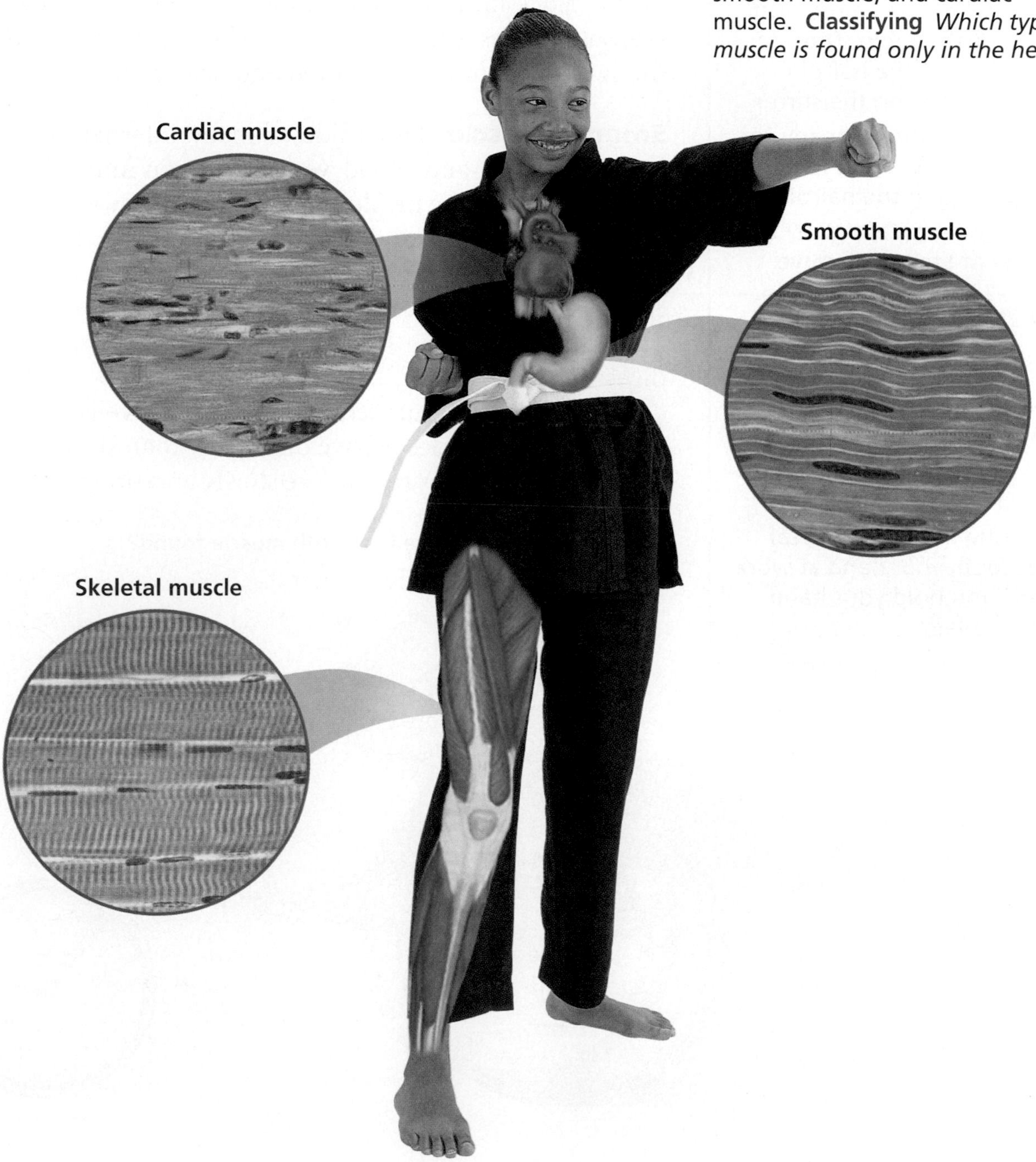

FIGURE 15
Types of Muscle
Your body has three types of muscle tissue: skeletal muscle, smooth muscle, and cardiac muscle. **Classifying** *Which type of muscle is found only in the heart?*

Cardiac muscle

Smooth muscle

Skeletal muscle

Get a Grip

Are skeletal muscles at work when you're not moving?

1. Hold a stirrer in front of you, parallel to a table top. Do not touch the table.

2. Have a partner place a hairpin on the stirrer.

3. Raise the stirrer until the "legs" of the hairpin just touch the table. The "head" of the hairpin should rest on the stirrer.

4. Hold the stirrer steady for 20 seconds. Observe what happens to the hairpin.

5. Grip the stirrer tighter and repeat Step 4. Observe.

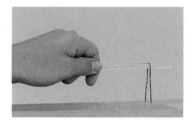

Inferring Are the skeletal muscles in your hand at work when you hold your hand still? Explain.

Skeletal Muscle Every time you walk across a room, you are using skeletal muscles. **Skeletal muscles** are attached to the bones of your skeleton and provide the force that moves your bones. At each end of a skeletal muscle is a tendon. A **tendon** is a strong connective tissue that attaches muscle to bone. Skeletal muscle cells appear banded, or striated. For this reason, skeletal muscle is sometimes called **striated** (STRY ay tid) **muscle.**

Because you have conscious control of skeletal muscles, they are classified as voluntary muscles. One characteristic of skeletal muscles is that they react very quickly. Think about what happens during a swim meet. Immediately after the starting gun sounds, a swimmer's leg muscles push the swimmer off the block into the pool. However, another characteristic of skeletal muscles is that they tire quickly. By the end of the race, the swimmer's muscles are tired and need a rest.

Smooth Muscle The inside of many internal organs, such as the stomach and blood vessels, contain **smooth muscles.** Smooth muscles are involuntary muscles. They work automatically to control certain movements inside your body, such as those involved in digestion. For example, as the smooth muscles of your stomach contract, they produce a churning action. The churning mixes the food with chemicals, and helps to digest the food.

Unlike skeletal muscles, smooth muscle cells are not striated. Smooth muscles behave differently than skeletal muscles, too. Smooth muscles react more slowly and tire more slowly.

 **Reading Checkpoint** Where is smooth muscle found?

Cardiac Muscle The tissue called **cardiac muscle** is found only in your heart. Cardiac muscle has some characteristics in common with both smooth muscle and skeletal muscle. Like smooth muscle, cardiac muscle is involuntary. Like skeletal muscle, cardiac muscle cells are striated. However, unlike skeletal muscle, cardiac muscle does not get tired. It can contract repeatedly. You call those repeated contractions heartbeats.

Muscles at Work

Has anyone ever asked you to "make a muscle"? If so, you probably tightened your fist, bent your arm at the elbow, and made the muscles in your upper arm bulge. Like other skeletal muscles, the muscles in your arm do their work by contracting, becoming shorter and thicker. Muscle cells contract when they receive messages from the nervous system. **Because muscle cells can only contract, not extend, skeletal muscles must work in pairs. While one muscle contracts, the other muscle in the pair relaxes to its original length.**

Muscles Work in Pairs Figure 16 shows the muscle action involved in bending the arm at the elbow. First, the biceps muscle on the front of the upper arm contracts to bend the elbow, lifting the forearm and hand. As the biceps contracts, the triceps on the back of the upper arm relaxes and returns to its original length. Then, to straighten the elbow, the triceps muscle contracts. As the triceps contracts to extend the arm, the biceps relaxes and returns to its original length. Another example of muscles that work in pairs are those in your thigh that bend and straighten the knee joint.

Go Online
PHSchool.com

For: More on muscle types
Visit: PHSchool.com
Web Code: ced-4014

FIGURE 16
Muscle Pairs

Because muscles can only contract, or shorten, they must work in pairs. To bend the arm at the elbow, the biceps contracts while the triceps returns to its original length. **Interpreting Diagrams** *What happens to each muscle to straighten the arm?*

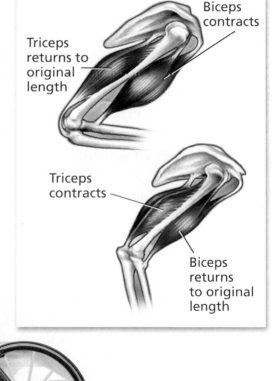

Triceps returns to original length

Biceps contracts

Triceps contracts

Biceps returns to original length

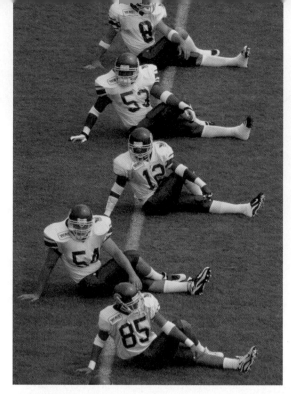

FIGURE 17
Preventing Muscle Injuries
When you warm up before exercising, you increase the flexibility of your muscles.

Muscular Strength and Flexibility Regular exercise is important for maintaining both muscular strength and flexibility. Exercise makes individual muscle cells grow in size. As a result, the whole muscle becomes thicker. The thicker a muscle is, the stronger the muscle is. When you stretch and warm up thoroughly before exercising, your muscles become more flexible. Stretching helps prepare your muscles for exercise or play.

Sometimes, despite taking proper precautions, muscles can become injured. A muscle strain, or pulled muscle, can occur when muscles are overworked or overstretched. Tendons can also be overstretched or partially torn. After a long period of exercise, a skeletal muscle can cramp. When a muscle cramps, the entire muscle contracts strongly and stays contracted. If you injure a muscle or tendon, it is important to follow medical instructions and to rest the injured area so it can heal.

 **Reading Checkpoint** **What are two ways to prepare the muscles for exercise?**

Section 4 Assessment

Target Reading Skill **Previewing Visuals** Refer to your questions and answers about Figure 15 to help you answer Question 1 below.

Reviewing Key Concepts

1. a. **Identifying** What are the three types of muscle tissue?
   b. **Comparing and Contrasting** How do voluntary and involuntary muscles differ? Give an example of each type of muscle.
   c. **Predicting** The muscles that move your fingers are attached to the bones in your fingers by tendons. Suppose one of the tendons in a person's index finger were cut. How would it affect movement in the finger?

2. a. **Identifying** Where might you find muscle pairs?
   b. **Describing** Describe how the muscles in your upper arm work together to bend and straighten your arm.
   c. **Applying Concepts** When exercising to build muscular strength, why is it important to exercise both muscles in a muscle pair equally?

Writing in Science

Comparison Paragraph Write a paragraph comparing smooth muscle tissue and skeletal muscle tissue. Include whether these muscle tissues are voluntary or involuntary, where they are found and what their functions are. In addition, describe what you might expect to see if you looked at these muscle tissues under a microscope.

A Look Beneath the Skin

Problem

What are some characteristics of skeletal muscles? How do skeletal muscles work?

Skills Focus

observing, inferring, classifying

Materials

- water
- paper towels
- scissors
- dissecting tray
- uncooked chicken wing, treated with bleach

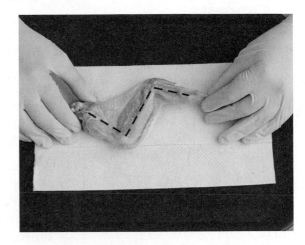

Procedure

1. Put on goggles, an apron, and protective gloves. **CAUTION:** *Wear gloves whenever you handle the chicken.*

2. Your teacher will give you a chicken wing. Rinse it well with water, dry it with paper towels, and place it in a dissecting tray.

3. Carefully extend the wing to find out how many major parts it has. Draw a diagram of the external structure. Label the upper arm, elbow, lower arm, and hand (wing tip).

4. Use scissors to remove the skin. Cut only through the skin. **CAUTION:** *Cut away from your body and your classmates.*

5. Examine the muscles, which are the bundles of pink tissue around the bones. Find the two groups of muscles in the upper arm. Hold the arm down at the shoulder, and alternately pull on each muscle group. Observe what happens.

6. Find the two groups of muscles in the lower arm. Hold down the arm at the elbow, and alternately pull on each muscle group. Then, make a diagram of the wing's muscles.

7. Find the tendons—shiny white tissue at the ends of the muscles. Notice what parts the tendons connect. Add the tendons to your diagram.

8. Remove the muscles and tendons. Find the ligaments, which are the whitish ribbon-shaped structures between bones. Add them to your diagram.

9. Dispose of the chicken parts according to your teacher's instructions. Wash your hands.

Analyze and Conclude

1. **Observing** How does a chicken wing move at the elbow? How does the motion compare to how your elbow moves? What type of joint is involved?

2. **Inferring** What happened when you pulled on one of the arm muscles? What muscle action does the pulling represent?

3. **Classifying** Categorize the muscles you observed as smooth, cardiac, or skeletal.

4. **Communicating** Why is it valuable to record your observations with accurate diagrams? Write a paragraph in which you describe what your diagrams show.

More to Explore

Use the procedures from this lab to examine an uncooked chicken thigh and leg. Compare how the chicken leg and a human leg move. *Obtain your teacher's permission before carrying out your investigation.*

The Skin

Reading Preview

Key Concepts
- What are the functions and the structures of skin?
- What habits can help keep your skin healthy?

Key Terms
- epidermis • melanin
- dermis • pore • follicle
- cancer

Target Reading Skill

Identifying Main Ideas As you read the section titled The Body's Tough Covering, write the main idea—the biggest or most important idea—in a graphic organizer like the one below. Then, write five supporting details. The supporting details give examples of the main idea.

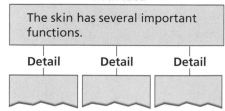

Main Idea

The skin has several important functions.

Detail	Detail	Detail

Discover Activity

What Can You Observe About Skin?

1. Using a hand lens, examine the skin on your hand. Look for pores and hairs on both the palm and back of your hand.
2. Place a plastic glove on your hand. After five minutes, remove the glove. Then, examine the skin on your hand with the hand lens.

Think It Over
Inferring Compare your hand before and after wearing the glove. What happened to the skin when you wore the glove? Why did this happen?

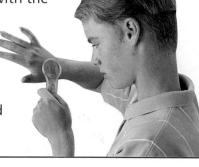

Here's a question for you: What's the largest organ in the human body? If your answer is the skin, you are right! If an adult's skin were stretched out flat, it would cover an area larger than 1.5 square meters—about the size of a mattress on a twin bed. You may think of the skin as nothing more than a covering that separates the inside of the body from the outside environment. If so, you'll be surprised to learn about the many important roles that the skin plays.

The Body's Tough Covering

The skin performs several major functions in the body. **The skin covers and protects the body from injury, infection, and water loss. The skin also helps regulate body temperature, eliminate wastes, gather information about the environment, and produce vitamin D.**

Protecting the Body The skin protects the body by forming a barrier that keeps disease-causing microorganisms and harmful substances outside the body. In addition, the skin helps keep important substances inside the body. Like plastic wrap that keeps food from drying out, the skin prevents the loss of important fluids such as water.

Maintaining Temperature Another function of the skin is to help the body maintain a steady temperature. Many blood vessels run throughout the skin. When you become too warm, these blood vessels enlarge and the amount of blood that flows through them increases. These changes allow heat to move from your body into the outside environment. In addition, sweat glands in the skin respond to excess heat by producing perspiration. As perspiration evaporates from your skin, your skin is cooled.

Eliminating Wastes Perspiration contains dissolved waste materials that come from the breakdown of chemicals during cellular processes. Thus, your skin is also helping to eliminate wastes whenever you perspire. For example, some of the wastes that come from the breakdown of proteins are eliminated in perspiration.

Gathering Information The skin also gathers information about the environment. To understand how the skin does this, place your fingertips on the skin of your arm and press down firmly. Then lightly pinch yourself. You have just tested some of the nerves in your skin. The nerves in skin provide information about such things as pressure, pain, and temperature. Pain messages are important because they warn you that something in your surroundings may have injured you.

Producing Vitamin D Lastly, some of the skin cells produce vitamin D in the presence of sunlight. Vitamin D is important for healthy bones because it helps the cells in your digestive system to absorb the calcium in your food. Your skin cells need only a few minutes of sunlight to produce all the vitamin D you need in a day.

✓ Reading Checkpoint How does your skin gather information about the environment?

FIGURE 18
Eliminating Wastes
Sweat glands in the skin produce perspiration, which leaves the body through pores. The inset photo shows beads of sweat on skin.
Relating Cause and Effect *In addition to eliminating wastes, what is another important function of perspiration?*

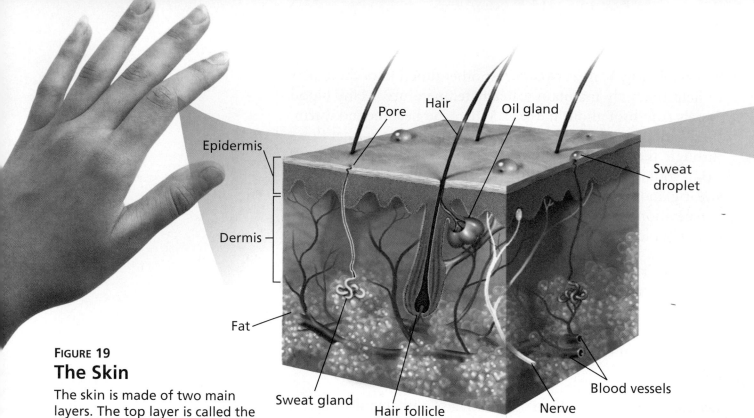

Pore Hair Oil gland

Epidermis

Sweat droplet

Dermis

Fat

Sweat gland

Hair follicle

Nerve

Blood vessels

FIGURE 19
The Skin

The skin is made of two main layers. The top layer is called the epidermis. The bottom layer is called the dermis.

Interpreting Diagrams *In which layer of the skin do you find blood vessels?*

The Epidermis

The skin is organized into two main layers, the epidermis and the dermis. The **epidermis** is the outer layer of the skin. In most places, the epidermis is thinner than the dermis. The epidermis does not have nerves or blood vessels. This is why you usually don't feel pain from very shallow scratches, and why shallow scratches do not bleed.

Epidermis Structure Like all cells, the cells in the epidermis have a life cycle. Each epidermal cell begins life deep in the epidermis, where cells divide to form new cells. The new cells mature and move upward in the epidermis as new cells form beneath them. After about two weeks, the cells die and become part of the epidermal surface layer. Under a microscope, this surface layer of dead cells resembles flat bags laid on top of one another. Cells remain in this layer for about two weeks. Then, they are shed and replaced by the dead cells below.

Epidermis Function In some ways, the cells of the epidermis are more valuable dead than alive. Most of the protection provided by the skin is due to the layer of dead cells on the surface. The thick layer of dead cells on your fingertips, for example, protects and cushions your fingertips. Also, the shedding of dead cells carries away bacteria and other substances that settle on the skin. Every time you rub your hands together, you lose thousands of dead skin cells and any bacteria on them.

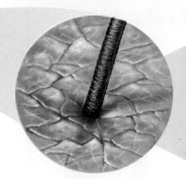

Hair follicle

Some cells in the inner layer of the epidermis help to protect the body, too. On your fingers, for example, some cells produce hard fingernails, which protect the fingertips from injury and help you scratch and pick up objects.

Other cells deep in the epidermis produce **melanin,** a pigment, or colored substance, that gives skin its color. The more melanin in your skin, the darker it is. Exposure to sunlight stimulates the skin to make more melanin. Melanin production helps to protect the skin from burning.

The Dermis

The **dermis** is the inner layer of the skin. Find the dermis in Figure 19. Notice that it is located below the epidermis and above a layer of fat. This fat layer pads the internal organs and helps keep heat in the body.

The dermis contains nerves and blood vessels. The dermis also contains sweat glands, hairs, and oil glands. Sweat glands produce perspiration, which reaches the surface through openings called **pores.** Strands of hair grow within the dermis in structures called **follicles** (FAHL ih kulz). The hair that you see above the skin's surface is made up of dead cells. Oil produced in glands around the hair follicles help to waterproof the hair. In addition, oil that reaches the surface of the skin helps to keep the skin moist.

 **Reading Checkpoint** What is the function of pores in the skin?

Lab zone Try This **Activity**

Sweaty Skin
This activity illustrates one of the skin's functions.

1. Wrap a wet cotton ball around the bulb of one thermometer. Place a second thermometer next to the first one.

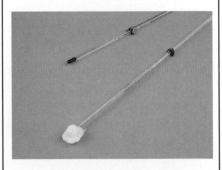

2. After two minutes, record the temperature reading on each thermometer.

3. Using a piece of cardboard, fan both of the thermometers for several minutes. The cardboard should be at least 10 cm from the thermometers. Record the temperatures.

Measuring Which of the thermometers had a lower temperature after Step 3? How does this activity relate to the role of skin in regulating body temperature?

Analyzing Data

Sunscreen Ratings

The graph shows how sunscreens with different sun protection factor (SPF) ratings extend the time three people can stay in the sun without beginning to get a sunburn.

1. **Reading Graphs** What does the height of each bar in the graph represent?

2. **Interpreting Data** How long can Person B stay in the sun without sunscreen before starting to burn? With a sunscreen of SPF 4? SPF 15?

3. **Inferring** Suppose that Person C was planning to attend an all-day picnic. Which sunscreen should Person C apply? Use data to support your answer.

4. **Calculating** Which is more effective at preventing sunburn—a sunscreen with SPF 4 or one with SPF 15? How much more effective is it? Show your work.

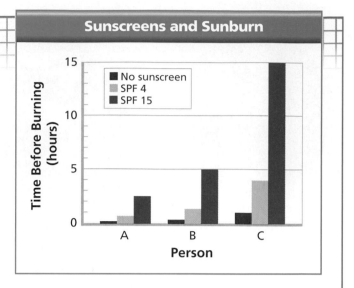

Sunscreens and Sunburn

5. **Drawing Conclusions** What does the number in the SPF rating stand for? *(Hint: Note the length of time each person can stay in the sun without sunscreen and compare this value to the length of time each can stay in the sun using SPF 4. Then, do the same for SPF 15.)*

Caring for Your Skin

Because your skin has so many vital functions, taking care of it is important. **Three simple habits can help you keep your skin healthy. Eat a healthful diet. Keep your skin clean and dry. Limit your exposure to the sun.**

Healthful Diet Your skin is always active. Eating a well-balanced diet provides the energy and raw materials needed for the growth and replacement of hair, nails, and skin cells. In addition to what you eat, a healthful diet also includes drinking plenty of water. That way, you can replace the water lost in perspiration.

Keeping Skin Clean When you wash your skin with mild soap, you get rid of dirt and harmful bacteria. Washing your skin also helps to control oiliness.

Good washing habits are particularly important during the teenage years when oil glands are more active. When glands become clogged with oil, the blackheads and whiteheads of acne can form. If acne becomes infected by skin bacteria, your doctor may prescribe an antibiotic to help control the infection.

For: Links on the skin
Visit: www.SciLinks.org
Web Code: scn-0415

Limiting Sun Exposure It is important to protect your skin from the harmful effects of the sun. Repeated exposure to sunlight can damage skin cells, and possibly lead to skin cancer. **Cancer** is a disease in which some cells in the body divide uncontrollably. In addition, repeated exposure to the sun can cause the skin to become leathery and wrinkled.

There are many things you can do to protect your skin from damage by the sun. When you are outdoors, always wear a hat, sunglasses, and use a sunscreen on exposed skin. Choose clothing made of tightly woven fabrics for the greatest protection. In addition, avoid exposure to the sun between the hours of 10 A.M. and 4 P.M. That is the time when sunlight is the strongest.

 **Reading Checkpoint** What health problems can result from repeated sun exposure?

FIGURE 20
Skin Protection
This person is wearing a hat to protect his skin from the sun.
Applying Concepts *What other behaviors can provide protection from the sun?*

Section 5 Assessment

🎯 **Target Reading Skill Identifying Main Ideas** Use your graphic organizer to help you answer Question 1 below.

Reviewing Key Concepts

1. a. Listing What are five important functions of the skin?
  b. Identifying How does the epidermis protect the body? What structure in the dermis helps to maintain body temperature?
  c. Inferring What could happen if the pores in your dermis become blocked?
2. a. Identifying What are three things you can do to keep your skin healthy?
  b. Explaining Why is it important to use sunscreen to protect your skin when outside?
  c. Making Judgments Do you think it is possible to wash your skin too much and damage it as a result? Why or why not?

Lab zone At-Home Activity

Protection From the Sun With a family member, look for products in your home that provide protection from the sun. You may also want to visit a store that sells these products. Make a list of the products and place them in categories, such as sunblocks, clothing, eye protectors, and other forms of protection. Explain to your family member why it is important to use such products.

Sun Safety

Problem

How well do different materials protect the skin from the sun?

Skills Focus

observing, predicting, interpreting data, drawing conclusions

Materials

- scissors
- photosensitive paper
- metric ruler
- white construction paper
- stapler
- pencil
- resealable plastic bag
- plastic knife
- 2 sunscreens with SPF ratings of 4 and 30
- staple remover
- 3 different fabrics

Procedure

PART 1 Sunscreen Protection

1. Read over the procedure for Part 1. Then, write a prediction about how well each of the sunscreens will protect against the sun.

2. Use scissors to cut two strips of photosensitive paper that measure 5 cm by 15 cm.

3. Divide each strip into thirds by drawing lines across the strips.

4. Cover one third of each strip with a square of white construction paper. Staple each square down.

5. Use a pencil to write the lower SPF rating on the back of the first strip. Write the other SPF rating on the back of the second strip.

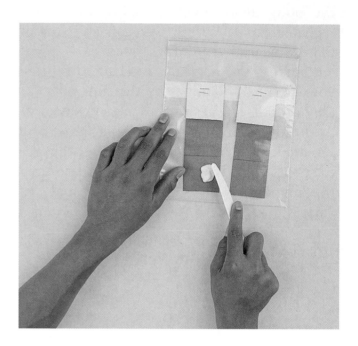

6. Place the two strips side by side in a plastic bag. Seal the bag, then staple through the white squares to hold the strips in place.

7. With a plastic knife, spread a thin layer of each sunscreen on the bag over the bottom square of its labeled strip. This is shown in the photo above. Make certain each strip has the same thickness of sunscreen. Be sure not to spread sunscreen over the middle squares.

8. Place the strips in sunlight until the color of the middle squares stops changing. Make sure the bag is sunscreen-side up when you place it in the sunlight.

9. Remove the staples from the bag, and then take out the strips. Take off the construction paper. Rinse the strips for one minute in cold water, then dry them flat.

10. Observe all the squares. Then, record your observations.

PART 2 Fabric Protection

11. Your teacher will provide three fabric pieces of different thicknesses.

12. Based on the procedure in Part 1, design an experiment to test how effective the three fabrics are in protecting against the sun. Write a prediction about which fabric you think will be most effective, next most effective, and least effective.

13. Obtain your teacher's approval before carrying out your experiment. Record all of your observations.

Analyze and Conclude

1. **Observing** Did the sunscreens protect against sun exposure? How do you know?

2. **Predicting** Which sunscreen provided more protection? Was your prediction correct? How would you predict a sunscreen with an SPF of 15 would compare to the sunscreens you tested?

3. **Interpreting Data** Did the fabrics protect against sun exposure? How do you know?

4. **Drawing Conclusions** Which of the fabrics provided the most protection? The least protection? How did your results compare with your predictions?

5. **Communicating** What advice would you give people about protecting their skin from the sun? Create a pamphlet in which you address this question by comparing the different sunscreens and fabrics you tested.

More to Explore

Design another experiment, this time to find out whether ordinary window glass protects skin against sun exposure. *Obtain your teacher's permission before carrying out your investigation.*

① Body Organization and Homeostasis

Key Concepts

- The levels of organization in the body consist of cells, tissues, organs, and organ systems.
- Homeostasis is the process by which an organism's internal environment is kept stable in spite of changes in the external environment.

Key Terms

cell	connective tissue
cell membrane	epithelial tissue
nucleus	organ
cytoplasm	organ system
tissue	homeostasis
muscle tissue	stress
nervous tissue	

② The Skeletal System

Key Concepts

- Your skeleton provides shape and support, enables you to move, protects your organs, produces blood cells, and stores minerals and other materials until your body needs them.
- Joints allow bones to move in different ways.
- Bones are complex living structures that undergo growth and development.
- A balanced diet and regular exercise are important for a lifetime of healthy bones.

Key Terms

skeleton
vertebra
joint
ligament
cartilage
compact bone
spongy bone
marrow
osteoporosis

③ Diagnosing Bone and Joint Injuries

Key Concepts

- Three common skeletal system injuries are fractures, dislocations, and sprains. Two ways to identify skeletal injuries are X-rays and magnetic resonance imaging (MRI).
- Ways to treat skeletal injuries include wearing a cast, joint replacement, and arthroscopy.

Key Terms

fracture	magnetic resonance
dislocation	imaging
sprain	arthritis
X-ray	arthroscope

④ The Muscular System

Key Concepts

- Your body has three types of muscle tissue—skeletal, smooth, and cardiac.
- Skeletal muscles work in pairs. While one muscle contracts, the other muscle in the pair relaxes to its original length.

Key Terms

involuntary muscle	striated muscle
voluntary muscle	smooth muscle
skeletal muscle	cardiac muscle
tendon	

⑤ The Skin

Key Concepts

- The skin has several functions: protection, maintaining temperature, eliminating wastes, gathering information, and making vitamin D.
- The two skin layers are epidermis and dermis.
- Three simple habits can help you keep your skin healthy. Eat a healthful diet. Keep your skin clean and dry. Limit your sun exposure.

Key Terms

epidermis	pore
melanin	follicle
dermis	cancer

Review and Assessment

Organizing Information

Concept Mapping Copy the concept map about the types of muscles onto a separate sheet of paper. Then complete it and add a title. (For more on Concept Mapping, see the Skills Handbook.)

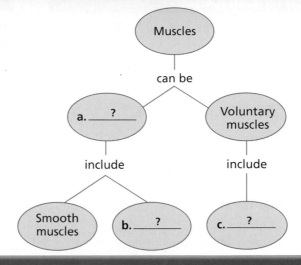

Reviewing Key Terms

Choose the letter of the best answer.

1. A group of similar cells that perform a similar function is called a(n)
   a. cell.   b. organ.
   c. tissue.   d. organ system.

2. A soft, connective tissue found inside some bones is
   a. cytoplasm.
   b. marrow.
   c. cartilage.
   d. osteoporosis.

3. The stretching and tearing of ligaments is
   a. a fracture.
   b. a dislocation.
   c. a sprain.
   d. osteoporosis.

4. Muscles that help the skeleton move are
   a. cardiac muscles.
   b. smooth muscles.
   c. skeletal muscles.
   d. involuntary muscles.

5. A colored substance that helps to keep the skin from burning is
   a. the dermis.   b. the epidermis.
   c. melanin.   d. a follicle.

If the statement is true, write _true_. If the statement is false, change the underlined word or words to make the statement true.

6. The <u>cytoplasm</u> directs the cell's activities.

7. Spongy bone is filled with <u>cartilage.</u>

8. <u>X-rays</u> produce images of soft tissues.

9. <u>Skeletal</u> muscle is called striated muscle.

10. The <u>epidermis</u> contains nerve endings and blood vessels.

Writing in Science

Descriptive Paragraph Pretend you are a writer for a science magazine for children. Write a few paragraphs that compare the characteristics of cartilage with the characteristics of bones. Be sure to explain the advantages of both types of materials.

Discovery
CHANNEL
SCHOOL™

Bones, Muscles, and Skin
Video Preview
Video Field Trip
▶ Video Assessment

Review and Assessment

Checking Concepts

11. Explain the relationship among cells, tissues, organs, and organ systems.

12. List the four kinds of movable joints. Describe the type of movement each joint allows.

13. Describe the structure of a bone.

14. How is arthroscopy used to treat injuries?

15. How does the appearance of smooth muscle differ from that of skeletal muscle?

16. Explain how skeletal muscles work in pairs.

17. How does the skin protect your body?

Thinking Critically

18. **Classifying** Identify each of the labeled parts of the cell.

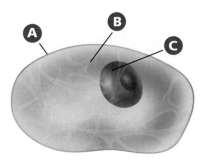

19. **Inferring** In addition to bone, cartilage, and fat, scientists classify blood as a connective tissue. Explain why.

20. **Making Generalizations** How is homeostasis important to survival?

21. **Making Judgments** A patient is admitted to the emergency room with a severe headache after a fall. What kind of image should be taken to diagnose the problem? Explain.

22. **Predicting** If smooth muscle had to be controlled consciously, what problems could you foresee in day-to-day living?

23. **Relating Cause and Effect** A person who is exposed to excessive heat may suffer from heatstroke. The first sign of heatstroke is that the person stops sweating. Why is heatstroke a life-threatening emergency?

Applying Skills

Use the graph to answer Questions 24–26.

The graph below shows the effects of the temperature of the environment on a boy's skin temperature and on the temperature inside his body.

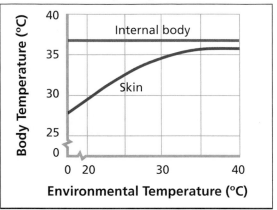

24. **Interpreting Data** As the temperature of the environment rises, what happens to the boy's internal body temperature? How does this demonstrate homeostasis?

25. **Inferring** What happens to the temperature of the boy's skin? Why is this pattern different from the pattern shown by the boy's internal body temperature?

26. **Predicting** Suppose the boy went outdoors on a chilly fall morning. Predict what would happen to his internal body temperature and his skin temperature. Explain.

Lab zone Chapter **Project**

Performance Assessment Before testing your prosthetic hand, explain to your classmates how and why you designed the hand the way you did. When you test the hand, observe how it picks up objects. How does it compare with a real human hand? How could you improve the function of your prosthetic hand?

80 ◆

Standardized Test Practice

Test-Taking Tip

Interpreting Graphs

If a question asks you to interpret a line graph, look first at the graph's title. This tells you the subject of the graph. Then, look at the labels on the horizontal and vertical axes. The labels represent the variables in the research and tell you what relationship is plotted on the graph.

Choose the letter that best answers the question or completes the statement.

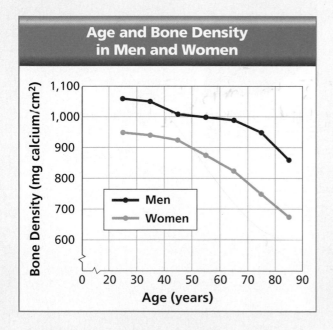

Age and Bone Density in Men and Women

1. Which of the following is the best example of organization in the human body?
   A An arm muscle is part of a tissue.
   B A nerve cell contains nerve tissue.
   C The stomach contains muscle cells.
   D The circulatory system is part of the heart.

2. A doctor cannot identify a sprained ankle by taking an X-ray because
   A X-rays pass through bones.
   B soft tissues block X-rays.
   C X-rays pass through soft tissues.
   D a sprained ankle cannot be viewed on an X-ray until the swelling decreases.

3. The muscles that you use to lift a book are examples of
   A cardiac muscle.
   B smooth muscle.
   C involuntary muscle.
   D skeletal muscle.

Use the graph below and your knowledge of science to answer Questions 4–5.

4. What difference is shown by the data in this graph?
   A The bones of women are more dense than the bones of men.
   B The bone density of men decreases less rapidly with age than does the bone density of women.
   C An average 55-year-old woman has stronger bones than an average 55-year-old man.
   D The bones of men contain less calcium than do the bones of women.

5. The independent variable in this study is
   A bone density.
   B milligrams of calcium.
   C different for men and for women.
   D age of the subjects.

Open-ended Question

6. Compare the dermis and the epidermis layers of the skin. Discuss the following: thickness, location, nerves, blood vessels, sweat glands, and cell life cycle.

Chapter 3

Food and Digestion

Let's eat! These baskets of vegetables offer ▶
a wide choice of tasty and healthful foods.

Food and Digestion

▶ Video Preview
Video Field Trip
Video Assessment

Lab zone™ Chapter **Project**

What's for Lunch?

When you're hungry and grab a snack, what do you choose? In this project, you'll take a close look at the foods you select each day.

Your Goal To compare your eating pattern to the recommendations in the Food Guide Pyramid

To complete this project successfully, you must

- keep an accurate record of everything you eat and drink for three days
- create graphs to compare your eating pattern with the recommendations in the Food Guide Pyramid
- make changes in your diet, if needed, during another three-day period

Plan It! Before you begin, study the Food Guide Pyramid in this chapter to understand how foods are grouped. Then, decide how to best keep an accurate, complete food log. How will you make sure you record everything you eat, including snacks and drinks? How will you decide which group each food falls into? How will you determine serving sizes? After your teacher approves your plan, start keeping your food log.

Food and Energy

Reading Preview

Key Concepts
- Why does your body need food?
- How do the six nutrients needed by the body help carry out essential processes?

Key Terms
- nutrient • calorie
- carbohydrate • glucose • fat
- protein • amino acid
- vitamin • mineral

Target Reading Skill
Outlining As you read, make an outline about the six groups of nutrients needed by the body. Use the red headings for the main ideas and the blue headings for the supporting ideas.

Food and Energy
I. Why You Need Food
A. Nutrients
B.
II. Carbohydrates
A.

Lab zone Discover **Activity**

Food Claims—Fact or Fiction?

1. Examine the list of statements at the right. Copy the list onto a separate sheet of paper.
2. Next to each statement, write *agree* or *disagree*. Give a reason for your response.
3. Discuss your responses with a small group of classmates. Compare the reasons you gave for agreeing or disagreeing with each statement.

Think It Over
Posing Questions List some other statements about nutrition that you have heard. How could you find out whether the statements are true?

Fact or Fiction?
a. Athletes need more protein in their diets than other people do.
b. The only salt that a food contains is the salt that you have added to it.
c. As part of a healthy diet, everyone should take vitamin supplements.

Imagine a Thanksgiving dinner—roast turkey on a platter, delicious stuffing, and lots of vegetables—an abundance of colors and aromas. Food is a central part of many celebrations, of times shared with friends and family. Food is also essential. Every living thing needs food to stay alive.

Why You Need Food

Foods provide your body with materials for growing and for repairing tissues. Food also provides energy for everything you do. For example, running, playing a musical instrument, reading, and even sleeping require energy. Food also helps your body maintain homeostasis. You read in Chapter 1 that the systems of the body work together to help keep the body's internal environment stable. By filling your energy needs, food enables your body to keep this balance during all your activities.

Nutrients Your body breaks down the foods you eat into nutrients. **Nutrients** (NOO tree unts) are the substances in food that provide the raw materials and energy the body needs to carry out all its essential processes. There are six groups of nutrients necessary for human health—carbohydrates, fats, proteins, vitamins, minerals, and water.

Energy When nutrients are used by the body for energy, the amount of energy they release can be measured in units called calories. One **calorie** is the amount of energy needed to raise the temperature of one gram of water by one degree Celsius. Most foods contain many thousands of calories of energy. Biologists use the term *Calorie,* with a capital *C,* to measure the energy in foods. One Calorie is the same as 1 kilocalorie (kcal) or 1,000 calories. For example, one serving of popcorn may contain 60 Calories (60 kcal), or 60,000 calories, of energy. The more Calories a food has, the more energy it contains.

You need to eat a certain number of Calories each day to meet your body's energy needs. Your daily energy requirement depends on your level of physical activity. Your needs also change as you grow and age. As an infant and child, you grew very rapidly, so you likely had very high energy needs. Your current growth and level of physical activity affect the number of Calories you need now. The more active you are, the greater your energy needs are.

✔ **Reading Checkpoint** How is energy in foods measured?

FIGURE 1
Burning Calories
The number of Calories you burn depends on your weight as well as your level of activity. The more active you are, the more Calories you burn.
Applying Concepts *Which activity do you think burns the most Calories per hour—playing basketball, walking, or reading?*

Playing basketball

Walking

Reading

FIGURE 2
Carbohydrates

Simple carbohydrates, or sugars, are found in fruits, milk, and some vegetables. Sugars are also added to cookies, candies, and soft drinks. Complex carbohydrates are found in rice, corn, pasta, and bread. Fruits, vegetables, nuts, and whole-grain foods also contain fiber.
Applying Concepts *Why is fiber important in the diet?*

Simple Carbohydrates

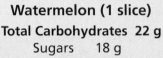

Brownie (1 square)
Total Carbohydrates 18 g
  Sugars   10 g
  Starches   7 g
  Fiber   1 g

Watermelon (1 slice)
Total Carbohydrates 22 g
  Sugars   18 g
  Starches   3 g
  Fiber   1 g

Milk (1 cup)
Total Carbohydrates 12 g
  Sugars   12 g
  Starches   0 g
  Fiber   0 g

Carbohydrates

The nutrients called **carbohydrates** (kahr boh HY drayts), which are composed of carbon, oxygen, and hydrogen, are a major source of energy. One gram of carbohydrate provides your body with four Calories of energy. **In addition to providing energy, carbohydrates provide the raw materials to make cell parts.** Based on their chemical structure, carbohydrates are divided into simple carbohydrates and complex carbohydrates.

Simple Carbohydrates Simple carbohydrates are also known as sugars. One sugar, **glucose** (GLOO kohs), is the major source of energy for your body's cells. However, most foods do not contain large amounts of glucose. The body converts other types of sugars, such as the sugar found in fruits, into glucose. Glucose is the form of sugar the body can most easily use.

Complex Carbohydrates Complex carbohydrates are made up of many sugar molecules linked together in a chain. Starch is a complex carbohydrate found in foods from plants, such as potatoes, rice, wheat, and corn. To use starch as an energy source, your body first breaks it down into smaller, individual sugar molecules. Only then can your body release the molecules' energy.

Like starch, fiber is a complex carbohydrate found in plants. But unlike starch, fiber cannot be broken down into sugar molecules by your body. Instead, fiber passes through the body and is eliminated.

Complex Carbohydrates

Yellow Corn (1 ear)
Total Carbohydrates 19 g
Sugars 2 g
Starches 15 g
Fiber 2 g

Pasta (1 cup)
Total Carbohydrates 40 g
Sugars 1 g
Starches 37 g
Fiber 2 g

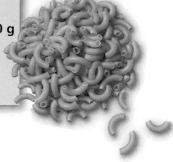

Wheat Bread (1 slice)
Total Carbohydrates 17 g
Sugars 3.5 g
Starches 12.0 g
Fiber 1.5 g

Because your body cannot digest it, fiber is not considered a nutrient. Fiber is an important part of the diet, however, because it helps keep the digestive system functioning properly.

Nutritionists' Recommendations Nutritionists recommend that 45 to 65 percent of the Calories in a diet come from carbohydrates. It is better to eat more complex carbohydrates, such as whole grains, than simple carbohydrates. Foods made with whole grains usually contain a variety of other nutrients. Foods made with a lot of sugar, such as candy and soft drinks, have few valuable nutrients. Also, while sugars can give you a quick burst of energy, starches provide a more even, long-term energy source.

 **Reading Checkpoint** What are two types of carbohydrates? Give an example of each.

Fats

Like carbohydrates, **fats** are energy-containing nutrients that are composed of carbon, oxygen, and hydrogen. However, fats contain more than twice the energy of an equal amount of carbohydrates. One gram of fat provides your body with nine Calories of energy. **In addition to providing energy, fats have other important functions. Fats form part of the cell membrane, the structure that forms the boundary of a cell. Fatty tissue protects and supports your internal organs and insulates your body.**

Lab zone Skills **Activity**

Predicting
You can do a test to see which foods contain starch.

1. Put on your apron.
2. Obtain food samples from your teacher. Predict which ones contain starch. Write down your predictions.
3. Use a plastic dropper to add three drops of iodine to each food sample. **CAUTION:** *Iodine can stain skin and clothing.* Handle it carefully. If the iodine turns blue-black, starch is present.

Which foods contain starch? Were your predictions correct?

FIGURE 3

Many foods contain saturated, unsaturated, and trans fats. Unsaturated fats are considered to be more healthful than saturated fats and trans fats.
Interpreting Graphs *Which item has the most unsaturated fat— butter, tub margarine, or olive oil?*

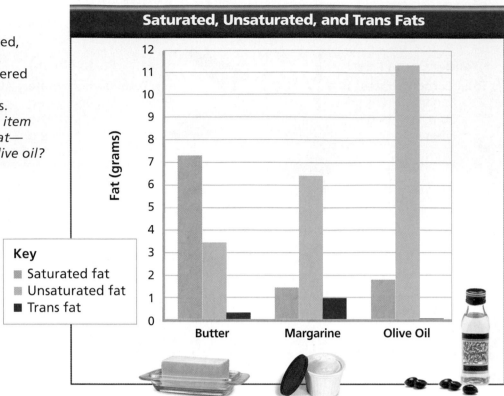

Saturated, Unsaturated, and Trans Fats

Key
■ Saturated fat
■ Unsaturated fat
■ Trans fat

Butter   Margarine   Olive Oil

Kinds of Fats

Fats may be classified as unsaturated or saturated based on their chemical structure. Unsaturated fats are usually liquid at room temperature. Most cooking oils are unsaturated fats. Saturated fats are usually solid at room temperature. Meat and dairy products contain relatively large amounts of saturated fat.

You may have heard about trans fat. Trans fats are made when manufacturers add hydrogen to vegetable oils. Foods containing trans fats stay fresh longer than foods containing unsaturated fats. Trans fats are found in margarine, chips, and commercially baked goods. Both trans fats and saturated fats are considered to be less healthful than unsaturated fats.

Cholesterol

Cholesterol (kuh LES tur awl) is a waxy, fatlike substance found only in animal products. Like fats, cholesterol is an important part of your body's cells. Your liver can make all of the cholesterol your body needs. Therefore, cholesterol is not a necessary part of the diet.

Nutritionists' Recommendations

Nutritionists recommend that no more than 30 percent of the Calories eaten each day come from fats. Extra fats and cholesterol in the diet can lead to a buildup of fatty material in the blood vessels. This fatty buildup can cause heart disease.

 **Reading Checkpoint** How can you tell the difference between most unsaturated fats and saturated fats?

Proteins

Proteins are nutrients that contain nitrogen as well as carbon, hydrogen, and oxygen. **Proteins are needed for tissue growth and repair. They also play an important part in chemical reactions within cells.** Proteins can serve as a source of energy, but they are a less important source of energy than carbohydrates or fats. About 10 to 35 percent of your daily Calorie intake should come from proteins.

Amino Acids Proteins are made up of small units called **amino acids** (uh MEE noh), which are linked together chemically to form large protein molecules. Thousands of different proteins are built from only about 20 different amino acids. Your body can make about half of the amino acids it needs. The others, called essential amino acids, must come from the foods you eat.

Complete and Incomplete Proteins Foods from animal sources, such as meat and eggs, are sources of complete proteins because these foods contain all the essential amino acids. Proteins from plant sources, such as beans, grains, and nuts, are called incomplete proteins because they are missing one or more essential amino acid. Different plant sources lack different amino acids. Therefore, to obtain all the essential amino acids from plant sources alone, people need to eat a wide variety of plant foods.

 **Reading Checkpoint** What are the units that make up proteins?

Math Skills

Percentage

A percentage (%) is a ratio that compares a number to 100. For example, 30% means 30 out of 100.

Suppose that a person eats a total of 2,000 Calories in one day. Of those Calories, 300 come from protein. Follow these steps to calculate the percentage of Calories that come from protein.

1. Write the comparison as a fraction:
$$\frac{300}{2,000}$$

2. Multiply the fraction by 100% to express it as a percentage:
$$\frac{300}{2,000} \times 100\% = 15\%$$

Practice Problem Suppose that 540 Calories of the person's 2,000 Calorie total come from fats. What percentage of the Calories comes from fats?

Vitamins and Minerals

Two kinds of nutrients—vitamins and minerals—are needed by the body in very small amounts. Unlike the other nutrients, vitamins and minerals do not provide the body with energy or raw materials. Instead, they help the body carry out various processes.

Vitamins act as helper molecules in a variety of chemical reactions in the body. Vitamin K, for example, helps your blood to clot when you get a cut or a scrape. Figure 6 lists the vitamins necessary for health. The body can make a few of these vitamins. For example, your skin can make vitamin D when exposed to sunlight. Most vitamins, however, must be obtained from foods.

Fat-Soluble and Water-Soluble Vitamins Vitamins are classified as either fat-soluble or water-soluble. Fat-soluble vitamins dissolve in fat, and they are stored in fatty tissues in the body. Vitamins A, D, E, and K are all fat-soluble vitamins. Water-soluble vitamins dissolve in water and are not stored in the body. This fact makes it especially important to include sources of water-soluble vitamins—vitamin C and all of the B vitamins—in your diet every day.

FIGURE 5
Eat Your Vegetables!
Fresh vegetables are full of vitamins and are fun to pick as well.

Importance of Vitamins Although vitamins are only needed in small amounts, a lack of certain vitamins in the diet can lead to health problems. In the 1700s, sailors on long voyages survived on hard, dry biscuits, salted meat, and not much else. Because of this limited diet, many sailors developed a serious disease called scurvy. People with scurvy suffer from bleeding gums, stiff joints, and sores that do not heal. Some may even die.

A Scottish doctor, James Lind, hypothesized that scurvy was the result of the sailors' poor diet. Lind divided sailors with scurvy into groups and fed different foods to each group. The sailors who were fed citrus fruits—oranges and lemons—recovered from the disease. Lind recommended that all sailors eat citrus fruits. When Lind's recommendations were carried out, scurvy disappeared. Today scientists know that scurvy is caused by the lack of vitamin C, which is found in citrus fruits.

 **Reading Checkpoint** **List the fat-soluble vitamins.**

FIGURE 6
Essential Vitamins
Both fat-soluble vitamins and water-soluble vitamins are necessary to maintain health. **Interpreting Tables** *What foods provide a supply of both vitamins E and K?*

Fat-Soluble Vitamins

Vitamin	Sources	Function
A	Dairy products; eggs; liver; yellow, orange, and dark green vegetables; fruits	Maintains healthy skin, bones, teeth, and hair; aids vision in dim light
D	Fortified dairy products; fish; eggs; liver; made by skin cells in presence of sunlight	Maintains bones and teeth; helps in the use of calcium and phosphorus
E	Vegetable oils; margarine; green, leafy vegetables; whole-grain foods; seeds; nuts	Aids in maintenance of red blood cells
K	Green, leafy vegetables; milk; liver; made by bacteria in the intestines	Aids in blood clotting

Water-Soluble Vitamins

Vitamin	Sources	Function
B1 (thiamin)	Pork; liver; whole-grain foods; legumes; nuts	Needed for breakdown of carbohydrates
B2 (riboflavin)	Dairy products; eggs; whole-grain breads and cereals; green, leafy vegetables	Needed for normal growth
B3 (niacin)	Many protein-rich foods; milk; eggs; meat; fish; whole-grain foods; nuts; peanut butter	Needed for release of energy
B6 (pyridoxine)	Green, leafy vegetables; meats; fish; legumes; fruits; whole-grain foods	Helps in the breakdown of proteins, fats, and carbohydrates
B12	Meats; fish; poultry; dairy products; eggs	Maintains healthy nervous system; needed for red blood cell formation
Biotin	Liver; meat; fish; eggs; legumes; bananas; melons	Aids in the release of energy
Folic acid	Green, leafy vegetables; legumes; seeds; liver	Needed for red blood cell formation
Pantothenic acid	Liver; meats; fish; eggs; whole-grain foods	Needed for the release of energy
C	Citrus fruits; tomatoes; potatoes; dark green vegetables; mangoes	Needed to form connective tissue and fight infection

FIGURE 7
Eating a variety of foods
each day provides your body
with the minerals it needs.
Interpreting Tables *Which
minerals play a role in
regulating water levels in
the body?*

Essential Minerals		
Mineral	Sources	Function
Calcium	Milk; cheese; dark green, leafy vegetables; tofu; legumes	Helps build bones and teeth; aids in blood clotting; muscle and nerve function
Chlorine	Table salt; soy sauce	Helps maintain water balance
Fluorine	Fluoridated drinking water; fish	Helps form bones and teeth
Iodine	Seafood, iodized salt	Helps in the release of energy
Iron	Red meats; seafood; green, leafy vegetables; legumes; dried fruits	Needed for red blood cell function
Magnesium	Green, leafy vegetables; legumes; nuts; whole-grain foods	Ais in muscle and nerve function; helps in the release of energy
Phosphorus	Meat; poultry; eggs; fish; dairy products	Helps produce healthy bones and teeth; helps in the release of energy
Potassium	Grains; fruits; vegetables; meat; fish	Helps maintain water balance; muscle and nerve function
Sodium	Table salt; soy sauce	Helps maintain water balance; nerve function

◄Source of calcium

◄Source of potassium

Source of sodium ►

Importance of Minerals Nutrients that are not made by living things are called **minerals.** Minerals are present in soil and are absorbed by plants through their roots. You obtain minerals by eating plant foods or animals that have eaten plants. Figure 7 lists some minerals you need. You probably know that calcium is needed for strong bones and teeth. Iron is needed for the proper functioning of red blood cells.

Both vitamins and minerals are needed by your body in small amounts to carry out chemical processes. If you eat a wide variety of foods, you probably will get enough vitamins and minerals. Most people who eat a balanced diet do not need to take vitamin or mineral supplements.

Reading Checkpoint What are minerals?

Water

Imagine that a boat is sinking. The people on board are getting into a lifeboat. They have room for only one of these items: a bag of fruit, a can of meat, a loaf of bread, or a jug of water. Which item should they choose?

You might be surprised to learn that the lifeboat passengers should choose the water. Although people can probably survive for weeks without food, they will die within days without fresh water. Water is the most abundant substance in the body. It accounts for about 65 percent of the average person's body weight.

Water is the most important nutrient because the body's vital processes—including chemical reactions such as the breakdown of nutrients—take place in water. Water makes up most of the body's fluids, including blood. Nutrients and other important substances are carried throughout the body dissolved in the watery part of the blood. Your body also needs water to produce perspiration, which helps regulate body temperature and remove wastes.

Under normal conditions, you need to take in about 2 liters of water every day. You can do this by drinking water and other beverages and by eating foods with lots of water, such as fruits and vegetables. If the weather is hot or you are exercising, you need to drink additional water to replace the water that you lose in sweat.

FIGURE 8
Water—An Essential Nutrient
All living things need water. Without regular water intake, an organism would not be able to carry out the processes that keep it alive.

Section 1 Assessment

Target Reading Skill Outlining Use the information in your outline about nutrients to help you answer the questions below.

Reviewing Key Concepts

1. a. **Identifying** Name two ways in which foods are used by the body.
   b. **Defining** What is a calorie? How does it relate to the amount of energy in foods?
   c. **Inferring** Why do young children and active teenagers have high energy needs?
2. a. **Listing** List the six nutrients that are needed by the body.
   b. **Summarizing** For each nutrient you listed, briefly describe the role it plays in the body.
   c. **Applying Concepts** Why is it especially important that vegetarians eat a varied diet?

Math Practice

3. **Percentage** Suppose that a person eats 2,500 Calories in one day. Of those Calories, 1,200 are from carbohydrates, 875 are from fat, and the rest are from protein. What percentages of the person's Calories are from carbohydrates, from fats, and from proteins?

Raisin' the Raisin Question

Problem

Raisins are a good source of the mineral iron. Which raisin bran cereal contains the most raisins?

Skills Focus

measuring, calculating, controlling variables

Materials

- balance
- beaker (250 mL)
- raisin bran cereals (several brands)

Procedure

1. Use a balance to find the mass of a clean 250-mL beaker. Record the mass in a data table like the one below.

2. Fill the beaker to the top with one of the brands of raisin bran cereal, but do not pack down the cereal. **CAUTION:** *Do not put any cereal in your mouth.* Write the brand name in the data table. Measure and record the mass of the beaker plus cereal. Subtract the mass of the empty beaker to get the mass of the cereal alone. Record the result.

3. Pour the cereal onto a paper towel. Separate the raisins from the bran and place the raisins back in the beaker. Measure and record the mass of the beaker plus raisins. Subtract the mass of the empty beaker to get the mass of the raisins alone. Record the result.

4. Repeat Steps 1–3 with each of the other brands of cereal.

Analyze and Conclude

1. **Measuring** Why did you first measure the mass of an empty beaker and then the mass of the beaker plus cereal?

2. **Calculating** Calculate the percentage mass of raisins in each cereal as follows:

$$\% \text{ Mass of raisins} = \frac{\text{Mass of raisins}}{\text{Mass of cereal}} \times 100\%$$

Record the results in your data table.

3. **Interpreting Data** Based on your observations, which brand of cereal had the greatest percentage of raisins by mass?

4. **Controlling Variables** Was it important that all of the cereal samples were collected in the same-size beaker? Why or why not?

5. **Communicating** Based on your results, write a paragraph that could be printed on a box of raisin bran cereal that would help consumers understand that this brand is the best source of iron.

Design an Experiment

In this investigation, you examined a *sample* of cereal rather than the contents of the entire box. Scientists often use samples because it is a more practical way to make observations. Redesign this experiment to improve upon the sampling technique and increase the accuracy of your results. *Obtain your teacher's permission before carrying out your investigation.*

Data Table						
	Mass (g)					Percentage Mass of Raisins (%)
Cereal Brand	Empty Beaker	Beaker plus Cereal	Cereal	Beaker plus Raisins	Raisins	

Healthy Eating

Reading Preview

Key Concepts
- How can the Food Guide Pyramid help you plan a healthy diet?
- What kind of information is included on food labels?

Key Terms
- Food Guide Pyramid
- Percent Daily Value
- Dietary Reference Intakes (DRIs)

Target Reading Skill

Asking Questions Before you read, preview the red headings. In a graphic organizer like the one below, ask a *what* or *how* question for each heading. As you read, write answers to your questions.

Healthy Eating

Question	Answer
What is the Food Guide Pyramid?	The Food Guide Pyramid classifies . . .

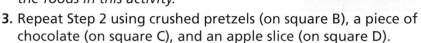

Discover **Activity**

Lab zone

Do Snack Foods Contain Fat?

1. Cut four small squares from a brown paper bag. Label them A, B, C, and D.
2. Rub some crushed potato chips on square A. **CAUTION:** *Do not eat any of the foods in this activity.*
3. Repeat Step 2 using crushed pretzels (on square B), a piece of chocolate (on square C), and an apple slice (on square D).
4. Remove any food. Allow the paper squares to dry.
5. Note which squares have spots of oil on them.

Think It Over
Classifying If a food contains fat, it will leave oily spots on the paper. What does this tell you about the foods you tested?

What does healthy eating mean to you? Eating more fresh fruits and vegetables? Not skipping breakfast? Cutting down on soft drinks and chips? You have just learned about the six types of nutrients—carbohydrates, fats, proteins, vitamins, minerals, and water—that are part of a healthy diet. You may now be wondering how you can use this information to make healthful choices in your diet.

With so many foods available, it may seem more difficult, not easier, to establish a healthful diet. Luckily, nutritionists have developed the Food Guide Pyramid and food labels as a way to help.

FIGURE 9
Healthy Food Choices
Fruits and vegetables are essential parts of a healthy diet. Some people enjoy picking these foods right off the plant.

The Food Guide Pyramid

The **Food Guide Pyramid** is a diagram that was developed to help people plan a healthy diet. **The Food Guide Pyramid classifies foods into six groups. It also indicates how many servings from each group should be eaten every day to maintain a healthy diet.**

The six food groups in the Food Guide Pyramid are shown in Figure 10. You can combine the advice within the pyramid with knowledge of your own food preferences. By doing this, you can have a healthy diet containing foods you like.

Go Online
active art

For: The Food Guide Pyramid activity
Visit: www.PHSchool.com
Web code: cep-4022

FIGURE 10
The Food Guide Pyramid
The Food Guide Pyramid recommends the number of servings that a person should eat each day from six food groups.

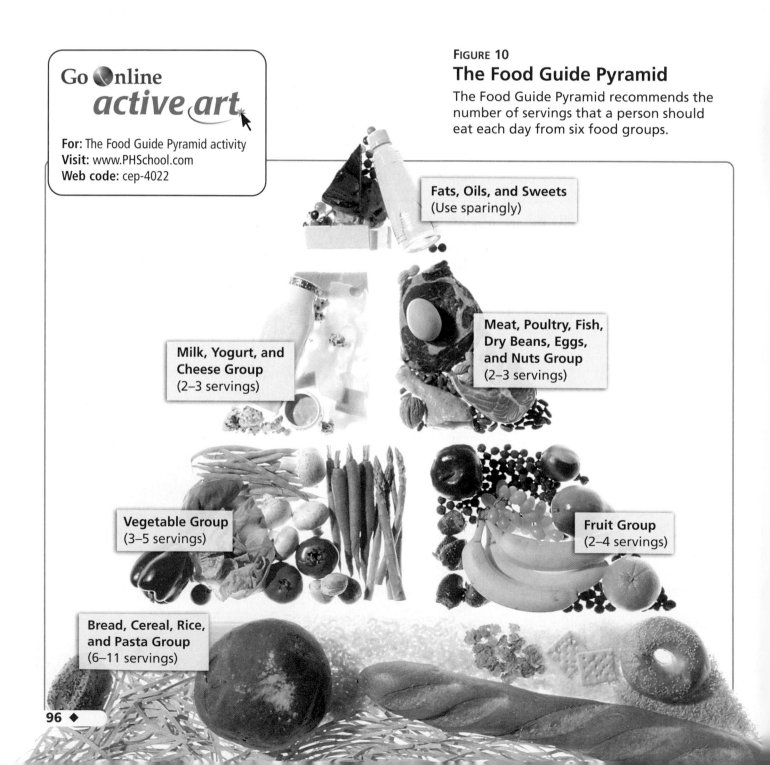

Fats, Oils, and Sweets
(Use sparingly)

Milk, Yogurt, and Cheese Group
(2–3 servings)

Meat, Poultry, Fish, Dry Beans, Eggs, and Nuts Group
(2–3 servings)

Vegetable Group
(3–5 servings)

Fruit Group
(2–4 servings)

Bread, Cereal, Rice, and Pasta Group
(6–11 servings)

Base of the Pyramid Notice in Figure 10 that the food group at the base of the pyramid includes foods made from grains, such as bread, cereal, rice, and pasta. These foods are rich in complex carbohydrates. These foods also provide proteins, fiber, vitamins, and some minerals. This bottom level is the widest part of the pyramid. The large size indicates that these foods should make up the largest part of the diet.

Middle of the Pyramid The second level in the pyramid is made of two food groups, the Fruit group and the Vegetable group. Fruits and vegetables are good sources of carbohydrates, fiber, vitamins, minerals, and water. Notice that this level is not as wide as the bottom level. This size difference indicates that people need fewer servings of these foods than of foods from the bottom level.

The third level of the pyramid contains the Milk, Yogurt, and Cheese group, and the Meat, Poultry, Fish, Dry Beans, Eggs, and Nuts group. Milk and other dairy products are rich in proteins, carbohydrates, vitamins, and minerals. The meat and poultry group contains foods that are high in protein. People need smaller amounts of food from the third level.

Top of the Pyramid At the top of the pyramid are foods containing large amounts of fat, sugar, or both. These foods contain few valuable nutrients. Notice that this is the smallest part of the pyramid. The small size indicates that intake of these foods should be limited. There is a good reason for this advice. Foods in the other groups already contain fats and sugars. Limiting the additional fats and sugars can help you prevent heart disease and other health problems.

 **Reading Checkpoint** Which food groups are in the second level of the Food Guide Pyramid?

Discovery CHANNEL SCHOOL

Food and Digestion

Video Preview
▶ Video Field Trip
Video Assessment

Lab zone Skills Activity

Graphing
You can graph the nutrient content in a meal. The meal of chicken, beans and rice, and salad has about 27 g of protein, 25 g of carbohydrates, and 4 g of fat. Use this information to draw a bar graph showing protein, carbohydrate, and fat content for this meal.

FIGURE 11
Healthful Eating
The Food Guide Pyramid can help you plan healthy meals. **Classifying** *Which of the food groups in the Food Guide Pyramid are contained in this meal of chicken, beans, rice, and salad?*

Food Labels

After a long day, you and your friends stop into a store on your way home from school. What snack should you buy? How can you make a wise choice? One thing you can do is to read the information provided on food labels. **Food labels allow you to evaluate a single food as well as to compare the nutritional value of two different foods.**

How to Read a Food Label Figure 12 shows a food label that might appear on a box of cereal. Refer to that label as you read about some of the important nutritional information it contains.

1 Serving Size This information tells you the size of a single serving and the number of servings in the container. The information on the rest of the label is based on serving size. If you eat twice the serving size, then you'll consume twice the number of Calories.

2 Calories This information tells you how much energy you get from one serving of this food, including how many Calories come from fat.

3 Percent Daily Value The **Percent Daily Value** shows you how the nutritional content of one serving fits into the recommended diet for a person who consumes 2,000 Calories a day. For example, one serving of this cereal contains 12% of the total amount of sodium a person should consume in one day. You might eat more or less than 2,000 Calories a day. But, you can still use this percentage as a general guide.

4 Ingredients The ingredients are listed in order by weight, starting with the main ingredient. The list can alert you to substances that have been added to a food to improve its flavor or color, or to keep it from spoiling. In addition, reading ingredients lists can help you avoid substances that make you ill.

Using Food Labels Food labels can help you make healthful food choices. Suppose you are shopping for breakfast cereals. By reading the labels, you might find that one cereal contains little fat and a high percentage of the Daily Values for complex carbohydrates and several vitamins. Another cereal might have fewer complex carbohydrates and vitamins, and contain significant amounts of fat. You can see that the first cereal would be a better choice as a regular breakfast food.

FIGURE 12
Food Label
By law, specific nutritional information must be listed on food labels.
Calculating *How many servings of this product would you have to eat to get 90% of the Daily Value for iron?*

98 ◆

Dietary Reference Intakes Food labels can also help you monitor the nutrients in your diet. Guidelines that show the amounts of nutrients that are needed every day are known as **Dietary Reference Intakes (DRIs).** For example, the DRIs for vitamins recommend that people your age get 45 milligrams of vitamin C every day.

DRIs also show how the Calories that people eat each day should be split among carbohydrates, fats, and proteins. The Percent Daily Values listed on food labels can help you make sure that you are meeting the DRIs for different nutrients.

 **What are Dietary Reference Intakes?**

FIGURE 13
Reading Food Labels
Food labels allow you to compare the nutritional content of similar kinds of foods.

Section 2 Assessment

Target Reading Skill **Asking Questions** Work with a partner to check the answers in your graphic organizer.

Reviewing Key Concepts

1. a. Identifying Into how many groups are foods in the Food Guide Pyramid classified?

b. Interpreting Diagrams Why are foods in the Bread, Cereal, Rice, and Pasta group placed at the bottom of the Food Guide Pyramid?

c. Applying Concepts Why might a runner need more servings from the Bread, Cereal, Rice, and Pasta group than a less active person?

2. a. Reviewing What are three kinds of information contained on food labels?

b. Explaining How can food labels help a person make healthy food choices?

c. Calculating Use Figure 12 to calculate the following: (1) the total number of Calories in 3 servings, (2) the number of servings needed to get 50 percent of the day's Daily Value for Vitamin C, and (3) the number of servings needed to get all the dietary fiber needed for the day.

Lab zone At-Home Activity

Menu Planning Work with a family member to plan menus for three days that meet the guidelines in the Food Guide Pyramid. Follow the recommended number of servings for each group. Remember to write down fats, such as butter or margarine, that may be used to add flavor to dishes. Include all snack items as well.

The Digestive Process Begins

Reading Preview

Key Concepts
- What functions are carried out in the digestive system?
- What roles do the mouth, esophagus, and stomach play in digestion?

Key Terms
- digestion • absorption
- saliva • enzyme • epiglottis
- esophagus • mucus
- peristalsis • stomach

Target Reading Skill
Using Prior Knowledge Before you read, look at the section headings and visuals to see what this section is about. Then write what you know about the digestive system in a graphic organizer like the one below. As you read, continue to write in what you learn.

What You Know
1. Food is digested in the stomach.
2.

What You Learned
1.
2.

Lab zone Discover **Activity**

How Can You Speed Up Digestion?
1. Obtain two plastic jars with lids. Fill the jars with equal amounts of water at the same temperature.
2. Place a whole sugar cube into one jar. Place a crushed sugar cube into the other jar.
3. Fasten the lids on the jars. Holding one jar in each hand, shake the two jars gently and for equal amounts of time.
4. Place the jars on a flat surface. Observe whether the whole cube or the crushed cube dissolves faster.

Think It Over
Predicting Use the results of this activity to predict which would take longer to digest: a large piece of food or one that has been cut up into many small pieces. Explain your answer.

In 1822, a man named Alexis St. Martin was wounded in the stomach. Dr. William Beaumont saved St. Martin's life. The wound, however, left an opening in St. Martin's stomach that never healed completely. Beaumont realized that by looking through the opening in St. Martin's abdomen, he could observe what was happening inside the stomach.

Beaumont observed that food changed chemically inside the stomach. He hypothesized that chemical reactions in the stomach broke down foods into smaller particles. Beaumont removed liquid from St. Martin's stomach and analyzed it. The stomach liquid contained an acid that played a role in the breakdown of foods into simpler substances.

Functions of the Digestive System

Beaumont's observations helped scientists understand the role of the stomach in the digestive system. **The digestive system has three main functions. First, it breaks down food into molecules the body can use. Then, the molecules are absorbed into the blood and carried throughout the body. Finally, wastes are eliminated from the body.** Figure 14 shows the organs of the digestive system, which is about 9 meters long from beginning to end.

Digestion The process by which your body breaks down food into small nutrient molecules is called **digestion.** There are two kinds of digestion—mechanical and chemical. In mechanical digestion, foods are physically broken down into smaller pieces. Mechanical digestion occurs when you bite into a sandwich and chew it into small pieces.

In chemical digestion, chemicals produced by the body break foods into their smaller chemical building blocks. For example, the starch in bread is broken down into individual sugar molecules.

Absorption and Elimination After your food is digested, the molecules are ready to be transported throughout your body. **Absorption** (ab SAWRP shun) is the process by which nutrient molecules pass through the wall of your digestive system into your blood. Materials that are not absorbed, such as fiber, are eliminated from the body as wastes.

Go Online
SciLINKS NSTA

For: Links on digestion
Visit: www.SciLinks.org
Web Code: scn-0423

✓ **Reading Checkpoint** **What is chemical digestion?**

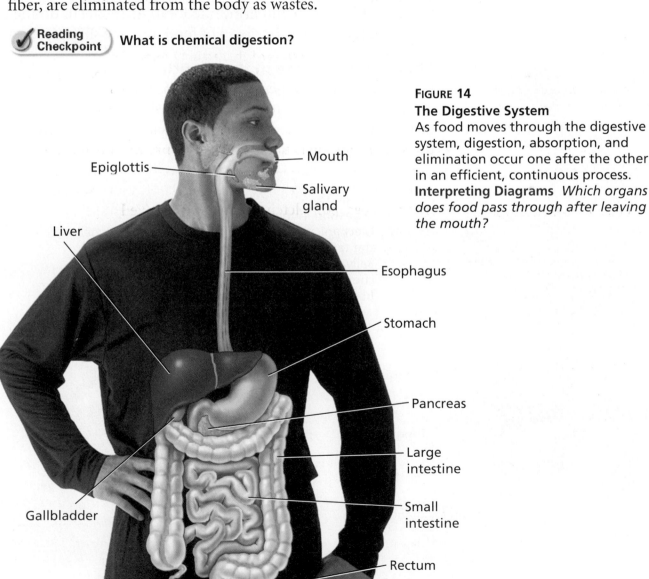

Epiglottis

Mouth

Salivary gland

Liver

Esophagus

Stomach

Pancreas

Large intestine

Small intestine

Gallbladder

Rectum

FIGURE 14
The Digestive System
As food moves through the digestive system, digestion, absorption, and elimination occur one after the other in an efficient, continuous process.
Interpreting Diagrams *Which organs does food pass through after leaving the mouth?*

The Mouth

Have you ever walked past a bakery or restaurant and noticed your mouth watering? Smelling or even just thinking about food when you're hungry is enough to start your mouth watering. This response isn't accidental. When your mouth waters, your body is preparing for the delicious meal it expects. **Both mechanical and chemical digestion begin in the mouth.** The fluid released when your mouth waters is **saliva** (suh LY vuh). Saliva plays an important role in both kinds of digestion.

Mechanical Digestion in the Mouth Your teeth carry out the first stage of mechanical digestion. Your center teeth, or incisors (in SY zurz), cut the food into bite-sized pieces. On either side of the incisors there are sharp, pointy teeth called canines (KAY nynz). These teeth tear and slash the food into smaller pieces. Behind the canines are the premolars and molars, which crush and grind the food. As the teeth do their work, saliva moistens the pieces of food into one slippery mass.

Chemical Digestion in the Mouth As mechanical digestion begins, so does chemical digestion. If you take a bite of a cracker and suck on it, the cracker begins to taste sweet. It tastes sweet because a chemical in the saliva has broken down the starch molecules in the cracker into sugar molecules.

FIGURE 15
Digestion in the Mouth
Mechanical digestion begins in the mouth, where the teeth cut and tear food into smaller pieces. Salivary glands release enzymes that begin chemical digestion. **Observing** *Which teeth are best suited for biting into a juicy apple?*

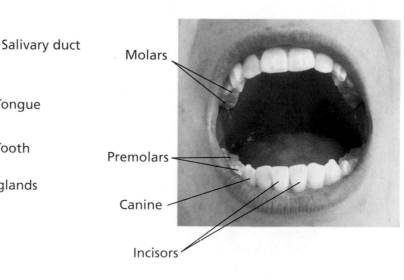

Salivary duct

Tongue

Tooth

Salivary glands

Molars

Premolars

Canine

Incisors

FIGURE 16
How Enzymes Work
The shape of an enzyme molecule is specific to
the shape of the food molecule it breaks down.
Here, an enzyme breaks down a starch into sugars.

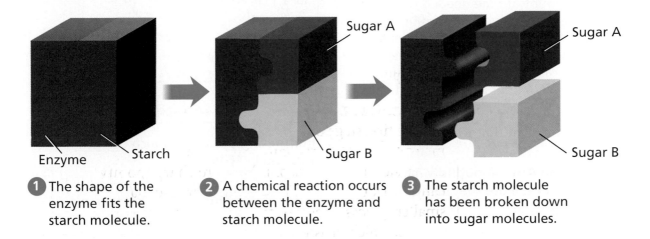

Enzyme   Starch   Sugar A   Sugar A
                           Sugar B   Sugar B

1 The shape of the
enzyme fits the
starch molecule.

2 A chemical reaction occurs
between the enzyme and
starch molecule.

3 The starch molecule
has been broken down
into sugar molecules.

The chemical in saliva that digests starch is an enzyme. **Enzymes** are proteins that speed up chemical reactions in the body. Your body produces many different enzymes. Each enzyme has a specific chemical shape. Its shape enables it to take part in only one kind of chemical reaction. An example of enzyme action is shown in Figure 16.

The Esophagus

If you've ever choked on food, your food may have "gone down the wrong way." That's because there are two openings at the back of your mouth. One opening leads to your windpipe, which carries air into your lungs. As you swallow, a flap of tissue called the **epiglottis** (ep uh GLAHT is) seals off your windpipe, preventing the food from entering. The food goes into the **esophagus** (ih SAHF uh gus), a muscular tube that connects the mouth to the stomach. The esophagus is lined with **mucus,** a thick, slippery substance produced by the body. Mucus makes food easier to swallow and move along.

Food remains in the esophagus for only about 10 seconds. **After food enters the esophagus, contractions of smooth muscles push the food toward the stomach.** These involuntary waves of muscle contraction are called **peristalsis** (pehr ih STAWL sis). Peristalsis also occurs in the stomach and farther down the digestive system. These muscular waves keep food moving in one direction.

Reading Checkpoint) **How is food prevented from entering the windpipe?**

Lab zone Try This Activity

Modeling Peristalsis

1. Obtain a clear, flexible plastic straw.
2. Hold the straw vertically and insert a small bead into the top of the straw. The bead should fit snugly into the straw. **CAUTION:** *Do not put the straw in your mouth or blow into the straw.*
3. Pinch the straw above the bead so the bead begins to move down the length of the tubing.
4. Repeat Step 3 until the bead exits the straw.

Making Models How does this action compare with peristalsis? What do the bead and the straw represent?

Chapter 3 ◆ 103

Protein Digestion

A scientist performed an experiment to determine the amount of time needed to digest protein. He placed small pieces of hard-boiled egg white (a protein) in a test tube containing hydrochloric acid, water, and the enzyme pepsin. He measured the rate at which the egg white was digested over a 24-hour period. His data are recorded in the graph.

1. **Reading Graphs** What do the values on the y-axis represent?

2. **Interpreting Data** After about how many hours would you estimate that half of the protein was digested?

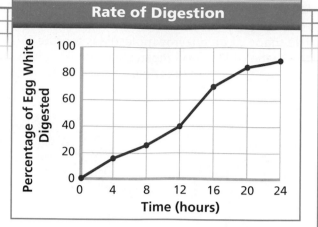

Rate of Digestion

3. **Interpreting Data** How much digestion occurred in 16 hours?

4. **Drawing Conclusions** During which 4-hour period did the most digestion take place?

The Stomach

When food leaves the esophagus, it enters the **stomach,** a J-shaped, muscular pouch located in the abdomen. As you eat, your stomach expands to hold all of the food that you swallow. **Most mechanical digestion and some chemical digestion occur in the stomach.**

Mechanical Digestion in the Stomach The process of mechanical digestion occurs as three strong layers of smooth muscle contract to produce a churning motion. This action mixes the food with fluids in somewhat the same way that clothes and soapy water are mixed in a washing machine.

Chemical Digestion in the Stomach Chemical digestion occurs as the churning food makes contact with digestive juice, a fluid produced by cells in the lining of the stomach. Digestive juice contains the enzyme pepsin. Pepsin chemically digests the proteins in your food, breaking them down into short chains of amino acids.

Digestive juice also contains hydrochloric acid, a very strong acid. Without this strong acid, your stomach could not function properly. First, pepsin works best in an acid environment. Second, the acid kills many bacteria that you swallow with your food.

Why doesn't stomach acid burn a hole in your stomach? The reason is that cells in the stomach lining also produce mucus, which coats and protects the stomach lining. Also, the cells that line the stomach are quickly replaced as they are damaged or worn out.

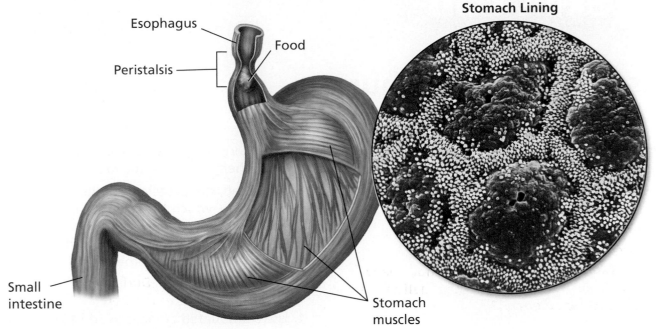

Esophagus

Food

Peristalsis

Small
intestine

Stomach
muscles

Stomach Lining

Food remains in the stomach until all of the solid material has been broken down into liquid form. A few hours after you finish eating, the stomach completes mechanical digestion of the food. By that time, most of the proteins have been chemically digested into shorter chains of amino acids. The food, now a thick liquid, is released into the next part of the digestive system. That is where final chemical digestion and absorption will take place.

 **Reading Checkpoint** What is pepsin?

FIGURE 17
The Stomach
The stomach has three layers of muscle that help to break down foods mechanically. The inset photo shows a microscopic view of the stomach lining. The yellow dots are mucus.
Relating Cause and Effect *What role does mucus play inside the stomach?*

Section 3 Assessment

🎯 **Target Reading Skill** **Using Prior Knowledge** Review your graphic organizer and revise it based on what you just learned in the section.

Reviewing Key Concepts

1. **a. Listing** What are the functions of the digestive system?
   b. Comparing and Contrasting Distinguish between mechanical and chemical digestion.
   c. Inferring Why must mechanical digestion start before chemical digestion?
2. **a. Reviewing** What key chemicals do the mouth and stomach contain?
   b. Describing How do pepsin and hydrochloric acid work together to digest food in the stomach?
   c. Predicting What could happen if your stomach didn't produce enough mucus? Explain.

Lab zone **At-Home Activity**

First Aid for Choking Explain to your family what happens when people choke on food. With your family, find out how to recognize when a person is choking and what to do to help the person. Learn about the Heimlich maneuver and how it is used to help someone who is choking.

As the Stomach Churns

Problem

What conditions are needed for the digestion of proteins in the stomach?

Skills Focus

interpreting data, controlling variables, drawing conclusions

Materials

- test-tube rack
- pepsin
- water
- 4 strips of blue litmus paper
- cubes of boiled egg white
- 10-mL plastic graduated cylinder
- 4 test tubes with stoppers
- marking pencil
- diluted hydrochloric acid
- plastic stirrers

Procedure

1. In this lab, you will investigate how acidic conditions affect protein digestion. Read over the entire lab to see what materials you will be testing. Write a prediction stating which conditions you think will speed up protein digestion. Then, copy the data table into your notebook.

2. Label four test tubes A, B, C, and D, and place them in a test-tube rack.

3. In this lab, the protein you will test is boiled egg white, which has been cut into cubes about 1 cm on each side. Add 3 cubes to each test tube. Note and record the size and overall appearance of the cubes in each test tube. **CAUTION:** *Do not put any egg white into your mouth.*

4. Use a graduated cylinder to add 10 mL of the enzyme pepsin to test tube A. Observe the egg white cubes to determine whether an immediate reaction takes place. Record your observations under Day 1 in your data table. If no changes occur, write "no immediate reaction."

5. Use a clean graduated cylinder to add 5 mL of pepsin to test tube B. Then rinse out the graduated cylinder and add 5 mL of water to test tube B. Observe whether or not an immediate reaction takes place.

6. Use a clean graduated cylinder to add 10 mL of hydrochloric acid to test tube C. Observe whether or not an immediate reaction takes place. **CAUTION:** *Hydrochloric acid can burn skin and clothing. Avoid direct contact with it. Wash any splashes or spills with plenty of water, and notify your teacher.*

Data Table				
Test Tube	Egg White Appearance		Litmus Color	
	Day 1	Day 2	Day 1	Day 2
A				
B				
C				
D				

7. Use a clean graduated cylinder to add 5 mL of pepsin to test tube D. Then, rinse the graduated cylinder and add 5 mL of hydrochloric acid to test tube D. Observe whether or not an immediate reaction takes place. Record your observations.

8. Obtain four strips of blue litmus paper. (Blue litmus paper turns pink in the presence of an acid.) Dip a clean plastic stirrer into the solution in each test tube, and then touch the stirrer to a piece of litmus paper. Observe what happens to the litmus paper. Record your observations.

9. Insert stoppers in the four test tubes and store the test tube rack as directed by your teacher.

10. The next day, examine the contents of each test tube. Note any changes in the size and overall appearance of the egg white cubes. Then, test each solution with litmus paper. Record your observations in your data table.

Analyze and Conclude

1. **Interpreting Data** Which materials were the best at digesting the egg white? What observations enabled you to determine this?

2. **Inferring** Is the chemical digestion of protein in food a fast or a slow reaction? Explain.

3. **Controlling Variables** Why was it important that the cubes of egg white all be about the same size?

4. **Drawing Conclusions** What did this lab show about the ability of pepsin to digest protein?

5. **Communicating** Write a paragraph in which you describe the purpose of test tube A and test tube C as they relate to the steps you followed in the procedure.

Design an Experiment

Design a way to test whether protein digestion is affected by the size of the food pieces. Write down your hypothesis and the procedure you will follow. *Obtain your teacher's permission before carrying out your investigation.*

Final Digestion and Absorption

Reading Preview

Key Concepts
- What digestive processes occur in the small intestine, and how are other digestive organs involved?
- What role does the large intestine play in digestion?

Key Terms
- small intestine • liver • bile
- gallbladder • pancreas
- villus • large intestine
- rectum • anus

Target Reading Skill

Identifying Main Ideas As you read the section titled The Small Intestine, write the main idea in a graphic organizer like the one below. Then, write three supporting details that further explain the main idea.

Main Idea

Chemical digestion takes place in the . . .

Detail	Detail	Detail

Lab zone Discover **Activity**

Which Surface Is Larger?

1. Work with a partner to carry out this investigation.
2. Begin by placing your hand palm-side down on a table. Keep your thumb and fingers tightly together. Lay string along the outline of your hand. Have your partner help you determine how long a string you need to outline your hand.
3. Use a metric ruler to measure the length of that string.

Think It Over
Predicting How long would you expect your hand outline to be if you spread out your thumb and fingers? Use string to test your prediction. Compare the two string lengths.

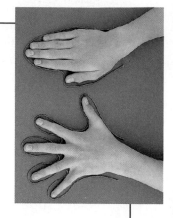

Have you ever been part of a huge crowd attending a concert or sports event? Barriers and passageways often guide people in the right direction. Ticket takers make sure that people enter in an orderly fashion.

In some ways, the stomach can be thought of as the "ticket taker" of the digestive system. Once the food has been changed into a thick liquid, the stomach releases a little of the liquid at a time into the next part of the digestive system. This slow, smooth passage of food through the digestive system ensures that digestion and absorption can take place efficiently.

The Small Intestine

After the thick liquid leaves the stomach, it enters the small intestine. The **small intestine** is the part of the digestive system where most chemical digestion takes place. You may wonder how the small intestine got its name. After all, at about 6 meters—longer than some full-sized cars—it makes up two thirds of the length of the digestive system. The small intestine was named for its small diameter. It is from 2 to 3 centimeters wide, about half the diameter of the large intestine.

When food reaches the small intestine, it has already been mechanically digested into a thick liquid. But chemical digestion has just begun. Starches and proteins have been partially broken down, but fats haven't been digested at all. **Almost all chemical digestion and absorption of nutrients takes place in the small intestine.** As the liquid moves into the small intestine, it mixes with enzymes and secretions that are produced by the small intestine, the liver, and the pancreas. The liver and the pancreas deliver their substances to the small intestine through small tubes.

The Liver As you can see in Figure 18, the **liver** is located in the upper right portion of the abdomen. It is the largest organ inside the body. The liver is like an extremely busy chemical factory and plays a role in many body processes. For example, it breaks down medicines, and it helps eliminate nitrogen from the body. **The role of the liver in the digestive system is to produce bile.**

Bile is a substance that breaks up fat particles. Bile flows from the liver into the **gallbladder,** the organ that stores bile. After you eat, bile passes through a tube from the gallbladder into the small intestine.

Bile is not an enzyme. It does not chemically digest foods. It does, however, physically break up large fat particles into smaller fat droplets. You can compare the action of bile on fats with the action of soap on a greasy frying pan. Soap physically breaks up the grease into small droplets that can mix with the soapy water and be washed away. Bile mixes with the fats in food to form small fat droplets. The droplets can then be chemically broken down by enzymes produced in the pancreas.

Lab zone Try This **Activity**

Break Up!
You can model the breakup of fat particles in the small intestine.

1. Fill two plastic jars half full of water. Add a few drops of oil to each jar.
2. Add about $\frac{1}{4}$ spoonful of baking soda to one jar.
3. Stir the contents of both jars. Record your observations.

Observing In which jar did the oil begin to break up? What substance does the baking soda represent?

FIGURE **18**
The Liver and Pancreas
Substances produced by the liver and pancreas aid in digestion.
Predicting *How would digestion be affected if the tube leading from the gallbladder to the small intestine became blocked?*

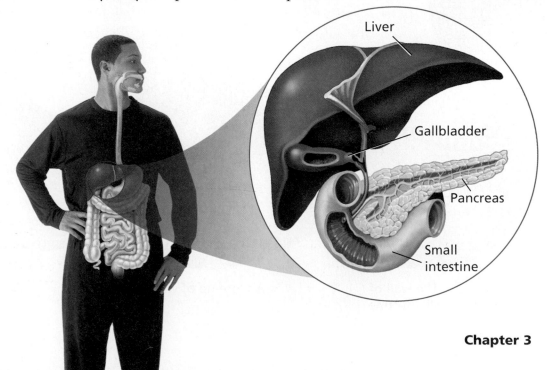

Liver

Gallbladder

Pancreas

Small intestine

The Pancreas The **pancreas** is a triangular organ that lies between the stomach and the first part of the small intestine. Like the liver, the pancreas plays a role in many body processes. **As part of the digestive system, the pancreas produces enzymes that flow into the small intestine and help break down starches, proteins, and fats.**

Digestive enzymes do not break down all food substances. Recall that the fiber in food isn't broken down. Instead, fiber thickens the liquid material in the intestine. This thickening makes it easier for peristalsis to push the material forward.

Absorption in the Small Intestine After chemical digestion takes place, the small nutrient molecules are ready to be absorbed by the body. The structure of the small intestine makes it well suited for absorption. The inner surface, or lining, of the small intestine looks bumpy. Millions of tiny finger-shaped structures called **villi** (VIL eye) (singular *villus*) cover the surface. The villi absorb nutrient molecules. Notice in Figure 19 that tiny blood vessels run through the center of each villus. Nutrient molecules pass from cells on the surface of a villus into blood vessels. The blood carries the nutrients throughout the body for use by body cells.

Villi greatly increase the surface area of the small intestine. If all the villi were laid out flat, the total surface area of the small intestine would be about as large as a tennis court. This increased surface enables digested food to be absorbed much faster than if the walls of the small intestine were smooth.

✔ **Reading Checkpoint** How does the pancreas aid in digestion?

FIGURE 19
The Small Intestine
Tiny finger-shaped projections called villi line the inside of the small intestine. Blood vessels in the villi are covered by a single layer of cells.
Relating Cause and Effect *How does the structure of the villi help them carry out their function?*

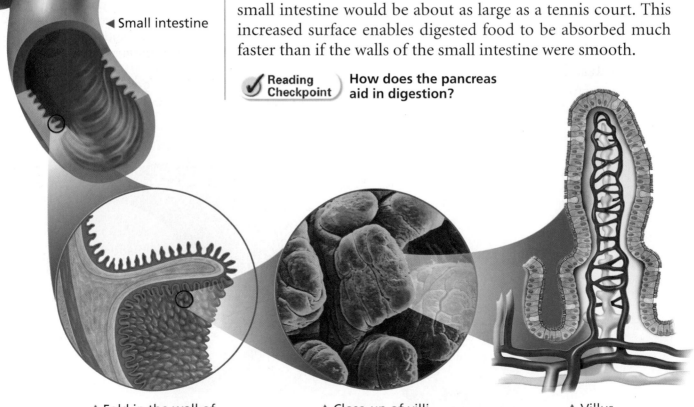

◀ Small intestine

▲ Fold in the wall of the small intestine

▲ Close-up of villi

▲ Villus

The Large Intestine

By the time material reaches the end of the small intestine, most nutrients have been absorbed. The remaining material moves from the small intestine into the large intestine. The **large intestine** is the last section of the digestive system. It is about 1.5 meters long—about as long as the average bathtub. It runs up the right-hand side of the abdomen, across the upper abdomen, and then down the left-hand side. The large intestine contains bacteria that feed on the material passing through. These bacteria normally do not cause disease. In fact, they are helpful because they make certain vitamins, including vitamin K.

The material entering the large intestine contains water and undigested food. **As the material moves through the large intestine, water is absorbed into the bloodstream. The remaining material is readied for elimination from the body.**

The large intestine ends in a short tube called the **rectum**. Here, waste material is compressed into a solid form. This waste material is eliminated from the body through the **anus,** a muscular opening at the end of the rectum.

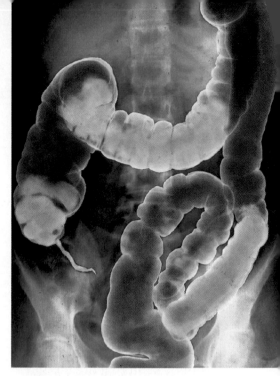

FIGURE 20
The Large Intestine
As material passes through the large intestine, most of the water is absorbed by the body. The remaining material will be eliminated from the body.

 **Reading Checkpoint**) What role do bacteria play in the large intestine?

Section 4 Assessment

Target Reading Skill

Identifying Main Ideas Use your graphic organizer to help you answer Question 1 below.

Reviewing Key Concepts

1. a. **Reviewing** What two digestive processes occur in the small intestine?
   b. **Explaining** Explain how bile produced by the liver and enzymes produced in the pancreas function in the small intestine.
   c. **Relating Cause and Effect** Some people are allergic to a protein in wheat. When these people eat foods made with wheat, a reaction destroys the villi in the small intestine. What problems would you expect these people to experience?
2. a. **Identifying** Which key nutrient is absorbed in the large intestine?
   b. **Describing** What happens as food moves through the large intestine?
   c. **Applying Concepts** Diarrhea is a condition in which waste material that is eliminated contains too much water. How might diarrhea upset homeostasis in the body? How could a person reduce the effects of diarrhea on the body?

Writing in Science

Sequence of Events Describe the journey of a bacon, lettuce, and tomato sandwich through a person's digestive system, starting in the mouth and ending with absorption. Include where digestion of fats, carbohydrates, and proteins take place. Use words like *first*, *next*, and *finally* in your writing.

1 Food and Energy

Key Concepts

- Foods provide the body with raw materials and energy.
- Carbohydrates provide energy as well as the raw materials to make cell parts.
- In addition to providing energy, fats form part of the cell membrane. Fatty tissue also protects and supports internal organs and insulates the body.
- Proteins are needed for tissue growth and repair. They also play an important part in chemical reactions within cells.
- Vitamins and minerals are needed in small amounts to carry out chemical processes.
- Water is the most important nutrient because the body's vital processes take place in water.

Key Terms

nutrient	protein
calorie	amino acid
carbohydrate	vitamin
glucose	mineral
fat	

2 Healthy Eating

Key Concepts

- The Food Guide Pyramid classifies foods into six groups. It also indicates how many servings from each group should be eaten every day.
- Food labels allow you to evaluate a single food as well as to compare the nutritional value of two different foods.

Key Terms

Food Guide Pyramid
Percent Daily Value
Dietary Reference Intakes (DRIs)

3 The Digestive Process Begins

Key Concepts

- The digestive system breaks down food into molecules the body can use. Then, the molecules are absorbed into the blood and carried throughout the body. Finally, wastes are eliminated.
- Both mechanical and chemical digestion begin in the mouth.
- In the esophagus, contractions of smooth muscles push the food toward the stomach.
- Most mechanical digestion and some chemical digestion occur in the stomach.

Key Terms

digestion	esophagus
absorption	mucus
saliva	peristalsis
enzyme	stomach
epiglottis	

4 Final Digestion and Absorption

Key Concepts

- Almost all chemical digestion and absorption of nutrients takes place in the small intestine.
- The liver produces bile, which breaks up fats.
- The pancreas produces enzymes that help break down starches, proteins, and fats.
- In the large intestine, water is absorbed into the bloodstream. The remaining material is readied for elimination.

Key Terms

small intestine	villus
liver	large intestine
bile	rectum
gallbladder	anus
pancreas	

Review and Assessment

Organizing Information

Sequencing Copy the flowchart about digestion onto a separate sheet of paper. Then, complete it and add a title. (For more on Sequencing, see the Skills Handbook.)

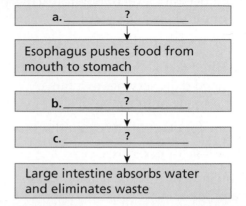

a. _____ ?

↓

Esophagus pushes food from mouth to stomach

↓

b. _____ ?

↓

c. _____ ?

↓

Large intestine absorbs water and eliminates waste

Reviewing Key Terms

Choose the letter of the best answer.

1. The building blocks of proteins are
   a. vitamins.
   b. minerals.
   c. amino acids.
   d. fats.

2. According to the Food Guide Pyramid, from which group should you eat the most servings?
   a. milk, yogurt, and cheese
   b. meat, poultry, fish, beans, eggs, and nuts
   c. vegetables
   d. bread, cereal, rice, and pasta

3. The enzyme in saliva chemically breaks down
   a. fats.
   b. proteins.
   c. glucose.
   d. starches.

4. Most mechanical digestion takes place in the
   a. liver.
   b. esophagus.
   c. stomach.
   d. small intestine.

5. Bile is produced by the
   a. liver.
   b. pancreas.
   c. small intestine.
   d. large intestine.

If the statement is true, write *true*. If it is false, change the underlined word or words to make the statement true.

6. Proteins that come from animal sources are <u>incomplete</u> proteins.

7. <u>Vitamins</u> are nutrients that are not made by living things.

8. To determine which of two cereals supplies more iron, check the <u>Percent Daily Value</u> on the food label.

9. <u>Absorption</u> moves food through the digestive system.

10. Most materials are absorbed into the bloodstream in the <u>large</u> intestine.

Writing in Science

Information Sheet You are a nutritionist assigned to work with a family trying to eat a more healthful diet. Write an instruction sheet outlining what kinds of foods they should eat. Provide some examples of each kind of food.

Food and Digestion

Video Preview
Video Field Trip
▶ Video Assessment

Review and Assessment

Checking Concepts

11. How does a person's level of physical activity affect his or her daily energy needs?

12. Why is fiber necessary in a person's diet?

13. Why does the Food Guide Pyramid give the recommended daily servings as a range instead of a single number?

14. Describe the function of the epiglottis.

15. Explain the role of peristalsis.

16. What is the function of the pancreas in the digestive process?

17. What is the function of villi?

Thinking Critically

18. **Applying Concepts** Before winter, animals that hibernate often prepare by eating foods high in fat. How is this behavior helpful?

19. **Predicting** Suppose a medicine killed all the bacteria in your body. How might this affect vitamin production in your body?

20. **Inferring** Why is it important for people to chew their food thoroughly before swallowing?

21. **Relating Cause and Effect** How does the condition illustrated in the diagram below affect the esophagus?

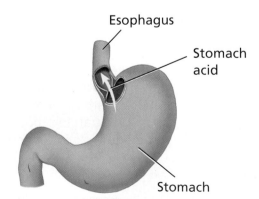

Esophagus

Stomach acid

Stomach

22. **Comparing and Contrasting** The digestive system is sometimes said to be "an assembly line in reverse." Identify some similarities and some differences between your digestive system and an assembly line.

Math Practice

23. **Percentage** Your aunt eats 250 Calories of protein and 1,800 Calories total for the day. Did she get enough protein on that particular day? Show your calculations.

Applying Skills

Use the table to answer Questions 24–27.

Comparing Nutrient Data

Food (1 cup)	Calcium (% Daily Value)	Calories	Calories From Fat
Chocolate milk	30	230	80
Low-fat milk	35	110	20
Plain yogurt	35	110	35

24. **Classifying** To which group in the Food Guide Pyramid do the foods in the chart belong? What is the recommended range of daily servings for that group?

25. **Interpreting Data** How many cups of low-fat milk provide 100% of the day's Daily Value for calcium?

26. **Calculating** Which of the foods meet the recommendation that no more than 30 percent of a food's Calories come from fat? Explain.

27. **Making Judgments** Which of the foods would be the most healthful choice for an afterschool snack? Explain your reasoning.

Lab zone Chapter **Project**

Performance Assessment Write a summary of what you've learned from keeping a food log. How close were your eating patterns to those recommended in the Food Guide Pyramid? How successful were you in making changes in your diet to match the Food Guide Pyramid?

Standardized Test Practice

Choose the letter that best answers the question or completes the statement.

1. Which of the following parts of the digestive system is best paired with its function?
   A esophagus—digests carbohydrates
   B liver—stores bile
   C small intestine—absorbs water
   D liver—produces bile

2. A food label on a cereal box gives you the following information: a serving size equals one cup and there are 110 Calories per serving. You measure the amount of cereal you plan to eat and find that it measures 1 1/2 cups. How many Calories will you consume?
   A 110 Calories
   B 165 Calories
   C 220 Calories
   D cannot be determined

Use the table below and your knowledge of science to answer Questions 3 and 4.

Length of Time Food Stays in Organ	
Organ	**Time**
Mouth	Less than 1 minute
Esophagus	Less than 1 minute
Stomach	1–3 hours
Small Intestine	1–6 hours
Large Intestine	12–36 hours

3. If a meal is eaten at noon, what is happening to the food at 2 P.M.?
   A Saliva is breaking down starch into sugar.
   B Proteins are being digested into short chains of amino acids.
   C Fats are being digested.
   D Digested food is being absorbed into the blood.

4. You can predict that the nutrients in food eaten at noon will not have been completely absorbed into the blood by
   A 1 P.M.
   B 6 P.M.
   C 9 P.M.
   D noon the next day.

5. You can infer that the body system most likely to develop problems if a person eats a diet that is deficient in vitamin D is the
   A digestive system.
   B skeletal system.
   C muscular system.
   D nervous system.

Open-Ended Question

6. Compare the processes of mechanical and chemical digestion. How are they similar? How are they different? Use the following terms in your answer: enzymes, physical change, chemical change.

Circulation

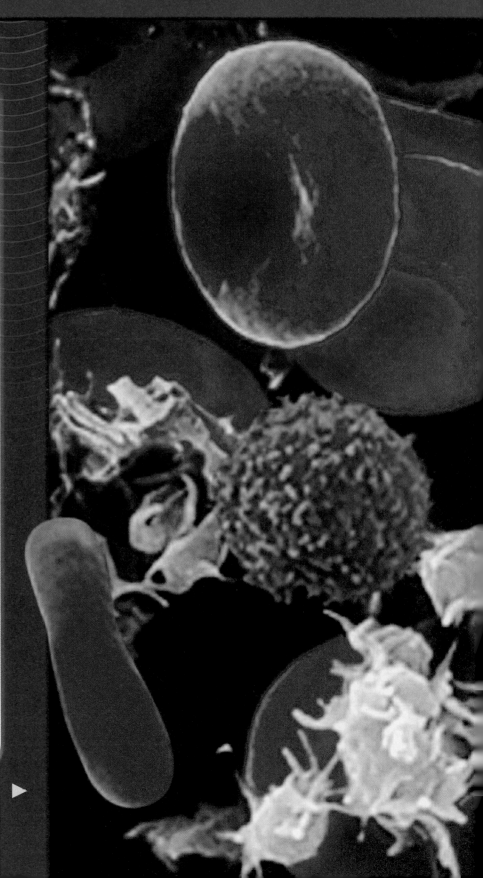

Academic Standards

This chapter addresses these Indiana standards.

The Nature of Science and Technology

7.1.5 Identify important contributions to science, mathematics, and technology by people of different cultures and times.

Scientific Thinking

7.2.6 Measure length, volume, weight, elapsed time, rates, or temperatures, and choose appropriate units.

The Physical Setting

7.3.12 Investigate how the temperature and acidity of a solution influence reaction rates.

The Living Environment

7.4.11 Explain that the amount of food energy a person needs depends on weight, age, sex, activity, and efficiency. Exercise is important to health.

Blood cells travel in blood vessels ▶ to all parts of the body.

Lab zone™ Chapter Project

Travels of a Red Blood Cell

Every day, you travel from home to school and back home again. Your travel path makes a loop, or circuit, ending where it began. In this chapter, you'll learn how your blood also travels in circuits. In this project, you'll create a display to show how blood circulates throughout the body.

Your Goal To design and construct a display showing a complete journey of a red blood cell through the human body

Your display must

- show a red blood cell that leaves from the heart and returns to the same place
- show where the exchange of oxygen and carbon dioxide takes place
- provide written descriptions of the circuits made by the red blood cell
- be designed following the safety guidelines in Appendix A

Plan It! Preview the chapter and find diagrams that show the heart, red blood cells, and the pathway of blood throughout the body. Then discuss the kinds of displays you could use, including a three-dimensional model, posters, a series of drawings, a flip book, or a video animation. Write down any content questions you'll need to answer.

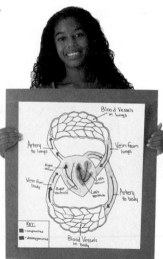

The Body's Transport System

Reading Preview

Key Concepts
• What are the functions of the cardiovascular system?
• What is the structure and function of the heart?
• What path does blood take through the cardiovascular system?

Key Terms
• cardiovascular system • heart
• atrium • ventricle • valve
• pacemaker • artery
• capillary • vein • aorta

Target Reading Skill
Sequencing As you read, make a cycle diagram like the one below that shows the path that blood follows as it circulates throughout the body. Write each step of the pathway in a separate circle.

Pathway of Blood

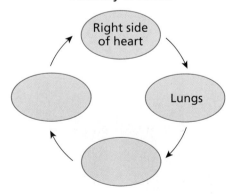

Lab zone · Discover **Activity**

How Hard Does Your Heart Work?

1. Every minute, your heart beats about 75 to 85 times. With each beat, it pumps about 60 milliliters of blood. Can you work as hard and fast as your heart does?

2. Cover a table or desk with newspapers. Place two large plastic containers side by side on the newspapers. Fill one with 2.5 liters of water, which is about the volume of blood that your heart pumps in 30 seconds. Leave the other container empty.

3. With a plastic cup that holds about 60 milliliters, transfer water as quickly as possible into the empty container, trying not to spill any. **CAUTION:** *Wipe up spills on the floor immediately.* Have a partner time you for 30 seconds. As you work, count how many transfers you make in 30 seconds.

4. Multiply your results by 2 to find the number of transfers in 1 minute.

Think It Over
Inferring Compare your performance with the number of times your heart beats every minute. What do your results tell you about the strength and speed of a heartbeat?

Late at night, a truck rolls through the darkness. Loaded with fresh fruits and vegetables, the truck is headed for a city supermarket. The driver steers off the interstate and onto a smaller highway. Finally, after driving through narrow city streets, the truck reaches its destination. As dawn breaks, store workers unload the cargo. At the same time, a garbage truck removes yesterday's trash and drives off down the road.

The Cardiovascular System

Like the roads that link all parts of the country, your body has a "highway" network, called the cardiovascular system, that links all parts of your body. The **cardiovascular system,** also called the circulatory system, consists of the heart, blood vessels, and blood. **The cardiovascular system carries needed substances to cells and carries waste products away from cells. In addition, blood contains cells that fight disease.**

Delivering Needed Materials Most substances that need to get from one part of the body to another are carried by blood. For example, blood carries oxygen from your lungs to your other body cells. Blood also transports the glucose your cells use to produce energy.

Removing Waste Products The cardiovascular system picks up wastes from cells. For example, when cells break down glucose, they produce carbon dioxide as a waste product. The carbon dioxide passes from the cells into the blood. The cardiovascular system then carries carbon dioxide to the lungs, where it is exhaled.

Fighting Disease The cardiovascular system also transports cells that attack disease-causing microorganisms. This process can help keep you from becoming sick. If you do get sick, these disease-fighting blood cells will kill the microorganisms and help you get well.

✓ **Reading Checkpoint** How does the cardiovascular system help fight disease?

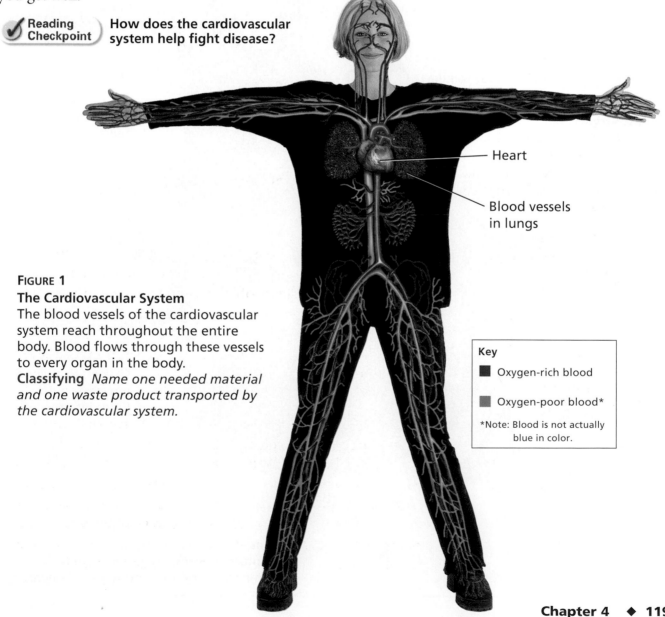

Heart

Blood vessels in lungs

FIGURE 1
The Cardiovascular System
The blood vessels of the cardiovascular system reach throughout the entire body. Blood flows through these vessels to every organ in the body.
Classifying *Name one needed material and one waste product transported by the cardiovascular system.*

Key
■ Oxygen-rich blood

■ Oxygen-poor blood*

*Note: Blood is not actually blue in color.

The Heart

Without the heart, blood wouldn't go anywhere. The **heart** is a hollow, muscular organ that pumps blood throughout the body. Your heart, which is about the size of your fist, is located in the center of your chest. The heart lies behind the sternum (breastbone) and inside the rib cage. These bones protect the heart from injury.

Each time the heart beats, it pushes blood through the blood vessels of the cardiovascular system. The heart is made of cardiac muscle, which can contract over and over without getting tired. Figure 2 shows the structure of the heart.

FIGURE 2
The Heart

Every second of your life, your heart pumps blood through your body. In a year, the heart pumps enough blood to fill more than 30 competition-size swimming pools.

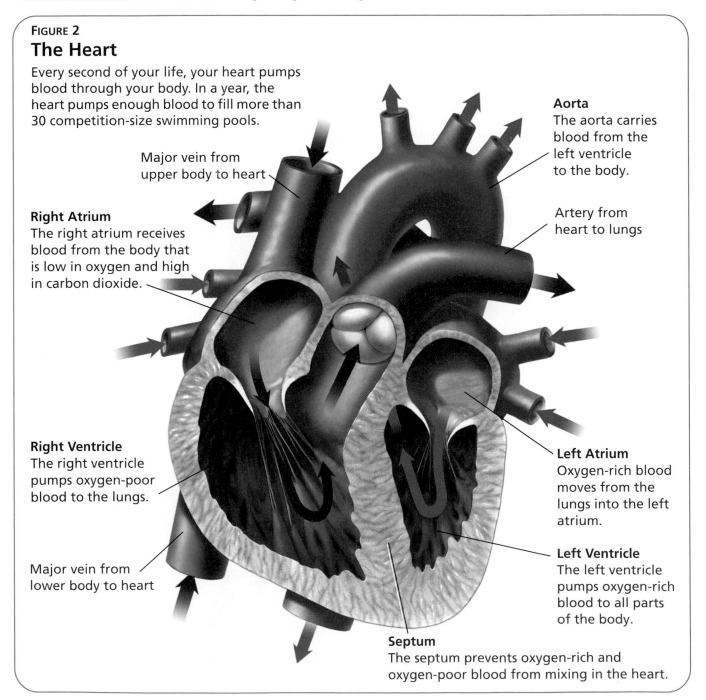

Major vein from upper body to heart

Aorta
The aorta carries blood from the left ventricle to the body.

Right Atrium
The right atrium receives blood from the body that is low in oxygen and high in carbon dioxide.

Artery from heart to lungs

Right Ventricle
The right ventricle pumps oxygen-poor blood to the lungs.

Left Atrium
Oxygen-rich blood moves from the lungs into the left atrium.

Major vein from lower body to heart

Left Ventricle
The left ventricle pumps oxygen-rich blood to all parts of the body.

Septum
The septum prevents oxygen-rich and oxygen-poor blood from mixing in the heart.

The Heart's Structure Notice in Figure 2 that the heart has a right side and a left side. **The right side of the heart is completely separated from the left side by a wall of tissue called the septum. Each side has two compartments, or chambers—an upper chamber and a lower chamber.** Each of the two upper chambers, called an **atrium** (AY tree um) (plural *atria*), receives blood that comes into the heart.

Each lower chamber, called a **ventricle,** pumps blood out of the heart. The atria are separated from the ventricles by valves. A **valve** is a flap of tissue that prevents blood from flowing backward. Valves are also located between the ventricles and the large blood vessels that carry blood away from the heart.

How the Heart Works The action of the heart has two main phases. In one phase, the heart muscle relaxes and the heart fills with blood. In the other phase, the heart muscle contracts and pumps blood forward. A heartbeat, which sounds something like *lub-dup*, can be heard during the pumping phase.

When the heart muscle relaxes, blood flows into the chambers. Then, the atria contract. This muscle contraction squeezes blood out of the atria, through the valves, and into the ventricles. Next, the ventricles contract. This contraction closes the valves between the atria and ventricles, making the *lub* sound and squeezing blood into large blood vessels. As the valves between the ventricles and the blood vessels snap shut, they make the *dup* sound. All of this happens in less than a second.

The Force of the Ventricles When muscle cells in the ventricles contract, they exert a force on the blood. A force is a push or a pull. The force exerted by the ventricles pushes blood out of your heart and into arteries.

The contraction of the left ventricle exerts much more force than the contraction of the right ventricle. The right ventricle pumps blood only to the lungs. In contrast, the left ventricle pumps blood throughout the body.

FIGURE 3
Open and Closed Heart Valves
As blood flows out of the heart and toward the lungs, it passes through a valve like the one in the photograph. **Applying Concepts** *What is the function of a closed heart valve?*

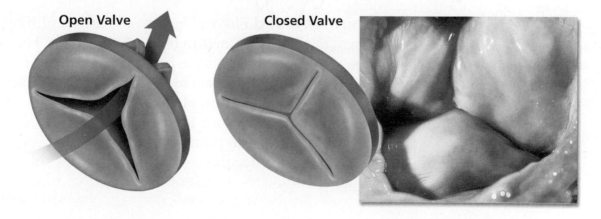

Open Valve   Closed Valve

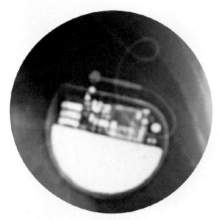

FIGURE 4
An Artificial Pacemaker
This pacemaker has been implanted beneath a patient's skin and connected with wires to the heart. The pacemaker will regulate the patient's heartbeat.

Lab zone **Skills Activity**

Creating Data Tables

Scientists measured the volume of blood that different organs receive, at rest and during vigorous exercise.

- At rest, the organs of the abdomen received about 1,400 mL of blood per minute (mL/min). During vigorous exercise, they received 600 mL/min.

- At rest, skeletal muscles received 1,200 mL/min. During vigorous exercise, they received about 12,500 mL/min.

- At rest, the kidneys received 1,100 mL/min. During vigorous exercise, they received about 600 mL/min.

Create a table to record these data. Then, use the data to explain why some organs receive more blood during exercise than others.

Regulation of Heartbeat A group of heart cells called the **pacemaker** sends out signals that make the heart muscle contract. The pacemaker is located in the right atrium of the heart.

The pacemaker constantly receives messages about the body's oxygen needs. It then adjusts the heart rate to match. For example, your heart beats much faster when you are exercising than when you are sitting quietly. When you exercise, the entire process from the beginning of one heartbeat to the beginning of the next can take less than half a second. Your muscles need more oxygen during exercise. Your rapid heartbeat supplies blood that carries the oxygen throughout your body.

In some people, the pacemaker becomes damaged as a result of disease or an accident. Damage to the pacemaker often results in an irregular or slow heartbeat. In the 1950s, doctors and engineers developed an artificial, battery-operated pacemaker. Modern artificial pacemakers are implanted beneath the skin and are connected by wires to the heart. Tiny electrical impulses travel from the battery through the wires, and make the heart contract.

 **Reading Checkpoint** **What is the function of the heart's pacemaker?**

Two Loops

After leaving the heart, blood travels in blood vessels through the body. Your body has three kinds of blood vessels—arteries, capillaries, and veins. **Arteries** are blood vessels that carry blood away from the heart. From the arteries, blood flows into tiny, narrow vessels called **capillaries.** In the capillaries, substances are exchanged between the blood and body cells. From capillaries, blood flows into **veins,** blood vessels that carry blood back to the heart.

Pattern of Blood Flow The overall pattern of blood flow through the body is something like a figure eight. The heart is at the center where the two loops cross. **In the first loop, blood travels from the heart to the lungs and then back to the heart. In the second loop, blood is pumped from the heart throughout the body and then returns again to the heart.** The heart is really two pumps, one on the right and one on the left. The right side pumps blood to the lungs, and the left side pumps blood to the rest of the body.

Blood travels in only one direction. If you were a drop of blood, you could start at any point and eventually return to the same point. The entire trip would take less than a minute. As you read about the path that blood takes through the cardiovascular system, trace the path in Figure 5.

Loop One: To the Lungs and Back When blood from the body flows into the right atrium, it contains little oxygen but a lot of carbon dioxide. This oxygen-poor blood is dark red. The blood then flows from the right atrium into the right ventricle. Then, the ventricle pumps the oxygen-poor blood into the arteries that lead to the lungs.

As blood flows through the lungs, large blood vessels branch into smaller ones. Eventually, blood flows through tiny capillaries that are in close contact with the air that comes into the lungs. The air in the lungs has more oxygen than the blood in the capillaries. Therefore, oxygen moves from the lungs into the blood. For the same reason, carbon dioxide moves in the opposite direction—from the blood into the lungs. As the blood leaves the lungs, it is now rich in oxygen and contains little carbon dioxide. This blood, which is bright red, flows to the left side of the heart and will be pumped through the second loop.

FIGURE 5
Direction of Blood Flow
Blood circulates through the body in two loops, with the heart at the center. Loop one goes from the heart to the lungs and back. Loop two circulates blood throughout the rest of the body.
Interpreting Diagrams *Where does the blood that enters the left atrium come from?*

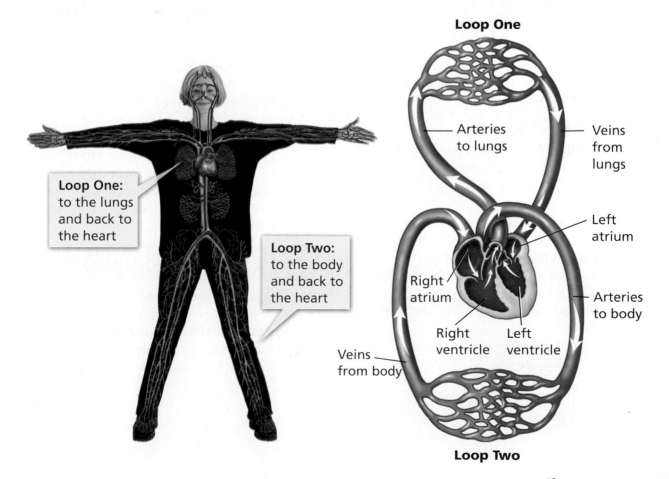

Loop One

Loop One:
to the lungs and back to the heart

Loop Two:
to the body and back to the heart

Arteries to lungs

Veins from lungs

Left atrium

Right atrium

Arteries to body

Right ventricle

Left ventricle

Veins from body

Loop Two

Loop Two: To the Body and Back The second loop begins as the left atrium fills with oxygen-rich blood coming from the lungs. The blood then moves into the left ventricle. From the left ventricle, the blood is pumped into the **aorta** (ay AWR tuh), the largest artery in the body.

Eventually, after passing through branching arteries, blood flows through tiny capillaries in different parts of your body, such as your brain, liver, and legs. These vessels are in close contact with body cells. Oxygen moves out of the blood and into the body cells. At the same time, carbon dioxide passes from the body cells into the blood. This blood, which is low in oxygen, then flows back to the right atrium of the heart through veins, completing the second loop.

FIGURE 6
Getting Blood to Body Cells
In loop two, oxygen-rich blood is pumped throughout the body. The oxygen moves out of the blood and into the body cells in this swimmer's arms and legs.

 **Reading Checkpoint** What is the largest artery in the body?

Section 1 Assessment

Target Reading Skill Sequencing Refer to your cycle diagram about the pathway of blood flow as you answer Question 3.

Reviewing Key Concepts

1. a. **Reviewing** What three functions does the cardiovascular system perform?
   b. **Comparing and Contrasting** Distinguish between substances that the cardiovascular system transports to cells and substances that it transports away from cells.
2. a. **Listing** Name the four chambers of the heart. What structures in the heart separate one chamber from another?
   b. **Summarizing** What function does the heart perform?
   c. **Predicting** What would happen if the valve between the right atrium and right ventricle did not work properly?

3. a. **Identifying** Where does blood returning from the body enter the heart?
   b. **Sequencing** Where does the blood move next?
   c. **Interpreting Diagrams** Review Figure 5. How does the blood in the artery leaving the right ventricle differ from the blood in the artery leaving the left ventricle? To where does the artery leaving the right ventricle carry blood?

Writing in Science

Comparison Paragraph Write a paragraph comparing the cardiovascular system in the body to a system of roads, telephone lines, or any other "network" you can think of. How are the two systems alike? How do they differ?

A Closer Look at Blood Vessels

Reading Preview

Key Concepts
- What are the structures and functions of arteries?
- What are the structures and functions of capillaries and veins?
- What causes blood pressure?

Key Terms
- coronary artery • pulse
- diffusion • blood pressure

Target Reading Skill
Comparing and Contrasting As you read, compare and contrast the three kinds of blood vessels by completing a table like the one below.

Comparing Blood Vessels

Blood Vessel	Function	Structure of Wall
Artery	Carries blood away from heart	
Capillary		
Vein		

Lab zone Discover **Activity**

How Does Pressure Affect Blood Flow?

1. Spread newspapers over a table or desktop. Then, fill a plastic squeeze bottle with water.

2. Hold the bottle over a dishpan. Squeeze the bottle with one hand. Observe how far the water travels. **CAUTION:** *Wipe up spills on the floor to prevent anyone from slipping.*

3. Now, grasp the bottle with both hands and squeeze again. Observe how far the water travels this time.

Think It Over
Inferring Blood is pushed through arteries with much more force than it is pushed through veins. Which part of the activity models an artery? Which part models a vein? Which organ in the body provides the pushing force for blood transport?

Like corridors in a large building, blood vessels run through all of the tissues of your body. Although some blood vessels are as wide as your thumb, most of them are much finer than a human hair. If all the arteries, capillaries, and veins in your body were hooked together end to end, they would stretch a distance of almost 100,000 kilometers. That's long enough to wrap around Earth twice—with a lot left over!

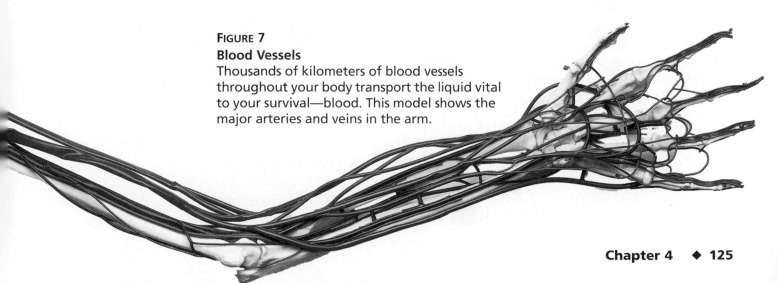

FIGURE 7
Blood Vessels
Thousands of kilometers of blood vessels throughout your body transport the liquid vital to your survival—blood. This model shows the major arteries and veins in the arm.

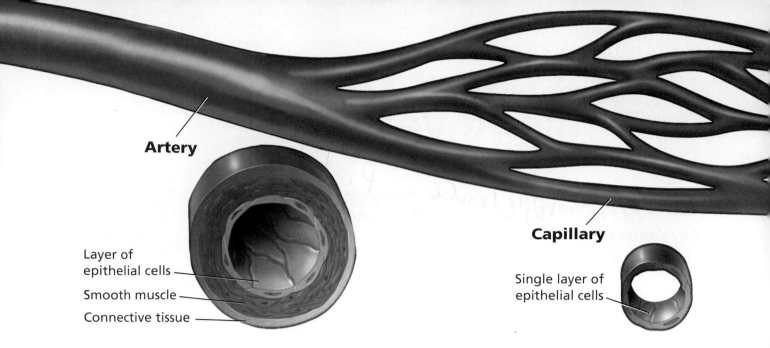

Artery

Layer of epithelial cells

Smooth muscle

Connective tissue

Capillary

Single layer of epithelial cells

FIGURE 8
Artery, Capillary, and Vein
The walls of arteries and veins have three layers. The walls of capillaries are only one cell thick. **Relating Cause and Effect** *How does material get from inside capillaries to body cells?*

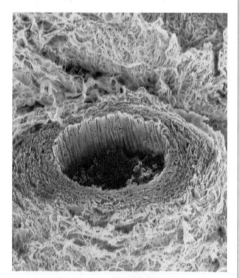

▲ The artery wall appears as a thick pink band surrounding a clump of red blood cells.

Arteries

When blood leaves the heart, it travels through arteries. The right ventricle pumps blood into the arteries that go to the lungs. The left ventricle pumps blood into the aorta. Smaller arteries branch off the aorta. The first branches, called the **coronary arteries,** carry blood to the heart itself. Other branches carry blood to the brain, intestines, and other organs. Each artery branches into smaller and smaller arteries.

Artery Structure **The walls of arteries are generally very thick. In fact, artery walls consist of three cell layers.** The innermost layer, which is made up of epithelial cells, is smooth. This smooth surface enables blood to flow freely. The middle layer consists mostly of muscle tissue. The outer wall is made up of flexible connective tissue. Because of this layered structure, arteries have both strength and flexibility. Arteries are able to withstand the enormous pressure of blood as it is pumped by the heart and to expand and relax between heart beats.

Pulse If you lightly touch the inside of your wrist, you can feel the artery in your wrist rise and fall repeatedly. This **pulse** is caused by the alternating expansion and relaxation of the artery wall. Every time the heart's ventricles contract, they send a spurt of blood out through all the arteries in your body. As this spurt travels through the arteries, it pushes the artery walls and makes them expand. After the spurt passes, the artery walls relax and become narrower again.

When you count the number of times an artery pulses beneath your fingers, you are counting heartbeats. By taking your pulse rate, you can determine how fast your heart is beating.

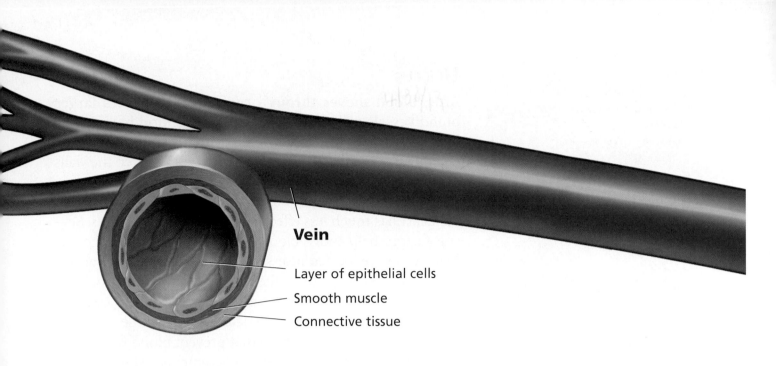

Vein

Layer of epithelial cells

Smooth muscle

Connective tissue

Regulating Blood Flow The layer of muscle in an artery acts as a control gate, adjusting the amount of blood sent to different organs. When the muscle contracts, the opening in the artery becomes smaller. When the muscle relaxes, the opening becomes larger. For example, after you eat, your stomach and intestines need a greater blood supply for digestion. The arteries leading to those organs open wider, and more blood flows through them. In contrast, when you are running, your stomach and intestines need less blood than the muscles in your legs. The arteries leading to the digestive organs become narrower, decreasing the blood flow to these organs.

 **Reading Checkpoint** What causes your pulse?

Capillaries

Eventually, blood flows from small arteries into the tiny capillaries. **In the capillaries, materials are exchanged between the blood and the body's cells. Capillary walls are only one cell thick.** Thus, materials can pass easily through them. Materials such as oxygen and glucose pass from the blood, through the capillary walls, to the cells. Cellular waste products travel in the opposite direction—from cells, through the capillary walls, and into the blood.

One way that materials are exchanged between the blood and body cells is by diffusion. **Diffusion** is the process by which molecules move from an area of higher concentration to an area of lower concentration. For example, glucose is more highly concentrated in the blood than it is in the body cells. Therefore, glucose diffuses from the blood into the body cells.

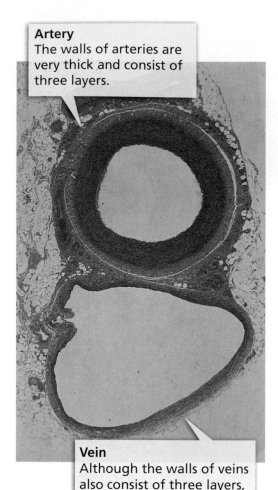

Artery
The walls of arteries are very thick and consist of three layers.

Vein
Although the walls of veins also consist of three layers, they are much thinner than the walls of arteries.

FIGURE 9
Artery and Vein
In this photo, you can compare the wall of an artery (top) with the wall of a vein (bottom).
Comparing and Contrasting *Where is the pushing force of the heart greater—in arteries or in veins?*

Veins

After blood moves through capillaries, it enters larger blood vessels called veins, which carry blood back to the heart. **The walls of veins, like those of arteries, have three layers, with muscle in the middle layer.** However, the walls of veins are generally much thinner than those of arteries.

By the time blood flows into veins, the pushing force of the heart has much less effect than it did in the arteries. Several factors help move blood through veins. First, because many veins are located near skeletal muscles, the contraction of the muscles helps push the blood along. For example, as you run or walk, the skeletal muscles in your legs contract and squeeze the veins in your legs. Second, larger veins in your body have valves in them that prevent blood from flowing backward. Third, breathing movements, which exert a squeezing pressure against veins in the chest, also force blood toward the heart.

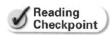 **Reading Checkpoint** How do skeletal muscles help move blood in veins?

Blood Pressure

Suppose that you are washing a car. You attach the hose to the faucet and turn on the faucet. The water flows out in a slow, steady stream. Then, while your back is turned, your little brother turns the faucet on all the way. Suddenly, the water spurts out rapidly, and the hose almost jumps out of your hand.

As water flows through a hose, it pushes against the walls of the hose, creating pressure on the walls. Pressure is the force that something exerts over a given area. When your brother turned on the faucet all the way, the additional water flow increased the pressure exerted on the inside of the hose. The extra pressure made the water spurt out of the nozzle faster.

What Causes Blood Pressure? Blood traveling through blood vessels behaves in a manner similar to that of water moving through a hose. Blood exerts a force, called **blood pressure,** against the walls of blood vessels. **Blood pressure is caused by the force with which the ventricles contract.** In general, as blood moves away from the heart, blood pressure decreases. This change happens because the farther away from the ventricle the blood moves, the lower its force is. Blood flowing near the heart arteries exerts the highest pressure. Blood pressure in arteries farther from the heart is much lower.

Measuring Blood Pressure Blood pressure can be measured with an instrument called a sphygmomanometer (sfig moh muh NAHM uh tur). A cuff is wrapped around the upper arm. Air is pumped into the cuff until the blood flow through the artery is stopped. As the pressure is released, the examiner listens to the pulse and records two numbers. Blood pressure is expressed in millimeters of mercury. The first number is a measure of the blood pressure while the heart's ventricles contract and pump blood into the arteries. The second number, which is lower, measures the blood pressure while the ventricles relax. The two numbers are expressed as a fraction: the contraction pressure over the relaxation pressure.

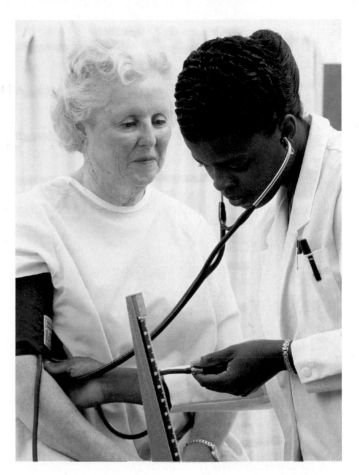

FIGURE 10
Measuring Blood Pressure
Blood pressure can be measured with a sphygmomanometer. A typical blood pressure reading for a healthy person is 120/80 or lower.

Section 2 Assessment

↻ **Target Reading Skill** Comparing and Contrasting Use the information in your table about blood vessels to help you answer the questions below.

Reviewing Key Concepts

1. a. Identifying In which direction do arteries carry blood?
  b. Explaining How does the structure of arteries enable them to withstand high pressure?
  c. Applying Concepts Arteries adjust the amount of blood flowing to different parts of the body, depending on where blood is needed. Use this fact to explain why you should not exercise vigorously shortly after you eat.
2. a. Reviewing What is the function of capillaries in the body?
  b. Summarizing Summarize the factors that enable blood in your leg veins to return to the heart in spite of the downward pull of gravity.

3. a. Defining What is blood pressure?
  b. Relating Cause and Effect Why is blood pressure lower in leg veins than in the aorta?
  c. Predicting How might having low blood pressure affect your body?

Math ➤ **Practice**

Before a run, you take your pulse rate for 30 seconds and count 29 beats. Immediately after the run, you count 63 beats in 30 seconds. After resting for 15 minutes, you count 31 beats in 30 seconds.

4. Calculating a Rate What was your pulse rate per minute before the run?
5. Calculating a Rate What was your pulse rate immediately after the run? After resting for 15 minutes?

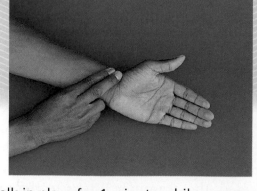

Heart Beat, Health Beat

Problem

How does physical activity affect your pulse rate?

Skills Focus

graphing, interpreting data, drawing conclusions

Materials

• graph paper
• watch with second hand or
  heart rate monitor

Procedure

1. Predict how your pulse rate will change as you go from resting to being active, then back to resting again. Then, copy the data table into your notebook.

2. Locate your pulse by placing the index and middle finger of one hand on your other wrist at the base of your thumb. Move the two fingers slightly until you feel your pulse. If you are using a heart rate monitor, see your teacher for instructions.

3. Work with a partner for the rest of this lab. Begin by determining your resting pulse rate. Count the number of beats in your pulse for exactly 1 minute while your partner times you. Record your resting pulse rate in your data table. **CAUTION:** *Do not complete the rest of this lab if there is any medical reason why you should avoid physical activities.*

Data Table	
Activity	Pulse Rate
Resting	
Walking	
Running	
Resting after exercise (1 min)	
Resting after exercise (3+ min)	

4. Walk in place for 1 minute while your partner times you. Stop and immediately take your pulse for 1 minute. Record the number in your data table.

5. Run in place for 1 minute. Take your pulse again, and record the result.

6. Sit down right away, and have your partner time you as you rest for 1 minute. Then, take your pulse rate again.

7. Have your partner time you as you rest for 3 more minutes. Then take your pulse rate again and record it.

Analyze and Conclude

1. **Graphing** Use the data you obtained to create a bar graph of your pulse rate under the different conditions you tested.

2. **Interpreting Data** What happens to the pulse rate when the physical activity has stopped?

3. **Inferring** What can you infer about the heartbeat when the pulse rate increases?

4. **Drawing Conclusions** What conclusion can you draw about the relationship between physical activity and a person's pulse rate?

5. **Communicating** How could you improve the accuracy of your pulse measurements? Write a paragraph in which you discuss this question in relation to the steps you followed in your procedure.

Design an Experiment

Design an experiment to determine whether the resting pulse rates of adults, teens, and young children differ. *Obtain your teacher's permission before carrying out your investigation.*

For: Data sharing
Visit: PHSchool.com
Web Code: ced-4032

Section 3

Blood and Lymph

Reading Preview

Key Concepts
- What are the components of blood?
- What determines the type of blood that a person can receive in transfusion?
- What are the structures and functions of the lymphatic system?

Key Terms
- plasma • red blood cell
- hemoglobin
- white blood cell • platelet
- lymphatic system • lymph
- lymph node

Target Reading Skill

Identifying Main Ideas As you read the section titled Blood, write the main idea in a graphic organizer like the one below. Then, write four supporting details that give examples of the main idea.

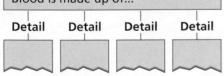

Main Idea

Blood is made up of...

Detail   Detail   Detail   Detail

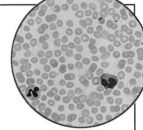

Lab zone Discover Activity

What Kinds of Cells Are in Blood?
1. Obtain a microscope slide of human blood. Look at the slide under the microscope, first under low power and then under high power.
2. Look carefully at the different kinds of cells that you see.
3. Make several drawings of each kind of cell. Use red pencil for the red blood cells.

Think It Over
Observing How many kinds of cells did you see? How do they differ from one another?

While riding your bike through the neighborhood, you take a tumble and scrape your knee. Your knee begins to sting, and you notice blood oozing from the wound. You go inside to clean the wound. As you do, you wonder, "Just what is blood?"

Blood

Blood may seem like just a plain red liquid, but it is actually a complex tissue that has several parts. **Blood is made up of four components: plasma, red blood cells, white blood cells, and platelets.** About 45 percent of the volume of blood is cells. The rest is plasma.

Plasma Most of the materials transported in the blood travel in the plasma. **Plasma** is the liquid part of the blood. Water makes up 90 percent of plasma. The other 10 percent is dissolved materials. Plasma carries nutrients, such as glucose, fats, vitamins, and minerals. Plasma also carries chemical messengers that direct body activities such as the uptake of glucose by your cells. In addition, many wastes produced by cell processes are carried away by plasma.

Protein molecules give plasma its yellow color. There are three groups of plasma proteins. One group helps to regulate the amount of water in blood. The second group, which is produced by white blood cells, helps fight disease. The third group of proteins interacts with platelets to form blood clots.

Red Blood Cells Without red blood cells, your body could not use the oxygen that you breathe in. **Red blood cells** take up oxygen in the lungs and deliver it to cells elsewhere in the body. Red blood cells, like most blood cells, are produced in bone marrow. Under a microscope, these cells look like disks with pinched-in centers. Because of their pinched shape, red blood cells are thin in the middle and can bend and twist easily. This flexibility enables them to squeeze through narrow capillaries.

A red blood cell is made mostly of **hemoglobin** (HEE muh gloh bin), which is an iron-containing protein that binds chemically to oxygen molecules. When hemoglobin combines with oxygen, the cells become bright red. Without oxygen, the cells are dark red. Thus, blood leaving the heart through the aorta is bright red, whereas blood returning from the body to the heart through veins is dark red. Hemoglobin picks up oxygen in the lungs and releases it as blood travels through capillaries in the rest of the body. Hemoglobin also picks up some of the carbon dioxide produced by cells. However, most of the carbon dioxide is carried by plasma. The blood carries the carbon dioxide to the lungs, where it is released from the body.

Mature red blood cells have no nuclei. Without a nucleus, a red blood cell cannot reproduce or repair itself. Mature red blood cells live only about 120 days. Every second, about 2 million red blood cells in your body die. Fortunately, your bone marrow produces new red blood cells at the same rate.

✓ **Reading Checkpoint** What is hemoglobin?

White Blood Cells Like red blood cells, white blood cells are produced in bone marrow. **White blood cells** are the body's disease fighters. Some white blood cells recognize disease-causing organisms, such as bacteria, and alert the body that it has been invaded. Other white blood cells produce chemicals to fight the invaders. Still others surround and kill the organisms.

White blood cells are different from red blood cells in several important ways. There are fewer of them—only about one white blood cell for every 500 to 1,000 red blood cells. White blood cells are also larger than red blood cells. In addition, white blood cells contain nuclei. Most white blood cells can live for months or even years.

FIGURE 11
Parts of Blood

Blood consists of liquid plasma and three kinds of cells—red blood cells, white blood cells, and platelets.
Observing *Describe the shape of a red blood cell.*

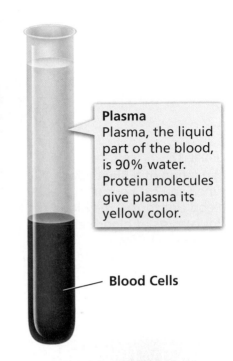

Plasma
Plasma, the liquid part of the blood, is 90% water. Protein molecules give plasma its yellow color.

— **Blood Cells**

Red Blood Cells
Oxygen is carried throughout your body by red blood cells. Your blood contains more red blood cells than any other kind of cell.

White Blood Cells
By finding and destroying disease-causing organisms, white blood cells fight disease.

Platelets
When you cut yourself, platelets help form the blood clot that stops the bleeding. Platelets aren't really whole cells. Instead, they are small pieces of cells and do not have nuclei.

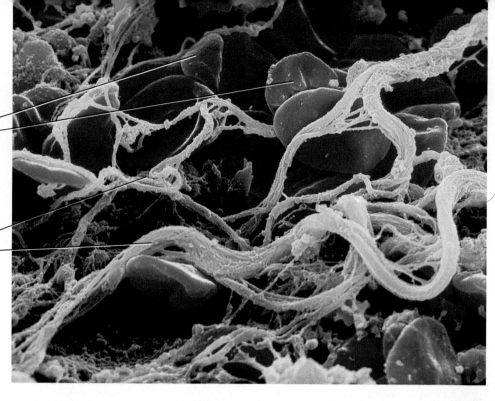

Red blood cells

Fibrin

FIGURE 12
Formation of a Blood Clot
When you cut your skin, a blood clot forms. The blood clot consists of blood cells trapped in a fiber net.
Relating Cause and Effect *How is this net of fibers produced?*

Lab zone Try This **Activity**

Caught in the Web

In this activity, you will model part of the process by which a blood clot forms.

1. Cover the opening of a sturdy plastic cup with a piece of cheesecloth. Use a rubber band to hold the cheesecloth in place.

2. Put some water, paper clips, and coins in another cup.

3. Carefully pour the water, coins, and paper clips into the middle of the cheesecloth.

Making Models The paper clips and coins represent blood cells. What does the cheesecloth represent? What starts the production of the substance that the cheesecloth represents?

Platelets When you scraped your knee, blood oozed out of the wound. After a short time, however, a blood clot formed, stopping the blood flow. **Platelets** (PLAYT lits) are cell fragments that play an important part in forming blood clots.

When a blood vessel is cut, platelets collect and stick to the vessel at the site of the wound. The platelets release chemicals that start a chain reaction. This series of reactions eventually produces a protein called fibrin (FY brin). Fibrin gets its name from the fact that it weaves a net of tiny fibers across the cut in the blood vessel. Look at Figure 12 to see how the fiber net traps the blood cells. As more and more platelets and blood cells become trapped in the net, a blood clot forms. A scab is a dried blood clot on the skin surface.

 Reading Checkpoint **What is the role of platelets?**

Blood Types

If a person loses a lot of blood—either from a wound or during surgery—he or she may be given a blood transfusion. A blood transfusion is the transfer of blood from one person to another. Most early attempts at blood transfusion failed, but no one knew why until the early 1900s. At that time, Karl Landsteiner, an Austrian American physician, tried mixing blood samples from pairs of people. Sometimes the two blood samples blended smoothly. In other cases, however, the red blood cells clumped together. This clumping accounted for the failure of many blood transfusions. If clumping occurs within the body, it clogs the capillaries and may lead to death.

Marker Molecules Landsteiner went on to discover that there are four major types of blood—A, B, AB, and O. Blood types are determined by proteins known as marker molecules that are on the red blood cells. If your blood type is A, you have the A marker. If your blood type is B, you have the B marker. People with type AB blood have both A and B markers. People with type O blood have neither A nor B markers.

Your plasma contains clumping proteins that recognize red blood cells with "foreign" markers (not yours) and make those cells clump together. For example, if you have blood type A, your blood contains clumping proteins that act against cells with B markers. So, if you receive a transfusion of type B blood, your clumping proteins will make the "foreign" type B cells clump together.

Safe Transfusions Landsteiner's work led to a better understanding of transfusions. **The marker molecules on your red blood cells determine your blood type and the type of blood that you can safely receive in transfusions.** A person with type A blood can receive transfusions of either type A or type O blood. Neither of these two blood types has B markers. Thus they would not be recognized as foreign by the clumping proteins in type A blood. A person with type AB blood can receive all blood types in transfusion because type AB blood has no clumping proteins. Figure 13 shows which transfusions are safe for each blood type.

If you ever receive a transfusion, your blood type will be checked first. Then, donated blood that you can safely receive will be found. This process is called cross matching. You may have heard a doctor on a television show give the order to "type and cross." The doctor wants to find out what blood type the patient has and then cross match it with donated blood.

Go Online
SciLINKS NSTA

For: Links on blood
Visit: www.SciLinks.org
Web Code: scn-0433

FIGURE 13
Blood Types and Their Markers
The chemical markers on a person's red blood cells determine the types of blood he or she can safely receive in a transfusion.
Interpreting Tables *What types of blood can be given safely to a person with blood type AB?*

Blood Types and Their Markers				
Blood Type Characteristic	**Blood Type A**	**Blood Type B**	**Blood Type AB**	**Blood Type O**
Marker Molecules on Red Blood Cells	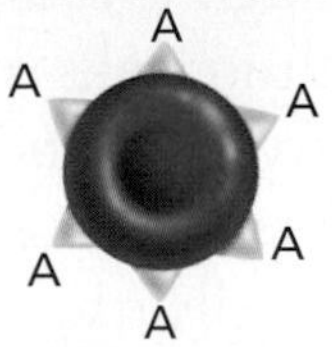 A A A A A	 B B B B B	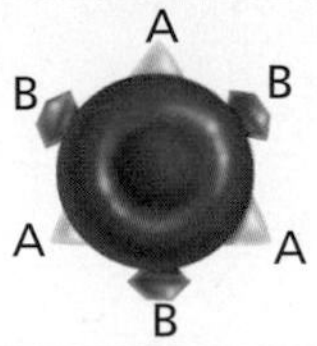 A B B A B	 (no markers)
Clumping Proteins	anti-B	anti-A	no clumping proteins	anti-A and anti-B
Blood Types That Can Be Safely Received in a Transfusion	A and O	B and O	A, B, AB, and O	O

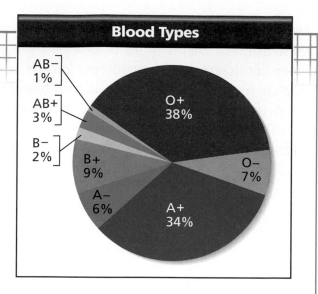

Blood Types

AB−
1%

AB+
3%

B−
2%

B+
9%

O+
38%

O−
7%

A−
6%

A+
34%

Blood Type Distribution

The circle graph shows the percentage of each blood type found in the U.S. population.

1. **Reading Graphs** What does each wedge of the graph represent?

2. **Interpreting Data** Rank the four major blood types—A, B, AB, and O—from least common to most common. What is the percentage of each type?

3. **Calculating** According to the graph, what percentage of the population is Rh positive? What percentage is Rh negative?

4. **Predicting** What type of blood can someone who is B negative (blood type B and Rh negative) receive? What percentage of the population does that represent?

5. **Creating Data Tables** Use the data to make a table of the eight possible blood types. Include columns for the A, B, AB, and O blood types, Rh factor (positive or negative), and percentage of the population.

Rh Factor Landsteiner also discovered the presence of another protein on red blood cells, which he called Rh factor. About 85 percent of the people he tested had this protein, and about 15 percent lacked it. Like the A, B, AB, and O blood types, the presence of Rh factor is determined by a marker on the red blood cell. If your blood type is Rh positive, you have the Rh marker. If your blood type is Rh negative, you lack the marker on your cells. If you are Rh negative and ever received Rh positive blood, you would develop Rh clumping proteins in your plasma. This situation is potentially dangerous.

 Reading Checkpoint **Where is the Rh marker found?**

The Lymphatic System

As blood travels through the capillaries in the cardiovascular system, some of the fluid leaks out. It moves through the walls of capillaries and into surrounding tissues. This fluid carries materials that the cells in the tissues need.

After bathing the cells, this fluid moves into your body's drainage system, called the **lymphatic system** (lim FAT ik). **The lymphatic system is a network of veinlike vessels that returns the fluid to the bloodstream.** The lymphatic system acts something like rain gutters after a rainstorm, carrying the excess fluid away.

Lymph Once the fluid is inside the lymphatic system, it is called **lymph.** Lymph consists of water and dissolved materials such as glucose. It also contains some white blood cells that have left the capillaries.

The lymphatic system has no pump, so lymph moves slowly. Lymphatic vessels, which are part of the cardiovascular system, connect to large veins in the chest. Lymph empties into these veins, and the fluid once again becomes part of blood plasma.

Lymph Nodes As lymph flows through the lymphatic system, it passes through small knobs of tissue called lymph nodes. The **lymph nodes** filter lymph, trapping bacteria and other disease-causing microorganisms in the fluid. When the body is fighting an infection, the lymph nodes enlarge. If you've ever had "swollen glands" when you've been sick, you've actually had swollen lymph nodes.

 **Reading Checkpoint** What is lymph?

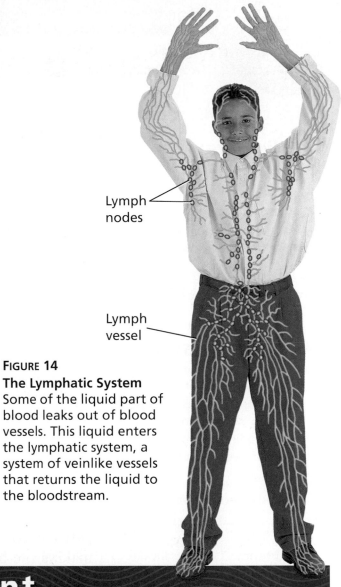

Lymph nodes

Lymph vessel

FIGURE 14
The Lymphatic System
Some of the liquid part of blood leaks out of blood vessels. This liquid enters the lymphatic system, a system of veinlike vessels that returns the liquid to the bloodstream.

Section 3 Assessment

Target Reading Skill Identifying Main Ideas
Use your graphic organizer to help you answer Question 1 below.

Reviewing Key Concepts

1. **a. Listing** Name the four components of blood. Identify whether each is a cell, a part of a cell, or a liquid.
   b. Summarizing Briefly describe what happens to stop the bleeding when you cut yourself.
   c. Relating Cause and Effect People with the disorder hemophilia do not produce the protein fibrin. Explain why hemophilia is a serious disorder.
2. **a. Reviewing** What is a marker molecule?
   b. Explaining Explain why a person with type O blood cannot receive a transfusion of type A blood.

   c. Predicting Can a person with type AB, Rh negative blood safely receive a transfusion of type O, Rh negative blood? Explain.
3. **a. Identifying** Where does lymph come from?
   b. Sequencing What happens to lymph after it travels through the lymphatic system?

Lab zone At-Home **Activity**

What's Your Blood Type? If possible, find out your blood type. Explain to family members the types of blood you can receive and to whom you can donate blood. Create a chart to help with your explanation.

Cardiovascular Health

Reading Preview

Key Concepts
- What are some diseases of the cardiovascular system?
- What behaviors can help maintain cardiovascular health?

Key Terms
- atherosclerosis • heart attack
- hypertension

Target Reading Skill

Asking Questions Before you read, preview the red headings. In a graphic organizer like the one below, ask a *what* or *how* question for each heading. As you read, write the answers to your questions.

Cardiovascular Health

Question	Answer
What are some cardiovascular diseases?	Cardiovascular diseases include...

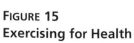

Lab zone — Discover **Activity**

Which Foods Are "Heart Healthy"?

1. Your teacher will give you an assortment of foods. If they have nutrition labels, read the information.
2. Sort the foods into three groups. In one group, put those foods that you think are good for your cardiovascular system. In the second group, put foods that you think might damage your cardiovascular system if eaten often. Place foods you aren't sure about in the third group.

Think It Over
Forming Operational Definitions How did you define a "heart-healthy" food?

Shortly after sunrise, when most people are just waking up, a team of rowers is already out on the river. Rhythmically, with perfectly coordinated movement, the rowers pull on the oars, making the boat glide swiftly through the water. Despite the chilly morning air, sweat glistens on the rowers' faces and arms. Inside their chests, their hearts are pounding, delivering blood to the arm and chest muscles that power the oars.

FIGURE 15
Exercising for Health
Strenuous exercise, such as rowing, requires a healthy cardiovascular system. In turn, exercise keeps the cardiovascular system healthy.

Healthy, unblocked artery

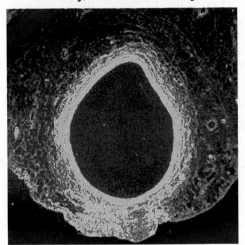

Partially blocked artery

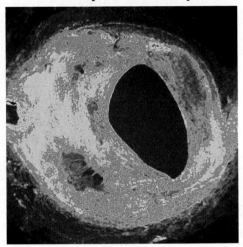

FIGURE 16
Effect of Atherosclerosis
The artery on the right shows atherosclerosis, which is caused by deposits of fat on the artery walls.
Relating Cause and Effect *What kind of diet can lead to atherosclerosis?*

Cardiovascular Diseases

Rowers cannot perform at their peaks unless their cardiovascular systems are in excellent condition. But cardiovascular health is important for all people, not just for athletes. Cardiovascular disease is the leading cause of death in the United States today. **Diseases of the cardiovascular system include atherosclerosis and hypertension.**

Atherosclerosis Compare the photos of the two arteries in Figure 16. The one on the left is a healthy artery. It has a large space in the center through which blood can flow easily. The artery on the right, in contrast, has a smaller space in the middle. This artery exhibits **atherosclerosis** (ath uh roh skluh ROH sis), a condition in which an artery wall thickens as a result of the buildup of fatty materials. One of these fatty materials is cholesterol, a waxy substance. Atherosclerosis results in a reduced flow of blood in the affected artery.

Atherosclerosis can develop in the coronary arteries, which supply the heart muscle. When that happens, the heart muscle receives less blood and therefore less oxygen. This condition may lead to a heart attack. A **heart attack** occurs when blood flow to part of the heart muscle is blocked. Cells die in the part of the heart that does not receive blood and oxygen. This permanently damages the heart.

Treatment for mild atherosclerosis usually includes a low-fat diet and a moderate exercise program. In addition, medications that lower the levels of cholesterol and fats in the blood may be prescribed. People with severe atherosclerosis may need to undergo surgery or other procedures to unclog the blocked arteries.

Lab zone Try This Activity

Blocking the Flow
Use this activity to model how fatty deposits affect the flow of blood through an artery.

1. Put a funnel in the mouth of a plastic jar. The funnel will represent an artery.

2. Slowly pour 100 mL of water into the funnel. Have your partner time how many seconds it takes for all the water to flow through the funnel. Then, discard the water.

3. Use a plastic knife to spread a small amount of paste along the bottom of the funnel's neck. Then, with a toothpick, carve out a hole in the paste so that the funnel is partly, but not completely, clogged.

4. Repeat Steps 1 and 2.

Predicting If the funnels were arteries, which one—blocked or unblocked—would do a better job of supplying blood to tissues? Explain.

Hypertension High blood pressure, or **hypertension** (hy pur TEN shun), is a disorder in which a person's blood pressure is consistently higher than normal—usually defined as greater than 140/90.

Hypertension makes the heart work harder to pump blood throughout the body. It also may damage the walls of the blood vessels. Over time, both the heart and arteries can be severely harmed by hypertension. Because people with hypertension often have no obvious symptoms to warn them of the danger until damage is severe, hypertension is sometimes called the "silent killer."

• Tech & Design in History •

Advances in Cardiovascular Medicine

Scientists today have an in-depth understanding of how the cardiovascular system works and how to treat cardiovascular problems. This timeline describes some of the advances in cardiovascular medicine.

1930s–1940s
Blood Banks
Charles Drew demonstrated that emergency blood transfusions could be done with plasma if whole blood was not available. During World War II, Drew established blood banks for storing donated blood. His work helped save millions of lives on and off the battlefield.

1958
Artificial Pacemaker
Electrical engineer Earl Baaken developed an external pacemaker to correct irregular heartbeats. A small electric generator connected to the pacemaker generated electric pulses that regulated heart rate. The first pacemakers had a fixed rate of 70 to 75 pulses per minute.

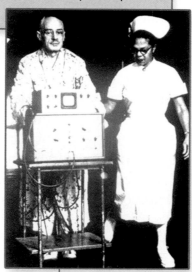

1961
Heart Valve Replacement
The first successful artificial heart valve was inserted into a patient's heart by surgeons Albert Starr and M. L. Edwards in Oregon. The valve was a rubberlike ball inside a stainless steel cage.

| 1930 | 1940 | 1950 | 1960 |

Hypertension and atherosclerosis are closely related. As the arteries narrow, blood pressure increases. For mild hypertension, regular exercise and careful food choices may be enough to lower blood pressure. People with hypertension may need to limit their intake of sodium, which can increase blood pressure. Sodium is found in table salt and in processed foods such as soups and packaged snack foods. For many people who have hypertension, however, medications are needed to reduce their blood pressure.

 **Reading Checkpoint** Why is hypertension called the "silent killer"?

Writing in Science

Research and Write Choose one of the scientists whose work is described in the timeline. Imagine that you are on a committee that has chosen this scientist to receive an award. Write the speech you would give at the award ceremony, explaining the scientist's contributions.

1967
First Heart Transplant
Christiaan Barnard, a South African surgeon, performed the first transplant of a human heart. Louis Washkanksky, the man who received the heart, lived for only 18 days after the transplant. But Barnard's work paved the way for future successes in transplanting hearts and other organs.

1977
Angioplasty
The first coronary balloon angioplasty was performed by Andreas Gruentizig and a team of surgeons in San Francisco. A balloon is inserted into the coronary artery and inflated, thus opening the artery. In 2001, more than two million angioplasties were performed worldwide.

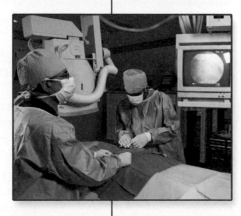

2001
Replacement Heart
The first replacement heart was implanted by a team of surgeons in Louisville, Kentucky. Unlike the first artificial heart, the Jarvik-7, the replacement heart has its own internal batteries. The patient does not have to be "plugged in" to an external power source. The first patient to receive the replacement heart lived for more than 500 days.

1970   **1980**   **1990**   **2000**

Keeping Healthy

Few young people have heart attacks, but signs of atherosclerosis can be found in some people as young as 18 to 20 years old. You can establish habits now that will lessen your risk of developing atherosclerosis and hypertension. **To help maintain cardiovascular health, people should exercise regularly; eat a balanced diet that is low in saturated fats and trans fats, cholesterol, and sodium; and avoid smoking.**

Exercise and Diet Do you participate in sports, ride a bike, swim, dance, or climb stairs instead of taking the elevator? Every time you do one of those activities, you are helping to strengthen your heart muscle and prevent atherosclerosis.

Foods that are high in cholesterol, saturated fats, and trans fats can lead to atherosclerosis. Foods such as red meats, eggs, and cheese are high in cholesterol. But because they also contain substances that your body needs, a smart approach might be to eat them only in small quantities. Foods that are high in saturated fat include butter, whole milk, and ice cream. Foods high in trans fat include margarine, potato chips, and doughnuts.

Avoid Smoking Smokers are more than twice as likely to have a heart attack as are nonsmokers. Every year, about 180,000 people in the United States who were smokers die from cardiovascular disease. If smokers quit, however, their risk of death from cardiovascular disease decreases.

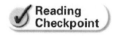 **Reading Checkpoint** What are some foods that are high in cholesterol?

FIGURE 17
Eating for Health
Eating foods that are low in fat can help keep your cardiovascular system healthy.
Applying Concepts *What are some heart-healthy low-fat foods?*

Section 4 Assessment

Target Reading Skill **Asking Questions** Use the answers to the questions you wrote about the headings to help you answer the questions below.

Reviewing Key Concepts

1. **a. Defining** What is atherosclerosis? What is hypertension?
   b. Relating Cause and Effect How do these two diseases affect the heart?
2. **a. Listing** List three things you can do to help your cardiovascular system stay healthy.
   b. Explaining Why it is important to exercise?
   c. Inferring Coronary heart disease is less common in some countries than in the United States. What factors might account for this difference?

Lab zone **At-Home Activity**

Heart-Healthy Activities With your family, discuss things you all can do to maintain heart health. Make a list of activities that you can enjoy together. You might also work with your family to cook and serve a "heart-healthy" meal. List the foods you would serve at the meal.

Do You Know Your A-B-O's?

Problem

Which blood types can safely receive transfusions of type A blood? Which can receive type O blood?

Skills Focus

interpreting data, drawing conclusions

Materials

- 4 paper cups
- 8 plastic petri dishes
- marking pen
- 4 plastic droppers
- white paper
- toothpicks
- four model "blood" types

Procedure

1. Write down your ideas about why type O blood might be in higher demand than other blood types. Then, make two copies of the data table in your notebook.

2. Label four paper cups A, B, AB, and O. Fill each cup about one-third full with the model "blood" supplied by your teacher. Place one clean plastic dropper into each cup. Use each dropper to transfer only that one type of blood.

3. Label the side of each of four petri dishes with a blood type: A, B, AB, or O. Place the petri dishes on a sheet of white paper.

4. Use the plastic droppers to place 10 drops of each type of blood in its labeled petri dish. Each sample represents the blood of a potential receiver of a blood transfusion. Record the original color of each sample in your data table as yellow, blue, green, or colorless.

5. Label your first data table Donor: Type A. To test whether each potential receiver can safely receive type A blood, add 10 drops of type A blood to each sample. Stir each mixture with a separate, clean toothpick.

6. Record the final color of each mixture in the data table. If the color stayed the same, write "safe" in the last column. If the color of the mixture changed, write "unsafe."

7. Label your second data table Donor: Type O. Obtain four clean petri dishes, and repeat Steps 3 through 6 to determine who could safely receive type O blood.

Analyze and Conclude

1. **Interpreting Data** Which blood types can safely receive a transfusion of type A blood? Type O blood?

2. **Inferring** Use what you know about marker molecules to explain why some transfusions of type A blood are safe while others are unsafe.

3. **Drawing Conclusions** If some blood types are not available, how might type O blood be useful?

4. **Communicating** Write a paragraph in which you discuss why it is important for hospitals to have an adequate supply of different types of blood.

More to Explore

Repeat this activity to find out which blood types can safely receive donations of type B and type AB blood.

Data Table			
Donor: Type _____			
Potential Receiver	Original Color	Final Color of Mixture	Safe or Unsafe?
A			
B			
AB			
O			

Heart-Lung Machines

What if you were too tired to make it through the day? What if walking up stairs left you out of breath and dizzy? These are symptoms that a person with a damaged heart may experience. A severely damaged heart may require surgery. While the heart is being repaired, blood must continue to circulate through the body around the heart. One way to bypass the heart during surgery is by using a heart-lung machine.

Repairing a Damaged Heart

A heart-lung machine takes over the functions of the heart and the lungs during heart surgery. Surgeons insert one tube into the right atrium and a second tube into the aorta. Oxygen-poor blood flows into the heart-lung machine from the right atrium. Within the machine, carbon dioxide is removed, oxygen is added, the blood is filtered, and the blood temperature is regulated. The filtered, oxygen-rich blood is then pumped through the second tube into the aorta, without flowing through the patient's heart. Once the surgical procedure is completed, doctors disconnect the machine and restart the heart.

Oxygen-rich blood from machine

Oxygen-poor blood to machine

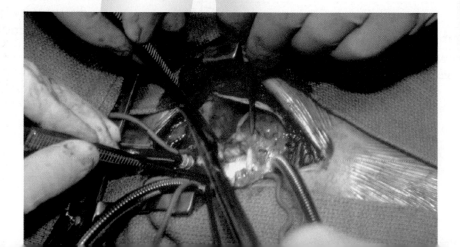

Heart-lung machine in use for open heart surgery ▶

Reservoir
The reservoir acts as a storage chamber for the blood and provides a constant supply and pressure to the pump.

Oxygen   Membrane
                    Red blood cell
                    White blood cell
                    Carbon dioxide
                    Platelet

Oxygen supply

Oxygenator
The oxygenator adds oxygen to blood cells and removes carbon dioxide.

Carbon dioxide return
Water in
Water out

Heat Exchanger
A heat exchanger warms or cools the blood as it moves through the heart-lung machine and back into the patient.

Pump
The pump circulates blood through the heart-lung machine and back into the patient.

Missing a Beat?

Heart valve repair and replacement, heart transplants, and coronary bypass surgery are a few of the surgeries that may use a heart-lung machine. Heart-lung machines have been credited with saving nearly one million lives around the world each year.

However, like all technologies, heart-lung machines pose certain risks. Use of the heart-lung machine has been associated with an increased risk of bleeding, stroke, kidney and lung problems, and memory loss. As with any surgical procedure, patients must consider the trade-offs.

Weigh the Impact

1. Identify the Need
What is the purpose of a heart-lung machine?

2. Research
Research to find out the success rate of bypass surgery using a heart-lung machine. Then research steps that patients might take to prevent the need for bypass surgery.

3. Write
Write a paragraph on steps patients might take to prevent the need for bypass surgery. Use your research and notes.

For: More on heart-lung machines
Visit: PHSchool.com
Web Code: ceh-4030

① The Body's Transport System

Key Concepts

- The cardiovascular system carries needed substances to cells and carries waste products away from cells. In addition, blood contains cells that fight disease.

- When the heart beats, it pushes blood through the blood vessels of the cardiovascular system.

- The right side of the heart is completely separated from the left side by a wall of tissue called the septum. Each side has two compartments, or chambers—an upper chamber and a lower chamber.

- Blood circulates in two loops. In the first loop, blood travels from the heart to the lungs and back to the heart. In the second loop, blood is pumped from the heart throughout the body and then returns to the heart.

Key Terms

cardiovascular system	pacemaker
heart	artery
atrium	capillary
ventricle	vein
valve	aorta

② A Closer Look at Blood Vessels

Key Concepts

- When blood leaves the heart, it travels through arteries. Artery walls are thick and consist of three cell layers.

- In the capillaries, materials are exchanged between the blood and the body's cells. Capillary walls are only one cell thick.

- After blood moves through capillaries, it enters larger blood vessels called veins, which carry blood back to the heart. The walls of veins have three layers, with muscle in the middle layer.

- Blood pressure is caused by the force with which the ventricles contract.

Key Terms

coronary artery	diffusion
pulse	blood pressure

③ Blood and Lymph

Key Concepts

- Blood is made up of four components: plasma, red blood cells, white blood cells, and platelets.

- The marker molecules on your red blood cells determine your blood type and the type of blood that you can safely receive in transfusions.

- The lymphatic system is a network of vein-like vessels that returns the fluid to the bloodstream.

Key Terms

plasma	platelet
red blood cell	lymphatic system
hemoglobin	lymph
white blood cell	lymph node

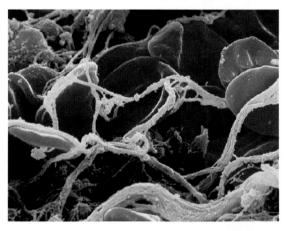

④ Cardiovascular Health

Key Concepts

- Diseases of the cardiovascular system include atherosclerosis and hypertension.

- To help maintain cardiovascular health, people should exercise regularly; eat a balanced diet that is low in saturated fats and trans fats, cholesterol, and sodium; and avoid smoking.

Key Terms

atherosclerosis	hypertension
heart attack	

Review and Assessment

Organizing Information

Comparing and Contrasting Copy the compare/contrast table about the two loops of the circulatory system onto a sheet of paper. Then complete it and add a title. (For more on Comparing and Contrasting, see the Skills Handbook.)

Loop	Side of heart where loop starts	Where blood flows to	Where blood returns to
Loop One	a. _____?_____	Lungs	b. _____?_____
Loop Two	Left side	c. _____?_____	d. _____?_____

Reviewing Key Terms

Choose the letter of the best answer.

1. The heart's upper chambers are called
   a. ventricles.
   b. atria.
   c. valves.
   d. arteries.

2. Nutrients are exchanged between the blood and body cells in the
   a. capillaries.
   b. veins.
   c. aorta.
   d. arteries.

3. The alternating expansion and relaxation of the artery that you feel in your wrist is your
   a. pulse.
   b. coronary artery.
   c. blood pressure.
   d. plasma.

4. Blood components that help the body to control bleeding are
   a. platelets.
   b. red blood cells.
   c. white blood cells.
   d. hemoglobin.

5. Cholesterol is a waxy substance associated with
   a. lymph nodes.
   b. white blood cells.
   c. atherosclerosis.
   d. plasma.

If the statement is true, write *true*. If it is false, change the underlined word or words to make the statement true.

6. The two lower chambers of the heart are called <u>atria</u>.

7. The <u>veins</u> are the narrowest blood vessels in the body.

8. <u>White blood cells</u> contain hemoglobin.

9. The <u>lymphatic system</u> is involved in returning fluid to the bloodstream.

10. Elevated blood pressure is called <u>atherosclerosis</u>.

Writing in Science

Letter Write a letter to a friend describing what you do to stay active. For example, do you participate in team sports, jog, or take long walks with your dog? Include in your letter additional ways you can be even more active.

DISCOVERY CHANNEL SCHOOL

Circulation

Video Preview
Video Field Trip
▶ Video Assessment

Review and Assessment

Checking Concepts

11. A red blood cell is moving through an artery in your leg. Describe the path that the blood cell will follow back to your heart. Identify the chamber of the heart to which it will return.

12. Contrast the forces with which the right and left ventricles contract. How does this relate to each ventricle's function?

13. How is a capillary's structure adapted to its function?

14. What is the function of hemoglobin?

15. What is lymph? How does lymph return to the cardiovascular system?

16. Give two reasons why food choices are important to cardiovascular health.

Thinking Critically

17. **Predicting** Some babies are born with an opening between the left and right ventricles of the heart. How would this heart defect affect the ability of the cardiovascular system to deliver oxygen to body cells?

18. **Classifying** Which two chambers of the heart shown below are the ventricles? Through which chamber does oxygen-poor blood enter the heart from the body?

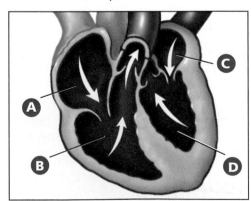

19. **Relating Cause and Effect** People who do not have enough iron in their diets sometimes develop a condition in which their blood cannot carry a normal amount of oxygen. Explain why this is so.

20. **Making Generalizations** Why is atherosclerosis sometimes called a "lifestyle disease"?

Math Practice

21. **Calculating a Rate** The veterinarian listens to your cat's heart and counts 30 beats in 15 seconds. What is your cat's heart rate?

Applying Skills

Use the graph to answer Questions 22–25.

The graph below shows how average blood pressure changes as men and women grow older.

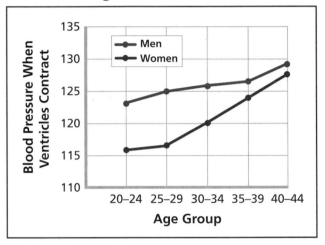

Changes in Blood Pressure

22. **Reading Graphs** What is plotted on each axis?

23. **Interpreting Data** At age 20, who is likely to have higher blood pressure—men or women?

24. **Drawing Conclusions** In general, what happens to blood pressure as people age?

25. **Predicting** Do you think that there is some age at which both men and women have about the same blood pressure? Use the graph lines to explain your prediction.

Lab zone Chapter **Project**

Performance Assessment You should now be ready to present your display. First show it to a small group of classmates to make sure it is clear and accurate. When you present your display, be ready to answer questions.

Standardized Test Practice

Standardized Test Practice

Test-Taking Tip
Anticipating the Answer
You can sometimes figure out an answer to a question before you look at the answer choices. After you answer the question in your mind, compare your answer with the answer choices. Choose the answer that most closely matches your own answer. Try to answer the sample question below before you look at the answer choices.

Sample Question
The upper chambers of the heart are the
  A ventricles.
  B valves.
  C atria.
  D capillaries.

Answer
Choice **C** is correct because the blood that comes into the heart enters through the atria, the upper chambers of the heart. Choice **A** is incorrect because ventricles are the lower chambers of the heart. Choices **B** and **D** are incorrect because valves and capillaries are not heart chambers.

Choose the letter of the best answer.

1. The most important function of the cardiovascular system is to
  A transport needed materials to body cells and remove wastes.
  B provide structural support for the lungs.
  C generate blood pressure so the arteries and veins do not collapse.
  D produce blood and lymph.

2. The correct sequence for the path of blood through the body is
  A heart—lungs—other body parts.
  B heart—lungs—heart—other body parts.
  C lungs—other body parts—heart.
  D heart—other body parts—lungs—heart.

3. A lab technician takes a blood sample from a patient's arm. The blood is bright red in color. You can infer that the sample most likely was taken from the patient's
  A vein.
  B artery.
  C lymph node.
  D capillary.

Use the table below and your knowledge of science to answer Questions 4 and 5.

Blood Types		
Blood Type	**Marker Molecules**	**Clumping Proteins**
A	A	anti-B
B	B	anti-A
AB	A and B	none
O	none	anti-A and anti-B

4. A person who has type O blood can safely receive blood from a person with
  A type O blood.
  B type A blood.
  C type AB blood.
  D type B blood.

5. A person who has type O blood can safely donate blood to a person with
  A type AB blood.
  B type O blood.
  C types A, B, AB, or O blood.
  D type A or type B blood.

Open-Ended Question

6. Explain what blood pressure is and what causes it. How is blood pressure measured and what is the significance of the two numbers in a blood pressure reading? Why can high blood pressure be dangerous?

Chapter 5

Respiration and Excretion

Academic Standards

This chapter addresses these Indiana standards.

Scientific Thinking

7.2.6 Measure length, volume, weight, elapsed time, rates, or temperatures, and choose appropriate units.

The Living Environment

7.4.14 Explain that the environment may contain dangerous levels of harmful substances. Public health requires monitoring of soil, air, and water quality.

Common Themes

7.7.2 Use different models to represent the same thing, noting that the model's type and complexity depend on its purpose.

7.7.3 Describe how systems usually change until they reach equilibrium, and remain that way unless their surroundings change.

Playing the pan flute requires ▶ strong, healthy lungs.

Chapter Project

Get the Message Out

Imagine that you're part of a team of writers and designers who create advertisements. You've just been given the job of creating anti-smoking ads for different age groups. As you read this chapter and learn about the respiratory system, you can use your knowledge in your ad campaign.

Your Goal To design three different anti-smoking ads: one telling young children about the dangers of smoking, the second one discouraging teenagers from trying cigarettes, and the third encouraging adult smokers to quit

To complete this project successfully, each ad must

● accurately communicate at least three health risks associated with smoking

● address at least two pressures that influence people to start or continue smoking

● use images and words in convincing ways that gear your message to each audience

Plan It! Brainstorm a list of reasons why people smoke. Consider the possible influences of family and friends as well as that of ads, movies, videos, and television. Also, decide which types of ads you will produce, such as magazine ads or billboards. After your teacher approves your plan, begin to design your ads.

The Respiratory System

Reading Preview

Key Concepts
• What are the functions of the respiratory system?
• What structures does air pass through as it travels to the lungs?
• What happens during gas exchange and breathing?

Key Terms
• respiration • cilia • pharynx
• trachea • bronchi • lungs
• alveoli • diaphragm • larynx
• vocal cords

Target Reading Skill
Sequencing As you read, make a flowchart that shows the path of air in the respiratory system. Write each step of the process in a separate box in the order in which it occurs.

Path of Air

Air enters the nose.

↓

To the pharynx

↓

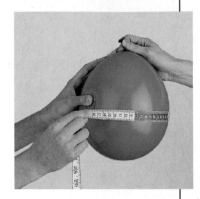

Lab zone Discover **Activity**

How Big Can You Blow Up a Balloon?

1. Take a normal breath, then blow as much air as possible into a balloon. Twist the end and hold it closed. Have your partner measure around the balloon at its widest point.
2. Let the air out of the balloon. Repeat Step 1 and calculate the average of the two measurements.
3. Compare your results with those of your classmates. The bigger the circumference, the greater the volume of air exhaled.

Think It Over
Inferring What factors might affect the volume of air a person can exhale?

Jerry, the main character in Doris Lessing's story "Through the Tunnel," is on vacation at the seaside. Day after day, he watches some older boys dive into deep water on one side of a huge rock. The boys mysteriously reappear on the other side. Jerry figures out that there must be an underwater tunnel in the rock. He finds the tunnel beneath the water and decides to swim through it. Once inside, though, he is terrified. The walls are slimy, and rocks scrape his body. He can barely see where he is going. But worst of all, Jerry has to hold his breath for far longer than ever before. The author describes Jerry this way: "His head was swelling, his lungs were cracking."

Hold your breath!

Respiratory System Functions

No one can go for very long without breathing. Your body cells need oxygen, and they get that oxygen from the air you breathe. **The respiratory system moves oxygen from the outside environment into the body. It also removes carbon dioxide and water from the body.**

Taking in Oxygen The oxygen your body needs comes from the atmosphere—the mixture of gases that blankets Earth. Your body doesn't use most of the other gases in the air you breathe in. When you exhale, most of the air goes back into the atmosphere.

Oxygen is needed for the energy-releasing chemical reactions that take place inside your cells. Like a fire, which cannot burn without oxygen, your cells cannot "burn" enough fuel to keep you alive without oxygen. The process in which oxygen and glucose undergo a complex series of chemical reactions inside cells is called **respiration.** Respiration, which is also called cellular respiration, is different from breathing. Breathing refers to the movement of air into and out of lungs. Respiration, on the other hand, refers to the chemical reactions inside cells. As a result of respiration, your cells release the energy that fuels growth and other cell processes.

Removing Carbon Dioxide and Water In addition to the release of energy, respiration produces carbon dioxide and water. Your respiratory system eliminates the carbon dioxide and some of the water through your lungs.

Math — Analyzing Data

The Air You Breathe

The air you breathe in contains several different gases, shown in the circle graph on the left. The air you breathe out contains the same gases, but in the amounts shown in the circle graph on the right.

1. **Reading Graphs** What does each wedge in the graphs represent?

2. **Interpreting Data** Based on the data, which gas is used by the body? Explain.

3. **Drawing Conclusions** Compare the percentage of carbon dioxide in inhaled air with the percentage in exhaled air. How can you account for the difference?

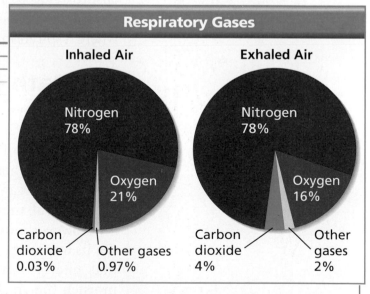

Respiratory Gases

Inhaled Air

Nitrogen 78%

Oxygen 21%

Carbon dioxide 0.03%

Other gases 0.97%

Exhaled Air

Nitrogen 78%

Oxygen 16%

Carbon dioxide 4%

Other gases 2%

4. **Inferring** Explain why the percentage of nitrogen is the same in both inhaled air and exhaled air.

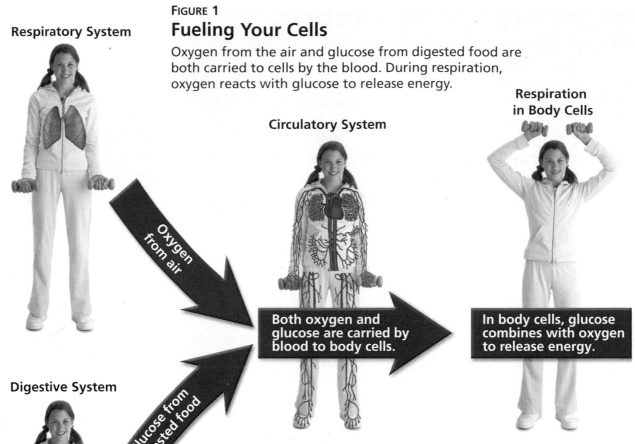

FIGURE 1
Fueling Your Cells

Oxygen from the air and glucose from digested food are both carried to cells by the blood. During respiration, oxygen reacts with glucose to release energy.

Respiratory System

Digestive System

Circulatory System

Respiration in Body Cells

Oxygen from air

Glucose from digested food

Both oxygen and glucose are carried by blood to body cells.

In body cells, glucose combines with oxygen to release energy.

Systems Working Together The respiratory system is just one of the body systems that makes respiration possible. As you can see in Figure 1, respiration could not take place without the digestive and circulatory systems as well. Your respiratory system brings oxygen into your lungs. Meanwhile, your digestive system absorbs glucose from the food you eat. Then, your circulatory system carries both the oxygen and the glucose to your cells, where respiration occurs.

The Path of Air

If you look toward a window on a bright day, you may see tiny particles dancing in the air. These particles include such things as floating grains of dust, plant pollen, and ash from fires. Though you can't see them, air also contains microorganisms. Some of these microorganisms can cause diseases in humans. When you breathe in, all these materials enter your body along with the air.

However, most of these materials never reach your lungs. On its way to the lungs, air passes through a series of structures that filter and trap particles. These organs also warm and moisten the air. **As air travels from the outside environment to the lungs, it passes through the following structures: nose, pharynx, trachea, and bronchi.** It takes air only a few seconds to complete the route from the nose to the lungs.

The Nose Air enters the body through the nose and then moves into spaces called the nasal cavities. Some of the cells lining the nasal cavities produce mucus. This sticky material moistens the air and keeps the lining from drying out. Mucus also traps particles such as dust.

The cells that line the nasal cavities have **cilia** (SIL ee uh), tiny hairlike extensions that can move together in a sweeping motion. The cilia sweep the mucus into the throat, where you swallow it. Stomach acid destroys the mucus, along with everything trapped in it.

Some particles and bacteria can irritate the lining of your nose or throat, causing you to sneeze. The powerful force of a sneeze shoots the particles out of your nose and into the air.

The Pharynx Next, air enters the **pharynx** (FAR ingks), or throat. The pharynx is the only part of the respiratory system that is shared with another system—the digestive system. Both the nose and the mouth connect to the pharynx.

Reading Checkpoint **What is the role of cilia?**

FIGURE 2
The Respiratory System
On its path from outside the body into the lungs, air passes through several structures that clean, warm, and moisten it. Once in the lungs, the oxygen in the air can enter your bloodstream.
Classifying *Which part of the respiratory system is also part of the digestive system?*

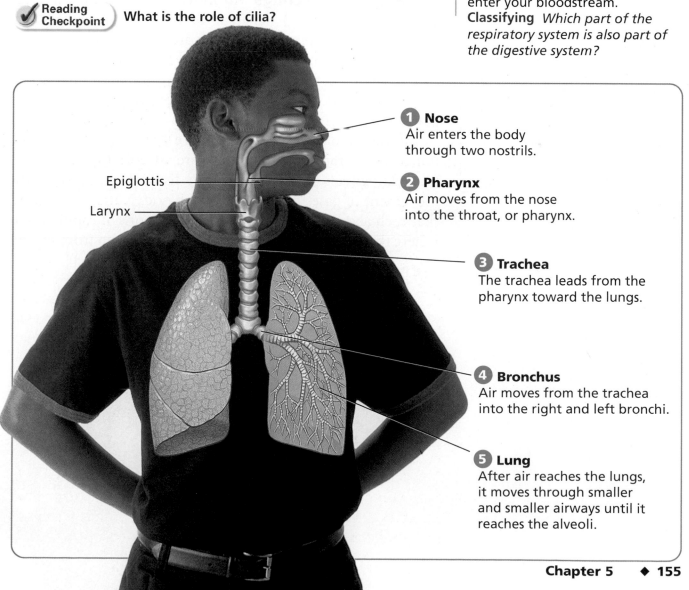

Epiglottis

Larynx

1 Nose
Air enters the body through two nostrils.

2 Pharynx
Air moves from the nose into the throat, or pharynx.

3 Trachea
The trachea leads from the pharynx toward the lungs.

4 Bronchus
Air moves from the trachea into the right and left bronchi.

5 Lung
After air reaches the lungs, it moves through smaller and smaller airways until it reaches the alveoli.

What Do You Exhale?

Learn whether carbon dioxide is present in exhaled air.

1. Label two test tubes *A* and *B*.

2. Fill each test tube with 10 mL of water and a few drops of bromthymol blue solution. Bromthymol blue solution turns green or yellow in the presence of carbon dioxide.

3. Using a straw, gently blow air into the liquid in test tube A for a few seconds. **CAUTION:** *Do not suck the solution back through the straw.*

4. Compare the solutions in the test tubes.

Predicting Suppose you had exercised immediately before you blew into the straw. Predict how this would have affected the results.

The Trachea From the pharynx, air moves into the **trachea** (TRAY kee uh), or windpipe. You can feel your trachea if you gently run your fingers down the center of your neck. The trachea feels like a tube with a series of ridges. The firm ridges are rings of cartilage that strengthen the trachea and keep it open.

The trachea, like the nose, is lined with cilia and mucus. The cilia in the trachea sweep upward, moving mucus toward the pharynx, where it is swallowed. The trachea's cilia and mucus continue the cleaning and moistening of air that began in the nose. If particles irritate the lining of the trachea, you cough. A cough, like a sneeze, sends the particles into the air.

Normally, only air—not food—enters the trachea. If food does enter the trachea, the food can block the opening and prevent air from getting to the lungs. When that happens, a person chokes. Fortunately, food rarely gets into the trachea. The epiglottis, a small flap of tissue that folds over the trachea, seals off the trachea while you swallow.

The Bronchi and Lungs Air moves from the trachea to the **bronchi** (BRAHNG ky) (singular *bronchus*), the passages that direct air into the lungs. The **lungs** are the main organs of the respiratory system. The left bronchus leads into the left lung, and the right bronchus leads into the right lung. Inside the lungs, each bronchus divides into smaller and smaller tubes in a pattern that resembles the branches of a tree.

At the end of the smallest tubes are structures that look like bunches of grapes. The "grapes" are **alveoli** (al VEE uh ly) (singular *alveolus*), tiny sacs of lung tissue specialized for the movement of gases between air and blood. Notice in Figure 3 that each alveolus is surrounded by a network of capillaries. It is here that the blood picks up its cargo of oxygen from the air.

Reading Checkpoint How is food prevented from entering the trachea?

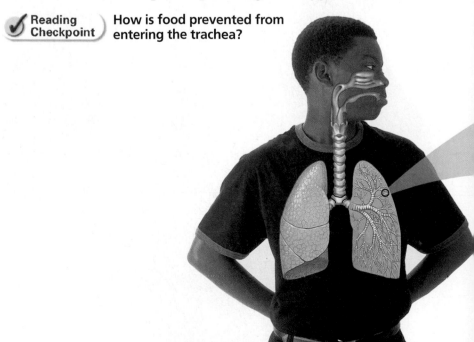

Gas Exchange

Because the walls of both the alveoli and the capillaries are very thin, certain materials can pass through them easily. **After air enters an alveolus, oxygen passes through the wall of the alveolus and then through the capillary wall into the blood. Carbon dioxide and water pass from the blood into the alveoli. This whole process is known as gas exchange.**

How Gas Exchange Occurs Imagine that you are a drop of blood beginning your journey through a capillary that wraps around an alveolus. When you begin that journey, you are carrying a lot of carbon dioxide and little oxygen. As you move through the capillary, oxygen gradually attaches to the hemoglobin in your red blood cells. At the same time, you are getting rid of carbon dioxide. At the end of your journey around the alveolus, you are rich in oxygen and poor in carbon dioxide.

Respiration and Excretion

Video Preview
▶Video Field Trip
Video Assessment

FIGURE 3

Gas Exchange in the Alveoli

Alveoli are hollow air sacs surrounded by capillaries. As blood flows through the capillaries, oxygen moves from the alveoli into the blood. At the same time, carbon dioxide moves from the blood into the alveoli.
Interpreting Diagrams *How is the structure of the alveoli important for gas exchange?*

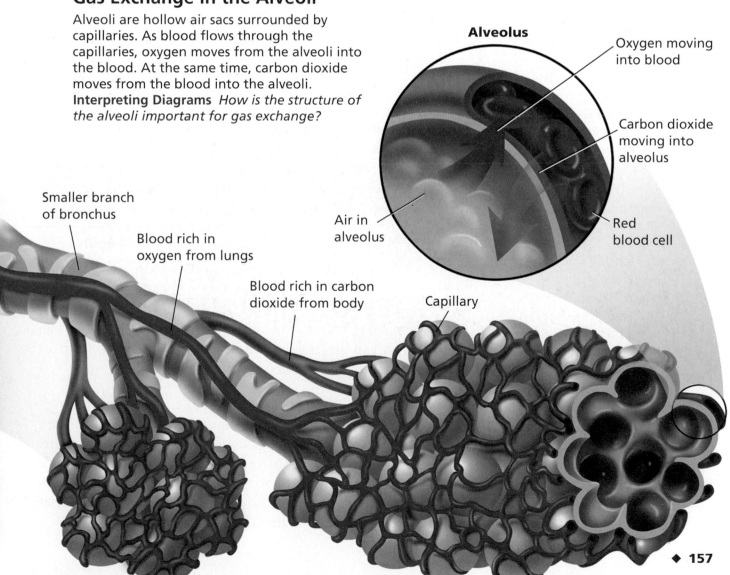

Alveolus

Oxygen moving into blood

Carbon dioxide moving into alveolus

Air in alveolus

Red blood cell

Smaller branch of bronchus

Blood rich in oxygen from lungs

Blood rich in carbon dioxide from body

Capillary

FIGURE 4
Oxygen for Activities
The huge surface area of the alveoli supplies the oxygen these trombone players need to march and play.

Math Skills

Surface Area

Surface area refers to the total area of all of the surfaces of a three-dimensional object. Consider a cube, which has six equal sides. Each side measures 2 cm by 2 cm.

1. To find the surface area of the cube, first calculate the area of one of the six sides:
   Area = length × width
   = 2 cm × 2 cm = 4 cm²
   Each side has an area of 4 cm².

2. Next, add the areas of the six sides together to find the total surface area:
   4 cm² + 4 cm² + 4 cm² + 4 cm² + 4 cm² + 4 cm² = 24 cm²
   The surface area of the cube is 24 cm².

Practice Problem Calculate the surface area of a cube whose side measures 3 cm.

Surface Area for Gas Exchange Your lungs can absorb a large amount of oxygen because of the large surface area of the alveoli. An adult's lungs contain about 300 million alveoli. If you opened the alveoli and spread them out on a flat surface, you would have a surface area of about 70 square meters.

The huge surface area of the alveoli enables the lungs to absorb a large amount of oxygen. The lungs can, therefore, supply the oxygen that people need—even when they are performing strenuous activities. When you play a wind instrument or a fast-paced game of basketball, you have your alveoli to thank.

Your lungs are not the only organs that provide a large surface area in a relatively small space. Recall from Chapter 2 that the small intestine contains numerous, tiny villi that increase the surface available to absorb food molecules.

 **Reading Checkpoint** What gases are exchanged across the alveoli?

How You Breathe

In an average day, you may breathe more than 20,000 times. The rate at which you breathe depends on your body's need for oxygen. The more oxygen you need, the faster you breathe.

Muscles for Breathing Breathing, like other body movements, is controlled by muscles. Figure 5 shows the structure of the chest, including the muscles that enable you to breathe. Notice that the lungs are surrounded by the ribs, which have muscles attached to them. At the base of the lungs is the **diaphragm** (DY uh fram), a large, dome-shaped muscle that plays an important role in breathing.

The Process of Breathing When you breathe, the actions of your rib muscles and diaphragm expand or contract your chest. As a result, air flows in or out.

Here's what happens when you inhale, or breathe in. The rib muscles contract, lifting the chest wall upward and outward. At the same time, the diaphragm contracts and moves downward. The combined action of these muscles makes the chest cavity larger. The same amount of air now occupies a larger space, causing the pressure of the air inside your lungs to decrease. This change means that the pressure of air inside the chest cavity is lower than the pressure of the atmosphere pushing on the body. Because of this difference in air pressure, air rushes into your chest, in the same way that air is sucked into a vacuum cleaner.

When you exhale, or breathe out, the rib muscles and diaphragm relax. This reduces the size of the chest cavity. This decrease in size squeezes air out of the lungs, the way squeezing a container of ketchup pushes ketchup out of the opening.

✓ **Reading Checkpoint** What muscles cause the chest to expand during breathing?

FIGURE 5
The Breathing Process
When you inhale, the diaphragm moves downward and pressure in the lungs decreases, causing air to flow in. When you exhale, the diaphragm moves upward and the pressure in the lungs increases, pushing the air out.
Interpreting Diagrams *How does the movement of the diaphragm affect the size of the chest cavity?*

Go Online
active art

For: The Breathing Process activity
Visit: PHSchool.com
Web Code: cep-4041

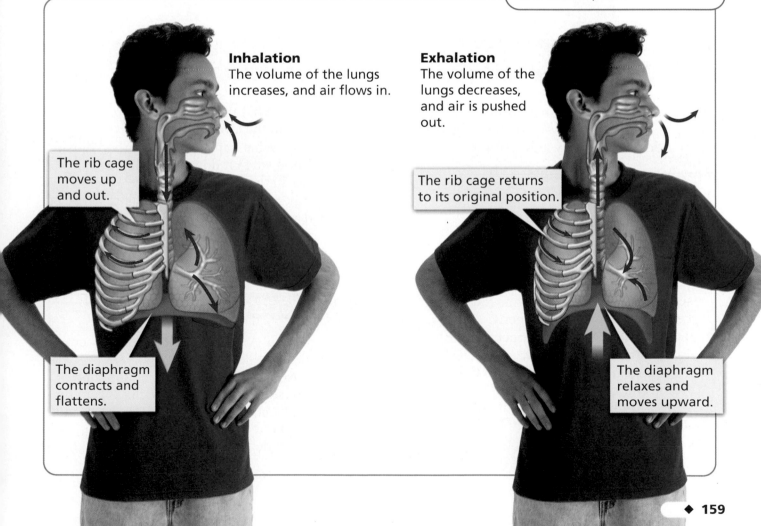

Inhalation
The volume of the lungs increases, and air flows in.

Exhalation
The volume of the lungs decreases, and air is pushed out.

The rib cage moves up and out.

The rib cage returns to its original position.

The diaphragm contracts and flattens.

The diaphragm relaxes and moves upward.

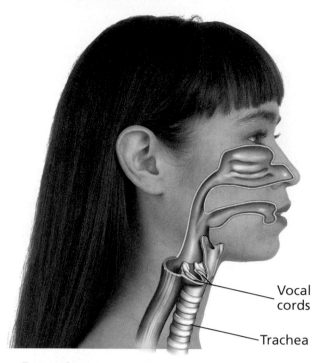

FIGURE 6
The Vocal Cords
Air moving over the vocal cords causes them to vibrate and produce sound.
Interpreting Diagrams *Where are the vocal cords located?*

Relating Breathing and Speaking The air that moves out of your lungs as you breathe also helps you speak. The **larynx** (LAR ingks), or voice box, is located in the top part of the trachea, underneath the epiglottis. Place your fingers on your Adam's apple, which sticks out from the front of your neck. You can feel some of the cartilage that makes up the larynx. Two **vocal cords,** folds of connective tissue that produce your voice, stretch across the opening of the larynx.

If you've ever let air out of a balloon while stretching its neck, you've heard the squeaking sound that the air makes. The neck of the balloon is something like your vocal cords. If you look at Figure 6 you can see that the vocal cords have a slitlike opening between them. When you speak, muscles make the vocal cords contract, narrowing the opening. Air from the lungs rushes through this opening. The movement of the vocal cords makes the air molecules vibrate, or move rapidly back and forth. This vibration creates a sound—your voice.

Section 1 Assessment

Target Reading Skill Sequencing With a partner, review your flowchart about the path of air. Add any necessary information.

Reviewing Key Concepts

1. a. **Listing** What are the functions of the respiratory system?
   b. **Comparing and Contrasting** Explain the difference between respiration and breathing.
   c. **Predicting** How might respiration in your body cells be affected if your respiratory system did not work properly?

2. a. **Identifying** Name the structures of the respiratory system.
   b. **Sequencing** Describe the path that a molecule of oxygen takes as it moves from the air outside your body into the alveoli.
   c. **Relating Cause and Effect** In a healthy person, how do coughing and sneezing protect the respiratory system?

3. a. **Reviewing** What three substances are exchanged in the alveoli?
   b. **Explaining** What happens to the carbon dioxide in the blood when it flows through the capillaries in the alveoli?
   c. **Applying Concepts** How would gas exchange be affected at the top of a tall mountain, where air pressure is lower and there is less oxygen than at lower elevations? Explain.

Math Practice

4. **Surface Area** A cube measures 4 cm × 4 cm on a side. Find its surface area.
5. **Surface Area** Suppose you cut up the cube into eight smaller cubes, each 2 cm × 2 cm on a side. If the larger cube represents a lung, and the smaller cubes represent alveoli, which would provide a larger surface area for oxygen exchange?

A Breath of Fresh Air

Problem

What causes your body to inhale and exhale air?

Skills Focus

making models, observing, drawing conclusions

Materials

- small balloon
- large balloon
- scissors
- transparent plastic bottle with narrow neck

Procedure

1. In your notebook, explain how you think air gets into the lungs during the breathing process.

2. Cut off and discard the bottom of a small plastic bottle. Trim the cut edge so there are no rough spots.

3. Stretch a small balloon; then blow it up a few times to stretch it further. Insert the round end of the balloon through the mouth of the bottle. Then, with a partner holding the bottle, stretch the neck of the balloon and pull it over the mouth of the bottle.

4. Stretch a large balloon; then blow it up a few times to stretch it further. Cut off and discard the balloon's neck.

5. Have a partner hold the bottle while you stretch the remaining part of the balloon over the bottom opening of the bottle, as shown in the photo.

6. Use one hand to hold the bottle firmly. With the knuckles of your other hand, push upward on the large balloon, causing it to form a dome. Remove your knuckles from the balloon, letting the balloon flatten. Repeat this procedure a few times. Observe what happens to the small balloon. Record your observations in your notebook.

Analyze and Conclude

1. **Making Models** Make a diagram of the completed model in your notebook. Add labels to show which parts of your model represent the chest cavity, diaphragm, lungs, and trachea.

2. **Observing** In this model, what is the position of the "diaphragm" just after you have made the model "exhale"? What do the lungs look like just after you have exhaled?

3. **Drawing Conclusions** In this model, how does the "diaphragm" move? How do these movements of the "diaphragm" affect the "lungs"?

4. **Communicating** Write a paragraph describing how this model shows that pressure changes are responsible for breathing.

More to Explore

How could you improve on this model to show more closely what happens in the chest cavity during the process of breathing? *Obtain your teacher's permission before carrying out your investigation.*

Smoking and Your Health

Reading Preview

Key Concepts
- What harmful chemicals are found in tobacco smoke?
- How can tobacco smoke affect a person's health over time?

Key Terms
- tar • carbon monoxide
- nicotine • addiction
- bronchitis • emphysema

Target Reading Skill

Relating Cause and Effect As you read, identify the effects of smoking on the body. Write the information in a graphic organizer like the one below.

Effects

Cause → Increase in breathing and heart rate due to carbon monoxide in smoke

Smoking →

→

Lab zone Discover **Activity**

What Are the Dangers of Smoking?

The graph shows the rate of lung cancer deaths in the United States from 1930 to 2000.

1. What was the rate of lung cancer deaths for males in 1930? For females?

2. What was the rate of lung cancer deaths for males in 1990? For females?

3. Did males or females show a faster rate of increase in the number of lung cancer deaths? How can you tell?

4. Cigarette smoking increased until 1965 but then decreased between 1965 and 1990. How does the trend in smoking compare with the rate of lung cancer deaths?

Think It Over
Predicting Do you think that the rate of lung cancer deaths is likely to increase, decrease, or remain the same by 2010? Explain.

(Graph: Death Rate per 100,000 People vs. Year, 1940–2000, showing Males and Females)

Whoosh! Millions of tiny but dangerous aliens are invading the respiratory system. The aliens are pulled into the mouth with an inhaled breath. The cilia trap some aliens, and others get stuck in mucus. But thousands of the invaders get past these defenses and enter the lungs. The aliens then land on the surface of the alveoli!

The "aliens" are not tiny creatures from space. They are the substances found in cigarette smoke. In this section you will learn how tobacco smoke damages the respiratory system.

A heavy smoker may smoke two packs of cigarettes in a day.

Chemicals in Tobacco Smoke

With each puff, a smoker inhales more than 4,000 different chemicals. **Some of the most deadly chemicals in tobacco smoke are tar, carbon monoxide, and nicotine.**

Tar The dark, sticky substance that forms when tobacco burns is called **tar.** When someone inhales tobacco smoke, some tar settles on cilia that line the trachea, bronchi, and smaller airways. Tar makes cilia clump together so they can't function to prevent harmful materials from getting into the lungs. Tar also contains chemicals that have been shown to cause cancer.

Carbon Monoxide When substances—including tobacco—are burned, a colorless, odorless gas called **carbon monoxide** is produced. Carbon monoxide is dangerous because its molecules bind to hemoglobin in red blood cells. When carbon monoxide binds to hemoglobin, it takes the place of some of the oxygen that the red blood cells normally carry. The carbon monoxide molecules are something like cars that are parked in spaces reserved for other cars.

When carbon monoxide binds to hemoglobin, red blood cells carry less than their normal load of oxygen throughout the body. To make up for the decrease in oxygen, the breathing rate increases and the heart beats faster. Smokers' blood may contain too little oxygen to meet their bodies' needs.

Nicotine Another dangerous chemical found in tobacco is **nicotine.** Nicotine is a stimulant drug that increases the activities of the nervous system and heart. It makes the heart beat faster and increases blood pressure. Over time, nicotine produces an **addiction,** or physical dependence. Smokers feel an intense craving for a cigarette if they go without one. Addiction to nicotine is one reason why smokers have difficulty quitting.

 **Reading Checkpoint** How does the tar in cigarettes affect the body?

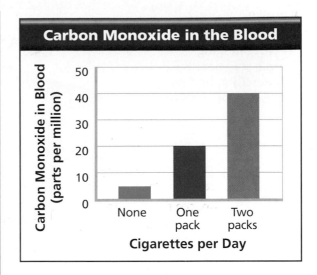

FIGURE 7
Carbon Monoxide in the Blood
The more cigarettes a person smokes, the more carbon monoxide he or she inhales.
Relating Cause and Effect *How does carbon monoxide deprive the body of oxygen?*

SURGEON GENERAL'S WARNING: Cigarette Smoke Contains Carbon Monoxide.

SURGEON GENERAL'S WARNING: Smoking Causes Lung Cancer, Heart Disease, Emphysema, and May Complicate Pregnancy.

SURGEON GENERAL'S WARNING: Smoking By Pregnant Women May Result in Fetal Injury, Premature Birth, and Low Birth Weight.

FIGURE 8
Staying Healthy by Not Smoking
People stay healthy by exercising and by choosing not to smoke.

Lung of a nonsmoker

Lab zone Skills Activity

Calculating

Heavy smokers may smoke two packs of cigarettes every day. Find out what one pack of cigarettes costs. Then, use that price to calculate how much a person would spend on cigarettes if he or she smoked two packs a day for 30 years.

Health Problems and Smoking

Tobacco smoke causes health problems in several ways. For example, because the cilia can't sweep away mucus, many smokers have a frequent cough. The mucus buildup also limits the space for airflow, thus decreasing oxygen intake. Because they are not getting enough oxygen, long-term or heavy smokers may be short of breath during even light exercise.

You probably know that smoking damages the respiratory system, but did you know that it strains the circulatory system as well? The respiratory and circulatory systems work together to get oxygen to body cells. If either system is damaged, the other one must work harder. Serious health problems can result from long-term smoking. **Over time, smokers can develop chronic bronchitis, emphysema, lung cancer, and atherosclerosis.** Every year in the United States, more than 400,000 people die from smoking-related illnesses. That's one out of every five deaths. Tobacco smoke is the most important preventable cause of major illness and death.

Chronic Bronchitis Bronchitis (brahng KY tis) is an irritation of the breathing passages in which the small passages become narrower than normal and may be clogged with mucus. People with bronchitis have difficulty breathing. If the irritation continues over a long time, it is called chronic bronchitis. Chronic bronchitis can cause permanent damage to the breathing passages. It is often accompanied by infection with disease-causing microorganisms. Chronic bronchitis is five to ten times more common in heavy smokers than in nonsmokers.

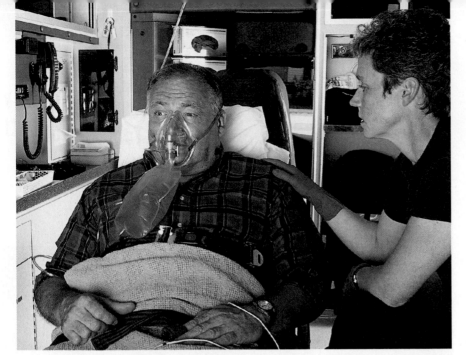

FIGURE 9
Effects of Smoking on the Lungs
Over time, smoking damages the lungs and leads to serious health problems. **Comparing and Contrasting** *Compare the lungs of a person with emphysema and a person with lung cancer to the lung of a nonsmoker shown in Figure 8.*

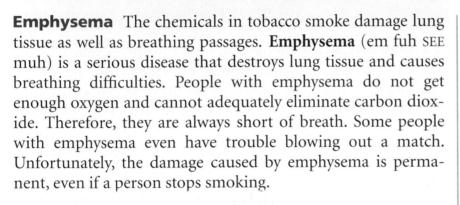

Lung with emphysema

Lung with cancer

Emphysema The chemicals in tobacco smoke damage lung tissue as well as breathing passages. **Emphysema** (em fuh SEE muh) is a serious disease that destroys lung tissue and causes breathing difficulties. People with emphysema do not get enough oxygen and cannot adequately eliminate carbon dioxide. Therefore, they are always short of breath. Some people with emphysema even have trouble blowing out a match. Unfortunately, the damage caused by emphysema is permanent, even if a person stops smoking.

Lung Cancer About 140,000 Americans die each year from lung cancer caused by smoking. Cigarette smoke contains more than 50 different chemicals that cause cancer, including the chemicals in tar. Cancerous growths, or tumors, take away space in the lungs that are used for gas exchange. Unfortunately, lung cancer is rarely detected early, when treatment would be most effective.

Atherosclerosis The chemicals in tobacco smoke also harm the circulatory system. Some of the chemicals get into the blood and are absorbed by the blood vessels. The chemicals then irritate the walls of the blood vessels. This irritation contributes to the buildup of fatty material on the blood vessel walls that causes atherosclerosis. Atherosclerosis can lead to heart attacks. Compared to nonsmokers, smokers are more than twice as likely to have heart attacks.

 **Reading Checkpoint** How does emphysema affect a person's lungs?

FIGURE 10
Passive Smoking
Billboards like this one increase people's awareness that nonsmokers can also suffer from the effects of tobacco smoke.

Go Online
SciLINKS NSTA

For: Links on respiratory disorders
Visit: www.SciLinks.org
Web Code: scn-0442

Passive Smoking Smokers are not the only people to suffer from the effects of tobacco smoke. In passive smoking, people involuntarily inhale the smoke from other people's cigarettes, cigars, or pipes. This smoke contains the same harmful chemicals that smokers inhale. Each year, passive smoking is associated with the development of bronchitis and other respiratory problems, such as asthma, in about 300,000 young children in the United States.

Section 2 Assessment

Target Reading Skill Relating Cause and Effect Refer to your graphic organizer about the effects of smoking on the body to help you answer the questions below.

Reviewing Key Concepts

1. **a. Listing** What are three harmful substances in tobacco smoke?
   b. Relating Cause and Effect How does each of the harmful substances directly affect the body?
   c. Developing Hypotheses Why might nicotine-containing products, such as chewing gums or skin patches, help a person who is trying to quit smoking?

2. **a. Reviewing** Identify four health problems that can develop in smokers over time.
   b. Describing How does smoking contribute to atherosclerosis?
   c. Inferring What effect would it have on the circulatory system if a person quit smoking?

Lab zone At-Home **Activity**

Warning Labels With a family member, make a list of the warning statements found on cigarette labels. What chemicals found in tobacco smoke and health problems do the labels identify? Summarize the information you find to share with the class.

The Excretory System

Reading Preview

Key Concepts
- What are the structures and function of the excretory system?
- How do the kidneys filter wastes from the blood?
- How does excretion contribute to homeostasis?

Key Terms
- excretion • urea • kidney
- urine • ureter
- urinary bladder • urethra
- nephron

Target Reading Skill
Previewing Visuals Before you read, preview Figure 11. Then, write two questions that you have about the diagram in a graphic organizer like the one below. As you read, answer your questions.

How the Kidneys Filter Wastes

Q.	Where are nephrons located?
A.	
Q.	

Lab zone Discover **Activity**

How Does Filtering a Liquid Change the Liquid?

1. Your teacher will give you 50 mL of a liquid in a small container. Pour a small amount of sand into the liquid.
2. Use a glucose test strip to determine whether glucose is present in the liquid.
3. Put filter paper in a funnel. Then, put the funnel into the mouth of a second container. Slowly pour the liquid through the funnel into the second container.
4. Look for any solid material on the filter paper. Remove the funnel, and carefully examine the liquid that passed through the filter.
5. Test the liquid again to see whether it contains glucose.

Think It Over
Observing Which substances passed through the filter, and which did not? How might a filtering device be useful in the body?

The human body faces a challenge that is a bit like trying to keep your room clean. Magazines, notebook paper, and CD wrappers tend to pile up in your room. You use all of these things, but sooner or later you must clean your room if you don't want to be buried in trash. Something similar happens in your body. As your cells use nutrients in respiration and other processes, wastes are created. Different organs in the body have roles for the removal of these wastes. The removal process is known as **excretion.**

If wastes were not removed from your body, they would pile up and make you sick. Excretion helps keep the body's internal environment stable and free of harmful materials. **The excretory system is the system in the body that collects wastes produced by cells and removes the wastes from the body.**

The Excretory System

Two wastes that your body must eliminate are excess water and urea. **Urea** (yoo REE uh) is a chemical that comes from the breakdown of proteins. **The structures of the excretory system that eliminate urea, water, and other wastes include the kidneys, ureters, urinary bladder, and urethra.**

Your two **kidneys,** which are the major organs of the excretory system, remove urea and other wastes from the blood. The kidneys act like filters. They remove wastes but keep materials that the body needs. The wastes are eliminated in **urine,** a watery fluid that contains urea and other wastes. Urine flows from the kidneys through two narrow tubes called **ureters** (yoo REE turz). The ureters carry urine to the **urinary bladder,** a sacklike muscular organ that stores urine. Urine leaves the body through a small tube called the **urethra** (yoo REE thruh).

 **Reading Checkpoint** What is the role of the ureters?

Filtration of Wastes

The kidneys are champion filters. Each of your kidneys contains about a million **nephrons,** tiny filtering factories that remove wastes from blood and produce urine. **The nephrons filter wastes in stages. First, both wastes and needed materials, such as glucose, are filtered out of the blood. Then, much of the needed material is returned to the blood, and the wastes are eliminated from the body.** Follow this process in Figure 11.

Filtering Out Wastes During the first stage of waste removal, blood enters the kidneys. Here, the blood flows through smaller and smaller arteries. Eventually it reaches a cluster of capillaries in a nephron. The capillaries are surrounded by a thin-walled, hollow capsule that is connected to a tube. In the capillary cluster, urea, glucose, and some water move out of the blood and into the capsule. Blood cells and most protein molecules do not move into the capsule. Instead, they remain in the capillaries.

Formation of Urine Urine forms from the filtered material in the capsule. This material flows through the long, twisting tube. As the liquid moves through the tube, many of the substances are returned to the blood. Normally, all the glucose, most of the water, and small amounts of other materials pass back into the blood in the capillaries that surround the tube. In contrast, urea and other wastes remain in the tube.

Lab zone Skills Activity

Classifying

A number of materials enter the kidney, where they are filtered by the nephrons.

- What materials enter a nephron?
- What materials are returned to the blood?
- What materials leave the body in urine?

168 ◆

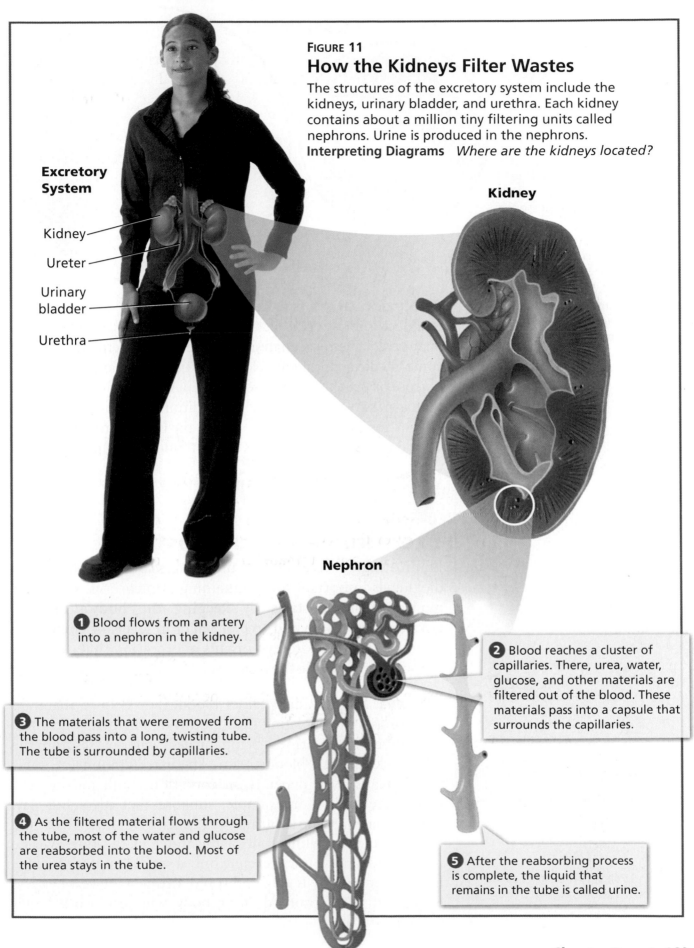

FIGURE 11

How the Kidneys Filter Wastes

The structures of the excretory system include the kidneys, urinary bladder, and urethra. Each kidney contains about a million tiny filtering units called nephrons. Urine is produced in the nephrons.
Interpreting Diagrams *Where are the kidneys located?*

Excretory System

Kidney

Ureter

Urinary bladder

Urethra

Kidney

Nephron

❶ Blood flows from an artery into a nephron in the kidney.

❷ Blood reaches a cluster of capillaries. There, urea, water, glucose, and other materials are filtered out of the blood. These materials pass into a capsule that surrounds the capillaries.

❸ The materials that were removed from the blood pass into a long, twisting tube. The tube is surrounded by capillaries.

❹ As the filtered material flows through the tube, most of the water and glucose are reabsorbed into the blood. Most of the urea stays in the tube.

❺ After the reabsorbing process is complete, the liquid that remains in the tube is called urine.

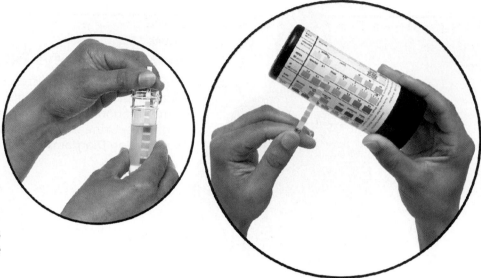

FIGURE 12
Analyzing Urine
Lab technicians can analyze urine by using a dipstick that changes color in the presence of glucose and other substances. The technician dips the dipstick into a urine sample and compares the results to a color chart.
Applying Concepts *What are two substances for which urine can be tested?*

Analyzing Urine for Signs of Disease When people go to a doctor for a medical checkup, they usually have their urine analyzed. A chemical analysis of urine can be useful in detecting some medical problems. Normally, urine contains almost no glucose or protein. If glucose is present in urine, it may indicate that a person has diabetes, a condition in which body cells cannot absorb enough glucose from the blood. Protein in urine can be a sign that the kidneys are not functioning properly.

 **Reading Checkpoint** What could it mean if there is glucose in the urine?

Excretion and Homeostasis

Eliminating wastes, such as urea, excess water, and carbon dioxide, is important for maintaining homeostasis. **Excretion maintains homeostasis by keeping the body's internal environment stable and free of harmful levels of chemicals. In addition to the kidneys, organs of excretion that maintain homeostasis include the lungs, skin, and liver.**

Kidneys As the kidneys filter blood, they help to maintain homeostasis by regulating the amount of water in your body. Remember that as urine is being formed, water passes from the tube back into the bloodstream. The exact amount of water that is reabsorbed depends on conditions both outside and within the body. For example, suppose that it's a hot day. You've been sweating a lot, and you haven't had much to drink. In that situation, almost all of the water in the tube will be reabsorbed, and you will excrete only a small amount of urine. If, however, the day is cool and you've drunk a lot of water, less water will be reabsorbed. Your body will produce a larger volume of urine.

Go Online
SciLINKS NSTA

For: Links on organs of excretion
Visit: www.SciLinks.org
Web Code: scn-0443

Lungs and Skin Most of the wastes produced by the body are removed through the kidneys. However, the lungs and skin remove some wastes from the body as well. When you exhale, carbon dioxide and some water are removed from the body by the lungs. Sweat glands in the skin also serve an excretory function because water and urea are excreted in perspiration.

Liver Have you ever torn apart a large pizza box so that it could fit into a wastebasket? If so, then you understand that some wastes need to be broken down before they can be excreted. The liver performs this function. For example, urea, which comes from the breakdown of proteins, is produced by the liver. The liver also converts part of the hemoglobin molecule from old red blood cells into substances such as bile. Because the liver produces a usable material from old red blood cells, you can think of the liver as a recycling facility.

FIGURE 13
Excretion Through the Lungs
Your lungs function as excretory organs. When you exhale on a cold morning, you can see the water in your breath.

 **Reading Checkpoint** What substances are excreted in perspiration?

Section 3 Assessment

Target Reading Skill Previewing Visuals
Compare your questions and answers about Figure 11 with those of a partner.

Reviewing Key Concepts

1. a. Reviewing What is the role of the excretory system in the body?
  b. Sequencing Name the structures of the excretory system in order of their roles in producing and eliminating urine. Describe the function of each structure.
2. a. Reviewing What are the two main stages of waste removal by the kidneys?
  b. Describing What happens as wastes are filtered in a nephron?
  c. Relating Cause and Effect Why is protein in the urine a sign that something could be wrong with the kidneys?

3. a. Identifying What is the role of excretion in maintaining homeostasis?
  b. Explaining How do the kidneys help maintain homeostasis?
  c. Predicting On a long bus trip, a traveler does not drink any water for several hours. How will the volume of urine she produces that day compare to the volume on a day when she drinks several glasses of water? Explain.

Writing in Science

Explanation Write a paragraph explaining how wastes are filtered in the kidneys. To help you with your writing, first make two lists—one that includes materials removed from the blood in the kidneys and one that includes materials returned to the blood.

Clues About Health

Problem

How can you test urine for the presence of glucose and protein?

Skills Focus

observing, interpreting data, drawing conclusions

Materials

- 6 test tubes
- test-tube rack
- 6 plastic droppers
- water
- glucose solution
- protein solution
- marking pencil
- white paper towels
- 6 glucose test strips
- Biuret solution
- 3 simulated urine samples

Procedure

PART 1 Testing for Glucose

1. Label six test tubes as follows: *W* for water, *G* for glucose, *P* for protein, and *A, B,* and *C* for three patients' "urine samples." Place the test tubes in a test-tube rack.

2. Label six glucose test strips with the same letters: *W, G, P, A, B,* and *C.*

3. Copy the data table into your notebook.

4. Fill each test tube about $\frac{3}{4}$ full with the solution that corresponds to its label.

5. Place glucose test strip W on a clean, dry section of a paper towel. Then, use a clean plastic dropper to place 2 drops of the water from test tube W on the test strip. Record the resulting color of the test strip in your data table. If no color change occurs, write "no reaction."

6. Use the procedure in Step 5 to test each of the other five solutions with the correctly labeled glucose test strip. Record the color of each test strip in the data table.

PART 2 Testing for Protein

7. Obtain a dropper bottle containing Biuret solution. Record the original color of the solution in your notebook.

8. Carefully add 30 drops of Biuret solution to test tube W. **CAUTION:** *Biuret solution can harm skin and damage clothing. Handle it with care.* Gently swirl the test tube to mix the two solutions together. Hold the test tube against a white paper towel to help you detect any color change. Observe the color of the final mixture, and record that color in your data table.

9. Repeat Step 8 for each of the other test tubes.

Data Table						
	Test Tube					
Test for	W (water)	G (glucose)	P (protein)	A (Patient A)	B (Patient B)	C (Patient C)
Glucose						
Protein						

Analyze and Conclude

1. **Observing** What color reaction occurred when you used the glucose test strip on sample W? On sample G?

2. **Interpreting Data** What do the changes in color you observed in Part 1 indicate? Explain.

3. **Observing** What happened when you added Biuret solution to test tube W? To test tube P?

4. **Interpreting Data** What do the changes in color of the Biuret solution you observed in Part II indicate? Explain.

5. **Drawing Conclusions** Which of the three patients' urine samples tested normal? How do you know?

6. **Drawing Conclusions** Which urine sample(s) indicated that diabetes might be present? How do you know?

7. **Drawing Conclusions** Which urine sample(s) indicated that kidney disease might be present? How do you know?

8. **Communicating** Do you think a doctor should draw conclusions about the presence of a disease based on a single urine sample? Write a paragraph in which you discuss this question based on what you know about gathering data in experiments.

More to Explore

Propose a way to determine whether a patient with glucose in the urine could reduce the level through changes in diet.

Study Guide

① The Respiratory System

Key Concepts

- The respiratory system moves oxygen from the outside environment into the body. It also removes carbon dioxide and water from the body.

- As air travels from the outside environment to the lungs, it passes through the following structures: nose, pharynx, trachea, and bronchi.

- After air enters an alveolus, oxygen passes through the wall of the alveolus and then through the capillary wall into the blood. Carbon dioxide and water pass from the blood into the alveoli. This whole process is known as gas exchange.

- When you breathe, the actions of your rib muscles and diaphragm expand or contract your chest, causing air to flow in or out.

Key Terms

respiration	lungs
cilia	alveoli
pharynx	diaphragm
trachea	larynx
bronchi	vocal cords

② Smoking and Your Health

Key Concepts

- Some of the most deadly chemicals in tobacco smoke are tar, carbon monoxide, and nicotine.

- Over time, smokers can develop chronic bronchitis, emphysema, lung cancer, and atherosclerosis.

Key Terms

tar	addiction
carbon monoxide	bronchitis
nicotine	emphysema

③ The Excretory System

Key Concepts

- The excretory system is the system in the body that collects wastes produced by cells and removes the wastes from the body.

- The structures of the excretory system that eliminate urea, water, and other wastes include the kidneys, ureters, the urinary bladder, and the urethra.

- The nephrons filter wastes in stages. First, both wastes and needed materials, such as glucose, are filtered from the blood into a nephron. Then, much of the needed material is returned to the blood, and the wastes are eliminated from the body.

- Excretion maintains homeostasis by keeping the body's internal environment stable and free of harmful levels of chemicals. In addition to the kidneys, organs of excretion that maintain homeostasis include the lungs, skin, and liver.

Key Terms

excretion	ureter
urea	urinary bladder
kidney	urethra
urine	nephron

SURGEON GENERAL'S WARNING: Cigarette Smoke Contains Carbon Monoxide.

SURGEON GENERAL'S WARNING: Smoking Causes Lung Cancer, Heart Disease, Emphysema, and May Complicate Pregnancy.

SURGEON GENERAL'S WARNING: Smoking By Pregnant Women May Result in Fetal Injury, Premature Birth, and Low Birth Weight.

Review and Assessment

Organizing Information

Sequencing Copy the flowchart about excretion onto a separate sheet of paper. Then, fill in the empty spaces and add a title. (For more on Sequencing, see the Skills Handbook.)

Blood flows into the nephron's capillary cluster.
↓
a. _____ ?
↓
b. _____ ?
↓
c. _____ ?
↓
d. _____ ?

Reviewing Key Terms

Choose the letter of the best answer.

1. The process in which glucose and oxygen react in cells to release energy is called
   a. excretion.
   b. respiration.
   c. bronchitis.
   d. emphysema.

2. The trachea divides into two tubes called
   a. bronchi.
   b. alveoli.
   c. ureters.
   d. vocal cords.

3. Your voice is produced by the
   a. pharynx.   b. larynx.
   c. trachea.   d. alveoli.

4. A colorless, odorless gas produced by burning tobacco is
   a. carbon monoxide.
   b. tar.
   c. nicotine.
   d. urea.

5. The filtration of wastes takes place inside the kidneys in the
   a. ureters.
   b. urethra.
   c. urinary bladder.
   d. nephrons.

If the statement is true, write *true*. If it is false, change the underlined word or words to make the statement true.

6. Dust particles trapped in mucus are swept away by tiny, hairlike <u>alveoli</u>.

7. Clusters of air sacs in the lungs are <u>bronchi</u>.

8. <u>Tar</u> is a chemical in tobacco smoke that makes the heart beat faster.

9. Urine leaves the body through the <u>ureter</u>.

10. Urine is stored in the <u>urethra</u>.

Writing in Science

Informational Brochure Pretend you are a doctor advising high-altitude climbers. Develop an informational brochure that focuses on the effects that high altitude has on the human body. Be sure to include one method climbers can use to become used to the higher altitudes.

Discovery CHANNEL SCHOOL™

Respiration and Excretion
Video Preview
Video Field Trip
▶ Video Assessment

Review and Assessment

Checking Concepts

11. Explain the difference between breathing and respiration.

12. Explain how the alveoli provide a large surface area for gas exchange in the lungs.

13. Describe how the diaphragm and rib muscles work together to control inhaling and exhaling.

14. Describe what happens when carbon monoxide enters the body. How does this affect the body?

15. Explain two ways in which the kidneys help to maintain homeostasis in the body.

Thinking Critically

16. **Comparing and Contrasting** How is respiration similar to the burning of fuel? How is it different?

17. **Relating Cause and Effect** What process is shown in the diagram below? What role do changes in pressure play in this process?

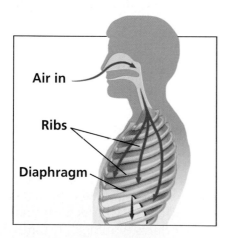

18. **Applying Concepts** Explain how babies can develop smoking-related respiratory problems.

19. **Making Judgments** Do you think that drugstores, which sell medicines, should also sell cigarettes and other tobacco products? Why or why not?

20. **Predicting** If the walls of the capillary cluster in a nephron were damaged or broken, what substance might you expect to find in urine that is not normally present? Explain.

Math Practice

21. **Surface Area** Which has a greater surface area, a cube that is 2 cm × 2 cm on a side, or eight cubes that are each 1 cm × 1 cm on a side? Show your work.

Applying Skills

Use your knowledge of the excretory system and the information in the data table below to answer Questions 22–25.

Average Daily Water Loss in Humans (mL)

Source	Normal Weather	Hot Weather	Extended Heavy Exercise
Lungs	350	250	650
Urine	1,400	1,200	500
Sweat	450	1,750	5,350
Digestive waste	200	200	200

22. **Interpreting Data** Identify the major source of water loss during normal weather and the major source of water loss during hot weather.

23. **Drawing Conclusions** How do the data for normal weather and hot weather show that the body is maintaining homeostasis?

24. **Calculating** What is the total amount of water lost on a hot-weather day? What is the total amount of water lost during extended heavy exercise?

25. **Inferring** Use the data to explain why it is important to drink a lot of water when you are exercising heavily.

Lab zone Chapter **Project**

Performance Assessment Your three anti-smoking ads should be ready for display. Be prepared to explain why you chose the message you did for each group of viewers. What health risks do each of your ads identify? Why do you think your ads would be effective?

ⓘ Standardized Test Practice

Choose the letter of the best answer.

1. Which of the following organs functions as both a respiratory organ and an excretory organ?

   A the liver

   B the lungs

   C the skin

   D the kidneys

2. The correct sequence of organs through which air travels when it is breathed into the body is

   A pharynx, nose, trachea, bronchi.

   B nose, trachea, pharynx, bronchi.

   C nose, pharynx, bronchi, trachea.

   0 nose, pharynx, trachea, bronchi.

The graph below shows the percentage of total lung function in people who have never smoked and in smokers from ages 25–75. Use the graph to answer Questions 3 and 4.

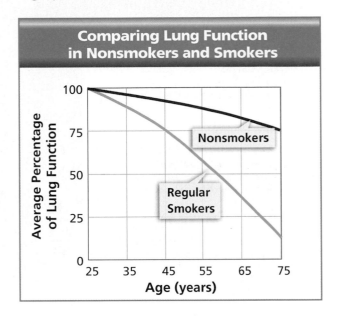

3. At approximately what age do the lungs of a smoker have the same capacity as the lungs of a 75-year-old who has never smoked?

   A 25

   B 45

   C 65

   D 75

4. What general conclusion about lung function and smoking could you draw from this graph?

   A Smoking does not affect lung function.

   B People who smoke are more likely to have greater lung function than those who have never smoked.

   C By the age of 50, a smoker will likely have 50 percent lung function.

   D Smoking significantly reduces the lung function of smokers compared to people who have never smoked.

Open-Ended Question

5. What is respiration? Explain where this process occurs and what body systems are involved in making respiration possible.

Fighting Disease

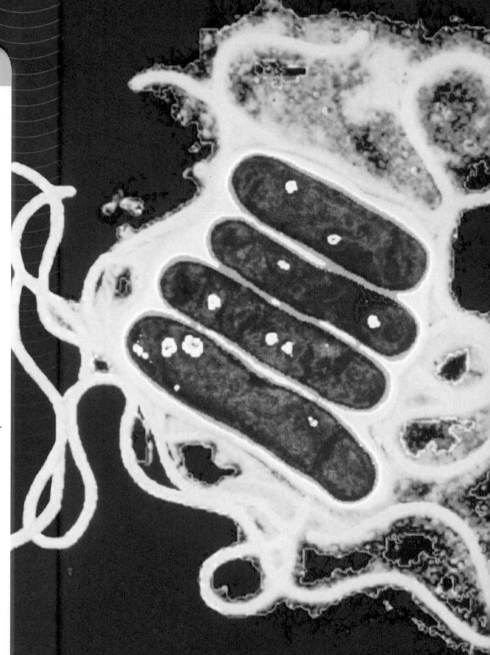

Academic Standards

This chapter addresses these Indiana standards.

The Living Environment

7.4.12 Explain that parasites can cause disease. A person can catch a cold many times because there are many different cold viruses.

7.4.13 Explain that white blood cells fight invaders. Antibodies produced by white blood cells can fight off subsequent invaders of the same kind.

Historical Perspectives

7.6.1 Describe old explanations for disease and the discovery that diseases are caused by microorganisms.

7.6.2 Explain how Louis Pasteur discovered that microorganisms can spoil food or cause diseases. Microorganisms can also be useful. Specific kinds of germs cause specific diseases.

interactive
Textbook

These rod-shaped bacteria *(Legionella)* ▶ cause Legionnaires' disease.

Lab zone™ Chapter **Project**

Stop the Invasion!

When you catch a cold, your body is under attack by cold viruses. Many other diseases are caused by viruses or bacteria that invade your body. In this project, you'll develop a series of informative news reports on how your body defends itself against such invasions.

Your Goal To create a series of imaginary news broadcasts from "battlefield sites" where the body is fighting an infectious disease

To complete this project successfully, you must

- choose a specific disease and represent the sequence of events that occurs when that disease strikes the body
- describe the stages of the disease as if they were battles between two armies
- present your story creatively in at least three reports, using newspaper, radio, or television news-reporting techniques

Plan It! With some classmates, list the techniques reporters use to make stories interesting or to explain complicated information. Also, recall the times you've had a cold, the flu, or another infectious disease. Write down how your body responded, how long you were sick, and any other useful information. Then select a specific disease to research.

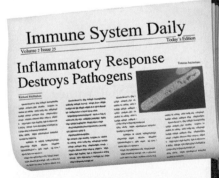

Infectious Disease

Reading Preview

Key Concepts
- What is the relationship between pathogens and infectious disease?
- What kinds of pathogens cause infectious diseases in humans?
- What are four ways that pathogens can spread?

Key Terms
- pathogen
- infectious disease
- toxin

Target Reading Skill

Using Prior Knowledge Before you read, look at the section headings and visuals to see what this section is about. Then write what you know about infectious diseases in a graphic organizer like the one below. As you read, continue to write in what you learn.

What You Know
1. Bacteria and viruses can cause disease.
2.

What You Learned
1.
2.

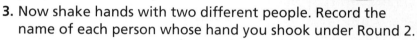

Lab zone Discover **Activity**

How Does a Disease Spread?

1. On a sheet of paper, write three headings: Round 1, Round 2, and Round 3.
2. Everyone in the class should shake hands with two people. Under Round 1, record the names of the people whose hand you shook.
3. Now shake hands with two different people. Record the name of each person whose hand you shook under Round 2.
4. Repeat Step 3. Under Round 3, record the names of the people whose hand you shook.

Think It Over

Calculating Suppose you had a disease that was spread by shaking hands. Everyone whose hand you shook has caught the disease and so has anyone who later shook hands with those people. Calculate how many people you "infected."

Before the twentieth century, surgery was a risky business. Even if people lived through an operation, they were not out of danger. After the operation, many patients' wounds became infected, and the patients often died. No one knew what caused these infections.

In the 1860s, a British surgeon named Joseph Lister hypothesized that microorganisms caused the infections. Before performing an operation, Lister washed his hands and surgical instruments with carbolic acid, a chemical that kills microorganisms. After the surgery, he covered the patient's wounds with bandages dipped in carbolic acid. Lister's results were dramatic. Before he used his new method, about 45 percent of his surgical patients died from infection. With Lister's new techniques, only 15 percent died.

Understanding Infectious Disease

Like the infections that Lister observed after surgery, many illnesses, such as ear infections and food poisoning, are caused by living things that are too small to see without a microscope. Organisms that cause disease are called **pathogens.**

Diseases that are caused by pathogens are called infectious diseases. An **infectious disease** is a disease that is caused by the presence of a living thing within the body. **When you have an infectious disease, pathogens have gotten inside your body and caused harm.** Pathogens make you sick by damaging individual cells, even though you may feel pain throughout your body. For example, when you have strep throat, pathogens have damaged cells in your throat.

Before Lister's time, people believed that things like evil spirits or swamp air led to sickness. Several scientists in the late 1800s contributed to the understanding of infectious diseases. In the 1860s, the French scientist Louis Pasteur showed that microorganisms cause certain kinds of diseases. Pasteur also showed that killing the microorganisms could prevent the spread of those diseases. In the 1870s and 1880s, the German physician Robert Koch demonstrated that each infectious disease is caused by a specific kind of pathogen. In other words, one kind of pathogen causes pneumonia, another kind causes chickenpox, and still another kind causes rabies.

 **Reading Checkpoint**) What causes infectious disease?

Go Online
PHSchool.com

For: More on infectious disease
Visit: PHSchool.com
Web Code: ced-4051

FIGURE 1
Preventing Infections
The illustration on the left shows how Lister used a carbolic steam sprayer to spread a mist of carbolic acid. The photo on the right shows a modern operating room.
Comparing and Contrasting *Identify some ways in which present-day surgery differs from surgery in Lister's time.*

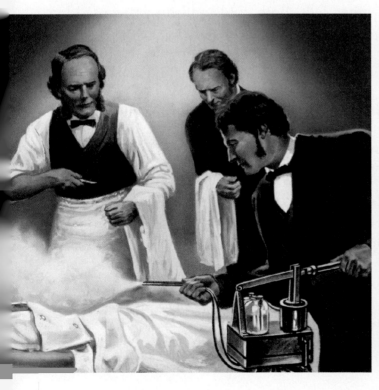

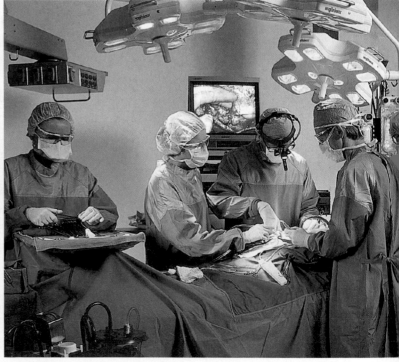

FIGURE 2

Pathogens
Most infectious diseases are caused by microscopic organisms.

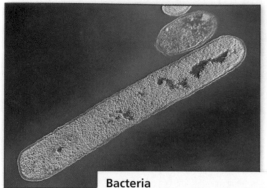

Bacteria
This rod-shaped bacterium causes tetanus, a disease that harms the nervous system.

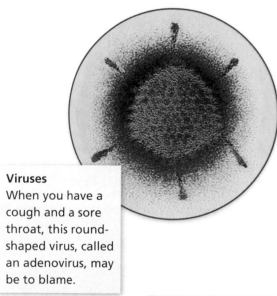

Viruses
When you have a cough and a sore throat, this round-shaped virus, called an adenovirus, may be to blame.

Fungi
This fungus causes ringworm, a disease that makes a round, ring-shaped skin rash.

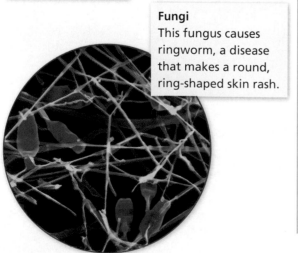

Kinds of Pathogens

You share Earth with many kinds of organisms. Most of these organisms are harmless, but some can make you sick. Some diseases are caused by multicelled animals, such as worms. However, most pathogens can be seen only with a microscope. **The four major groups of human pathogens are bacteria, viruses, fungi, and protists.** Look at Figure 2 to see some examples of pathogens.

Bacteria Bacteria are one-celled microorganisms. They cause a wide variety of diseases, including ear infections, food poisoning, and strep throat.

Some bacterial pathogens damage body cells directly. Strep throat is caused by streptococcus bacteria that invade cells in your throat. Other bacterial pathogens damage cells indirectly by producing a poison, or **toxin.** For example, if the bacteria that cause tetanus get into a wound, they produce a toxin that damages the nervous system. Tetanus is also called lockjaw because the nerve damage can lock the jaw muscles.

Viruses Viruses are tiny particles, much smaller than bacteria. Viruses cannot reproduce unless they are inside living cells. The cells are damaged or destroyed in the process, releasing new viruses to infect other cells. Both colds and flu are caused by viruses that invade cells in the respiratory system. There are more than 200 kinds of cold viruses, each of which can give you a sore throat and runny nose.

Fungi Fungi, which include molds and yeasts, also cause some infectious diseases. Fungi grow best in warm, dark, and moist areas. Two examples of fungal diseases are athlete's foot and ringworm.

Protists Protists are also a cause of disease. Malaria, an infection of the blood that is common in tropical areas, is one disease caused by protists. Other diseases caused by protists are African sleeping sickness and amebic dysentery.

 **Reading Checkpoint** What is required in order for viruses to reproduce?

How Pathogens Are Spread

Like all living things, pathogens need food and a place to live and reproduce. Unfortunately, your body may be the right place to meet a pathogen's needs. You can become infected by a pathogen in several ways. **Pathogens can spread through contact with either an infected person; soil, food, or water; a contaminated object; or an infected animal.**

Infected People Pathogens often pass from one person to another through direct physical contact, such as kissing and shaking hands. For example, if you kiss someone who has an open cold sore, cold-sore viruses may get into your body.

Diseases are also spread through indirect contact with an infected person. For example, when a person with a cold or the flu sneezes, pathogens shoot into the air. Other people may catch a cold or the flu if they inhale these pathogens.

Soil, Food, and Water Some pathogens occur naturally in the environment. The bacteria that cause botulism, a severe form of food poisoning, live in soil. Botulism bacteria can produce toxins in foods that have been improperly canned.

Some pathogens can contaminate food and water. If people then eat the food or drink the water, they may become sick. Some pathogens that cause severe diarrhea are spread through contaminated food and water. Cholera and dysentery are two deadly diseases that spread through food or water.

Cholera Cases, London, 1854

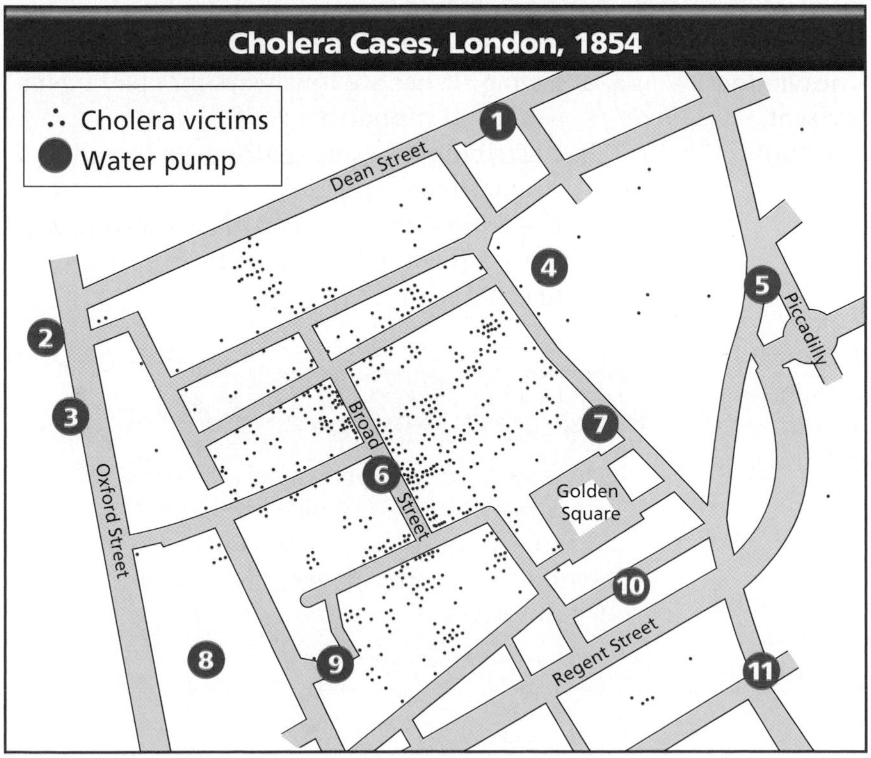

FIGURE 3
Cholera is a deadly disease caused by cholera bacteria. The map shows the location of cholera cases in the 1854 epidemic in London, England.
Inferring *How are cholera bacteria spread?*

FIGURE 4
Deer Ticks and Lyme Disease
The tiny deer tick may carry the bacteria that cause Lyme disease, a serious condition that can damage the joints.
Problem Solving *How might people reduce their risk of catching Lyme disease?*

Contaminated Objects Some pathogens can survive for a time outside a person's body. People can come into contact with pathogens by using objects, such as towels or silverware, that have been handled by an infected person. Colds and flu can be spread in this way. Tetanus bacteria can enter the body if a person steps on a contaminated object.

Infected Animals If an animal that is infected with certain pathogens bites a person, it can pass the pathogens to the person. People can get rabies, a serious disease that affects the nervous system, from the bite of an infected animal, such as a dog or a raccoon. Lyme disease and Rocky Mountain spotted fever are both spread by tick bites. For example, if a deer tick that is carrying Lyme disease bacteria bites a person, the person may get Lyme disease. The protist that causes malaria is transferred by the bites of mosquitoes that live in tropical regions.

 **Reading Checkpoint** Name a disease that can be spread by an animal bite.

Section 1 Assessment

Target Reading Skill Using Prior Knowledge Review your graphic organizer and revise it based on what you just learned in the section.

Reviewing Key Concepts

1. **a. Defining** What is a pathogen?
   b. Explaining How do pathogens cause infectious disease?
   c. Relating Cause and Effect How did Pasteur and Koch contribute to the understanding of the causes of infectious disease?

2. **a. Identifying** Name four kinds of pathogens that cause disease in humans.
   b. Explaining In what two ways do bacteria cause disease?
   c. Comparing and Contrasting Compare and contrast bacteria and viruses—both in terms of their size and how they cause disease.

3. **a. Listing** What are four ways that pathogens can infect humans?
   b. Describing How are pathogens spread by contaminated objects?
   c. Applying Concepts If you have a cold, what steps can you take to keep from spreading it to other people? Explain.

Writing in Science

Speech Write a short speech that Joseph Lister might have delivered to other surgeons to convince them to use his surgical techniques. In the speech, Lister should explain why his techniques were so successful.

The Body's Defenses

Reading Preview

Key Concepts
- How does the body's first line of defense guard against pathogens?
- What happens during the inflammatory response?
- How does the immune system respond to pathogens?
- How does HIV affect the immune system and how does it spread?

Key Terms
- inflammatory response
- phagocyte • immune response
- lymphocyte • T cell
- antigen • B cell • antibody
- AIDS • HIV

⟳ Target Reading Skill
Building Vocabulary After you read this section, reread the paragraphs that contain definitions of Key Terms. Use all the information you have learned to write a definition of each Key Term in your own words.

Discover **Activity**

Which Pieces Fit Together?
1. Your teacher will give you a piece of paper with one jagged edge.
2. One student in the class has a piece of paper with a jagged edge that matches yours, like two pieces of a jigsaw puzzle. Find the student whose paper matches yours and fit the two edges together.

Think It Over
Inferring Imagine that one piece of paper in each matching pair is a pathogen. The other is a cell in your body that defends your body against the invading pathogen. How many kinds of invaders can each defender cell recognize?

Your eyes are glued to the video screen. Enemy troops have gotten through an opening in the wall. Your soldiers have held back most of the invaders. However, some enemy soldiers are breaking through the defense lines. You need your backup defenders. They can zap invaders with their more powerful weapons. If your soldiers can fight off the enemy until the backup team arrives, you can save your fortress.

Video games create fantasy wars, but in your body, real battles happen all the time. In your body, the "enemies" are invading pathogens. You are hardly ever aware of these battles. The body's disease-fighting system is so effective that most people get sick only occasionally. By eliminating pathogens that can harm your cells, your body maintains homeostasis.

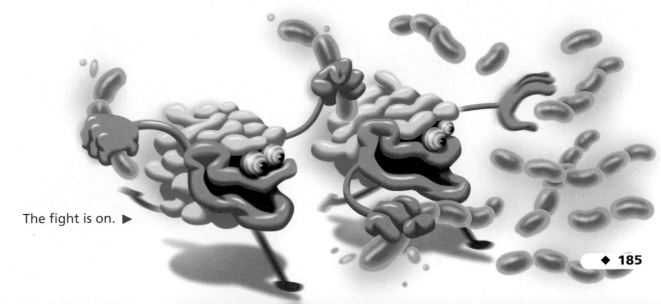

The fight is on. ▶

Barriers That Keep Pathogens Out

Your body has three lines of defense against pathogens. The first line consists of barriers that keep most pathogens from getting into the body. You do not wear a sign that says "Pathogens Keep Out," but that doesn't matter. **In the first line of defense, the surfaces of the skin, breathing passages, mouth, and stomach function as barriers to pathogens. These barriers trap and kill most pathogens with which you come into contact.**

Skin When pathogens land on the skin, they are exposed to destructive chemicals in oil and sweat. Even if these chemicals don't kill them, the pathogens may fall off with dead skin cells. If the pathogens manage to stay on the skin, they must get through the tightly packed dead cells that form a barrier on top of living skin cells. Most pathogens get through the skin only when it is cut. Scabs form over cuts so rapidly that the period in which pathogens can enter the body in this way is very short.

Breathing Passages Pathogens can also enter the body when you inhale. The nose, pharynx, trachea, and bronchi, however, contain mucus and cilia. Together, the mucus and cilia trap and remove most of the pathogens that enter the respiratory system. In addition, irritation by pathogens may make you sneeze or cough. Both actions force the pathogens out of your body.

Mouth and Stomach Some pathogens are found in foods, even if the foods are handled safely. The saliva in your mouth contains destructive chemicals, and your stomach produces acid. Most pathogens that you swallow are destroyed by saliva or stomach acid.

✓ **Reading Checkpoint** How do your breathing passages help keep pathogens out of your body?

FIGURE 5
Barriers to Pathogens
The surfaces of your skin and breathing passages are the first line of defense for keeping pathogens out of your body. **Relating Cause and Effect** *How can washing your hands help prevent infection?*

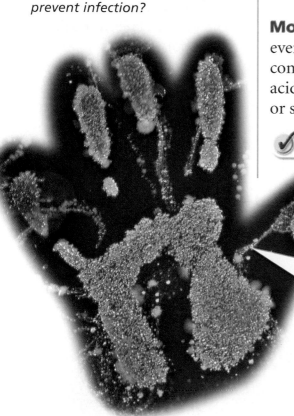

Skin
The dots in this photo are colonies of bacteria living on a person's hand.

Breathing Passages
Cilia that line the trachea help keep pathogens out of the lungs.

186 ◆

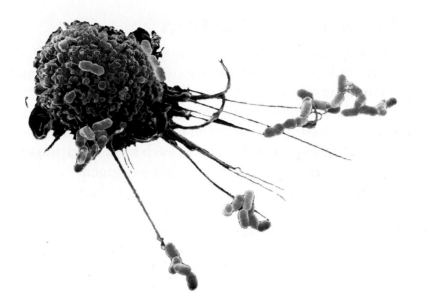

FIGURE 6
Phagocytes Destroy Pathogens
Caught! A phagocyte (shown in red) is a white blood cell that engulfs and destroys bacteria (shown in green). As phagocytes do their job, the body shows visible signs of inflammation, which include redness and swelling.

The Inflammatory Response

In spite of barriers, pathogens sometimes get into your body and begin to damage cells. When body cells are damaged, they release chemicals that trigger the **inflammatory response,** which is the body's second line of defense. **In the inflammatory response, fluid and white blood cells leak from blood vessels into nearby tissues. The white blood cells then fight the pathogens.** Because the inflammatory response is the same regardless of the pathogen, it is called the body's general defense.

White Blood Cells All white blood cells are disease fighters. However, there are different types of white blood cells, each with its own particular function. The type involved in the inflammatory response are the phagocytes. A **phagocyte** (FAG uh syt) is a white blood cell that engulfs pathogens and destroys them by breaking them down.

Inflammation During the inflammatory response, blood vessels widen in the area affected by the pathogens. This enlargement increases blood flow to the area. As a result, more disease-fighting white blood cells are delivered to the area. The enlarged blood vessels, and the fluid that leaks out of them, make the affected area red and swollen. If you touch the swollen area, it will feel slightly warmer than normal.

Fever In some cases, chemicals produced during the inflammatory response cause a fever. Although fever makes you feel bad, it actually helps your body fight the infection. Some pathogens do not grow and reproduce well at higher temperatures.

 **Reading Checkpoint** What role do white blood cells play in the inflammatory response?

Fighting Disease

Video Preview
▶ **Video Field Trip**
Video Assessment

The Immune System

If a pathogen infection is severe enough to cause a fever, it triggers the body's third line of defense—the **immune response.** The immune response is controlled by the immune system, the body's disease-fighting system. **The cells of the immune system can distinguish between different kinds of pathogens. The immune system cells react to each kind of pathogen with a defense targeted specifically at that pathogen.**

The white blood cells that distinguish between different kinds of pathogens are called **lymphocytes** (LIM fuh syts). There are two major kinds of lymphocytes—T lymphocytes and B lymphocytes, which are also called T cells and B cells. In Figure 7, you can see how T cells and B cells work together to destroy flu viruses.

T Cells A major function of **T cells** is to identify pathogens and distinguish one kind of pathogen from another. You have tens of millions of T cells circulating in your blood. Each kind of T cell recognizes a different kind of pathogen. What T cells actually recognize are marker molecules, called antigens, found on each pathogen. **Antigens** are molecules that the immune system recognizes either as part of your body or as coming from outside your body.

You can think of antigens as something like the uniforms that athletes wear. When you watch a track meet, you can look at the runners' uniforms to tell which school each runner comes from. Like athletes from different schools, each different pathogen has its own kind of antigen. Antigens differ from one another because each kind of antigen has a different chemical structure. T cells distinguish one chemical structure from another.

B Cells The lymphocytes called **B cells** produce proteins that help destroy pathogens. These proteins are called **antibodies.** Each kind of B cell produces only one kind of antibody, and each kind of antibody has a different structure. Antigen and antibody molecules fit together like pieces of a puzzle. An antigen on a flu virus will only bind to one kind of antibody—the antibody that acts against that flu virus.

When antibodies bind to the antigens on a pathogen, they mark the pathogen for destruction. Some antibodies make pathogens clump together. Others keep pathogens from attaching to the body cells that they might damage. Still other antibodies make it easier for phagocytes to destroy the pathogens.

Reading Checkpoint What is the function of an antibody?

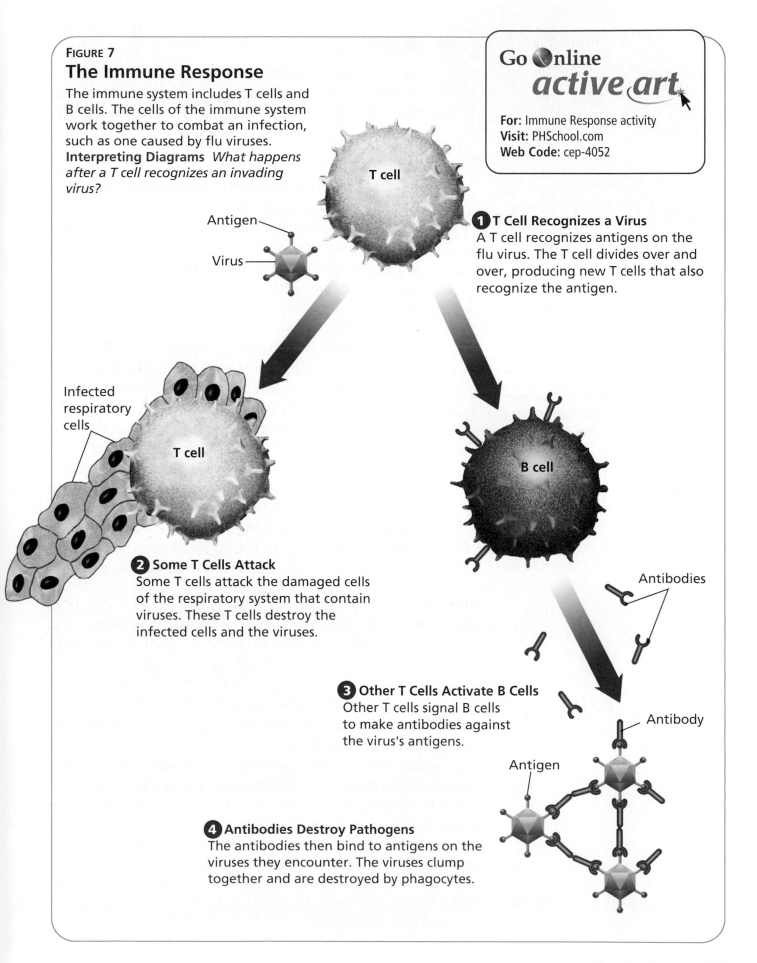

FIGURE 7

The Immune Response

The immune system includes T cells and B cells. The cells of the immune system work together to combat an infection, such as one caused by flu viruses. **Interpreting Diagrams** *What happens after a T cell recognizes an invading virus?*

Go Online
active art

For: Immune Response activity
Visit: PHSchool.com
Web Code: cep-4052

Antigen

Virus

T cell

❶ T Cell Recognizes a Virus
A T cell recognizes antigens on the flu virus. The T cell divides over and over, producing new T cells that also recognize the antigen.

Infected respiratory cells

T cell

B cell

❷ Some T Cells Attack
Some T cells attack the damaged cells of the respiratory system that contain viruses. These T cells destroy the infected cells and the viruses.

Antibodies

❸ Other T Cells Activate B Cells
Other T cells signal B cells to make antibodies against the virus's antigens.

Antibody

Antigen

❹ Antibodies Destroy Pathogens
The antibodies then bind to antigens on the viruses they encounter. The viruses clump together and are destroyed by phagocytes.

Chapter 6 ◆ **189**

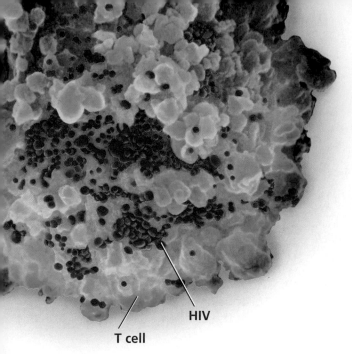

AIDS

Acquired immunodeficiency syndrome, or **AIDS,** is a disease caused by a virus that attacks the immune system. The virus that causes AIDS is called the human immunodeficiency virus, or **HIV.**

How HIV Affects the Body **HIV is the only kind of virus known to attack the human immune system directly and destroy T cells.** Once it invades the body, HIV enters T cells and reproduces inside them. People can be infected with HIV—that is, have the virus living in their T cells—for years before they become sick. More than 40 million people in the world, including more than 3 million children under 15, are infected with HIV.

Eventually, HIV begins to destroy the T cells it has infected. As the viruses destroy T cells, the body loses its ability to fight disease. Most persons infected with HIV eventually develop the symptoms of AIDS.

Because their immune systems no longer function properly, people with AIDS become sick with diseases not normally found in people with healthy immune systems. Many people survive attack after attack of such diseases. But eventually their immune systems fail, ending in death. At this time, there is no cure for AIDS. However, new drug treatments allow many people with the disease to survive much longer than in the past.

How HIV Is Spread Like all other viruses, HIV can only reproduce inside cells. However, the virus can survive for a short time outside the human body in body fluids, such as blood and the fluids produced by the male and female reproductive systems.

HIV can spread from one person to another only if body fluids from an infected person come in contact with those of an uninfected person. Sexual contact is one way in which this can happen. HIV may also pass from an infected woman to her baby during pregnancy or childbirth or through breast milk. In addition, infected blood can spread HIV. For example, if an infected drug user shares a needle, the next person who uses the needle may also become infected. Before 1985, HIV was sometimes transmitted through blood transfusions. Since 1985, however, all donated blood in the United States has been tested for signs of HIV. If blood is identified as infected, it is not used in transfusions.

FIGURE 9
How HIV Is Not Spread
You cannot get HIV, the virus that causes AIDS, by hugging someone infected with the virus.

How HIV Is Not Spread It is important to know the many ways in which HIV is *not* spread. HIV does not live on skin, so you cannot be infected by hugging or shaking hands with an infected person. You can't get infected by using a toilet seat after it has been used by someone with HIV. HIV is also not spread when you bump into someone while playing sports.

 **Reading Checkpoint** What disease is caused by HIV?

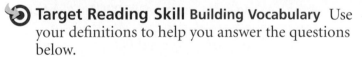

Section 2 Assessment

 **Target Reading Skill** **Building Vocabulary** Use your definitions to help you answer the questions below.

Reviewing Key Concepts

1. a. **Listing** Name four barriers that prevent pathogens from getting into the body.
   b. **Explaining** Briefly describe how each barrier prevents infections.
   c. **Predicting** What could happen if you got a cut that did not heal?

2. a. **Reviewing** What triggers the inflammatory response?
   b. **Describing** How does the inflammatory response defend against invading pathogens?
   c. **Relating Cause and Effect** Why is the presence of large numbers of white blood cells in a wound a sign of infection?

3. a. **Identifying** Identify the cells that are part of the immune system.
   b. **Sequencing** Outline the steps involved in the immune response.

4. a. **Reviewing** Where in the body does HIV reproduce?
   b. **Summarizing** What are three ways that HIV can be passed from one person to another?

Writing in Science

Explanation An antigen and antibody can be compared to a lock and key. Write a paragraph in which you explain how the lock-and-key model is a good way to describe the relationship between an antigen and antibody.

The Skin as a Barrier

Problem

How does the skin act as a barrier to pathogens?

Skills Focus

observing, making models, controlling variables

Materials

- 4 sealable plastic bags
- 4 fresh apples
- rotting apple
- cotton swabs
- marking pen
- paper towels
- toothpick
- rubbing alcohol

Procedure

1. Read over the entire procedure to see how you will treat each of four fresh apples. Write a prediction in your notebook about the change(s) you expect to see in each apple. Then, copy the data table into your notebook.

2. Label four plastic bags *1, 2, 3,* and *4.*

3. Wash your hands with soap and water. Then, gently wash four fresh apples with water and dry them carefully with paper towels. Place one apple into plastic bag 1, and seal the bag.

4. Insert a toothpick tip into a rotting apple and withdraw it. Lightly draw the tip of the toothpick down the side of the second apple without breaking the skin. Repeat these actions three more times, touching the toothpick to different parts of the apple without breaking the skin. Insert the apple into plastic bag 2, and seal the bag.

5. Insert the toothpick tip into the rotting apple and withdraw it. Use the tip to make a long, thin scratch down the side of the third apple. Be sure to pierce the apple's skin. Repeat these actions three more times, making additional scratches on different parts of the apple. Insert the apple into plastic bag 3, and seal the bag.

6. Repeat Step 5 with the fourth apple. However, before you place the apple into the bag, dip a cotton swab in rubbing alcohol, and swab the scratches. Then, place the apple into plastic bag 4, and seal the bag. **CAUTION:** *Alcohol and its vapors are flammable. Work where there are no sparks, exposed flames, or other heat sources.*

Data Table				
Date	Apple 1 (no contact with decay)	Apple 2 (contact with decay, unbroken skin)	Apple 3 (contact with decay, scratched, untreated)	Apple 4 (contact with decay, scratched, treated with alcohol)

7. Store the four bags in a warm, dark place. Wash your hands thoroughly with soap and water.

8. Every day for one week, remove the apples from their storage place and observe them without opening the bags. Record your observations, and return the bags to their storage location. At the end of the activity, dispose of the unopened bags as directed by your teacher.

Analyze and Conclude

1. **Observing** How did the appearance of the four apples compare?

2. **Inferring** Explain the differences you observed in Question 1.

3. **Making Models** In this experiment, what condition in the human body is each of the four fresh apples supposed to model?

4. **Controlling Variables** What is the purpose of Apple 1 in this experiment? Explain.

5. **Making Models** What is the role of the rotting apple in this experiment?

6. **Communicating** Write a paragraph in which you explain how this investigation shows why routine cuts and scrapes should be cleaned and bandaged.

Design an Experiment

Using apples as you did in this activity, design an experiment to model how washing hands can prevent the spread of disease. *Obtain your teacher's permission before carrying out your investigation.*

Preventing Infectious Disease

Reading Preview

Key Concepts
- How does the body acquire active immunity?
- How does passive immunity occur?

Key Terms
- immunity • active immunity
- vaccination • vaccine
- antibiotic • passive immunity

Target Reading Skill
Comparing and Contrasting As you read, compare and contrast active immunity and passive immunity in a Venn diagram like the one below. Write the similarities in the space where the circles overlap and the differences on the left and right sides.

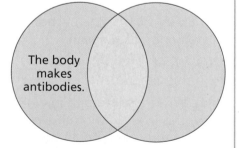

Active Immunity   Passive Immunity

The body makes antibodies.

Lab zone Discover **Activity**

What Substances Can Kill Pathogens?
1. Your teacher will give you a variety of products, such as disinfectant cleansers and mouthwashes, that claim to kill pathogens. Read the labels to learn the pathogens that each product is supposed to destroy.
2. Also note the ingredients in each product that act against pathogens. These are labeled "active ingredients."

Think It Over
Designing Experiments How could you determine which of two different cleansers is more effective at killing bacteria? Design an experiment to find out. Do not perform the experiment without obtaining your teacher's approval.

Ask an adult if he or she remembers having the chickenpox. Chances are, the response will be, "Wow, did I itch!" But someone who has had chickenpox can be pretty sure of never getting that disease again. As people recover from some diseases, they develop immunity to the diseases. **Immunity** is the body's ability to destroy pathogens before they can cause disease. There are two basic types of immunity—active and passive.

Active Immunity

Someone who has been sick with chickenpox was invaded by chickenpox viruses. The immune system responded to the virus antigens by producing antibodies. The next time chickenpox viruses invade the body, a healthy immune system will produce antibodies so quickly that the person will not become sick with chickenpox. This reaction is called **active immunity** because the body has produced the antibodies that fight the disease pathogens. **A person acquires active immunity when their own immune system produces antibodies in response to the presence of a pathogen.** Active immunity can result from either getting the disease or being vaccinated.

The Immune Response When someone gets a disease such as chickenpox, active immunity is produced by the immune system as part of the immune response. Remember that during the immune response, T cells and B cells help destroy the pathogens. After the person recovers, some T cells and B cells keep the "memory" of the pathogen's antigen. If that kind of pathogen enters the body again, these memory cells recognize the antigen. The memory cells start the immune response so quickly that the person usually does not get sick. Active immunity often lasts for many years, and sometimes it lasts for life.

Vaccination A second way to gain active immunity is by being vaccinated. **Vaccination** (vac suh NAY shun), or immunization, is the process by which harmless antigens are deliberately introduced into a person's body to produce active immunity. Vaccinations are given by injection, by mouth, or through a nasal spray. Vaccinations can prevent polio, chickenpox, and other diseases.

The substance that is used in a vaccination is called a vaccine. A **vaccine** (vak SEEN) usually consists of pathogens that have been weakened or killed but can still trigger the immune system to go into action. The T cells and B cells still recognize and respond to the antigens of the weakened or dead pathogen. When you receive a vaccination with weakened pathogens, you usually do not get sick. However, your immune system responds by producing memory cells and active immunity to the disease.

FIGURE 10
Vaccination

Follow the steps below to see how vaccinations work. **Classifying** *Why do vaccinations produce active immunity?*

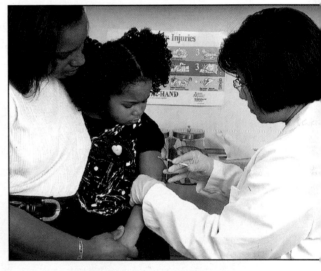

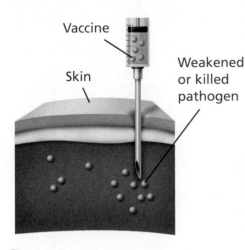

❶ A person receives an injection with weakened or killed pathogens.

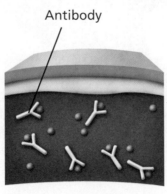

❷ The immune system produces antibodies against the disease. It also produces memory cells.

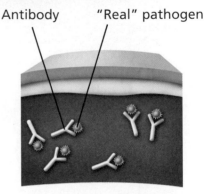

❸ If the "real" pathogen invades later, memory cells help to produce antibodies that disable the pathogen.

Go Online
PLANET DIARY

For: More on disease prevention
Visit: PHSchool.com
Web Code: ced-4053

When You Do Get Sick You develop immunity to certain diseases either because you have had the diseases or because you have been vaccinated against them. However, no one is immune to all diseases.

Unfortunately, you probably will become sick from time to time. Sometimes, when you become sick, medications can help you get better. If you have a disease that is caused by bacteria, you may be given an antibiotic. An **antibiotic** (an tih by AHT ik) is a chemical that kills bacteria or slows their growth without harming body cells. Unfortunately, there are no medications that are effective against viral illnesses, including the common cold. The best way to deal with most viral diseases is to get plenty of rest.

Science and **History**

Fighting Infectious Disease

From ancient times, people have practiced methods for preventing disease and caring for sick people. About 200 years ago, people began to learn much more about the causes of infectious diseases and how to protect against them.

1796 Edward Jenner
Edward Jenner, a country doctor in England, successfully vaccinated a child against smallpox, a deadly viral disease. Jenner used material from the sore of a person with cowpox, a mild but similar disorder. Although Jenner's procedure was successful, he did not understand why it worked.

1868 Louis Pasteur
In France, Louis Pasteur showed that microorganisms were the cause of disease in silkworms. Pasteur reasoned that he could control the spread of disease by killing microorganisms. He also proposed that infectious disease in humans are caused by microorganisms.

1854 Florence Nightingale
As an English nurse caring for British soldiers during the Crimean War, Florence Nightingale insisted that army hospitals be kept clean. By doing this, she saved many soldiers' lives. She is considered to be the founder of the modern nursing profession.

| 1800 | 1840 | 1880 |

Although some medicines don't kill pathogens, they may help you feel more comfortable while you get better. Many of these are over-the-counter medications—drugs that can be purchased without a doctor's prescription. Such medications may reduce fever, clear your nose so you can breathe more easily, or stop a cough. Be sure you understand and follow the instructions for all types of medications.

While you recover, be sure to get plenty of rest. Drink plenty of fluids. Unless your stomach is upset, try to eat well-balanced meals. And if you don't start to feel better in a short time, you should see a doctor.

Reading Checkpoint What is an antibiotic?

Writing in Science

Research and Write Learn more about the work of one of these scientists. Then, imagine that a new hospital is going to be dedicated to that person and that you have been chosen to deliver the dedication speech. Write a speech that praises the person's contributions to fighting disease.

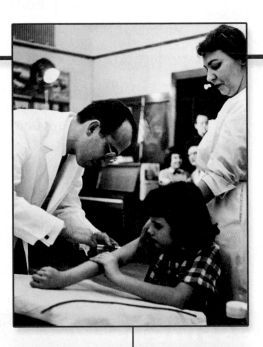

1928 Alexander Fleming
In Britain, Alexander Fleming observed that bacteria growing on laboratory plates were killed when various kinds of fungi grew on the same plate. He discovered that one fungus produced a substance that killed bacteria—penicillin.

1952 Jonas Salk
In 1952, there were more than 57,000 cases of polio, making it one of the most dreaded diseases known at the time. That same year, Jonas Salk, a professor at a medical university in the United States, showed that people injected with killed polio viruses did not get the disease, but produced antibodies against it.

1985 Mathilde Krim
Mathilde Krim, an American biomedical researcher, founded The American Foundation for AIDS Research, or AmFAR. Krim recognized that AIDS was a serious threat to public health and has dedicated her life to supporting AIDS research.

1920   **1960**   **2000**

Passive Immunity

Some diseases, such as rabies, are so uncommon that people rarely receive vaccinations against them. However, if a person is bitten by an animal that might have rabies, the person is usually given injections that contain antibodies to the rabies antigen. The protection that the person acquires this way is an example of passive immunity. **Passive immunity** results when antibodies are given to a person—the person's immune system does not make them. **A person acquires passive immunity when the antibodies that fight the pathogen come from a source other than the person's body.** Unlike active immunity, which is long-lasting, passive immunity usually lasts no more than a few months.

A baby acquires passive immunity to some diseases before birth. This immunity results from antibodies that are passed from the mother's blood into the baby's blood during pregnancy. After birth, these antibodies protect the baby for a few months. By then, the baby's own immune system has begun to function fairly efficiently.

FIGURE 11
Passive Immunity
This baby has acquired passive immunity from her mother.
Relating Cause and Effect *How do babies acquire passive immunity?*

 **Reading Checkpoint** **What is one disease for which you can acquire passive immunity?**

Section 3 Assessment

Target Reading Skill Comparing and Contrasting Use the information in your Venn diagram about active immunity and passive immunity to help you answer the questions below.

Reviewing Key Concepts

1. **a. Defining** What is active immunity?
   b. Explaining What are two ways in which active immunity can be acquired?
   c. Applying Concepts After receiving certain vaccinations, some children may develop mild symptoms of the disease. Explain why.
2. **a. Reviewing** What is passive immunity?
   b. Describing How is passive immunity acquired?
   c. Inferring Why does passive immunity usually not last for very long?

Lab zone At-Home **Activity**

Vaccination History With a family member, make a list of all the vaccinations you have received. For each, note when you received the vaccination. Then, with your family member, learn about one of the diseases against which you were vaccinated. What kind of pathogen causes the disease? What are the symptoms of the disease? Is the disease still common in the United States?

Noninfectious Disease

Reading Preview

Key Concepts
- What causes allergies?
- How does diabetes affect the body?
- What are the effects of cancer on the body?

Key Terms
- noninfectious disease
- allergy • allergen
- histamine • asthma • insulin
- diabetes • tumor • carcinogen

Target Reading Skill

Asking Questions Before you read, preview the red headings. In a graphic organizer like the one below, ask a *what* or *how* question for each heading. As you read, answer your questions.

Noninfectious Disease

Question	Answer
What is an allergy?	An allergy is a disorder in which . . .

Lab zone **Discover Activity**

What Happens When Airflow Is Restricted?

1. Asthma is a disorder in which breathing passages become narrower than normal. This activity will help you understand how this condition affects breathing. **CAUTION:** *Do not perform this activity if you have a medical condition that affects your breathing.* Begin by breathing normally, first through your nose and then through your mouth. Observe how deeply you breathe.

2. Put one end of a drinking straw in your mouth. Then, gently pinch your nostrils shut so that you cannot breathe through your nose.

3. With your nostrils pinched closed, breathe by inhaling air through the straw. Continue breathing this way for thirty seconds.

Think It Over
Observing Compare your normal breathing pattern to that when breathing through the straw. Which way were you able to take deeper breaths? Did you ever feel short of breath?

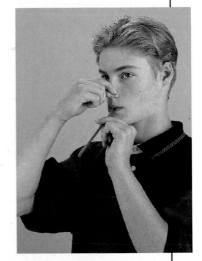

Americans are living longer today than ever before. A person who was born in 2000 can expect to live about 77 years. In contrast, a person born in 1950 could expect to live only about 68 years, and a person born in 1900 only about 50 years.

Progress against infectious disease is one reason why life spans have increased. However, as infectious diseases have become less common, noninfectious diseases have grown more common. **Noninfectious diseases** are diseases that are not caused by pathogens in the body. Unlike infectious diseases, noninfectious diseases cannot be transmitted from person to person. One noninfectious disease, cardiovascular disease, is the leading cause of death in the United States. Allergies, diabetes, and cancer are other noninfectious diseases.

◀ People live longer today than ever before.

Drawing Conclusions

Two weeks ago, after you ate strawberry shortcake with whipped cream, you broke out in an itchy rash. The ingredients in the dessert were strawberries, sugar, flour, butter, eggs, vanilla, baking powder, salt, and cream. Last night, you ate a strawberry tart with whipped cream and again broke out in a rash. The ingredients were strawberries, sugar, cornstarch, milk, eggs, flour, shortening, salt, and vanilla.

You think that you may be allergic to strawberries. Do you have enough evidence to support this conclusion? If so, why? If not, what additional evidence do you need?

Allergies

Spring has arrived. Flowers are in bloom, and the songs of birds fill the air. Unfortunately, for some people, sneezing is another sound that fills the air. People who sneeze and cough in the spring may not have colds. Instead, they may be suffering from allergies to plant pollen. An **allergy** is a disorder in which the immune system is overly sensitive to a foreign substance—something not normally found in the body. **An allergy develops in response to various foreign substances that set off a series of reactions in the body.**

Allergens Any substance that causes an allergy is called an **allergen**. In addition to different kinds of pollen, allergens include dust, molds, some foods, and even some medicines. If you are lucky, you have no allergies at all. However, the bodies of many people react to one or more allergens.

Allergens may get into your body when you inhale them, eat them in food, or touch them with your skin. When lymphocytes encounter an allergen, they produce antibodies to that allergen. These antibodies, unlike the ones made during the immune response, signal cells in the body to release a substance called histamine. **Histamine** (HIS tuh meen) is a chemical that is responsible for the symptoms of an allergy, such as sneezing and watery eyes. Drugs that interfere with the action of histamine, called antihistamines, may lessen this reaction. However, if you have an allergy, the best strategy is to try to avoid the substance to which you are allergic.

FIGURE 12
Allergens
Some people have allergic reactions to plant pollen, dust mites, or cats.

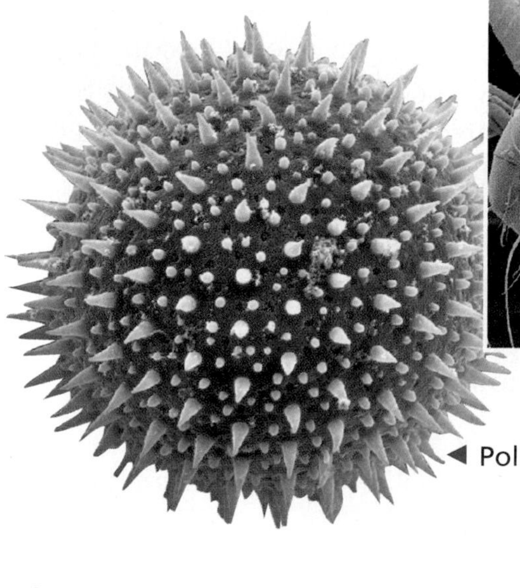

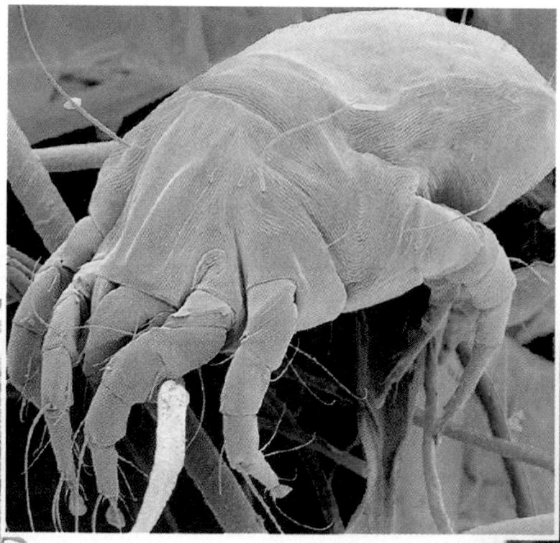

Dust Mite ▲

◄ Pollen

◄ Cat

Asthma Some allergic reactions can create a condition called asthma. **Asthma** (AZ muh) is a disorder in which the respiratory passages narrow significantly. This narrowing causes the person to wheeze and become short of breath. Asthma attacks may be brought on by factors other than allergies, such as stress and exercise.

 **Reading Checkpoint** What is asthma?

Diabetes

The pancreas is an organ with many different functions. One function is to produce a chemical called insulin. **Insulin** (IN suh lin) enables body cells to take in glucose from the blood and use it for energy. In the condition known as **diabetes** (dy uh BEE tis), either the pancreas fails to produce enough insulin or the body's cells fail to properly use insulin. **As a result, a person with diabetes has high levels of glucose in the blood and may even excrete glucose in the urine. The person's body cells, however, do not have enough glucose.**

Effects of Diabetes If untreated, people with diabetes may lose weight, feel weak, and be hungry all the time. These symptoms occur because body cells are unable to take in the glucose they need. In addition, diabetics may urinate frequently and feel thirsty as the kidneys work to eliminate the excess glucose from the body. The long-term effects of diabetes are serious and can include blindness, kidney failure, and heart disease.

Forms of Diabetes There are two main forms of diabetes. Type I diabetes usually begins in childhood or early adulthood. In Type I diabetes, the pancreas produces little or no insulin. People with this condition must get insulin injections.

Type II diabetes usually develops during adulthood. In this condition, either the pancreas does not make enough insulin, or body cells do not respond normally to insulin. People with Type II diabetes may be able to control their symptoms through proper diet, weight control, and exercise.

 **Reading Checkpoint** What are two symptoms of diabetes?

Go Online
SciLINKS

For: Links on noninfectious disease
Visit: www.SciLinks.org
Web Code: scn-0454

FIGURE 13
Glucose Testing
Many people with diabetes must test their blood frequently to determine the level of glucose in their blood.
Relating Cause and Effect *What accounts for the high level of glucose in the blood of diabetics?*

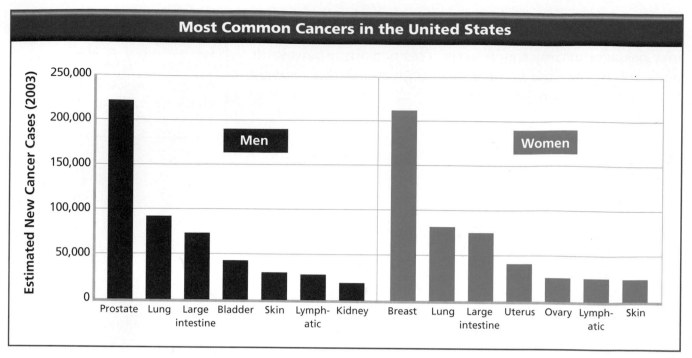

Most Common Cancers in the United States

Estimated New Cancer Cases (2003)

Men: Prostate, Lung, Large intestine, Bladder, Skin, Lymphatic, Kidney

Women: Breast, Lung, Large intestine, Uterus, Ovary, Lymphatic, Skin

FIGURE 14
The graph shows the leading types of cancer that affect men and women in the United States.
Reading Graphs *Do more women or men develop lung cancer each year?*

Cancer

Under normal conditions, the body produces new cells at about the same rate that other cells die. In a condition known as cancer, however, the situation is quite different. **Cancer is a disease in which cells multiply uncontrollably, over and over, destroying healthy tissue in the process.**

How Cancer Develops As cells divide over and over, they often form abnormal tissue masses called **tumors**. Not all tumors are cancerous. Cancerous tumors invade and destroy the healthy tissue around them. Cancer cells can break away from a tumor and invade blood or lymph vessels. The blood or lymph carries the cancer cells to other parts of the body, where they may begin to divide and form new tumors. Unless stopped by treatment, cancer progresses through the body.

Causes of Cancer Different factors may work together in causing cells to become cancerous. One such factor is the characteristics that people inherit from their parents. Because of their inherited characteristics, some people are more likely than others to develop certain kinds of cancer. For example, if you are female, and your mother or grandmother has breast cancer, you have an increased chance of developing breast cancer.

Some substances or factors in the environment, called **carcinogens** (kahr SIN uh junz), can cause cancer. The tar in cigarette smoke is an example of a carcinogen. Ultraviolet light, which is part of sunlight, can also be a carcinogen.

Cancer Treatment Surgery, drugs, and radiation are all used to treat cancer. If cancer is detected before it has spread, doctors may remove the cancerous tumors through surgery. After surgery, radiation or drugs may be used to make sure all the cancer cells have been killed.

Radiation treatment uses high-energy waves to kill cancer cells. When these rays are aimed at tumors, the intense energy damages and kills cancer cells more than it damages normal cells. Drug therapy is the use of chemicals to destroy cancer cells. Many of these chemicals, however, destroy some normal cells as well.

Cancer Prevention As with other diseases, the best way to fight cancer is to prevent it. People can reduce their risk of cancer by avoiding carcinogens, such as those found in tobacco. Even chewing tobacco and snuff contain carcinogens, which can cause mouth cancers. A low-fat diet that includes plenty of fruits and vegetables can help prevent cancers of the digestive system.

People can also increase their chance of surviving cancer by having regular medical checkups. The earlier cancer is detected, the more likely it can be treated successfully.

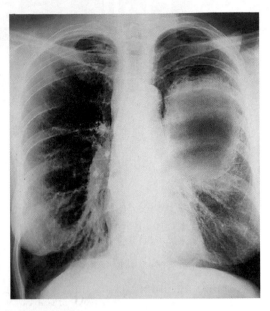

FIGURE 15
Lung Tumor
The large orange mass in the X-ray is a cancerous tumor in the lung.

 **Reading Checkpoint** What is a carcinogen?

Section 4 Assessment

Target Reading Skill Asking Questions Use the answers to the questions you wrote about the headings to help you answer the questions below.

Reviewing Key Concepts

1. a. **Defining** What is an allergy?
   b. **Describing** Describe how the body reacts to the presence of an allergen.
   c. **Inferring** You and your friends go to a movie. When you enter the theater, you start to sneeze and your throat feels scratchy. Explain what you think is happening.
2. a. **Identifying** What is the function of insulin in the body?
   b. **Explaining** How does diabetes affect the level of glucose in the blood and in body cells?

3. a. **Reviewing** What is a cancerous tumor?
   b. **Relating Cause and Effect** Describe how cancerous tumors harm the body.
   c. **Applying Concepts** Why do doctors look for cancerous tumors in the lymphatic system when someone is diagnosed with cancer?

Lab zone At-Home **Activity**

Family History of Allergies Explain to your family what allergies are and how allergens affect the body. Make a list of any substances to which your family members are allergic. Use this list to determine whether certain allergies occur frequently in your family.

Causes of Death, Then and Now

Problem

How do the leading causes of death today compare with those in 1900?

Skills Focus

graphing, interpreting data, drawing conclusions

Materials

- colored pencils
- rulers
- calculator (optional)
- protractor
- compass

Procedure

1. The data table on the next page shows the leading causes of death in the United States in 1900 and today. Examine the data and note that one cause of death—accidents—is not a disease. The other causes are labeled either "I," indicating an infectious disease, or "NI," indicating a noninfectious disease.

PART 1 Comparing Specific Causes of Death

2. Look at the following causes of death in the data table: (a) pneumonia and influenza, (b) heart disease, (c) accidents, and (d) cancer. Construct a bar graph that compares the numbers of deaths from each of those causes in 1900 and today. Label the horizontal axis *"Causes of Death."* Label the vertical axis *"Deaths per 100,000 People."* Draw two bars side by side for each cause of death. Use a key to show which bars refer to 1900 and which refer to today.

PART 2 Comparing Infectious and Noninfectious Causes of Death

3. In this part of the lab, you will make two circle graphs showing three categories: infectious diseases, noninfectious diseases, and "other." You may want to review the information on creating circle graphs on page 262 of the Skills Handbook.

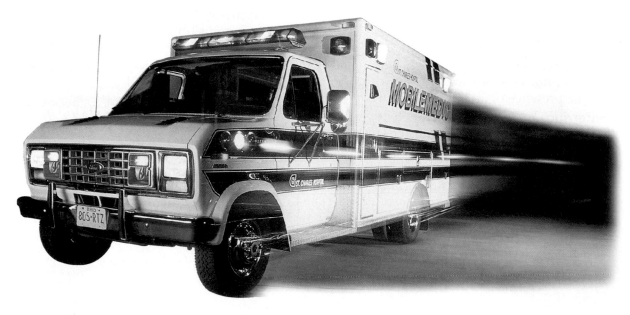

Ten Leading Causes of Death in the United States, 1900 and Today			
1900		**Today**	
Cause of Death	**Deaths Per 100,000**	**Cause of Death**	**Deaths Per 100,000**
Pneumonia, influenza (I)*	215	Heart disease (NI)	246
Tuberculosis (I)	185	Cancer (NI)	194
Diarrhea (I)	140	Stroke (NI)	57
Heart disease (NI)	130	Lung disease (NI)	43
Stroke (NI)	110	Accidents	34
Kidney disease (NI)	85	Diabetes (NI)	25
Accidents	75	Pneumonia, influenza (I)	22
Cancer (NI)	65	Alzheimer's disease (NI)	19
Senility (NI)	55	Kidney disease (NI)	14
Diphtheria (I)	40	Septicemia (I)	11
Total	**1,100**	**Total**	**665**

* (I) indicates an infectious disease. (NI) indicates a noninfectious disease.

4. Start by grouping the data from 1900 into the three categories—infectious diseases, noninfectious diseases, and other causes. Calculate the total number of deaths for each category. Then find the size of the "pie slice" (the number of degrees) for each category, and construct your circle graph. To find the size of the infectious disease slice for 1900, for example, use the following formula:

$$\frac{\text{Number of deaths from infectious diseases}}{1{,}100 \text{ deaths total}} = \frac{x}{360°}$$

5. Calculate the percentage represented by each category using this formula:

$$\frac{\text{Numbers of degrees in a slice}}{360°} \times 100 = \blacksquare\%$$

6. Repeat Steps 4 and 5 using the data from today to make the second circle graph. What part of the formula in Step 4 do you need to change?

Analyze and Conclude

1. **Observing** What information did you learn from examining the data table in Step 1?

2. **Graphing** According to your bar graph, which cause of death showed the greatest increase between 1900 and today? The greatest decrease?

3. **Interpreting Data** In your circle graphs, which category decreased the most from 1900 to today? Which increased the most?

4. **Drawing Conclusions** Suggest an explanation for the change in the number of deaths due to infectious diseases from 1900 to today.

5. **Communicating** In a paragraph, explain how graphs help you identify patterns and other information in data that you might otherwise overlook.

More to Explore

Write a question related to the data table that you have not yet answered. Then create a graph or work with the data in other ways to answer your question.

Cancer and the Environment

Reading Preview

Key Concepts
- How can people's environments affect their risk of cancer?
- What are three carcinogens found in the environment?

Target Reading Skill
Relating Cause and Effect

As you read, identify environmental carcinogens and the types of cancer they cause. Write the information in a graphic organizer like the one below.

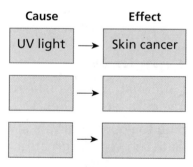

Cause		Effect
UV light	→	Skin cancer
	→	
	→	

Discover Activity

What Does Sunlight Do to the Beads?

1. Your teacher will give you beads that change color under certain conditions. Thread five beads on a pipe cleaner. Observe what the beads look like.

2. Wrap the pipe cleaner around your wrist. Go outdoors for 1 minute. Observe what happens to the beads.

Think It Over
Developing Hypotheses The ultraviolet light in sunlight causes the reaction you observed. Form a hypothesis about how you might prevent the beads from reacting as they did. How can you test your hypothesis?

You are trapped in a place that is dark, tight, and so warm that you can hardly breathe. You climb upwards, carefully feeling for footholds as you inch along. The surfaces are so warm that your knees feel hot as they scrape against the walls. Grimy dirt falls on your face, and you blink to keep it out of your eyes. This story sounds like a nightmare. But it was real life for the children who worked as chimney sweeps in the 1700s.

In 1775, about one million people lived in London, England. Their homes were heated by coal fires. Because burning coal produces lots of black soot, the soot had to be cleaned out of the chimneys regularly. Chimney sweeps did this job by crawling into the chimneys and scraping the soot off the walls.

1770s
Making Observations
Percival Pott notices that chimney sweeps have a high rate of skin cancer.

1775
Developing a Hypothesis
Pott hypothesizes that something in soot causes skin cancer.

1775
Testing the Hypothesis
Pott recommends that chimney sweeps bathe frequently, thus removing the cancer-causing soot.

Linking Cancer to the Environment

Because chimney sweeps had to be small and thin enough to fit inside a chimney, most chimney sweeps were children. The chimney sweeps were a type of indentured servant. The master would teach them the trade in exchange for housing. At the end of a hard day, chimney sweeps were covered with soot, but few washed it off. The chimney sweeps often slept in their soot sacks and bathed infrequently.

A Link Between Soot and Cancer Percivall Pott, a London doctor, saw many chimney sweeps at his medical clinic. Pott noticed that the chimney sweeps often had soot ground deeply into their skin. He also observed that a high number of chimney sweeps developed skin cancer. Pott hypothesized that something in soot caused cancer. He recommended frequent bathing to reduce the risk of skin cancer. Many years later, scientists identified the carcinogens in soot. They are the same substances that make up the tar in cigarette smoke.

Carcinogens in the Environment Percivall Pott was one of the first scientists to recognize the connection between the environment and cancer. **The environment may contain carcinogens. To reduce the risk of cancer, carcinogens need to be removed or people need to be protected from them.**

Pott's work led to efforts to control environmental carcinogens. In the United States, the Environmental Protection Agency (EPA) is in charge of enforcing environmental laws. The EPA identifies environmental carcinogens and develops strategies for protecting people from them.

✓ **Reading Checkpoint** How could chimney sweeps reduce their risk of skin cancer?

FIGURE 16
Soot and Skin Cancer
Percivall Pott hypothesized that there was a connection between soot and skin cancer in chimney sweeps. **Drawing Conclusions** *What additional evidence supported Pott's hypothesis?*

1892
Collecting Data
Later evidence shows that chimney sweeps who bathe regularly develop skin cancer at a lower rate than sweeps who rarely bathe.

Early 1900s
Confirming the Hypothesis
Certain substances in soot are found to cause skin cancer in laboratory animals.

Skin Cancer

The graph shows the frequency of skin cancer in the United States from 1998 to 2003.

1. **Reading Graphs** What variable is being plotted on the *y*-axis?

2. **Interpreting Data** How many cases of skin cancer were estimated for women in 1998? In 2003?

3. **Calculating** Using the data from Question 2, calculate the increase in the number of skin cancer cases among women.

4. **Calculating** What was the difference in the number of skin cancer cases for men and women in 1999?

5. **Predicting** Based on these graphs, do you think the number of skin cancers will increase, decrease, or remain the same in the next five years? Explain your answer.

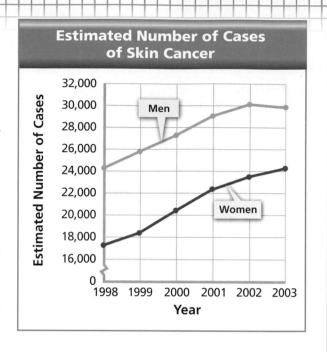

Estimated Number of Cases of Skin Cancer

Environmental Carcinogens Today

Scientists have identified many carcinogens found in the environment. **Three important environmental carcinogens are ultraviolet light, vinyl chloride, and arsenic.**

Ultraviolet Light Skin cancer can result from overexposure to sunlight. Ultraviolet light is the part of sunlight that causes cancer. Fortunately, as sunlight arrives on Earth from the sun, much of the ultraviolet light is absorbed before it can reach Earth's surface. Ozone, a gas present high in Earth's atmosphere, absorbs most of the ultraviolet light.

In the 1970s and 1980s, scientists noticed that ozone levels in the upper atmosphere were decreasing. This decrease in ozone means that more ultraviolet light can reach Earth's surface. At the same time, new cases of skin cancer have increased markedly. Although the causes of the increase in skin cancer are complicated, many scientists say that it is linked to the loss of ozone in the atmosphere.

Vinyl Chloride Vinyl chloride is a manufactured material that exists as a colorless gas at normal temperatures. Most vinyl chloride is used to make polyvinyl chloride, or PVC. PVC is used in a wide variety of plastic products, including pipes, coatings for wires, packaging, upholstery, housewares, and car parts.

Go Online
SciLINKS ⟨NSTA⟩

For: Links on cancer
Visit: www.SciLinks.org
Web Code: scn-0455

People can be exposed to vinyl chloride by breathing in the vapors. Repeatedly inhaling the vapors over long periods can result in cancers of the liver, brain, or lungs. For example, people who work in the manufacturing of vinyl chloride have an increased risk of liver cancer. In spite of the potential hazards, production of vinyl chloride continues because it is used in so many everyday products.

Arsenic Arsenic is a substance that occurs naturally in soil and rock. At one time, it was widely used in pesticides. Since the 1970s, however, it has been used more and more as a wood preservative. Wood treated with CCA, a chemical that contains arsenic, is called pressure-treated wood. Pressure-treated wood is resistant to rotting and decay. Pressure-treated wood is used for utility poles and building lumber.

Arsenic has long been recognized as poisonous and is lethal if consumed in large doses. More recently, arsenic has been reported to increase the risk of cancers of the liver, bladder, kidneys, and lungs. In 2002, the EPA announced that CCA in wood products for home use would be eliminated by 2004.

FIGURE 17
Making the Environment Safer
People who clean up environmental carcinogens must wear protective suits to prevent touching or inhaling these substances.

 **Reading Checkpoint** What kinds of cancers might result from inhaling vinyl chloride?

Section 5 Assessment

Target Reading Skill Relating Cause and Effect Refer to your graphic organizer about environmental carcinogens to help you answer Question 2.

Reviewing Key Concepts

1. a. **Reviewing** What did Percivall Pott observe about the relationship between skin cancer and soot?
   b. **Developing Hypotheses** In your own words, write a possible hypothesis that explains Pott's observations about chimney sweeps.
   c. **Designing Experiments** How could you use methods similar to those used by Pott and others to study the relationship between skin cancer and another carcinogen?

2. a. **Listing** Name three carcinogens found in the environment.
   b. **Relating Cause and Effect** What is the relationship between ultraviolet light, ozone, and skin cancer?
   c. **Predicting** If ozone levels in the atmosphere continue to decrease, what could happen to the number of skin cancer cases? Explain.

Lab zone At-Home **Activity**

Warning Labels With a family member, read the labels on various products around your home. Do any of the products contain cancer warnings? Work with your family to identify ways to protect yourselves from exposure to carcinogens contained in common everyday products.

① Infectious Disease

Key Concepts

- When you have an infectious disease, pathogens have gotten inside your body and caused harm.
- The four major groups of human pathogens are bacteria, viruses, fungi, and protists.
- Pathogens can spread through contact with either an infected person; soil, food, or water; a contaminated object; or an infected animal.

Key Terms

pathogen
infectious disease
toxin

② The Body's Defenses

Key Concepts

- In the first line of defense, the surfaces of the skin, breathing passages, mouth, and stomach function as barriers to pathogens. These barriers trap and kill most pathogens with which you come into contact.
- In the inflammatory response, fluid and white blood cells leak from blood vessels into nearby tissues. The white blood cells then fight the pathogens.
- The cells of the immune system can distinguish between different kinds of pathogens. The immune system cells react to each kind of pathogen with a defense targeted specifically at that pathogen.
- HIV is the only kind of virus known to attack the human immune system directly and destroy T cells. HIV can spread from one person to another only if body fluids from an infected person come in contact with those of an uninfected person.

Key Terms

inflammatory response	antigen
phagocyte	B cell
immune response	antibody
lymphocyte	AIDS
T cell	HIV

③ Preventing Infectious Disease

Key Concepts

- A person acquires active immunity when their own immune system produces antibodies in response to the presence of a pathogen.
- A person acquires passive immunity when the antibodies that fight the pathogen come from a source other than the person's body.

Key Terms

immunity	vaccine
active immunity	antibiotic
vaccination	passive immunity

④ Noninfectious Disease

Key Concepts

- An allergy develops in response to various foreign substances that set off a series of reactions in the body.
- A diabetic has high levels of glucose in the blood and excretes glucose in the urine. The person's body cells do not have enough glucose.
- Cancer is a disease in which cells multiply uncontrollably and destroy healthy tissue.

Key Terms

noninfectious disease	insulin
allergy	diabetes
allergen	tumor
histamine	carcinogen
asthma	

⑤ Cancer and the Environment

Key Concepts

- To reduce the risk of cancer, environmental carcinogens need to be removed or people need to be protected from them.
- Three important environmental carcinogens are ultraviolet light, vinyl chloride, and arsenic.

Review and Assessment

Go Online
PHSchool.com
For: Self-Assessment
Visit: PHSchool.com
Web Code: cea-4050

Organizing Information

Sequencing Copy the flowchart showing what happens after strep bacteria begin to multiply in the throat. Then complete it and add a title. (For more on Sequencing, see the Skills Handbook.)

T cell recognizes bacterial antigen.
a._____ ?
b._____ ?
c._____ ?
d._____ ?

Reviewing Key Terms

Choose the letter of the best answer.

1. Some bacteria produce poisons called
   a. histamines.   **b.** toxins.
   c. phagocytes.   **d.** pathogens.

2. Antibodies are produced by
   a. phagocytes.   **b.** B cells.
   c. T cells.   **d.** pathogens.

3. A chemical that kills bacteria or slows their growth without harming body cells is called a(n)
   a. pathogen.
   b. antibiotic.
   c. allergen.
   d. histamine.

4. High levels of glucose in the blood may be a sign of
   a. an allergy.
   b. AIDS.
   c. cancer.
   d. diabetes.

5. A carcinogen causes
   a. cancer.
   b. AIDS.
   c. an infectious disease.
   d. an allergy.

If the statement is true, write *true*. If it is false, change the underlined word or words to make the statement true.

6. Bacteria, viruses, fungi, and protists are the major human <u>phagocytes</u>.

7. A <u>T cell</u> engulfs pathogens and destroys them.

8. Vaccination produces <u>active immunity.</u>

9. During an allergic reaction, cells in the body release the chemical <u>insulin</u>.

10. A <u>tumor</u> is a mass of cancer cells.

Writing in Science

Newspaper Article Suppose you are a reporter who is able to travel inside the human body and document how the body fights a virus. Write an article on the battle between the virus and the human immune system, describing the different ways the body fights pathogens.

DISCOVERY CHANNEL SCHOOL

Fighting Disease
Video Preview
Video Field Trip
▶ Video Assessment

Review and Assessment

Checking Concepts

11. List four ways in which a person can become infected with a pathogen.

12. Explain why it is difficult for pathogens to get to a part of the body in which they can cause disease.

13. What is the relationship between antigens and antibodies?

14. Describe two ways in which active immunity is acquired. What do they have in common?

15. How does diabetes harm the body?

16. Identify two factors that can make a person likely to develop cancer.

Thinking Critically

17. **Applying Concepts** Can you catch a cold by sitting in a chilly draft? Explain.

18. **Interpreting Diagrams** Identify each structure labeled below and its role in the immune response.

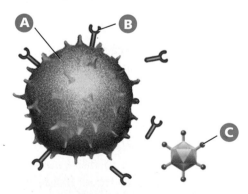

19. **Relating Cause and Effect** Why is the immune system successful in fighting most pathogens but is unsuccessful in fighting HIV?

20. **Comparing and Contrasting** Compare and contrast active immunity and passive immunity. Then, describe one way in which a person can acquire each type of immunity.

21. **Making Judgments** What precautions can people take to decrease their risk of skin cancer?

Applying Skills

Use the graph to answer Questions 22–25.

A glucose tolerance test can check for diabetes. A doctor gives a patient a sugar drink and measures the blood glucose level over a 2 hour period. The graph below shows the results of this test for two people.

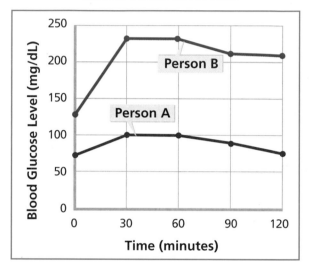

22. **Reading Graphs** What was each person's glucose level at the start of the test?

23. **Interpreting Data** Which person's blood glucose level rose more quickly during the first 30 minutes?

24. **Interpreting Data** Which person's blood glucose level returned to near the starting level after 2 hours? Which person's blood glucose level remained elevated after 2 hours?

25. **Drawing Conclusions** Which person may have diabetes? Explain your answer.

Lab zone Chapter **Project**

Performance Assessment Before you present your news broadcasts, make sure any sound effects and props support the story. Do your broadcasts help people better understand how the body fights disease?

① Standardized Test Practice

Use the data table to answer Questions 2 and 3.

Test-Taking Tip

Interpreting a Data Table

To answer questions about a data table, first read the title of the table. Next, look at the headings of the columns and rows to see how the data are organized. Do not spend a lot of time examining all the data because you may not need total understanding to answer the questions.

Sample Question

According to the data table, which of the statements below is true?

SARS* Cases (Nov. 2002 – July 2003)		
Country	**No. of Cases**	**No. of Deaths**
Canada	251	43
China, mainland	5,327	349
China, Taiwan	346	37
Singapore	238	33
United States	29	0

*SARS (severe acute respiratory syndrome) is a respiratory disease caused by a virus.

   A Most of the people who got SARS died.
   B Most SARS cases were in mainland China.
   C Most SARS cases were in North America.
   D Most SARS cases were in Singapore.

Answer

The correct answer is **B**. There were 5,327 SARS cases in mainland China—more than the 280 cases in North America (choice **C**) or the 238 cases in Singapore (choice **D**). Choice **A** is incorrect because most people did not die from SARS.

Choose the letter of the best answer.

1. All of the following are the body's defenses against pathogens EXCEPT
   A a physical barrier such as the skin.
   B the inflammatory response.
   C the immune response.
   D attack by red blood cells.

Cancer: New Cases and Survival Rates		
Type of Cancer	**Estimated New Cases (2003)**	**Five-Year Survival Rate (1992–1998)**
Prostate (males)	221,000	97%
Breast (females)	211,000	86%
Lung	172,000	15%
Colon and rectum	148,000	62%
Bladder	57,000	82%
Melanoma (skin)	54,000	89%

2. The type of cancer with the best five-year survival rate is
   A prostate cancer.
   B bladder cancer.
   C breast cancer.
   D lung cancer.

3. A reasonable inference that can be made from the data is that
   A lung cancer is easy to diagnose and hard to treat.
   B prostate cancer is hard to diagnose and hard to treat.
   C very few females survive for five years after being diagnosed with breast cancer.
   D lung cancer is the most common cancer.

4. Which of the following is paired correctly?
   A diabetes: infectious disease
   B AIDS: noninfectious disease
   C rabies: infectious disease
   D allergy: infectious disease

Open-Ended Question

5. What is diabetes? What causes diabetes and what effects does it have on the body? How is diabetes usually treated?

Chapter 7

The Nervous System

Academic Standards

This chapter addresses these Indiana standards.

The Physical Setting

7.3.20 Describe that seeing occurs when light waves enter the eye, just as sound is heard when sound waves enter the ear.

The Living Environment

7.4.14 Explain that the environment may contain dangerous levels of harmful substances. Public health requires monitoring of soil, air, and water quality.

Common Themes

7.7.1 Explain that the output from one part of a system can become the input to other parts, and that this can control the whole system.

Without your nervous system, ▶ a sport like windsurfing would be impossible!

Lab zone™ Chapter **Project**

Tricks and Illusions

Things aren't always what they seem. For example, an optical illusion is a picture or other visual effect that tricks you into seeing something incorrectly. In this project, you'll investigate how your senses sometimes can be fooled by illusions.

Your Goal To set up a science fair booth to demonstrate how different people respond to one or more illusions

To complete this project, you must

- try out a variety of illusions, including some that involve the senses of hearing or touch as well as sight
- select one or more illusions and set up an experiment to monitor people's responses to the illusions
- learn why the illusions fool the senses
- follow the safety guidelines in Appendix A

Plan It! In a small group, discuss optical illusions or other illusions that you know about. Look in books to learn about others. Try them out. Which illusions would make an interesting experiment? How could you set up such an experiment at a science fair?

How the Nervous System Works

Reading Preview

Key Concepts
- What are the functions of the nervous system?
- What is the structure of a neuron and what kinds of neurons are found in the body?
- How do nerve impulses travel from one neuron to another?

Key Terms
- stimulus • response
- neuron • nerve impulse
- dendrite • axon • nerve
- sensory neuron • interneuron
- motor neuron • synapse

⊙ Target Reading Skill
Previewing Visuals Before you read, preview Figure 3. Then, write two questions that you have about the diagram in a graphic organizer like the one below. As you read, answer your questions.

The Path of a Nerve Impulse

Q.	What is a sensory neuron?
A.	
Q.	

Lab zone ╲ Discover **Activity**

How Simple Is a Simple Task?
1. Trace the outline of a penny in twelve different places on a piece of paper.
2. Number the circles 1 through 12. Write the numbers randomly, in no particular order.
3. Now, pick up the penny again. Put it in each circle, one after another, in numerical order, beginning with 1 and ending with 12.

Think It Over
Inferring Make a list of all the sense organs, muscle movements, and thought processes used in this activity. Compare your list with your classmates' lists. What organ system coordinated all the different processes involved in this task?

The ball whizzes toward the soccer goalie. She lunges for the ball, and in one swift movement blocks it from entering the net. To tend goal, soccer players need excellent coordination and keen vision. In addition, they must remember what they have learned from years of practice.

Whether or not you play soccer, you too need coordination, memory, and the ability to learn. Your nervous system carries out all these functions. The nervous system includes the brain, spinal cord, and nerves that run throughout the body. It also includes sense organs, such as the eyes and ears.

Functions of the Nervous System
The Internet lets people gather information from anywhere in the world with the click of a button. Like the Internet, your nervous system is a communications network. But it is much more efficient than the Internet.

The nervous system receives information about what is happening both inside and outside your body. It also directs the way in which your body responds to this information. In addition, your nervous system helps maintain homeostasis. Without your nervous system, you could not move, think, feel pain, or taste a spicy taco.

Receiving Information Because of your nervous system, you are aware of what is happening in the environment around you. For example, you know that a fly is buzzing around your head, that the wind is blowing, or that a friend is telling a funny joke. Your nervous system also checks conditions inside your body, such as the level of glucose in your blood.

Responding to Information Any change or signal in the environment that can make an organism react is called a **stimulus** (STIM yoo lus) (plural: *stimuli*). A buzzing fly is a stimulus. After your nervous system analyzes the stimulus, it causes a response. A **response** is what your body does in reaction to a stimulus—you swat at the fly.

Some nervous system responses, such as swatting a fly, are voluntary, or under your control. However, many processes necessary for life, such as heart rate, are controlled by involuntary actions of the nervous system.

Maintaining Homeostasis The nervous system helps maintain homeostasis by directing the body to respond appropriately to the information it receives. For example, when you are hungry, your nervous system prompts you to eat. This action maintains homeostasis by supplying your body with the nutrients and energy it needs.

Reading Checkpoint) **What is a stimulus?**

FIGURE 1
The Nervous System at Work
The zooming soccer ball is a stimulus. The goalie responds by lunging toward the ball and blocking the shot.
Interpreting Diagrams How does the goalie's nervous system help her body maintain homeostasis?

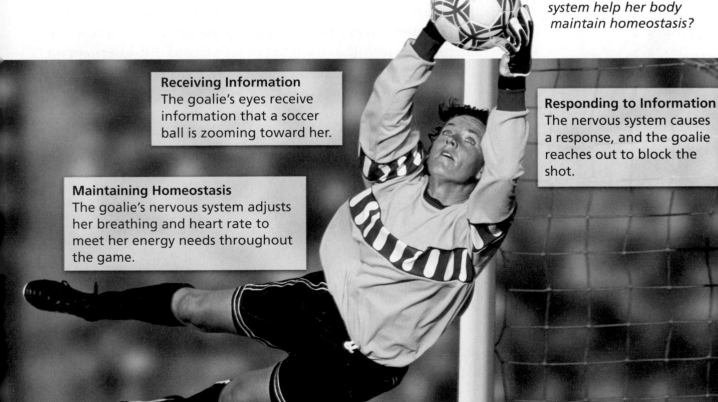

Receiving Information
The goalie's eyes receive information that a soccer ball is zooming toward her.

Responding to Information
The nervous system causes a response, and the goalie reaches out to block the shot.

Maintaining Homeostasis
The goalie's nervous system adjusts her breathing and heart rate to meet her energy needs throughout the game.

FIGURE 2
Structure of a Neuron
A neuron has one axon and many dendrites that extend from the cell body.

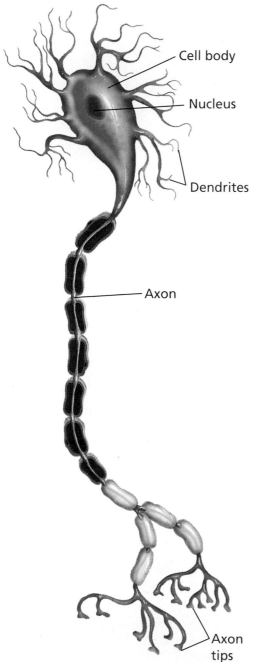

Cell body

Nucleus

Dendrites

Axon

Axon tips

Go Online
PHSchool.com

For: More on nerve impulses
Visit: PHSchool.com
Web Code: ced-4061

The Neuron

Your nervous system includes various organs, tissues, and cells. For example, your brain is an organ, and the nerves running throughout your body are tissues. The cells that carry information through your nervous system are called **neurons** (NOO rahnz), or nerve cells. The message that a neuron carries is called a **nerve impulse.**

The Structure of a Neuron The structure of a neuron enables it to carry nerve impulses. **A neuron has a large cell body that contains the nucleus, threadlike extensions called dendrites, and an axon.** The **dendrites** carry impulses toward the neuron's cell body. The **axon** carries impulses away from the cell body. Nerve impulses begin in a dendrite, move toward the cell body, and then move down the axon. A neuron can have many dendrites, but it has only one axon. An axon, however, can have more than one tip, so the impulse can go to more than one other cell.

Axons and dendrites are sometimes called nerve fibers. Nerve fibers are often arranged in parallel bundles covered with connective tissue, something like a package of uncooked spaghetti wrapped in cellophane. A bundle of nerve fibers is called a **nerve.**

Kinds of Neurons **Three kinds of neurons are found in the body—sensory neurons, interneurons, and motor neurons.** Figure 3 shows how these three kinds of neurons work together.

A **sensory neuron** picks up stimuli from the internal or external environment and converts each stimulus into a nerve impulse. The impulse travels along the sensory neuron until it reaches an interneuron, usually in the brain or spinal cord. An **interneuron** is a neuron that carries nerve impulses from one neuron to another. Some interneurons pass impulses from sensory neurons to motor neurons. A **motor neuron** sends an impulse to a muscle or gland, and the muscle or gland reacts in response.

 **Reading Checkpoint** **What is the function of an axon?**

How a Nerve Impulse Travels

Every day of your life, billions of nerve impulses travel through your nervous system. Each of those nerve impulses begins in the dendrites of a neuron. The impulse moves rapidly toward the neuron's cell body and then down the axon until it reaches the axon tip. A nerve impulse travels along the neuron in the form of electrical and chemical signals. Nerve impulses can travel as fast as 120 meters per second!

FIGURE 3

The Path of a Nerve Impulse

When you hear your phone ring, you pick it up to answer it. Many sensory neurons, interneurons, and motor neurons are involved in this action.

Interpreting Diagrams *To where does the impulse pass from the sensory neurons?*

Receptors in ear

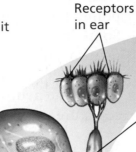

1 Sensory Neuron
Nerve impulses begin when receptors pick up stimuli from the environment. Receptors in the ear pick up the sound of the phone ringing. The receptors trigger nerve impulses in sensory neurons.

2 Interneuron
From the sensory neurons, the nerve impulse passes to interneurons in the brain. Your brain interprets the impulses from many interneurons and makes you realize that the phone is ringing. Your brain also decides that you should answer the phone.

Muscle in hand

3 Motor neuron
Impulses then travel along thousands of motor neurons. The motor neurons send the impulses to muscles. The muscles carry out the response, and you reach for the phone.

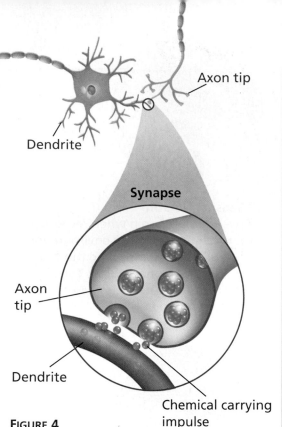

Axon tip

Dendrite

Synapse

Axon tip

Dendrite

Chemical carrying impulse

FIGURE 4
The Synapse
When a nerve impulse reaches the tip of an axon, chemicals are released into the gap at the synapse. The chemicals carry the nerve impulse across the gap.

The Synapse What happens when a nerve impulse reaches the axon tip at the end of a neuron? At that point, the impulse can pass to the next structure. Sometimes the structure is the dendrite of another neuron. Other times, the structure is a muscle or a cell in another organ, such as a sweat gland. The junction where one neuron can transfer an impulse to another structure is called a **synapse** (SIN aps).

How an Impulse is Transferred Figure 4 shows a synapse between the axon tip of one neuron and the dendrite of another neuron. Notice that a small gap separates these two structures. **For a nerve impulse to be carried along at a synapse, it must cross the gap between the axon and the next structure. The axon tips release chemicals that carry the impulse across the gap.**

You can think of the gap at a synapse as a river, and an axon as a road that leads up to the riverbank. The nerve impulse is like a car traveling on the road. To get to the other side, the car has to cross the river. The car gets on a ferry boat, which carries it across the river. The chemicals that the axon tips release are like the ferry, carrying the nerve impulse across the gap.

Section 1 Assessment

Target Reading Skill Previewing Visuals Refer to your questions and answers about Figure 3 to help you answer Question 2 below.

Reviewing Key Concepts

1. **a. Listing** What are three functions of the nervous system?
   b. Describing Give an example of a stimulus and describe how the nervous system produces a response.
   c. Predicting Your heart rate is controlled by involuntary actions of the nervous system. What would life be like if your heartbeat were under voluntary control?

2. **a. Identifying** Identify the three kinds of neurons that are found in the nervous system.
   b. Explaining How do the three kinds of neurons interact to carry nerve impulses?

   c. Comparing and Contrasting How do sensory neurons and motor neurons differ?

3. **a. Reviewing** What is a synapse?
   b. Sequencing Outline the steps by which a nerve impulse reaches and then crosses the gap at a synapse.

Lab zone At-Home **Activity**

Pass the Salt, Please During dinner, ask a family member to pass the salt and pepper to you. Observe what your family member then does. Explain that the words you spoke were a stimulus and that the family member's reaction was a response. Discuss other examples of stimuli and responses with your family.

Ready or Not!

Problem

Do people's reaction times vary at different times of the day?

Skills Focus

developing hypotheses, controlling variables, drawing conclusions

Material

• meter stick

Procedure

PART 1 Observing a Response to a Stimulus

1. Have your partner hold a meter stick with the zero end about 50 cm above a table.

2. Get ready to catch the meter stick by positioning the top of your thumb and forefinger just at the zero position, as shown in the photograph.

3. Your partner should drop the meter stick without any warning. Using your thumb and forefinger only (no other part of your hand), catch the meter stick as soon as you can. Record the distance in centimeters that the meter stick fell. This distance is a measure of your reaction time.

PART 2 Designing Your Experiment

4. With your partner, discuss how you can use the activity from Part 1 to find out whether people's reaction times vary at different times of day. Consider the questions below. Then, write up your experimental plan.
   • What hypothesis will you test?
   • What variables do you need to control?
   • How many people will you test? How many times will you test each person?

5. Submit your plan for your teacher's review. Make any changes your teacher recommends. Create a data table to record your results. Then, perform your experiment.

Analyze and Conclude

1. **Inferring** In this lab, what is the stimulus? What is the response? Is the response voluntary or involuntary? Explain.

2. **Developing Hypotheses** What hypothesis did you test in Part 2?

3. **Controlling Variables** In Part 2, why was it important to control all variables except the time of day?

4. **Drawing Conclusions** Based on your results in Part 2, do people's reaction times vary at different times of the day? Explain.

5. **Communicating** Write a paragraph to explain why you can use the distance on the meter stick as a measure of reaction time.

More to Explore

Do you think people can do arithmetic problems more quickly and accurately at certain times of the day? Design an experiment to investigate this question. *Obtain your teacher's permission before carrying out your investigation.*

Divisions of the Nervous System

Reading Preview

Key Concepts
- What are the structures and functions of the central nervous system?
- What are the structures and functions of the peripheral nervous system?
- What is a reflex?
- What are two ways in which the nervous system can be injured?

Key Terms
- central nervous system
- peripheral nervous system
- brain • spinal cord
- cerebrum • cerebellum
- brain stem
- somatic nervous system
- autonomic nervous system
- reflex • concussion

Target Reading Skill
Building Vocabulary After you read this section, reread the paragraphs that contain definitions of Key Terms. Use all the information you have learned to write a definition of each Key Term in your own words.

Lab zone Discover **Activity**

How Does Your Knee React?

1. Sit on a table or counter so that your legs dangle freely. Make sure that your partner is not directly in front of your legs.

2. Have your partner use the side of his or her hand to tap one of your knees gently just below the kneecap. Observe what happens to your leg. Note whether you have any control over your reaction.

3. Change places with your partner. Repeat Steps 1 and 2.

Think It Over
Inferring When might it be an advantage for your body to react very quickly and without your conscious control?

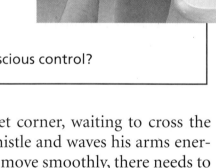

You are standing at a busy street corner, waiting to cross the street. A traffic cop blows his whistle and waves his arms energetically. For the heavy traffic to move smoothly, there needs to be a traffic cop and responsive drivers. The traffic cop coordinates the movements of the drivers, and they maneuver the cars safely through the intersection.

Similarly, your nervous system has two divisions that work together. The **central nervous system** consists of the brain and spinal cord. The **peripheral nervous system** (puh RIF uh rul) includes all the nerves located outside of the central nervous system. The central nervous system is like a traffic cop. The peripheral nervous system is like the drivers and pedestrians.

The traffic cop keeps everybody moving.

Central Nervous System

You can see the central and peripheral nervous systems in Figure 5. **The central nervous system is the control center of the body. It includes the brain and spinal cord.** All information about what is happening in the world inside or outside your body is brought to the central nervous system. The **brain,** located in the skull, is the part of the central nervous system that controls most functions in the body. The **spinal cord** is the thick column of nervous tissue that links the brain to most of the nerves in the peripheral nervous system.

Most impulses from the peripheral nervous system travel through the spinal cord to get to the brain. Your brain then directs a response. The response usually travels from the brain, through the spinal cord, and then to the peripheral nervous system.

For example, here is what happens when you reach under the sofa to find a lost quarter. Your fingers move over the floor, searching for the quarter. When your fingers finally touch the quarter, the stimulus of the touch triggers nerve impulses in sensory neurons in your fingers. These impulses travel through nerves of the peripheral nervous system to your spinal cord. Then the impulses race up to your brain. Your brain interprets the impulses, telling you that you've found the quarter. Your brain starts nerve impulses that move down the spinal cord. From the spinal cord, the impulses travel through motor neurons in your arm and hand. The impulses in the motor neurons cause your fingers to grasp the quarter.

 **Reading Checkpoint** What are the parts of the central nervous system?

Go Online
active art

For: Nervous System activity
Visit: PHSchool.com
Web Code: cep-4062

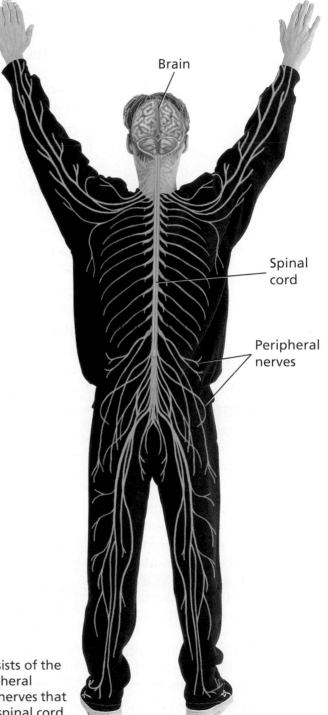

Brain

Spinal cord

Peripheral nerves

FIGURE 5
The Nervous System
The central nervous system consists of the brain and spinal cord. The peripheral nervous system includes all the nerves that branch out from the brain and spinal cord.

The Brain and Spinal Cord

Your brain contains about 100 billion neurons, all of which are interneurons. Each of those neurons may receive messages from up to 10,000 other neurons and may send messages to about 1,000 more! Three layers of connective tissue cover the brain. The space between the middle layer and innermost layer is filled with a watery fluid. The skull, the layers of connective tissue, and the fluid all help protect the brain from injury.

There are three main regions of the brain that receive and process information. These are the cerebrum, the cerebellum, and the brain stem. Find each in Figure 6.

Cerebrum The largest part of the brain is called the cerebrum. The **cerebrum** (suh REE brum) interprets input from the senses, controls movement, and carries out complex mental processes such as learning and remembering. Because of your cerebrum, you can locate your favorite comic strip in the newspaper, read it, and laugh at its funny characters.

The cerebrum is divided into a right and a left half. The right half sends impulses to skeletal muscles on the left side of the body. In contrast, the left half controls the right side of the body. When you reach with your right hand for a pencil, the messages that tell you to do so come from the left half of the cerebrum. In addition, each half of the cerebrum controls slightly different kinds of mental activity. The right half is usually associated with creativity and artistic ability. The left half is usually associated with mathematical skills and logical thinking.

As you can see in Figure 6, certain areas of the cerebrum are associated with smell, touch, taste, hearing, and vision. Other areas control movement, speech, written language, and abstract thought.

Cerebellum and Brain Stem The second largest part of your brain is called the cerebellum. The **cerebellum** (sehr uh BEL um) coordinates the actions of your muscles and helps you keep your balance. When you walk, the impulses that tell your feet to move start in your cerebrum. However, your cerebellum gives you the muscular coordination and sense of balance that keep you from falling down.

The **brain stem,** which lies between the cerebellum and spinal cord, controls your body's involuntary actions—those that occur automatically. For example, neurons in the brain stem regulate your breathing and help control your heartbeat.

 **Reading Checkpoint** What actions does the brain stem control?

FIGURE 6

The Brain

Each of the three main parts of the human brain—the cerebrum, cerebellum, and brain stem—carries out specific functions. **Interpreting Diagrams** *What are three functions of the cerebrum?*

Cerebrum
The cerebrum is the largest part of the brain. Different areas of the cerebrum control such functions as movement, the senses, speech, and abstract thought.

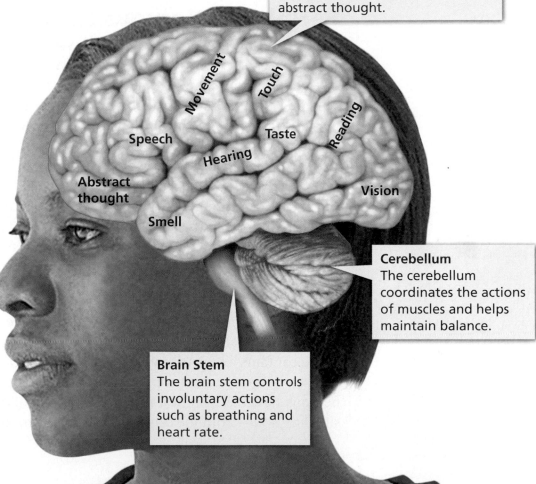

Movement

Touch

Speech

Taste

Reading

Hearing

Abstract thought

Vision

Smell

Cerebellum
The cerebellum coordinates the actions of muscles and helps maintain balance.

Brain Stem
The brain stem controls involuntary actions such as breathing and heart rate.

Top View of Cerebrum

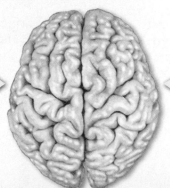

Left Half
The left half of the cerebrum is associated with mathematical and logical thinking.

Right Half
The right half of the cerebrum is associated with creativity and artistic ability.

The Spinal Cord Run your fingers down the center of your back to feel the bones of the vertebral column. The vertebral column surrounds and protects the spinal cord. **The spinal cord is the link between your brain and the peripheral nervous system.** The layers of connective tissue that surround and protect the brain also cover the spinal cord. In addition, like the brain, the spinal cord is further protected by a watery fluid.

Peripheral Nervous System

The second division of the nervous system is the peripheral nervous system. **The peripheral nervous system consists of a network of nerves that branch out from the central nervous system and connect it to the rest of the body. The peripheral nervous system is involved in both involuntary and voluntary actions.**

A total of 43 pairs of nerves make up the peripheral nervous system. Twelve pairs originate in the brain. The other 31 pairs—the spinal nerves—begin in the spinal cord. One nerve in each pair goes to the left side of the body, and the other goes to the right. As you can see in Figure 7, spinal nerves leave the spinal cord through spaces between the vertebrae.

How Spinal Nerves Function A spinal nerve is like a two-lane highway. Impulses travel on a spinal nerve in two directions—both to and from the central nervous system. Each spinal nerve contains axons of both sensory and motor neurons. The sensory neurons carry impulses from the body to the central nervous system. The motor neurons carry impulses in the opposite direction—from the central nervous system to the body.

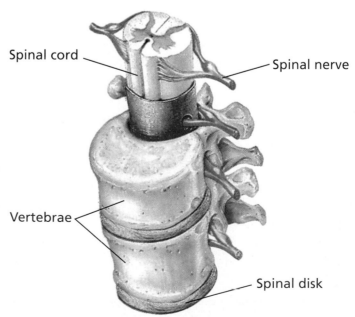

FIGURE 7

The Spinal Nerves
The spinal nerves, which connect to the spinal cord, emerge from spaces between the vertebrae. Each spinal nerve consists of both sensory and motor neurons.

Spinal cord

Spinal nerve

Vertebrae

Spinal disk

FIGURE 8
Somatic and Autonomic Nervous Systems
The somatic nervous system controls voluntary actions. The autonomic nervous system controls involuntary actions. **Classifying** *Which system helps regulate the artist's heartbeat?*

Actions Controlled by the Somatic Nervous System
• Hands shape the clay.
• Foot turns the wheel.
• Mouth smiles.

Actions Controlled by the Autonomic Nervous System
• Heartbeat is regulated.
• Breathing rate is kept steady.
• Body temperature remains constant.

Somatic and Autonomic Systems The nerves of the peripheral nervous system can be divided into two groups, the somatic (soh MAT ik) and autonomic (awt uh NAHM ik) nervous systems. The nerves of the **somatic nervous system** control voluntary actions such as using a fork or tying your shoes. In contrast, nerves of the **autonomic nervous system** control involuntary actions. For example, the autonomic nervous system regulates the contractions of the smooth muscles that adjust the diameter of blood vessels.

Reading Checkpoint What kinds of actions are controlled by the autonomic nervous system?

Reflexes

Imagine that you are watching an adventure movie. The movie is so thrilling that you don't notice a fly circling above your head. When the fly zooms right in front of your eyes, however, your eyelids immediately blink shut. You didn't decide to close your eyes. The blink, which is a **reflex**, is a response that happened automatically. **A reflex is an automatic response that occurs very rapidly and without conscious control. Reflexes help to protect the body.** If you did the Discover activity on page 182, you saw another example of a reflex.

 **Try This Activity**

You Blinked!

Can you make yourself *not* blink? To answer this question, try the following activity.

1. Put on safety goggles.
2. Have your partner stand across from you and gently toss ten cotton balls toward your goggles. Your partner should not give you any warning before tossing the cotton balls.
3. Count the number of times you blink and the number of times you are able to keep from blinking.

Interpreting Data Compare the two numbers. Why is blinking considered a reflex?

A Reflex Pathway As you have learned, the contraction of skeletal muscles is usually controlled by the brain. However, in some reflex actions, skeletal muscles contract with the involvement of the spinal cord only—not the brain.

Figure 9 shows the reflex action that occurs when you touch a sharp object. When your finger touches the object, sensory neurons send impulses to the spinal cord. The impulses may then pass to interneurons in the spinal cord. From there the impulses pass directly to motor neurons in your arm and hand. The muscles then contract, and your hand jerks up and away from the sharp object. By removing your hand quickly, this reflex protects you from getting badly cut.

Signaling the Brain At the same time that some nerve impulses make your arm muscles contract, other nerve impulses travel up your spinal cord to your brain. When these impulses reach your brain, your brain interprets them. You then feel a sharp pain in your finger.

It takes longer for the pain impulses to get to the brain and be interpreted than it does for the reflex action to occur. By the time you feel the pain, you have already moved your hand away.

✓ **Reading Checkpoint** What is an example of a reflex?

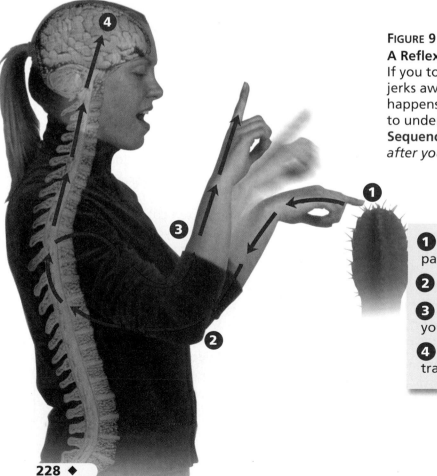

FIGURE 9
A Reflex Action
If you touch a sharp object, your hand immediately jerks away. This action, which is known as a reflex, happens automatically. Follow the numbered steps to understand how a reflex happens.
Sequencing *Do you pull your hand away before or after you feel the pain? Explain.*

❶ Sensory neurons in your fingertip detect a pain stimulus.

❷ Nerve impulses travel to your spinal cord.

❸ Nerve impulses return to motor neurons in your hand, and you pull your hand away.

❹ As you pull your hand away, nerve impulses travel to your brain. You feel the pain.

Nervous System Injuries

The nervous system can suffer injuries that interfere with its functioning. **Concussions and spinal cord injuries are two ways in which the central nervous system can be damaged.**

Concussions A **concussion** is a bruiselike injury of the brain. A concussion occurs when the soft tissue of the brain collides against the skull. Concussions can happen when you bump your head in a hard fall, an automobile accident, or a contact sport such as football.

With most concussions, you may have a headache for a short time, but the injured tissue heals by itself. However, with more serious concussions, you may lose consciousness, experience confusion, or feel drowsy after the injury. To decrease your chances of getting a brain injury, wear a helmet during activities in which you risk bumping your head.

Spinal Cord Injuries Spinal cord injuries occur when the spinal cord is cut or crushed. As a result, axons in the injured region are damaged, so impulses cannot pass through them. This type of injury usually results in paralysis, which is the loss of movement in some part of the body. Car crashes are the most common cause of spinal cord injuries.

FIGURE 10
Protecting the Nervous System
You can help protect yourself from a spinal cord injury by wearing a seatbelt when you travel in a car.

 Reading Checkpoint **What is paralysis?**

Section 2 Assessment

Target Reading Skill Building Vocabulary Use your definitions to help you answer the questions below.

Reviewing Key Concepts

1. **a. Listing** What two structures are part of the central nervous system?
   b. Describing Describe the functions of the three main regions of the brain.
   c. Relating Cause and Effect What symptoms might indicate that a person's cerebellum has been injured?
2. **a. Identifying** What are the two groups of nerves into which the peripheral nervous system is divided?
   b. Comparing and Contrasting How do the functions of the two groups of peripheral nerves differ?

3. **a. Defining** What is a reflex?
   b. Sequencing Trace the pathway of a reflex in the nervous system.
   c. Inferring How do reflexes help protect the body from injury?
4. **a. Reviewing** What is a concussion?
   b. Applying Concepts How can you reduce your risk of concussion?

Writing in Science

Comparison Paragraph Write a paragraph in which you compare the functions of the left and right halves of the cerebrum. Discuss what kinds of mental activities each half controls as well as which side of the body it controls.

Should People Be Required to Wear Bicycle Helmets?

Bicycling is an enjoyable activity. Unfortunately, many bicyclists are injured while riding. Each year, more than 500,000 people in the United States are treated in hospitals for bicycling injuries. Many of those people suffer head injuries. Head injuries can affect everything your brain does—thinking, remembering, seeing, and being able to move.

Depending on the age group and geographic location, helmet use ranges from less than 10 percent to about 80 percent of bicyclists. What is the best way to get bicyclists to protect themselves from head injury?

The Issues

Should Laws Require the Use of Bicycle Helmets?

Experts estimate that bicycle helmets could reduce the risk of bicycle-related head injuries by as much as 85 percent. Today, about 19 states have passed laws requiring bicycle riders to wear helmets. Most of these statewide laws, however, apply only to children.

Some supporters of helmet laws want to see the laws extended to all riders. They claim that laws are the most effective way to increase helmet use.

What Are the Drawbacks of Helmet Laws?

Opponents of helmet laws believe it is up to the individual to decide whether or not to wear a helmet. They say it is not the role of government to stop people from taking risks. They argue that, rather than making people pay fines if they don't wear bicycle helmets, governments should educate people about the benefits of helmets. Car drivers should also be educated about safe driving procedures near bicycles.

Are There Alternatives to Helmet Laws?

Instead of laws requiring people to wear helmets, some communities and organizations have set up educational programs that teach about the advantages of helmets. Effective programs teach about the dangers of head injuries and the protection that helmets provide. Effective education programs, though, can be expensive. They also need to reach a wide audience, including children, teens, and adults.

You Decide

1. Identify the Problem
In your own words, explain the issues concerning laws requiring people to wear bicycle helmets.

2. Analyze the Options
List two different plans for increasing helmet use by bicycle riders. List at least one advantage and one drawback of each plan.

3. Find a Solution
You are a member of the city government hoping to increase helmet use. Write a speech outlining your position for either a helmet law or an alternative plan. Support your position.

Go Online
PHSchool.com

For: More on bicycle helmets
Visit: PHSchool.com
Web Code: ceh-4060

The Senses

Reading Preview

Key Concepts
- How do your eyes enable you to see?
- How do you hear and maintain your sense of balance?
- How do your senses of smell and taste work together?
- How is your skin related to your sense of touch?

Key Terms
- cornea • pupil • iris • lens
- retina • nearsightedness
- farsightedness • eardrum
- cochlea • semicircular canal

Target Reading Skill

Outlining As you read, make an outline about the senses. Use the red headings for the main ideas and the blue headings for the supporting ideas.

The Senses
I. Vision
A. How light enters your eye
B.
C.

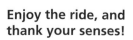

Lab zone Discover **Activity**

What's in the Bag?

1. Your teacher will give you a paper bag that contains several objects. Your challenge is to use only your sense of touch to identify each object. You will not look inside the bag.

2. Put your hand in the bag and carefully touch each object. Observe the shape of each object. Note whether its surface is rough or smooth. Also note other characteristics, such as its size, what it seems to be made of, and whether it can be bent.

3. After you have finished touching each object, write your observations on a sheet of paper. Then, write your inference about what each object is.

Think It Over
Observing What could you determine about each object without looking at it? What could you not determine?

You waited in line to get on the ride, and now it's about to begin. You grip the wheel as the bumper cars jerk into motion. The next thing you know, you are zipping around crazily and bumping into cars driven by your friends.

You can thrill to the motion of amusement park rides because of your senses. The sense organs pick up information about your environment, change the information into nerve impulses, and send the impulses to your brain. Your brain then interprets the information. Your senses and brain working together enable you to respond to things in your environment, such as the other bumper cars around you.

Enjoy the ride, and thank your senses!

Pupil in Bright Light

Pupil in Dim Light

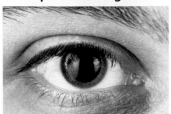

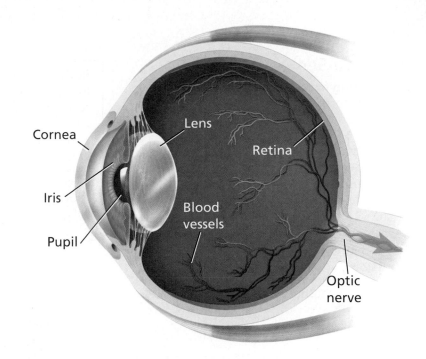

Cornea

Lens

Retina

Iris

Blood vessels

Pupil

Optic nerve

Vision

Your eyes are the sense organs that enable you to see the objects in your environment. They let you see this textbook in front of you, the window across the room, and the world outside the window. **Your eyes respond to the stimulus of light. They convert that stimulus into impulses that your brain interprets, enabling you to see.**

How Light Enters Your Eye When rays of light strike the eye, they pass through the structures shown in Figure 11. First, the light strikes the **cornea** (KAWR nee uh), the clear tissue that covers the front of the eye. The light then passes through a fluid-filled chamber behind the cornea and reaches the pupil. The **pupil** is the opening through which light enters the eye.

You may have noticed that people's pupils change size when they go from a dark room into bright sunshine. In bright light, the pupil becomes smaller. In dim light, the pupil becomes larger. The size of the pupil is adjusted by muscles in the iris. The **iris** is a circular structure that surrounds the pupil and regulates the amount of light entering the eye. The iris also gives the eye its color. If you have brown eyes, it is actually your irises that are brown.

How Light Is Focused Light that passes through the pupil strikes the lens. The **lens** is a flexible structure that focuses light. The lens of your eye functions something like the lens of a camera, which focuses light on photographic film. Because of the way in which the lens of the eye bends the light rays, the image it produces is upside down and reversed. Muscles that attach to the lens adjust its shape, producing an image that is in focus.

FIGURE 11
The Eye

The eye is a complex organ that allows you to sense light. The pupil is the opening through which light enters the eye. In bright light, the pupil becomes smaller. In dim light, the pupil enlarges and allows more light to enter the eye.
Interpreting Diagrams *What structure adjusts the size of the pupil?*

DISCOVERY
CHANNEL
SCHOOL

The Nervous System

Video Preview
▶ Video Field Trip
Video Assessment

FIGURE 12
How You See

Light coming from an object enters your eye and is focused by the lens. The light produces an upside-down image on your retina. Receptors in your retina then send impulses to your cerebrum, which turns the image right-side up. **Comparing and Contrasting** *Which receptors work best in dim light?*

Rods and Cones
Receptors in the retina include rods (shown in green) and cones (shown in blue).

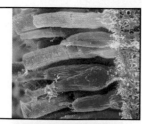

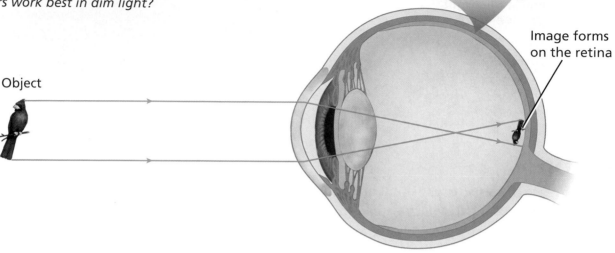

Object

Image forms on the retina

How You See an Image After passing through the lens, the focused light rays pass through a transparent, jellylike fluid. Then the light rays strike the **retina** (RET 'n uh), the layer of receptor cells that lines the back of the eye. The retina contains about 130 million receptor cells that respond to light. There are two types of receptors: rods and cones. Rod cells work best in dim light and enable you to see black, white, and shades of gray. In contrast, cone cells work best in bright light and enable you to see colors. This difference between rods and cones explains why you see colors best in bright light, but you see only shadowy gray images in dim light.

When light strikes the rods and cones, nerve impulses travel to the cerebrum through the optic nerves. One optic nerve comes from the left eye and the other one comes from the right eye. In the cerebrum, two things happen. The brain turns the reversed image right-side up, and it also combines the images from each eye to produce a single image.

Correcting Nearsightedness A lens—whether it is in your eye or in eyeglasses—is a curved, transparent object that bends light rays as they pass through it. If the lens of the eye does not focus light properly on the retina, vision problems result. The lenses in eyeglasses can help correct vision problems.

Lab zone Try This **Activity**

Working Together
Discover how your two eyes work together.

1. With your arms fully extended, hold a drinking straw in one hand and a pipe cleaner in the other.
2. With both eyes open, try to insert the pipe cleaner into the straw.
3. Now close your right eye. Try to insert the pipe cleaner into the straw.
4. Repeat Step 3 with your left eye closed.

Inferring How does closing one eye affect your ability to judge distances?

FIGURE 13
Correcting Vision Problems

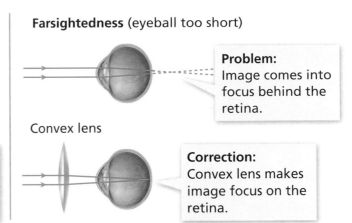

Nearsightedness (eyeball too long)

Problem:
Image comes into focus in front of the retina.

Concave lens

Correction:
Concave lens makes image focus on the retina.

Farsightedness (eyeball too short)

Problem:
Image comes into focus behind the retina.

Convex lens

Correction:
Convex lens makes image focus on the retina.

People with **nearsightedness** can see nearby objects clearly. However, they have trouble seeing objects far away. Nearsightedness results when the eyeball is too long. Because of the extra length that light must travel to reach the retina, distant objects do not focus sharply on the retina. Instead, the lens of the eye makes the image come into focus at a point in front of the retina, as shown in Figure 13.

To correct nearsightedness, eyeglasses with concave lenses are worn. A concave lens is thicker at the edges than it is in the center. When light rays pass through a concave lens, they are bent away from the center of the lens. The concave lenses in glasses make light rays spread out before they reach the lens of the eye. After the rays pass through the lens of the eye, they focus on the retina rather than in front of it.

Correcting Farsightedness People with **farsightedness** can see distant objects clearly. Nearby objects, however, look blurry. The eyeballs of people with farsightedness are too short. Because of this, the lens of the eye bends light from nearby objects so that the image does not focus properly on the retina. If light could pass through the retina, the image would come into sharp focus at a point behind the retina, as shown in Figure 13.

Convex lenses are used to help correct farsightedness. A convex lens is thicker in the middle than at the edges. The convex lens makes the light rays bend toward each other before they reach the eye. Then the lens of the eye bends the rays even more. This bending makes the image focus exactly on the retina.

 **Reading Checkpoint** What type of lens corrects nearsightedness?

Hearing and Balance

What wakes you up in the morning? Maybe an alarm clock buzzes, or perhaps your parent calls you. On a summer morning, you might hear birds singing. Whatever wakes you up, there's a good chance that it's a sound of some sort. **Your ears are the sense organs that respond to the stimulus of sound. The ears convert the sound to nerve impulses that your brain interprets.** So when you hear an alarm clock or another morning sound, your brain tells you that it's time to wake up.

How Sound Is Produced Sound is produced by vibrations. The material that is vibrating, or moving rapidly back and forth, may be almost anything—a guitar string, an insect's wings, or a stereo speaker.

The vibrations move outward from the source of the sound, something like ripples moving out from a stone dropped in water. The vibrations cause particles, such as the gas molecules that make up air, to vibrate. In this way, sound is carried. When you hear a friend's voice, for example, sound has traveled from your friend's larynx to your ears. In addition to being able to travel through gases such as those in air, sound waves can also travel through liquids, such as water, and solids, such as wood.

Math ▶ Analyzing Data

Sound Intensity

Sound intensity, or loudness, is measured in units called decibels. The threshold of hearing for the human ear is 0 decibels. For every 10-decibel increase, the sound intensity increases ten times. Thus, a 20-decibel sound is ten times more intense than a 10-decibel sound, not twice as intense. A 30-decibel sound is 100 times more intense than a 10-decibel sound. Sound levels for several sound sources are shown in the bar graph.

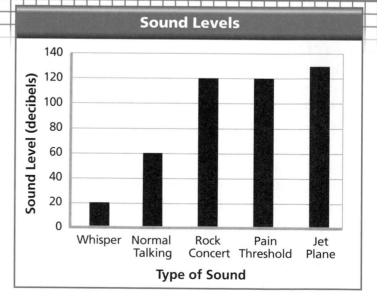

1. **Reading Graphs** What unit of measure is represented on the y-axis? What is represented on the x-axis?

2. **Interpreting Data** What is the sound intensity in decibels of a whisper? Normal talking? A rock concert?

3. **Calculating** How much more intense is normal talking than a whisper? Explain.

4. **Predicting** Based on the graph, what types of sound could be painful if you were exposed to them?

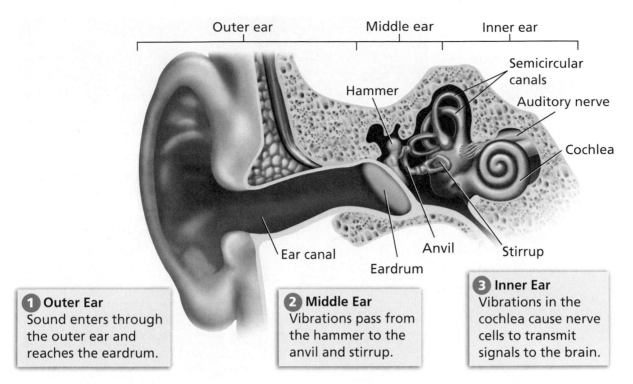

Outer ear | Middle ear | Inner ear

Hammer

Semicircular canals

Auditory nerve

Cochlea

Ear canal

Eardrum

Anvil

Stirrup

1 Outer Ear
Sound enters through the outer ear and reaches the eardrum.

2 Middle Ear
Vibrations pass from the hammer to the anvil and stirrup.

3 Inner Ear
Vibrations in the cochlea cause nerve cells to transmit signals to the brain.

FIGURE 14
The Ear
Sound waves enter the outer ear and make structures in the middle ear vibrate. When the vibrations reach the inner ear, nerve impulses travel to the cerebrum through the auditory nerve. **Predicting** *What would happen if the bones of the middle ear were stuck together and could not move?*

The Outer Ear The ear is structured to receive sound vibrations. The three regions of the ear—the outer ear, middle ear, and inner ear—are shown in Figure 14. The visible part of the outer ear is shaped like a funnel. This funnel-like shape enables the outer ear to gather sound waves. The sound vibrations then travel down the ear canal, which is also part of the outer ear.

The Middle Ear At the end of the ear canal, sound vibrations reach the eardrum. The **eardrum,** which separates the outer ear from the middle ear, is a membrane that vibrates when sound strikes it. Your eardrum vibrates in much the same way that a drum vibrates when it is struck. Vibrations from the eardrum pass to the middle ear, which contains the three smallest bones in the body—the hammer, anvil, and stirrup. These bones are named for their shapes. The vibrating eardrum makes the hammer vibrate. The hammer passes the vibrations to the anvil, and the anvil passes them to the stirrup.

The Inner Ear The stirrup vibrates against a thin membrane that covers the opening of the inner ear. The membrane channels the vibrations into the fluid in the cochlea. The **cochlea** (KAHK le uh) is a snail-shaped tube that is lined with receptor cells that respond to sound. When the fluid in the cochlea vibrates, it stimulates these receptors. Sensory neurons then send nerve impulses to the cerebrum through the auditory nerve. These impulses are interpreted as sounds that you hear.

Go Online
SciLINKS

For: Links on the senses
Visit: www.SciLinks.org
Web Code: scn-0463

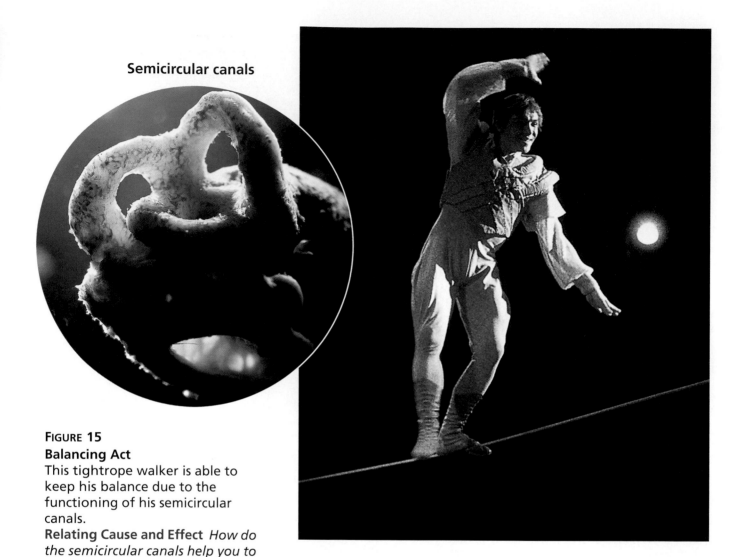

Semicircular canals

FIGURE 15
Balancing Act
This tightrope walker is able to keep his balance due to the functioning of his semicircular canals.
Relating Cause and Effect *How do the semicircular canals help you to maintain balance?*

The Inner Ear and Balance Structures in your inner ear control your sense of balance. Above the cochlea in your inner ear are the **semicircular canals,** which are the structures in the ear that are responsible for your sense of balance. You can see how these structures got their name if you look at Figure 15. These canals, as well as the two tiny sacs located behind them, are full of fluid. The canals and sacs are also lined with tiny cells that have hairlike extensions.

When your head moves, the fluid in the semicircular canals is set in motion. The moving fluid makes the cells' hairlike extensions bend. This bending produces nerve impulses in sensory neurons. The impulses travel to the cerebellum. The cerebellum then analyzes the impulses to determine the way your head is moving and the position of your body. If the cerebellum senses that you are losing your balance, it sends impulses to muscles that help you restore your balance.

 **Reading Checkpoint** Where in the ear are the semicircular canals located?

Smell and Taste

You walk into the house and smell the aroma of freshly baked cookies. You bite into one and taste its rich chocolate flavor. When you smelled the cookies, receptors in your nose reacted to chemicals carried by the air from the cookies to your nose. When you took a bite of a cookie, taste buds on your tongue responded to chemicals in the food. These food chemicals were dissolved in saliva, which came in contact with your taste buds.

The senses of smell and taste work closely together. Both depend on chemicals in food or in the air. The chemicals trigger responses in receptors in the nose and mouth. Nerve impulses then travel to the brain, where they are interpreted as smells or tastes.

The nose can distinguish at least 50 basic odors. In contrast, there are only five main taste sensations—sweet, sour, salty, bitter, and a meatlike taste called *umami*. When you eat, however, you experience a much wider variety of tastes. The flavor of food is influenced by both smell and taste. When you have a cold, foods may not taste as good as they usually do. That is because a stuffy nose decreases your ability to smell food.

Lab zone Skills **Activity**

Designing Experiments

Can people tell one food from another if they can taste the foods but not smell them? Design an experiment to find out. Use these foods: a peeled pear, a peeled apple, and a peeled raw potato. Be sure to control all variables except the one you are testing. Write your hypothesis and a description of your procedure. Obtain your teacher's approval before carrying out your experiment.

✓ Reading Checkpoint What basic tastes can the tongue detect?

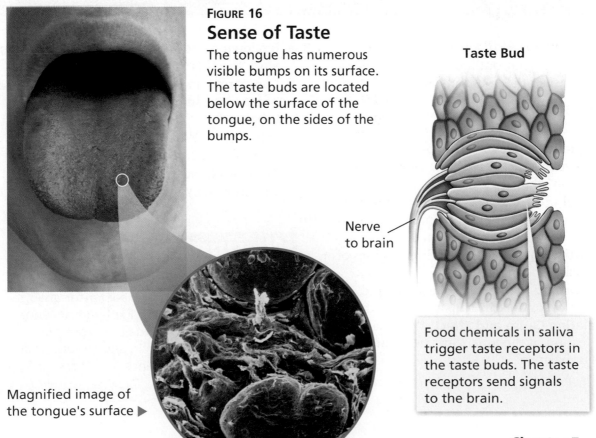

FIGURE 16
Sense of Taste

The tongue has numerous visible bumps on its surface. The taste buds are located below the surface of the tongue, on the sides of the bumps.

Magnified image of the tongue's surface ▶

Taste Bud

Nerve to brain

Food chemicals in saliva trigger taste receptors in the taste buds. The taste receptors send signals to the brain.

Touch

Unlike vision, hearing, balance, smell, and taste, the sense of touch is not found in one specific place. Instead, the sense of touch is found in all areas of your skin. Your skin is your largest sense organ! **Your skin contains different kinds of touch receptors that respond to a number of stimuli.** Some of these receptors respond to light touch and others to heavy pressure. Still other receptors pick up sensations of pain and temperature change.

The receptors that respond to light touch are in the upper part of the dermis. They tell you when something brushes against your skin. These receptors also let you feel the textures of objects, such as smooth glass and rough sandpaper. Receptors deeper in the dermis pick up the feeling of pressure. Press down hard on the top of your desk, for example, and you will feel pressure in your fingertips.

The dermis also contains receptors that respond to temperature and pain. Pain is unpleasant, but it can be one of the body's most important feelings because it alerts the body to possible danger. Have you ever stepped into a bathtub of very hot water and then immediately pulled your foot out? If so, you can appreciate how pain can trigger an important response in your body.

FIGURE 17
Reading by Touch
People who are blind use their sense of touch to read. To do this, they run their fingers over words written in Braille. Braille uses raised dots to represent letters and numbers. Here, a teacher shows a blind child how to read Braille.

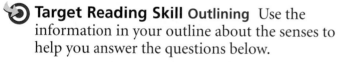

Section 3 Assessment

> **Target Reading Skill Outlining** Use the information in your outline about the senses to help you answer the questions below.

Reviewing Key Concepts

1. a. **Listing** What are the parts of the eye?
   b. **Sequencing** Describe the process by which the eye produces an image. Begin at the point at which light is focused by the lens.
   c. **Inferring** If nearby objects seem blurry, what type of vision problem might you have? How can it be corrected?
2. a. **Identifying** What are the three regions of the ear?
   b. **Describing** Describe the location and function of the eardrum and the cochlea.
   c. **Relating Cause and Effect** Why may an infection of the inner ear cause you to lose your balance?

3. a. **Reviewing** How do the senses of taste and smell work together?
   b. **Comparing and Contrasting** How are the senses of taste and smell similar? How are they different?
4. a. **Identifying** What kinds of touch receptors are found in the skin?
   b. **Applying Concepts** What happens in the dermis when you accidentally touch a hot stove?

Writing in Science

Cause-and-Effect Paragraph Write a description of how you feel after an amusement park ride. Explain how your feeling is related to the structure and function of the semicircular canals. Be sure to include a topic sentence and three to four supporting points.

Alcohol and Other Drugs

Reading Preview

Key Concepts
- What are the immediate and long-term effects of drug abuse?
- What are some commonly abused drugs and how does each affect the body?
- How does alcohol abuse harm the body?

Key Terms
- drug • drug abuse
- tolerance • addiction
- withdrawal • depressant
- stimulant • anabolic steroid
- alcoholism

Target Reading Skill
Relating Cause and Effect As you read, identify commonly abused drugs and how they affect the body. Write the information in a graphic organizer like the one below.

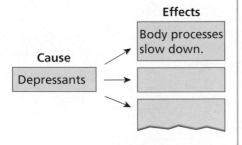

Effects

Body processes slow down.

Cause

Depressants

Lab zone Discover **Activity**

How Can You Best Say No?

1. In this activity, you will use marbles to represent drugs. Your teacher will divide the class into groups of three students. In each group, your teacher will appoint two students to try to convince the other person to take the "drugs."

2. Depending on your role, you should think of arguments to get the person to accept the marbles or arguments against accepting them. After everyone has had a chance to think of arguments, begin the discussion.

3. After a while, students in each group should exchange roles.

Think It Over

Inferring What role does peer pressure play in whether or not a person decides to abuse drugs?

Drugs! You probably hear and see that word in a lot of places. Drugstores sell drugs to relieve headaches, soothe upset stomachs, and stop coughs. Radio and television programs and magazine articles explore drug-related problems. Your school probably has a program to educate students about drugs. When people talk about drugs, what do they mean? To a scientist, a **drug** is any chemical taken into the body that causes changes in a person's body or behavior. Many drugs affect the functioning of the central nervous system.

Drug Abuse

The deliberate misuse of drugs for purposes other than medical ones is called **drug abuse.** Even medicines can be abused drugs if they are used in a way for which they were not intended. Many abused drugs, however, such as cocaine and heroin, are illegal under any circumstances. The use of these drugs is against the law because their effects on the body are almost always dangerous.

Go Online
SciLINKS NSTA

For: Links on drug addiction
Visit: www.SciLinks.org
Web Code: scn-0464

Effects of Abused Drugs Abused drugs start to affect the body shortly after they are taken. **Most commonly abused drugs, such as marijuana, alcohol, and cocaine, are especially dangerous because of their immediate effects on the brain and other parts of the nervous system. In addition, long-term drug abuse can lead to addiction and other health and social problems.**

Different drugs have different effects. Some drugs cause nausea and a fast, irregular heartbeat. Others can cause sleepiness. Drug abusers may also experience headaches, dizziness, and trembling. Alcohol can cause confusion, poor muscle coordination, and blurred vision. These effects are especially dangerous in situations in which an alert mind is essential, such as driving a car.

Most abused drugs can alter, or change, a person's mood and feelings. Because of this effect, these drugs are often called mood-altering drugs. For example, the mood of a person under the influence of marijuana may change from calm to anxious. Alcohol can sometimes make a person angry and even violent. Mood-altering drugs also affect patterns of thinking and the way in which the brain interprets information from the senses.

Tolerance If a person takes a drug regularly, the body may develop a tolerance to the drug. **Tolerance** is a state in which a drug user needs larger and larger amounts of the drug to produce the same effect on the body. Tolerance can cause people to take a very large amount of a drug, or an overdose. People who take an overdose may become unconscious or even die.

FIGURE 18
Drug Abuse
Drug abuse can have serious consequences. However, there are ways to tell if someone is abusing drugs and ways to help that person. **Interpreting Diagrams**
What are two ways you can help if someone you know is abusing drugs?

Signs of Drug Abuse

- Sudden changes in mood
- Lying, cheating
- Forgetfulness, withdrawn attitude, aggressiveness
- Poor coordination
- Slurred speech

Addiction For many commonly abused drugs, repeated use can result in addiction. In **addiction,** the body becomes physically dependent on the drug. If a drug addict misses a few doses of the drug, the body reacts to the lack of the drug. The person may experience headaches, dizziness, fever, vomiting, body aches, and muscle cramps. The person is experiencing **withdrawal,** a period of adjustment that occurs when a person stops taking a drug on which the body is dependent.

Some drugs may also cause a person to become emotionally dependent on them. The person becomes accustomed to the feelings and moods produced by the drug. Therefore, the person has a strong desire to continue using the drug.

Other Effects of Drug Abuse Drugs can also affect a person's health indirectly. Some drug users sometimes share needles. When a person uses a needle to inject a drug, some of the person's blood remains in the needle after it is withdrawn. If the person has HIV or another pathogen in the blood, the next person to use the needle may become infected with the pathogen.

The abuse of drugs also has serious legal and social effects. A person who is caught using or selling an illegal drug may have to pay a fine or go to jail. Drug abuse can also make a person unable to get along with others. Drug abusers often have a hard time doing well in school or holding a job.

Reading Checkpoint What is withdrawal?

Lab zone Skills **Activity**

Communicating

Plan a 30-second television commercial aimed at teenagers to help them avoid the pressure to try drugs. Your commercial should reveal some harmful effects of drugs and give strategies for avoiding drugs. Create several storyboards to show what the commercial will look like. Then, write a script for your commercial.

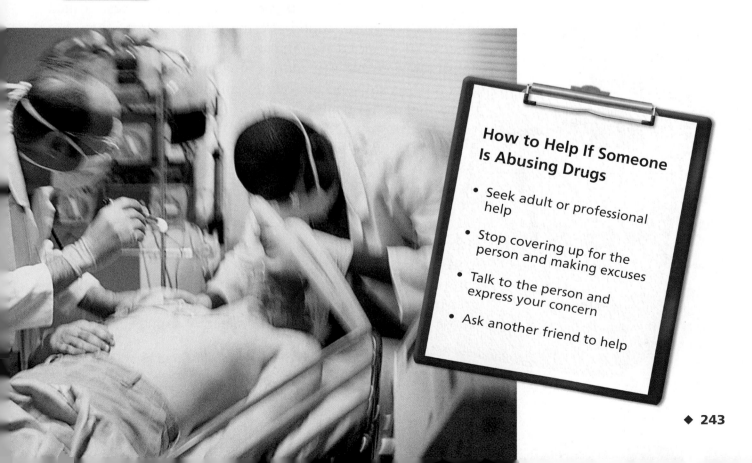

How to Help If Someone Is Abusing Drugs

- Seek adult or professional help
- Stop covering up for the person and making excuses
- Talk to the person and express your concern
- Ask another friend to help

Kinds of Abused Drugs

There are many kinds of drugs, with a wide range of effects on the body. Some are legitimate medicines that a doctor prescribes to help the body fight disease and injury. However, many kinds of drugs are frequently abused. **Commonly abused drugs include depressants, stimulants, inhalants, hallucinogens, anabolic steroids, and alcohol. Many drugs affect the central nervous system, while others affect the overall chemical balance in the body.** Figure 20 lists and describes the characteristics of some commonly abused drugs.

Depressants   Notice in Figure 20 that some drugs are classified as depressants. **Depressants** are drugs that slow down the activity of the central nervous system. When people take depressants, their muscles relax and they may become sleepy. They may take longer than normal to respond to stimuli. For example, depressants may prevent people from reacting quickly to the danger of a car rushing toward them. Alcohol and narcotics, such as heroin, are depressants.

Stimulants   In contrast to depressants, **stimulants** speed up body processes. They make the heart beat faster and make the breathing rate increase. Cocaine and nicotine are stimulants, as are amphetamines (am FET uh meenz). Amphetamines are prescription drugs that are sometimes sold illegally.

Inhalants and Hallucinogens   Some substances, called inhalants, produce mood-altering effects when they are inhaled, or breathed in. Inhalants include paint thinner, nail polish remover, and some kinds of cleaning fluids. Hallucinogens, such as LSD and mescaline, can make people see or hear things that do not really exist.

Steroids   Some athletes try to improve their performance by taking drugs known as steroids. **Anabolic steroids** (an uh BAH lik STEER oydz) are synthetic chemicals that are similar to hormones produced in the body.

Anabolic steroids may increase muscle size and strength. However, steroids can cause mood changes that lead to violence. In addition, steroid abuse can cause serious health problems, such as heart damage, liver damage, and increased blood pressure. Steroid use is especially dangerous for teenagers, whose growing bodies can be permanently damaged.

 **Reading Checkpoint**   What kinds of drugs are classified as stimulants?

FIGURE 19
Making a Statement About Drug Abuse
Many teens are becoming active in antidrug campaigns.

FIGURE 20
Abused drugs can have many serious effects on the body. **Interpreting Tables** *What are the long-term effects of using inhalants?*

Some Effects of Commonly Abused Drugs				
Drug Type	**Short-Term Effects**	**Long-Term Effects**	**Addiction?**	**Emotional Dependence?**
Marijuana (including hashish)	Unclear thinking, loss of coordination, increased heart rate	Difficulty with concentration and memory; respiratory disease and lung cancer	Probably not	Yes
Nicotine (in cigarettes, cigars, chewing tobacco)	Stimulant; nausea, loss of appetite, headache	Heart and lung disease, difficulty breathing, heavy coughing	Yes, strongly so	Yes
Alcohol	Depressant; decreased alertness, poor reflexes, nausea, emotional depression	Liver and brain damage, inadequate nutrition	Yes	Yes
Inhalants (glue, nail polish remover, paint thinner)	Sleepiness, nausea, headaches, emotional depression	Damage to liver, kidneys, and brain; hallucinations	No	Yes
Cocaine (including crack)	Stimulant; nervousness, disturbed sleep, loss of appetite	Mental illness, damage to lining of nose, irregular heartbeat, heart or breathing failure, liver damage	Yes	Yes, strongly so
Amphetamines	Stimulant; restlessness, rapid speech, dizziness	Restlessness, irritability, irregular heartbeat, liver damage	Possible	Yes
Hallucinogens (LSD, mescaline, PCP)	Hallucinations, anxiety, panic; thoughts and actions not connected to reality	Mental illness; fearfulness; behavioral changes, including violence	No	Yes
Barbiturates (Phenobarbital, Nembutal, Seconal)	Depressant; decreased alertness, slowed thought processes, poor muscle coordination	Sleepiness, irritability, confusion	Yes	Yes
Tranquilizers (Valium, Xanax)	Depressant; blurred vision, sleepiness, unclear speech, headache, skin rash	Blood and liver disease	Yes	Yes
Narcotics (opium, codeine, morphine, heroin)	Depressant; sleepiness, nausea, hallucinations	Convulsion, coma, death	Yes, very rapid development	Yes, strongly so
Anabolic steroids	Mood swings	Heart, liver, and kidney damage; hypertension; overgrowth of skull and facial bones	No	Yes

Chapter 7 ◆ 245

Alcohol

Alcohol is a drug found in many beverages, including beer, wine, cocktails, and hard liquor. Alcohol is a powerful depressant. In all states, it is illegal for people under the age of 21 to buy or possess alcohol. In spite of this fact, alcohol is the most commonly abused legal drug in people aged 12 to 17.

How Alcohol Affects the Body Alcohol is absorbed by the digestive system quickly. If a person drinks alcohol on an empty stomach, the alcohol enters the blood and gets to the brain and other organs almost immediately. If alcohol is drunk with a meal, it takes longer to get into the blood.

The chart in Figure 21 describes what alcohol does to the body. The more alcohol in the blood, the more serious the effects. The amount of alcohol in the blood is usually expressed as blood alcohol concentration, or BAC. A BAC value of 0.1 percent means that one tenth of one percent of the fluid in the blood is alcohol. In some states, if car drivers have a BAC of 0.08 percent or more, they are legally drunk. In other states, drivers with a BAC of 0.1 are considered legally drunk.

Alcohol produces serious negative effects, including loss of normal judgment, at a BAC of less than 0.08 percent. This loss of judgment can have serious consequences. People who have been drinking may not realize that they cannot drive a car safely. About every two minutes, a person in the United States is injured in a car crash related to alcohol.

FIGURE 21
Alcohol's Effects
Alcohol affects every system of the body. It also impacts a person's thought processes, judgment, and reaction time. In the bottom photo, a police officer tests the blood alcohol concentration of a driver suspected of drinking.

Short-Term Effects of Alcohol	
Body System	**Effect**
Cardiovascular system	Heartbeat rate and blood pressure increase.
Digestive system	Alcohol is absorbed directly from the stomach and small intestine, which allows it to enter the bloodstream quickly.
Excretory system	The kidneys produce more urine, causing the drinker to excrete more water than usual.
Nervous system	Vision becomes blurred. Speech becomes unclear. Control of behavior is reduced. Judgment becomes poor.
Skin	Blood flow to the skin increases, causing rapid loss of body heat.

Long-Term Alcohol Abuse Many adults drink occasionally and in moderation, without serious safety or health problems. However, heavy drinking, especially over a long period, can result in significant health problems. **Alcohol abuse can cause the destruction of cells in the brain and liver, and can lead to addiction and emotional dependence.** Damage to the brain can cause mental disturbances, such as hallucinations and loss of consciousness. The liver, which breaks down alcohol for elimination from the body, can become so scarred that it does not function properly. In addition, long-term alcohol abuse can increase the risk of getting certain kinds of cancer.

Abuse of alcohol can result in **alcoholism,** a disease in which a person is both physically addicted to and emotionally dependent on alcohol. To give up alcohol, as with any addictive drug, alcoholics must go through withdrawal. To give up drinking, alcoholics need both medical and emotional help. Medical professionals, psychologists, and organizations such as Alcoholics Anonymous can help a person stop drinking.

 **Reading Checkpoint** What organs are affected by alcohol abuse?

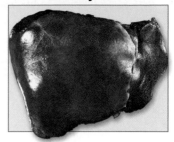
Healthy Liver

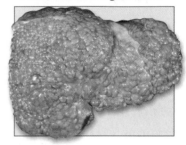
Alcohol-damaged Liver

FIGURE 22
Alcohol's Effect on the Liver
Long-term alcohol abuse can cause serious damage to the liver. **Relating Cause and Effect** *What other effects can alcohol abuse have on the body?*

Section 4 Assessment

Target Reading Skill Relating Cause and Effect Refer to your graphic organizer about commonly abused drugs to help you answer Question 2.

Reviewing Key Concepts

1. **a. Defining** In your own words, explain what a drug is. What is drug abuse?
   b. Explaining How can the repeated use of some drugs lead to addiction and emotional dependence?
   c. Applying Concepts What reasons would you give someone to not try drugs in the first place?
2. **a. Listing** Name some commonly abused depressants and stimulants.
   b. Comparing and Contrasting Contrast the effects that depressants and stimulants have on the body.

   c. Inferring Why might a person's risk of a heart attack increase with the use of stimulants?
3. **a. Reviewing** What type of drug is alcohol? What immediate effects does alcohol have on the body?
   b. Explaining What are the effects of long-term alcohol abuse?
   c. Relating Cause and Effect Based on alcohol's effect on the nervous system, explain why drinking and driving is extremely dangerous.

Lab zone **At-Home Activity**

Medicine Labels Collect several medicine bottles and read the warning labels. Make a list of the kinds of warnings you find. Discuss these warnings with a family member. Why do you think medicines provide warnings?

With Caffeine or Without?

Problem

What body changes does caffeine produce in blackworms *(Lumbriculus)*?

Skills Focus

observing, controlling variables, drawing conclusions

Materials

- blackworms
- plastic dropper
- adrenaline solution
- stereomicroscope
- paraffin specimen trough
- noncarbonated spring water
- beverages with and without caffeine
- stopwatch or clock with second hand

Procedure

PART 1 Observing the Effects of a Known Stimulant

1. Use a dropper to remove one worm and a drop or two of water from the blackworm population provided by your teacher.

2. Place the worm and the water in the trough of the paraffin block. Use the dropper or the corner of a paper towel to remove any excess water that does not fit in the trough. Let the blackworm adjust for a few minutes.

3. Place the paraffin block under the stereomicroscope. Select the smallest amount of light and the lowest possible power to view the blackworm.

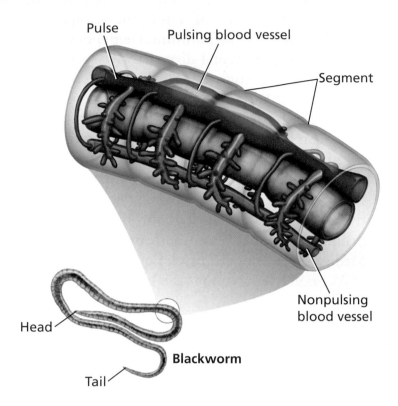

Pulse · Pulsing blood vessel · Segment · Nonpulsing blood vessel · Head · **Blackworm** · Tail

4. Look through the stereomicroscope and locate a segment near the middle of the worm. Count the number of times blood pulses through this segment for 30 seconds. Multiply this number by two to get the pulse in beats per minute. Record the pulse in your data table.

Data Table	
Condition	Pulse Rate
No adrenaline	
With adrenaline	
Beverage without caffeine	
Beverage with caffeine	

5. Remove the block from the stereomicroscope. Use the dropper to add 1 drop of adrenaline solution to the trough. (Adrenaline is a substance produced by the human body that acts as a stimulant.) Let the worm sit in the adrenaline solution for 5 minutes.

6. Place the paraffin block under the stereomicroscope. Again locate a segment near the middle of the worm. Count the number of pulses through this segment for 30 seconds. Multiply this number by two to get the pulse in beats per minute. Record the blackworm's pulse with adrenaline.

PART 2 Testing the Effects of Caffeine

7. Using the procedures you followed in Part 1, design an experiment that tests the effect of caffeine on the blackworm's pulse. You can use beverages with and without caffeine in your investigation. Be sure to write a hypothesis and control all necessary variables.

8. Submit your experimental plan to your teacher for review. After making any necessary changes, carry out your experiment.

Analyze and Conclude

1. **Observing** In Part 1, what was the blackworm's pulse rate before you added adrenaline? After you added adrenaline?

2. **Interpreting Data** Use the data you collected in Part 1 to explain how you know that adrenaline acts as a stimulant.

3. **Controlling Variables** In the experiment you performed in Part 2, what was your control? Explain.

4. **Drawing Conclusions** Based on your results in Part 2, does caffeine act as a stimulant? Explain your answer.

5. **Communicating** Write a paragraph to explain how you think your body would react to drinks with caffeine and without caffeine. Use the results from this investigation to support your viewpoint.

Design an Experiment

Do you think that "decaffeinated" products will act as a stimulant in blackworms? Design a controlled experiment to find out. *Obtain your teacher's permission before carrying out your investigation.*

① How the Nervous System Works

Key Concepts

- The nervous system directs how your body responds to information about what is happening inside and outside your body. Your nervous system also helps maintain homeostasis.

- The three kinds of neurons found in the body are sensory neurons, interneurons, and motor neurons.

- For a nerve impulse to be carried along at a synapse, it must cross the gap between an axon and the next structure.

Key Terms

stimulus	axon
response	nerve
neuron	sensory neuron
nerve impulse	interneuron
dendrite	motor neuron
	synapse

② Divisions of the Nervous System

Key Concepts

- The central nervous system is the control center of the body. It includes the brain and spinal cord.

- The peripheral nervous system consists of a network of nerves that branch out from the central nervous system and connect it to the rest of the body.

- A reflex is an automatic response that occurs very rapidly and without conscious control.

- Concussions and spinal cord injuries are two ways the central nervous system can be damaged.

Key Terms

central nervous system	brain stem
peripheral nervous system	somatic nervous system
brain	autonomic nervous system
spinal cord	reflex
cerebrum	concussion
cerebellum	

③ The Senses

Key Concepts

- The eyes convert light into nerve impulses that your brain interprets, enabling you to see.

- The ears convert sound into nerve impulses that your brain interprets, enabling you to hear. Structures in your inner ear control your sense of balance.

- The senses of smell and taste work together.

- The skin contains touch receptors that respond to a number of stimuli.

Key Terms

cornea	nearsightedness
pupil	farsightedness
iris	eardrum
lens	cochlea
retina	semicircular canal

④ Alcohol and Other Drugs

Key Concepts

- Most abused drugs are dangerous because of their immediate effects on the nervous system. Long-term drug abuse can lead to addiction and other health and social problems.

- Commonly abused drugs include depressants, stimulants, inhalants, steroids, and alcohol.

- Alcohol use can destroy cells in the brain and liver, and lead to addiction.

Key Terms

drug
drug abuse
tolerance
addiction
withdrawal
depressant
stimulant
anabolic steroid
alcoholism

Review and Assessment

Organizing Information

Concept Mapping Copy the concept map about neurons and their functions onto a separate sheet of paper. Then, complete it and add a title. (For more on Concept Mapping, see the Skills Handbook.)

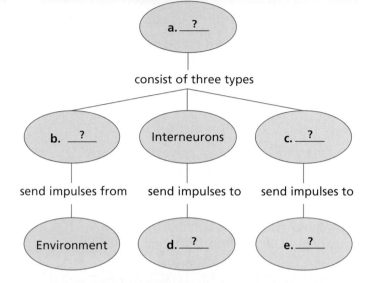

Reviewing Key Terms

Choose the letter of the best answer.

1. A change or signal in the environment that makes the nervous system react is called a
   a. stimulus.
   b. response.
   c. nerve impulse.
   d. synapse.

2. The structures that carry messages toward a neuron's cell body are
   a. axons.
   b. dendrites.
   c. nerves.
   d. nerve impulses.

3. Which structure links the brain and the peripheral nervous system?
   a. the cerebrum
   b. the cerebellum
   c. the cochlea
   d. the spinal cord

4. Which structure adjusts the size of the pupil?
   a. the cornea   **b.** the retina
   c. the lens   **d.** the iris

5. Physical dependence on a drug is called
   a. withdrawal.   **b.** response.
   c. addiction.   **d.** tolerance.

If the statement is true, write *true*. If it is false, change the underlined word or words to make the statement true.

6. A nerve message is also called a <u>synapse</u>.

7. The <u>cerebrum</u> is the part of the brain that controls involuntary actions.

8. In <u>nearsightedness</u>, a person can see distant objects clearly.

9. The <u>cochlea</u> is part of the inner ear.

10. Alcohol is a <u>depressant</u>.

Writing in Science

Descriptive Paragraph Draw a diagram of the human eye, and label the key parts. Then, write a paragraph that describes how each part helps a person "see" an image.

The Nervous System

Video Preview
Video Field Trip
▶ Video Assessment

Review and Assessment

Checking Concepts

11. Compare the functions of axons and dendrites.

12. How do the cerebrum and cerebellum work together when you ride a bicycle?

13. What is the function of the autonomic nervous system?

14. What is the result if the spinal cord is cut?

15. Describe how lenses in eyeglasses correct nearsightedness and farsightedness.

16. List in order all the structures in your ear that must vibrate before you hear a sound.

17. How do anabolic steroids affect the body?

Thinking Critically

18. Inferring How might the number of nerve impulses compare between the two synapses shown below? Explain.

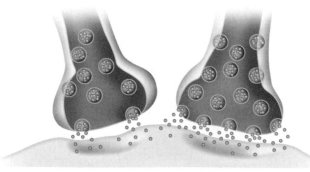

19. Relating Cause and Effect When a person has a stroke, blood flow to part of the brain is reduced, and some brain cells die. Suppose that after a stroke, a woman is unable to move her right arm and right leg. In which side of her brain did the stroke occur? Explain.

20. Applying Concepts As a man walks barefoot along a beach, he steps on a sharp shell. His foot automatically jerks upward, even before he feels pain. What process is this an example of? How does it help protect the man?

21. Making Judgments If someone tried to persuade you to take drugs, what arguments would you use as a way of refusing? Why do you think these arguments would be effective?

Applying Skills

Use the graph to answer Questions 22–25.

A person with normal vision stood at different distances from an eye chart and tried to identify the letters on the chart. The line graph gives the results.

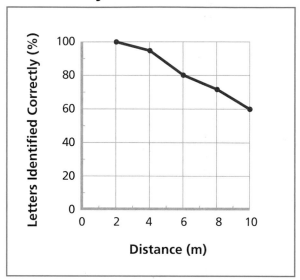

Eye Chart Results

22. Reading Graphs What variable is plotted on the *x*-axis? On the *y*-axis?

23. Interpreting Data As the distance from the eye chart increases, what happens to the percentage of letters identified correctly?

24. Controlling Variables What was the manipulated variable in this experiment? What was the responding variable?

25. Predicting How would you expect the results to differ for a farsighted person? Explain.

Lab zone Chapter **Project**

Performance Assessment Explain to your classmates how you set up your experiment, which illusions you used, which senses were involved in the illusions, and why the illusions worked. Include information on how the nervous system was involved in your illusions.

◑ Standardized Test Practice

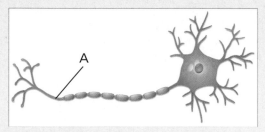
Choose the letter of the best answer.

1. A scientist studying the brain is studying part of the
   A peripheral nervous system.
   B somatic nervous system.
   C autonomic nervous system.
   D central nervous system.

Use the diagram below and your knowledge of science to answer Questions 2 and 3.

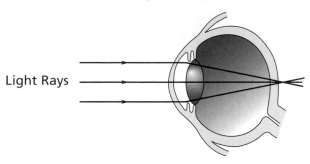

Light Rays

2. To correct the vision of the eye shown above, a lens would have to make the light rays
   A bend toward each other before they reach the eye's lens.
   B spread out before they reach the eye's lens.
   C focus on the eye's lens.
   D focus behind the retina.

3. Which of the following correctly pairs the vision problem in the eye shown above with the proper corrective lens?
   A farsightedness; convex lens
   B farsightedness; concave lens
   C nearsightedness; convex lens
   D nearsightedness; concave lens

4. The brain stem is involved in controlling
   A breathing.
   B the ability to learn.
   C movement of skeletal muscles.
   D balance.

5. You can infer that a person who has lost his or her sense of smell is also likely to have a poor
   A sense of balance.
   B sense of touch.
   C sense of taste.
   D sense of hearing.

Open-Ended Question

6. Outline the path of the reflex action that takes place when you step on a tack. What is the advantage of the nerve impulse not needing to go through the brain before action is taken?

The Olympic Games

Discus Thrower
This ancient marble statue is called *Discobolus*, ancient Greek for "discus thrower." The statue is a Roman copy of a statue made in Greece about 2,500 years ago.

What event—

- **is the dream of athletes around the world?**
- **has the motto "faster, higher, stronger"?**
- **supports amateur sports?**

The Olympic games began more than 2,500 years ago in Olympia, Greece. For one day every four years, the best athletes in Greece gathered to compete. The games honored the Greek god Zeus. The ancient Greeks valued both physical and intellectual achievement. A winning athlete at the Olympic games was rewarded with a lifetime of honor and fame.

For more than a thousand years, the Greeks held the games at Olympia every four years. The games were discontinued in A.D. 394, when the Romans ruled Greece.

Centuries later, in the 1880s, Pierre de Coubertin, a Frenchman, convinced the United States and other nations to bring back the Olympic games. Coubertin hoped that the modern Olympics would promote world peace by bringing together athletes from all nations. The modern Olympics began in Athens in 1896.

Today the summer and winter Olympics alternate every two years. For several weeks, athletes from all around the world experience the excitement of competing against each other. Only a few know the joy of winning. But, all who participate learn about fair play, striving toward a goal, and becoming a little bit faster and stronger through training.

Olympic Torch, 2002
Here the flame burns in Salt Lake City, Utah. It's a symbol of the spirit of competition and fair play.

Sports in Ancient Greece

The ancient Greeks valued physical fitness as much as an educated mind. Men and boys exercised regularly by wrestling, sprinting, throwing the discus, and tossing the javelin. Greek philosophy taught that a sound mind and body created a well-balanced person. Greek art glorified the muscles and movement of the human body in magnificent sculptures and paintings.

The first recorded Olympic games were held in 776 B.C. That year a cook named Coroebus from Elis, Greece, won the only event in the games—a sprint of about 192 meters. The prize was a wreath of olive leaves. In ancient Greece, an olive wreath was the highest mark of honor.

Over the next 130 years, other events were added to the games, including longer running events, wrestling, chariot racing, boxing, and the pentathlon. *Pent-* comes from the Greek word meaning "five." A pentathlon included five competitions: a long jump, javelin toss, discus throw, foot race, and wrestling. Early records indicate that women were not allowed to compete in the games.

Ancient Greece
Rival city-states, such as Athens and Sparta, sent their best athletes to the games at Olympia.

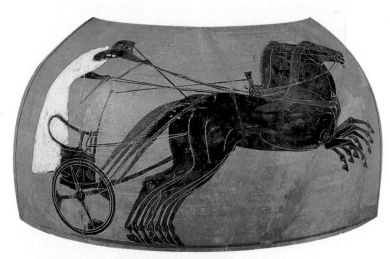

Amphora
Chariot racing became a popular sport in the ancient Olympics. This scene is painted on a Greek amphora, a pottery jar for olive oil or wine.

Social Studies Activity

The Olympics encourage peaceful competition among athletes from many nations. But political conflicts sometimes have disrupted or canceled the games. For example, the 1916 games were canceled because of World War I. Other Olympics are remembered for the achievements of certain athletes, such as Babe Didrikson in 1932. Find out what political events affected particular Olympics during the twentieth century. Or research outstanding athletes at different games. Report your findings to the class.

Modern Olympic Games

Jackie Joyner-Kersee
Jackie jumps to her second gold medal at the 1988 Olympic games.

At the 1988 Olympic games in Seoul, South Korea, Jackie Joyner-Kersee was one of the star athletes. She won two gold medals there. In total, between 1984 and 1996, she won six Olympic medals (three of them gold), making her one of the world's greatest athletes.

Jackie grew up in East St. Louis, Illinois, where she started running and jumping at age ten. Although she was a natural at the long jump, she wasn't a fast runner. But her coach, Mr. Fennoy, encouraged her. After her final Olympics, Jackie wrote an autobiography—a story of her life. Here is an excerpt from her book *A Kind of Grace*.

After school the boys' and girls' teams jogged to Lincoln Park's irregular-shaped track and makeshift long-jump pit. The track was a 36-inch-wide strip of black cinders sprinkled amid the rest of the dirt and grass. We called it the bridle path because that's what it looked like. We ran over, around and through the potholes, rocks, glass and tree limbs that littered the track. After practice, we jogged another two or three miles around the neighborhood to complete our workout.

In winter, when it was too cold to practice outside, we trained inside the Lincoln High building. Every afternoon after school and at 9:00 every Saturday morning, the team of twenty-five girls split into groups on the two floors and ran along the brown concrete corridors. When it was time for hurdling drills, Mr. Fennoy set up hurdles in the center of the hallway on the second floor, and put us through our paces. We sprinted and leaped past the doors to the math and science classrooms.

We ran to the end of the hall, turned around and repeated the drill in the opposite direction.

The running drills, exhausting as they were, eventually paid off. In 1977, between the ninth and tenth grade, I developed booster rockets and cut an astonishing four seconds off my 440 time. I surged to the front of the pack in practice heats. By the time we entered Lincoln High as tenth-graders, I was the fastest 440 runner on the team. The last was—at long last—first.

Language Arts Activity

What does Jackie mean by "the last was—at long last—first"? How did she get to be first? Some people say that Jackie was just a natural athlete. Jackie herself says, "I think it was my reward for all those hours of work on the bridle path, the neighborhood sidewalks and the schoolhouse corridors."

Think about a period in your life when you had to prepare for a math competition, a recital, a performance, a sports event, or other event. Write a short autobiographical sketch describing how you worked to improve your performance.

Yelena Yelesina
Yelena Yelesina of Russia won the women's high jump at the 2000 Olympics in Sydney, Australia. How much higher did she jump than the 1952 winner?

Women's High Jump	
Year	Height
1952	65.75
1960	72.75
1968	71.5
1976	76.0
1984	79.5
1992	79.5
2000	79.0

Olympic Records

To prepare for the Olympic games, top athletes train for years. Sometimes they even move to climates that will help them prepare to compete in their sports. Skiers, for example, might move to a mountain region where they can train year-round. Athletes also use the most advanced equipment available in their sport. This scientific approach to training has helped athletes set new records for speed, height, and distance. In addition, measurement tools such as timing clocks have become more precise. As a result, athletes can now break records by just a few hundredths of a second.

The table and graph at right show how the winning height in the women's high jump has changed over many Olympic games. Notice that the high jump measures height in inches.

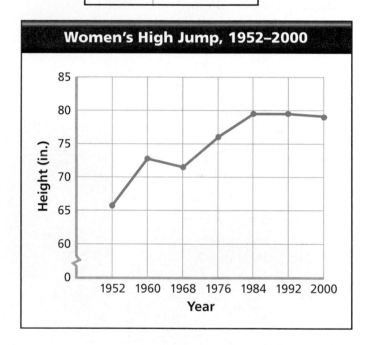

Women's High Jump, 1952–2000

Math Activity

The line graph above shows how the heights in the Olympic women's high jump have changed since 1952. Use the table at right, showing times for the men's 400-meter run, to create your own line graph.

How did the winning performance in the men's 400-meter run change over time? How does your graph differ from that of the women's high jump? Why do the graphs differ?

Men's 400-Meter Run	
Year	Time in Seconds
1952	45.90
1960	44.90
1968	43.86
1976	44.26
1984	44.27
1992	43.50
2000	43.84

High-Tech Training

Recent technology has made training for the Olympics a different process from that used in previous Olympic games. Today's high-tech equipment enables athletes to focus on specific aspects in their training.

One technology that is widely used today is video imaging. Olympic athletes such as figure skaters, gymnasts, and divers use video imaging. Using a video camera that links to a laptop computer, a coach can videotape an athlete practicing. Using software in the laptop, the coach and athlete can immediately replay a routine, like a dive, and discuss possible improvements. Some software allows the user to superimpose one video clip routine "on top" of another for comparison.

If you are a runner, you might use a watch with a chronometer, or timekeeper. But some athletes today use another new technology, sometimes called "wrist-top computers." These watches can measure an athlete's heart rate, speed, distance, and time. Many of these "mini machines" can also be connected to a computer so that athletes can compare their performances.

A third new technology, called a diagnostic system, tracks an athlete's constantly shifting body systems. Each training session can be adapted to provide enough—but not too much—of a workout. Electrodes are attached to the athlete's ankles, wrists, chest, and forehead. In 20 minutes, while the athlete is lying down, the system records and analyzes information, from heart rate and oxygen usage to how well the central nervous system, liver, and kidneys are functioning. These measurements can give all types of athletes an overall picture of their conditioning.

High-Tech Machines
The athlete on this workout machine can monitor her time, distance, speed, calories burned, heart rate, and other data (right). A transmitter attached to the chest sends data to a wrist-top computer that displays the athlete's heart rate and other data (above).

Science Activity

Athletes who are in the best shape often have very low resting heart and breathing rates. Some have resting heart rates below 40 bpm (beats per minute). Yet, while exercising, their heart and breathing rates can speed up to more than 170 bpm. Compare yourself to a top athlete.

1. In a sitting position, feel your pulse and count your heartbeats for 10 seconds. Multiply that number by 6 to get your resting bpm. Record the number. Next, count how many times you inhale and exhale in 30 seconds. Multiply that number by 2 to get your resting breathing rate. Record the data.

2. Walk up and down a staircase with at least 5 steps for 10 minutes without stopping. Keep your pace steady. As soon as the 10 minutes are up, measure your heart and breathing rates again. Record the data. **CAUTION:** *Do not do this part of the activity if you have any limiting physical and/or cardiovascular condition.*

3. What is your heartbeat range before and after exercise? How does that range compare to the top athlete described above? What is your breathing rate range?

Working Out

1. Warm-up
(5–10 minutes)
Slowly move the muscles to be used in the workout.

2. Stretch
(5–10 minutes)
Stretch the muscles to be used in the workout.

3. Workout
(20–45 minutes)
Do an activity such as walking, running, swimming, gymnastics, or riding a bicycle.

4. Cool-down
(5–10 minutes)
Move the muscles used in the workout at a reduced pace.

5. Stretch
(5–10 minutes)
Stretch the muscles used in the workout.

Tie It Together

Plan an Olympic Day!

Design a competition that can be held at your school. Decide the time, place, and kind of contests to hold. Remember that the ancient Greeks honored intellect as well as athletics. So you could include games that test the mind as well as the body.

Research the decathlon, pentathlon, heptathlon, and marathon in the ancient and modern Olympics. You could design your own pentathlon that includes athletic and nonathletic events.

To organize the Olympic day, you should

- set up the sports contests by measuring and marking the ground for each event
- find stopwatches, meter sticks, tape measures, and any necessary equipment
- locate or make prizes for first, second, and third place in each event
- enlist volunteers to compete in the events
- assign someone to take notes and to write a newspaper story on your Olympic day

Chapter

8

Plate Tectonics

Academic Standards

This chapter addresses these Indiana standards.

The Physical Setting

7.3.3 Describe how climates sometimes changed abruptly in the past because of changes in Earth's crust.

7.3.4 Explain how heat flow and movement within Earth cause earthquakes and volcanic eruptions and create mountains and ocean basins.

7.3.7 Give examples of some changes in Earth's surface that are abrupt and some changes that happen very slowly.

7.3.9 Explain that deeply buried sedimentary rock may be changed by pressure and heat. Describe that these changed rock layers may be become land surface and even mountains, and subsequently erode.

Common Themes

7.7.2 Use different models to represent the same thing, noting that the model's type and complexity depend on its purpose.

interactive Textbook

The huge gash in the ground is a rift valley formed where the mid-Atlantic ridge cuts through Iceland. ▶

Lab zone™ Chapter **Project**

Make a Model of Earth

In this chapter, you will learn how movements deep within Earth help to create mountains and other surface features. As you read this chapter, you will build a model that shows Earth's interior.

Your Goal To build a three-dimensional model that shows Earth's surface features, as well as a cutaway view of Earth's interior

Your model must

- be built to scale to show the layers of Earth's interior
- include at least three of the plates that form Earth's surface, as well as two landmasses or continents
- show how the plates push together, pull apart, or slide past each other and indicate their direction of movement
- follow the safety guidelines in Appendix A

Plan It! Think about the materials you could use to make a three-dimensional model. How will you show what happens beneath the crust? As you learn about sea-floor spreading and plate tectonics, add the appropriate features to your model.

Earth's Interior

Reading Preview

Key Concepts
- How have geologists learned about Earth's inner structure?
- What are the characteristics of Earth's crust, mantle, and core?

Key Terms
- seismic waves • pressure
- crust • basalt • granite
- mantle • lithosphere
- asthenosphere • outer core
- inner core

Target Reading Skill

Using Prior Knowledge Before you read, look at the section headings and visuals to see what this section is about. Then write what you know about Earth's interior in a graphic organizer like the one below. As you read, write what you learn.

What You Know
1. Earth's crust is made of rock.
2.

What You Learned
1.
2.

Discover Activity

How Do Scientists Find Out What's Inside Earth?

1. Your teacher will provide you with three closed film canisters. Each canister contains a different material. Your goal is to determine what is inside each canister—even though you can't directly observe what it contains.
2. Tape a paper label on each canister.
3. To gather evidence about what is in the canisters, you may tap, roll, shake, or weigh them. Record your observations.
4. What differences do you notice between the canisters? Apart from their appearance on the outside, are the canisters similar in any way? How did you obtain this evidence?

Think It Over
Inferring From your observations, what can you infer about the contents of the canisters? How is a canister like Earth?

Imagine watching an island grow! That's exactly what you can do on the island of Hawaii. On the south side of the island, molten material pours out of cracks in Mount Kilauea (kee loo AY uh) and flows into the ocean. As this lava flows over the land, it cools and hardens into rock.

The most recent eruptions of Mount Kilauea began in 1983. An area of cracks 7 kilometers long opened in Earth's surface. Through the cracks spurted "curtains of fire"—fountains of hot liquid rock from deep inside Earth. Since that time, the lava has covered more than 100 square kilometers of land with a layer of rock. When the lava reaches the sea, it extends the borders of the island into the Pacific Ocean.

FIGURE 1
Lava Flows in Hawaii
These people are watching lava from vents in Kilauea flow into the Pacific Ocean.

FIGURE 2
Getting Beneath the Surface
Geologists (left) examine rocks for clues about what's inside Earth. Even though caves like this one in Georgia (below) may seem deep, they reach only a relatively short distance beneath the surface.

Exploring Inside Earth

Earth's surface is constantly changing. Throughout our planet's long history, its surface has been lifted up, pushed down, bent, and broken. Thus Earth looks different today from the way it did millions of years ago.

Volcanic eruptions like those at Mount Kilauea make people wonder, What's inside Earth? Yet this question is very difficult to answer. Much as geologists would like to, they cannot dig a hole to the center of Earth. The extreme conditions in Earth's interior prevent exploration far below the surface.

The deepest mine in the world, a gold mine in South Africa, reaches a depth of 3.8 kilometers. But that mine only scratches the surface. You would have to travel more than 1,600 times that distance—over 6,000 kilometers—to reach Earth's center. **Geologists have used two main types of evidence to learn about Earth's interior: direct evidence from rock samples and indirect evidence from seismic waves.** The geologists in Figure 2 are observing rock on Earth's surface.

Evidence From Rock Samples   Rocks from inside Earth give geologists clues about Earth's structure. Geologists have drilled holes as much as 12 kilometers into Earth. The drills bring up samples of rock. From these samples, geologists can make inferences about conditions deep inside Earth, where these rocks formed. In addition, forces inside Earth sometimes blast rock to the surface from depths of more than 100 kilometers. These rocks provide more information about the interior.

Evidence From Seismic Waves   Geologists cannot look inside Earth. Instead, they must rely on indirect methods of observation. Have you ever hung a heavy picture on a wall? If you have, you know that you can knock on the wall to locate the wooden beam underneath the plaster that will support the picture. When you knock on the wall, you listen carefully for a change in the sound.

To study Earth's interior, geologists also use an indirect method. But instead of knocking on walls, they use seismic waves. When earthquakes occur, they produce **seismic waves** (SYZ mik). Geologists record the seismic waves and study how they travel through Earth. The speed of seismic waves and the paths they take reveal the structure of the planet.

Using data from seismic waves, geologists have learned that Earth's interior is made up of several layers. Each layer surrounds the layers beneath it, much like the layers of an onion. In Figure 3, you can see how seismic waves travel through the layers that make up Earth.

✔ **Reading Checkpoint**   **What causes seismic waves?**

Earthquake   Path of seismic waves

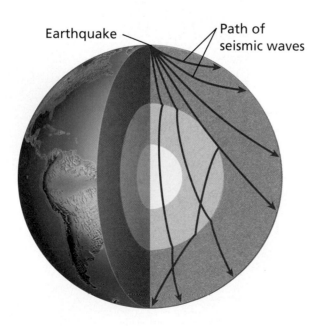

FIGURE 3
Seismic Waves
Scientists infer Earth's inner structure by recording and studying how seismic waves travel through Earth.

Depth

0

0.5 m

1 m

Pressure
Increases

1.5 m

2 m

A Journey to the Center of Earth

The three main layers of Earth are the crust, the mantle, and the core. These layers vary greatly in size, composition, temperature, and pressure. If you could travel through these layers to the center of Earth, what would your trip be like? To begin, you will need a vehicle that can travel through solid rock. The vehicle will carry scientific instruments to record changes in temperature and pressure as you descend.

Temperature   As you start to tunnel beneath the surface, the surrounding rock is cool. Then at about 20 meters down, your instruments report that the rock is getting warmer. For every 40 meters that you descend from that point, the temperature rises 1 Celsius degree. This rapid rise in temperature continues for several tens of kilometers. After that, the temperature increases more slowly, but steadily. The high temperatures inside Earth are the result of heat left over from the formation of the planet. In addition, radioactive substances inside Earth release energy. This further heats the interior.

Pressure   During your journey to the center of Earth, your instruments record an increase in pressure in the surrounding rock. **Pressure** results from a force pressing on an area. Because of the weight of the rock above, pressure inside Earth increases as you go deeper. The deeper you go, the greater the pressure. Pressure inside Earth increases much as it does in the swimming pool in Figure 4.

The Crust

Your journey to the center of Earth begins in the crust. The **crust** is the layer of rock that forms Earth's outer skin. **The crust is a layer of solid rock that includes both dry land and the ocean floor.** On the crust you find rocks and mountains. The crust also includes the soil and water that cover large parts of Earth's surface.

This outer rind of rock is much thinner than the layer that lies beneath it. In fact, you can think of Earth's crust as being similar to the paper-thin skin of an onion. The crust is thickest under high mountains and thinnest beneath the ocean. In most places, the crust is between 5 and 40 kilometers thick. But it can be up to 70 kilometers thick beneath mountains.

The crust beneath the ocean is called oceanic crust. Oceanic crust consists mostly of rocks such as basalt. **Basalt** (buh SAWLT) is dark rock with a fine texture. Continental crust, the crust that forms the continents, consists mainly of rocks such as granite. **Granite** is a rock that usually is a light color and has a coarse texture.

Reading Checkpoint What is the main type of rock in oceanic crust?

FIGURE 5
Earth's Interior
Earth's interior is divided into layers: the crust, mantle, outer core, and inner core.
Interpreting Diagrams *Which of Earth's layers is the thickest?*

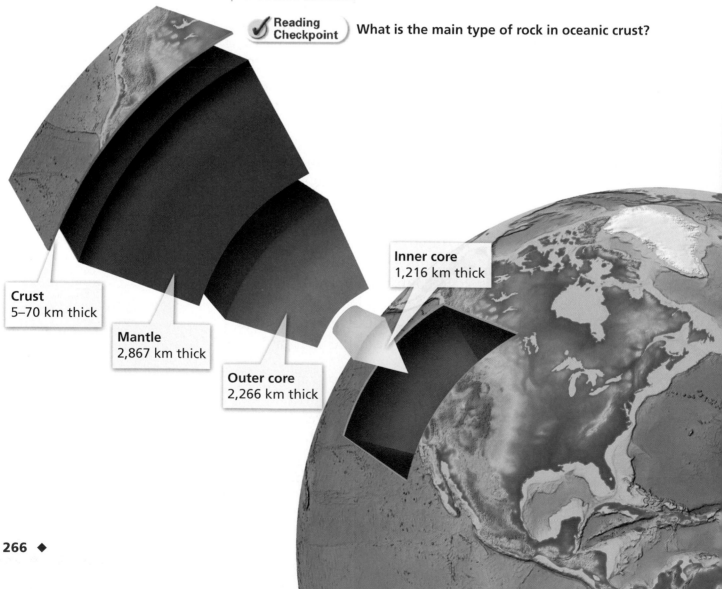

Crust
5–70 km thick

Mantle
2,867 km thick

Outer core
2,266 km thick

Inner core
1,216 km thick

The Mantle

Your journey downward continues. About 40 kilometers beneath the surface, you cross a boundary. Below the boundary is the solid material of the **mantle,** a layer of hot rock. **Earth's mantle is made up of rock that is very hot, but solid. Scientists divide the mantle into layers based on the physical characteristics of those layers. Overall, the mantle is nearly 3,000 kilometers thick.**

The Lithosphere The uppermost part of the mantle is very similar to the crust. The uppermost part of the mantle and the crust together form a rigid layer called the **lithosphere** (LITH uh sfeer). In Greek, *lithos* means "stone." As you can see in Figure 6, the lithosphere averages about 100 kilometers thick.

The Asthenosphere Below the lithosphere, your vehicle encounters material that is hotter and under increasing pressure. As a result, the part of the mantle just beneath the lithosphere is less rigid than the rock above. Like road tar softened by the heat of the sun, this part of the mantle is somewhat soft—it can bend like plastic. This soft layer is called the **asthenosphere** (as THEN uh sfeer). In Greek, *asthenes* means "weak." Although the asthenosphere is softer than the rest of the mantle, it's still solid. If you kicked it, you would stub your toe.

The Lower Mantle Beneath the asthenosphere, the mantle is solid. This solid material extends all the way to Earth's core.

✔ **Reading Checkpoint** What is the asthenosphere?

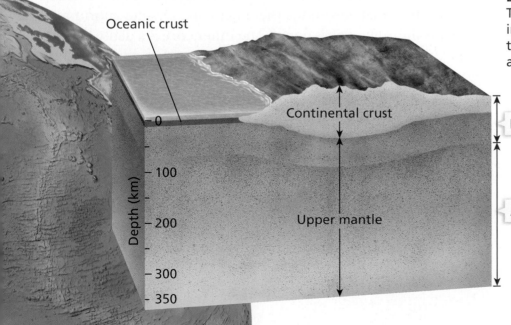

FIGURE 6
Lithosphere and Asthenosphere
The rigid lithosphere, which includes the crust, rests on the softer material of the asthenosphere.

Oceanic crust

Continental crust

Lithosphere

Asthenosphere

Depth (km)
0
100
200
300
350

Upper mantle

Temperature Inside Earth

The graph shows how temperatures change between Earth's surface and the bottom of the mantle. On this graph, the temperature at Earth's surface is 0°C. Study the graph carefully and then answer the questions.

1. **Reading Graphs** As you move from left to right on the *x*-axis, how does depth inside Earth change?

2. **Estimating** What is the temperature at the boundary between the lithosphere and the asthenosphere?

3. **Estimating** What is the temperature at the boundary between the lower mantle and the core?

4. **Interpreting Data** How does temperature change with depth in Earth's interior?

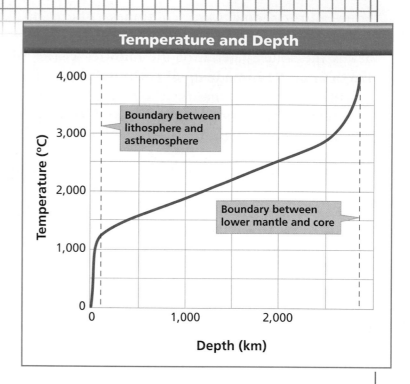

Temperature and Depth

Boundary between lithosphere and asthenosphere

Boundary between lower mantle and core

The Core

After traveling through the mantle, you reach Earth's core. **The core is made mostly of the metals iron and nickel. It consists of two parts—a liquid outer core and a solid inner core.** Together, the inner and outer core are 3,486 kilometers thick.

Outer Core and Inner Core The **outer core** is a layer of molten metal that surrounds the inner core. Despite enormous pressure, the outer core is liquid. The **inner core** is a dense ball of solid metal. In the inner core, extreme pressure squeezes the atoms of iron and nickel so much that they cannot spread out and become liquid.

Most of the current evidence suggests that both parts of the core are made of iron and nickel. But scientists have found data suggesting that the core also contains substances such as oxygen, sulfur, and silicon. Scientists must seek more data before they decide which of these other substances is most important.

 **Reading Checkpoint** What is the main difference between the outer core and the inner core?

Bar Magnet's Magnetic Field
The pattern of iron filings was made by sprinkling them on paper placed under a bar magnet.

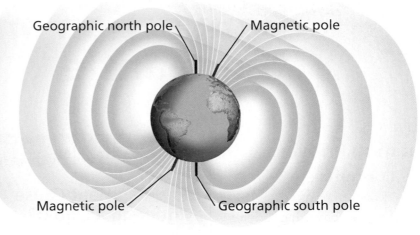

Geographic north pole   Magnetic pole

Magnetic pole   Geographic south pole

Earth's Magnetic Field
Like a magnet, Earth's magnetic field has north and south poles.

The Core and Earth's Magnetic Field Scientists think that movements in the liquid outer core create Earth's magnetic field. Because Earth has a magnetic field, the planet acts like a giant bar magnet. As you can see in Figure 7, the magnetic field affects the whole Earth.

Consider an ordinary bar magnet. If you place it on a piece of paper and sprinkle iron filings on the paper, the iron filings line up with the bar's magnetic field. If you could cover the entire planet with iron filings, they would form a similar pattern. When you use a compass, the compass needle aligns with the lines of force in Earth's magnetic field.

FIGURE 7
Earth's Magnetic Field
Just as a bar magnet is surrounded by its own magnetic field, Earth's magnetic field surrounds the planet.
Relating Cause and Effect *If you shifted the magnet beneath the paper, what would happen to the iron filings?*

Section 1 Assessment

Target Reading Skill **Using Prior Knowledge**
Review your graphic organizer and revise it based on what you just learned in the section.

Reviewing Key Concepts

1. a. **Explaining** Why is it difficult to determine Earth's inner structure?
   b. **Inferring** How are seismic waves used to provide evidence about Earth's interior?
2. a. **Listing** List Earth's three main layers.
   b. **Comparing and Contrasting** What is the difference between the lithosphere and the asthenosphere? In which layer is each located?

c. **Classifying** Classify each of the following layers as liquid, solid, or solid but able to flow slowly: lithosphere, asthenosphere, lower mantle, outer core, inner core.

Writing in Science

Narrative Write a narrative of your own imaginary journey to the center of Earth. Your narrative should describe the layers of Earth through which you travel and how temperature and pressure change beneath the surface.

Convection and the Mantle

Reading Preview

Key Concepts
- How is heat transferred?
- What causes convection currents?
- What causes convection currents in Earth's mantle?

Key Terms
- radiation • conduction
- convection • density
- convection current

 **Target Reading Skill**

Outlining An outline shows the relationship between major ideas and supporting ideas. As you read, make an outline about heat transfer. Use the red headings for the main topics and the blue headings for the subtopics.

Convection and the Mantle
I. Types of Heat Transfer
A. Radiation
B.
C.
II. Convection Currents

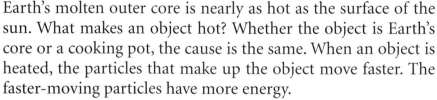 **Discover Activity**

How Can Heat Cause Motion in a Liquid?

1. Carefully pour some hot water into a small, shallow pan. Fill a clear, plastic cup about half full with cold water. Place the cup in the pan.
2. Allow the water to stand for two minutes until all motion stops.
3. Fill a plastic dropper with some food coloring. Then, holding the dropper under the water's surface and slightly away from the edge of the cup, gently squeeze a small droplet of the food coloring into the water.
4. Observe the water for one minute.
5. Add another droplet at the water's surface in the middle of the cup and observe again.

Think It Over

Inferring How do you explain what happened to the droplets of food coloring? Why do you think the second droplet moved in a way that was different from the way the first droplet moved?

Earth's molten outer core is nearly as hot as the surface of the sun. What makes an object hot? Whether the object is Earth's core or a cooking pot, the cause is the same. When an object is heated, the particles that make up the object move faster. The faster-moving particles have more energy.

If you have ever touched a hot pot accidentally, you have discovered for yourself (in a painful way) that heat moves. In this case, it moved from the hot pot to your hand. The movement of energy from a warmer object to a cooler object is called heat transfer. To explain how heat moves from Earth's core through the mantle, you need to know how heat is transferred.

Types of Heat Transfer

Heat always moves from a warmer substance to a cooler substance. For example, holding an ice cube will make your hand begin to feel cold in a few seconds. But is the coldness in the ice cube moving to your hand? No! Since cold is the absence of heat, it's the heat in your hand that moves to the ice cube. This is one of the ways that heat is transferred. **There are three types of heat transfer: radiation, conduction, and convection.**

Radiation The transfer of energy through space is called **radiation.** Heat transfer by radiation takes place with no direct contact between a heat source and an object. Sunlight is radiation that warms Earth's surface. Other familiar forms of radiation include the heat you feel around a flame or open fire.

Conduction Heat transfer within a material or between materials that are touching is called **conduction.** For example, a spoon in a pot of soup heats up by conduction, as shown in Figure 8. Heat moves from the hot soup and the pot to the particles that make up the spoon. The particles near the bottom of the spoon vibrate faster as they are heated, so they bump into other particles and heat them, too. Gradually the entire spoon heats up. When your hand touches the spoon, conduction transfers heat from the spoon directly to your skin. Then you feel the heat. Conduction is responsible for some of the heat transfer inside Earth.

> **Reading Checkpoint** What is conduction?

FIGURE 8
Conduction
In conduction, the heated particles of a substance transfer heat through contact with other particles in the substance. Conduction heats the spoon and the pot itself. That's why you need a mitt to protect your hand from the hot handle.

Go Online
PHSchool.com

For: More on convection currents in the mantle
Visit: PHSchool.com
Web Code: cfd-1012

Convection Heat can also be transferred by the movement of fluids—liquids and gases. **Convection** is heat transfer by the movement of currents within a fluid. During convection, heated particles of fluid begin to flow. This flow transfers heat from one part of the fluid to another.

Heat transfer by convection is caused by differences of temperature and density within a fluid. **Density** is a measure of how much mass there is in a volume of a substance. For example, rock is more dense than water because a given volume of rock has more mass than the same volume of water.

When a liquid or gas is heated, the particles move faster and spread apart. As a result, the particles of the heated fluid occupy more space. The fluid's density decreases. But when a fluid cools, its particles move more slowly and settle together more closely. As the fluid becomes cooler, its density increases.

Convection Currents

When you heat soup on a stove, convection occurs in the soup, as shown in Figure 9. As the soup at the bottom of the pot gets hot, it expands and therefore becomes less dense. The warm, less dense soup moves upward and floats over the cooler, denser soup. At the surface, the warm soup cools, becoming denser. Then gravity pulls this cooler, denser soup back down to the bottom of the pot, where it is heated again.

A constant flow begins as the cooler, denser soup sinks to the bottom of the pot and the warmer, less dense soup rises. A **convection current** is the flow that transfers heat within a fluid. **Heating and cooling of the fluid, changes in the fluid's density, and the force of gravity combine to set convection currents in motion.** Convection currents continue as long as heat is added. Without heat, convection currents eventually stop.

✓ **Reading Checkpoint** What is the role of gravity in creating convection currents?

FIGURE 9
Convection Currents
Differences in temperature and density cause convection currents. In the pot, convection currents arise because the soup close to the heat source is hotter and less dense than the soup near the surface.

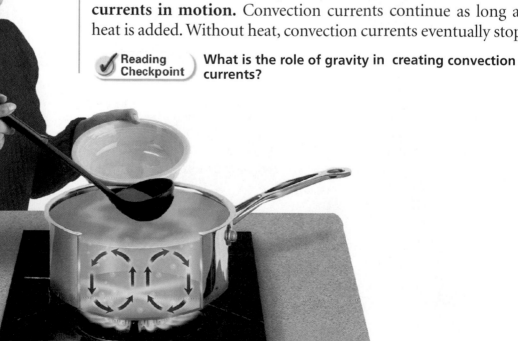

Convection Currents in Earth

In Earth's mantle, large amounts of heat are transferred by convection currents, as shown in Figure 10. **Heat from the core and the mantle itself causes convection currents in the mantle.**

How is it possible for mantle rock to flow? Over millions of years, the great heat and pressure in the mantle cause solid mantle rock to flow very slowly. Many geologists think that plumes of mantle rock rise slowly from the bottom of the mantle toward the top. The hot rock eventually cools and sinks back through the mantle. Over and over, the cycle of rising and sinking takes place. Convection currents like these have been moving inside Earth for more than four billion years!

There are also convection currents in the outer core. These convection currents cause Earth's magnetic field.

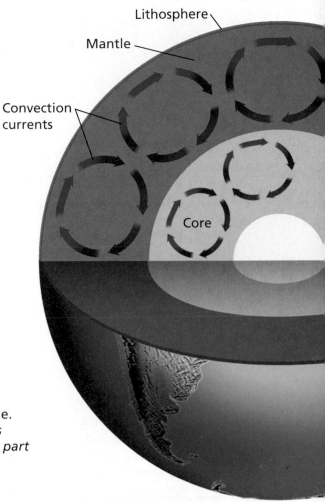

Lithosphere

Mantle

Convection currents

Core

FIGURE 10
Mantle Convection
Most geologists think that convection currents rise and sink through the mantle.
Applying Concepts *What part of Earth's interior is like the soup in the pot? What part is like the burner on the stove?*

Section 2 Assessment

⊙ **Target Reading Skill** **Outlining** Use the information in your outline about heat transfer to help you answer the questions below.

Reviewing Key Concepts

1. **a. Listing** What are the three types of heat transfer?
   b. Explaining How is heat transferred through space?
2. **a. Defining** What is a convection current?
   b. Relating Cause and Effect In general, what happens to the density of a fluid as it becomes hotter?
   c. Summarizing Describe how convection currents form.
3. **a. Identifying** Name two layers of Earth in which convection currents take place.
   b. Relating Cause and Effect What causes convection currents in the mantle?
   c. Predicting What will happen to the convection currents in the mantle if Earth's interior eventually cools down? Explain.

Lab zone **At-Home Activity**

Tracing Heat Flow Convection currents may keep the air inside your home at a comfortable temperature. Air is made up of gases, so it is a fluid. Regardless of the type of home heating system, heated air circulates through a room by convection. You may have tried to adjust the flow of air in a stuffy room by opening a window. When you did so, you were making use of convection currents. With an adult family member, study how your home is heated. Look for evidence of convection currents.

Drifting Continents

Reading Preview

Key Concepts
- What was Alfred Wegener's hypothesis about the continents?
- What evidence supported Wegener's hypothesis?
- Why was Wegener's hypothesis rejected by most scientists of his day?

Key Terms
- continental drift • Pangaea
- fossil

🎯 Target Reading Skill
Identifying Supporting Evidence As you read, identify the evidence that supports the hypothesis of continental drift. Write the evidence in a graphic organizer like the one below.

Evidence

Hypothesis

Earth's continents have moved. ← Shape of continents

← (blank)

← (blank)

How Are Earth's Continents Linked Together?
1. Find the oceans and the seven continents on a globe showing Earth's physical features.
2. How much of the globe is occupied by the Pacific Ocean? Does most of Earth's dry land lie in the Northern or Southern Hemisphere?
3. Find the points or areas where most of the continents are connected. Find the points at which several of the continents almost touch, but are not connected.
4. Examine the globe more closely. Find the great belt of mountains running from north to south along the western side of North and South America. Can you find another great belt of mountains on the globe?

Think It Over
Posing Questions What questions can you pose about how oceans, continents, and mountains are distributed on Earth's surface?

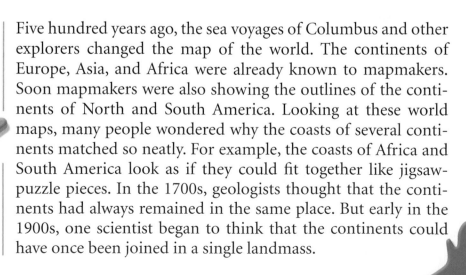

Five hundred years ago, the sea voyages of Columbus and other explorers changed the map of the world. The continents of Europe, Asia, and Africa were already known to mapmakers. Soon mapmakers were also showing the outlines of the continents of North and South America. Looking at these world maps, many people wondered why the coasts of several continents matched so neatly. For example, the coasts of Africa and South America look as if they could fit together like jigsaw-puzzle pieces. In the 1700s, geologists thought that the continents had always remained in the same place. But early in the 1900s, one scientist began to think that the continents could have once been joined in a single landmass.

FIGURE 11
Continental Puzzle Today's continents provide clues about Earth's history.
Observing *Which coastlines of continents seem to match up like jigsaw-puzzle pieces?*

Continental Drift

In 1910, a young German scientist named Alfred Wegener (VAY guh nur) became curious about the relationship of the continents. He hypothesized that Earth's continents had moved! **Wegener's hypothesis was that all the continents were once joined together in a single landmass and have since drifted apart.** Wegener's idea that the continents slowly moved over Earth's surface became known as **continental drift.**

According to Wegener, the continents drifted together to form the supercontinent **Pangaea** (pan JEE uh). *Pangaea* means "all lands." According to Wegener, Pangaea existed about 300 million years ago. This was the time when reptiles and winged insects first appeared. Tropical forests, which later formed coal deposits, covered large parts of Earth's surface.

Over tens of millions of years, Pangaea began to break apart. The pieces of Pangaea slowly moved toward their present-day locations. These pieces became the continents as they are today.

Wegener gathered evidence from different scientific fields to support his ideas about continental drift. He studied land features, fossils, and evidence of climate change. In 1915, Wegener published his evidence for continental drift in a book called *The Origin of Continents and Oceans.*

Go Online
SCiLINKS NSTA

For: Links on continental drift
Visit: www.SciLinks.org
Web Code: scn-1013

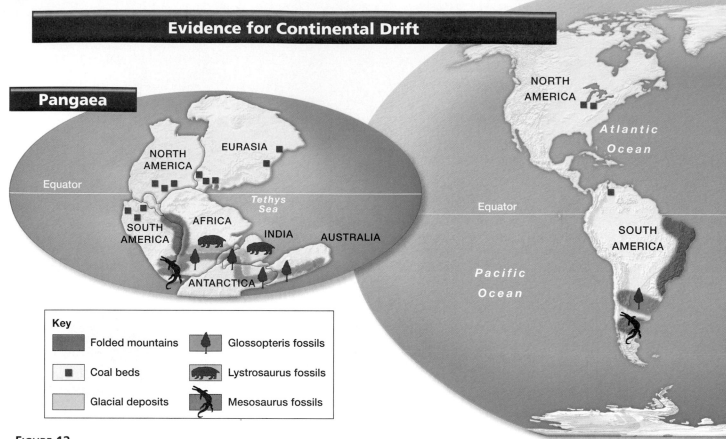

Pangaea

Key

■ Folded mountains		▲ Glossopteris fossils	
■ Coal beds		Lystrosaurus fossils	
Glacial deposits		Mesosaurus fossils	

FIGURE 12
Fossils and rocks found on different continents provide evidence that Earth's landmasses once were joined together in the supercontinent Pangaea.
Inferring *What do the matching mountain ranges in Africa and South America show, according to Wegener's hypothesis?*

Evidence From Land Features As shown in Figure 12, mountains and other features on the continents provided evidence for continental drift. For example, when Wegener pieced together maps of Africa and South America, he noticed that mountain ranges on both continents line up. He noticed that European coal fields match up with coal fields in North America.

Evidence From Fossils Wegener also used fossils to support his argument for continental drift. A **fossil** is any trace of an ancient organism that has been preserved in rock. For example, *Glossopteris* (glaw SAHP tuh ris), was a fernlike plant that lived 250 million years ago. *Glossopteris* fossils have been found in rocks in Africa, South America, Australia, India, and Antarctica. The occurrence of *Glossopteris* on these widely separated landmasses convinced Wegener that Pangaea had existed.

Other examples include fossils of the freshwater reptiles *Mesosaurus* and *Lystrosaurus*. These fossils have also been found in places now separated by oceans. Neither reptile could have swum great distances across salt water. Wegener inferred that these reptiles lived on a single landmass that has since split apart.

Lystrosaurus

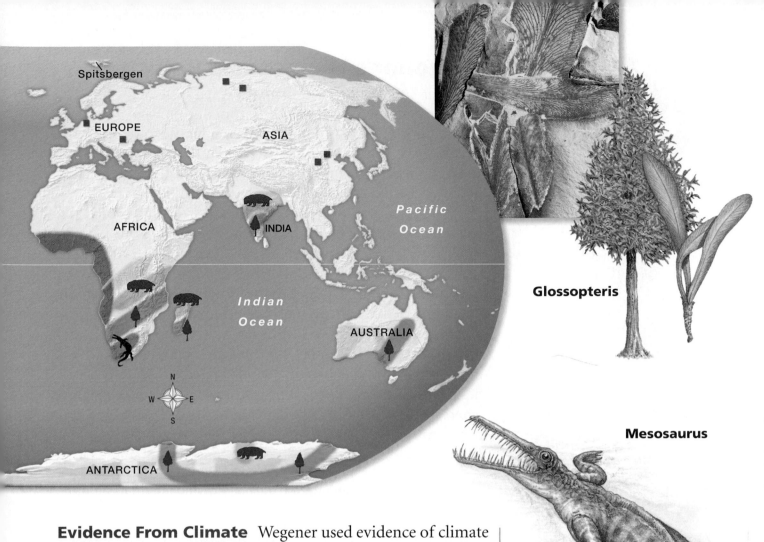

Glossopteris

Mesosaurus

Evidence From Climate Wegener used evidence of climate change to support his hypothesis. As a continent moves toward the equator, its climate becomes warmer. As a continent moves toward the poles, its climate becomes colder. But the continent carries with it the fossils and rocks that formed at its previous locations. For example, fossils of tropical plants are found on Spitsbergen, an island in the Arctic Ocean. When these plants lived about 300 million years ago, the island must have had a warm and mild climate. According to Wegener, Spitsbergen must have been located closer to the equator.

Geologists found evidence that when it was warm in Spitsbergen, the climate was much colder in South Africa. Deep scratches in rocks showed that continental glaciers once covered South Africa. Continental glaciers are thick layers of ice that cover hundreds of thousands of square kilometers. But the climate of South Africa is too mild today for continental glaciers to form. Wegener concluded that when Pangaea existed, South Africa was much closer to the South Pole. According to Wegener, the climates of Spitsbergen and South Africa changed because these landmasses had moved.

 **Reading Checkpoint** **How would continental drift affect a continent's climate?**

Wegener's Hypothesis Rejected

Wegener attempted to explain how continental drift took place. He suggested that the continents plowed across the ocean floors. **Unfortunately, Wegener could not provide a satisfactory explanation for the force that pushes or pulls the continents.** Because Wegener could not identify the cause of continental drift, most geologists rejected his idea.

For geologists to accept continental drift, they would also have had to change their ideas about how mountains form. In the early 1900s, many geologists thought that mountains formed because Earth was slowly cooling and shrinking. According to this hypothesis, mountains formed when the crust wrinkled like the skin of a dried-up apple.

Wegener said that if these geologists were correct, then mountains should be found all over Earth's surface. But mountains usually occur in narrow bands along the edges of continents. Wegener developed a hypothesis that better explained where mountains occur and how they form. Wegener proposed that when continents collide, their edges crumple and fold. The folding continents push up huge mountains.

✓ **Reading Checkpoint** According to Wegener, how do mountains form?

FIGURE 13
Alfred Wegener
Although scientists rejected his theory, Wegener continued to collect evidence on continental drift and to update his book. He died in 1930 on an expedition to explore Greenland's continental glacier.

Section 3 Assessment

Target Reading Skill

Identifying Supporting Evidence Refer to your graphic organizer about continental drift as you answer Question 2 below.

Reviewing Key Concepts

1. **a. Identifying** Who proposed the concept of continental drift?
   b. Summarizing According to the hypothesis of continental drift, how would a world map have changed over the last 250 million years?
2. **a. Reviewing** What evidence supported the hypothesis of continental drift?
   b. Explaining How did fossils provide evidence for continental drift?
   c. Forming Hypotheses Deposits of coal have been found beneath the ice of Antarctica. But coal only forms in warm swamps. Use Wegener's hypothesis to explain how coal could be found so near to the South Pole.

3. **a. Explaining** Why did most scientists reject Wegener's hypothesis of continental drift?
   b. Making Judgments Do you think the scientists of Wegener's time should have accepted his hypothesis? Why or why not?

Lab zone At-Home **Activity**

Moving the Continents Using a world map and tracing paper, trace the outlines of the continents that border the Atlantic Ocean. Label the continents. Then use scissors to carefully cut your map along the edges of the continents. Throw away the Atlantic Ocean. Place the two remaining pieces on a dark surface and ask family members to try to fit the two halves together. Explain to them about continental drift and Pangaea.

Sea-Floor Spreading

Reading Preview

Key Concepts
- What is the process of sea-floor spreading?
- What is the evidence for sea-floor spreading?
- What happens at deep-ocean trenches?

Key Terms
- mid-ocean ridge • sonar
- sea-floor spreading
- deep-ocean trench
- subduction

Target Reading Skill
Sequencing Make a flowchart to show the process of sea-floor spreading.

```
┌─────────────────────────┐
│   Magma erupts along    │
│    mid-ocean ridge      │
└─────────────────────────┘
            │
            ▼
┌─────────────────────────┐
│                         │
└─────────────────────────┘
            │
            ▼
┌─────────────────────────┐
│                         │
└──────────────∨∨─────────┘
```

Discover Activity

What Is the Effect of a Change in Density?
1. Partially fill a sink or dishpan with water.
2. Open up a dry washcloth in your hand. Does the washcloth feel light or heavy?
3. Moisten one edge of the washcloth in the water. Then gently place the washcloth so that it floats on the water's surface. Observe the washcloth carefully (especially at its edges) as it starts to sink.
4. Remove the washcloth from the water and open it up in your hand. Is the mass of the washcloth the same as, less than, or greater than when it was dry?

Think It Over
Observing How did the washcloth's density change? What effect did this change in density have on the washcloth?

Deep in the ocean, the temperature is near freezing. There is no light, and living things are generally scarce. Yet some areas of the deep-ocean floor are teeming with life. One of these areas is the East Pacific Rise. This area forms part of the Pacific Ocean floor off the coasts of Mexico and South America. Here, ocean water sinks through cracks, or vents, in the crust. The water is heated by contact with hot material from the mantle. The hot water then spurts back into the ocean.

Around these hot-water vents live some of the most bizarre creatures ever discovered. Giant, red-tipped tube worms sway in the water. Nearby sit giant clams nearly a meter across. Strange spider-like crabs scuttle by. Surprisingly, the geological features of this strange environment provided some of the best evidence for Wegener's hypothesis of continental drift.

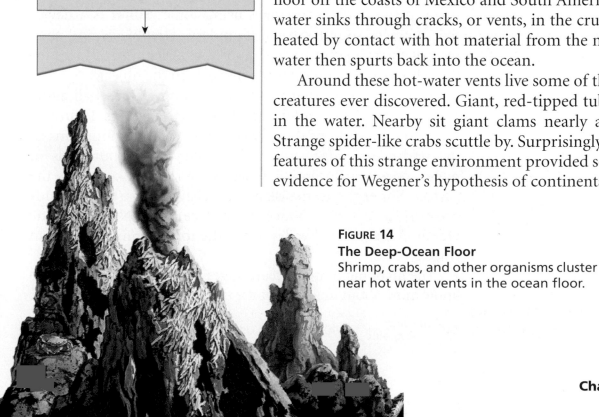

FIGURE 14
The Deep-Ocean Floor
Shrimp, crabs, and other organisms cluster near hot water vents in the ocean floor.

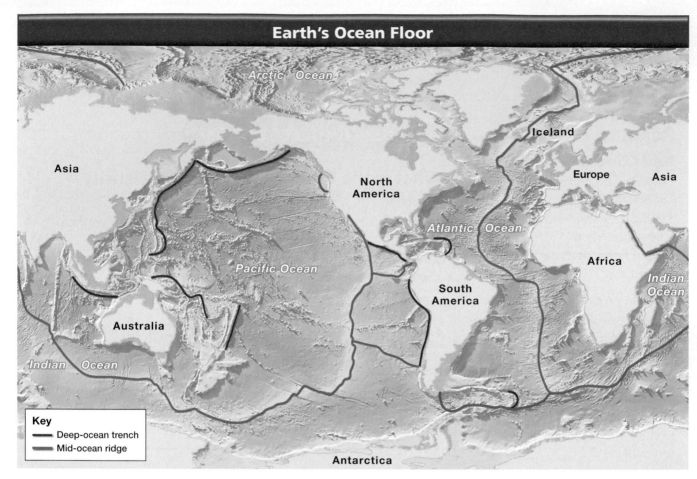

Earth's Ocean Floor

Arctic Ocean

Asia

North America

Iceland

Europe

Asia

Atlantic Ocean

Africa

Pacific Ocean

South America

Indian Ocean

Australia

Indian Ocean

Key
—— Deep-ocean trench
▬▬ Mid-ocean ridge

Antarctica

FIGURE 15
The mid-ocean ridge system is more than 50,000 kilometers long.
Interpreting Maps *What is unusual about Iceland?*

Mid-Ocean Ridges

The East Pacific Rise is just one of many **mid-ocean ridges** that wind beneath Earth's oceans. In the mid-1900s, scientists mapped the mid-ocean ridges using sonar. **Sonar** is a device that bounces sound waves off underwater objects and then records the echoes of these sound waves. The time it takes for the echo to arrive indicates the distance to the object.

Mid-ocean ridges curve like the seam of a baseball along the sea floor. They extend into all of Earth's oceans. Figure 15 shows the location of these ridges. Most of the mountains in the mid-ocean ridge system lie hidden under hundreds of meters of water. But in a few places the ridge pokes above the surface. For example, the island of Iceland is a part of the mid-ocean ridge that rises above the surface in the North Atlantic Ocean. A steep-sided valley splits the top of some mid-ocean ridges.

The mapping of mid-ocean ridges made scientists curious to know more about them. What are the ridges? How do they form?

 **Reading Checkpoint** What device is used to map the ocean floor?

What Is Sea-Floor Spreading?

Harry Hess, an American geologist, was one of the scientists who studied mid-ocean ridges. Hess carefully examined maps of the mid-ocean ridge system. Then he began to think about the ocean floor in relation to the problem of continental drift. Finally, he reached a startling conclusion: Maybe Wegener was right! Perhaps the continents do move.

In 1960, Hess proposed a radical idea. He suggested that a process he called **sea-floor spreading** continually adds new material to the ocean floor. **In sea-floor spreading, the sea floor spreads apart along both sides of a mid-ocean ridge as new crust is added. As a result, the ocean floors move like conveyor belts, carrying the continents along with them.** Look at Figure 16 to see the process of sea-floor spreading.

Sea-floor spreading begins at a mid-ocean ridge, which forms along a crack in the oceanic crust. Along the ridge, molten material that forms several kilometers beneath the surface rises and erupts. At the same time, older rock moves outward on both sides of the ridge. As the molten material cools, it forms a strip of solid rock in the center of the ridge. When more molten material flows into the crack, it forms a new strip of rock.

 **Reading Checkpoint** How does new oceanic crust form?

Go Online
PHSchool.com

For: More on sea-floor spreading
Visit: PHSchool.com
Web Code: cfd-1014

FIGURE 16
Sea-Floor Spreading
Molten material erupts through the valley that runs along the center of some mid-ocean ridges. This material hardens to form the rock of the ocean floor.
Applying Concepts *What happens to the rock along the ridge when new molten material erupts?*

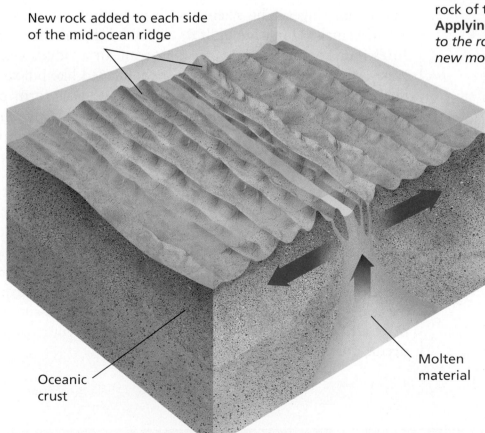

New rock added to each side of the mid-ocean ridge

Oceanic crust

Molten material

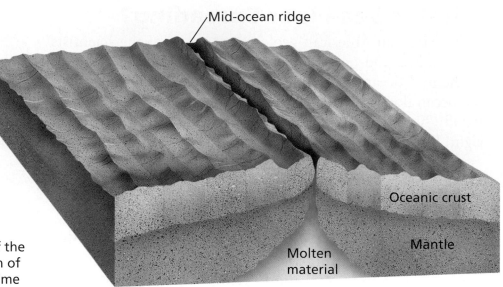

Mid-ocean ridge

Oceanic crust

Mantle

Molten material

Rock formed when Earth's magnetic field was normal

Rock formed when Earth's magnetic field was reversed

FIGURE 17
Magnetic Stripes
Magnetic stripes in the rock of the ocean floor show the direction of Earth's magnetic field at the time the rock hardened.
Interpreting Diagrams *How are these matching stripes evidence of sea-floor spreading?*

Evidence for Sea-Floor Spreading

Several types of evidence supported Hess's theory of sea-floor spreading: eruptions of molten material, magnetic stripes in the rock of the ocean floor, and the ages of the rocks themselves. This evidence led scientists to look again at Wegener's hypothesis of continental drift.

Evidence From Molten Material In the 1960s, scientists found evidence that new material is indeed erupting along mid-ocean ridges. The scientists dived to the ocean floor in *Alvin*, a small submarine built to withstand the crushing pressures four kilometers down in the ocean. In a ridge's central valley, *Alvin's* crew found strange rocks shaped like pillows or like toothpaste squeezed from a tube. Such rocks form only when molten material hardens quickly after erupting under water. These rocks showed that molten material has erupted again and again along the mid-ocean ridge.

Evidence From Magnetic Stripes When scientists studied patterns in the rocks of the ocean floor, they found more support for sea-floor spreading. In Section 1 you read that Earth behaves like a giant magnet, with a north pole and a south pole. Surprisingly, Earth's magnetic poles have reversed themselves many times during Earth's history. The last reversal happened 780,000 years ago. If the magnetic poles suddenly reversed themselves today, you would find that your compass needle points south.

Scientists discovered that the rock that makes up the ocean floor lies in a pattern of magnetized "stripes." These stripes hold a record of reversals in Earth's magnetic field. The rock of the ocean floor contains iron. The rock began as molten material that cooled and hardened. As the rock cooled, the iron bits inside lined up in the direction of Earth's magnetic poles. This locked the iron bits in place, giving the rocks a permanent "magnetic memory."

Using sensitive instruments, scientists recorded the magnetic memory of rocks on both sides of a mid-ocean ridge. They found that stripes of rock that formed when Earth's magnetic field pointed north alternate with stripes of rock that formed when the magnetic field pointed south. As shown in Figure 17, the pattern is the same on both sides of the ridge.

Evidence From Drilling Samples The final proof of sea-floor spreading came from rock samples obtained by drilling into the ocean floor. The *Glomar Challenger,* a drilling ship built in 1968, gathered the samples. The *Glomar Challenger* sent drilling pipes through water six kilometers deep to drill holes in the ocean floor. This feat has been compared to using a sharp-ended wire to dig a hole into a sidewalk from the top of the Empire State Building.

Samples from the sea floor were brought up through the pipes. Then the scientists determined the age of the rocks in the samples. They found that the farther away from a ridge the samples were taken, the older the rocks were. The youngest rocks were always in the center of the ridges. This showed that sea-floor spreading really has taken place.

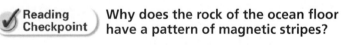

Reading Checkpoint Why does the rock of the ocean floor have a pattern of magnetic stripes?

FIGURE 18
Sea-Floor Drilling
The *Glomar Challenger* was the first research ship designed to drill samples of rock from the deep-ocean floor.

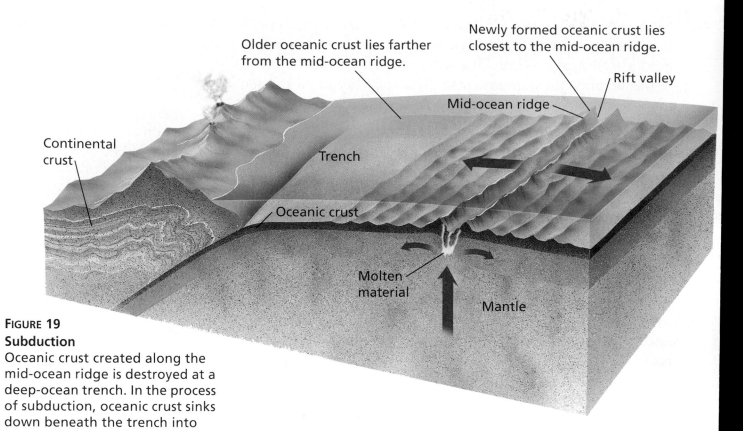

Older oceanic crust lies farther from the mid-ocean ridge.

Newly formed oceanic crust lies closest to the mid-ocean ridge.

Rift valley

Mid-ocean ridge

Continental crust

Trench

Oceanic crust

Molten material

Mantle

FIGURE 19
Subduction
Oceanic crust created along the mid-ocean ridge is destroyed at a deep-ocean trench. In the process of subduction, oceanic crust sinks down beneath the trench into the mantle.
Drawing Conclusions *Where would the densest oceanic crust be found?*

DISCOVERY
CHANNEL
SCHOOL

Plate Tectonics

Video Preview
▶ Video Field Trip
Video Assessment

Subduction at Trenches

How can the ocean floor keep getting wider and wider? The answer is that the ocean floor generally does not just keep spreading. Instead, the ocean floor plunges into deep underwater canyons called **deep-ocean trenches.** At a deep-ocean trench, the oceanic crust bends downward. What occurs at trenches? **In a process taking tens of millions of years, part of the ocean floor sinks back into the mantle at deep-ocean trenches.**

The Process of Subduction The process by which ocean floor sinks beneath a deep-ocean trench and back into the mantle is called **subduction** (sub DUK shun). As subduction occurs, crust closer to a mid-ocean ridge moves away from the ridge and toward a deep-ocean trench. Sea-floor spreading and subduction work together. They move the ocean floor as if it were on a giant conveyor belt.

New oceanic crust is hot. But as it moves away from the mid-ocean ridge, it cools and becomes more dense. Eventually, as shown in Figure 19, gravity pulls this older, denser oceanic crust down beneath the trench. The sinking crust is like the washcloth in the Discover activity at the beginning of this section. As the dry washcloth floating on the water gets wet, its density increases and it begins to sink.

Subduction and Earth's Oceans The processes of subduction and sea-floor spreading can change the size and shape of the oceans. Because of these processes, the ocean floor is renewed about every 200 million years. That is the time it takes for new rock to form at the mid-ocean ridge, move across the ocean, and sink into a trench.

The vast Pacific Ocean covers almost one third of the planet. And yet it is shrinking. How can that be? Sometimes a deep ocean trench swallows more oceanic crust than a mid-ocean ridge can produce. Then, if the ridge does not add new crust fast enough, the width of the ocean will shrink. In the Pacific Ocean, subduction through the many trenches that ring the ocean is occurring faster than new crust can be added.

On the other hand, the Atlantic Ocean is expanding. Unlike the Pacific Ocean, the Atlantic Ocean has only a few short trenches. As a result, the spreading ocean floor has virtually nowhere to go. In most places, the oceanic crust of the Atlantic Ocean floor is attached to the continental crust of the continents around the ocean. So as the Atlantic's ocean floor spreads, the continents along its edges also move. Over time, the whole ocean gets wider.

FIGURE 20
Growing an Ocean
Because of sea-floor spreading, the distance between Europe and North America is increasing by a few centimeters per year.

 **Reading Checkpoint** **Why is the Pacific Ocean shrinking?**

Section 4 Assessment

Target Reading Skill **Sequencing** Refer to your flowchart on sea-floor spreading as you answer the questions below.

Reviewing Key Concepts

1. **a. Naming** What scientist helped to discover the process of sea-floor spreading?
   b. Identifying Along what feature of the ocean floor does sea-floor spreading begin?
   c. Sequencing What are the steps in the process of sea-floor spreading?
2. **a. Reviewing** What three types of evidence provided support for the theory of sea-floor spreading?
   b. Applying Concepts How do rocks along the central valley of the mid-ocean ridge provide evidence of sea-floor spreading?
   c. Predicting Where would you expect to find the oldest rock on the ocean floor?

3. **a. Defining** What is a deep-ocean trench?
   b. Relating Cause and Effect What happens to oceanic crust at a deep-ocean trench?

Writing in Science

Description Write a description of what you might see if you could explore a mid-ocean ridge in a vessel like the *Alvin*. In your description, be sure to include the main features of the ocean floor along and near the ridge.

Modeling Sea-Floor Spreading

Problem

How does sea-floor spreading add material to the ocean floor?

Skills Focus

making models

Materials

- scissors
- colored marker
- metric ruler
- 2 sheets of unlined paper

Procedure

1. Draw stripes across one sheet of paper, parallel to the short sides of the paper. The stripes should vary in spacing and thickness.

2. Fold the paper in half lengthwise and write the word "Start" at the top of both halves of the paper. Using the scissors, carefully cut the paper in half along the fold line to form two strips.

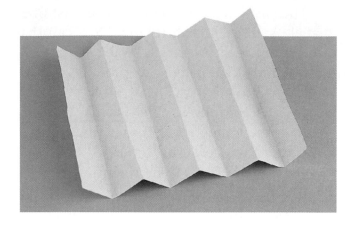

3. Lightly fold the second sheet of paper into eighths. Then unfold it, leaving creases in the paper. Fold this sheet in half lengthwise.

4. Starting at the fold, draw lines 5.5 cm long on the middle crease and the two creases closest to the ends of the paper.

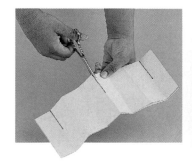

5. Now carefully cut along the lines you drew. Unfold the paper. There should be three slits in the center of the paper.

6. Put the two striped strips of paper together so their Start labels touch one another. Insert the Start ends of the strips up through the center slit and then pull them toward the side slits.

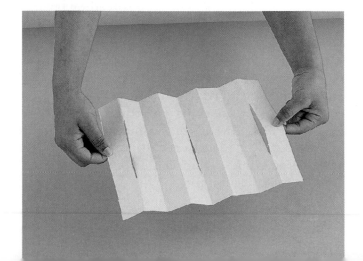

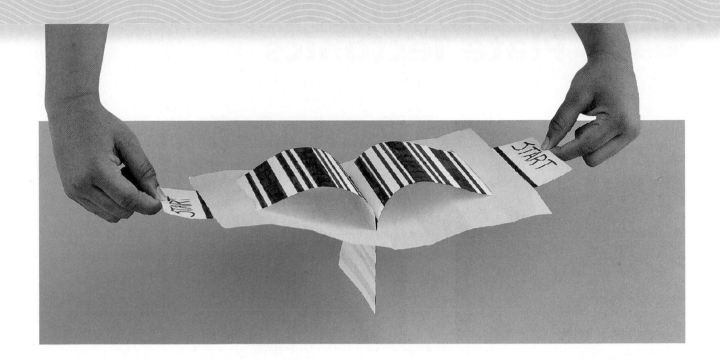

7. Insert the ends of the strips into the side slits. Pull the ends of the strips and watch what happens at the center slit.

8. Practice pulling the strips until you can make the two strips come up through the center and go down through the sides at the same time.

Analyze and Conclude

1. **Making Models** What feature of the ocean floor does the center slit stand for? What prominent feature of the ocean floor is missing from the model at this point?

2. **Making Models** What do the side slits stand for? What does the space under the paper stand for?

3. **Comparing and Contrasting** As shown by your model, how does the ocean floor close to the center slit differ from the ocean floor near a side slit? How does this difference affect the depth of the ocean?

4. **Making Models** What do the stripes on the strips stand for? Why is it important that your model have an identical pattern of stripes on both sides of the center slit?

5. **Applying Concepts** Explain how differences in density and temperature provide some of the force needed to cause sea-floor spreading and subduction.

6. **Communicating** Use your own words to describe the process of sea-floor spreading. What parts of the process were not shown by your model?

More to Explore

How could you modify your model to show an island that formed where a large amount of molten rock erupted from the mid-ocean ridge? How could you show what would happen to the island over a long period of time?

Section

5 The Theory of Plate Tectonics

Reading Preview

Key Concepts

- What is the theory of plate tectonics?
- What are the three types of plate boundaries?

Key Terms

- plate
- scientific theory
- plate tectonics
- fault
- divergent boundary
- rift valley
- convergent boundary
- transform boundary

Target Reading Skill

Building Vocabulary A definition states the meaning of a word or phrase by telling about its most important feature or function. After you read the section, reread the paragraphs that contain definitions of Key Terms. Use all the information you have learned to write a definition of each Key Term in your own words.

Lab zone Discover Activity

How Well Do the Continents Fit Together?

1. Using a world map in an atlas, trace the shape of each continent and Madagascar on a sheet of paper. Also trace the shape of India and the Arabian Peninsula.
2. Carefully cut apart the landmasses, leaving Asia and Europe as one piece. Separate India and the Arabian Peninsula from Asia.
3. Piece together the continents as they may have looked before the breakup of Pangaea. Then attach your reconstruction of Pangaea to a sheet of paper.

Think It Over

Drawing Conclusions How well did the pieces of your continents fit together? Do your observations support the idea that today's landmasses were once joined together? Explain.

Have you ever dropped a hard-boiled egg? If so, you may have noticed that the eggshell cracked in an irregular pattern of pieces. Earth's lithosphere, its solid outer shell, is not one unbroken layer. It is more like that cracked eggshell. It's broken into pieces separated by jagged cracks.

A Canadian scientist, J. Tuzo Wilson, observed that there are cracks in the continents similar to those on the ocean floor. In 1965, Wilson proposed a new way of looking at these cracks. According to Wilson, the lithosphere is broken into separate sections called **plates.** The plates fit together along cracks in the lithosphere. As shown in Figure 22, the plates carry the continents or parts of the ocean floor, or both. Wilson combined what geologists knew about sea-floor spreading, Earth's plates, and continental drift into a single theory. A **scientific theory** is a well-tested concept that explains a wide range of observations.

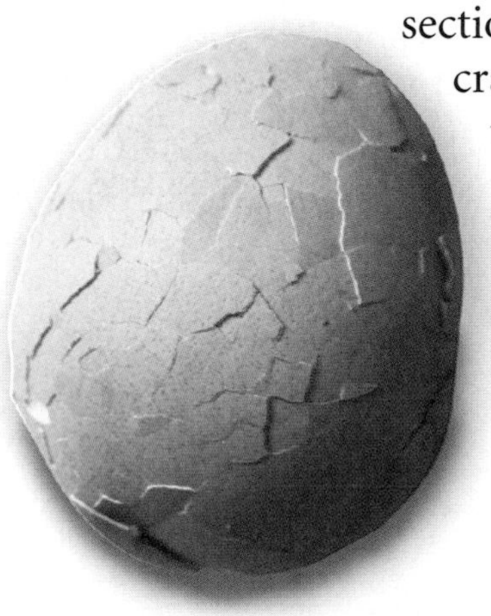

FIGURE 21
A Cracked Eggshell
Earth's lithosphere is broken into plates like the cracked shell of a hard-boiled egg.

How Plates Move

The theory of **plate tectonics** (tek TAHN iks) states that pieces of Earth's lithosphere are in slow, constant motion, driven by convection currents in the mantle. **The theory of plate tectonics explains the formation, movement, and subduction of Earth's plates.**

How can Earth's plates move? What force is great enough to move the heavy continents? Geologists think that movement of convection currents in the mantle is the major force that causes plate motion. During subduction, gravity pulls one edge of a plate down into the mantle. The rest of the plate also moves. This slow movement is similar to what happens in a pot of soup when gravity causes the cooler, denser soup near the surface to sink.

As the plates move, they collide, pull apart, or grind past each other, producing spectacular changes in Earth's surface. These changes include volcanoes, mountain ranges, and deep-ocean trenches.

Lab zone Skills **Activity**

Predicting

Study the map of Earth's plates in Figure 22. Notice the arrows that show the direction of plate movement. Now find the Nazca plate on the map. Which direction is it moving? Find the South American plate and describe its movement. What do you think will happen as these plates continue to move?

FIGURE 22
Plate boundaries divide the lithosphere into large plates.
Interpreting Maps *Which plates include only ocean floor? Which plates include both continents and ocean floor?*

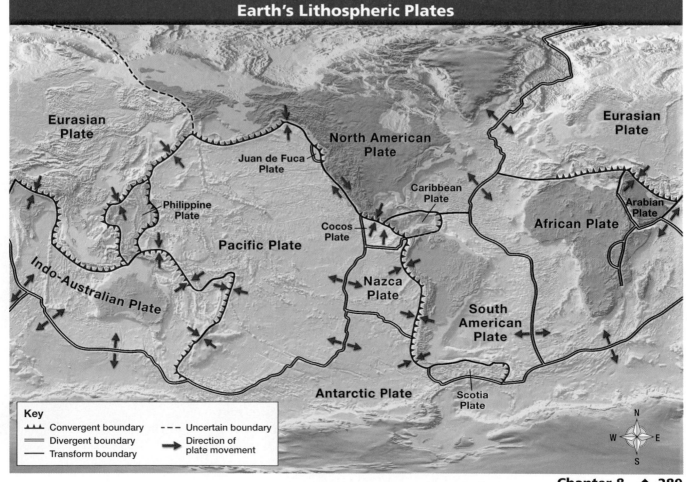

Earth's Lithospheric Plates

Eurasian Plate

Juan de Fuca Plate

North American Plate

Philippine Plate

Pacific Plate

Cocos Plate

Caribbean Plate

Eurasian Plate

Arabian Plate

African Plate

Indo-Australian Plate

Nazca Plate

South American Plate

Antarctic Plate

Scotia Plate

Key
⩕⩕⩕ Convergent boundary
═══ Divergent boundary
─── Transform boundary
--- Uncertain boundary
→ Direction of plate movement

N W E S

Chapter 8 ♦ 289

Plate Boundaries

The edges of Earth's plates meet at plate boundaries. Plate boundaries extend deep into the lithosphere. **Faults**—breaks in Earth's crust where rocks have slipped past each other—form along these boundaries. **As shown in Figure 23, there are three kinds of plate boundaries: divergent boundaries, convergent boundaries, and transform boundaries. A different type of plate movement occurs along each type of boundary.**

Scientists have used instruments on satellites to measure plate motion very precisely. The plates move at amazingly slow rates: from about 1 to 24 centimeters per year. The North American and Eurasian plates are moving apart at a rate of 2.5 centimeters per year. That's about as fast as your fingernails grow. This may not seem like much, but these plates have been moving apart for tens of millions of years.

Divergent Boundaries The place where two plates move apart, or diverge, is called a **divergent boundary** (dy VUR junt). Most divergent boundaries occur along the mid-ocean ridges where sea-floor spreading occurs.

Divergent boundaries also occur on land. When a divergent boundary develops on land, two of Earth's plates slide apart. A deep valley called a **rift valley** forms along the divergent boundary. For example, the Great Rift Valley in East Africa marks a deep crack in the African continent.

FIGURE 23
Plate Tectonics

Plate movements have built many of the features of Earth's land surfaces and ocean floors.
Predicting *What will eventually happen if a rift valley continues to pull apart?*

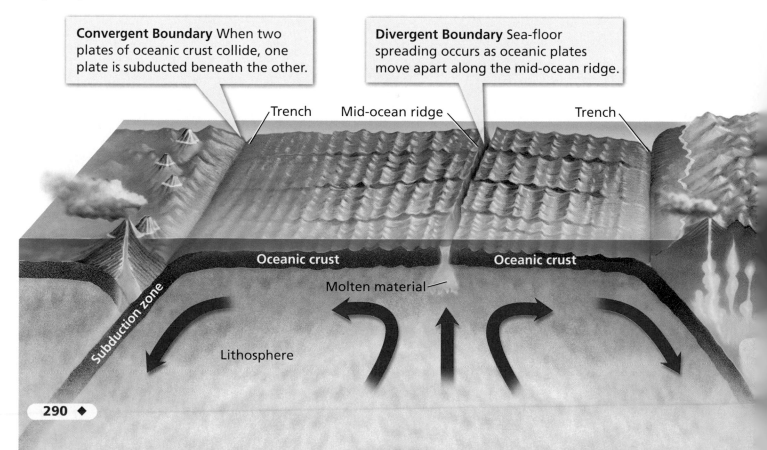

Convergent Boundary When two plates of oceanic crust collide, one plate is subducted beneath the other.

Divergent Boundary Sea-floor spreading occurs as oceanic plates move apart along the mid-ocean ridge.

Trench   Mid-ocean ridge   Trench

Oceanic crust   Oceanic crust

Molten material

Subduction zone

Lithosphere

Convergent Boundaries The place where two plates come together, or converge, is called a **convergent boundary** (kun VUR junt). When two plates converge, the result is called a collision. When two plates collide, the density of the plates determines which one comes out on top.

Oceanic crust becomes cooler and denser as it spreads away from the mid-ocean ridge. Where two plates carrying oceanic crust meet at a trench, the plate that is more dense sinks under the other plate.

Sometimes a plate carrying oceanic crust collides with a plate carrying continental crust. Oceanic crust is more dense than continental crust. The less dense continental crust can't sink under the more dense oceanic crust. Instead, subduction occurs as the oceanic plate sinks beneath the continental plate.

When two plates carrying continental crust collide, subduction does not take place. Neither piece of crust is dense enough to sink very far into the mantle. Instead, the collision squeezes the crust into mighty mountain ranges.

Transform Boundaries A **transform boundary** is a place where two plates slip past each other, moving in opposite directions. Earthquakes often occur along transform boundaries, but crust is neither created nor destroyed.

Reading Checkpoint What features form where two continental plates come together?

Math Skills

Calculating a Rate

To calculate the rate of plate motion, divide the distance the plate moves by the time it takes to move that distance.

$$\text{Rate} = \frac{\text{Distance}}{\text{Time}}$$

For example, a plate takes 2 million years to move 156 km. Calculate its rate of motion.

$$\frac{156 \text{ km}}{2,000,000 \text{ years}} = 7.8 \text{ cm per year}$$

Practice Problem The Pacific plate is sliding past the North American plate. It has taken 10 million years for the plate to move 600 km. What is the Pacific plate's rate of motion?

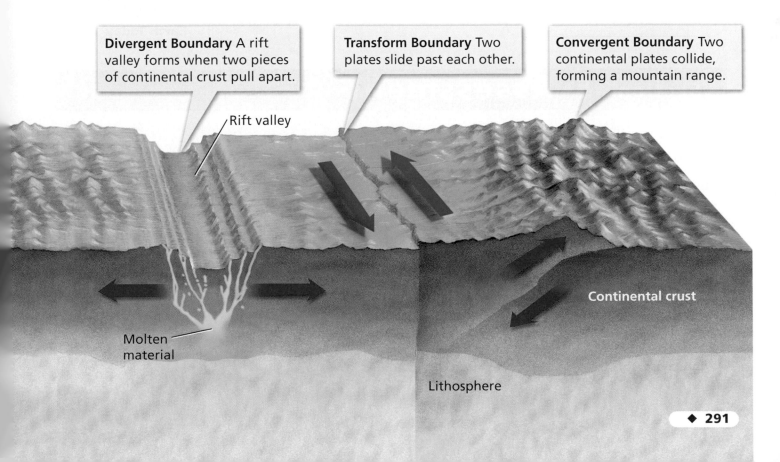

Divergent Boundary A rift valley forms when two pieces of continental crust pull apart.

Transform Boundary Two plates slide past each other.

Convergent Boundary Two continental plates collide, forming a mountain range.

Rift valley

Molten material

Lithosphere

Continental crust

225 Million Years Ago

Plate Motions Over Time The movement of Earth's plates has greatly changed Earth's surface. Geologists have evidence that, before Pangaea existed, other supercontinents formed and split apart over billions of years. Pangaea itself formed when Earth's landmasses drifted together about 260 million years ago. Then, about 225 million years ago, Pangaea began to break apart. Figure 24 shows how major landmasses have moved since the breakup of Pangaea.

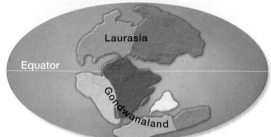
180–200 Million Years Ago

FIGURE 24
Continental Drift
It has taken the continents about 225 million years since the breakup of Pangaea to move to their present locations. **Posing Questions** *What questions would you need to answer in order to predict where the continents will be in 50 million years?*

135 Million Years Ago

Earth Today

Go Online
active art

For: Continental Drift activity
Visit: PHSchool.com
Web Code: cfp-1015

Section 5 Assessment

Target Reading Skill **Building Vocabulary** Use your definitions to help answer the questions.

Reviewing Key Concepts

1. a. **Defining** What are plates?
   b. **Summarizing** In your own words, what is the theory of plate tectonics?
   c. **Relating Cause and Effect** What do scientists think causes the movement of Earth's plates?
2. a. **Listing** What are the three types of plate boundaries?
   b. **Describing** Describe the type of movement that occurs at each type of plate boundary.
   c. **Predicting** What is likely to occur at a plate boundary where oceanic crust collides with continental crust?

Math **Practice**

3. **Calculating a Rate** There are two islands on opposite sides of a mid-ocean ridge in the Atlantic Ocean. During the last 8 million years, the distance between the islands has increased by 200 kilometers. Calculate the rate at which the two plates are diverging.

Modeling Mantle Convection Currents

Problem

How might convection in Earth's mantle affect tectonic plates?

Skills Focus

making models, observing

Materials

- large plastic bottle • food coloring • small glass jar • aluminum foil or plastic wrap
- rubber band • several paper hole punches or small pieces of paper • tap water

Procedure

1. Fill the large bottle about half full with cold tap water.

2. Partly fill the small jar with hot tap water and stir in 6 drops of food coloring. Carefully add enough hot water to fill the jar to the brim.

3. Cover the top of the jar with aluminum foil or plastic wrap and secure with a rubber band.

4. Carefully lower the jar into the bottle of tap water.

5. Place the pieces of paper on the surface of the water.

6. Without disturbing the water, use the tip of the pencil to make two small holes about 2–4 mm in diameter in the material covering the jar.

7. Predict what will happen to the colored water and to the pieces of paper floating on the surface.

8. Observe the contents of the jar, as well as the paper pieces on the surface of the water.

Analyze and Conclude

1. **Observing** Describe what happened to the colored water and to the pieces of paper after the holes were punched in the material covering the jar.

2. **Drawing Conclusions** How did your prediction compare with what actually happened to the colored water and pieces of paper?

3. **Inferring** What type of heat transfer took place in the bottle? Describe how the transfer occurred.

4. **Making Models** Which part of your model represents a tectonic plate? Which part represents Earth's mantle?

5. **Communicating** How well do you think this lab modeled the movement of Earth's plates? What similarities exist between this model and actual plate movement? What factors weren't you able to model in this lab?

Designing Experiments

Repeat this activity, but develop a plan to measure the temperature of the water inside the large bottle. Is there a difference in temperature between the water's surface and the water near the top of the small jar? Do you observe any change in the convection currents as the water temperature changes? With your teacher's approval, carry out your plan.

Equator Pangaea

① Earth's Interior

Key Concepts

- Geologists have used two main types of evidence to learn about Earth's interior: direct evidence from rock samples and indirect evidence from seismic waves.

- The three main layers of Earth are the crust, the mantle, and the core. These layers vary greatly in size, composition, temperature, and pressure.

- The crust is a layer of solid rock that includes both dry land and the ocean floor.

- Earth's mantle is made up of rock that is very hot, but solid. Scientists divide the mantle into layers based on physical characteristics.

- The core is made mostly of the metals iron and nickel. It consists of two parts—a liquid outer core and a solid inner core.

Key Terms

- seismic waves • pressure • crust • basalt
- granite • mantle • lithosphere
- asthenosphere • outer core • inner core

② Convection and the Mantle

Key Concepts

- There are three types of heat transfer: radiation, conduction, and convection.

- Heating and cooling of the fluid, changes in the fluid's density, and the force of gravity combine to set convection currents in motion.

- Heat from the core and the mantle itself causes convection currents in the mantle.

Key Terms

- radiation • conduction • convection
- density • convection current

③ Drifting Continents

Key Concepts

- Wegener's hypothesis was that all the continents had once been joined together in a single landmass and have since drifted apart.

- Wegener gathered evidence from different scientific fields to support his ideas about continental drift. He studied land features, fossils, and evidence of climate change.

- Wegener could not provide a satisfactory explanation for the force that pushes or pulls the continents.

Key Terms

- continental drift • Pangaea • fossil

④ Sea-Floor Spreading

Key Concepts

- In sea-floor spreading, the sea floor spreads apart along both sides of a mid-ocean ridge as new crust is added. As a result, the ocean floors move like conveyor belts, carrying the continents along with them.

- Several types of evidence supported Hess's theory of sea-floor spreading: eruptions of molten material, magnetic stripes in the rock of the ocean floor, and the ages of the rocks.

- In a process taking tens of millions of years, part of the ocean floor sinks back into the mantle at deep-ocean trenches.

Key Terms

- mid-ocean ridge • sonar • sea-floor spreading
- deep-ocean trench • subduction

⑤ The Theory of Plate Tectonics

Key Concepts

- The theory of plate tectonics explains the formation, movement, and subduction of Earth's plates.

- There are three kinds of plate boundaries: divergent boundaries, convergent boundaries, and transform boundaries. A different type of plate movement occurs along each.

Key Terms

- plate • scientific theory • plate tectonics
- fault • divergent boundary • rift valley
- convergent boundary • transform boundary

Review and Assessment

Go Online
PHSchool.com

For: Self-assessment
Visit: PHSchool.com
Web Code: cfa-1010

Organizing Information

Comparing and Contrasting Fill in the compare-and-contrast table to compare the characteristics of the different types of plate boundaries.

Type of Plate Boundary	Type of Motion	Effect on Crust	Feature(s) Formed
a. ___?___ boundary	Plates slide past each other.	b. ___?___	c. ___?___
d. ___?___ boundary	e. ___?___	Subduction or mountain building	f. ___?___
g. ___?___ boundary	h. ___?___	i. ___?___	Mid-ocean ridge, ocean floor

Reviewing Key Terms

Choose the letter of the best answer.

1. The relatively soft layer of the upper mantle is the
   a. asthenosphere.
   b. lithosphere.
   c. inner core.
   d. continental crust.

2. The transfer of heat by the direct contact of particles of matter is
   a. pressure.
   b. radiation.
   c. conduction.
   d. convection.

3. Subduction of the ocean floor takes place at
   a. the lower mantle.
   b. mid-ocean ridges.
   c. rift valleys.
   d. trenches.

4. The process that powers plate tectonics is
   a. radiation.
   b. convection.
   c. conduction.
   d. subduction.

5. Two plates collide with each other at
   a. a divergent boundary.
   b. a convergent boundary.
   c. the boundary between the mantle and the crust.
   d. a transform boundary.

If the statement is true, write *true*. If it is false, change the underlined word or words to make the statement true.

6. Continental <u>crust</u> is made of rocks such as granite.

7. Slow movements of mantle rock called <u>radiation</u> transfer heat in the mantle.

8. <u>The single landmass that broke apart 250 million years ago was Pangaea.</u>

9. <u>Mid-ocean ridges</u> are places where oceanic crust sinks back to the mantle.

10. When two continental plates diverge, a <u>transform boundary</u> forms.

Writing in Science

Prediction Now that you have learned about the theory of plate tectonics, write a paragraph predicting what the shape and positions of Earth's continents will be 50 million years in the future. Include what would happen to the oceans if continental landmasses became connected in new ways or drifted from their present locations.

Discovery CHANNEL SCHOOL

Plate Tectonics

Video Preview
Video Field Trip
▶ Video Assessment

Review and Assessment

Checking Concepts

11. What kinds of indirect evidence do geologists use to study the structure of Earth?

12. How do temperature and pressure change as you go deeper into Earth?

13. What happens in Earth's interior to produce Earth's magnetic field? Describe the layer where the magnetic field is produced.

14. Why are there convection currents in the mantle?

15. Why are the oldest parts of the ocean floor no older than about 200 million years old?

16. How do magnetic stripes form on the ocean floor? Why are these stripes significant?

Thinking Critically

17. Comparing and Contrasting How are oceanic and continental crust alike? How do they differ?

18. Sequencing Place these terms in correct order so they begin at Earth's surface and move toward the center: inner core, asthenosphere, lower mantle, lithosphere, outer core.

19. Predicting In the diagram below, a plate of oceanic crust is colliding with a plate of continental crust. What will happen? Why?

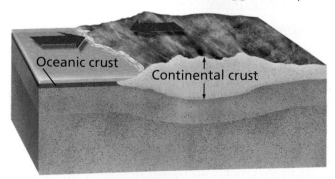

20. Relating Cause and Effect What do many geologists think is the driving force of plate tectonics? Explain.

21. Making Judgments Scientists refer to plate tectonics as a *theory*. What is a theory? How is plate tectonics a theory? Why isn't continental drift considered a theory? (*Hint*: Refer to the Skills Handbook for more on theories.)

Math Practice

22. Calculating a Rate It takes 100,000 years for a plate to move about 14 kilometers. Calculate the rate of plate motion.

Applying Skills

Use the map to answer Questions 23–25.

Geologists think that a new plate boundary is forming in the Indian Ocean. The part of the plate carrying Australia is twisting away from the part of the plate carrying India.

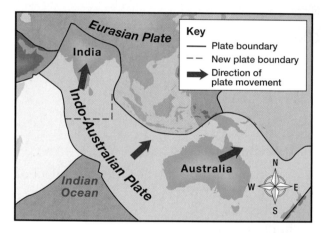

23. Interpreting Maps In what direction is the part of the plate carrying Australia moving? In what direction is the part carrying India moving?

24. Predicting As India and Australia move in different directions, what type of plate boundary will form between them?

25. Inferring What features could occur where the northern part of the Indo-Australian plate is colliding with the Eurasian plate?

Lab zone Chapter **Project**

Performance Assessment Present your model to the class. Point out the types of plate boundaries on your model. Discuss the plate motions and landforms that result in these areas.

ⓘ Standardized Test Practice

Choose the letter that best answers the question or completes the statement.

1. Which of the following is evidence for sea-floor spreading?
     A matching patterns of magnetic stripes in the ocean floor
     B volcanic eruptions along mid-ocean ridges
     C older rock found farther from mid-ocean ridges
     D all of the above

2. Wegener thought the continents moved because fossils of the same organisms are found on widely separated continents. Wegener's use of fossil evidence is an example of a(n)
     A prediction.
     B observation.
     C inference.
     D controlled experiment.

3. The table below shows the movement of rock away from a mid-ocean ridge, and the time in years it takes sea-floor spreading to move the rock that distance.

Distance (meters)	Time (years)
50	4,000
100	8,000
150	12,000

What is the speed of the rock?

  A 0.0125 m per year   **B** 12.5 m per year
  C 80 m per year   **D** 200,000 m per year

4. Which of the following best describes the process in the diagram below?
     A Converging plates form a transform boundary.
     B Converging plates form volcanoes.
     C Diverging plates form a mid-ocean ridge.
     D Diverging plates form a rift valley.

Open-Ended Question

5. Today, the Mediterranean Sea lies between Europe and Africa. But the African plate is moving toward the Eurasian plate at a rate of a few centimeters per year. Predict how this area will change in 100 million years. In your answer, first explain how the Mediterranean Sea will change. Then explain what will happen on land.

Academic Standards

This chapter addresses these Indiana standards.

The Physical Setting

7.3.4 Explain how heat flow and movement within Earth cause earthquakes and volcanic eruptions and create mountains and ocean basins.

7.3.7 Give examples of abrupt and very slow changes in Earth's surface.

Common Themes

7.7.2 Use different models to represent the same thing, noting that the model's type and complexity depend on its purpose.

An earthquake destroyed this freeway in Oakland, California, in 1989. ▶

Lab zone™ Chapter **Project**

Design and Build an Earthquake-Safe House

Earthquakes like the ones that caused the damage in this picture are proof that our planet is subject to great forces from within. Earthquakes remind us that we live on the moving pieces of Earth's crust. In this Chapter Project you will design a structure that can withstand earthquakes.

Your Goal To design, build, and test a model structure that is earthquake resistant

Your structure must

● be made of materials that have been approved by your teacher
● be built to specifications agreed on by your class
● be able to withstand several "earthquakes" of increasing intensity
● be built following the safety guidelines in Appendix A

Plan It! Before you design your model, find out how earthquakes damage structures such as homes, office buildings, and highways. Preview the chapter to find out how engineers design structures to withstand earthquakes. Then choose materials for your structure and sketch your design. When your teacher has approved your design, build and test your structure.

Forces in Earth's Crust

Reading Preview

Key Concepts
- How does stress in the crust change Earth's surface?
- Where are faults usually found, and why do they form?
- What land features result from the forces of plate movement?

Key Terms
- stress • tension
- compression • shearing
- normal fault • hanging wall
- footwall • reverse fault
- strike-slip fault • anticline
- syncline • plateau

Target Reading Skill

Building Vocabulary
A definition states the meaning of a word or phrase. As you read, write a definition of each Key Term in your own words.

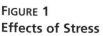

Lab zone Discover **Activity**

How Does Stress Affect Earth's Crust?

1. Put on your goggles.
2. Holding a popsicle stick at both ends, slowly bend it into an arch.
3. Release the pressure on the popsicle stick and observe what happens.
4. Repeat Steps 1 and 2. This time, however, keep bending the ends of the popsicle stick toward each other. What happens to the wood?

Think It Over
Predicting Think of the popsicle stick as a model for part of Earth's crust. What do you think might eventually happen as the forces of plate movement bend the crust?

The movement of Earth's plates creates enormous forces that squeeze or pull the rock in the crust as if it were a candy bar. These forces are examples of **stress,** a force that acts on rock to change its shape or volume. (A rock's volume is the amount of space the rock takes up.) Because stress is a force, it adds energy to the rock. The energy is stored in the rock until the rock changes shape or breaks.

If you try to break a caramel candy bar in two, it may only bend and stretch at first. Like a candy bar, many types of rock can bend or fold. But beyond a certain limit, even these rocks will break.

FIGURE 1
Effects of Stress
Powerful forces in Earth's crust caused the ground beneath this athletic field in Taiwan to change its shape.

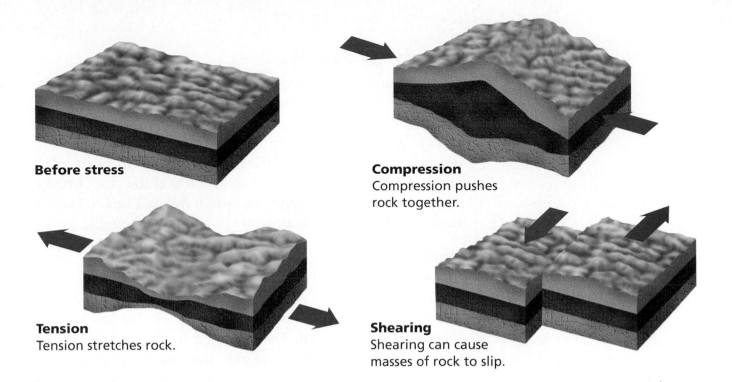

Before stress

Compression
Compression pushes rock together.

Tension
Tension stretches rock.

Shearing
Shearing can cause masses of rock to slip.

Types of Stress

Three different kinds of stress can occur in the crust—tension, compression, and shearing. **Tension, compression, and shearing work over millions of years to change the shape and volume of rock.** These forces cause some rocks to become brittle and snap. Other rocks bend slowly, like road tar softened by the sun. Figure 2 shows how stress affects the crust.

Most changes in the crust occur so slowly that they cannot be observed directly. But if you could speed up time so a billion years passed by in minutes, you could see the crust bend, stretch, break, tilt, fold, and slide. The slow shift of Earth's plates causes these changes.

Tension The stress force called **tension** pulls on the crust, stretching rock so that it becomes thinner in the middle. The effect of tension on rock is somewhat like pulling apart a piece of warm bubble gum. Tension occurs where two plates are moving apart.

Compression The stress force called **compression** squeezes rock until it folds or breaks. One plate pushing against another can compress rock like a giant trash compactor.

Shearing Stress that pushes a mass of rock in two opposite directions is called **shearing.** Shearing can cause rock to break and slip apart or to change its shape.

FIGURE 2
Stress in Earth's Crust
Stress forces push, pull, or twist the rocks in Earth's crust.
Relating Cause and Effect *Which type of stress tends to shorten part of the crust?*

 **Reading Checkpoint** How does shearing affect rock in Earth's crust?

Kinds of Faults

When enough stress builds up in rock, the rock breaks, creating a fault. Recall that a fault is a break in the rock of the crust where rock surfaces slip past each other. The rocks on both sides of a fault can move up or down or sideways. **Most faults occur along plate boundaries, where the forces of plate motion push or pull the crust so much that the crust breaks. There are three main types of faults: normal faults, reverse faults, and strike-slip faults.**

Normal Faults Tension in Earth's crust pulls rock apart, causing **normal faults.** In a normal fault, the fault is at an angle, so one block of rock lies above the fault while the other block lies below the fault. The block of rock that lies above is called the **hanging wall.** The rock that lies below is called the **footwall.** Look at Figure 3 to see how the hanging wall lies above the footwall. When movement occurs along a normal fault, the hanging wall slips downward. Normal faults occur where plates diverge, or pull apart. For example, normal faults are found along the Rio Grande rift valley in New Mexico, where two pieces of Earth's crust are under tension.

FIGURE 3
Kinds of Faults

There are three main kinds of faults: normal faults, reverse faults, and strike-slip faults.
Inferring *Which half of a normal fault would you expect to form the floor of a valley? Why?*

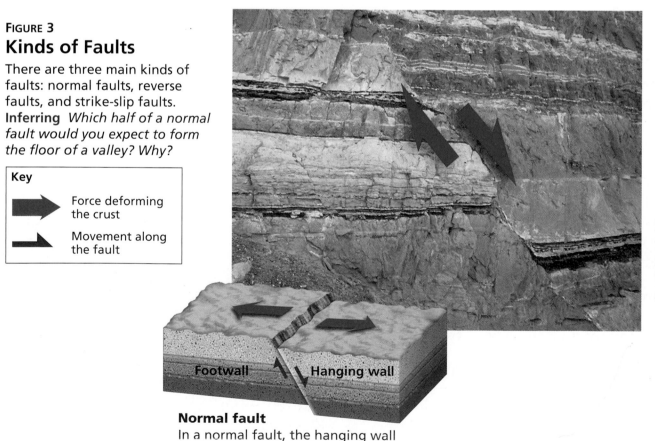

Key

Force deforming the crust

Movement along the fault

Footwall   Hanging wall

Normal fault
In a normal fault, the hanging wall slips down relative to the footwall.

Reverse Faults In places where the rock of the crust is pushed together, compression causes reverse faults to form. A **reverse fault** has the same structure as a normal fault, but the blocks move in the opposite direction. Look at Figure 3 to see how the rocks along a reverse fault move. As in a normal fault, one side of a reverse fault lies at an angle above the other side. The rock forming the hanging wall of a reverse fault slides up and over the footwall. Movement along reverse faults produced part of the northern Rocky Mountains in the western United States and Canada.

Strike-Slip Faults In places where plates move past each other, shearing creates strike-slip faults. In a **strike-slip fault,** the rocks on either side of the fault slip past each other sideways, with little up or down motion. A strike-slip fault that forms the boundary between two plates is called a transform boundary. The San Andreas fault in California is an example of a strike-slip fault that is a transform boundary.

For: Links on faults
Visit: www.SciLinks.org
Web Code: scn-1021

 **Reading Checkpoint** What is the difference between a hanging wall and a footwall?

Reverse fault
In a reverse fault, the hanging wall moves up relative to the footwall.

Strike-slip fault
Rocks on either side of a strike-slip fault slip past each other.

FIGURE 4
Effects of Folding
Compression and folding of the crust produce anticlines, which arch upward, and synclines, which dip downward. Over millions of years, folding can push up high mountain ranges. **Predicting** *If the folding in the diagram continued, what kind of fault might form?*

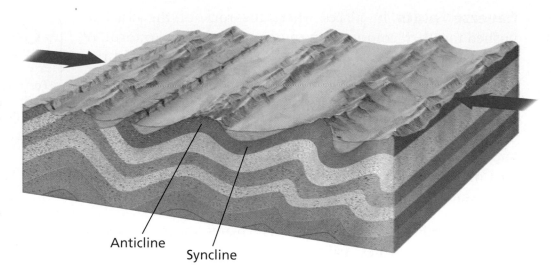

Anticline   Syncline

Changing Earth's Surface

The forces produced by the movement of Earth's plates can fold, stretch, and uplift the crust. **Over millions of years, the forces of plate movement can change a flat plain into landforms such as anticlines and synclines, folded mountains, fault-block mountains, and plateaus.**

Folding Earth's Crust Sometimes plate movement causes the crust to fold. Have you ever skidded on a rug that wrinkled up as your feet pushed it across the floor? Much as the rug wrinkles, rock stressed by compression may bend without breaking. Folds are bends in rock that form when compression shortens and thickens part of Earth's crust. A fold can be only a few centimeters across or hundreds of kilometers wide. You can often see small folds in the rock exposed where a highway has been cut through a hillside.

Geologists use the terms anticline and syncline to describe upward and downward folds in rock. A fold in rock that bends upward into an arch is an **anticline**, shown in Figure 4. A fold in rock that bends downward to form a valley is a **syncline.** Anticlines and synclines are found in many places where compression forces have folded the crust. The central Appalachian Mountains in Pennsylvania are folded mountains made up of parallel ridges (anticlines) and valleys (synclines).

The collision of two plates can cause compression and folding of the crust over a wide area. Folding produced some of the world's largest mountain ranges. The Himalayas in Asia and the Alps in Europe formed when pieces of the crust folded during the collision of two plates.

Lab zone Try This **Activity**

Modeling Stress
You can model the stresses that create faults.

1. Knead a piece of plastic putty until it is soft.
2. Push the ends of the putty toward the middle.
3. Pull the ends apart.
4. Push half of the putty one way and the other half in the opposite direction.

Classifying Which step in this activity models the type of stress that would produce anticlines and synclines?

Stretching Earth's Crust When two normal faults cut through a block of rock, a fault-block mountain forms. You can see a diagram of this process in Figure 5. How does this process begin? Where two plates move away from each other, tension forces create many normal faults. When two of these normal faults form parallel to each other, a block of rock is left lying between them. As the hanging wall of each normal fault slips downward, the block in between moves upward, forming a fault-block mountain.

If you traveled by car from Salt Lake City to Los Angeles, you would cross the Great Basin. This region contains many ranges of fault-block mountains separated by broad valleys, or basins.

 **Reading Checkpoint** What type of plate movement causes fault-block mountains to form?

FIGURE 5
Fault-Block Mountains
As tension forces pull the crust apart, two parallel normal faults can form a range of fault-block mountains, like the Beaverhead Range in Idaho.

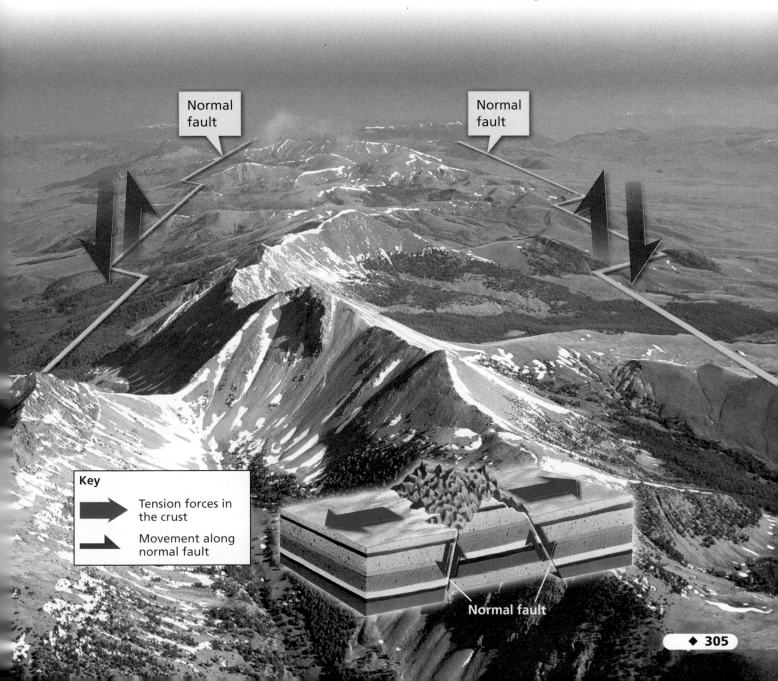

Normal fault

Normal fault

Key

Tension forces in the crust

Movement along normal fault

Normal fault

FIGURE 6
The Kaibab Plateau
The flat land on the horizon is the Kaibab Plateau, which forms the North Rim of the Grand Canyon in Arizona. The Kaibab Plateau is part of the Colorado Plateau.

Uplifting Earth's Crust The forces that raise mountains can also uplift, or raise, plateaus. A **plateau** is a large area of flat land elevated high above sea level. Some plateaus form when forces in Earth's crust push up a large, flat block of rock. Like a fancy sandwich, a plateau consists of many different flat layers, and is wider than it is tall.

Forces deforming the crust uplifted the Colorado Plateau in the "Four Corners" region of Arizona, Utah, Colorado, and New Mexico. Much of the Colorado Plateau lies more than 1,500 meters above sea level. Figure 6 shows one part of that plateau in northern Arizona.

Section 1 Assessment

Target Reading Skill Building Vocabulary
Refer to your definitions of the Key Terms to help you answer the following questions.

Reviewing Key Concepts

1. a. **Reviewing** What are the three main types of stress in rock?
   b. **Relating Cause and Effect** How does tension change the shape of Earth's crust?
   c. **Comparing and Contrasting** Compare the way that compression affects the crust to the way that tension affects the crust.
2. a. **Describing** What is a fault?
   b. **Explaining** Why do faults often occur along plate boundaries?
   c. **Relating Cause and Effect** What type of fault is formed when plates diverge, or pull apart? What type of fault is formed when plates are pushed together?

3. a. **Listing** Name five kinds of landforms caused by plate movement.
   b. **Relating Cause and Effect** What are three landforms produced by compression in the crust? What landform is produced by tension?

Lab zone **At-Home Activity**

Modeling Faults To model Earth's crust, roll modeling clay into layers and then press the layers together to form a rectangular block. Use a plastic knife to slice through the block at an angle, forming a fault. Explain which parts of your model represent the land surface, the hanging wall, and the footwall. Then show the three ways in which the sides of the fault can move.

Earthquakes and Seismic Waves

Reading Preview

Key Concepts
- How does the energy of an earthquake travel through Earth?
- What are the scales used to measure the strength of an earthquake?
- How do scientists locate the epicenter of an earthquake?

Key Terms
- earthquake • focus
- epicenter • P wave
- S wave • surface wave
- Mercalli scale • magnitude
- Richter scale • seismograph
- moment magnitude scale

⟳ Target Reading Skill
Identifying Main Ideas As you read Types of Seismic Waves, write the main idea in a graphic organizer like the one below. Then write three supporting details. The supporting details further explain the main idea.

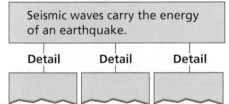

Main Idea

Seismic waves carry the energy of an earthquake.

Detail	Detail	Detail

Lab zone | Discover **Activity**

How Do Seismic Waves Travel Through Earth?

1. Stretch a spring toy across the floor while a classmate holds the other end. Do not overstretch the toy.
2. Gather together about four coils of the spring toy and release them. In what direction do the coils move?
3. Once the spring toy has stopped moving, jerk one end of the toy from side to side once. Be certain your classmate has a secure grip on the other end. In what direction do the coils move?

Think It Over
Observing Describe the two types of wave motion that you observed in the spring toy.

Earth is never still. Every day, worldwide, there are several thousand earthquakes. An **earthquake** is the shaking and trembling that results from the movement of rock beneath Earth's surface. Most earthquakes are too small to notice. But a large earthquake can produce dramatic changes in Earth's surface and cause great damage.

The forces of plate movement cause earthquakes. Plate movements produce stress in Earth's crust, adding energy to rock and forming faults. Stress increases along a fault until the rock breaks. An earthquake begins. In seconds, the earthquake releases an enormous amount of stored energy.

Most earthquakes begin in the lithosphere within about 100 kilometers of Earth's surface. The **focus** (FOH kus) is the area beneath Earth's surface where rock that is under stress breaks, triggering an earthquake. The point on the surface directly above the focus is called the **epicenter** (EP uh sen tur).

Types of Seismic Waves

Like a pebble thrown into a pond, an earthquake produces vibrations called waves. These waves carry energy as they travel outward. During an earthquake, seismic waves race out from the focus in all directions. Seismic waves are vibrations that travel through Earth carrying the energy released during an earthquake. The seismic waves move like ripples in a pond. **Seismic waves carry energy from an earthquake away from the focus, through Earth's interior, and across the surface.** That's what happened in 2002, when a powerful earthquake ruptured the Denali fault in Alaska, shown in Figure 7.

There are three main categories of seismic waves: P waves, S waves, and surface waves. An earthquake sends out two types of waves from its focus: P waves and S waves. When these waves reach Earth's surface at the epicenter, surface waves develop.

FIGURE 7

Seismic Waves

This diagram shows an earthquake along the Denali fault. An earthquake occurs when rocks fracture deep in the crust. The seismic waves move out in all directions from the focus.
Interpreting Diagrams *At what point do seismic waves first reach the surface?*

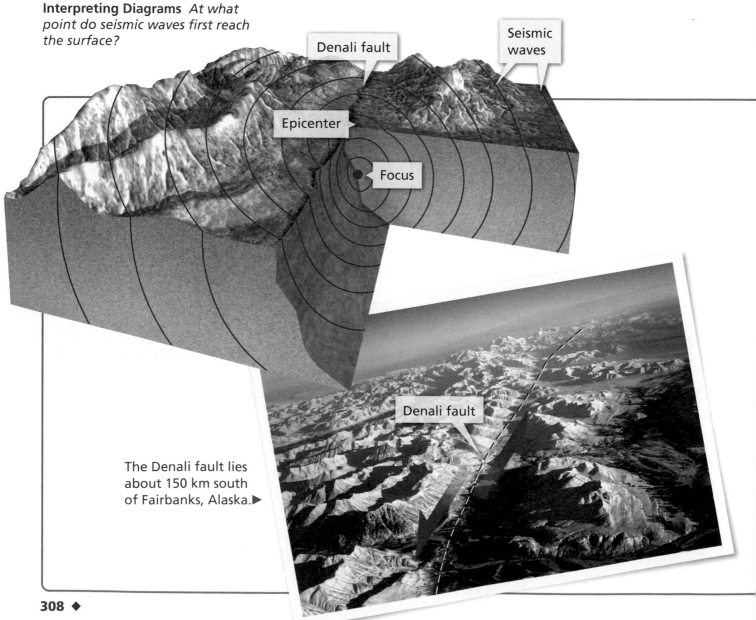

The Denali fault lies about 150 km south of Fairbanks, Alaska.▶

P Waves The first waves to arrive are primary waves, or P waves. **P waves** are seismic waves that compress and expand the ground like an accordion. Like the other types of seismic waves, P waves can damage buildings. Look at Figure 7 to see how P waves move.

S Waves After P waves come secondary waves, or S waves. **S waves** are seismic waves that vibrate from side to side as well as up and down. They shake the ground back and forth. When S waves reach the surface, they shake structures violently. Unlike P waves, which travel through both solids and liquids, S waves cannot move through liquids.

Surface Waves When P waves and S waves reach the surface, some of them become surface waves. **Surface waves** move more slowly than P waves and S waves, but they can produce severe ground movements. Some surface waves make the ground roll like ocean waves. Other surface waves shake buildings from side to side.

✓ Reading Checkpoint Which type of seismic wave causes the ground to roll like ocean waves?

Go Online
active art

For: Seismic Waves activity
Visit: PHSchool.com
Web Code: cfp-1022

P waves ▼
The crust vibrates forward and back along the path of the wave.

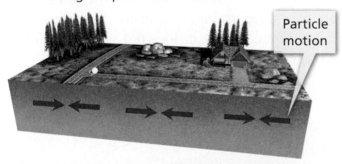

Particle motion

Direction of waves ⟶

S waves ▼
The crust vibrates from side to side and up and down.

Particle motion

Direction of waves ⟶

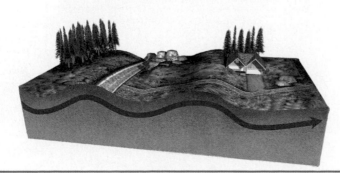

◄ Surface waves
The ground surface rolls with a wavelike motion.

Measuring Earthquakes

When an earthquake occurs, people want to know "How big was the quake?" and "Where was it centered?" When geologists want to know the size of an earthquake, they must consider many factors. As a result, there are at least 20 different measures for rating earthquakes, each with its strengths and shortcomings. **Three commonly used methods of measuring earthquakes are the Mercalli scale, the Richter scale, and the moment magnitude scale.**

The Mercalli Scale The **Mercalli scale** was developed to rate earthquakes according to the level of damage at a given place. The 12 steps of the Mercalli scale, shown in Figure 9, describe an earthquake's effects. The same earthquake can have different Mercalli ratings because it causes different amounts of ground motion at different locations.

The Richter Scale An earthquake's **magnitude** is a number that geologists assign to an earthquake based on the earthquake's size. Geologists determine magnitude by measuring the seismic waves and fault movement that occur during an earthquake. The **Richter scale** is a rating of an earthquake's magnitude based on the size of the earthquake's seismic waves. The seismic waves are measured by a **seismograph.** A seismograph is an instrument that records and measures seismic waves. The Richter scale provides accurate measurements for small, nearby earthquakes. But it does not work well for large or distant earthquakes.

Slight Damage

Moderate Damage

Great Destruction

FIGURE 8
Levels of Earthquake Damage
The level of damage caused by an earthquake varies depending on the magnitude of the earthquake and the distance from the epicenter.

FIGURE 9
The Mercalli Scale
The Mercalli scale uses Roman numerals to rank earthquakes by how much damage they cause.
Applying Concepts *How would you rate the three examples of earthquake damage in Figure 8?*

I–III
People notice vibrations like those from a passing truck. Unstable objects disturbed.

IV–VI
Slight damage. People run outdoors.

VII–IX
Moderate to heavy damage. Buildings jolted off foundations or destroyed.

X–XII
Great destruction. Cracks appear in ground. Waves seen on surface.

The Moment Magnitude Scale Geologists today often use the **moment magnitude scale,** a rating system that estimates the total energy released by an earthquake. The moment magnitude scale can be used to rate earthquakes of all sizes, near or far. You may hear news reports that mention the Richter scale. But the number they quote is almost always the moment magnitude for that earthquake.

To rate an earthquake on the moment magnitude scale, geologists first study data from seismographs. The data show what kinds of seismic waves the earthquake produced and how strong they were. The data also help geologists infer how much movement occurred along the fault and the strength of the rocks that broke when the fault slipped. Geologists use all this information to rate the quake on the moment magnitude scale.

Reading Checkpoint What evidence do geologists use to rate an earthquake on the moment magnitude scale?

Lab zone Skills **Activity**

Classifying
Classify the earthquake damage at these locations using the Mercalli scale.

1. Many buildings are destroyed; cracks form in the ground.
2. Several old brick buildings and a bridge collapse.
3. Canned goods fall off shelves; walls crack; people go outside to see what's happening.

FIGURE 10
Collecting Seismic Data
This geologist is checking data collected after an earthquake. These data can be used to pinpoint the epicenter of an earthquake.

Comparing Magnitudes An earthquake's magnitude tells geologists how much energy was released by the earthquake. Each one-point increase in magnitude represents the release of roughly 32 times more energy. For example, a magnitude 6 quake releases 32 times as much energy as a magnitude 5 quake, and about 1,000 times as much as a magnitude 4 quake.

The effects of an earthquake increase with magnitude. People scarcely notice earthquakes with magnitudes below 3. Earthquakes with a magnitude below 5 are small and cause little damage. Those with a magnitude between 5 and 6 can cause moderate damage. Earthquakes with a magnitude above 6 can cause great damage. Fortunately, the most powerful earthquakes, with a magnitude of 8 or above, are rare. During the twentieth century, only two earthquakes measured above 9 on the moment magnitude scale. These earthquakes occurred in Chile in 1960 and in Alaska in 1964.

Locating the Epicenter

Geologists use seismic waves to locate an earthquake's epicenter. Seismic waves travel at different speeds. P waves arrive at a seismograph first, with S waves following close behind. To tell how far the epicenter is from the seismograph, scientists measure the difference between the arrival times of the P waves and S waves. The farther away an earthquake is, the greater the time between the arrival of the P waves and the S waves.

Math Analyzing Data

Seismic Wave Speeds
Seismographs at five observation stations recorded the arrival times of the P and S waves produced by an earthquake. These data are shown in the graph.

1. **Reading Graphs** What variable is shown on the *x*-axis of the graph? The *y*-axis?

2. **Reading Graphs** How long did it take the S waves to travel 2,000 km?

3. **Estimating** How long did it take the P waves to travel 2,000 km?

4. **Calculating** What is the difference in the arrival times of the P waves and the S waves at 2,000 km? At 4,000 km?

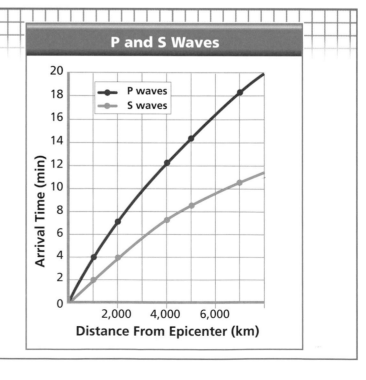

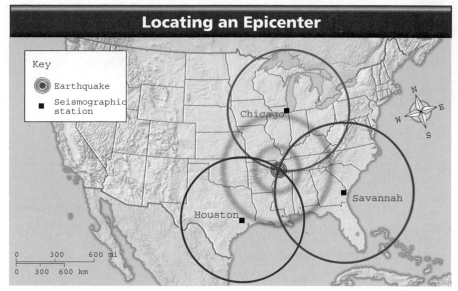

Locating an Epicenter

Key
- ◎ Earthquake
- ■ Seismographic station

Chicago

Houston

Savannah

| 0 | 300 | 600 mi |
| 0 | 300 | 600 km |

FIGURE 11
The map shows how to find the epicenter of an earthquake using data from three seismographic stations. **Measuring** *Use the map scale to determine the distances from Savannah and Houston to the epicenter. Which is closer?*

Geologists then draw at least three circles using data from different seismographs set up at stations all over the world. The center of each circle is a particular seismograph's location. The radius of each circle is the distance from that seismograph to the epicenter. As you can see in Figure 11, the point where the three circles intersect is the location of the epicenter.

 **Reading Checkpoint** What do geologists measure to determine the distance from a seismograph to an epicenter?

Section 2 Assessment

Target Reading Skill
Identifying Main Ideas Use your graphic organizer to help you answer Question 1 below.

Reviewing Key Concepts
1. a. **Reviewing** How does energy from an earthquake reach Earth's surface?
   b. **Describing** What kind of movement is produced by each of the three types of seismic waves?
   c. **Sequencing** When do P waves arrive at the surface in relation to S waves and surface waves?
2. a. **Defining** What is an earthquake's magnitude?
   b. **Describing** How is magnitude measured using the Richter scale?
   c. **Applying Concepts** What are the advantages of using the moment magnitude scale to measure an earthquake?

3. a. **Explaining** What type of data do geologists use to locate an earthquake's epicenter?
   b. **Interpreting Maps** Study the map in Figure 11 above. Then describe the method that scientists use to determine the epicenter of an earthquake.

Writing in Science

News Report As a television news reporter, you are covering an earthquake rated between IV and V on the Mercalli scale. Write a short news story describing the earthquake's effects. Your lead paragraph should tell *who, what, where, when,* and *how.* (*Hint:* Refer to Figure 9 for examples of earthquake damage.)

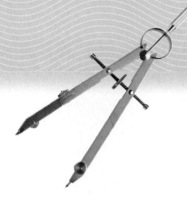

Finding the Epicenter

Problem

How can you locate an earthquake's epicenter?

Skills Focus

interpreting data, drawing conclusions

Materials

- drawing compass with pencil
- outline map of the United States

Data Table		
City	Difference in P and S Wave Arrival Times	Distance to Epicenter
Denver, Colorado	2 min 10 s	
Houston, Texas	3 min 55 s	
Miami, Florida	5 min 40 s	

Procedure

1. Make a copy of the data table showing differences in earthquake arrival times.

2. The graph shows how the difference in arrival time between P waves and S waves depends on the distance from the epicenter of the earthquake. Find the difference in arrival time for Denver on the *y*-axis of the graph. Follow this line across to the point at which it crosses the curve. To find the distance to the epicenter, read down from this point to the *x*-axis of the graph. Enter this distance in the data table.

3. Repeat Step 2 for Houston and Miami.

4. Set your compass at a radius equal to the distance from Denver to the earthquake epicenter that you previously recorded in your data table.

5. Draw a circle with the radius determined in Step 4, using Denver as the center. Draw the circle on your copy of the map. (*Hint:* Draw your circles carefully. You may need to draw some parts of the circles off the map.)

6. Repeat Steps 4 and 5 for Houston and Miami.

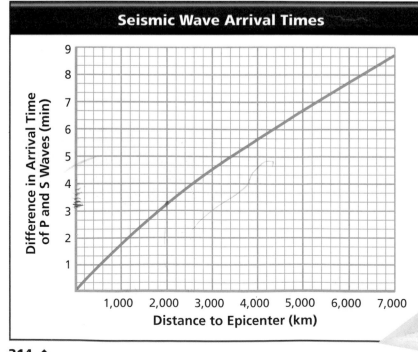

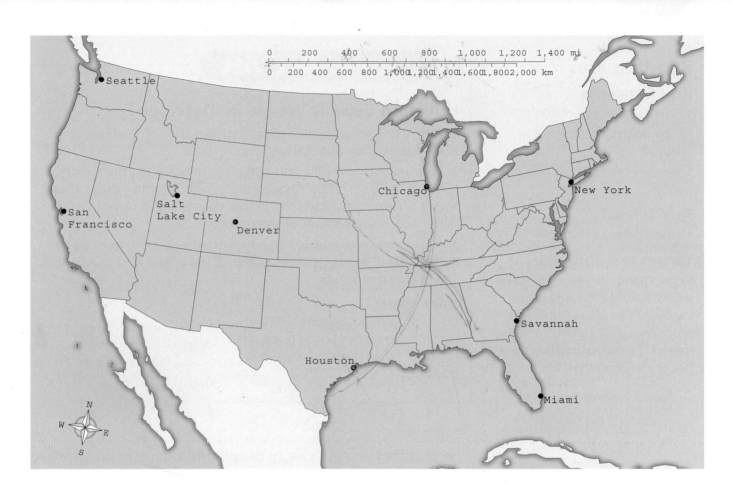

Analyze and Conclude

1. **Drawing Conclusions** Observe the three circles you have drawn. Where is the earthquake's epicenter?

2. **Measuring** Which city on the map is closest to the earthquake epicenter? How far, in kilometers, is this city from the epicenter?

3. **Inferring** In which of the three cities listed in the data table would seismographs detect the earthquake first? Last?

4. **Estimating** About how far from San Francisco is the epicenter that you found? What would be the difference in arrival times of the P waves and S waves for a recording station in San Francisco?

5. **Interpreting Data** What happens to the difference in arrival times between P waves and S waves as the distance from the earthquake increases?

6. **Communicating** Review the procedure you followed in this lab and then answer the following question. When you are trying to locate an epicenter, why is it necessary to know the distance from the epicenter for at least three recording stations?

More to Explore

You have just located an earthquake's epicenter. Now look at the map of Earth's Lithospheric Plates on page 203. What conclusions can you draw from this map about the cause of earthquakes in this area?

Monitoring Earthquakes

Reading Preview

Key Concepts
- How do seismographs work?
- How do geologists monitor faults?
- How are seismographic data used?

Key Terms
- seismogram • friction

⊙ Target Reading Skill
Sequencing As you read, make a flowchart like the one below that shows how a seismograph produces a seismogram. Write each step of the process in a separate box in the order in which it occurs.

How a Seismograph Works

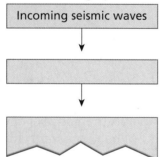

Incoming seismic waves

Discover Activity

How Can Seismic Waves Be Detected?

1. ✂ Using scissors, cut 4 plastic stirrers in half. Each piece should be about 5 cm long.
2. Your teacher will give you a pan containing gelatin. Gently insert the 8 stirrer pieces into the gelatin, spacing them about 2–3 cm apart in a row. The pieces should stand upright, but not touch the bottom of the pan.
3. At the opposite end of the pan from the stirrers, gently tap the surface of the gelatin once with the eraser end of a pencil. Observe the results.

Think It Over
Inferring What happened to the stirrer pieces when you tapped the gelatin? What was responsible for this effect?

Look at the beautiful vase in the photo. You might be surprised to learn that the vase is actually a scientific instrument. Can you guess what it was designed to do? Zhang Heng, an astronomer, designed and built this earthquake detection device in China nearly 2,000 years ago. It is said to have detected an earthquake centered several hundred kilometers away.

Earthquakes are dangerous, so people want to monitor them. To *monitor* means to "watch closely." Like the ancient Chinese, many societies have used technology to determine when and where earthquakes have occurred. During the late 1800s, scientists developed seismographs that were much more sensitive and accurate than any earlier devices.

FIGURE 12
Earthquake Detector
Nearly 2,000 years ago, a Chinese scientist invented this instrument to detect earthquakes.

The Seismograph

A simple seismograph can consist of a heavy weight attached to a frame by a spring or wire. A pen connected to the weight rests its point on a drum that can rotate. As the drum rotates slowly, the pen draws a straight line on paper wrapped tightly around the drum. **Seismic waves cause the seismograph's drum to vibrate. But the suspended weight with the pen attached moves very little. Therefore, the pen stays in place and records the drum's vibrations.**

Measuring Seismic Waves When you write a sentence, the paper stays in one place while your hand moves the pen. But in a seismograph, it's the pen that remains stationary while the paper moves. Why is this? All seismographs make use of a basic principle of physics: Whether it is moving or at rest, every object resists any change to its motion. A seismograph's heavy weight resists motion during a quake. But the rest of the seismograph is anchored to the ground and vibrates when seismic waves arrive.

Reading a Seismogram You have probably seen a zigzag pattern of lines used to represent an earthquake. The pattern of lines, called a **seismogram,** is the record of an earthquake's seismic waves produced by a seismograph. Study the seismogram in Figure 13 and notice when the P waves, S waves, and surface waves arrive. The height of the jagged lines drawn on the seismograph's drum is greater for a more severe earthquake or for an earthquake close to the seismograph.

✓ **Reading Checkpoint** What is a seismogram?

FIGURE 13
Recording Seismic Waves
A seismograph records seismic waves, producing a seismogram. Today, electronic seismographs contain sensors instead of pens. **Interpreting Diagrams** *What is the function of the weight in the seismograph?*

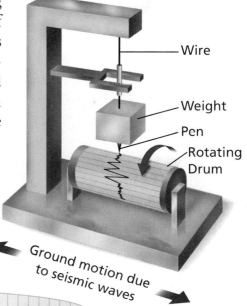

Seismograph

Wire

Weight

Pen

Rotating Drum

Ground motion due to seismic waves

Seismogram

Earlier

Later

P waves travel fastest and arrive first.

S waves arrive shortly after P waves.

Surface waves produce the largest disturbance on the seismogram.

Instruments That Monitor Faults

Along a fault, scientists may detect a slight rise or fall in the elevation and tilt of the land. Geologists hypothesize that such changes signal a buildup of stress in rock. Increasing stress could eventually lead to an earthquake. **To monitor faults, geologists have developed instruments to measure changes in elevation, tilting of the land surface, and ground movements along faults.** Some of the instruments that geologists use to monitor these movements include tiltmeters, creep meters, laser-ranging devices, and satellites.

Tiltmeters A tiltmeter measures tilting or raising of the ground. If you have ever used a carpenter's level, you have used a type of tiltmeter. The tiltmeters used by geologists consist of two bulbs that are filled with a liquid and connected by a hollow stem. Notice that if the land rises or falls slightly, the liquid will flow from one bulb to the other. Each bulb contains a measuring scale to measure the depth of the liquid in that bulb. Geologists read the scales to measure the amount of tilt occurring along the fault.

Creep Meters A creep meter uses a wire stretched across a fault to measure horizontal movement of the ground. On one side of the fault, the wire is anchored to a post. On the other side, the wire is attached to a weight that can slide if the fault moves. Geologists determine how much the fault has moved by measuring how much the weight has moved against a scale.

Laser-Ranging Devices A laser-ranging device uses a laser beam to detect horizontal fault movements. The device times a laser beam as it travels to a reflector and back. Thus, the device can detect any change in distance to the reflector.

GPS Satellites Scientists can monitor changes in elevation as well as horizontal movement along faults using a network of Earth-orbiting satellites called GPS. GPS, the Global Positioning System, was developed to help ships and planes find their routes. As shown in Figure 14, GPS can also be used to locate points on Earth's surface with great precision. Using GPS, scientists measure tiny movements of markers set up on the opposite sides of a fault.

 **Reading Checkpoint** How does a creep meter work?

FIGURE 14
Motion Detectors

To detect slight motions along faults, geologists use several types of devices.

Comparing and Contrasting *Which of these devices measure horizontal movement? Which ones measure vertical movement?*

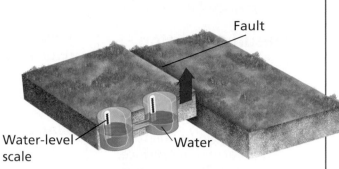

Tiltmeter
A tiltmeter measures vertical movement.

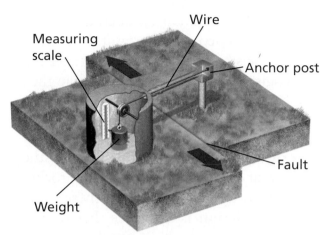

Creep Meter
A creep meter measures horizontal movement.

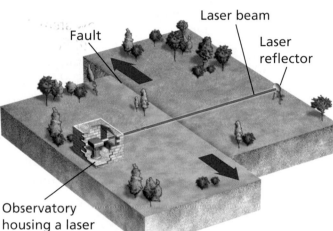

Laser-Ranging Device
A laser-ranging device measures horizontal movement.

GPS Satellites
Ground-based receivers use the GPS satellite system to measure changes in elevation and tilt of the land as well as horizontal movement along a fault.

Lab zone **Skills Activity**

Measuring Friction
You can measure the force of friction.

1. Place a small weight on a smooth, flat tabletop. Use a spring scale to pull the weight across the surface. How much force is shown on the spring scale? (*Hint:* The unit of force is newtons.)
2. Tape a piece of sandpaper to the tabletop. Repeat Step 1, pulling the weight across the sandpaper.

Is the force of friction greater for a smooth surface or for a rough surface?

Using Seismographic Data

Scientists collect and use seismographic data in a variety of ways. **Seismographs and fault-monitoring devices provide data used to map faults and detect changes along faults. Geologists are also trying to use these data to develop a method of predicting earthquakes.**

Mapping Faults Faults are often hidden by a thick layer of rock or soil. How can geologists map a hidden fault?

When seismic waves encounter a fault, the waves are reflected off the fault. Seismographs can detect these reflected seismic waves. Geologists then use these data to map the fault's length and depth. Knowing the location of hidden faults helps scientists determine the earthquake risk for the area.

Monitoring Changes Along Faults Geologists study the types of movement that occur along faults. How rocks move along a fault depends on how much friction there is between the sides of the fault. **Friction** is the force that opposes the motion of one surface as it moves across another surface. Friction exists because surfaces are not perfectly smooth.

Where friction along a fault is low, the rocks on both sides of the fault slide by each other without much sticking. Therefore stress does not build up, and big earthquakes are unlikely. Where friction is moderate, the sides of the fault jam together. Then from time to time they jerk free, producing small earthquakes. Where friction is high, the rocks lock together and do not move. In this case, stress increases until it is strong enough to overcome the friction force. For example, in most places along the San Andreas fault in California, friction is high and the plates lock. Stress builds up until an earthquake occurs.

FIGURE 15
Earthquake Risk in California
The map shows the probability of a strong earthquake along the San Andreas fault. A high percent probability means that a quake might be more likely to occur. **Inferring** *What do scientists think is the risk of an earthquake near San Francisco?*

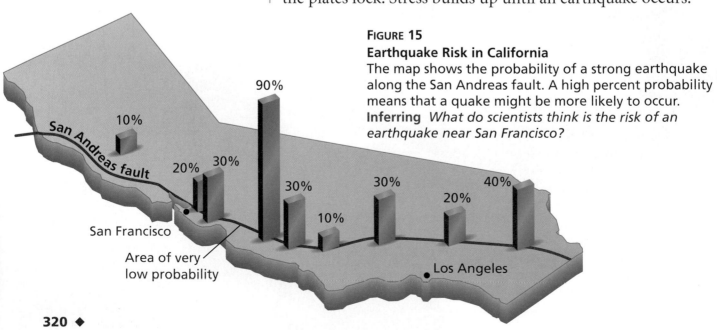

90%
10%
San Andreas fault
20% 30%
30%
10%
30%
40%
20%
San Francisco
Area of very low probability
Los Angeles

320 ◆

Figure 15 shows how geologists in California have used data about how the San Andreas fault moves. They have tried to estimate the earthquake risk along different parts of the fault. Unfortunately, this attempt at forecasting earthquakes has not worked yet.

Trying to Predict Earthquakes Even with data from many sources, geologists can't predict when and where a quake will strike. Usually, stress along a fault increases until an earthquake occurs. Yet sometimes stress builds up along a fault, but an earthquake fails to occur. Or, one or more earthquakes may relieve stress along another part of the fault. Exactly what will happen remains uncertain.

The problem of predicting earthquakes is one of many scientific questions that remain unsolved. If you become a scientist, you can work to find answers to these questions. Much remains to be discovered!

 **Reading Checkpoint** Why is it difficult to predict earthquakes?

FIGURE 16
Seismographic Data
A geologist interprets a seismogram. Understanding changes that precede earthquakes may help in efforts to predict them.

Section 3 Assessment

Target Reading Skill Sequencing Refer to your flowchart about seismographs as you answer Question 1.

Reviewing Key Concepts

1. a. **Defining** What is a seismograph?
   b. **Explaining** How does a seismograph record seismic waves?
   c. **Predicting** A seismograph records a strong earthquake and a weak earthquake. How would the seismograms for the two earthquakes compare?
2. a. **Reviewing** What four instruments are used to monitor faults?
   b. **Describing** What changes does each instrument measure?
   c. **Inferring** A satellite that monitors a fault detects an increasing tilt in the land surface along the fault. What could this change in the land surface indicate?

3. a. **Listing** What are three ways in which geologists use seismographic data?
   b. **Explaining** How do geologists use seismographic data to make maps of faults?
   c. **Making Generalizations** Why do geologists collect data on friction along the sides of faults?

Writing in Science

Patent Application You are an inventor who has created a simple device that can detect an earthquake. To protect your rights to the invention, you apply for a patent. In your patent application, describe your device and how it will indicate the direction and strength of an earthquake. You may include a sketch.

Design a Seismograph

Problem

Can you design and build a seismograph that can record the movements of simulated earthquakes?

Skills Focus

designing, evaluating, troubleshooting

Materials

- large book
- pencil
- pen
- 2 strips of paper
- optional materials provided by your teacher

Procedure

PART 1   Research and Investigate

1. With two lab partners, create a model of a seismograph. Begin by placing a large book on a table.

2. Wind a strip of paper about one meter long around a pencil.

3. Hold the pencil with the paper wound around it in one hand. In your other hand, hold a pen against the paper.

4. As you hold the pen steady, have one lab partner slowly pull on the paper so that it slides across the book.

5. After a few seconds, the other lab partner should jiggle the book gently for 10 seconds to model a weak earthquake, and then for 10 seconds to model a strong earthquake.

6. Observe the pen markings on the paper strip. Compare how the seismograph recorded the weak earthquake and the strong earthquake. Record your observations in your notebook.

7. Repeat Steps 1–6 with a new paper strip. Compare the two paper strips to see how consistent your seismograph recordings were. Record your observations.

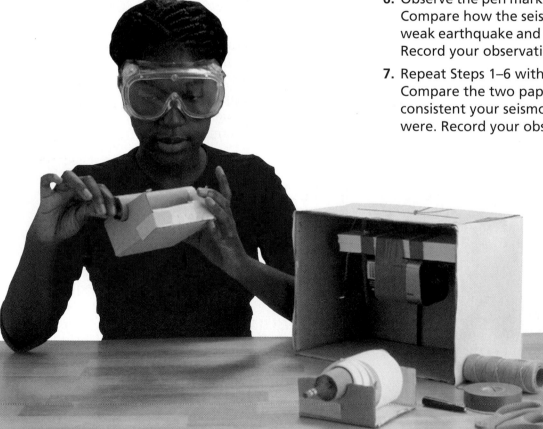

PART 2   Design and Build

8. Using what you learned from the seismo-graph model in Part 1, develop your own design for a seismograph. Your seismograph should be able to
   - record vibrations continuously for 30 seconds
   - produce a seismogram that can distinguish between gentle and strong earthquakes
   - record seismic readings consistently from trial to trial

9. Sketch your design on a sheet of paper. Then make a list of the materials you will need. Materials might include a heavy weight, a roll of paper, a pen, wood blocks, wood dowels, and duct tape.

10. Obtain your teacher's approval for your design. Then construct your seismograph.

PART 3   Evaluate and Redesign

11. Test your seismograph in a series of simu-lated earthquakes of different strengths. Evaluate how well your seismograph func-tions. Does it meet the criteria outlined in Step 8? Make note of any problems.

12. Based on your tests, decide how you could improve the design of your seismograph. Then make any necessary changes to your seismograph and test how it functions.

Analyze and Conclude

1. **Evaluating** What problems or shortcomings did you encounter with the seismograph you tested in Part 1? Why do you think these problems occurred?

2. **Designing a Solution** How did you incorpo-rate what you learned in Part 1 into your seismograph design in Part 2? For example, what changes did you make to improve con-sistency from trial to trial?

3. **Troubleshooting** As you designed, built, and tested your seismograph, what problems did you encounter? How did you solve these problems?

4. **Working With Design Constraints** What limi-tations did factors such as gravity, materials, costs, time, or other factors place on the design and function of your seismograph? Describe how you adapted your design to work within these limitations.

5. **Evaluating the Impact on Society** Why is it important for scientists around the world to have access to accurate and durable seismo-graphs?

Communicate

Write an advertisement trying to "sell" your seis-mograph. In your ad, explain how your design and evaluation process helped you improve your seis-mograph. Include a labeled sketch of your design.

Volcanoes and Plate Tectonics

Reading Preview

Key Concepts
- Where are most of Earth's volcanoes found?
- How do hot spot volcanoes form?

Key Terms
- volcano • magma • lava
- Ring of Fire • island arc
- hot spot

Target Reading Skill
Asking Questions Before you read, preview the red headings. In a graphic organizer like the one below, ask a *where, what,* or *how* question for each heading. As you read, write the answers to your questions.

Volcanoes and Plate Tectonics

Question	Answer
Where are volcanoes found?	Most volcanoes are found along plate boundaries.

Discover Activity

Where Are Volcanoes Found on Earth's Surface?

1. Look at the map of Earth's Active Volcanoes on page 83. What symbols are used to represent volcanoes? What other symbols are shown on the map?

2. Do the locations of the volcanoes form a pattern? Do the volcanoes seem related to any other features on Earth's surface?

Think About It
Developing Hypotheses Develop a hypothesis to explain where Earth's volcanoes are located.

In 2002, Mount Etna erupted in glowing fountains and rivers of molten rock. Located on the island of Sicily in the Mediterranean Sea, Mount Etna is Europe's largest volcano. Over the last 2,500 years, it has erupted often. The ancient Greeks believed that Mount Etna was one home of Hephaestus, the Greek god of fire. Beneath the volcano was the forge where Hephaestus made beautiful metal objects for the other Greek gods.

The eruption of a volcano is among the most awe-inspiring events on Earth. A **volcano** is a weak spot in the crust where molten material, or magma, comes to the surface. **Magma** is a molten mixture of rock-forming substances, gases, and water from the mantle. When magma reaches the surface, it is called **lava.** After lava has cooled, it forms solid rock. Lava released during volcanic activity builds up Earth's surface.

FIGURE 17
Lava Flow on Mount Etna
A lava flow from Mount Etna in Sicily almost buried this small building.

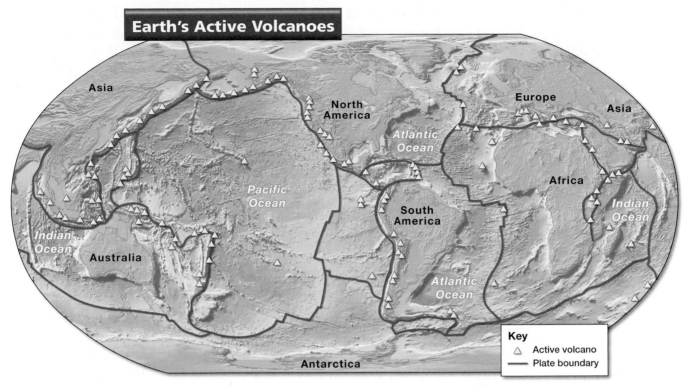

Earth's Active Volcanoes

Asia

North
America

Europe

Asia

Atlantic
Ocean

Pacific
Ocean

Africa

South
America

Indian
Ocean

Indian
Ocean

Australia

Atlantic
Ocean

Antarctica

Key
△ Active volcano
— Plate boundary

FIGURE 18
Many of Earth's volcanoes are located along the boundaries of tectonic plates. The Ring of Fire is a belt of volcanoes that circles the Pacific Ocean. **Observing** *What other regions have a large number of volcanoes?*

Volcanoes and Plate Boundaries

There are about 600 active volcanoes on land. Many more lie beneath the sea, where it is difficult for scientists to observe and map them. Figure 18 shows the location of some of Earth's major volcanoes. Notice how volcanoes occur in belts that extend across continents and oceans. One major volcanic belt is the **Ring of Fire,** formed by the many volcanoes that rim the Pacific Ocean.

Volcanic belts form along the boundaries of Earth's plates. At plate boundaries, huge pieces of the crust diverge (pull apart) or converge (push together). As a result, the crust often fractures, allowing magma to reach the surface. Most volcanoes form along diverging plate boundaries such as mid-ocean ridges and along converging plate boundaries where subduction takes place. For example, Mount Etna formed near the boundary of the Eurasian and African plates.

Diverging Boundaries Volcanoes form along the mid-ocean ridges, which mark diverging plate boundaries. Recall that ridges are long, underwater mountain ranges that some-times have a rift valley down their center. Along the rift valley, lava pours out of cracks in the ocean floor, gradually building new mountains. Volcanoes also form along diverging plate boundaries on land. For example, there are several large volca-noes along the Great Rift Valley in East Africa.

Go Online
PLANET DIARY

For: More on volcanoes
Visit: PHSchool.com
Web Code: cfd-1031

Converging Boundaries Many volcanoes form near converging plate boundaries where oceanic plates return to the mantle. Volcanoes may form where two oceanic plates collide or where an oceanic plate collides with a continental plate. Figure 19 shows how converging plates produce volcanoes.

Many volcanoes occur near boundaries where two oceanic plates collide. Through subduction, the older, denser plate sinks beneath a deep-ocean trench into the mantle. Some of the rock above the subducting plate melts and forms magma. Because the magma is less dense than the surrounding rock, it rises toward the surface. Eventually, the magma breaks through the ocean floor, creating volcanoes.

The resulting volcanoes create a string of islands called an **island arc.** The curve of an island arc echoes the curve of its deep-ocean trench. Major island arcs include Japan, New Zealand, Indonesia, the Philippines, the Aleutians, and the Caribbean islands.

Volcanoes also occur where an oceanic plate is subducted beneath a continental plate. Collisions of this type produced the volcanoes of the Andes Mountains in South America and the volcanoes of the Pacific Northwest in the United States.

Reading Checkpoint How did the volcanoes in the Andes Mountains form?

FIGURE 19
Volcanoes at Converging Boundaries
Volcanoes often form where two oceanic plates collide or where an oceanic plate collides with a continental plate. In both situations, an oceanic plate sinks beneath a trench. Rock above the plate melts to form magma, which then erupts to the surface as lava.

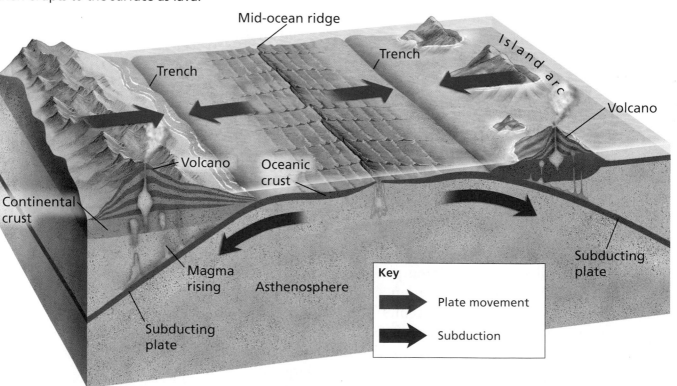

Mid-ocean ridge

Trench

Trench

Island arc

Volcano

Volcano

Oceanic crust

Continental crust

Magma rising

Asthenosphere

Subducting plate

Subducting plate

Key

→ Plate movement

→ Subduction

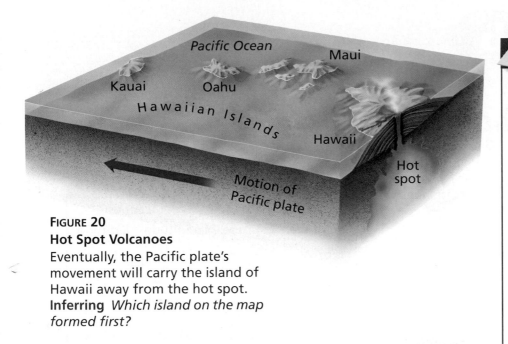

FIGURE 20
Hot Spot Volcanoes
Eventually, the Pacific plate's movement will carry the island of Hawaii away from the hot spot.
Inferring *Which island on the map formed first?*

Hot Spot Volcanoes

Some volcanoes result from "hot spots" in Earth's mantle. A **hot spot** is an area where material from deep within the mantle rises and then melts, forming magma. **A volcano forms above a hot spot when magma erupts through the crust and reaches the surface.** Some hot spot volcanoes lie in the middle of plates far from any plate boundaries. Other hot spots occur on or near plate boundaries.

A hot spot in the ocean floor can gradually form a series of volcanic mountains. For example, the Hawaiian Islands formed one by one over millions of years as the Pacific plate drifted over a hot spot. Hot spots can also form under the continents. Yellowstone National Park in Wyoming marks a hot spot under the North American plate.

Lab zone **Try This Activity**

Hot Spot in a Box

1. Fill a plastic box half full of cold water. This represents the mantle.
2. Mix red food coloring with hot water in a small, narrow-necked bottle to represent magma.
3. Hold your finger over the mouth of the bottle as you place the bottle in the center of the box. The mouth of the bottle must be under water.
4. Float a flat piece of plastic foam on the water above the bottle to model a tectonic plate.
5. Take your finger off the bottle and observe what happens to the "magma."

Making Models Move the plastic foam slowly along. Where does the magma touch the "plate"? How does this model a hot spot volcano?

Section 4 Assessment

Target Reading Skill **Asking Questions** Work with a partner to check the answers in your graphic organizer.

Reviewing Key Concepts

1. **a. Defining** What is a volcano?
   b. Reviewing Where are most volcanoes located?
   c. Relating Cause and Effect What causes volcanoes to form at a diverging plate boundary?
2. **a. Defining** What is a hot spot?
   b. Summarizing How does a hot spot volcano form?
   c. Predicting What features form as an oceanic plate moves across a hot spot?

Writing in Science

Travel Brochure As a travel agent, you are planning a Pacific Ocean cruise that will visit volcanoes in the Ring of Fire and Hawaii. Write a travel brochure describing the types of volcanoes the group will see and explaining why the volcanoes formed where they did.

Mapping Earthquakes and Volcanoes

Problem

Is there a pattern in the locations of earthquakes and volcanoes?

Skills Focus

interpreting data

Materials

- outline world map showing longitude and latitude
- 4 pencils of different colors

Procedure

1. Use the information in the table to mark the location of each earthquake on the world map. Use a colored pencil to draw a letter E inside a circle at each earthquake location.

2. Use a pencil of a second color to mark the volcanoes on the world map. Indicate each volcano with the letter V inside a circle.

3. Use a third pencil to lightly shade the areas in which earthquakes are found.

4. Use a fourth colored pencil to lightly shade the areas in which volcanoes are found.

Analyze and Conclude

1. **Interpreting Data** How are earthquakes distributed on the map? Are they scattered evenly or concentrated in zones?

2. **Interpreting Data** How are volcanoes distributed? Are they scattered evenly or concentrated in zones?

3. **Inferring** From your data, what can you infer about the relationship between earthquakes and volcanoes?

4. **Communicating** Suppose you added the locations of additional earthquakes and volcanoes to your map. Would the overall pattern of earthquakes and volcanoes change? Explain in writing why you think the pattern would or would not change.

Earthquakes and Volcanoes			
Earthquakes		Volcanoes	
Longitude	Latitude	Longitude	Latitude
120° W	40° N	150° W	60° N
110° E	5° S	70° W	35° S
77° W	4° S	120° W	45° N
88° E	23° N	61° W	15° N
121° E	14° S	105° W	20° N
34° E	7° N	75° W	0°
74° W	44° N	122° W	40° N
70° W	30° S	30° E	40° N
10° E	45° N	60° E	30° N
85° W	13° N	160° E	55° N
125° E	23° N	37° E	3° S
30° E	35° N	145° E	40° N
140° E	35° N	120° E	10° S
12° E	46° N	14° E	41° N
75° E	28° N	105° E	5° S
150° W	61° N	35° E	15° N
68° W	47° S	70° W	30° S
175° E	41° S	175° E	39° S
121° E	17° N	123° E	38° N

More to Explore

On a map of the United States, locate active volcanoes and areas of earthquake activity. Determine the distance from your home to the nearest active volcano.

Volcanic Eruptions

Reading Preview

Key Concepts
- What happens when a volcano erupts?
- What are the two types of volcanic eruptions?
- What are a volcano's stages of activity?

Key Terms
- magma chamber • pipe
- vent • lava flow • crater
- pyroclastic flow • dormant
- extinct

🎯 Target Reading Skill
Using Prior Knowledge Before you read, look at the section headings to see what the section is about. Then write what you know about how a volcano erupts in a graphic organizer like the one below. As you read, write what you learn.

What You Know
1. Lava flows out of a volcano.
2.

What You Learned
1.
2.

Lab zone Discover **Activity**

What Are Volcanic Rocks Like?
Volcanoes produce lava, which hardens into rock. Two of these rocks are pumice and obsidian.

1. Observe samples of pumice and obsidian with a hand lens.
2. How would you describe the texture of the pumice? What could have caused this texture?
3. Observe the surface of the obsidian. How does the surface of the obsidian differ from pumice?

Think It Over
Developing Hypotheses What could have produced the difference in texture between the two rocks? Explain your answer.

Pumice

Obsidian

In Hawaii, there are many myths about Pele (PAY lay), the fire goddess of volcanoes. Pele lives in the depths of Hawaii's erupting volcanoes. According to legend, when Pele is angry, she causes a volcanic eruption. One result of an eruption is "Pele's hair," a fine, threadlike rock formed by lava. Pele's hair forms when lava sprays out of the ground like water from a fountain. As it cools, the lava stretches and hardens into thin strands, as shown in Figure 21.

Where does this lava come from? Lava begins as magma, which usually forms in the asthenosphere. The materials of the asthenosphere are under great pressure. Liquid magma is less dense than the solid material around it. Therefore, magma flows upward into any cracks in the rock above. As magma rises, it sometimes becomes trapped beneath layers of rock. But if an opening in weak rock allows the magma to reach the surface, a volcano forms.

FIGURE 21
Pele's Hair
Pele's hair is a type of rock formed from lava. Each strand is as fine as spun glass.

Magma Reaches Earth's Surface

A volcano is more than a large, cone-shaped mountain. Inside a volcano is a system of passageways through which magma moves.

Inside a Volcano All volcanoes have a pocket of magma beneath the surface and one or more cracks through which the magma forces its way. Beneath a volcano, magma collects in a pocket called a **magma chamber.** The magma moves upward through a **pipe,** a long tube in the ground that connects the magma chamber to Earth's surface. You can see these features in Figure 23.

Molten rock and gas leave the volcano through an opening called a **vent.** Often, there is one central vent at the top of a volcano. However, many volcanoes also have other vents that open on the volcano's sides. A **lava flow** is the area covered by lava as it pours out of a vent. A **crater** is a bowl-shaped area that may form at the top of a volcano around the central vent.

A Volcanic Eruption What pushes magma to the surface? The explosion of a volcano is similar to the soda water bubbling out of a warm bottle of soda pop. You cannot see the carbon dioxide gas in a bottle of soda pop because it is dissolved in the liquid. But when you open the bottle, the pressure is released. The carbon dioxide expands and forms bubbles, which rush to the surface. Like the carbon dioxide in soda pop, dissolved gases are trapped in magma. These dissolved gases are under tremendous pressure.

FIGURE 22
Lava Burp
During an eruption on Mount Kilauea, the force of a bursting gas bubble pushes up a sheet of red-hot lava.

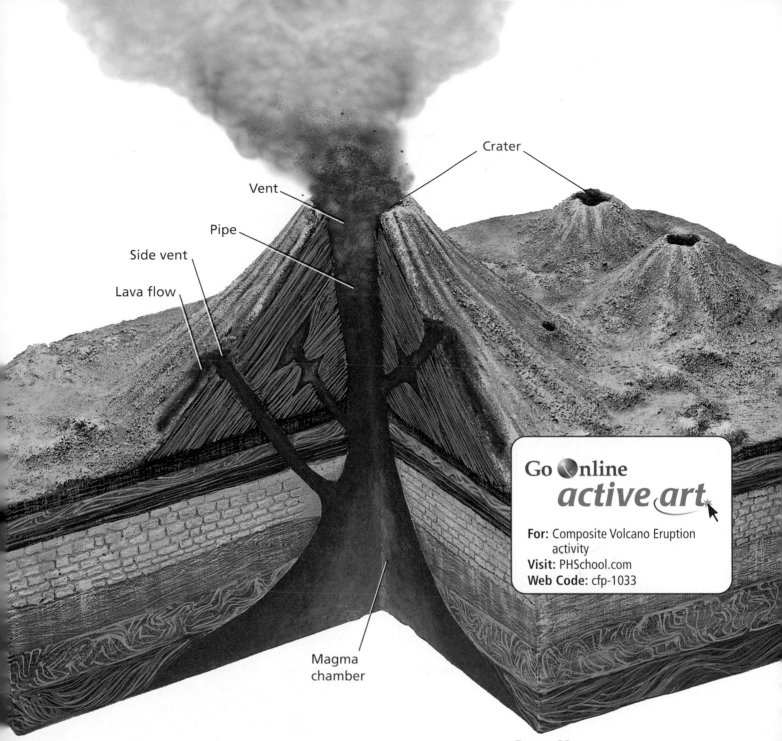

Vent

Pipe

Side vent

Lava flow

Crater

Magma chamber

FIGURE 23
A Volcano Erupts
A volcano forms where magma breaks through Earth's crust and lava flows over the surface.
Interpreting Diagrams *What part of a volcano connects the vent with the magma chamber?*

As magma rises toward the surface, the pressure of the surrounding rock on the magma decreases. The dissolved gases begin to expand, forming bubbles. As pressure falls within the magma, the size of the gas bubbles increases greatly. These expanding gases exert an enormous force. **When a volcano erupts, the force of the expanding gases pushes magma from the magma chamber through the pipe until it flows or explodes out of the vent.** Once magma escapes from the volcano and becomes lava, the remaining gases bubble out.

 **Reading Checkpoint** What happens to the pressure in magma as the magma rises toward the surface?

Kinds of Volcanic Eruptions

Some volcanic eruptions occur gradually. Others are dramatic explosions. **Geologists classify volcanic eruptions as quiet or explosive.** The physical properties of its magma determine how a volcano erupts. Whether an eruption is quiet or explosive depends on the magma's silica content and viscosity.

Quiet Eruptions A volcano erupts quietly if its magma is low in silica. Low-silica magma has low viscosity and flows easily. The gases in the magma bubble out gently. Lava with low viscosity oozes quietly from the vent and can flow for many kilometers. Quiet eruptions can produce both pahoehoe and aa.

The Hawaiian Islands were formed from quiet eruptions. On the Big Island of Hawaii, lava pours out of the crater near the top of Mount Kilauea. But lava also flows out of long cracks on the volcano's sides. Quiet eruptions have built up the Big Island over hundreds of thousands of years.

Explosive Eruptions A volcano erupts explosively if its magma is high in silica. High-silica magma has high viscosity, making it thick and sticky. The high-viscosity magma does not always flow out of the crater. Instead, it builds up in the volcano's pipe, plugging it like a cork in a bottle. Dissolved gases, including water vapor, cannot escape from the thick magma. The trapped gases build up pressure until they explode. The erupting gases and steam push the magma out of the volcano with incredible force. That's what happened during the eruption of Mount St. Helens, shown in Figure 24.

Before Eruption

During Eruption

An explosive eruption breaks lava into fragments that quickly cool and harden into pieces of different sizes. The smallest pieces are volcanic ash—fine, rocky particles as small as a speck of dust. Pebble-sized particles are called cinders. Larger pieces, called bombs, may range from the size of a base-ball to the size of a car. A **pyroclastic flow** (py roh KLAS tik) occurs when an explosive eruption hurls out a mixture of hot gases, ash, cinders, and bombs.

Pumice and obsidian, which you observed if you did the Discover Activity, form from high-silica lava. Obsidian forms when lava cools very quickly, giving it a smooth, glossy surface like glass. Pumice forms when gas bubbles are trapped in fast-cooling lava, leaving spaces in the rock.

 **Reading Checkpoint** What is a pyroclastic flow?

FIGURE 24
An Explosive Eruption
Mount St. Helens in Washington State erupted at 8:30 A.M. on May 18, 1980. The explosion blew off the top of the mountain, leaving a huge crater and causing great destruction.

After Eruption

Volcano Hazards Although quiet eruptions and explosive eruptions produce different hazards, both types of eruption can cause damage far from the crater's rim.

During a quiet eruption, lava flows from vents, setting fire to, and then burying, everything in its path. A quiet eruption can cover large areas with a thick layer of lava.

During an explosive eruption, a volcano can belch out hot clouds of deadly gases as well as ash, cinders, and bombs. Volcanic ash can bury entire towns. If it becomes wet, the heavy ash can cause roofs to collapse. If a jet plane sucks ash into its engine, the engine may stall. Eruptions can cause landslides and avalanches of mud, melted snow, and rock. The Science and History timeline shows the effects of several explosive eruptions.

Reading Checkpoint How does volcanic ash cause damage?

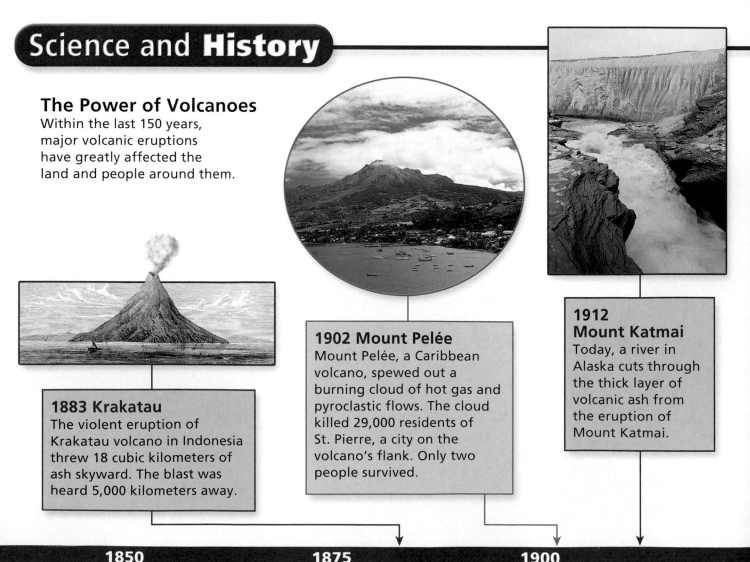

Science and History

The Power of Volcanoes
Within the last 150 years, major volcanic eruptions have greatly affected the land and people around them.

1883 Krakatau
The violent eruption of Krakatau volcano in Indonesia threw 18 cubic kilometers of ash skyward. The blast was heard 5,000 kilometers away.

1902 Mount Pelée
Mount Pelée, a Caribbean volcano, spewed out a burning cloud of hot gas and pyroclastic flows. The cloud killed 29,000 residents of St. Pierre, a city on the volcano's flank. Only two people survived.

1912 Mount Katmai
Today, a river in Alaska cuts through the thick layer of volcanic ash from the eruption of Mount Katmai.

| 1850 | 1875 | 1900 |

Stages of Volcanic Activity

The activity of a volcano may last from less than a decade to more than 10 million years. Most long-lived volcanoes, however, do not erupt continuously. Geologists try to determine a volcano's past and whether the volcano will erupt again.

Life Cycle of a Volcano Geologists often use the terms *active, dormant,* or *extinct* to describe a volcano's stage of activity. An active, or live, volcano is one that is erupting or has shown signs that it may erupt in the near future. A dormant, or sleeping, volcano is like a sleeping bear. Scientists expect a **dormant** volcano to awaken in the future and become active. An **extinct,** or dead, volcano is unlikely to erupt again.

The time between volcanic eruptions may span hundreds to many thousands of years. People living near a dormant volcano may be unaware of the danger. But a dormant volcano can become active at any time.

2002 Mount Etna
Bulldozers constructed a wall against a scalding river of lava creeping down the slopes of Mount Etna in Sicily.

1991 Mount Pinatubo
Pinatubo in the Philippines spewed out huge quantities of ash that rose high into the atmosphere and buried nearby areas.

1980 Mount St. Helens
When Mount St. Helens in Washington exploded, it blasted one cubic kilometer of volcanic material skyward.

1950 1975 2000

FIGURE 25
Volcano Watch
Near Mount Kilauea in Hawaii, these geologists are testing instruments to monitor temperatures in and around a crater.

Monitoring Volcanoes Geologists have been more successful in predicting volcanic eruptions than in predicting earthquakes. Geologists use instruments to detect changes in and around a volcano. These changes may give warning a short time before a volcano erupts. But geologists cannot be certain about the type of eruption or how powerful it will be.

Geologists use tiltmeters and other instruments to detect slight surface changes in elevation and tilt caused by magma moving underground. They monitor any gases escaping from the volcano. A temperature increase in underground water may be a sign that magma is nearing the surface. Geologists also monitor the many small earthquakes that occur around a volcano before an eruption. The upward movement of magma triggers these quakes.

 **Reading Checkpoint** How do geologists monitor volcanoes?

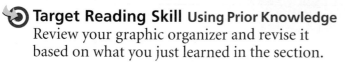

Section 5 Assessment

Target Reading Skill Using Prior Knowledge Review your graphic organizer and revise it based on what you just learned in the section.

Reviewing Key Concepts

1. a. **Listing** What are the main parts of a volcano?
   b. **Sequencing** Describe the order of parts through which magma travels as it moves to the surface.
   c. **Relating Cause and Effect** As a volcano erupts, what force pushes magma out of a volcano onto the surface?
2. a. **Identifying** What are the two main kinds of volcanic eruptions?
   b. **Explaining** What properties of magma help to determine the type of eruption?
   c. **Inferring** What do lava flows made of pahoehoe and aa indicate about the type of volcanic eruption that occurred?

3. a. **Naming** What are the three stages of volcanic activity?
   b. **Predicting** Which is more likely to be dangerous—a volcano that erupts frequently or a volcano that has been inactive for a hundred years? Why?

Writing in Science

Interview You are a television news reporter who will be interviewing a geologist. The geologist has just returned from studying a nearby volcano that may soon erupt. Write the questions that you would ask. Be sure to ask about the evidence that an eruption is coming, the type of eruption expected, and any hazards that will result. Write an answer for each question.

Remote Sensing

You can't see all sides of a large landform, such as a volcano, when you are standing close to it on the ground. Remote sensing, which involves studying Earth from above, provides people with a "birds-eye view" of just about any landform.

Radar Image of Mauna Loa
This synthetic aperture radar image of Mauna Loa was taken aboard the space shuttle *Endeavour* in 1994.

What Is Imaging Radar?

One kind of remote sensing is imaging radar (**ra**dio **d**etection and **r**anging). It uses an antenna to send microwave signals from space to Earth's surface. Signals are reflected back from the surface to the antenna and converted to digital data that is later recorded as images. Synthetic aperture radar (SAR) is a technology that produces images with fine detail. SAR can make images any time, day or night, and can even "see" Earth's surface through clouds and dust.

How Is Imaging Radar Used?

Notice the varying colors in the radar image of Mauna Loa shown in the photograph at the top of this page. These color differences are caused by differences in surface roughness of the lava flows. Smoother pahoehoe flows appear red and rougher aa flows appear yellow and white.

The ability to detect such different types of surfaces makes imaging radar a particularly useful tool for mapping lava flows and other volcanic landforms. It also is used to track and study a variety of Earth processes such as deforestation, ocean dynamics, soil erosion, and desertification.

Mauna Loa
This ground view of Mauna Loa was taken with regular color photography.

Weigh the Impact

1. Identify the Need
Explain why a single radar image would be more useful in mapping a volcano than a single photograph taken on the ground.

2. Research
Use scientific texts and articles to find out more about how imaging radar works and how different types of surfaces appear on radar images.

3. Write
Summarize your findings in a report. Be sure to include in your report a radar image and a description of what the different colors in the image represent.

Study Guide

1 Forces in Earth's Crust

Key Concepts

- Shearing, tension, and compression work over millions of years to change the shape and volume of rock.

- Faults usually occur along plate boundaries, where the forces of plate motion push or pull the crust so much that the crust breaks. There are three main types of faults: strike-slip faults, normal faults, and reverse faults.

- Over millions of years, the forces of plate movement can change a flat plain into landforms such as anticlines and synclines, folded mountains, fault-block mountains, and plateaus.

Key Terms

- stress • tension • compression • shearing
- normal fault • hanging wall • footwall
- reverse fault • strike-slip fault • anticline
- syncline • plateau

2 Earthquakes and Seismic Waves

Key Concepts

- Seismic waves carry energy from an earthquake away from the focus, through Earth's interior, and across the surface.

- There are three categories of seismic waves: P waves, S waves, and surface waves.

- Three commonly used ways of measuring earthquakes are the Mercalli scale, the Richter scale, and the moment magnitude scale.

Key Terms

- earthquake • focus • epicenter • P wave
- S wave • surface wave • magnitude
- Mercalli scale • Richter scale • seismograph
- moment magnitude scale

3 Monitoring Earthquakes

Key Concepts

- During an earthquake, seismic waves cause the seismograph's drum to vibrate. But the suspended weight with the pen attached moves very little. Therefore, the pen stays in place and records the drum's vibrations.

- To monitor faults, geologists have developed instruments to measure changes in elevation, tilting of the land surface, and ground movements along faults.

- Seismographs and fault-monitoring devices provide data used to map faults and detect changes along faults. Geologists are also trying to use these data to develop a method of predicting earthquakes.

Key Terms

- seismogram • friction

4 Volcanoes and Plate Tectonics

Key Concepts

- Volcanic belts form along the boundaries of Earth's plates.

- A volcano forms above a hot spot when magma erupts through the crust and reaches the surface.

Key Terms

- volcano • magma • lava • Ring of Fire
- island arc • hot spot

5 Volcanic Eruptions

Key Concepts

- When a volcano erupts, the force of the expanding gases pushes magma from the magma chamber through the pipe until it flows or explodes out of the vent.

- Geologists classify volcanic eruptions as quiet or explosive.

- Geologists often use the terms *active, dormant,* or *extinct* to describe a volcano's stage of activity.

Key Terms

- magma chamber • pipe • vent • lava flow
- crater • pyroclastic flow • dormant
- extinct

Review and Assessment

Go Online
PHSchool.com
For: Self-assessment
Visit: PHSchool.com
Web Code: cla-0060

Organizing Information

Relating Cause and Effect Fill in the cause-and-effect graphic organizer to show how different stress forces produce different kinds of faults.

Cause of Fault		Effect
Compression produces	→	___?___ fault
___?___ produces	→	Normal fault
___?___ produces	→	___?___ fault

Reviewing Key Terms

Choose the letter of the best answer.

1. The force that causes part of the crust to become shorter and thicker is
   a. tension.
   b. compression.
   c. shearing.
   d. normal force.

2. When the hanging wall of a fault slips down with respect to the footwall, the result is a
   a. reverse fault.
   b. syncline.
   c. normal fault.
   d. strike-slip fault.

3. Which of the following is a rating of earthquake damage at a particular location?
   a. moment magnitude scale
   b. focus scale
   c. Mercalli scale
   d. Richter scale

4. The largest waves on a seismogram are
   a. P waves.
   b. S waves.
   c. surface waves.
   d. tsunamis.

5. Magma becomes lava when it reaches a volcano's
   a. geyser.
   b. magma chamber.
   c. pipe.
   d. vent.

If the statement is true, write *true*. If it is false, change the underlined word or words to make the statement true.

6. <u>Anticline</u> forces squeeze or pull the rock in Earth's crust.

7. Rock uplifted by <u>normal faults</u> creates fault-block mountains.

8. An earthquake's <u>epicenter</u> is located deep underground.

9. As <u>S waves</u> move through the ground, they cause it to compress and then expand.

10. In a volcano, magma moves upward through a <u>pipe.</u>

Writing in Science

Cause-and-Effect Paragraph Now that you have learned about the awesome power of earthquakes, write a paragraph about how earthquakes cause damage. Discuss both the natural and human-made factors that contribute to an earthquake's destructive power.

DISCOVERY CHANNEL SCHOOL

Earthquakes

Video Preview
Video Field Trip
▶ Video Assessment

Review and Assessment

Checking Concepts

11. What process causes stress in Earth's crust?

12. Explain how a fault-block mountain forms.

13. What type of stress in the crust results in the formation of folded mountains? Explain.

14. What are plateaus and how do they form?

15. Describe what happens along a fault beneath Earth's surface when an earthquake occurs.

16. How is the amount of energy released by an earthquake related to its magnitude?

17. What process causes volcanoes to form along the mid-ocean ridge?

18. What are two ways volcanoes can form near converging plate boundaries?

Thinking Critically

19. **Classifying** Look at the diagram of a fault below. Describe how the hanging wall moves in relation to the footwall. What kind of fault is this?

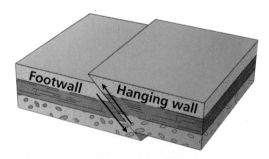

20. **Analyzing Data** A geologist has data about an earthquake from two seismographic stations. Is this enough information to determine the location of the epicenter? Why or why not?

21. **Predicting** A community has just built a street across a strike-slip fault that has frequent earthquakes. How will movement along the fault affect the street?

22. **Comparing and Contrasting** Compare the way in which an island arc forms with the way in which a hot spot volcano forms.

Applying Skills

Refer to the diagram to answer Questions 23–26.

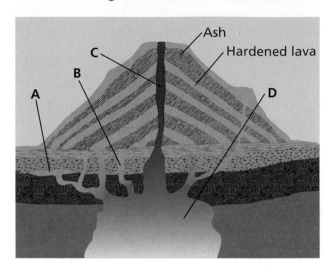

23. **Classifying** What is this volcano made of? How do geologists classify a volcano made of these materials?

24. **Developing Hypotheses** What is the feature labeled A in the diagram? What is the feature labeled B? How do these features form?

25. **Predicting** What is the feature labeled C in the diagram? If this feature becomes plugged with hardened magma, what could happen to the volcano? Explain.

26. **Inferring** What is the feature labeled D in the diagram? What can you infer about this feature if the volcano becomes dormant?

Lab zone Chapter **Project**

Performance Assessment Before testing how your model withstands an earthquake, explain to your classmates how and why you changed your model. When your model is tested, observe how it withstands the earthquake. How would a real earthquake compare with the method used to test your model? If it were a real building, could your structure withstand an earthquake? How could you improve your model?

Standardized Test Practice

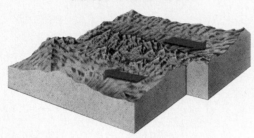
Choose the letter that best answers the question or completes the statement.

1. Stress will build until an earthquake occurs if friction along a fault is
   A decreasing.
   B high.
   C low.
   D changed to heat.

2. To estimate the total energy released by an earthquake, a geologist should use the
   A Mercalli scale.
   B Richter scale.
   C epicenter scale.
   D moment magnitude scale.

3. If magma is low in silica, it will cause
   A an explosive eruption.
   B pyroclastic flow.
   C a quiet eruption.
   D pumice deposits.

4. Which step in a volcanic eruption occurs just before the volcano erupts?
   A Magma collects in the magma chamber.
   B Lava hardens to form volcanic rock.
   C Expanding gases push magma through the pipe.
   D The roof of the empty magma chamber collapses.

5. The diagram below shows the formation of what volcanic feature?
   A crater
   B island arc volcano
   C hot spot
   D mid-ocean ridge

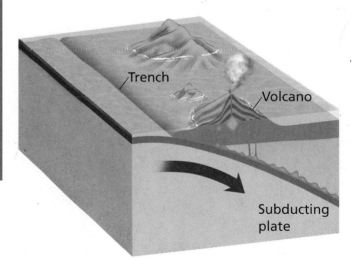

Open-Ended Question

6. Explain the process that forms a strike-slip fault and leads to an earthquake along the fault. In your answer, discuss the force that causes stress in Earth's crust, the type of stress that produces a strike-slip fault, the characteristics of a strike-slip fault, and what happens before and during the earthquake.

Chapter
10
Minerals

 Academic Standards

This chapter addresses these Indiana standards.

The Nature of Science

7.1.5 Identify important contributions to science, mathematics, and technology by people of different cultures and times.

Scientific Thinking

7.2.6 Measure length, volume, weight, elapsed time, rates, or temperatures, and choose appropriate units.

The Physical Setting

7.3.8 Describe how sediments are buried and bonded together by dissolved minerals to form solid rock.

This cave beneath a California mountain ▶ sparkles with thousands of calcite crystals.

Lab zone™ Chapter **Project**

Growing a Crystal Garden

Minerals occur in an amazing variety of colors and shapes—from clear, tiny cubes of halite (table salt), to the masses of calcite crystals in the photograph, to precious rubies and sapphires. In this project, you will grow crystals to see how different types of chemicals form different crystal shapes.

Your Goal To design and grow a crystal garden

To complete this project successfully, you must

- create a three dimensional garden scene as a base on which to grow crystals
- prepare at least two different crystal-growth solutions
- observe and record the shapes and growth rates of your crystals
- follow the safety guidelines in Appendix A

Plan It! Begin by deciding what materials you will use to create your garden scene. Your teacher will suggest a variety of materials and also describe the types of crystal-growth solutions that you can use. Then, design and build a setting for your crystal garden and add the solutions. Observe and record the growth of the crystals. Finally, display your finished crystal garden to your class. Be prepared to describe your procedure, observations, and conclusions.

Properties of Minerals

Reading Focus

Key Concepts
- What is a mineral?
- How are minerals identified?

Key Terms
- mineral • inorganic
- crystal • streak • luster
- Mohs hardness scale
- cleavage • fracture

Target Reading Skill

Outlining An outline shows the relationship between major ideas and supporting ideas. As you read, make an outline about the properties of minerals. Use the red headings for the main topics and the blue headings for the subtopics.

Properties of Minerals
I. What is a mineral?
A. Naturally occurring
B. Inorganic
C.
D.
E.
II. Identifying minerals

Lab zone Discover Activity

What Is the True Color of a Mineral?

1. Examine samples of magnetite and black hematite. Both minerals contain iron. Describe the color and appearance of the two minerals. Are they similar or different?
2. Rub the black hematite across the back of a porcelain or ceramic tile. Observe the color of the streak on the tile.
3. Wipe the tile clean before you test the next sample.
4. Rub the magnetite across the back of the tile. Observe the color of the streak.

Think It Over

Observing Does the color of each mineral match the color of its streak? How could this streak test be helpful in identifying them as two different minerals?

Look at the two different substances in Figure 1. On the left are beautiful quartz crystals. On the right is a handful of coal. Both are solid materials that form beneath Earth's surface. But only one is a mineral. To determine which of the two is a mineral, you need to become familiar with the characteristics of minerals. Then you can decide what's a mineral and what's not!

What Is a Mineral?

A mineral is a naturally occurring, inorganic solid that has a crystal structure and a definite chemical composition. For a substance to be a **mineral,** it must have all five of these characteristics.

Naturally Occurring To be classified as a mineral, a substance must be formed by processes that occur in the natural world. The mineral quartz forms naturally as magma cools and hardens deep beneath Earth's surface. Materials made by people, such as plastic, brick, glass, and steel, are not minerals.

Inorganic A mineral must also be **inorganic.** This means that the mineral cannot form from materials that were once part of a living thing. For example, coal forms naturally in the crust. But geologists do not classify coal as a mineral because it comes from the remains of plants that lived millions of years ago.

Solid A mineral is always a solid, with a definite volume and shape. The particles that make up a solid are packed together very tightly, so they cannot move like the particles that make up a liquid.

Crystal Structure The particles of a mineral line up in a pattern that repeats over and over again. The repeating pattern of a mineral's particles forms a solid called a **crystal.** A crystal has flat sides, called faces, that meet at sharp edges and corners. The quartz in Figure 1 has a crystal structure. In contrast, most coal lacks a crystal structure.

Definite Chemical Composition A mineral has a definite chemical composition or range of compositions. This means that a mineral always contains certain elements in definite proportions.

Almost all minerals are compounds. For example, a crystal of the mineral quartz has one atom of silicon for every two atoms of oxygen. Each compound has its own properties, or characteristics, which usually differ greatly from the properties of the elements that form it.

Some elements occur in nature in a pure form, and not as part of a compound with other elements. Elements such as copper, silver, and gold are also minerals. Almost all pure, solid elements are metals.

FIGURE 1
Quartz and Coal
Quartz (below) has all the characteristics of a mineral. But coal (above) is formed from the remains of plants, lacks a crystal structure, and has no definite chemical composition.

✓ **Reading Checkpoint** What does the phrase "definite chemical composition" mean?

Mineral Characteristics	Quartz	Coal
Naturally occurring	✓	✓
Inorganic	✓	No
Solid	✓	✓
Crystal structure	✓	No
Definite chemical composition	✓	No

Identifying Minerals

Geologists have identified about 3,800 minerals. Because there are so many different kinds of minerals, telling them apart can often be a challenge. **Each mineral has characteristic properties that can be used to identify it.** When you have learned to recognize the properties of minerals, you will be able to identify many common minerals around you.

You can see some of the properties of a mineral just by looking at a sample. To observe other properties, however, you need to conduct tests on that sample. As you read about the properties of minerals, think about how you could use them to identify a mineral.

Color The color of a mineral is an easily observed physical property. But the color of a mineral alone often provides too little information to make an identification. All three minerals in Figure 2 are the color gold, yet only one is the real thing. Color can be used to identify only those few minerals that always have their own characteristic color. The mineral malachite is always green. The mineral azurite is always blue. No other minerals look quite the same as these.

Gold   Pyrite   Chalcopyrite

FIGURE 2
Color of Minerals
These women in India are searching for bits of gold in river sand. Just because a mineral is gold in color doesn't mean it really is gold. Chalcopyrite and pyrite, also known as "fool's gold," are similar in color to real gold.

FIGURE 3
Streak
A mineral's streak can be the same as or quite different from its color.
Observing *How do the streaks of these minerals compare with their colors?*

Malachite ▶

Hematite ▶

▲ Galena

Streak A streak test can provide a clue to a mineral's identity. The **streak** of a mineral is the color of its powder. You can observe a streak by rubbing a mineral against a piece of unglazed porcelain tile, as shown in Figure 3. Even though the color of the mineral may vary, its streak does not. Surprisingly, the streak color and the mineral color are often different. For example, although pyrite has a gold color, it always produces a greenish black streak. Real gold, on the other hand, produces a golden yellow streak.

Luster Another simple test to identify a mineral is to check its luster. **Luster** is the term used to describe how light is reflected from a mineral's surface. Minerals containing metals are often shiny. For example, galena is an ore of lead that has a bright, metallic luster. Quartz has a glassy luster. Some of the other terms used to describe luster include earthy, waxy, and pearly. Figure 4 shows the luster of several minerals.

 **Reading Checkpoint** What characteristic of minerals does the term *luster* describe?

FIGURE 4
Geologists use many different terms to describe the luster of minerals.
Interpreting Tables *Which mineral has an earthy luster?*

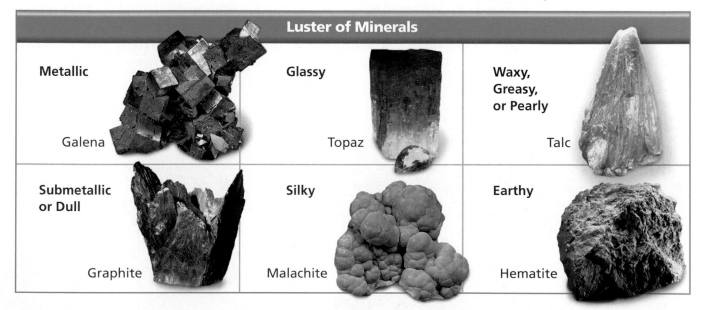

Luster of Minerals		
Metallic Galena	**Glassy** Topaz	**Waxy, Greasy, or Pearly** Talc
Submetallic or Dull Graphite	**Silky** Malachite	**Earthy** Hematite

Calculating Density

To calculate the density of a mineral, divide the mass of the mineral sample by its volume.

$$\text{Density} = \frac{\text{Mass}}{\text{Volume}}$$

For example, if a sample of olivine has a mass of 237 g and a volume of 72 cm^3, then the density is

$$\frac{237\ \text{g}}{72\ \text{cm}^3} = 3.3\ \text{g/cm}^3$$

Practice Problem A sample of calcite has a mass of 324 g and a volume of 120 cm^3. What is its density?

Density Each mineral has a characteristic density. Recall that density is the mass in a given space, or mass per unit volume. No matter what the size of a mineral sample, the density of that mineral always remains the same.

You can compare the density of two mineral samples of about the same size. Just pick them up and heft them, or feel their weight, in your hands. You may be able to feel the difference between low-density quartz and high-density galena. If the two samples are the same size, the galena will be almost three times as heavy as the quartz.

But heft provides only a rough measure of density. When geologists measure density, they use a balance to determine the precise mass of a mineral sample. Then they place the mineral in water to determine how much water the sample displaces. The volume of the displaced water equals the volume of the sample. Dividing the sample's mass by its volume gives the density of the mineral:

$$\text{Density} = \frac{\text{Mass}}{\text{Volume}}$$

Hardness When you identify a mineral, one of the best clues you can use is the mineral's hardness. In 1812, Friedrich Mohs, an Austrian mineral expert, invented a test to describe the hardness of minerals. Called the **Mohs hardness scale,** this scale ranks ten minerals from softest to hardest. Look at Figure 5 to see which mineral is the softest and which is the hardest.

FIGURE 5

Mohs Hardness Scale

Geologists determine a mineral's hardness by comparing it to the hardness of the minerals on the Mohs scale.

Talc
The softest known mineral, talc flakes when scratched by a fingernail.

Gypsum
A fingernail can easily scratch it.

Calcite
A fingernail cannot scratch it, but a copper penny can.

Fluorite
A steel knife can easily scratch it.

Apatite
A steel knife can scratch it.

1 2 3 4 5

Mineral Density

Use the line graph of the mass and volume of pyrite samples to answer the questions.

1. **Reading Graphs** What is the mass of Sample B? What is the volume of Sample B?

2. **Calculating** What is the density of Sample B?

3. **Reading Graphs** What is the mass of Sample C? What is the volume of Sample C?

4. **Calculating** What is the density of Sample C?

5. **Comparing and Contrasting** Compare the density of Sample B to that of Sample C.

6. **Predicting** A piece of pyrite has a volume of 40 cm³. What is its mass?

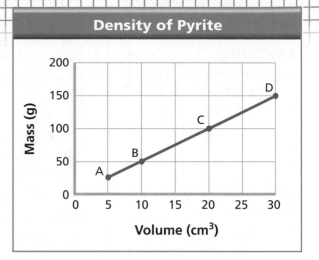

Density of Pyrite

Mass (g) vs *Volume (cm³)*

7. **Drawing Conclusions** Does the density of a mineral depend on the size of the mineral sample? Explain.

Hardness can be determined by a scratch test. A mineral can scratch any mineral softer than itself, but can be scratched by any mineral that is harder. To determine the hardness of azurite, a mineral not on the Mohs scale, you could try to scratch it with talc, gypsum, or calcite. But none of these minerals scratch azurite. Apatite, rated 5 on the scale, does scratch azurite. Therefore, azurite's hardness is about 4.

Feldspar
It can't be scratched by a steel knife, but it can scratch window glass.

Quartz
It can scratch steel and hard glass easily.

Topaz
It can scratch quartz.

Corundum
It can scratch topaz.

Diamond
The hardest known mineral, diamond can scratch all other substances.

6   7   8   9   10

Crystal Systems The crystals of each mineral grow atom by atom to form that mineral's crystal structure. Geologists classify these structures into six groups based on the number and angle of the crystal faces. These groups are called crystal systems. For example, all halite crystals are cubic. Halite crystals have six square faces that meet at right angles, forming a perfect cube.

Sometimes, the crystal structure is obvious from the mineral's appearance. Crystals that grow in an open space can be almost perfectly formed. But crystals that grow in a tight space are often incompletely formed. In other minerals, the crystal structure is visible only under a microscope. A few minerals, such as opal, are considered minerals even though their particles are not arranged in a crystal structure. Figure 6 shows minerals that belong to each of the six crystal systems.

Cleavage and Fracture The way a mineral breaks apart can help to identify it. A mineral that splits easily along flat surfaces has the property called **cleavage**. Whether a mineral has cleavage depends on how the atoms in its crystals are arranged. The arrangement of atoms in the mineral causes it to break apart more easily in one direction than another. Look at the photo of mica in Figure 7. Mica separates easily in only one direction, forming flat sheets. Therefore, mica has cleavage. Feldspar is another common mineral that has cleavage.

FIGURE 6
Properties of Minerals
All crystals of the same mineral have the same crystal structure. Each mineral also has other characteristic properties.
Interpreting Data *Which mineral has the lowest density?*

Magnetite
Crystal System: Cubic
Color: Black
Streak: Black
Luster: Metallic
Hardness: 6
Density (g/cm³): 5.2
Special Property: Magnetic

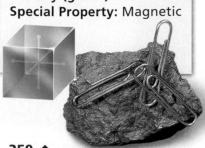

Quartz
Crystal System: Hexagonal
Color: Transparent, various colors
Streak: Colorless
Luster: Glassy
Hardness: 7
Density (g/cm³): 2.6
Special Property: Fractures like broken glass

Rutile
Crystal System: Tetragonal
Color: Black or reddish brown
Streak: Light brown
Luster: Metallic or gemlike
Hardness: 6–6.5
Density (g/cm³): 4.2–4.3
Special Property: Not easily melted

Fracture

When quartz fractures, the break looks like the surface of a seashell.

Cleavage

Mica cleaves into thin, flat sheets that are almost transparent.

Most minerals do not split apart evenly. Instead, they have a characteristic type of fracture. **Fracture** describes how a mineral looks when it breaks apart in an irregular way. Geologists use a variety of terms to describe fracture. For example, quartz has a shell-shaped fracture. When quartz breaks, it produces curved, shell-like surfaces that look like chipped glass. Pure metals, like copper and iron, have a hackly fracture—they form jagged points. Some soft minerals that crumble easily like clay have an earthy fracture. Minerals that form rough, irregular surfaces when broken have an uneven fracture.

FIGURE 7
Cleavage and Fracture
How a mineral breaks apart can help to identify it.
Applying Concepts *How would you test a mineral to determine whether it has cleavage or fracture?*

 **Reading Checkpoint**   **Compare the fracture of quartz to the fracture of a pure metal, such as iron.**

Go Online
active art

For: Crystal Systems activity
Visit: PHSchool.com
Web Code: cfp-1041

Sulfur
Crystal System: Orthorhombic
Color: Lemon yellow to yellowish brown
Streak: White
Luster: Greasy
Hardness: 2
Density (g/cm³): 2.0–2.1
Special Property: Melts easily

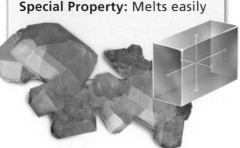

Azurite
Crystal System: Monoclinic
Color: Blue
Streak: Pale blue
Luster: Glassy to dull or earthy
Hardness: 3.5–4
Density (g/cm³): 3.8
Special Property: Reacts to acid

Microcline Feldspar
Crystal System: Triclinic
Color: Pink, white, red-brown, or green
Streak: Colorless
Luster: Glassy
Hardness: 6
Density (g/cm³): 2.6
Special Property: Cleaves well in two directions

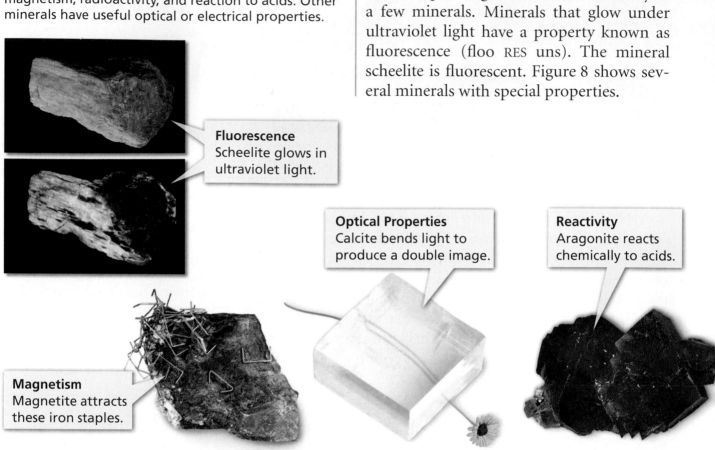

FIGURE 8
Special Properties
The special properties of minerals include fluorescence, magnetism, radioactivity, and reaction to acids. Other minerals have useful optical or electrical properties.

Fluorescence
Scheelite glows in ultraviolet light.

Optical Properties
Calcite bends light to produce a double image.

Reactivity
Aragonite reacts chemically to acids.

Magnetism
Magnetite attracts these iron staples.

Special Properties Some minerals can be identified by special physical properties. For example, magnetism occurs naturally in a few minerals. Minerals that glow under ultraviolet light have a property known as fluorescence (floo RES uns). The mineral scheelite is fluorescent. Figure 8 shows several minerals with special properties.

Section 1 Assessment

Target Reading Skill Outlining Use the information in your outline about the properties of minerals to help you answer the questions.

Reviewing Key Concepts

1. **a. Defining** Write a definition of "mineral" in your own words.
   b. Explaining What does it mean to say that a mineral is inorganic?
   c. Classifying Amber is a precious material used in jewelry. It forms when the resin of pine trees hardens into stone. Is amber a mineral? Explain.
2. **a. Listing** Name eight properties that can be used to identify minerals.
   b. Comparing and Contrasting What is the difference between fracture and cleavage?

   c. Predicting Graphite is a mineral made up of carbon atoms that form thin sheets. But the sheets are only weakly held together. Predict whether graphite will break apart with fracture or cleavage. Explain.

Math Practice

3. **Calculating Density** The mineral platinum is an element that often occurs as a pure metal. If a sample of platinum has a mass of 430 g and a volume of 20 cm³, what is its density?

Go Online
PHSchool.com

For: Data sharing
Visit: PHSchool.com
Web Code: cfd-1041

Finding the Density of Minerals

Problem

How can you compare the density of different minerals?

Skills Focus

measuring

Materials (per student)

- graduated cylinder, 100-mL
- 3 mineral samples: pyrite, quartz, and galena
- water
- balance

Procedure

1. Check to make sure the mineral samples are small enough to fit in the graduated cylinder.

2. Copy the data table into your notebook. Place the pyrite on the balance and record its mass in the data table.

3. Fill the cylinder with water to the 50-mL mark.

4. Carefully place the pyrite in the cylinder of water. Try not to spill any of the water.

5. Read the level of the water on the scale of the graduated cylinder. Record the level of the water with the pyrite in it.

6. Calculate the volume of water displaced by the pyrite. To do this, subtract the volume of water without the pyrite from the volume of water with the pyrite. Record your answer.

7. Calculate the density of the pyrite by using this formula.

$$\text{Density} = \frac{\text{Mass of mineral}}{\text{Volume of water displaced by mineral}}$$

(Note: Density is expressed as g/cm^3. One mL of water has a volume of $1\ cm^3$.)

8. Remove the water and mineral from the cylinder.

9. Repeat Steps 2–8 for quartz and galena.

Analyze and Conclude

1. **Interpreting Data** Which mineral had the highest density? The lowest density?

2. **Measuring** How does finding the volume of the water that was displaced help you find the volume of the mineral itself?

3. **Drawing Conclusions** Does the shape of a mineral sample affect its density? Explain.

4. **Predicting** Would the procedure you used in this lab work for a substance that floats or one that dissolves in water?

Designing Experiments

Pyrite is sometimes called "fool's gold" because its color and appearance are similar to real gold. Design an experiment to determine if a sample that looks like gold is in fact real gold.

Data Table			
	Pyrite	Quartz	Galena
Mass of Mineral (g)			
Volume of Water Without Mineral (mL)	50	50	50
Volume of Water With Mineral (mL)			
Volume of Water Displaced (mL)			
Volume of Water Displaced (cm³)			
Density (g/cm³)			

How Minerals Form

Reading Focus

Key Concepts
• How do minerals form from magma and lava?
• How do minerals form from water solutions?

Key Terms
• geode • crystallization
• solution • vein

Target Reading Skill
Asking Questions Before you read, preview the red headings. In a graphic organizer like the one below, ask a *how* or *what* question for each heading. As you read, write answers to your questions.

Formation of Minerals

Question	Answer
How do minerals form from magma?	

Discover **Activity**

How Does the Rate of Cooling Affect Crystals?

1. ☠ Put on your goggles. Use a plastic spoon to place a small amount of salol near one end of each of two microscope slides. You need just enough to form a spot 0.5 to 1.0 cm in diameter.

2. 🔥 🧪 Carefully hold one slide with tongs. Warm it gently over a lit candle until the salol is almost completely melted. **CAUTION:** *Move the slide in and out of the flame to avoid cracking the glass.*

3. Set the slide aside to cool slowly. While the first slide is cooling, hold the second slide with tongs and heat it as in Step 2.

4. Cool the second slide quickly by placing it on an ice cube. Carefully blow out the candle.

5. Observe the slides under a hand lens. Compare the appearance of the crystals that form on the two slides.

6. Wash your hands when you are finished.

Think It Over
Developing Hypotheses Which sample had larger crystals? If a mineral forms by rapid cooling, would you expect the crystals to be large or small?

On a rock-collecting field trip, you spot an egg-shaped rock about the size of a football. No, it's not a dinosaur egg—but what is it? You collect the rock and bring it to a geologic laboratory. There, you carefully split the rock open. The rock is hollow! Its inside surface sparkles with large, colorful amethyst crystals.

You have found a geode (JEE ohd). A **geode** is a rounded, hollow rock that is often lined with mineral crystals. Crystals form inside a geode when water containing dissolved minerals seeps into a crack or hollow in a rock. Slowly, crystallization occurs, lining the inside with large crystals that are often perfectly formed. **Crystallization** is the process by which atoms are arranged to form a material with a crystal structure. In general, minerals can form in two ways: by crystallization of magma and lava or by crystallization of materials dissolved in water.

Amethyst geode ▼

Minerals From Magma and Lava

Many minerals form from magma and lava. **Minerals form as hot magma cools inside the crust, or as lava hardens on the surface. When these liquids cool to a solid state, they form crystals.** The size of the crystals depends on several factors. The rate at which the magma cools, the amount of gas the magma contains, and the chemical composition of the magma all affect crystal size.

When magma remains deep below the surface, it cools slowly over many thousands of years. Slow cooling leads to the formation of large crystals, like the amethyst crystals in a geode. If the crystals remain undisturbed while cooling, they grow by adding atoms according to a regular pattern.

Magma closer to the surface cools much faster than magma that hardens deep below ground. With more rapid cooling, there is no time for magma to form large crystals. Instead, small crystals form. If magma erupts to the surface and becomes lava, the lava will also cool quickly and form minerals with small crystals.

 **Reading Checkpoint** What size crystals form when magma cools rapidly?

Minerals From Solutions

Sometimes the elements and compounds that form minerals can be dissolved in water to form solutions. A **solution** is a mixture in which one substance is dissolved in another. **When elements and compounds that are dissolved in water leave a solution, crystallization occurs.** Minerals can form in this way underground and in bodies of water on Earth's surface.

FIGURE 9
Selenite Crystals
These huge selenite crystals in a cave in Mexico formed from the crystallization of minerals in a solution.

Minerals formed
by evaporation

A gypsum "rose" forms by
evaporation of a mineral solution.

Water containing
dissolved minerals

Minerals Formed by Evaporation Some minerals form when solutions evaporate. If you stir salt crystals into a beaker of water, the salt dissolves, forming a solution. But if you allow the water in the solution to evaporate, it will leave salt crystals on the bottom of the beaker. In a similar way, deposits of the mineral halite formed over millions of years when ancient seas slowly evaporated. In the United States, such halite deposits are found in the Midwest, the Southwest, and along the Gulf Coast. Other useful minerals that can form by evaporation include gypsum and calcite.

Minerals From Hot Water Solutions Deep underground, magma can heat water to a high temperature. Sometimes, the elements and compounds that form a mineral dissolve in this hot water. When the water solution begins to cool, the elements and compounds leave the solution and crystallize as minerals. The silver in Figure 10 was deposited from a hot water solution.

Pure metals that crystallize from hot water solutions underground often form veins. A **vein** is a narrow channel or slab of a mineral that is different from the surrounding rock. Solutions of hot water and metals often flow through cracks within the rock. Then the metals crystallize into veins that resemble the streaks of fudge in vanilla fudge ice cream.

 **Reading Checkpoint** What is a vein?

Go Online
PHSchool.com

For: More on mineral formation
Visit: PHSchool.com
Web Code: cfd-1042

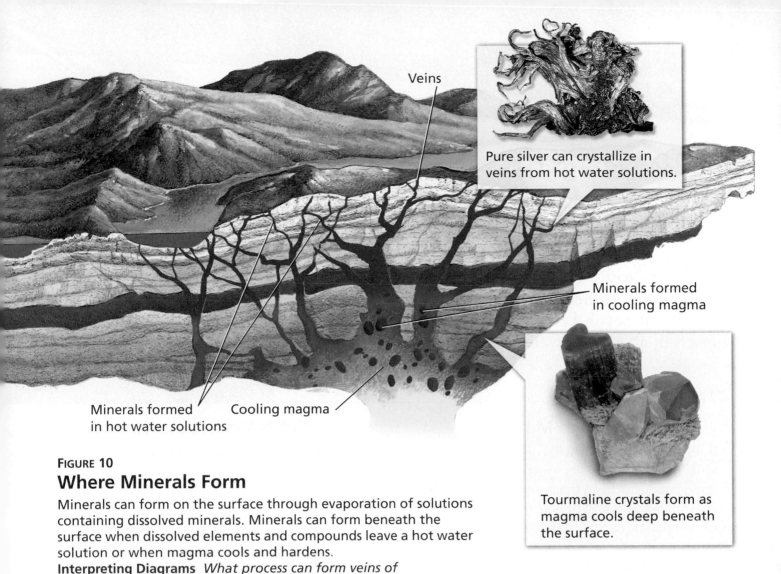

Veins

Pure silver can crystallize in veins from hot water solutions.

Minerals formed in cooling magma

Minerals formed in hot water solutions

Cooling magma

Tourmaline crystals form as magma cools deep beneath the surface.

FIGURE 10

Where Minerals Form

Minerals can form on the surface through evaporation of solutions containing dissolved minerals. Minerals can form beneath the surface when dissolved elements and compounds leave a hot water solution or when magma cools and hardens.
Interpreting Diagrams *What process can form veins of underground minerals?*

Section 2 Assessment

Target Reading Skill Asking Questions Use your chart to explain two ways in which minerals can form on Earth's surface.

Reviewing Key Concepts

1. **a. Defining** What is crystallization?
   b. Relating Cause and Effect What factors affect the size of the crystals that form as magma cools?
   c. Predicting Under what conditions will cooling magma produce minerals with large crystals?
2. **a. Defining** What is a solution?
   b. Explaining What are two ways in which minerals can form from a solution?
   c. Relating Cause and Effect Describe the process by which a deposit of rock salt, or halite, could form from a solution.

Writing in Science

Dialogue Suppose that you are a scientist exploring a cave. The light on your helmet suddenly reveals a wall covered with large crystals. Scientists on the surface ask you about your observations. Write a dialogue made up of their questions and your replies. Include the different ways in which the minerals you see might have formed.

Who Owns the Ocean's Minerals?

Rich mineral deposits lie on and just beneath the ocean floor. Coastal nations have the right to mine deposits near their shores. Today, they are mining minerals from the continental shelf. But mineral deposits on the ocean floor beyond are open for all nations. Who owns these valuable underwater minerals?

The Issues

Who Can Afford to Mine?

Mining the ocean floor will cost a huge amount of money. New technologies must be developed to obtain mineral deposits from the ocean floor. Only wealthy industrial nations will be able to afford the costs. Industrial nations that have spent money on mining think that they should keep the profits. But developing nations that lack money and technology and landlocked nations disagree.

What Rights Do Nations Have?

By 2003, 157 nations had signed the Law of the Sea treaty. Among other things, this treaty stated that ocean mineral deposits are the common property of all people. It also stated that mining profits must be shared among all nations. Some people think that, because of the treaty, wealthy nations should share their technology and any profits they get from mining the ocean floor.

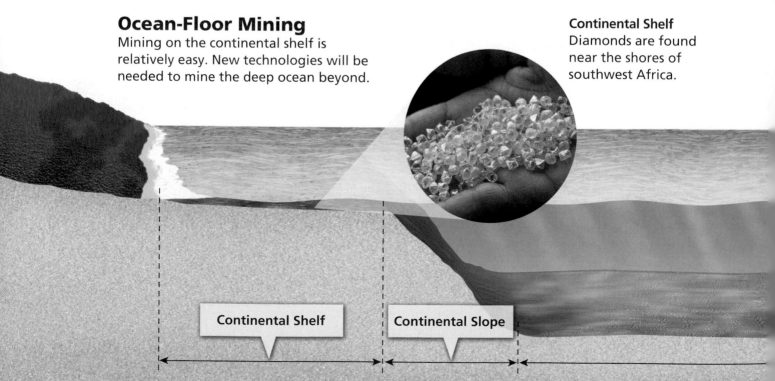

Ocean-Floor Mining
Mining on the continental shelf is relatively easy. New technologies will be needed to mine the deep ocean beyond.

Continental Shelf
Diamonds are found near the shores of southwest Africa.

Continental Shelf

Continental Slope

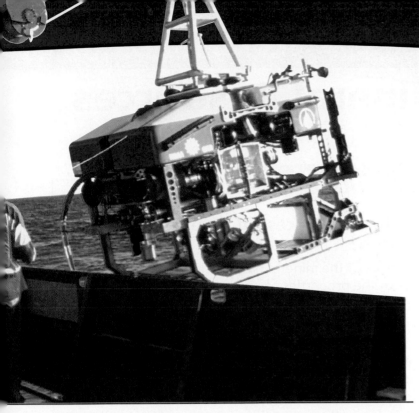

How Can the Wealth Be Shared?

What can nations do to prevent conflict over mining the ocean floor? They might arrange a compromise. Perhaps wealthy nations should contribute part of their profits to help developing or landlocked nations. Developing nations could pool their money for ocean-floor mining. Whatever nations decide, some regulations for ocean-floor mining are necessary. In the future, these resources will be important to everyone.

What Would You Do?

1. Identify the Problem
Summarize the controversy about ocean mineral rights.

2. Analyze the Options
Research this topic at the library or on the Internet. Then compare the concerns of wealthy nations with those of developing nations. How could you reassure developing nations that they will not be left out?

3. Find a Solution
Look at a map of the world. Who should share the mineral profits from the Pacific Ocean? From the Atlantic Ocean? Write one or two paragraphs stating your opinion. Support your ideas with facts.

Go Online
PHSchool.com

For: More on who owns the ocean's minerals
Visit: PHSchool.com
Web Code: cfh-1040

Abyssal Plain
Minerals called manganese nodules form on the deep ocean floor. The metals cobalt, iron, nickel, and copper are also found here.

Mid-Ocean Ridge
Rich mineral deposits form from hot water solutions near mid-ocean ridges. Mining for gold, silver, copper, and other minerals might be possible here.

Abyssal Plain

Mid-Ocean Ridge

Using Mineral Resources

Reading Focus

Key Concepts
- How are minerals used?
- How are ores processed to obtain metals?

Key Terms
- gemstone
- ore
- smelting
- alloy

Target Reading Skill
Using Prior Knowledge Before you read, look at the section headings and visuals to see what this section is about. Then write what you know about mineral resources in a graphic organizer like the one below. As you read, write what you learn.

What You Know
1. The gems used in jewelry are minerals.
2.

What You Learned
1.
2.

Lab zone Discover Activity

How Are Minerals Processed Before They Are Used?

1. Examine a piece of the mineral bauxite carefully. Use your knowledge of the properties of minerals to describe it.
2. Examine an aluminum can. (The metal aluminum comes from bauxite.) Compare the properties of the aluminum can with the properties of bauxite.
3. Examine a piece of the mineral graphite and describe its properties.
4. Examine the lead in a pencil. (Pencil lead is made from graphite.) Compare the properties of the pencil lead with the properties of graphite.

Think It Over
Posing Questions How does each mineral compare to the object made from it? To understand how bauxite and graphite are made into useful materials, what questions would you need to answer?

More than a thousand years ago, the Hopewell people lived in the Ohio River valley. These ancient Native Americans are famous for the mysterious earthen mounds they built near the river. There these people left beautiful objects made from minerals. Some of these objects are tools chipped from flint (a variety of quartz). Others are animals made from thin sheets of copper, like the fish in Figure 11.

To obtain these minerals, the Hopewell people traded with peoples across North America. The copper, for example, came from near Lake Superior. There, copper could be found as a pure metal. Because pure copper is soft, it was easy to shape into ornaments or weapons.

FIGURE 11
Hopewell Fish
The ancient Hopewell people used a thin sheet of copper to make this fish.

The Uses of Minerals

Like the Hopewell people, modern civilizations use many minerals. You are surrounded by materials that come from minerals, such as the metal body and window glass of a car. **Minerals are the source of gemstones, metals, and a variety of materials used to make many products.** How many products that are made from minerals can you name? You might be surprised at how important minerals are in everyday life.

Gemstones Beautiful gemstones such as rubies and sapphires have captured the imagination of people throughout the ages. Usually, a **gemstone** is a hard, colorful mineral that has a brilliant or glassy luster. People value gemstones for their color, luster, and durability, and for the fact that they are rare. Once a gemstone is cut and polished, it is called a gem. Gems are used mainly for jewelry and decoration. They are also used for mechanical parts and for grinding and polishing.

Metals Some minerals are the sources of metals such as aluminum, iron, copper, or silver. Metals are generally not as hard as gemstones. But metals are useful because they can be stretched into wire, flattened into sheets, and hammered or molded without breaking. Metal tools and machinery, the metal filament in a light bulb, aluminum foil, and the steel beams used to frame office buildings all began as minerals inside Earth's crust.

Other Useful Minerals There are many other useful minerals besides metals and gems. People use materials from these minerals in foods, medicines, fertilizers, and building materials. The very soft mineral talc is ground up to make talcum powder. Clear crystals of the mineral calcite are used in optical instruments such as microscopes. Quartz, a mineral found in sand, is used in making glass as well as in electronic equipment and watches. Gypsum, a soft, white mineral, is used to make wallboard, cement, and stucco.

 **Reading Checkpoint** How do people use talc and calcite?

FIGURE 12
Gems
Precious gems like the diamonds and large blue sapphires on this necklace are among the most valuable minerals.
Observing *How would you describe the luster of these gems?*

DISCOVERY CHANNEL SCHOOL™

Minerals

Video Preview
▶ Video Field Trip
Video Assessment

Producing Metals From Minerals

How is a mineral containing metal made into a finished product? **To produce metal from a mineral, a rock containing the mineral must be located through prospecting and mined, or removed from the ground. Then the rock must be processed to extract the metal.** Look at the Tech & Design in History timeline to see how the technology of producing metals has developed through the ages.

A rock that contains a metal or other useful mineral that can be mined and sold at a profit is called an **ore.** Unlike the copper used by the Hopewell people, most metals do not occur in a pure form. A metal usually occurs as a mineral that is a combination of that metal and other elements. Much of the world's copper, for example, comes from ores containing the mineral chalcopyrite (kal koh PY ryt). In addition to copper, chalcopyrite contains iron and sulfur.

• Tech & Design in History •

Advances in Metal Technology
For thousands of years, people have been inventing and improving methods for smelting metals and making alloys.

4000 B.C. Copper
The island of Cyprus was one of the first places where copper was mined and smelted. In fact, the name of the island provided the name of the metal. In Latin, *aes cyprium* meant "metal of Cyprus." It was later shortened to *cuprum*, meaning "copper." The sculpted figure is carrying a large piece of smelted copper.

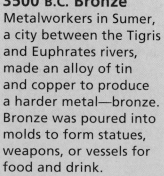

3500 B.C. Bronze
Metalworkers in Sumer, a city between the Tigris and Euphrates rivers, made an alloy of tin and copper to produce a harder metal—bronze. Bronze was poured into molds to form statues, weapons, or vessels for food and drink.

1500 B.C. Iron
The Hittites learned to mine and smelt iron ore. Because iron is stronger than copper or bronze, its use spread rapidly. Tools and weapons could be made of iron. This iron dagger was made in Austria several hundred years after the Hittites' discovery.

| 4000 B.C. | 2500 B.C. | 1000 B.C. |

Prospecting A prospector is anyone who searches, or prospects, for an ore deposit. Geologists prospect for ores by observing rocks on the land surface and by studying maps of rocks beneath the surface. Geologists can often map the size and shape of an ore deposit by making careful measurements of Earth's magnetic field over the deposit. This works well for minerals that contain magnetic elements such as iron and nickel.

Mining The geologist's map of an ore deposit helps miners decide how to remove the ore from the ground. There are three types of mines: strip mines, open pit mines, and shaft mines. In strip mining, earthmoving equipment scrapes away soil to expose ore. In open pit mining, miners use giant earthmoving equipment to dig a tremendous pit and remove ore deposits. For ore deposits that occur in veins, miners dig shaft mines. Shaft mines often have a network of tunnels that extend deep into the ground, following the veins of ore.

Writing in Science

Diary Entry When people discover how to use metals in a new way, the discovery often produces big changes in the way those people live. Choose a development in the history of metals to research. Write a diary entry telling how the discovery happened and how it changed people's lives.

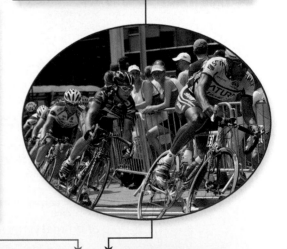

A.D. 1960s Space-Age Alloys
Scientists working on the space program have developed light and strong alloys for use in products ranging from bicycles to soda cans. For example, a new alloy of nickel and titanium can "remember" its shape. It is used for eyeglasses that return to their original shape after being bent.

**A.D. 500
Early Steel-Making**
Sri Lankans made steel in outdoor furnaces. Steady winds blowing over the top of the furnace's front wall created the high temperatures needed to make steel. Because their steel was so much harder than iron, the Sri Lankans were able to trade it throughout the Indian Ocean region.

**A.D. 1860s
Modern Steel-Making**
Steel-making techniques invented by Henry Bessemer and William Siemens made it possible to produce steel cheaply on a large scale. Siemens' invention, the open-hearth furnace, is still widely used, although more modern methods account for most steel production today.

A.D. 500   **A.D. 2000**

Smelting Ores must be processed before the metals they contain can be used. In the process of **smelting,** an ore is mixed with other substances and then melted to separate the useful metal from other elements the ore contains. Look at Figure 13 to see how smelting separates iron metal from hematite, a common form of iron ore.

❶ Iron ore is crushed and mixed with crushed limestone and coke (baked coal), which is rich in carbon.

❷ The mixture is placed in a blast furnace, where extremely hot air is blown through, making the coke burn easily.

❸ As the coke burns, chemical changes in the mixture produce carbon dioxide gas and molten iron.

❹ The dense, molten iron sinks to the bottom of the furnace. Impurities left in the ore combine with the limestone to create slag.

❺ The slag and molten iron are poured off through taps.

FIGURE 13
Smelting Iron Ore
Iron ores must be smelted to separate the iron from the oxygen and other substances in the ores. Then the iron is refined and processed into steel.
Inferring *Why does the molten iron sink to the bottom of the blast furnace?*

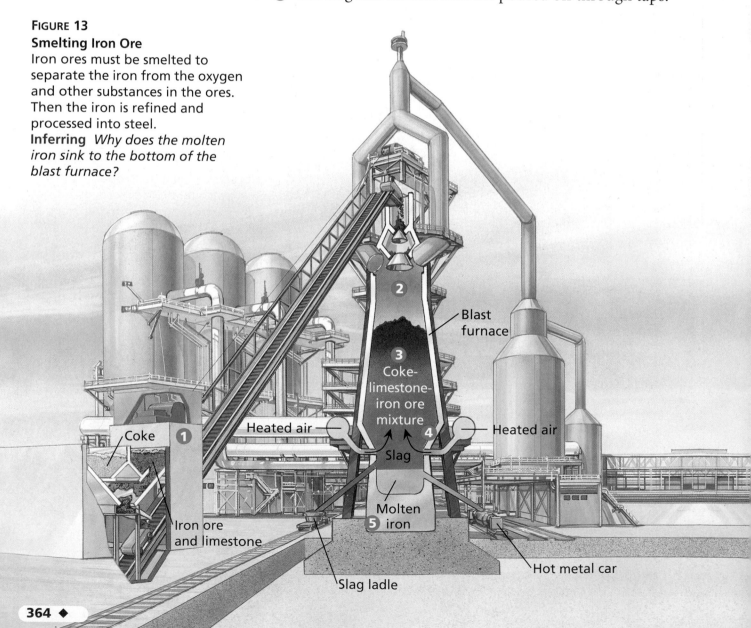

364 ◆

Further Processing After smelting, additional processing is needed to remove impurities from the metal. After the iron is purified, a small amount of carbon may be added to it. The result is steel, which is harder and stronger than iron. Steel is an **alloy,** a solid mixture of two or more elements, at least one of which is a metal. To be considered an alloy, the mixture must have the characteristic properties of a metal.

After adding carbon to iron, steelmakers may add other elements to create alloys with specific properties. For stronger steel, the metal manganese is added. For rust-resistant steel, the metals chromium and nickel are added. Figure 14 shows how rust-resistant stainless steel was used in the construction of one of America's most famous monuments.

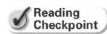 **Reading Checkpoint** What is an alloy?

FIGURE 14
The Gateway Arch
The Gateway Arch in St. Louis, Missouri, is covered in stainless steel.

Section 3 Assessment

Target Reading Skill Using Prior Knowledge Review your graphic organizer and revise it based on what you just learned in the section.

Reviewing Key Concepts

1. a. **Defining** What are gemstones? Why are they valuable?
   b. **Listing** What properties of metals make them useful to humans?
   c. **Problem Solving** Suppose that you are designing a machine with many small, moving parts that will need to run constantly. Would you make the parts from metal or gemstone? Explain your answer.
2. a. **Identifying** What is an ore?
   b. **Summarizing** Explain the steps that must take place before an ore can be made into a useful product.
   c. **Inferring** Which material formed during smelting is denser—molten metal or slag? How can you tell?

Lab zone At-Home **Activity**

Rust Protection You can demonstrate to your family how rust damages objects that contain iron. Obtain three iron nails. Coat one of the nails with petroleum jelly and coat the second nail with clear nail polish. Do not put anything on the third nail. Place all the nails in a glass of water with a little vinegar. (The vinegar speeds up the rusting process.) Allow the nails to stand in the glass overnight. Which nails show signs of rusting? Explain these results to your family.

A Mouthful Of Minerals

Problem

What effect do the minerals in toothpaste have on the toothpaste's ability to clean?

Skills Focus

observing, controlling variables, drawing conclusions

Materials

• samples of 3 different types of toothpaste
• worn-out toothbrushes
• tap water
• a ceramic tile stained on the unglazed side with a felt-tip marker or pen

Procedure

1. Copy the data table into your notebook.

2. Your teacher will give you samples of toothpaste, a list of the mineral or minerals in each type of toothpaste, a toothbrush, and a ceramic tile.

3. In your data table, record the substances found in each toothpaste sample. Common minerals in toothpaste include mica, calcite, and quartz (silica). Toothpaste also may include compounds such as sodium bicarbonate (baking soda), sodium fluoride, aluminum or calcium phosphates, and titanium dioxide.

4. For each toothpaste sample, predict how effective you think it will be in removing the stain from the tile. Record your predictions in the data table.

5. Put a pea-sized amount of the first toothpaste onto a toothbrush. **CAUTION:** *Do not ingest any of the toothpaste.*

6. Brush one of the stain marks on the tile 50 times. As you brush, try to use the same amount of force for each stroke.

7. Using tap water, rinse the tile to remove all of the paste. Then rinse the toothpaste out of the toothbrush.

8. Repeat Steps 5–7 for the other toothpaste samples, using a different stain mark for each test. Be sure to brush with the same amount of force and for the same number of times.

9. Compare how well the different toothpastes cleaned the stains. Record your observations in the data table.

Analyze and Conclude

1. **Classifying** Which mineral or minerals were found in all of the toothpastes tested? Did any toothpaste contain minerals not found in the other toothpastes?

2. **Observing** Which toothpaste was most effective in removing stains from the tile?

3. **Interpreting Data** Were your predictions about which toothpaste would be most effective correct?

4. **Interpreting Data** Does the toothpaste that was most effective in cleaning the tile differ in mineral content from the other toothpastes that were tested?

Data Table			
Toothpaste	Minerals Present	Predictions	Observations
1			
2			
3			

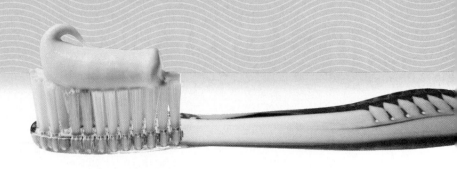

5. **Controlling Variables** What was the independent variable in this experiment? What was the dependent variable? Why did you use the same amount of toothpaste, force, and number of brushstrokes in each trial?

6. **Drawing Conclusions** How do the minerals in toothpaste affect the toothpaste's cleaning ability? Explain.

7. **Developing Hypotheses** Your teeth have the same composition as apatite, which has a hardness of 5 on the Mohs scale. What would be the advantages and disadvantages of using a toothpaste containing a mineral that is harder than apatite? Softer than apatite? Explain.

8. **Communicating** Write a lab report for this experiment. In your report, describe your predictions, your procedure, how you controlled variables, and whether or not your results supported your predictions.

Design Your Own Experiment

Some brands of toothpaste claim that they whiten teeth. Design an experiment to test the effectiveness of different kinds of whitening toothpaste. Make a data table to organize your findings. *Obtain your teacher's permission before carrying out your investigation.*

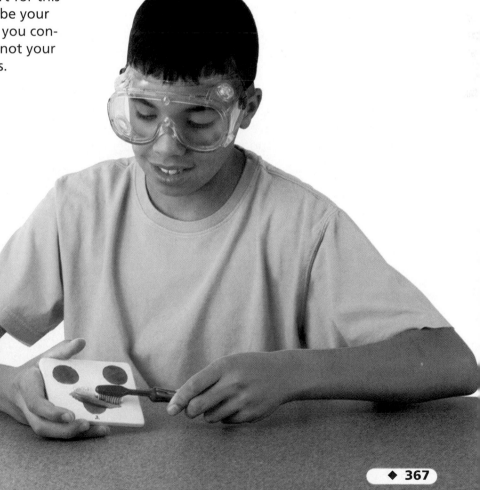

1 Properties of Minerals

Key Concepts

- A mineral is a naturally occurring, inorganic solid that has a crystal structure and a definite chemical composition.

- Each mineral has characteristic properties that can be used to identify it.

- Density can be determined with the following formula:

$$\text{Density} = \frac{\text{Mass}}{\text{Volume}}$$

Key Terms

mineral
inorganic
crystal
streak
luster
Mohs hardness scale
cleavage
fracture

2 How Minerals Form

Key Concepts

- Minerals form as hot magma cools inside the crust, or as lava hardens on the surface. When these liquids cool to a solid state, they form crystals.

- When elements and compounds that are dissolved in water leave a solution, crystallization of minerals occurs.

Key Terms

geode
crystallization
solution
vein

3 Mineral Resources

Key Concepts

- Minerals are the source of gemstones, metals, and a variety of materials used to make many products.

- To produce metal from a mineral, a rock containing the mineral must be located through prospecting and mined, or removed from the ground. Then the rock must be processed to extract the metal.

Key Terms

gemstone
ore
smelting
alloy

Review and Assessment

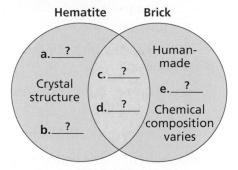
Organizing Information

Comparing and Contrasting Fill in the Venn diagram to compare the characteristics of a mineral and a material that is not a mineral.

Hematite   Brick

a. ___?___
Crystal structure
c. ___?___
d. ___?___
b. ___?___

Human-made
e. ___?___
Chemical composition varies

Reviewing Key Terms

Choose the letter of the best answer.

1. Because minerals do not come from once-living material, they are said to be
   a. crystalline.
   b. solid.
   c. colorful.
   d. inorganic.

2. In a mineral, the particles line up in a repeating pattern to form a(n)
   a. element.
   b. crystal.
   c. mixture.
   d. compound.

3. Which characteristic is used to determine the color of a mineral's powder?
   a. luster
   b. fracture
   c. cleavage
   d. streak

4. Halite is a mineral formed through the evaporation of
   a. magma.
   b. a vein.
   c. a solution.
   d. lava.

5. Minerals from which metals can be removed in usable amounts are called
   a. gemstones.   b. crystals.
   c. alloys.   d. ores.

If the statement is true, write _true_. If it is false, change the underlined word or words to make the statement true.

6. A hollow rock lined with crystals is a <u>geode</u>.

7. <u>Fracture</u> is the term that describes how a mineral reflects light from its surface.

8. Mineral deposits beneath Earth's surface that are different from the surrounding rocks are called <u>veins</u>.

9. Hard, shiny crystals used in jewelry are called <u>ores</u>.

10. Steel is an example of a(n) <u>alloy</u>.

Writing in Science

Descriptive Paragraph Choose a mineral such as gold or jade. Write a paragraph about the properties of this mineral. Explain why it is valuable and how it is useful to society.

Minerals

Video Preview
Video Field Trip
▶ Video Assessment

Review and Assessment

Checking Concepts

11. How does the composition of most minerals differ from a pure element?

12. How can the streak test be helpful in identifying minerals?

13. How do geologists use different types of crystal shapes to classify minerals?

14. Describe two ways that minerals can form.

15. Which mineral in the table below would make the best gemstone? Explain your answer.

Properties of Minerals

Mineral	Hardness	Density (g/cm³)	Luster
Galena	2.5	7.5	metallic
Fluorite	4.0	3.3	glassy
Corundum	9.0	4.0	glassy
Talc	1.0	2.8	pearly

16. Describe what happens to a mineral during smelting.

Thinking Critically

17. Classifying Obsidian is a solid that occurs in volcanic areas. Obsidian forms when magma cools very quickly, creating a type of glass. In glass, the particles are not arranged in an orderly pattern as in a crystal. Should obsidian be classified as a mineral? Explain why or why not.

18. Comparing and Contrasting Color and luster are both properties of minerals. How are they similar? How are they different? How can each be used to help identify a mineral?

19. Relating Cause and Effect Describe how a vein of ore forms underground. What is the energy source for this process?

20. Predicting What would happen if steel-makers forgot to add enough chromium and nickel to a batch of stainless steel?

Math Practice

21. Calculating A platinum ring has a volume of 0.8 cm³ and a mass of 15.2 g. What is its density?

22. Calculating A diamond has a mass of 10.56 g and a volume of 3 cm³. Calculate the density of the diamond.

Applying Skills

Use the photograph below to answer Questions 23–25.

You have found a sample of the mineral wulfenite. The wulfenite has a hardness of about 3 on the Mohs hardness scale and a density of 6.8 g/cm³. The mineral contains oxygen as well as the metals lead and molybdenum.

23. Observing Describe wulfenite's color and luster and the shape of its crystals.

24. Inferring Did the wulfenite form slowly or quickly? Explain your answer.

25. Drawing Conclusions Is wulfenite hard enough for use as a gem? What would you use these crystals for? Explain.

Lab zone Chapter **Project**

Performance Assessment Share your crystal garden with a classmate. Can your classmate identify which solution created which crystals? Do your data show differences in crystal growth rates? Which materials worked best for crystals to grow on? Share the answers to these questions when you present your project.

Standardized Test Practice

Test-Taking Tip

Choosing Among Similar Answers

Sometimes two or more answers to a question are almost identical. If you do not read each answer carefully, you may select an incorrect answer.

Sample Question

Which of the following is the best definition of a mineral?

A a naturally occurring, inorganic solid that has a crystal shape and a definite chemical composition

B a naturally occurring, inorganic solid that forms through crystallization of melted materials

C a naturally occurring, inorganic solid that forms through crystallization of materials dissolved in water

D a naturally occurring, organic solid that has a crystal shape and a definite chemical composition

Answer

Choices **A** and **D** are similar, but the correct answer is **A**. **D** is incorrect because minerals do not contain organic material. Although correct, **B** and **C** are not the most complete definition of a mineral.

Choose the letter of the best answer.

1. Which of the following is a mineral?
   A salt
   B pearl
   C coal
   D cement

2. You could distinguish gold from pyrite (fool's gold) by
   A comparing their hardness.
   B testing their chemical composition.
   C comparing their density.
   D all of the above

3. Veins of silver can be found in rock. These veins formed when
   A hot water solutions escaped from cracks in the rock.
   B hot water solutions crystallized in cracks in the rock.
   C magma crystallized in cracks in the rock.
   D hot water solutions evaporated in cracks in the rock.

4. An ore is a mineral that
   A is beautiful and rare.
   B can be mined at a profit.
   C is dense and metallic.
   D is light and durable.

5. The following diagrams show four different mineral samples. Based on these diagrams, what property is the same for all four minerals?

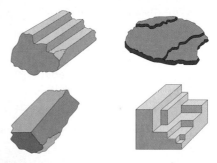

   A crystal structure
   B cleavage
   C hardness
   D color

Open-Ended Question

6. A geologist finds an unknown mineral while working in a national park. The geologist is carrying a kit that contains a geologic hammer, a jackknife, a hand lens, a piece of tile, and a penny. In a paragraph, describe how the geologist could use these items to determine some of the mineral's properties.

Chapter

11 Rocks

Rock climbers need to know the characteristics of rock. ▶

◢ Lab zone™ Chapter **Project**

Collecting Rocks

Each rock, whether a small pebble or a mountain peak, tells a story. The rocks in your own community tell part of the story of Earth's crust.

In this chapter, you will learn how three different types of rocks form. You can apply what you learn about rocks to create your own rock collection and explore the properties of your rocks.

Your Goal To make a collection of the rocks in your area

To complete this project, you must

● collect samples of rocks, keeping a record of where you found each sample
● describe the characteristics of your rocks, including their color, texture, and density
● classify each rock as igneous, sedimentary, or metamorphic
● create a display for your rock collection
● follow the safety guidelines in Appendix A

Plan It! With your classmates and teacher, brainstorm locations in your community where rocks are likely to be found. Are there road cuts, outcroppings of bedrock, riverbanks, or beaches where you could safely and legally collect your rocks? Plan your rock-hunting expeditions. Collect your rocks, and then describe, test, and classify your rock collection.

Classifying Rocks

Reading Focus

Key Concepts
- What characteristics do geologists use to identify rocks?
- What are the three main groups of rocks?

Key Terms
- rock-forming mineral • granite
- basalt • grains • texture
- igneous rock
- sedimentary rock
- metamorphic rock

Target Reading Skill

Asking Questions Before you read, preview the red headings. In a graphic organizer like the one below, ask a *what* or *how* question for each heading. As you read, write answers to your questions.

Question	Answer
What does a rock's color tell about the rock?	

Lab zone Discover **Activity**

How Do Rocks Compare?

1. Look at samples of conglomerate and marble with a hand lens.
2. Describe the two rocks. What is the color and texture of each?
3. Try scratching the surface of each rock with the edge of a penny. Which rock seems harder?
4. Hold each rock in your hand. Allowing for the fact that the samples aren't exactly the same size, which rock seems denser?

Think It Over

Observing Based on your observations, how would you compare the physical properties of marble and conglomerate?

Conglomerate

Marble

If you were a geologist, how would you examine a rock for the first time? You might use a camera or notebook to record information about the setting where the rock was found. Then, you would use a chisel or the sharp end of a rock hammer to remove samples of the rock. Finally, you would break open the samples with a hammer to examine their inside surfaces. You must look at the inside of a rock because the effects of ice, liquid water, and weather can change the outer surface of a rock.

You can find interesting rocks almost anywhere. The rock of Earth's crust forms mountains, hills, valleys, beaches, even the ocean floor. **When studying a rock sample, geologists observe the rock's mineral composition, color, and texture.**

FIGURE 1
Inspecting a Rock
This geologist is using a hand lens to observe a piece of shale.

Quartz

Feldspar

Hornblende

Granite

Mica

Mineral Composition and Color

Rocks are made of mixtures of minerals and other materials. Some rocks contain only a single mineral. Others contain several minerals. For example, the granite in Figure 2 is made up of the minerals quartz, feldspar, hornblende, and mica. About 20 minerals make up most of the rocks of Earth's crust. These minerals are known as **rock-forming minerals.** Appendix B at the back of this book lists some of the most common rock-forming minerals.

A rock's color provides clues to the rock's mineral composition. For example, **granite** is generally a light-colored rock that has high silica content. **Basalt,** shown in Figure 3, is a dark-colored rock that is low in silica. But as with minerals, color alone does not provide enough information to identify a rock.

Geologists observe the shape and color of crystals in a rock to identify the minerals that the rock contains. In identifying rocks, geologists also use some of the tests that are used to identify minerals. For example, testing the surface of a rock with acid determines whether the rock includes minerals made of compounds called carbonates.

 **Reading Checkpoint** How would you define "rock-forming mineral"?

FIGURE 2
Minerals in Granite
Granite is made up of quartz, feldspar, hornblende, and mica. It may also contain other minerals.
Observing *Which mineral seems most abundant in the sample of granite shown?*

FIGURE 3
Basalt
Basalt is a dark-colored rock that has low silica content. Unlike granite, basalt has mineral crystals that are too small to be seen without a hand lens.

Texture

As with minerals, color alone does not provide enough information to identify a rock. But a rock's texture is very useful in identifying a rock. Most rocks are made up of particles of minerals or other rocks, which geologists call **grains.** Grains give the rock its texture. To a geologist, a rock's **texture** is the look and feel of the rock's surface. Some rocks are smooth and glassy. Others are rough or chalky. To describe a rock's texture, geologists use terms based on the size, shape, and pattern of the grains.

FIGURE 4
Rock Textures
Texture helps classify rocks.
Comparing and Contrasting *How would you compare the texture of diorite with the texture of gneiss?*

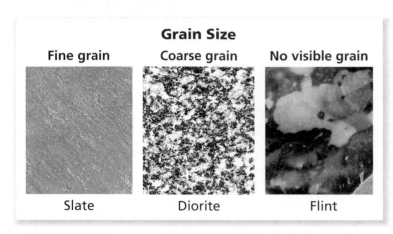

Grain Size

Fine grain	Coarse grain	No visible grain
Slate	Diorite	Flint

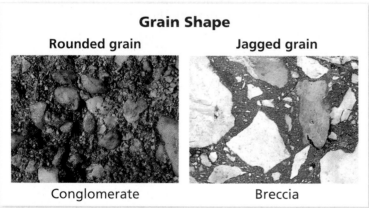

Grain Shape

Rounded grain	Jagged grain
Conglomerate	Breccia

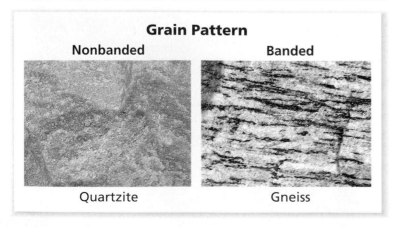

Grain Pattern

Nonbanded	Banded
Quartzite	Gneiss

Grain Size Often, the grains in a rock are large and easy to see. Such rocks are said to be coarse-grained. In other rocks, the grains are so small that they can only be seen with a microscope. These rocks are said to be fine-grained. Notice the difference in texture between the fine-grained slate and the coarse-grained diorite in Figure 4 at left. Some rocks have no visible grain even when they are examined under a microscope.

Grain Shape The grains in a rock vary widely in shape. Some grains look like tiny particles of sand. Others look like small seeds or exploding stars. In some rocks, such as granite, the grain results from the shapes of the crystals that form the rock. In other rocks, the grain shape results from fragments of several rocks. These fragments can be smooth and rounded or they can be jagged.

Grain Pattern The grains in a rock often form patterns. Some grains lie in flat layers that look like a stack of pancakes. Other grains form swirling patterns. Some rocks have grains of different colors in bands, like the gneiss (NYS) in Figure 4. In other rocks, the grains occur randomly throughout.

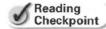 **Reading Checkpoint** What does it mean to say that a rock is coarse-grained?

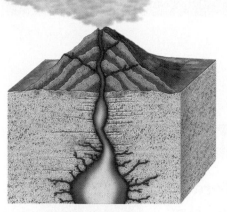

Igneous Rock forms when magma or lava cools and hardens.

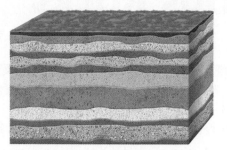

Sedimentary Rock forms when pieces of rock are pressed and cemented together.

Metamorphic Rock forms from other rocks that are changed by heat and pressure.

How Rocks Form

Using color, texture, and mineral composition, geologists can classify a rock according to its origin. A rock's origin is how the rock formed. **Geologists classify rocks into three major groups: igneous rock, sedimentary rock, and metamorphic rock.**

Each of these groups of rocks forms in a different way. **Igneous rock** (IG nee us) forms from the cooling of magma or lava. Most **sedimentary rock** (sed uh MEN tur ee) forms when particles of other rocks or the remains of plants and animals are pressed and cemented together. Sedimentary rock forms in layers that are buried below the surface. **Metamorphic rock** (met uh MAWR fik) forms when an existing rock is changed by heat, pressure, or chemical reactions. Most metamorphic rock forms deep underground.

FIGURE 5
Kinds of Rocks
Rocks can be igneous, sedimentary, or metamorphic, depending on how the rock formed.

For: More on rock identification
Visit: PHSchool.com
Web Code: cfd-1051

Section 1 Assessment

Target Reading Skill Asking Questions Work with a partner to check the answers in your graphic organizer about the section headings.

Reviewing Key Concepts

1. **a. Naming** What three characteristics do geologists use to identify rocks?
   b. Defining What are the grains of a rock?
   c. Comparing and Contrasting In your own words, compare the grain size, shape, and pattern of the conglomerate and breccia in Figure 4.
2. **a. Reviewing** What are the three main groups of rocks?
   b. Explaining How do igneous rocks form?
   c. Classifying Gneiss is a kind of rock that forms when heat and pressure inside Earth change granite. To what group of rocks does gneiss belong?

Writing in Science

Wanted Poster Write a paragraph for a wanted poster in which you describe the characteristics of granite. In your wanted poster, be sure to describe granite's mineral composition, color, and texture. Also mention the group of rocks to which granite belongs.

Igneous Rocks

Reading Focus

Key Concepts
- What characteristics are used to classify igneous rocks?
- How are igneous rocks used?

Key Terms
- extrusive rock • intrusive rock

Target Reading Skill
Identifying Main Ideas As you read Classifying Igneous Rocks, write the main idea in a graphic organizer like the one below. Then write three supporting details that further explain the main idea.

Main Idea

Igneous rocks are classified by origin, texture, and composition.

Detail	Detail	Detail

Lab zone Discover Activity

How Do Igneous Rocks Form?
1. Use a hand lens to examine samples of granite and obsidian.
2. Describe the texture of both rocks using the terms coarse, fine, or glassy.
3. Which rock has coarse-grained crystals? Which rock has no crystals or grains?

Think It Over
Inferring Granite and obsidian are igneous rocks. From your observations, what can you infer about how each type of rock formed?

Obsidian

Granite

The time is 4.6 billion years ago. You are in a spacecraft orbiting Earth. Do you see the blue and green globe of Earth that astronauts today see from space? No—instead, Earth looks like a charred and bubbling marshmallow heated over hot coals.

Soon after Earth formed, the planet's interior became so hot that magma formed. Lava repeatedly flowed over the surface. The lava quickly hardened, forming a rocky crust. Because this early crust was denser than the material beneath it, chunks of crust sank into Earth's interior. This allowed more lava to erupt over the surface and harden to form rock.

Classifying Igneous Rocks

The first rocks to form on Earth probably looked like the igneous rocks that can be seen today. Igneous rock is any rock that forms from magma or lava. The name *igneous* comes from the Latin word *ignis*, meaning "fire." **Igneous rocks are classified according to their origin, texture, and mineral composition.**

Origin Igneous rock may form on or beneath Earth's surface. **Extrusive rock** is igneous rock formed from lava that erupted onto Earth's surface. Basalt is the most common extrusive rock. Basalt forms much of the crust, including the oceanic crust, shield volcanoes, and lava plateaus.

Igneous rock that formed when magma hardened beneath Earth's surface is called **intrusive rock.** The most abundant intrusive rock in continental crust is granite. Batholiths made of granite form the core of many mountain ranges.

Texture The texture of an igneous rock depends on the size and shape of its mineral crystals. The only exceptions to this rule are the different types of volcanic glass—igneous rock that lacks a crystal structure.

Igneous rocks may be similar in mineral composition and yet have very different textures. Rapidly cooling lava forms fine-grained igneous rocks with small crystals. Slowly cooling magma forms coarse-grained rocks with large crystals. Therefore, intrusive and extrusive rocks usually have different textures.

Intrusive rocks have larger crystals than extrusive rocks. If you examine a coarse-grained rock such as granite, you can easily see that the crystals vary in size and color. Some intrusive rocks, like the porphyry in Figure 6, have a texture that looks like a gelatin dessert with chopped-up fruit mixed in.

Extrusive rocks have a fine-grained or glassy texture. Basalt is a fine-grained extrusive rock. It consists of crystals too small to be seen without a microscope. Obsidian is an extrusive rock that cooled very rapidly without forming crystals. As a result, obsidian has the smooth, shiny texture of a thick piece of glass.

FIGURE 6
Igneous Rock Textures
Igneous rocks such as rhyolite, pegmatite, and porphyry can vary greatly in texture depending on whether they are intrusive or extrusive.
Relating Cause and Effect *What conditions caused rhyolite to have a fine-grained texture?*

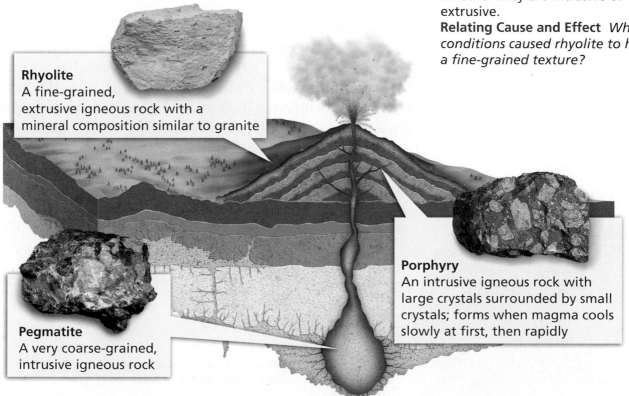

Rhyolite
A fine-grained, extrusive igneous rock with a mineral composition similar to granite

Pegmatite
A very coarse-grained, intrusive igneous rock

Porphyry
An intrusive igneous rock with large crystals surrounded by small crystals; forms when magma cools slowly at first, then rapidly

Math ▶ Analyzing Data

Mineral Mixture

Granite is a mixture of light-colored minerals such as feldspar and quartz and dark-colored minerals including hornblende and mica. But, granite can vary in mineral composition, affecting its color and texture.

Study the circle graph and then answer the questions.

1. **Reading Graphs** What mineral is most abundant in granite?

2. **Reading Graphs** About what percentage of granite is made up of dark minerals?

3. **Calculating** If the amount of quartz increases to 35 percent and the amount of dark-colored minerals stays the same, what percentage of the granite will be made up of feldspar?

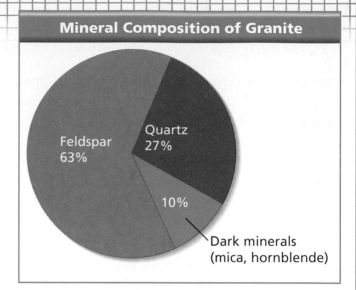

Mineral Composition of Granite

Feldspar 63%

Quartz 27%

10%

Dark minerals (mica, hornblende)

4. **Predicting** How would the color of the granite change if it contained less feldspar and more mica and hornblende?

Mineral Composition You may recall that the silica content of magma and lava can vary. Lava that is low in silica usually forms dark-colored rocks such as basalt. Basalt contains feldspar as well as certain dark-colored minerals, but does not contain quartz.

Magma that is high in silica usually forms light-colored rocks, such as granite. Granite's mineral composition determines its color—light gray, red, pink, or nearly black. Granite that is rich in reddish feldspar is a speckled pink. But granite rich in hornblende and dark mica is light gray with dark specks. Quartz crystals in granite add light gray or smoky specks.

Geologists can make thin slices of a rock, such as the gabbro in Figure 7. They study the rock's crystals under a microscope to determine the rock's mineral composition.

 Reading Checkpoint How can mineral composition affect a rock's color?

FIGURE 7
Thin Section of a Rock
This thin slice of gabbro, viewed under a microscope, contains olivine, feldspar, and other minerals.

Uses of Igneous Rocks

Many igneous rocks are hard, dense, and durable. **People throughout history have used igneous rock for tools and building materials.**

Building Materials Granite has a long history as a building material. More than 3,500 years ago, the ancient Egyptians used granite for statues like the one shown in Figure 8. About 600 years ago, the Incas of Peru carefully fitted together great blocks of granite and other igneous rocks to build a fortress near Cuzco, their capital city. In the United States during the 1800s and early 1900s, granite was widely used to build bridges and public buildings and for paving streets with cobblestones. Today, thin, polished sheets of granite are used in curbstones, floors, and kitchen counters. Basalt is crushed to make gravel that is used in construction.

Other Uses Igneous rocks such as pumice and obsidian also have important uses. The rough surface of pumice makes it a good abrasive for cleaning and polishing. Ancient native Americans used obsidian to make sharp tools for cutting and scraping. Perlite, formed from the heating of obsidian, is often mixed with soil for starting vegetable seeds.

FIGURE 8
Durable Granite
The ancient Egyptians valued granite for its durability. These statues from a temple in Luxor, Egypt, were carved in granite.

 **Reading Checkpoint** What igneous rock is most often used as a building material?

Section 2 Assessment

Target Reading Skill Identifying Main Ideas Use your graphic organizer about the characteristics of igneous rock to help you answer Question 1 below.

Reviewing Key Concepts

1. a. **Explaining** How are igneous rocks classified?
   b. **Defining** What are extrusive rocks and intrusive rocks?
   c. **Comparing and Contrasting** Compare granite and basalt in terms of their origin and texture. Which is extrusive? Which is intrusive?
2. a. **Summarizing** What are two common uses of igneous rocks?
   b. **Reviewing** What characteristics make igneous rocks useful?
   c. **Making Judgments** Would pumice be a good material to use to make a floor? Explain.

Lab zone At-Home Activity

The Rocks Around Us Many common household products contain minerals found in igneous rock. For example, glass contains quartz, which is found in granite. Research one of the following materials and the products in which it is used: garnet, granite, perlite, pumice, or vermiculite. Explain to family members how the rock or mineral formed and how it is used.

Sedimentary Rocks

Reading Focus

Key Concepts
- How do sedimentary rocks form?
- What are the three major types of sedimentary rocks?
- How are sedimentary rocks used?

Key Terms
- sediment • erosion
- deposition • compaction
- cementation • clastic rock
- organic rock • chemical rock

Target Reading Skill

Outlining As you read, make an outline about sedimentary rocks. Use the red section headings for the main topics and the blue headings for the subtopics.

Sedimentary Rocks
I. From sediment to rock
A. Erosion
B.
II.
A.

Lab zone Discover **Activity**

How Does Pressure Affect Particles of Rock?

1. Place a sheet of paper over a slice of soft bread.
2. Put a stack of several heavy books on top of the paper. After 10 minutes, remove the books. Observe what happened to the bread.
3. Slice the bread so you can observe its cross section.
4. Carefully slice a piece of fresh bread and compare its cross section to that of the pressed bread.

Think It Over

Observing How did the bread change after you removed the books? Describe the texture of the bread. How does the bread feel? What can you predict about how pressure affects the particles that make up sedimentary rocks?

Visitors to Badlands National Park in South Dakota see some of the strangest scenery on Earth. The park contains jagged peaks, steep cliffs, and deep canyons sculpted in colorful rock that is layered like a birthday cake. The layers of this cake are red, orange, pink, yellow, or tan. These rocks formed over millions of years as particles of mud, sand, and volcanic ash were deposited in thick layers. The mud and sand slowly changed to sedimentary rock. Then, uplift of the land exposed the rocks to the forces that wear away Earth's surface.

Badlands National Park ▲

From Sediment to Rock

If you have ever walked along a stream or beach you may have noticed tiny sand grains, mud, and pebbles. These are particles of sediment. **Sediment** is small, solid pieces of material that come from rocks or living things. In addition to particles of rock, sediment may include shells, bones, leaves, stems, and other remains of living things. Sedimentary rocks form when sediment is deposited by water and wind. **Most sedimentary rocks are formed through a series of processes: erosion, deposition, compaction, and cementation.** Figure 9 shows how sedimentary rocks form.

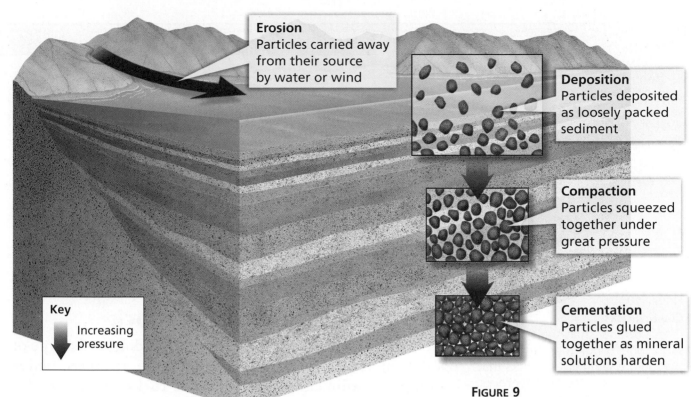

Erosion
Particles carried away from their source by water or wind

Deposition
Particles deposited as loosely packed sediment

Compaction
Particles squeezed together under great pressure

Cementation
Particles glued together as mineral solutions harden

Key
Increasing pressure

FIGURE 9
How Sedimentary Rocks Form
Sedimentary rocks form through the deposition, compaction, and cementation of sediments over millions of years.
Relating Cause and Effect *What conditions are necessary for sedimentary rocks to form?*

Erosion Destructive forces are constantly breaking up and wearing away all the rocks on Earth's surface. These forces include heat and cold, rain, waves, and grinding ice. The forces of erosion form sediment. In **erosion,** running water, wind, or ice loosen and carry away fragments of rock.

Deposition Eventually, the moving water, wind, or ice slows and deposits the sediment in layers. If water is carrying the sediment, rock fragments and other materials sink to the bottom of a lake or ocean. **Deposition** is the process by which sediment settles out of the water or wind carrying it.

Compaction The process that presses sediments together is **compaction.** Thick layers of sediment build up gradually over millions of years. These heavy layers press down on the layers beneath them. The weight of new layers further compacts the sediments, squeezing them tightly together. The layers often remain visible in sedimentary rock.

Cementation While compaction is taking place, the minerals in the rock slowly dissolve in the water. **Cementation** is the process in which dissolved minerals crystallize and glue particles of sediment together. In cementation, dissolved minerals seep into the spaces between particles and then harden.

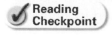 **Reading Checkpoint** What is deposition?

For: Links on sedimentary rocks
Visit: www.SciLinks.org
Web Code: scn-1053

Shale
Fossils are often found in shale, which splits easily into flat pieces.

Sandstone
Many small holes between sand grains allow sandstone to absorb water.

Conglomerate
Rock fragments with rounded edges make up conglomerate.

FIGURE 10
Clastic Rocks
Clastic rocks such as shale, sandstone, conglomerate, and breccia are sedimentary rocks that form from particles of other rocks.

Lab zone Try This **Activity**

Rock Absorber

Here's how to find out if water can soak into rock.

1. Using a hand lens, compare samples of sandstone and shale.
2. Use a balance to measure the mass of each rock.
3. Place the rocks in a pan of water and watch closely. Which sample has bubbles escaping? Predict which sample will gain mass.
4. Leave the rocks submerged in the pan overnight.
5. The next day, remove the rocks from the pan and find the mass of each rock.

Drawing Conclusions How did the masses of the two rocks change after soaking? What can you conclude about each rock?

Types of Sedimentary Rock

Geologists classify sedimentary rocks according to the type of sediments that make up the rock. **There are three major groups of sedimentary rocks: clastic rocks, organic rocks, and chemical rocks.** Different processes form each of these types of sedimentary rocks.

Clastic Rocks Most sedimentary rocks are made up of broken pieces of other rocks. A **clastic rock** is a sedimentary rock that forms when rock fragments are squeezed together. These fragments can range in size from clay particles that are too small to be seen without a microscope to large boulders that are too heavy for you to lift. Clastic rocks are grouped by the size of the rock fragments, or particles, of which they are made. Common clastic rocks include shale, sandstone, conglomerate, and breccia (BRECH ee uh), shown in Figure 10.

Shale forms from tiny particles of clay. Water must deposit the clay particles in thin, flat layers. Sandstone forms from the sand on beaches, the ocean floor, riverbeds, and sand dunes. Most sand particles consist of quartz.

Some sedimentary rocks contain a mixture of rock fragments of different sizes. If the fragments have rounded edges, they form a clastic rock called conglomerate. A rock made up of large fragments with sharp edges is called breccia.

Organic Rocks Not all sedimentary rocks are made from particles of other rocks. **Organic rock** forms where the remains of plants and animals are deposited in thick layers. The term "organic" refers to substances that once were part of living things or were made by living things. Two important organic sedimentary rocks are coal and limestone, shown in Figure 11.

Breccia
Rock fragments with sharp edges form breccia.

Coal
Swamp plants that formed millions of years ago slowly changed to form coal.

Limestone
Coquina is a form of limestone in which the shells that makeup the rock are easy to see.

Coal forms from the remains of swamp plants buried in water. As layer upon layer of plant remains build up, the weight of the layers squeezes the decaying plants. Over millions of years, they slowly change into coal.

Limestone forms in the ocean, where many living things, such as coral, clams, and oysters, have hard shells or skeletons made of calcite. When these animals die, their shells pile up on the ocean floor. Over millions of years, these layers of sediment can grow to a depth of hundreds of meters. Slowly, compaction and cementation change the sediment to limestone.

Chemical Rocks When minerals that are dissolved in a solution crystallize, **chemical rock** forms. For example, limestone can form when calcite that is dissolved in lakes, seas, or underground water comes out of solution and forms crystals. This kind of limestone is considered a chemical rock. Chemical rocks can also form from mineral deposits left when seas or lakes evaporate. For example, rock salt is made of the mineral halite, which forms by evaporation.

 **Reading Checkpoint** How does coal form?

FIGURE 11
Organic Rocks
Organic rocks such as coal and limestone are sedimentary rocks that form from the remains of living things.

FIGURE 12
Chemical Rocks
These rock "towers" in Mono Lake California, are made of tufa, a form of limestone. Tufa is a chemical rock that forms from solutions containing dissolved materials. **Classifying** *What type of sedimentary rock is tufa?*

Uses of Sedimentary Rocks

People have used sedimentary rocks throughout history for many different purposes, including building materials and tools. For example, people made arrowheads out of flint for thousands of years. Flint is a hard rock, yet it can be shaped to a point. Flint is formed when small particles of silica settle out of water.

Sedimentary rocks such as sandstone and limestone have been used as building materials for thousands of years. Both types of stone are soft enough to be cut easily into blocks or slabs. You may be surprised to learn that the White House in Washington, D.C., is built of sandstone. Builders today use sandstone and limestone on the outside walls of buildings. Limestone also has many industrial uses. For example, limestone is used in making cement and steel.

FIGURE 13
Carving Marble
This stone carver is sculpting a block of pink marble.

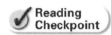 **Reading Checkpoint** Why are sandstone and limestone useful as building materials?

Section 3 Assessment

Target Reading Skill Outlining Use the information in your outline about sedimentary rocks to help you answer the questions below.

Reviewing Key Concepts

1. **a. Defining** What is sediment?
   b. Sequencing Place these steps in the formation of sedimentary rock in the proper sequence: compaction, erosion, cementation, deposition.
   c. Inferring In layers of sedimentary rock, where would you expect to find the oldest sediment? Explain your answer.
2. **a. Listing** What are the three main types of sedimentary rock?
   b. Explaining Which type of sedimentary rock forms from the remains of living things? Explain how this sedimentary rock forms.
   c. Relating Cause and Effect What process causes deposits of rock salt to form? What type of sedimentary rock is rock salt?

3. **a. Listing** What are some uses of sedimentary rocks?
   b. Predicting The particles of sediment that make up shale are not usually cemented. Would shale be a good choice of building material in a wet climate?

Writing in Science

Explaining a Process Suppose that a large mass of granite lies exposed on Earth's surface. Explain the steps in the process by which the granite could become sedimentary rock. Your answer should also state which of the main types of sedimentary rock will result from this process.

Rocks From Reefs

Reading Focus

Key Concepts
- How do coral reefs form?
- What evidence do limestone deposits from coral reefs provide about Earth's history?

Key Term
- coral reef

Target Reading Skill
Using Prior Knowledge
Before you read, look at the section headings to see what this section is about. Then write what you know about coral reefs in a graphic organizer like the one below. As you read, write what you learn.

What You Know
1. Coral reefs grow in the oceans.
2.

What You Learned
1.
2.

Discover Activity

How Does a Rock React to Acid?
1. Using a hand lens, observe the color and texture of limestone and coquina.
2. Put on your goggles and apron.
3. Obtain a small amount of dilute hydrochloric acid from your teacher. Hydrochloric acid is used to test rocks for the presence of the mineral calcite.

   Using a plastic dropper, place a few drops of dilute hydrochloric acid on the limestone. **CAUTION:** *Hydrochloric acid can cause burns.*
4. Record your observations.
5. Repeat Steps 2 through 4 with the sample of coquina and observe the results.
6. Rinse the rock samples with lots of water before returning them to your teacher. Wash your hands.

Think It Over
Drawing Conclusions How did the two rocks react to the test? A piece of coral reacts to hydrochloric acid the same way as limestone and coquina. What could you conclude about the mineral composition of coral?

Off the coast of Florida lies a "city" in the sea. It is a coral reef providing both food and shelter for many sea animals. The reef shimmers with life—clams, sponges, sea urchins, starfish, marine worms and, of course, fish. Schools of brilliantly colored fish dart in and out of forests of equally colorful corals. Octopuses lurk in underwater caves, scooping up crabs that pass too close. A reef forms a sturdy wall that protects the shoreline from battering waves. This city was built by billions of tiny, soft-bodied animals that have skeletons made of calcite.

FIGURE 14
A City in the Sea
A coral reef provides food and shelter for many different kinds of living things.

Go Online
PLANET DIARY

For: More on coral landforms
Visit: PHSchool.com
Web Code: cfd-1054

FIGURE 15
Coral Animals and Reefs
The coral animals in the close-up feed on tiny organisms carried their way by the movement of ocean water. (The view has been magnified to show detail.) The aerial photograph shows an island in the South Pacific Ocean that is ringed by a coral reef (light blue areas). **Inferring** *Why are there no coral reefs in the dark blue areas of ocean water?*

Coral Reefs

Coral animals are tiny relatives of jellyfish that live together in vast numbers. They produce skeletons that grow together to form a structure called a **coral reef.**

How Coral Animals Live Most coral animals are smaller than your fingernail. Each one looks like a small sack with a mouth surrounded by tentacles. These animals use their tentacles to capture and eat microscopic creatures that float by.

Tiny algae grow within the body of each coral animal. The algae provide substances that the coral animals need to live. In turn, the coral animals provide a framework for the algae to grow on. Like plants, algae need sunlight. Below 40 meters, there is not enough light for the algae to grow. For this reason, almost all coral growth occurs within 40 meters of the water's surface.

How a Coral Reef Forms To form their skeletons, coral animals absorb the element calcium from the ocean water. The calcium is then combined with carbon and oxygen to form calcite. Recall that calcite is a mineral. **When coral animals die, their skeletons remain. More corals build on top of them, gradually forming a coral reef.**

Coral animals cannot grow in cold water. As a result, coral reefs form only in the warm, shallow water of tropical oceans. Reefs are most abundant around islands and along the eastern coasts of continents. In the United States, only the coasts of southern Florida and Hawaii have coral reefs.

Over thousands of years, reefs may grow to be hundreds of kilometers long and hundreds of meters thick. Reefs usually grow outward toward the open ocean. If the sea level rises or if the sea floor sinks, the reef will grow upward, too.

✓ **Reading Checkpoint** What conditions of light and temperature do coral animals require?

Limestone From Coral Reefs

A coral reef is really organic limestone. **Limestone deposits that began as coral reefs provide evidence of how plate motions have changed Earth's surface. These deposits also provide evidence of past environments.**

Limestone from coral reefs has been forming in Earth's oceans for more than 400 million years. The limestone formed when shallow seas covered the low-lying parts of the continents. The limestone was exposed when the seas retreated. Later, plate motions slowly moved these limestone deposits far from the tropical oceans where they formed. In the United States, reefs that formed millions of years ago are exposed in Wisconsin, Illinois, Indiana, Texas, New Mexico, and many other places.

Deposits of organic limestone help geologists understand past environments. Where geologists find fossils of an ancient coral reef, they know that the reef formed in an area with a warm climate and shallow ocean water. In North America, these conditions existed for millions of years when much of the continent lay closer to the equator than it does today. Shallow seas covered the central part of North America, allowing large coral reefs to form. Today, the reefs are thick deposits of sedimentary rock.

FIGURE 16
Limestone From Coral
A band of light-colored limestone marks an ancient reef that forms part of Guadalupe Peak in Texas. This reef is now 2,600 meters above sea level!

Section 4 Assessment

Target Reading Skill Using Prior Knowledge
Review your graphic organizer about coral reefs and revise it based on what you just learned.

Reviewing Key Concepts

1. a. **Describing** What is a coral animal?
   b. **Summarizing** How do coral animals build a coral reef?
   c. **Predicting** If sea level rises above a coral reef, what may happen to the reef?
2. a. **Identifying** What type of rock is made up of ancient coral?
   b. **Inferring** A geologist finds an area where the rocks were formed from an ancient coral reef. What can the geologist infer about the ancient environment where the rocks formed?

Lab zone At-Home Activity

Earth's Coral Reefs Obtain a globe or world map. Find the lines that represent the tropic of Cancer and the tropic of Capricorn. The area that lies between these two lines, called the Tropics, is where most coral reefs form in warm ocean water. Locate the northeast coast of Australia, the Red Sea, and groups of tropical islands in the Caribbean Sea, Indian Ocean, and Pacific Ocean. Point out these features to family members and explain that these are areas where coral reefs occur today.

Metamorphic Rocks

Reading Preview

Key Concepts
- Under what conditions do metamorphic rocks form?
- How do geologists classify metamorphic rocks?
- How are metamorphic rocks used?

Key Term
- foliated

Target Reading Skill
Previewing Visuals Before you read, preview Figure 17. Then write two questions that you have about metamorphic rocks in a graphic organizer like the one below. As you read, answer your questions.

Metamorphic Rocks

Q.	Why do the crystals in gneiss line up in bands?
A.	
Q.	

Lab zone Discover **Activity**

How Do Grain Patterns Compare?

1. Using a hand lens, observe samples of gneiss and granite. Look carefully at the grains or crystals in both rocks.
2. Observe how the grains or crystals are arranged in both rocks. Draw a sketch of both rocks and describe their textures.

Think It Over
Inferring Within the crust, some granite becomes gneiss. What do you think must happen to cause this change?

Every metamorphic rock is a rock that has changed its form. In fact, the word *metamorphic* comes from the Greek words *meta*, meaning "change," and *morphosis*, meaning "form." But what causes a rock to change into metamorphic rock? The answer lies inside Earth.

Heat and pressure deep beneath Earth's surface can change any rock into metamorphic rock. When rock changes into metamorphic rock, its appearance, texture, crystal structure, and mineral content change. Metamorphic rock can form out of igneous, sedimentary, or other metamorphic rock.

Collisions between Earth's plates can push the rock down toward the heat of the mantle. Pockets of magma rising through the crust also provide heat that can produce metamorphic rocks. The deeper a rock is buried in the crust, the greater the pressure on that rock. Under high temperature and pressure many times greater than at Earth's surface, the minerals in a rock can be changed into other minerals. The rock has become a metamorphic rock.

Types of Metamorphic Rocks

While metamorphic rocks are forming, high temperatures change the size and shape of the grains, or mineral crystals, in the rock. Extreme pressure squeezes rock so tightly that the mineral grains may line up in flat, parallel layers. **Geologists classify metamorphic rocks according to the arrangement of the grains that make up the rocks.**

Foliated Rocks Metamorphic rocks that have their grains arranged in parallel layers or bands are said to be **foliated.** The term *foliated* comes from the Latin word for "leaf." It describes the thin, flat layering found in most metamorphic rocks. Foliated rocks—including slate, schist, and gneiss—may split apart along these bands. In Figure 17, notice how the crystals in granite have been flattened to create the foliated texture of gneiss.

One common foliated rock is slate. Heat and pressure change the sedimentary rock shale into slate. Slate is basically a denser, more compact version of shale. During the change, new minerals such as mica form in the slate.

Nonfoliated Rocks Some metamorphic rocks are nonfoliated. The mineral grains in these rocks are arranged randomly. Metamorphic rocks that are nonfoliated do not split into layers. Marble and quartzite are two metamorphic rocks that have a nonfoliated texture. Quartzite forms out of sandstone. The weakly cemented quartz particles in the sandstone recrystallize to form quartzite, which is extremely hard. Notice in Figure 17 how much smoother quartzite looks than sandstone.

 **Reading Checkpoint** What is a foliated rock?

FIGURE 17
Forming Metamorphic Rocks
Great heat and pressure can change one type of rock into another. **Observing** *How does slate differ from shale?*

Lab zone Try This **Activity**

A Sequined Rock

1. Make three balls of clay about 3 cm in diameter. Gently mix about 25 sequins into one ball.

2. Use a 30-cm piece of string to cut the ball in half. How are the sequins arranged?

3. Roll the clay with the sequins back into a ball. Stack the three balls with the sequin ball in the middle. Set these on a block of wood. With another block of wood, press slowly down until the stack is about 3 cm high.

4. Use the string to cut the stack in half. How are the sequins arranged?

Making Models What do the sequins in your model rock represent? Is this rock foliated or nonfoliated?

Granite
igneous

Sandstone
sedimentary

Shale
sedimentary

Heat and pressure

Heat and pressure

Heat and pressure

Gneiss
metamorphic, foliated

Quartzite
metamorphic, nonfoliated

Slate
metamorphic, foliated

◆ **391**

FIGURE 18
The Lincoln Memorial
The statue of Abraham Lincoln in the Lincoln Memorial in Washington, D.C., is made of gleaming white marble.

Uses of Metamorphic Rock

Certain metamorphic rocks are important materials for building and sculpture. Marble and slate are two of the most useful metamorphic rocks. Marble usually forms when limestone is subjected to heat and pressure deep beneath the surface. Because marble has a fine, even grain, it can be cut into thin slabs or carved into many shapes. And marble is easy to polish. These qualities have led architects and sculptors to use marble for many buildings and statues. For example, one of America's most famous sculptures is in the Lincoln Memorial in Washington, D.C. Sculptor Daniel Chester French carved this portrait of Abraham Lincoln in gleaming white marble.

Like marble, slate comes in a variety of colors, including gray, black, red, and purple. Because it is foliated, slate splits easily into flat pieces. These pieces can be used for flooring, roofing, outdoor walkways, chalkboards, and as trim for stone buildings.

 **Reading Checkpoint** What characteristics of slate make it useful?

Section 5 Assessment

Target Reading Skill Previewing Visuals Compare your questions and answers about Figure 17 with those of a partner.

Reviewing Key Concepts

1. **a. Explaining** What does *metamorphic* mean?
   b. Relating Cause and Effect Where and under what conditions are metamorphic rocks formed?
2. **a. Identifying** What characteristic of metamorphic rocks do geologists use to classify them?
   b. Explaining How does a foliated metamorphic rock form?
   c. Classifying Which of the rocks in Figure 17 is foliated? How can you tell?
3. **a. Identifying** What is the main use of metamorphic rocks?
   b. Making Judgments Which might be more useful for carving chess pieces—marble or slate? Explain your answer.

Lab zone **At-Home Activity**

Rocks Around the Block How are rocks used in your neighborhood? Take a walk with your family to see how many uses you can observe. Identify statues, walls, and buildings made from rocks. Can you identify which type of rock was used? Look for limestone, sandstone, granite, and marble. Share a list of the rocks you found with your class. For each rock, include a description of its color and texture, where you observed the rock, and how it was used.

Lab zone Skills Lab

Mystery Rocks

Problem

What properties can be used to classify rocks?

Skills Focus

inferring, classifying

Materials

- 1 "mystery rock"
- 2 unknown igneous rocks
- 2 unknown sedimentary rocks
- 2 unknown metamorphic rocks
- hand lens

Procedure

1. For this activity, you will be given six rocks and one sample that is not a rock. They are labeled A through G.
2. Copy the data table into your notebook.
3. Using the hand lens, examine each rock for clues that show the rock formed from molten material. Record the rock's color and texture. Observe if there are any crystals or grains in the rock.
4. Use the hand lens to look for clues that show the rock formed from particles of other rocks. Observe the texture of the rock to see if it has any tiny, well-rounded grains.
5. Use the hand lens to look for clues that show the rock formed under heat and pressure. Observe if the rock has a flat layer of crystals or shows colored bands.
6. Record your observations in the data table.

Analyze and Conclude

1. **Inferring** Infer from your observations the group in which each rock belongs.
2. **Classifying** Which of the samples could be classified as igneous rocks? What physical properties do these rock share with the other samples? How are they different?
3. **Classifying** Which of the samples could be classified as sedimentary rocks? How do you think these rocks formed? What are the physical properties of these rocks?
4. **Classifying** Which of the samples could be classified as metamorphic rocks? What are their physical properties?
5. **Drawing Conclusions** Decide which sample is not a rock. How did you determine that the sample you chose is not a rock? What do you think the "mystery rock" is? Explain.
6. **Communicating** What physical property was most useful in classifying rocks? Which physical property was least useful? Explain your answer.

More to Explore

Can you name each rock? Use a field guide to rocks and minerals to find the specific name of each rock sample.

Data Table				
Sample	Color	Texture (fine, medium, or coarse-grained)	Foliated or Banded	Rock Group (igneous, metamorphic, sedimentary)
A				
B				

The Rock Cycle

Reading Preview

Key Concepts
• What is the rock cycle?
• What is the role of plate tectonics in the rock cycle?

Key Term
• rock cycle

◉ Target Reading Skill
Sequencing As you read, make a cycle diagram that shows the stages in the rock cycle. Write each stage of the rock cycle in a separate circle in your diagram.

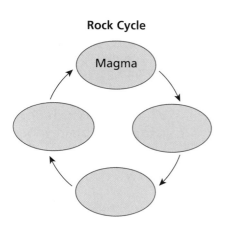

Rock Cycle

Magma

Lab zone **Discover Activity**

Which Rock Came First?

1. Referring to the photos at the right, make sketches of quartzite, granite, and sandstone on three index cards.
2. Observe the color and texture of each rock. Look for similarities and differences.
3. To which major group does each rock belong?

Think It Over
Developing Hypotheses How are quartzite, granite, and sandstone related? Arrange your cards in the order in which these three rocks formed. Given enough time in Earth's crust, what might happen to the third rock in your series?

Sandstone   **Quartzite**   **Granite**

Earth's rocks are not as unchanging as they seem. **Forces deep inside Earth and at the surface produce a slow cycle that builds, destroys, and changes the rocks in the crust.** The **rock cycle** is a series of processes on Earth's surface and in the crust and mantle that slowly change rocks from one kind to another.

A Cycle of Many Pathways

Here's one possible pathway through the rock cycle, shown in Figure 19. The igneous rock granite formed beneath the surface. Then, the forces of mountain building slowly pushed the granite upward, forming a mountain. Slowly, water and wind wore away the granite. These granite particles became sand, carried by streams to the ocean. Over millions of years, layers of sandy sediment piled up on the ocean floor. Slowly, the sediment changed to sandstone, a sedimentary rock. Over time, the sandstone became deeply buried. Heat and pressure changed the rock's texture from gritty to smooth. The sandstone changed into the metamorphic rock quartzite. But metamorphic rock does not end the rock cycle, which continues for millions of years.

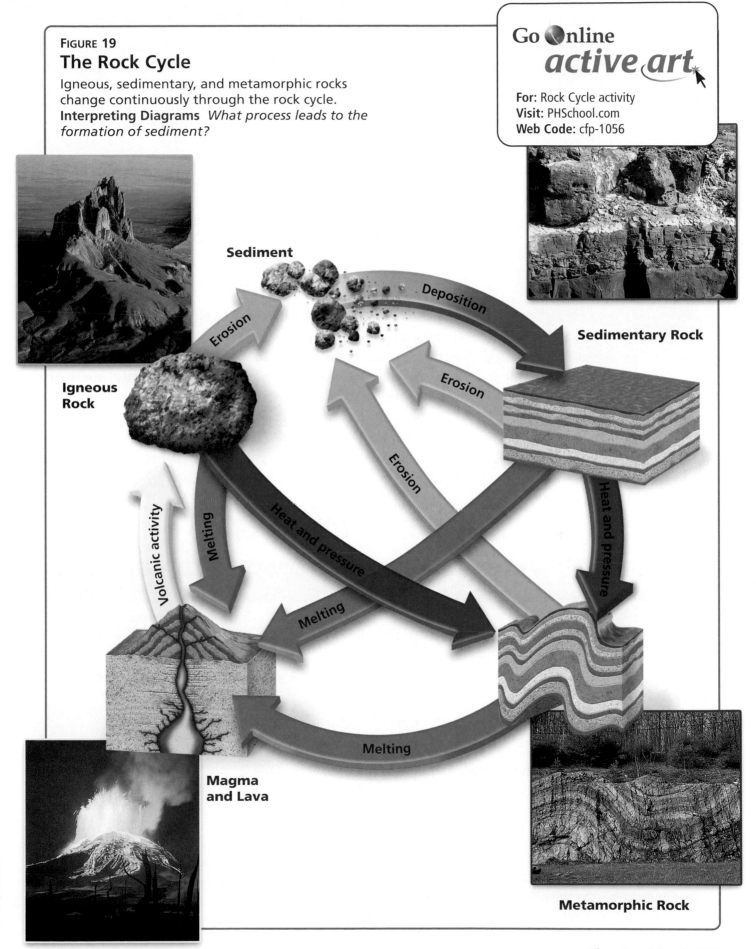

FIGURE 19
The Rock Cycle
Igneous, sedimentary, and metamorphic rocks
change continuously through the rock cycle.
Interpreting Diagrams *What process leads to the
formation of sediment?*

Go Online
active art

For: Rock Cycle activity
Visit: PHSchool.com
Web Code: cfp-1056

Sediment

Deposition

Erosion

Igneous
Rock

Sedimentary Rock

Erosion

Erosion

Heat and pressure

Heat and pressure

Volcanic activity

Melting

Melting

Melting

Magma
and Lava

Metamorphic Rock

The Rock Cycle and Plate Tectonics

The changes of the rock cycle are closely related to plate tectonics. **Plate movements start the rock cycle by helping to form magma, the source of igneous rocks. Plate movements also cause faulting, folding, and other motions of the crust that help to form sedimentary and metamorphic rocks.**

Igneous Rocks Where oceanic plates move apart, magma formed from melted mantle rock moves upward and fills the gap with new igneous rock. Where an oceanic plate is subducted beneath a continental plate, magma forms and rises. The result is a volcano made of igneous rock. A collision of continental plates may push rocks so deep that they melt and form magma. This magma slowly cools and hardens to form igneous rock.

Sedimentary and Metamorphic Rocks The collision of continental plates produces faults, folds, and uplift of the crust. Eventually, the collision could push up a mountain range. Then, erosion begins. The mountains eventually are worn away, leading to the formation of sedimentary rock.

A collision between continental plates can also push rocks down deep into the mantle. There, heat and pressure could change the rocks to metamorphic rock. And so the rock cycle continues, for hundreds of millions of years.

 **Reading Checkpoint** How can plate movements help to form metamorphic rock?

FIGURE 20
Moving Up in the World
This fossil trilobite lived on an ocean floor about 500 million years ago. As plate tectonics moved pieces of Earth's crust, the rock containing this fossil became part of a mountain.

Section 6 Assessment

Target Reading Skill **Sequencing** Review your cycle diagram about the rock cycle with a partner. Add any necessary information.

Reviewing Key Concepts

1. a. Defining Write a definition of the rock cycle in your own words.
   b. Sequencing Begin with igneous rock and explain how it could change through two more steps in the rock cycle.
2. a. Reviewing How do plate movements help to form igneous rocks?
   b. Relating Cause and Effect How can the collision of plates lead to the formation of sedimentary rock?
   c. Predicting What would be likely to happen to the rock cycle if Earth's interior cooled so much that plate motions stopped?

Writing in Science

Rock Legend Pick one type of rock and write a possible "biography" of the rock as it moves through the rock cycle. Your story should state the type of rock, how the rock formed, and how it might change.

Testing Rock Flooring

Problem
What kind of building stone makes the best flooring?

Skills Focus
designing experiments, controlling variables, drawing conclusions

Suggested Materials
- steel nail • wire brush • water
- plastic dropper • hand lens
- samples of igneous, sedimentary, and metamorphic rocks with flat surfaces
- greasy materials such as butter and crayons
- materials that form stains, such as ink and paints

Procedure

1. Brainstorm with your partner the qualities of good flooring. For example, good flooring should resist stains, scratches, and grease marks, and be safe to walk on when wet.

2. Predict what you think is the best building stone for a kitchen floor. Why is it the best?

3. Write the steps you plan to follow in answering the problem question. As you design your plan, consider the following factors:
   - What igneous, sedimentary, and metamorphic rocks will you test? (Pick at least one rock from each group.)
   - What materials or equipment will you need to acquire, and in what amounts?
   - What tests will you perform on the samples?
   - How will you control the variables in each test?
   - How will you measure each sample's resistance to staining, grease, and scratches?
   - How will you measure slipperiness?

4. Review your plan. Will it lead to an answer to the problem question?

5. Check your procedure and safety plan with your teacher.

6. Create a data table that includes a column in which you predict how each material will perform in each test.

Analyze and Conclude

1. **Interpreting Data** Which material performed the best on each test? Which performed the worst on each test?

2. **Drawing Conclusions** Which material is best for the kitchen flooring? Which material would you least want to use?

3. **Drawing Conclusions** Do your answers support your initial prediction? Why or why not?

4. **Applying Concepts** The person installing the floor might want stone that is easy to cut to the correct size or shape. What other qualities would matter to the flooring installer?

5. **Communicating** Based on your results, write an advertisement for the building stone that performed best as a flooring material.

Design an Experiment
Suppose you are trying to select flooring material for a laboratory where heavy equipment is frequently moved across the floor. Make a hypothesis predicting which type of stone flooring will be strongest. Then design an experiment to compare how well each type resists breakage.

Chapter 11

Study Guide

1 Classifying Rocks

Key Concepts

- When studying a rock sample, geologists observe the rock's mineral composition, color, and texture.
- Geologists classify rocks into three major groups: igneous rock, sedimentary rock, and metamorphic rock.

Key Terms

rock-forming mineral	texture
granite	igneous rock
basalt	sedimentary rock
grains	metamorphic rock

2 Igneous Rocks

Key Concepts

- Igneous rocks are classified according to their origin, texture, and mineral composition.
- People throughout history have used igneous rock for tools and building materials.

Key Terms

extrusive rock
intrusive rock

3 Sedimentary Rocks

Key Concepts

- Most sedimentary rocks are formed through a series of processes: erosion, deposition, compaction, and cementation.
- There are three major groups of sedimentary rocks: clastic rocks, organic rocks, and chemical rocks.
- People have used sedimentary rocks throughout history for many different purposes, including building materials and tools.

Key Terms

sediment	cementation
erosion	clastic rock
deposition	organic rock
compaction	chemical rock

4 Rocks From Reefs

Key Concepts

- When coral animals die, their skeletons remain. More corals build on top of them, gradually forming a reef.
- Limestone deposits that began as coral reefs provide evidence of how plate motions have changed Earth's surface. These deposits also provide evidence of past environments.

Key Term

coral reef

5 Metamorphic Rocks

Key Concepts

- Heat and pressure deep beneath Earth's surface can change any rock into metamorphic rock.
- Geologists classify metamorphic rocks according to the arrangement of the grains that make up the rocks.
- Certain metamorphic rocks are important materials for building and sculpture.

Key Term

foliated

6 The Rock Cycle

Key Concepts

- Forces deep inside Earth and at the surface produce a slow cycle that builds, destroys, and changes the rocks in the crust.
- Plate movements start the rock cycle by helping to form magma, the source of igneous rocks. Plate movements also cause faulting, folding, and other motions of the crust that help to form sedimentary and metamorphic rocks.

Key Term

rock cycle

Review and Assessment

Organizing Information

Concept Mapping Copy the concept map about classifying rocks onto a separate sheet of paper. Then complete it and give it a title. (For more on concept maps, see the Skills Handbook.)

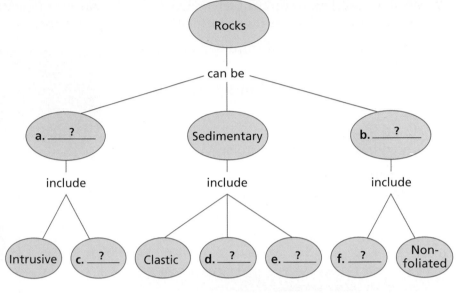

Reviewing Key Terms

Choose the letter of the best answer.

1. A rock formed from fragments of other rocks is a(n)
   a. metamorphic rock.   **b.** extrusive rock.
   c. sedimentary rock.   **d.** igneous rock.

2. An igneous rock containing large crystals is most likely a(n)
   a. chemical rock.   **b.** extrusive rock.
   c. foliated rock.   **d.** intrusive rock.

3. A sedimentary rock formed from pieces of other rocks is called a(n)
   a. organic rock.   **b.** chemical rock.
   c. clastic rock.   **d.** compacted rock.

4. A deposit of organic limestone on land probably formed millions of years ago as a(n)
   a. extrusive rock.   **b.** coral reef.
   c. chemical rock.   **d.** metamorphic rock.

5. A metamorphic rock in which the grains line up in parallel bands is a
   a. clastic rock.   **b.** nonclastic rock.
   c. nonfoliated rock.   **d.** foliated rock.

6. In the rock cycle, the process by which an igneous rock changes to a sedimentary rock must begin with
   a. cementation.
   b. deposition.
   c. erosion.
   d. compaction.

Writing in Science

Field Guide Research and write a field guide for geologists and visitors to an area such as the Grand Canyon. Describe the types of rocks you might find there, what the rocks look like, and what their properties are. Briefly explain the kinds of forces that shaped the rocks in the area you chose.

Discovery CHANNEL SCHOOL

Rocks

Video Preview
Video Field Trip
▶ Video Assessment

Review and Assessment

Checking Concepts

7. What is the relationship between an igneous rock's texture and where it was formed?

8. Why can water pass easily through sandstone but not through shale?

9. Describe how a rock can form by evaporation. What type of rock is it?

10. How do the properties of a rock change when it becomes a metamorphic rock?

11. What are the sources of the heat that helps metamorphic rocks to form?

12. What are two things that could happen to a metamorphic rock to continue the rock cycle?

Thinking Critically

13. Developing Hypotheses The sedimentary rocks limestone and sandstone are used as building materials. However, they wear away more rapidly than marble and quartzite, the metamorphic rocks that are formed from them. Why do you think this is so?

14. Inferring A geologist finds an area where the rocks are layers of coal and shale as shown in the diagram below. What kind of environment probably existed in this area millions of years ago when these rocks formed?

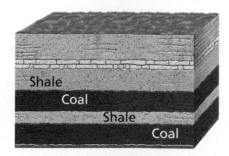

15. Comparing and Contrasting How are clastic rocks and organic rocks similar? How are they different?

16. Predicting Would you be less likely to find fossils in metamorphic rocks than in sedimentary rocks? Explain your answer.

Applying Skills

Answer Questions 17–20 using the photos of three rocks.

Ⓐ

Ⓑ

Ⓒ

17. Observing How would you describe the texture of each rock?

18. Classifying Which of the three rocks would you classify as a metamorphic rock? Why?

19. Inferring A rock's texture gives clues about how the rock formed. What can you infer about the process by which Rock B formed?

20. Relating Cause and Effect What conditions led to the formation of the large crystals in Rock C? Explain your answer.

Lab zone Chapter **Project**

Performance Assessment Construct a simple display for your rocks. It should show your classification for each rock sample. In your presentation, describe where you hunted and what kinds of rocks you found. Were any rocks hard to classify? Did you find rocks from each of the three major groups? Can you think of any reason why certain types of rocks would not be found in your area?

Choose the letter of the best answer.

1. You find a rock in which the grains are arranged in parallel bands of white and black crystals. The rock is probably a(n)
   A igneous rock.
   B sedimentary rock.
   C metamorphic rock.
   D reef rock.

2. Many sedimentary rocks have visible layers because of the process of
   A eruption.
   B deposition.
   C intrusion.
   D crystallization.

3. Rock salt, made of the mineral halite, is an organic sedimentary rock. A deposit of rock salt is most likely to be formed when
   A magma cools and hardens inside Earth.
   B hot water solutions form veins of rock salt.
   C the minerals form a solution in magma.
   D a solution of halite and water evaporates.

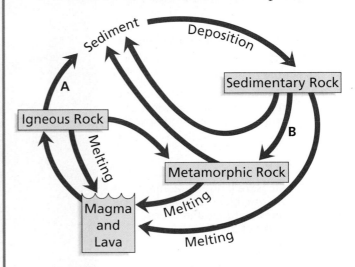

Use the diagram above to answer Questions 4 and 5.

4. If the heat and pressure inside Earth cause a rock to melt, the material that formed would be
   A metamorphic rock.
   B magma.
   C sedimentary rock.
   D igneous rock.

5. How can a metamorphic rock change into a sedimentary rock?
   A erosion and deposition
   B melting and crystallization
   C heat and pressure
   D all of the above

Open-Ended Question

6. You are studying some moon rocks. Some of the moon rocks are made up of jagged pieces of other rocks. The pieces are cemented together by fine, dust-sized particles called rock powder. How would you classify this type of moon rock? Explain how you used the rock's characteristics to classify it.

Chapter 12

Mapping Earth's Surface

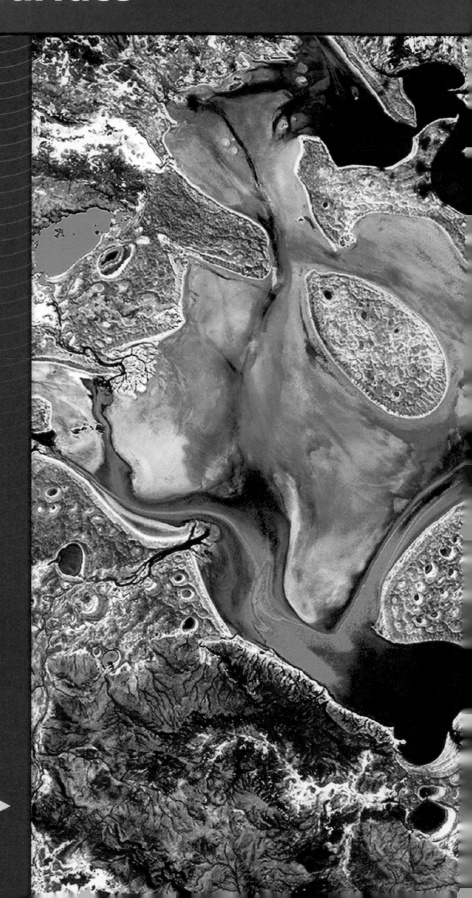

Academic Standards

This chapter addresses these Indiana standards.

The Nature of Science

7.1.11 Illustrate how numbers can be represented by sequences of only two symbols and how that affects the storage of information.

Scientific Thinking

7.2.6 Measure length, volume, weight, elapsed time, rates, or temperatures, and choose appropriate units.

The Physical Setting

7.3.7 Give examples of abrupt and very slow changes in Earth's surface.

7.3.8 Describe how sediments are buried and bonded together by dissolved minerals to form solid rock.

Common Themes

7.7.2 Use different models to represent the same thing, noting that the model's type and complexity depend on its purpose.

This satellite image shows Lake Carnegie in Western Australia. ▶

Lab zone™ Chapter Project

Getting on the Map

For this chapter project, you will select a small piece of land and draw a map of its physical features.

Your Goal To create a scale map of a small area of your neighborhood

To complete this project, you must
- work with your teacher or an adult family member
- choose and measure a small square or rectangular piece of land
- use a compass to locate north
- draw a map to scale
- use symbols and a key to represent natural and human-made features of the land
- follow the safety guidelines in Appendix A

Plan It! Start by looking for a suitable site. Your site should be about 300 to 1,000 square meters in area. It could be part of a park, playground, or backyard. Look for an area that includes interesting natural features such as trees, a stream, and changes in elevation or slope. There may be some human-made structures on your site, such as a park bench or sidewalk. Once you have chosen a site, measure its boundaries and sketch its physical features. Then brainstorm ideas for symbols to include on your map. When you have completed your map, including a key and map scale, present it to your class.

Exploring Earth's Surface

Reading Preview

Key Concepts

- What does the topography of an area include?
- What are the main types of landforms?

Key Terms

- topography • elevation
- relief • landform • plain
- mountain • mountain range
- plateau • landform region

Target Reading Skill

Comparing and Contrasting
As you read, compare and contrast the characteristics of landforms by completing a table like the one below.

Characteristics of Landforms

Landform	Elevation	Relief
Plain	a. ____?____	Low
Mountain	b. ____?____	c. ____?____
d. ____?____	High	e. ____?____

Lab zone **Discover Activity**

What Is the Land Like Around Your School?

1. On a piece of paper, draw a small square to represent your school.
2. Choose a word that describes the type of land near your school, such as flat, hilly, or rolling. Write the word next to the square.
3. Use a magnetic compass to determine the direction of north. Assume that north is at the top of your piece of paper.
4. If you travel due north 1 kilometer from your school, what type of land do you find? Choose a word to describe the land in this area. Write that word to the north of the square.
5. Repeat Step 4 for areas located 1 kilometer east, south, and west of your school.

Think It Over
Forming Operational Definitions What phrase could you use to describe the land in your area?

In 1804, an expedition set out from St. Louis to explore the land between the Mississippi River and the Pacific Ocean. The United States had just purchased a part of this vast territory, called Louisiana, from France. Before the Louisiana Purchase, the United States stretched from the Atlantic coast westward to the Mississippi River. Few United States citizens had traveled west of the Mississippi. None had ever traveled over land all the way to the Pacific.

Led by Meriwether Lewis and William Clark, the expedition first traveled up the Missouri River. Then the group crossed the Rocky Mountains and followed the Columbia River to the Pacific Ocean. They returned by a similar route. The purpose of the expedition was to map America's interior.

On the journey to the Pacific, the Lewis and Clark expedition traveled more than 5,000 kilometers. As they traveled, Lewis and Clark observed many changes in topography. **Topography** (tuh PAWG ruh fee) is the shape of the land. An area's topography may be flat, sloping, hilly, or mountainous.

◄ **The compass used by Meriwether Lewis**

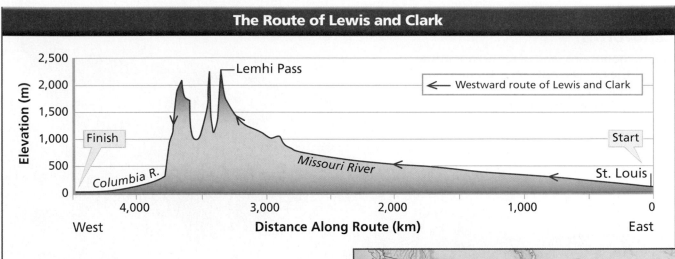

The Route of Lewis and Clark

Elevation (m) — Westward route of Lewis and Clark

Lemhi Pass

Finish

Start

Columbia R.

Missouri River

St. Louis

Distance Along Route (km)

West — 4,000 — 3,000 — 2,000 — 1,000 — 0 — East

Topography

The topography of an area includes the area's elevation, relief, and landforms. The desktop where you do homework probably has piles of books, papers, and other objects of different sizes and shapes. Your desktop has both elevation and relief!

Elevation The height above sea level of a point on Earth's surface is its **elevation.** When Lewis and Clark started in St. Louis, they were about 140 meters above sea level. By the time they reached Lemhi Pass in the Rocky Mountains, they were more than 2,200 meters above sea level. Look at Figure 1 to see the changes in elevation along Lewis and Clark's route.

Relief The difference in elevation between the highest and lowest parts of an area is its **relief.** Early in their journey, Lewis and Clark encountered flat or rolling land with low relief, or small differences in elevation. In the Rocky Mountains, they crossed huge mountains separated by deep valleys. These areas had high relief, or great differences in elevation.

Landforms If you followed the route of the Lewis and Clark expedition, you would see many different landforms. A **landform** is a feature of topography, such as a hill or valley, formed by the processes that shape Earth's surface. Different landforms have different combinations of elevation and relief.

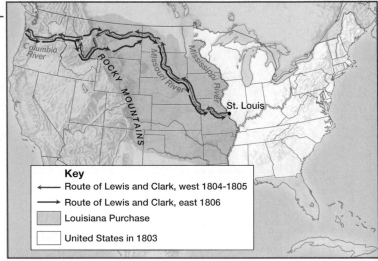

FIGURE 1
The route of the Lewis and Clark expedition crossed regions that differed greatly in elevation and relief. **Interpreting Graphs** *How much elevation did Lewis and Clark gain between St. Louis and Lemhi Pass?*

Reading Checkpoint What is the difference between elevation and relief?

FIGURE 2
Landforms

Plains, mountains, and plateaus are just a few of the many landforms that make up the topography of Earth's surface.
Forming Operational Definitions *Based on this illustration, how would you define "mountains"?*

Plains
Plains may occur along a continent's edges or in the interior.

Types of Landforms

Landforms vary greatly in size and shape—from level plains extending as far as the eye can see, to low, rounded hills that you could climb on foot, to jagged mountains that would take you many days to walk around. **There are three main types of landforms: plains, mountains, and plateaus.**

Plains A **plain** is a landform made up of nearly flat or gently rolling land with low relief. A plain that lies along a seacoast is called a coastal plain. In North America, a coastal plain extends around the continent's eastern and southeastern shores. Coastal plains have both low elevation and low relief.

A plain that lies away from the coast is called an interior plain. Although interior plains have low relief, their elevation can vary. The broad interior plains of North America are called the Great Plains.

The Great Plains extend north from Texas into Canada. The Great Plains extend west to the Rocky Mountains from the states of North and South Dakota, Nebraska, Kansas, Oklahoma, and Texas. At the time of the Lewis and Clark expedition, the Great Plains were a vast grassland.

Mountains
A mountain's base usually covers an area of at least several square kilometers, but its peak may rise to a point. Mountains often have steeply sloping sides.

Plateaus
The top of a plateau forms a level surface.

Mountains A **mountain** is a landform with high elevation and high relief. Mountains usually occur as part of a mountain range. A **mountain range** is a group of mountains that are closely related in shape, structure, and age. After crossing the Great Plains, the Lewis and Clark expedition crossed a rugged mountain range in Idaho called the Bitterroot Mountains.

The different mountain ranges in a region make up a mountain system. The Bitterroot Mountains are one mountain range in the mountain system known as the Rocky Mountains.

Mountain ranges and mountain systems in a long, connected chain form a larger unit called a mountain belt. The Rocky Mountains are part of a great mountain belt that stretches down the western sides of North America and South America.

Plateaus A landform that has high elevation and a more or less level surface is called a **plateau.** A plateau is rarely perfectly smooth on top. Streams and rivers may cut into the plateau's surface. The Columbia Plateau in Washington State is an example. The Columbia River, which the Lewis and Clark expedition followed, slices through this plateau. The many layers of rock that make up the Columbia Plateau are stacked about 1,500 meters thick.

Lab zone Skills **Activity**

Classifying
You take a direct flight across the United States from Walla Walla in Washington State to Washington, D.C. You have a window seat. Write a postcard to friends describing the major landforms that you see on your trip. Use Figure 3 to determine what the land is like along your route.

Landform Regions of the United States

Key
- Coastal plains
- Interior plains or lowlands
- Mountains
- Plateaus or uplands
- Basins and mountains

FIGURE 3
The United States has many different landform regions.
Interpreting Maps *In what regions are Charleston, Santa Fe, and Topeka?*

Landform Regions A large area of land where the topography is made up mainly of one type of landform is called a **landform region.** The Great Plains and Rocky Mountains are major landform regions. Other terms can be used to describe landform regions. For example, an upland is a region of hilly topography. A lowland is a region of plains with low elevation. A basin is lower than the mountains around it.

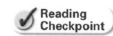 Reading Checkpoint **What terms can be used to describe landform regions?**

Section 1 Assessment

Target Reading Skill Comparing and Contrasting Use the information in your table to help answer Question 2 below.

Reviewing Key Concepts

1. **a. Defining** What is elevation?
   b. Comparing and Contrasting What is relief? How does it differ from elevation?
   c. Calculating What is the relief in an area where the highest point is 1,200 meters above sea level and the lowest point is 200 meters above sea level?

2. **a. Listing** What are the three main types of landforms?
   b. Describing What are the characteristics of a mountain?
   c. Sequencing Place these features in order from smallest to largest: mountain system, mountain range, mountain belt, mountain.

 **Writing in Science**

Description Look at Figure 3. Choose one of the landform regions on the map. Research the characteristics of your landform region using an encyclopedia or other reference. Write a description of the region, including characteristics such as elevation, relief, and the types of landforms found there.

Models of Earth

Reading Preview

Key Concepts
- How do maps and globes represent Earth's surface?
- What reference lines are used to locate points on Earth?
- What are three common map projections?

Key Terms
- map • globe • scale
- symbol • key • degree
- equator • hemisphere
- prime meridian • latitude
- longitude • map projection

⊙ Target Reading Skill

Asking Questions Before you read, preview the red headings. In a graphic organizer like the one below, ask a question for each heading. As you read, write the answers to your questions.

Models of Earth

Question	Answer
What are maps and globes?	

How Can You Flatten the Curved Earth?

1. Using a felt-tip pen, make a rough sketch of the outlines of the continents on the surface of an orange or grapefruit.
2. Using a plastic knife, carefully peel the orange. If possible, keep the peel in one large piece so that the continents remain intact.
3. Try to lay the pieces of orange peel flat on a table.

Think It Over
Observing What happens to the continents when you try to flatten the pieces? Is there any way to keep the shapes of the continents from being distorted?

Today, people know that Earth is a sphere located in space and moving around the sun. But it took hundreds of years to develop this scientific model of Earth. Around 600 B.C., one early Greek scientist, Thales of Miletus, hypothesized that Earth is a disk floating in a pool of water. Another Greek scientist, Anaximander, suggested that Earth is a cylinder floating in space. (He thought that people lived on the flat top of the cylinder!)

Around 350 B.C., the Greek scientist Aristotle used evidence from everyday observations to support the idea that Earth is a sphere. For example, Aristotle pointed out that a ship sailing away from shore appears to sink beneath the horizon because Earth's surface is curved. If Earth were flat, the ship would simply appear smaller as it moved away.

After Aristotle, other Greek scientists used the knowledge that Earth is a sphere to help them measure the size of Earth. Eratosthenes, a Greek scientist who lived in Egypt more than 2,200 years ago, calculated Earth's size. Using measurements and principles of geometry and astronomy, he arrived at a figure that was accurate to within 14 percent.

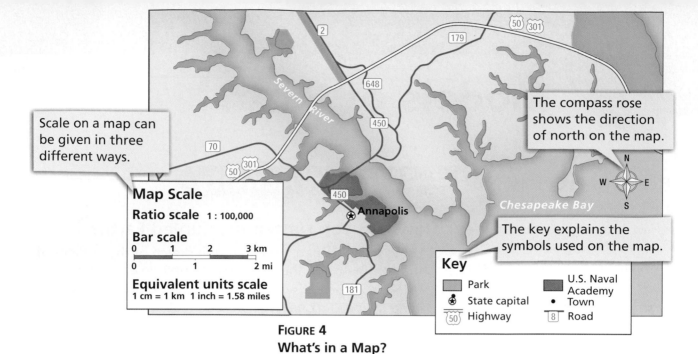

Scale on a map can be given in three different ways.

The compass rose shows the direction of north on the map.

Map Scale

Ratio scale 1 : 100,000

Bar scale

0   1   2   3 km

0   1   2 mi

Equivalent units scale
1 cm = 1 km 1 inch = 1.58 miles

The key explains the symbols used on the map.

Key

Park

State capital

Highway

U.S. Naval Academy

Town

Road

Annapolis

Chesapeake Bay

FIGURE 4

What's in a Map?
A map is drawn to scale, uses symbols explained in a map key, and usually has a compass rose to show direction. This map shows the area around Annapolis, Maryland.
Interpreting Maps *What is the scale of this map?*

Scales and Ratios

A ratio compares two numbers by division. For example, the scale of a map given as a ratio is 1 : 250,000. At this scale, the distance between two points on the map measures 23.5 cm. How would you find the actual distance?

1. Write the scale as a fraction.

$$\frac{1}{250,000}$$

2. Write a proportion. Let *d* represent the distance between the two points.

$$\frac{1}{250,000} = \frac{23.5 \text{ cm}}{d}$$

3. Write the cross products.

$$1 \times d = 250,000 \times 23.5 \text{ cm}$$
$$d = 5,875,000 \text{ cm}$$

(*Hint:* To convert cm to km, divide *d* by 100,000.)

Practice Problem A map's scale is 1 : 25,000. If two points are 4.7 cm apart on the map, how far apart are they on the ground?

Maps and Globes

Maps and globes show the shape, size, and position of Earth's surface features. A **map** is a flat model of all or part of Earth's surface as seen from above. A **globe** is a sphere that represents Earth's entire surface. A globe correctly shows the relative size, shape, and position of landmasses and bodies of water, much as if you were viewing Earth from space.

Maps and globes are drawn to scale and use symbols to represent topography and other features on Earth's surface. A map's **scale** relates distance on a map to a distance on Earth's surface. Scale is often given as a ratio. For example, one unit on a map could equal 25,000 units on the ground. So one centimeter on the map would represent 0.25 kilometer. This scale, "one to twenty-five thousand," would be written "1 : 25,000." Figure 4 shows three ways of giving a map's scale.

Mapmakers use shapes and pictures called **symbols** to stand for features on Earth's surface. A symbol can represent a physical feature, such as a river, lake, mountain, or plain. A symbol also can stand for a human-made feature, such as a highway, city, or airport. A map's **key,** or legend, is a list of all the symbols used on the map with an explanation of their meaning.

Maps also include a compass rose or north arrow. The compass rose helps relate directions on the map to directions on Earth's surface. North usually is located at the top of the map.

Reading Checkpoint Where can you find the meaning of the symbols on a map?

An Earth Reference System

When you play checkers, the grid of squares helps you to keep track of where each piece should be. To find a point on Earth's surface, you need a reference system like the grid of squares on a checkerboard. Of course, Earth itself does not have grid lines, but most maps and globes show a grid. Because Earth is a sphere, the grid curves to cover the entire planet. **Two of the lines that make up the grid, the equator and prime meridian, are the baselines for measuring distances on Earth's surface.**

Measuring in Degrees To locate positions on Earth's surface, scientists use units called degrees. You probably know that degrees are used to measure the distance around a circle. As you can see in Figure 6, a **degree** (°) is $\frac{1}{360}$ of the distance around a circle. Degrees can also be used to measure distances on the surface of a sphere. On Earth's surface, each degree is a measure of an angle formed by lines drawn from the center of Earth to points on the surface. To help locate points precisely, degrees are further divided into smaller units called minutes and seconds.

FIGURE 6
Degrees Around
Distances around a circle are measured in degrees.
Interpreting Diagrams *How many degrees are there in one quarter of the distance around the circle?*

360°/0°

270°

90°

180°

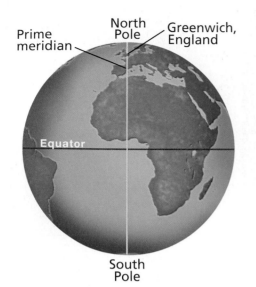

North Pole
Prime meridian
Greenwich, England
Equator
South Pole

FIGURE 7
Equator and Prime Meridian
The equator and prime meridian divide Earth's surface into hemispheres.

The Equator Halfway between the North and South poles, the **equator** forms an imaginary line that circles Earth. The equator divides Earth into the Northern and Southern hemispheres. A **hemisphere** (HEM ih sfeer) is one half of the sphere that makes up Earth's surface. If you started at the equator and traveled to one of the poles, you would travel 90 degrees—one quarter of the distance in a full circle.

Science and History

Maps and Technology

Centuries ago, people invented instruments for determining compass direction, latitude, and longitude. Mapmakers developed techniques to show Earth's surface accurately.

1154
Scientific Mapmaking
The Arab mapmaker Al-Idrisi made several world maps for King Roger of Sicily. Idrisi's maps marked a great advance over other maps of that time. They showed the Arabs' grasp of scientific mapmaking and geography. But unlike modern maps, these maps placed south at the top!

Around 1300
Charts for Navigation
Lines representing wind directions criss-crossed a type of map called a portolan chart. These charts also showed coastlines and harbors. A sea captain would use a portolan chart and a compass when sailing from one harbor to another.

Around 1100
Magnetic Compass
Because the needle of a magnetic compass points north, ships at sea could tell direction even when the sun and stars were not visible. Arabs and Europeans adopted this Chinese invention by the 1200s.

| 1100 | 1200 | 1300 | 1400 |

The Prime Meridian Another imaginary line, called the **prime meridian,** makes a half circle from the North Pole to the South Pole. The prime meridian passes through Greenwich, England. Places east of the prime meridian are in the Eastern Hemisphere. Places west of the prime meridian are in the Western Hemisphere.

If you started at the prime meridian and traveled west along the equator, you would travel through 360 degrees before returning to your starting point. At 180 degrees east or west of the prime meridian is another half circle that lies directly opposite the prime meridian.

 **Reading Checkpoint** What two hemispheres are separated by the equator?

Writing in Science

Writing in Science Choose one period on the timeline to learn more about. Use the library to find information about maps in that time. Who used maps? Why were they important? Share what you learn in the form of a letter written by a traveler or explorer who is using a map of that period.

**1569
Map Projections**
Flemish mapmaker Gerardus Mercator invented the first modern map projection, which bears his name. Mercator and his son, Rumold, also made an atlas and maps of the world such as the one shown above.

**1595
Determining Latitude**
To find latitude, sailors used a variety of instruments, including the backstaff. The navigator sighted along the backstaff's straight edge to measure the angle of the sun or North Star above the horizon. Later improvements led to modern instruments for navigation.

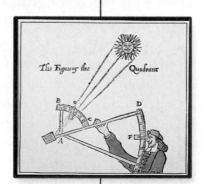

**1763
Determining Longitude**
John Harrison, a carpenter and mechanic, won a prize from the British navy for building a highly accurate clock called a chronometer. Harrison's invention made finding longitudes quicker and easier. With exact longitudes, mapmakers could greatly improve the accuracy of their maps.

| 1500 | 1600 | 1700 | 1800 |

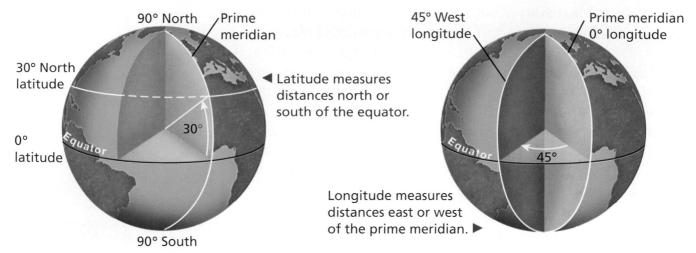

FIGURE 8
Latitude and Longitude
Points on Earth's surface can be located using the grid of latitude and longitude lines.

Locating Points on Earth's Surface

Using the equator and prime meridian, mapmakers have constructed a grid made up of lines of latitude and longitude. **The lines of latitude and longitude form a grid that can be used to find locations anywhere on Earth.**

Latitude The equator is the starting line for measuring **latitude,** or distance in degrees north or south of the equator. The latitude of the equator is 0°. Between the equator and each pole are 90 evenly spaced, parallel lines called lines of latitude. Each degree of latitude is equal to about 111 kilometers.

A line of latitude is defined by the angle it makes with the equator and the center of Earth. Figure 8 shows how lines drawn from the center of Earth to the equator and from the center of Earth to 30° North form an angle of 30 degrees.

Longitude The distance in degrees east or west of the prime meridian is called **longitude.** There are 360 lines of longitude that run from north to south, meeting at the poles. Each line represents one degree of longitude. A degree of longitude equals about 111 kilometers at the equator. But at the poles, where the lines of longitude come together, the distance decreases to zero.

The prime meridian, which is the starting line for measuring longitude, is at 0°. The longitude lines in each hemisphere are numbered up to 180 degrees. Half of the lines of longitude are in the Eastern Hemisphere, and half are in the Western Hemisphere.

Each line of longitude is defined by the angle it makes with the prime meridian and the center of Earth. As you can see in Figure 8, a line drawn from the center of Earth to the prime meridian and a line drawn from the center of Earth to 45° West form an angle of 45 degrees at the equator.

Lab zone Try This Activity

Where in the World?

Using a globe, determine what city is found at each of the following points:

    2° S 79° W

    38° N 9° W

    34° N 135° E

    34° S 58° W

    55° N 3° W

    1° N 103° E

What word is spelled by the first letters of these cities?

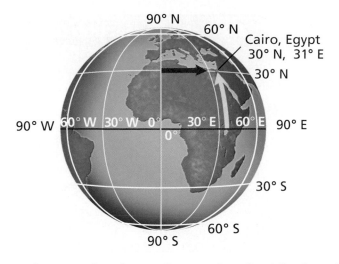

90° N
60° N
Cairo, Egypt
30° N, 31° E
30° N

90° W 60° W 30° W 0° 30° E 60° E 90° E
0°

30° S

60° S
90° S

◄ Cairo, Egypt, is located where
the latitude line 30° N crosses
the longitude line 31° E.

Go Online
SciLINKS NSTA

For: Links on latitude and longitude
Visit: www.SciLinks.org
Web Code: scn-0712

Using Latitude and Longitude The location of any point on Earth's surface can be expressed in terms of the latitude and longitude lines that cross at that point. For example, you can see on the map in Figure 9 that New Orleans is located where the line for 30° North latitude crosses the line for 90° West longitude. Notice that each longitude line crosses the latitude lines, including the equator, at a right angle.

 **Reading Checkpoint** How are longitude lines numbered?

FIGURE 9
Every point on Earth's surface has a particular latitude and longitude.
Interpreting Maps *What are the latitude and longitude of Mexico City? Of Sydney?*

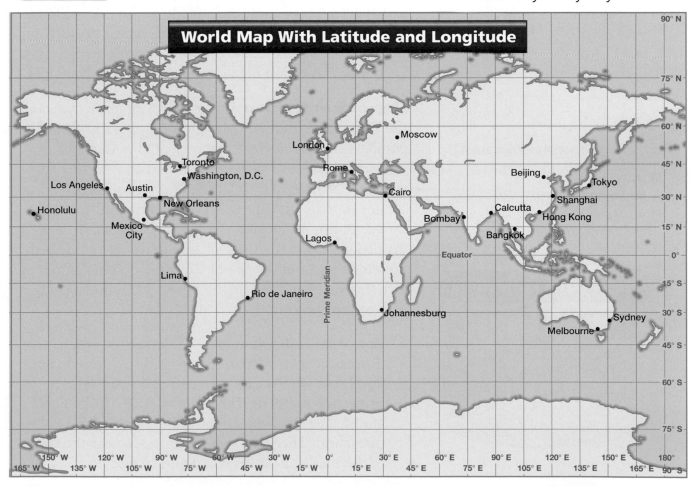

World Map With Latitude and Longitude

FIGURE 10

A Mercator projection is based on a cylinder with grid lines that has been flattened. On a Mercator projection, lines of longitude are parallel, so shapes near the poles are distorted.

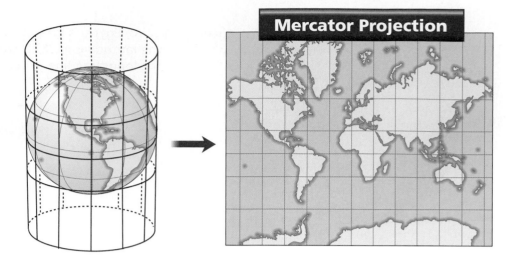

Mercator Projection

Map Projections

To show Earth's curved surface on a flat map, mapmakers use map projections. A **map projection** is a framework of lines that helps in transferring points on Earth's three-dimensional surface onto a flat map. Features such as continents, oceans, islands, rivers, and lakes might appear to have somewhat different sizes and shapes on different map projections. All projections distort the shapes of these features to some extent. **Three common map projections are the Mercator projection, the equal-area projection, and the conic projection.** Each map projection has advantages and disadvantages.

Mercator Projection On a Mercator projection, all the lines of latitude and longitude appear as straight, parallel lines that form a rectangle. On a Mercator projection, the size and shape of landmasses near the equator are distorted only a little. But as you can see in Figure 10, size and shape become more and more distorted as you go toward the poles. The reason for this distortion is that the lines of longitude on the map do not come together at the poles as they do on a globe. In fact, the North and South poles cannot be shown using a Mercator projection.

FIGURE 11

An equal-area projection shows areas correctly, but distorts some shapes around its edges.
Comparing and Contrasting *Why does Greenland appear larger on the Mercator projection than on the equal-area projection?*

Equal-Area Projection

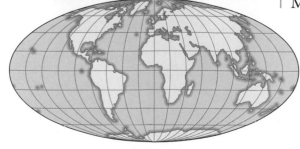

Equal-Area Projection To solve the problem of distortion on Mercator projections, mapmakers developed equal-area projections. An equal-area projection correctly shows the relative sizes of Earth's landmasses. But an equal-area projection also has distortion. The shapes of landmasses near the edges of the map appear stretched and curved.

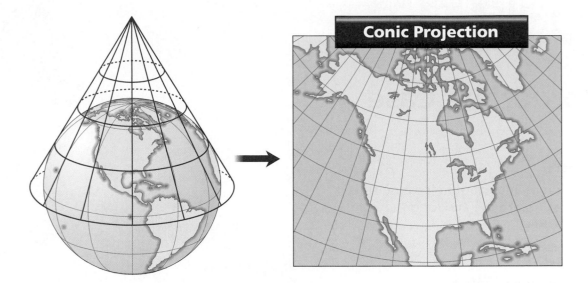

Conic Projection

Conic Projection Suppose you placed a clear plastic cone over a globe, as shown in Figure 12. Then you could trace the lines of latitude and longitude onto the cone, unwrap the cone, and place it flat. The result would be a conic projection. In a conic projection, lines of longitude appear as straight lines while lines of latitude are curved. There is little distortion on maps that use this projection to show limited parts of Earth's surface. A conic projection is frequently used for maps of the continental United States.

FIGURE 12
A conic projection is based on a cone that covers part of Earth and is then rolled out flat. A conic projection's grid is formed from straight lines of longitude and curved lines of latitude.

 **Reading Checkpoint** Why is a conic projection best suited to showing only part of Earth's surface?

Section 2 Assessment

🎯 **Target Reading Skill** Asking Questions
Work with a partner to check the answers in your graphic organizer.

Reviewing Key Concepts

1. **a. Defining** What is a map?
   b. Explaining What information does a globe present?
   c. Comparing and Contrasting How are maps and globes similar? How are they different?
2. **a. Identifying** What two lines are baselines for measurements on Earth's surface?
   b. Explaining How are these baselines used to locate points on Earth's surface?
   c. Interpreting Maps Look at the map in Figure 9. If you fly due north from Lima, through how many degrees of latitude must you travel to reach Washington, D.C.?

3. **a. Listing** What are three common map projections?
   b. Comparing and Contrasting What are the advantages and disadvantages of each of the three projections?

Math ▶ **Practice**

4. **Scales and Ratios** A globe has a scale of 1 : 40,000,000. Using a piece of string, you determine that the shortest distance between two cities on the globe is 7 cm. What is the actual distance between the two cities?

A Borderline Case

Problem

Which was more important in locating state borders: lines of latitude and longitude or physical features?

Skills Focus

classifying, observing, inferring

Materials

- United States map with latitude, longitude, and state borders
- tracing paper
- paper clips
- colored pencils

Procedure

1. Lay a sheet of tracing paper on top of a map of the United States.
2. Trace over the Pacific and Atlantic coasts of the United States with a blue pencil.
3. Using the blue pencil, trace all Great Lakes shorelines that reach nearby states.
4. Trace all state borders that go exactly north-south with a red pencil. (*Hint:* Some straight-line borders that appear to run north-south, such as the western border of Maine, do not follow lines of longitude.)
5. Use a green pencil to trace all state borders or sections of state borders that go exactly east-west. (*Hint:* Straight-line borders that are slanted, such as the southern border of Nevada, do not follow lines of latitude.)
6. Now use a blue pencil to trace the borders that follow rivers.
7. Use a brown pencil to trace any borders that are not straight lines or rivers.

Analyze and Conclude

1. **Classifying** How many state boundaries are completely defined by longitude and latitude? How many are partially defined by longitude and latitude? How many states do not use either one to define their borders?
2. **Observing** What feature is most often used to define a state border when longitude and latitude are not used? Give specific examples.
3. **Observing** Study the physical map of the United States in Appendix A. What other physical features are used to define borders? Which state borders are defined by these features?
4. **Inferring** In which region of the country were lines of latitude and longitude most important in determining state borders? What do you think is the reason for this?
5. **Communicating** Pick any state and describe its borders as accurately as you can in terms of latitude, longitude, and physical features.

More to Explore

Research the history of your state to find out when and how its borders were established. Are your state's borders based on longitude and latitude, landforms and topography, or both?

Review a map of your county or state. Are any features other than borders related to longitude and latitude? Which features seem to follow landforms and topography?

Maps and Computers

Reading Preview

Key Concepts
- How does computer mapping differ from earlier ways of making maps?
- What sources of data are used in making computer maps?

Key Terms
- surveying • digitizing
- satellite image • pixel
- Global Positioning System

Target Reading Skill

Identifying Main Ideas As you read the Maps and Computers section, write the main idea in a graphic organizer like the one below. Then write three supporting details that further explain the main idea.

Main Idea

Computers use digitized data to make maps.

Detail	Detail	Detail

Discover Activity

Can You Make a Pixel Picture?

1. With a pencil, draw a square grid of lines spaced 1 centimeter apart. The grid should have 6 squares on each side.
2. On the grid, draw the outline of a simple object, such as an apple.
3. Using a different color pencil, fill in all squares that are completely inside the object. If a square is mostly inside the object, fill it in completely. If it is mostly outside, leave it blank.
4. Each square on your grid represents one pixel, or bit of information, about your picture. Looking at your pixel picture, can you recognize the shape you started with?

Think It Over
Predicting How would the pixel picture change if you drew the object smaller? How would the pixel picture look if you used graph paper with squares that are smaller than your grid?

For centuries, mapmakers drew maps by hand. Explorers made maps by sketching coastlines as seen from their ships. More accurate maps were made by locating points on Earth's surface in a process called surveying. In **surveying,** mapmakers determine distances and elevations using instruments and the principles of geometry. In the twentieth century, people learned to make maps using photographs taken from airplanes.

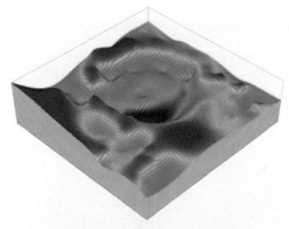

▲ A computer produced this digital model of part of Earth's surface.

Computer Mapping

Since the 1970s, computers have revolutionized mapmaking. **With computers, mapmakers can store, process, and display map data electronically.**

All of the data used in computer mapping must be written in numbers. The process by which mapmakers convert the location of map points to numbers is called **digitizing.** These numbers are stored on a computer as a series of 0's and 1's. The digitized data can easily be displayed on a computer screen, modified, and printed in map form.

For: More on satellite mapping
Visit: PHSchool.com
Web Code: cfd-2013

Sources of Map Data

Computer mapmakers use these up-to-the-minute data to produce maps quickly and easily. Computers can automatically make maps that might take a person hundreds of hours to draw by hand. **Computers produce maps using data from many sources, including satellites and the Global Positioning System.**

Data From Satellites Much of the data used in computer mapping is gathered by satellites in space. Mapping satellites use electronic devices to collect computer data about the land surface. Pictures of the surface based on these data are called **satellite images.**

A satellite image is made up of thousands of tiny dots called **pixels.** A painting made of pixels would have many separate dots of color. Each pixel in a satellite image contains information on the color and brightness of a small part of Earth's surface. For example, the pixels that represent a forest differ in color and brightness from the pixels that represent farmland. The data in each pixel are stored on a computer. When the satellite image is printed, the computer translates these digitized data into colors.

FIGURE 13

Views of Yellowstone

These views of Yellowstone National Park show how computers have changed the technology of mapmaking. Yellowstone Lake is near the center of both images.

◀ This early map of the Yellowstone region was produced through surveys on the ground.

This satellite image made by the Landsat ▶ Thematic Mapper enables scientists to compare areas affected by forest fires (orange) with unburnt forest (green).

Beginning in 1972, the United States launched a series of Landsat satellites designed to observe Earth's surface. Today, Landsat is just one of many different satellites used for this purpose. As a Landsat satellite orbits Earth, it collects and stores data about a strip of the surface that is 185 kilometers wide. The satellite relays the data back to a station on Earth, where computers use the data to create images. Landsat images show what covers the land surface—plants, soil, sand, rock, water, or snow and ice. Large, human-made features such as cities are also visible.

Scientists learn to identify specific features by the "signature," or combination of colors and shapes, that the feature makes on a satellite image. In a satellite image, areas covered by grass, trees, or crops are often shown as red, water as black or blue, and cities as bluish gray. Landsat images may show features such as grasslands, forests, and agricultural crops, as well as deserts, mountains, or cities.

Data From the Global Positioning System Today mapmakers can collect data for maps using the Global Positioning System, or GPS. The **Global Positioning System** is a method of finding latitude, longitude, and elevation of points on Earth's surface using a network of satellites. To learn more about GPS, look at the Technology and Society feature on pages 24 and 25.

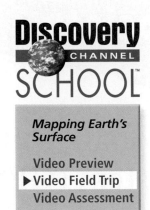

Mapping Earth's Surface
Video Preview
▶ Video Field Trip
Video Assessment

 **Reading Checkpoint** **What is a satellite image?**

Section 3 Assessment

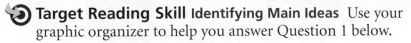

Target Reading Skill Identifying Main Ideas Use your graphic organizer to help you answer Question 1 below.

Reviewing Key Concepts

1. a. **Explaining** In what form is the information for a map stored on a computer?
   b. **Defining** What is digitizing?
   c. **Applying Concepts** What are the advantages of computer mapping?
2. a. **Reviewing** How do satellites gather data for a satellite image?
   b. **Explaining** In what form are data for a satellite image stored?
   c. **Summarizing** Summarize the process by which Landsat produces a satellite image of part of Earth's surface.

Lab zone **At-Home Activity**

Maps in the News Most of the maps that you see today in newspapers and magazines are made using computers. With family members, look through newspapers and news magazines. How many different types of maps can you find? Explain to your family the map's scale, symbols, and key. After you have studied the map, try to state the main point of the information shown on the map.

Global Positioning System (GPS)

Today, being lost could be a thing of the past for many people. Why? A system of satellites orbiting nearly 20,200 km above Earth can be used to pinpoint one's location anywhere on Earth as well as in the air.

Satellite
Each of two dozen GPS satellites continually sends out its current location and the exact time to receivers controlled by GPS users.

Location, Location, Location!

The Global Positioning System, or GPS, allows a user to locate his or her position anywhere on or above Earth to within a few meters or less. Hikers, drivers, boaters, and pilots use GPS to navigate. While its major use is navigation, GPS also has many scientific applications. Geologists use GPS to map some of the most rugged terrains on Earth. Points located with GPS can be entered into a computer and plotted to make maps. Archaeologists use GPS to map sites without disturbing ancient artifacts. Biologists can use the system to track threatened and endangered species.

Navigation
GPS systems aboard ships and boats have simplified navigation.

Keeping GPS on Track

GPS has become indispensable to surveyors and mappers, many types of scientists and engineers, and many ordinary people who need to know where they are. But like all technologies, GPS has limitations. To receive signals from GPS satellites, receivers need an unobstructed view of the sky. Dense forests and tall buildings can prevent the receivers from picking up signals.

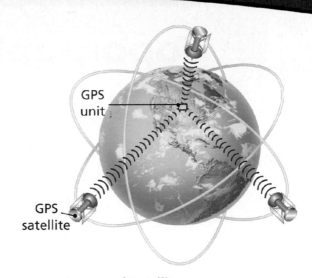

System of Satellites
At least three satellites must be above the horizon to pinpoint a location.

Receiver
GPS receivers are the size of a typical cellular phone. These devices receive and process satellite signals to determine the receiver's precise location.

Weigh the Impact

1. Identify the Need
Think about activities in which knowing one's precise location is important. Make a list of at least five activities.

2. Research
Research the activities you listed in Question 1 to find out if GPS has been applied to them.

3. Write
Choose one application of GPS mentioned in this feature. Or, propose an application of this guidance system that you think might be useful. Write one or two paragraphs to explain the application or how you think GPS might be applied to an activity.

For: More on GPS
Visit: PHSchool.com
Web Code: cfh-2010

Topographic Maps

Reading Preview

Key Concepts
- How do mapmakers represent elevation, relief, and slope?
- How do you read a topographic map?
- What are some uses of topographic maps?

Key Terms
- topographic map
- contour line
- contour interval
- index contour

Target Reading Skill

Using Prior Knowledge Before you read, write what you know about topographic maps in a graphic organizer like the one below. As you read, write what you learn.

What You Know
1. Some maps show where mountains and plains are.
2.

What You Learned
1.
2.

Discover Activity

Can a Map Show Relief?

1. Carefully cut the corners off 8 pieces of cardboard so that they look rounded. Each piece should be at least 1 centimeter smaller than the one before.
2. Trim the long sides of the two largest pieces so that the long sides appear wavy. Don't cut more than 0.5 centimeter into the cardboard.
3. Trace the largest cardboard piece on a sheet of paper.
4. Trace the next largest piece inside the tracing of the first. Don't let any lines cross.
5. Trace the other cardboard pieces, from largest to smallest, one inside the other, on the same paper.
6. Stack the cardboard pieces beside the paper in the same order they were traced. Compare the stack of cardboard pieces with your drawing. How are they alike? How are they different?

Think It Over
Making Models If the cardboard pieces are a model of a landform, what do the lines on the paper represent?

An orienteering meet is not an ordinary race. Participants compete to see how quickly they can find a series of locations called control points. The control points are scattered over a large park or state forest. Orienteers choose a set number of control points, and then visit the points in any order. In this sport, your ability to read a map and use a compass is often more important than how fast you can run. In a major meet, there may be several hundred orienteers on dozens of teams.

At the start of an orienteering meet, you would need to consult your map. But the maps used in orienteering are different from road maps or maps in an atlas—they're topographic maps.

FIGURE 14
Orienteering
Orienteering helps people develop the skill of using a map and compass.

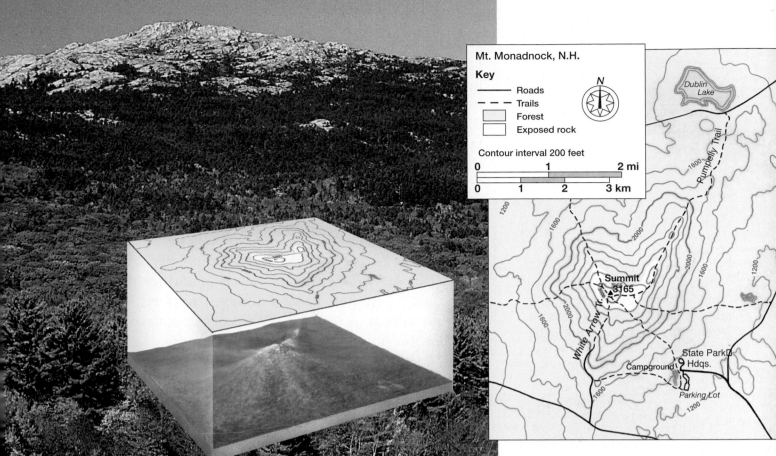

FIGURE 15
Contour Lines
The contour lines on a topographic map represent elevation and relief.
Comparing and Contrasting *What information does the topographic map provide that the photograph does not?*

Mapping Earth's Topography

A **topographic map** (tahp uh GRAF ik) is a map showing the surface features of an area. Topographic maps use symbols to portray the land as if you were looking down on it from above. Topographic maps provide highly accurate information on the elevation, relief, and slope of the ground surface.

Mapmakers use contour lines to represent elevation, relief, and slope on topographic maps. On a topographic map, a **contour line** connects points of equal elevation. In the United States, most topographic maps give contour intervals in feet rather than meters.

The change in elevation from contour line to contour line is called the **contour interval.** The contour interval for a given map is always the same. For example, the map in Figure 15 has a contour interval of 200 feet. If you start at one contour line and count up 10 contour lines, you have reached an elevation 2,000 feet above where you started. Usually, every fifth contour line, known as an index contour, is darker and heavier than the others. **Index contours** are labeled with the elevation in round units, such as 1,600 or 2,000 feet above sea level.

Go **Online**
active art

For: Topographic Map activity
Visit: PHSchool.com
Web Code: cfp-2014

Reading Checkpoint) **What do all the points connected by a contour line have in common?**

Reading a Topographic Map

Looking at a topographic map with many squiggly contour lines, you may feel as if you are gazing into a bowl of spaghetti. But with practice, you can learn to read a topographic map like the one in Figure 16. **To read a topographic map, you must familiarize yourself with the map's scale and symbols and interpret the map's contour lines.**

Scale Topographic maps are usually large-scale maps. Large-scale maps show a close-up view of part of Earth's surface. In the United States, many topographic maps are at a scale of 1 : 24,000, or 1 centimeter equals 0.24 kilometers. At this scale, a map can show the details of elevation and features such as rivers and coastlines. Large buildings, airports, and major highways appear as outlines at the correct scale. Symbols are used to show houses and other small features.

FIGURE 16
Topographic Map
The different types of symbols on topographic maps provide data on elevation, relief, slopes, and human-made features. This United States Geological Survey map shows part of Tennessee.

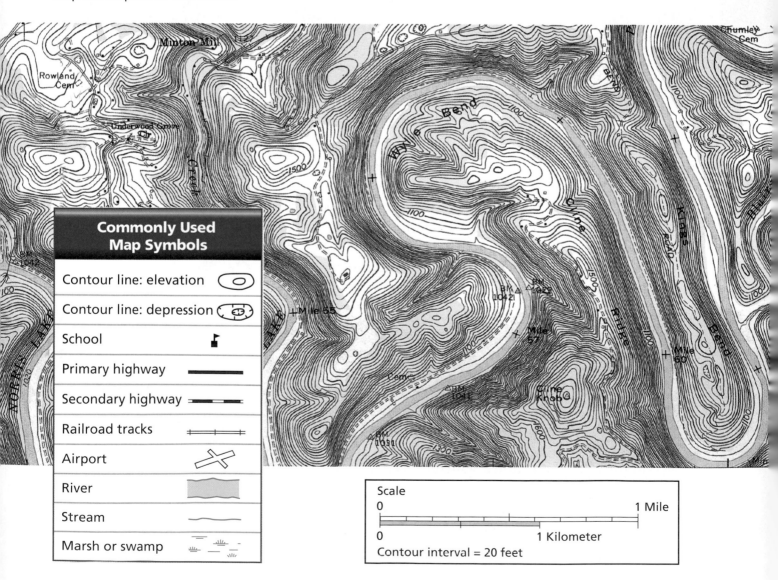

Commonly Used Map Symbols

Contour line: elevation	
Contour line: depression	
School	
Primary highway	
Secondary highway	
Railroad tracks	
Airport	
River	
Stream	
Marsh or swamp	

Scale
0 — 1 Mile
0 — 1 Kilometer
Contour interval = 20 feet

Mapping Elevation Data

The map shows the elevation data points on which the contour lines are based. Study the map and the map key, then answer the questions.

1. **Reading Maps** What is the contour interval on this map?

2. **Reading Maps** What color are the lowest points on the map? What range of elevations do these points represent?

3. **Reading Maps** What color are the highest points on the map?

4. **Applying Concepts** What is the elevation of the contour line labeled A?

5. **Inferring** Is the area between B and C a ridge or a valley? How can you tell?

6. **Interpreting Data** Describe how elevation changes along the trail from point D to point C.

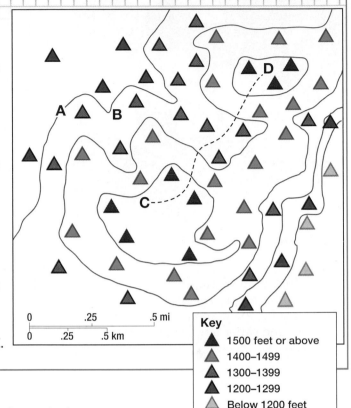

| 0 | .25 | .5 mi |
| 0 | .25 | .5 km |

Key

▲	1500 feet or above
▲	1400–1499
▲	1300–1399
▲	1200–1299
△	Below 1200 feet
—	Contour line
--	Trail

Contour interval = 100 feet

Symbols Mapmakers use a great variety of symbols on topographic maps. If you were drawing a map, what symbols would you use to represent a forest, a campground, an orchard, a swamp, or a school? Look at Figure 16 to see the symbols that are often used for these and other features.

Interpreting Contour Lines To find the elevation of a feature, begin at the labeled index contour, which is a heavier line than regular contour lines. Then, count the number of contour lines up or down to the feature.

Reading contour lines is the first step toward "seeing" an area's topography. Look at the topographic map in Figure 16. The closely spaced contour lines indicate steep slopes. The widely spaced contour lines indicate gentle slopes or relatively flat areas. A contour line that forms a closed loop with no other contour lines inside it indicates a hilltop. A closed loop with dashes inside indicates a depression, or hollow in the ground.

The shape of contour lines also help to show ridges and valleys. V-shaped contour lines pointing downhill indicate a ridge line. V-shaped contour lines pointing uphill indicate a valley. A stream in the valley flows toward the open end of the V.

 **Reading Checkpoint** How are hilltops and depressions represented using contour lines?

Lab zone Skills Activity

Interpreting Data
Study the topographic map in Figure 16. Where are the steepest slopes on the map found? How can you tell? What is the difference in elevation between the river and the top of Cline Knob?

Uses of Topographic Maps

Topographic maps have many uses in science and engineering, business, government, and everyday life. Suppose that you are an engineer planning a route for a highway over a mountain pass. Your design for the highway needs to solve several problems. To design a safe highway, you need a route that avoids the steepest slopes. To protect the area's water supply, the highway must stay a certain distance from rivers and lakes. You also want to find a route that avoids houses and other buildings. How would you solve these problems and find the best route for the highway? You would probably begin by studying topographic maps.

Businesses use topographic maps to help decide where to build new stores, housing, or factories. Local governments use them to decide where to build new schools and other public buildings. Topographic maps have recreational uses, too. If you were planning a bicycle trip, you could use a topographic map to see where your trip would be flat or hilly.

FIGURE 17
Using Topographic Maps
Topographic maps provide the data necessary for the planning of highways, bridges, and other large construction projects.

 **Reading Checkpoint** How do businesses use topographic maps?

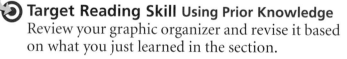

Section 4 Assessment

Target Reading Skill Using Prior Knowledge Review your graphic organizer and revise it based on what you just learned in the section.

Reviewing Key Concepts

1. **a. Defining** What is a topographic map?
   b. Explaining How do topographic maps represent elevation and relief?
   c. Calculating If the contour interval on a topographic map is 50 meters, how much difference in elevation do 12 contour lines represent?
2. **a. Reviewing** What do you need to know about a topographic map in order to read it?
   b. Comparing and Contrasting Compare the way steep slopes are represented on a topographic map with the way gentle slopes are represented.
   c. Inferring Reading a map, you see V-shaped contour lines that point uphill. What land feature would you find in this area?

3. **a. Listing** What are four main uses of topographic maps?
   b. Problem Solving Suppose that your community needs a large, flat site for a new athletic field. How could you use a topographic map of your area to identify possible sites?

Writing in Science

Giving Directions Write a descriptive paragraph of a simple route from one point on the map on page 28 to another point. Your paragraph should provide the starting point, but not the end point. Include details such as distance, compass direction, and topography along the route. Share your paragraph with classmates to see if they can follow your directions.

A Map in a Pan

Problem

How can you make a topographic map?

Skills Focus

making models, interpreting maps

Materials

- deep-sided pan
- water
- marking pencil
- modeling clay
- clear, hard sheet of plastic
- metric ruler
- sheet of unlined white paper
- food coloring

Procedure

1. Place a lump of clay on the bottom of a pan. Shape the clay into a model of a hill.

2. Pour colored water into the pan to a depth of 1 centimeter to represent sea level.

3. Place a sheet of hard, clear plastic over the container.

4. Trace the outline of the pan on the plastic sheet with a marking pencil. Then, looking straight down into the pan, trace the outline the water makes around the edges of the clay model. Remove the plastic sheet from the pan.

5. Add another centimeter of water to the pan, bringing the depth of the water to 2 centimeters. Replace the plastic sheet exactly as before, then trace the water level again.

6. Repeat Step 5 several times. Stop when the next addition of water would completely cover your model.

7. Remove the plastic sheet. Trace the outlines that you drew on the plastic sheet onto a sheet of paper.

Analyze and Conclude

1. **Interpreting Maps** Looking at your topographic map, how can you tell which parts of your model hill have a steep slope? A gentle slope?

2. **Interpreting Maps** How can you tell from the map which point on the hill is the highest?

3. **Interpreting Maps** Are there any ridges or valleys on your map?

4. **Applying Concepts** Is there any depression on your map where water would collect after it rained? What symbol should you use to identify this depression?

5. **Making Models** Compare your map with the clay landform. How are they alike? How are they different? How could you improve your map as a model of the landform?

More to Explore

Obtain a topographic map that includes an interesting landform such as a mountain, canyon, river valley, or coastline. After studying the contour lines on the map, make a sketch of what you think the landform looks like. Then build a scale model of the landform using clay or layers of cardboard or foamboard. How does your model landform compare with your sketch?

① Exploring Earth's Surface

Key Concepts

- The topography of an area includes the area's elevation, relief, and landforms.
- There are three main types of landforms: plains, mountains, and plateaus.

Key Terms
topography
elevation
relief
landform
plain
mountain
mountain range
plateau
landform region

② Models of Earth

Key Concepts

- Maps and globes are drawn to scale and use symbols to represent topography and other features on Earth's surface.
- Two of the lines that make up the grid, the equator and prime meridian, are the baselines for measuring distances on Earth's surface.
- The lines of latitude and longitude form a grid that can be used to find locations anywhere on Earth.
- Three common map projections are the Mercator projection, the equal-area projection, and the conic projection.

Key Terms
map
globe
scale
symbol
key
degree
equator
hemisphere
prime meridian
latitude
longitude
map projection

③ Maps and Computers

Key Concepts

- With computers, mapmakers can store, process, and display map data electronically.
- Computers produce maps using data from many sources, including satellites and the Global Positioning System.

Key Terms
surveying
digitizing
satellite image
pixel
Global Positioning System

④ Topographic Maps

Key Concepts

- Mapmakers use contour lines to represent elevation, relief, and slope on topographic maps.
- To read a topographic map, you must familiarize yourself with the map's scale and symbols and interpret the map's contour lines.
- Topographic maps have many uses in science and engineering, business, government, and everyday life.

Key Terms
topographic map
contour line
contour interval
index contour

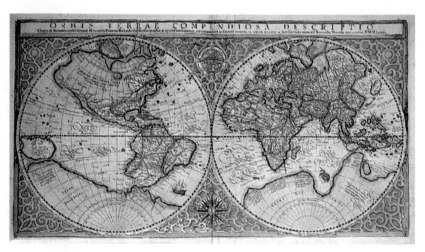

Review and Assessment

Organizing Information

Concept Mapping Copy the concept map. Then complete the map to show the characteristics of the different types of landforms. (For more about Concept Mapping, see the Skills Handbook.)

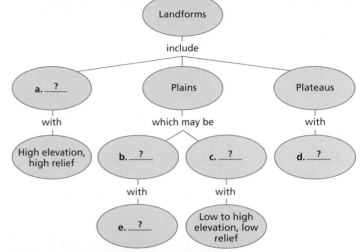

Reviewing Key Terms

Choose the letter of the best answer.

1. A landform that has high elevation but a mostly flat surface is a
   a. plain.   **b.** mountain.
   c. mountain range. **d.** plateau.

2. The equator divides Earth into two equal halves called
   a. globes.   **b.** hemispheres.
   c. degrees.   **d.** pixels.

3. Latitude is a measurement of distance north or south of the
   a. hemisphere.   **b.** equator.
   c. index contour. **d.** prime meridian.

4. To show Earth's curved surface on a flat map, mapmakers choose different
   a. map projections. **b.** globes.
   c. scales.   **d.** landform regions.

5. The digitized data on a computer map is made up of
   a. index contours.   **b.** pixels.
   c. contour intervals. **d.** symbols.

6. On a topographic map, relief is shown using
   a. lines of latitude. **b.** lines of longitude.
   c. map projections.   **d.** contour lines.

If the statement is true, write *true*. If it is false, change the underlined word or words to make the statement true.

7. <u>Relief</u> is a landform's height above sea level.

8. The <u>equator</u> is a half circle that extends from the North Pole to the South Pole.

9. If an airplane flew around Earth in a straight line from east to west, the airplane would cross lines of <u>longitude.</u>

10. An <u>index contour</u> is labeled to indicate the elevation along a contour line.

Writing in Science

Advertisement Suppose that you are a manufacturer of GPS tracking and mapping devices. Write an advertisement that describes as many uses for your device as you can think of.

DISCOVERY CHANNEL **SCHOOL**

Mapping Earth's Surface

Video Preview
Video Field Trip
▶ Video Assessment

Review and Assessment

Checking Concepts

11. Compare the elevation of a coastal plain to that of an interior plain.

12. What is a mountain range?

13. What do geologists call an area where there is mostly one kind of topography?

14. The South Island of New Zealand lies at about 170° E. What hemisphere is it in?

15. What is one advantage of a Mercator projection? What is one disadvantage?

16. What information does a map's contour interval provide?

17. How do the contour lines on a topographic map indicate the slope of the land?

Math Practice

18. **Scale and Ratios** Earth's diameter is about 13,000 kilometers. If a globe has a diameter of 0.5 meter, write the globe's scale as a ratio. What distance on Earth would 1 centimeter on the globe represent?

Thinking Critically

19. **Applying Concepts** Which would be more likely to show a shallow, 1.5-meter-deep depression in the ground: a 1-meter contour interval or a 5-meter contour interval?

20. **Interpreting Maps** Use the map below to answer the question. What is the latitude and longitude of Point A? In which two hemispheres is Point A located?

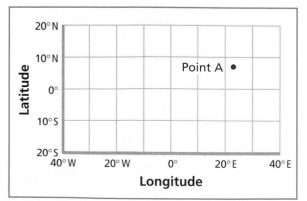

21. **Comparing and Contrasting** How would the colors in a satellite image of an area compare with those in a color photograph of the same area?

22. **Problem Solving** Describe one way in which you could use a topographic map of your community.

Applying Skills

Use the map below to answer Questions 23–25.

This map shows part of Acadia National Park in Maine. The contour interval is 20 feet.

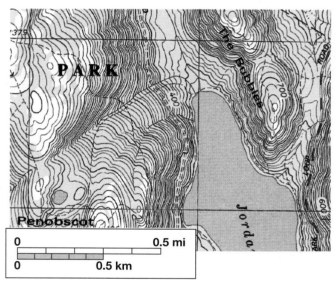

23. **Interpreting Maps** What is the elevation of the large lake? Which of the two Bubbles is higher?

24. **Calculating** Use the map scale to calculate the distance from the top of Penobscot Mountain to the large lake.

25. **Inferring** How can you tell whether the streams flow into or out of the large lake?

Lab zone Chapter **Project**

Performance Assessment Present your map to the class. What symbols did you use to represent the natural and physical features of your site? How did you measure and locate them on your map? How accurate is your map? Does your map give others a clear idea of what the land looks like?

⚖ Standardized Test Practice

Choose the letter of the best answer.

1. On a map, what is the height above sea level of a point on Earth's surface?
  A topography   **B** relief
  C elevation   **D** latitude

2. You are an engineer preparing to build a new highway exit. You will need to look at details of the area where the new exit will be located. Which map scale would it be best to use, in order to see the needed topographic details?
  A 1 centimeter = 0.25 kilometers
  B 1 centimeter = 10.0 kilometers
  C 1 centimeter = 5.0 kilometers
  D 1 centimeter = 2.5 kilometers

Use the map below and your knowledge of science to answer Questions 3–4.

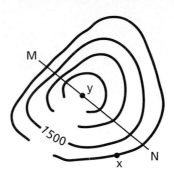

Contour interval = 15 meters

3. A topographic profile shows the shape or relief of the land along a given line. Along line M-N on the map, which of the following would the profile most closely resemble?

  A 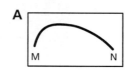   **B**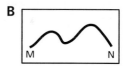

  C 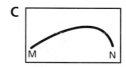   **D**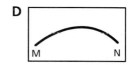

4. What is the elevation of the point marked *x* on the map?
  A 1400 meters   **B** 1500 meters
  C 1485 meters   **D** 1515 meters

5. How is longitude measured?
  A in degrees east or west of the prime meridian
  B in degrees east or west of the equator
  C in degrees north or south of the prime meridian
  D in kilometers east or west of the prime meridian

Open-Ended Question

6. Write a paragraph comparing a topographic map of an area with a satellite image of the same area. Assume that both are at the same scale. In your answer, explain how the topographic map and the satellite image are similar and how they are different.

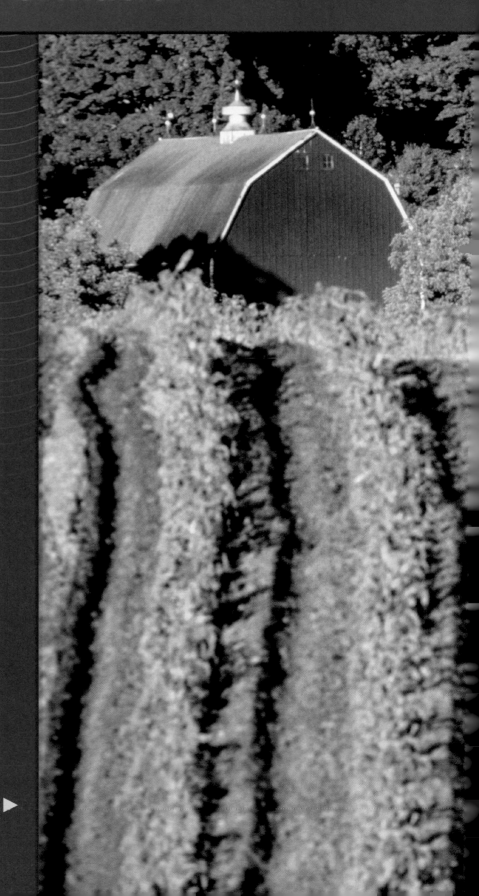

Chapter

13

Weathering and Soil Formation

The rich soil on this farm is a ► valuable natural resource.

Chapter **Project**

Lab zone™

Soils for Seeds

The process of weathering affects all rocks exposed on Earth's surface. Weathering breaks rock into smaller and smaller particles. When the rock particles mix with other ingredients, such as leaves, the mixture is called soil. In this project you will test how soil and other growing materials affect the growth of plants.

Your Goal To determine how soil composition affects the growth of bean seeds

To complete this project, you must

- compare the particle size, shape, and composition of different growing materials
- compare how bean seeds grow in several different growing materials
- determine what type of soil or growing material is best for young bean plants
- follow the safety guidelines in Appendix A

Plan It! In a group, brainstorm what types of soil and other growing materials you will use in your experiment. What are the different variables that affect the growth of plants? How will you measure the growth of your bean plants? Plan your experiment and obtain your teacher's approval. As you carry out your experiment, observe and record the growth of your plants. Then present your results to your class.

Rocks and Weathering

Reading Preview

Key Concepts
- How do weathering and erosion affect Earth's surface?
- What are the causes of mechanical weathering and chemical weathering?
- What determines how fast weathering occurs?

Key Terms
- weathering
- erosion
- uniformitarianism
- mechanical weathering
- abrasion
- ice wedging
- chemical weathering
- oxidation
- permeable

Target Reading Skill

Relating Cause and Effect A cause makes something happen. An effect is what happens. As you read, identify the causes of chemical weathering. Write them in a graphic organizer like the one below.

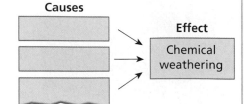

Causes

Effect

Chemical weathering

Lab zone Discover **Activity**

How Fast Can It Fizz?

1. Place a fizzing antacid tablet in a small beaker. Then grind up a second tablet and place it in another beaker. The whole tablet is a model of solid rock. The ground-up tablet is a model of rock fragments.

2. Add 100 mL of warm water to the beaker containing the whole tablet. Then stir with a stirring rod until the tablet dissolves completely. Use a stopwatch to time how long it takes.

3. Add 100 mL of warm water to the beaker containing the ground-up tablet. Then stir until all of the ground-up tablet dissolves. Time how long it takes.

Think It Over
Drawing Conclusions Which dissolved faster, the whole antacid tablet or the ground-up tablet? What variable affected how long it took each of them to dissolve?

Imagine a hike that lasts for months and covers hundreds of kilometers. Each year, many hikers go on such treks. They hike trails that run the length of America's great mountain ranges. For example, the John Muir Trail follows the Sierra Nevada mountains. The Sierras extend about 640 kilometers along the eastern side of California. In the east, the Appalachian Trail follows the Appalachian Mountains. The Appalachians stretch more than 3,000 kilometers from Alabama to Canada.

The two trails cross very different landscapes. The Sierras are rocky and steep, with many peaks rising 3,000 meters above sea level. The Appalachians are more rounded and gently sloping, and are covered with soil and plants. The highest peaks in the Appalachians are less than half the elevation of the highest peaks in the Sierras. Which mountain range do you think is older? The Appalachians formed more than 250 million years ago. The Sierras formed only within the last 10 million years. The forces that wear down rock on Earth's surface have had much longer to grind down the Appalachians.

Weathering and Erosion

The process of mountain building thrusts rock up to the surface of Earth. There, the rock is exposed to weathering. **Weathering** is the process that breaks down rock and other substances at Earth's surface. Heat, cold, water, and ice all contribute to weathering. So do the oxygen and carbon dioxide in the atmosphere. Repeated freezing and thawing, for example, can crack rock apart into smaller pieces. Rainwater can dissolve minerals that bind rock together. You don't need to go to the mountains to see examples of weathering. The forces that wear down mountains also cause bicycles to rust, paint to peel, sidewalks to crack, and potholes to form.

The forces of weathering break rocks into smaller and smaller pieces. Then the forces of erosion carry the pieces away. **Erosion** (ee ROH zhun) is the removal of rock particles by wind, water, ice, or gravity. **Weathering and erosion work together continuously to wear down and carry away the rocks at Earth's surface.** The weathering and erosion that geologists observe today also shaped Earth's surface millions of years ago. How do geologists know this? Geologists make inferences based on the principle of **uniformitarianism** (yoon uh fawrm uh TAYR ee un iz um). This principle states that the same processes that operate today operated in the past.

There are two kinds of weathering: mechanical weathering and chemical weathering. Both types of weathering act slowly, but over time they break down even the biggest, hardest rocks.

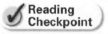 **Reading Checkpoint** What is the difference between weathering and erosion?

FIGURE 1
Effects of Weathering
The jagged peaks of the Sierra Nevadas (bottom) formed within the last 10 million years. The more gently sloping Appalachians (top) have been exposed to weathering for 250 million years.
Inferring *How can you tell that the Sierra Nevadas formed much more recently than the Appalachians?*

FIGURE 2
Forces of Mechanical Weathering

Mechanical weathering affects all the rock on Earth's surface.

Forming Operational Definitions *Study the examples of mechanical weathering, then write a definition of each term in your own words.*

Freezing and Thawing
When water freezes in a crack in a rock, it expands and makes the crack bigger. The process of ice wedging also widens cracks in sidewalks and causes potholes in streets.

Ice

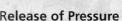

Release of Pressure
As erosion removes material from the surface of a mass of rock, pressure on the rock is reduced. This release of pressure causes the outside of the rock to crack and flake off like the layers of an onion.

Animal Actions
Animals that burrow in the ground—including moles, gophers, prairie dogs, and some insects—loosen and break apart rocks in the soil.

Mechanical Weathering

If you hit a rock with a hammer, the rock may break into pieces. Like a hammer, some forces of weathering break rock into pieces. The type of weathering in which rock is physically broken into smaller pieces is called **mechanical weathering.** These smaller pieces of rock have the same composition as the rock they came from. If you have seen rocks that arc cracked or split in layers, then you have seen rocks that are undergoing mechanical weathering. Mechanical weathering works slowly. But over very long periods of time, it does more than wear down rocks. Mechanical weathering eventually wears away whole mountains.

Abrasion
Sand and other rock particles that are carried by wind, water, or ice can wear away exposed rock surfaces like sandpaper on wood. Wind-driven sand helped shape the rocks shown here.

Plant Growth
Roots of trees and other plants enter cracks in rocks. As roots grow, they force the cracks farther apart. Over time, the roots of even small plants can pry apart cracked rocks.

The causes of mechanical weathering include freezing and thawing, release of pressure, plant growth, actions of animals, and abrasion. The term **abrasion** (uh BRAY zhun) refers to the grinding away of rock by rock particles carried by water, ice, wind, or gravity.

In cool climates, the most important force of mechanical weathering is the freezing and thawing of water. Water seeps into cracks in rocks and then freezes when the temperature drops. Water expands when it freezes. Ice therefore acts like a wedge that forces things apart. Wedges of ice in rocks widen and deepen cracks. This process is called **ice wedging.** When the ice melts, the water seeps deeper into the cracks. With repeated freezing and thawing, the cracks slowly expand until pieces of rock break off.

 **Reading Checkpoint** How does ice wedging weather rock?

Go Online
PHSchool.com

For: More on weathering
Visit: PHSchool.com
Web Code: cfd-2021

Chemical Weathering

In addition to mechanical weathering, another type of weathering attacks rock. **Chemical weathering** is the process that breaks down rock through chemical changes. **The causes of chemical weathering include the action of water, oxygen, carbon dioxide, living organisms, and acid rain.**

Each rock is made up of one or more minerals. Chemical weathering can produce new minerals as it breaks down rock. For example, granite is made up of several minerals, including feldspar, quartz, and mica. As a result of chemical weathering, granite eventually changes the feldspar minerals to clay minerals.

Chemical weathering creates holes or soft spots in rock, so the rock breaks apart more easily. Chemical and mechanical weathering often work together. As mechanical weathering breaks rock into pieces, more surface area becomes exposed to chemical weathering. The Discover activity at the beginning of this section shows how increasing the surface area increases the rate of a chemical reaction.

FIGURE 3

Weathering and Surface Area
As weathering breaks apart rock, the surface area exposed to weathering increases. The total volume of the rock stays the same even though the rock is broken into smaller and smaller pieces.
Predicting *What will happen to the surface area if each cube is again divided into four cubes?*

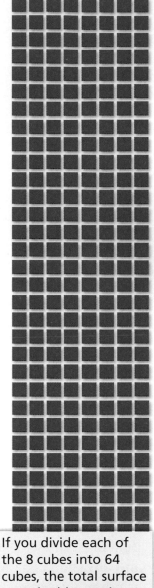

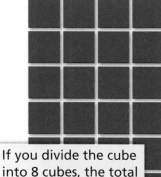

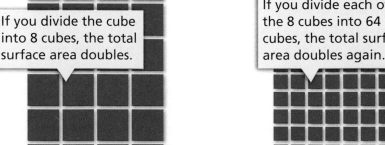

The surface area of a cube is equal to 6 times the area of each side.

If you divide the cube into 8 cubes, the total surface area doubles.

If you divide each of the 8 cubes into 64 cubes, the total surface area doubles again.

FIGURE 4
Effects of Chemical Weathering
Acid rain chemically weathered these stone gargoyles on the cathedral of Notre Dame in Paris, France.

Water Water is the most important cause of chemical weathering. Water weathers rock by dissolving it. When a rock or other substance dissolves in water, it mixes uniformly throughout the water to make a solution. Over time, many rocks will dissolve in water.

Oxygen The oxygen gas in air is an important cause of chemical weathering. If you have ever left a bicycle or metal tool outside in the rain, then you have seen how oxygen can weather iron. Iron combines with oxygen in the presence of water in a process called **oxidation.** The product of oxidation is rust. Rock that contains iron also oxidizes, or rusts. Rust makes rock soft and crumbly and gives it a red or brown color.

Carbon Dioxide Another gas found in air, carbon dioxide, also causes chemical weathering. Carbon dioxide dissolves in rainwater and in water that sinks through air pockets in the soil. The result is a weak acid called carbonic acid. Carbonic acid easily weathers rocks such as marble and limestone.

Living Organisms Imagine a seed landing on a rock face. As it sprouts, its roots push into cracks in the rock. As the plant's roots grow, they produce weak acids that slowly dissolve rock around the roots. Lichens—plantlike organisms that grow on rocks—also produce weak acids that chemically weather rock.

Acid Rain Over the past 150 years, people have been burning large amounts of coal, oil, and gas for energy. Burning these fuels can pollute the air with sulfur, carbon, and nitrogen compounds. Such compounds react chemically with the water vapor in clouds, forming acids. These acids mix with raindrops and fall as acid rain. Acid rain causes very rapid chemical weathering.

 **Reading Checkpoint** How can plants cause chemical weathering?

Lab zone Try This Activity

Rusting Away
Here's how you can observe weathering.

1. Moisten some steel wool and place it in a closed container so it will not dry out.

2. Observe the steel wool after a few days. What has happened to it?

3. Take a new piece of steel wool and squeeze it between your fingers. Remove the steel wool from the container and squeeze it between your fingers. What happens? Wash your hands when you have finished.

Predicting If you kept the steel wool moist for a longer time, what would eventually happen to it? How is the weathering of steel wool like the weathering of a rock?

Which Weathered Faster?

The graph shows the rate of weathering for two identical pieces of limestone that weathered in different locations.

1. **Reading Graphs** What does the *x*-axis of the graph represent?

2. **Reading Graphs** What does the *y*-axis of the graph represent?

3. **Reading Graphs** How much thickness did Stone A lose in 1,000 years? How much thickness did Stone B lose in the same period?

4. **Drawing Conclusions** Which stone weathered at a faster rate?

5. **Inferring** Since the two identical pieces of limestone weathered at different rates, what can you infer caused the difference in their rates of weathering?

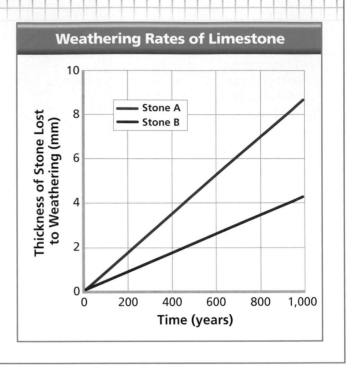

Weathering Rates of Limestone

Stone A
Stone B

Thickness of Stone Lost to Weathering (mm)

Time (years)

Rate of Weathering

Visitors to New England's historic cemeteries may notice a surprising fact. Slate tombstones carved in the 1700s are less weathered and easier to read than marble gravestones from the 1800s. Why is this so? Some kinds of rocks weather more rapidly than others. **The most important factors that determine the rate at which weathering occurs are the type of rock and the climate.**

Type of Rock The minerals that make up the rock determine how fast it weathers. Rock made of minerals that do not dissolve easily in water weathers slowly. Rock made of minerals that dissolve easily in water weathers faster.

Some rock weathers more easily because it is permeable. **Permeable** (PUR mee uh bul) means that a material is full of tiny, connected air spaces that allow water to seep through it. Permeable rock weathers chemically at a fast rate. Why? As water seeps through the spaces in the rock, it dissolves and removes material broken down by weathering.

Climate Climate refers to the average weather conditions in an area. Both chemical and mechanical weathering occur faster in wet climates. Rainfall provides the water needed for chemical changes as well as for freezing and thawing.

Granite

Marble

Chemical reactions occur faster at higher temperatures. That is why chemical weathering occurs more quickly where the climate is both hot and wet. Granite, for example, is a very hard rock that forms when molten material cools inside Earth. Granite weathers so slowly in cool climates that it is often used as a building stone. But in hot and wet climates, granite weathers more rapidly and eventually crumbles apart.

 **Reading Checkpoint** **How does rainfall affect the rate of weathering?**

FIGURE 5
Which Rock Weathers Faster?
These two tombstones are about the same age and are in the same cemetery, yet one has weathered much less than the other.
Inferring *Which type of stone weathers faster, granite or marble? Explain.*

Section 1 Assessment

Target Reading Skill **Relating Cause and Effect** Refer to your graphic organizer about the causes of chemical weathering to help you answer Question 2 below.

Reviewing Key Concepts

1. **a. Defining** What is weathering?
   b. Defining What is erosion?
   c. Predicting Over millions of years, how do weathering and erosion change a mountain made of solid rock?
2. **a. Defining** What is chemical weathering?
   b. Comparing and Contrasting Compare and contrast mechanical weathering and chemical weathering.
   c. Classifying Classify each as chemical or mechanical weathering: freezing or thawing, oxidation, water dissolving chemicals in rock, abrasion, acid rain.
3. **a. Identifying** What are two factors that affect the rate of weathering?
   b. Relating Cause and Effect A granite monument is placed outside for 200 years in a region with a cool, dry climate. What would its rate of weathering be? Explain.

Lab zone **At-Home Activity**

Ice in a Straw Demonstrate one type of weathering for your family. Plug one end of a drinking straw with a small piece of clay. Fill the straw with water. Now plug the top of the straw with clay. Make sure that the clay plugs do not leak. Lay the straw flat in the freezer overnight. Remove the straw the next day. What happened to the clay plugs? What process produced this result? Be sure to dispose of the straw so that no one will use it for drinking.

Rock Shake

Problem

How will shaking and acid conditions affect the rate at which limestone weathers?

Skills Focus

interpreting data, calculating, drawing conclusions

Materials

- 300 mL of water
- balance
- paper towels
- masking tape
- 2 pieces of thin cloth
- marking pen or pencil
- 300 mL of vinegar, an acid
- plastic graduated cylinder, 250 mL
- 80 small pieces of water-soaked limestone
- 4 watertight plastic containers with screw-on caps, 500 mL

Procedure

PART 1 Day 1

1. Using masking tape, label the four 500-mL containers A, B, C, and D.

2. Separate the 80 pieces of limestone into four sets of 20.

3. Copy the data table in your notebook. Then place the first 20 pieces of limestone on the balance and record their mass in the data table. Place the rocks in container A.

4. Repeat Step 3 for the other sets of rocks and place them in containers B, C, and D.

5. Pour 150 mL of water into container A and container B. Put caps on both containers.

6. Pour 150 mL of vinegar into container C and container D. Put caps on both containers.

7. Predict the effect of weathering on the mass of the limestone pieces. Which will weather more: the limestone in water or the limestone in vinegar? (*Hint:* Vinegar is an acid.) Also predict the effect of shaking on the limestone in containers B and D. Record your predictions in your notebook.

8. Allow the pieces to soak overnight.

Data Table				
Container	Total Mass at Start	Total Mass Next Day	Change in Mass	Percent Change in Mass
A (water, no shaking)				
B (water, shaking)				
C (vinegar, no shaking)				
D (vinegar, shaking)				

PART 2 Day 2

9. Screw the caps tightly on containers B and D. Shake both containers for 10 to 15 minutes. Make sure that each container is shaken for exactly the same amount of time and at the same intensity. After shaking, set the containers aside. Do not shake containers A and C.

10. Open the top of container A. Place one piece of thin cloth over the opening of the container. Carefully pour all of the water out through the cloth into a waste container. Be careful not to let any of the pieces flow out with the water. Dry these pieces carefully and record their mass in your data table.

11. Next, determine how much limestone was lost through weathering in container A. (*Hint*: Subtract the mass of the limestone pieces remaining on Day 2 from the mass of the pieces on Day 1.)

12. Repeat Steps 10 and 11 for containers B, C, and D.

Analyze and Conclude

1. **Calculating** Calculate the percent change in mass of the 20 pieces for each container.

$$\% \text{ change} = \frac{\text{Change in mass} \times 100}{\text{Total mass at start}}$$

Record the results in the data table.

2. **Interpreting Data** Do your data show a change in mass of the 20 pieces in each of the four containers?

3. **Interpreting Data** Is there a greater change in total mass for the pieces in one container than for the pieces in another? Explain.

4. **Drawing Conclusions** How correct were your predictions of how shaking and acid would affect the weathering of limestone? Explain.

5. **Developing Hypotheses** If your data showed a greater change in the mass of the pieces in one of the containers, how might this change be explained?

6. **Drawing Conclusions** Based on your data, which variable do you think was more responsible for breaking down the limestone: the vinegar or the shaking? Explain.

7. **Communicating** Write a paragraph that explains why you allowed two of the containers to stand without shaking, and why you were careful to shake the other two containers for the same amount of time.

Design an Experiment

Would your results for this experiment change if you changed the variables? For example, you could soak or shake the pieces for a longer time, or test rocks other than limestone. You could also test whether adding more limestone pieces (30 rather than 20 in each set) would make a difference in the outcome. Design an experiment on the rate of weathering to test the effects of changing one of these variables. *Have your teacher approve your plan before you begin.*

How Soil Forms

Reading Preview

Key Concepts
- What is soil made of and how does it form?
- How do scientists classify soils?
- What is the role of plants and animals in soil formation?

Key Terms
- soil
- bedrock
- humus
- fertility
- loam
- soil horizon
- topsoil
- subsoil
- litter
- decomposer

Target Reading Skill
Building Vocabulary A definition states the meaning of a word or phrase by telling about its most important feature or function. Carefully read the definition of each Key Term and also read the neighboring sentences. Then write a definition of each Key Term in your own words.

Lab zone Discover **Activity**

What Is Soil?
1. Use a toothpick to separate a sample of soil into individual particles. With a hand lens, try to identify the different types of particles in the sample. Wash your hands when you are finished.
2. Write a "recipe" for the sample of soil, naming each of the "ingredients" that you think the soil contains. Include what percentage of each ingredient would be needed to make up the soil.
3. Compare your recipe with those of your classmates.

Think It Over
Forming Operational Definitions Based on your observations, how would you define *soil*?

A bare rock surface does not look like a spot where a plant could grow. But look more closely. In that hard surface is a small crack. Over many years, mechanical and chemical weathering will slowly enlarge the crack. Rain and wind will bring bits of weathered rock, dust, and dry leaves. The wind also may carry tiny seeds. With enough moisture, a seed will sprout and take root. Then, a few months later, the plant blossoms.

What Is Soil?

The crack in the rock seems to have little in common with a flower garden containing thick, rich soil. But soil is what the weathered rock and other materials in the crack have started to become. **Soil** is the loose, weathered material on Earth's surface in which plants can grow.

One of the main ingredients of soil comes from bedrock. **Bedrock** is the solid layer of rock beneath the soil. Once exposed at the surface, bedrock gradually weathers into smaller and smaller particles that are the basic material of soil.

Soil Composition Soil is more than just particles of weathered bedrock. **Soil is a mixture of rock particles, minerals, decayed organic material, water, and air.** Together, sand, silt, and clay make up the portion of soil that comes from weathered rock.

The decayed organic material in soil is called humus. **Humus** (HYOO mus) is a dark-colored substance that forms as plant and animal remains decay. Humus helps create spaces in soil for the air and water that plants must have. Humus also contains substances called nutrients, including nitrogen, sulfur, phosphorus, and potassium. Plants need nutrients in order to grow. As plants grow, they absorb nutrients from the soil.

Fertile soil is rich in the nutrients that plants need to grow. The **fertility** of soil is a measure of how well the soil supports plant growth. Soil that is rich in humus has high fertility. Sandy soil containing little humus has low fertility.

Soil Texture Sand feels coarse and grainy, but clay feels smooth and silky. These differences are differences in texture. Soil texture depends on the size of individual soil particles.

The particles of rock in soil are classified by size. As you can see in Figure 7, the largest soil particles are gravel. The smallest soil particles are clay. Clay particles are smaller than the period at the end of this sentence.

Soil texture is important for plant growth. Soil that is mostly clay has a dense, heavy texture. Some clay soils hold a lot of water, so plants grown in them may "drown" for lack of air. In contrast, sandy soil has a coarse texture. Water quickly drains through it, so plants may die for lack of water.

Soil that is made up of about equal parts of clay, sand, and silt is called **loam.** It has a crumbly texture that holds both air and water. Loam is best for growing most types of plants.

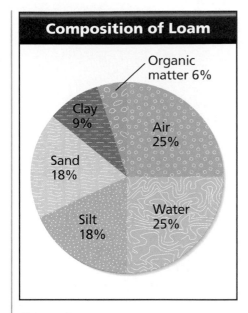

Composition of Loam

Organic matter 6%
Clay 9%
Air 25%
Sand 18%
Silt 18%
Water 25%

FIGURE 6
Loam, a type of soil, is made up of air, water, and organic matter as well as materials from weathered rock. **Interpreting Graphs** *What two materials make up the major portion of this soil?*

FIGURE 7
Soil particles range in size from gravel to clay particles too small to be seen by the unaided eye. The sand, silt, and clay shown here have been enlarged.

Soil Particle Size

Clay	Silt	Sand	Gravel
Less than $\frac{1}{256}$ mm	Less than $\frac{1}{16}$ mm	Less than 2 mm	2 mm and larger

The Process of Soil Formation

Soil forms as rock is broken down by weathering and mixes with other materials on the surface. Soil is constantly being formed wherever bedrock is exposed. Soil formation continues over a long period of time.

Gradually, soil develops layers called horizons. A **soil horizon** is a layer of soil that differs in color and texture from the layers above or below it.

If you dug a hole in the ground about half a meter deep, you would see the different soil horizons. Figure 8 shows how soil scientists classify the soil into three horizons. The A horizon is made up of **topsoil,** a crumbly, dark brown soil that is a mixture of humus, clay, and other minerals. The B horizon, often called **subsoil,** usually consists of clay and other particles washed down from the A horizon, but little humus. The C horizon contains only partly weathered rock.

The rate at which soil forms depends on the climate and type of rock. Remember that weathering occurs most rapidly in areas with a warm, rainy climate. As a result, soil develops more quickly in these areas. In contrast, weathering and soil formation take place slowly in areas where the climate is cold and dry.

Some types of rock weather and form soil faster than others. For example, limestone, a type of rock formed from the shells and skeletons of once-living things, weathers faster than granite. Thus, soil forms more quickly from limestone than from granite.

Go Online
active art

For: Soil Layers activity
Visit: PHSchool.com
Web Code: cfp-2022

FIGURE 8
Soil Layers
Soil horizons form in three steps.
Inferring *Which soil horizon is responsible for soil's fertility? Explain.*

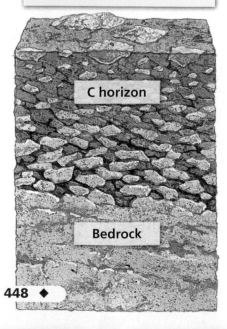

❶ The C horizon forms as bedrock weathers and rock breaks up into soil particles.

C horizon

Bedrock

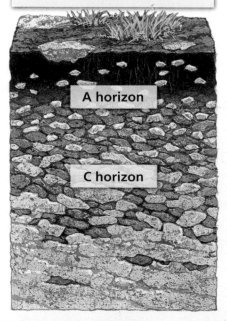

❷ The A horizon develops as plants add organic material to the soil and plant roots weather pieces of rock.

A horizon

C horizon

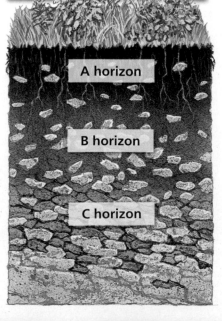

❸ The B horizon develops as rainwater washes clay and minerals from the A horizon to the B horizon.

A horizon

B horizon

C horizon

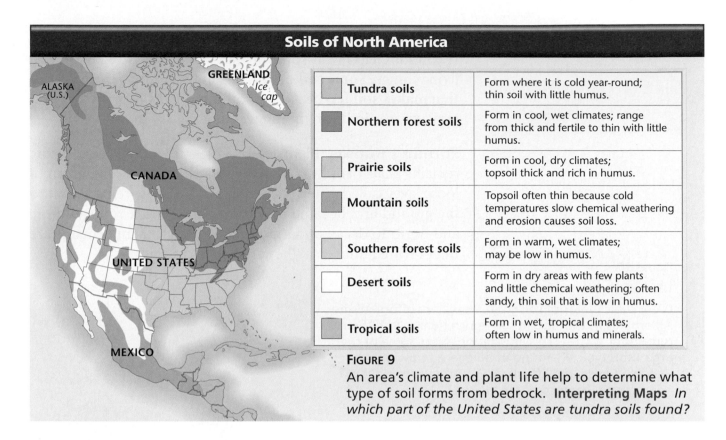

Soils of North America

	Tundra soils	Form where it is cold year-round; thin soil with little humus.
	Northern forest soils	Form in cool, wet climates; range from thick and fertile to thin with little humus.
	Prairie soils	Form in cool, dry climates; topsoil thick and rich in humus.
	Mountain soils	Topsoil often thin because cold temperatures slow chemical weathering and erosion causes soil loss.
	Southern forest soils	Form in warm, wet climates; may be low in humus.
	Desert soils	Form in dry areas with few plants and little chemical weathering; often sandy, thin soil that is low in humus.
	Tropical soils	Form in wet, tropical climates; often low in humus and minerals.

FIGURE 9
An area's climate and plant life help to determine what type of soil forms from bedrock. **Interpreting Maps** *In which part of the United States are tundra soils found?*

Soil Types

If you were traveling across the hills of north-central Georgia, you would see soils that seem to be made of red clay. In other parts of the country, soils can be black, brown, yellow, or gray. In the United States alone, there are thousands of different types of soil.

Scientists classify the different types of soil into major groups based on climate, plants, and soil composition. Fertile soil can form in regions with hot, wet climates, but rain may wash humus and minerals out of the A horizon. In mountains and polar regions with cold, dry climates, the soil is often very thin. The thickest, most fertile soil forms in climate regions with moderate temperatures and rainfall.

The most common plants found in a region are also used to help classify the soil. For example, grassland soils are very different from forest soils. In addition, scientists classify soil by its composition—whether it is rocky, sandy, or rich in clay. Other factors in the classification of soil include the type of bedrock and the amount of time the soil has been developing.

Major soil types found in North America include forest, prairie, desert, mountain, tundra, and tropical soils. Look at Figure 9 to see where each of the major soil types is found.

 **Reading Checkpoint** What major soil types are found in North America?

Lab zone Try This Activity

A Square Meter of Soil

1. Outdoors, measure an area of one square meter. Mark your square with string.
2. Observe the color and texture of the soil at the surface and a few centimeters below the surface. Is it dry or moist? Does it contain sand, clay, or gravel? Are there plants, animals, or humus?
3. When you finish, leave the soil as you found it. Wash your hands.

Drawing Conclusions What can you conclude about the soil's fertility? Explain.

Living Organisms in Soil

If you look closely at soil, you can see that it is teeming with living things. **Some soil organisms make humus, the material that makes soil fertile. Other soil organisms mix the soil and make spaces in it for air and water.**

Forming Humus Plants contribute most of the organic remains that form humus. As plants shed leaves, they form a loose layer called **litter.** When plants die, their remains fall to the ground and become part of the litter. Plant roots also die and begin to decay underground. Although plant remains are full of stored nutrients, they are not yet humus.

FIGURE 10
Life in Soil

Every cubic meter of soil contains billions of organisms. All organisms that live in soil enrich humus with their remains or wastes. This illustration shows some of the organisms typically found in northern forest soil.
Relating Cause and Effect *Which organisms in the art help air and water to enter the soil?*

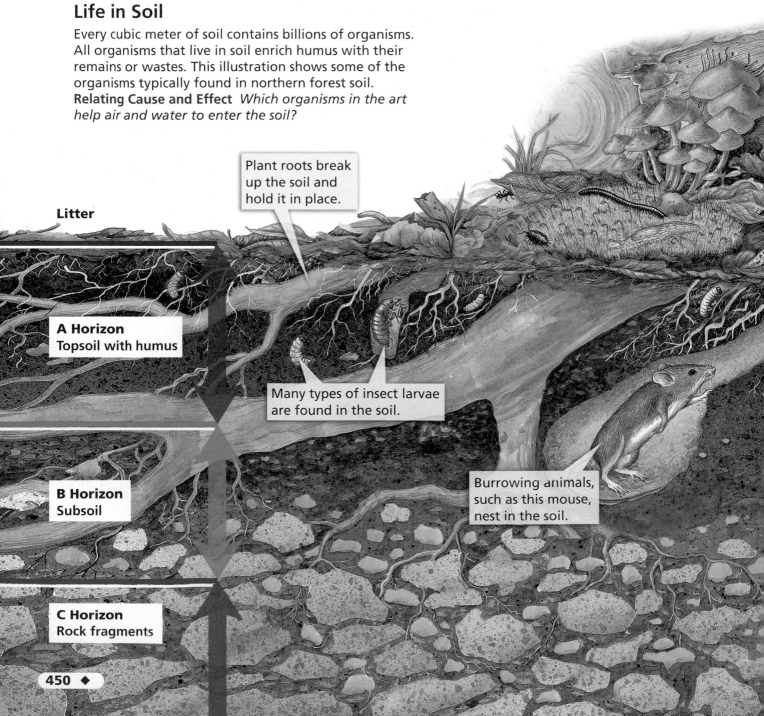

Plant roots break up the soil and hold it in place.

Litter

A Horizon
Topsoil with humus

Many types of insect larvae are found in the soil.

Burrowing animals, such as this mouse, nest in the soil.

B Horizon
Subsoil

C Horizon
Rock fragments

Humus forms in a process called decomposition. During decomposition, organisms that live in soil turn dead organic material into humus. These organisms are called decomposers. **Decomposers** are the organisms that break the remains of dead organisms into smaller pieces and digest them with chemicals.

Soil decomposers include fungi, bacteria, worms, and other organisms. Fungi are organisms such as molds and mushrooms. Fungi grow on, and digest, plant remains. Bacteria are microscopic decomposers that cause decay. Bacteria attack dead organisms and their wastes in soil. Very small animals, such as mites and worms, also decompose dead organic material and mix it with the soil.

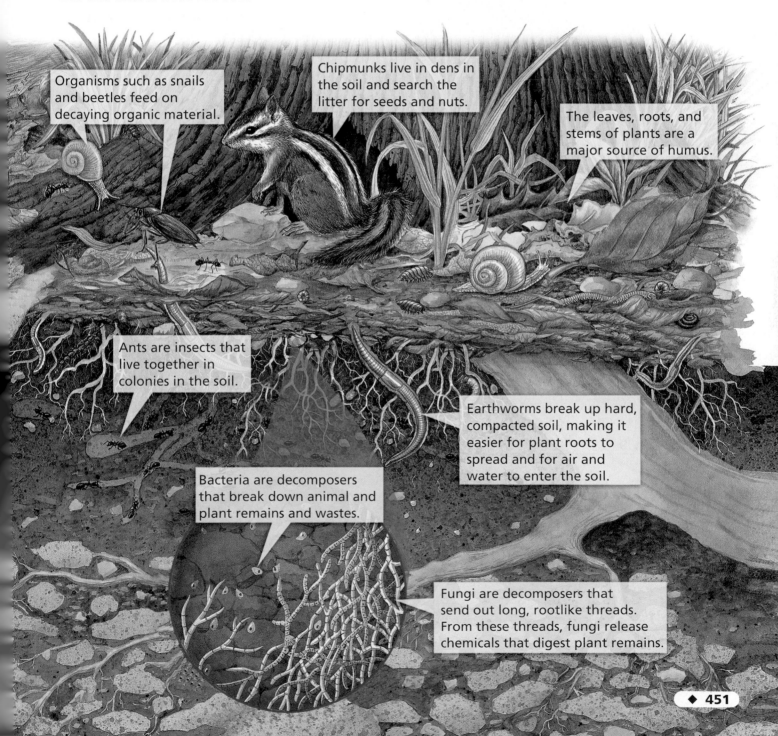

FIGURE 11
Soil Mixers
Earthworms break up the soil, allowing in air and water. An earthworm eats its own weight in soil every day. **Predicting** *How fertile is soil that contains many earthworms likely to be? Explain.*

Mixing the Soil Earthworms do most of the work of mixing humus with other materials in soil. As earthworms eat their way through the soil, they carry humus down to the subsoil and subsoil up to the surface. Earthworms also pass out the soil they eat as waste. The waste soil is enriched with substances that plants need to grow, such as nitrogen.

Many burrowing mammals such as mice, moles, prairie dogs, and gophers break up hard, compacted soil and mix humus through it. These animals also add nitrogen to the soil when they produce waste. They add organic material when they die and decay.

Earthworms and burrowing animals also help to aerate, or mix air into, the soil. Plant roots need the oxygen that this process adds to the soil.

 **Reading Checkpoint** Which animals are most important in mixing humus into the soil?

Section 2 Assessment

Target Reading Skill

Building Vocabulary Use your definitions to help you answer the questions below.

Reviewing Key Concepts

1. a. Describing What five materials make up soil?
   b. Explaining How do soil horizons form?
   c. Sequencing Place these terms in the correct order starting from the surface: C horizon, subsoil, bedrock, topsoil.
2. a. Reviewing What are three main factors used to classify soils?
   b. Interpreting Maps Soil forms more rapidly in warm, wet areas than in cold, dry areas. Study the map in Figure 9. Which soil type on the map would you expect to form most slowly? Explain.

3. a. Identifying What are two main ways in which soil organisms contribute to soil formation?
   b. Describing Give examples of three types of decomposers and describe their effects on soil.
   c. Predicting What would happen to the fertility of a soil if all decomposers were removed? Explain.

Writing in Science

Product Label Write a product label for a bag of topsoil. Your label should give the soil a name that will make consumers want to buy it, state how and where the soil formed, give its composition, and suggest how it can be used.

Consumer Lab

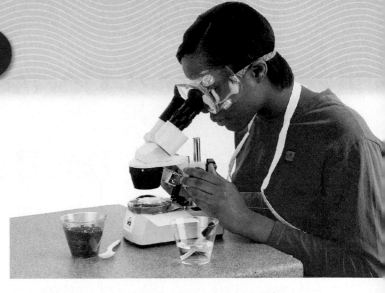

Comparing Soils

Problem

What are the characteristics of two samples of soil?

Skills Focus

observing, inferring, developing hypotheses

Materials

- 20–30 grams of local soil
- 20–30 grams of bagged topsoil
- plastic spoon • plastic dropper • toothpick
- water • stereomicroscope
- plastic petri dish or jar lid
- graph paper ruled with 1- or 2-mm spacing

Procedure

1. Obtain a sample of local soil. As you observe the sample, record your observations in your lab notebook.

2. Spread half of the sample on the graph paper. Spread the soil thinly so that you can see the lines on the paper through the soil. Using the graph paper as a background, estimate the sizes of the particles that make up the soil.

3. Place the rest of the sample in the palm of your hand, rub it between your fingers, and squeeze it. Is it soft or gritty? Does it clump together or crumble when you squeeze it?

4. Place about half the sample in a plastic petri dish. Using the dropper, add water one drop at a time. Watch how the sample changes. Does any material in the sample float? As the sample gets wet, do you notice any odor? (*Hint:* If the wet soil has an odor or contains material that floats, it is likely to contain organic material.)

5. Look at some of the soil under the stereomicroscope. (*Hint:* Use the toothpick to separate the particles in the soil.) Sketch what you see. Label the particles, such as gravel, organic matter, or strangely shaped grains.

6. Repeat Steps 1–5 with the topsoil. Be sure to record your observations.

7. Clean up and dispose of your samples as directed by your teacher. **CAUTION:** *Wash your hands when you finish handling soil.*

Analyze and Conclude

1. **Observing** Did you observe any similarities between the local soil sample and the topsoil? Any differences?

2. **Inferring** What can you infer about the composition of both types of soil from the different sizes of their particles? From your observations of texture? From how the samples changed when water was added?

3. **Inferring** Do you think that both types of soil were formed in the same way? Explain.

4. **Developing Hypotheses** Based on your observations and study of the chapter, develop a hypothesis about which soil would be better for growing flowers and vegetables.

5. **Communicating** Write a report for consumers that summarizes your analysis of the two soil samples. Be sure to describe what factors you analyzed and give a suggestion for which soil consumers should use for growing flowers and vegetables.

Design an Experiment

In Question 4 you developed a hypothesis about which soil would be better for growing flowers and vegetables. Design an experiment that would test this hypothesis. Be sure to indicate how you would control variables. *After you receive your teacher's approval, carry out your experiment.*

Reading Preview

Key Concepts
- Why is soil a valuable resource?
- How can soil lose its value?
- What are some ways that soil can be conserved?

Key Terms
- sod • natural resource
- Dust Bowl • soil conservation
- contour plowing
- conservation plowing
- crop rotation

Target Reading Skill

Previewing Visuals Before you read, preview Figure 13, The Dust Bowl. Then write two questions that you have about the photo and map in a graphic organizer like the one below. As you read, answer your questions.

The Dust Bowl

Q.	Where was the Dust Bowl?
A.	
Q.	

Prairie grasses and wildflowers ▼

Discover **Activity**

How Can You Keep Soil From Washing Away?

1. Pour about 500 mL of soil into a pie plate, forming a pile.
2. Devise a way to keep the soil from washing away when water is poured over it. To protect the pile of soil, you may use craft sticks, paper clips, pebbles, modeling clay, strips of paper, or other materials approved by your teacher.
3. After arranging your materials to protect the soil, hold a container filled with 200 mL of water about 20 cm above the center of the soil. Slowly pour the water in a stream onto the pile of soil.
4. Compare your pan of soil with those of your classmates.

Think It Over

Observing Based on your observations, what do you think is the best way to prevent soil on a slope from washing away?

Suppose you were a settler traveling west in the mid 1800s. Much of your journey would have been through vast, open grasslands called prairies. After the forests and mountains of the East, the prairies were an amazing sight. Grass taller than a person rippled and flowed in the wind like a sea of green.

The prairie soil was very fertile. It was rich with humus because of the tall grass. The **sod**—the thick mass of tough roots at the surface of the soil—kept the soil in place and held onto moisture.

The prairies covered a vast area. They included Iowa and Illinois, as well as the eastern parts of Kansas, Nebraska, and North and South Dakota. Today, farms growing crops such as corn, soybeans, and wheat have replaced the prairies. But prairie soils are still among the most fertile in the world.

The Value of Soil

A **natural resource** is anything in the environment that humans use. **Soil is one of Earth's most valuable natural resources because everything that lives on land, including humans, depends directly or indirectly on soil.** Plants depend directly on the soil to live and grow. Humans and animals depend on plants—or on other animals that depend on plants—for food.

Fertile soil is valuable because there is a limited supply. Less than one eighth of the land on Earth has soils that are well suited for farming. Soil is also in limited supply because it takes a long time to form. It can take hundreds of years for just a few centimeters of soil to form. The thick, fertile soil of the prairies took many thousands of years to develop.

 **Reading Checkpoint** Why is fertile soil valuable?

Soil Damage and Loss

Human activities and changes in the environment can affect the soil. **The value of soil is reduced when soil loses its fertility and when topsoil is lost due to erosion.**

Loss of Fertility Soil can be damaged when it loses its fertility. Soil that has lost its fertility is said to be exhausted. This type of soil loss occurred in large parts of the South in the late 1800s. Soils in which only cotton had been grown were exhausted. Many farmers abandoned their farms. Early in the 1900s in Alabama, a scientist named George Washington Carver developed new crops and farming methods that helped to restore soil fertility in the South. Peanuts were one crop that helped make the soil fertile again. Peanut plants are legumes. Legumes have small lumps on their roots that contain nitrogen-fixing bacteria. These bacteria make nitrogen, an important nutrient, available in a form that plants can use.

FIGURE 12
Restoring Soil Fertility
George Washington Carver (1864–1943) taught new methods of soil conservation. He also encouraged farmers to plant peanuts, which helped restore soil fertility.
Applying Concepts *What nutrient do peanut plants add to the soil?*

The Dust Bowl

Key

- Dust Bowl
- Other areas affected by dust storms

Montana, North Dakota, Wyoming, South Dakota, Rocky Mountains, Nebraska, Iowa, Colorado, Kansas, Missouri, Oklahoma, New Mexico, Texas, Mississippi River

FIGURE 13
The Dust Bowl
The Dust Bowl ruined farmland in western Oklahoma and parts of the surrounding states. Wind blew dry particles of soil into great clouds of dust that traveled thousands of kilometers.

Go Online

*Sci*LINKS. **NSTA**

For: Links on soil conservation
Visit: www.SciLinks.org
Web Code: scn-0723

Loss of Topsoil Whenever soil is exposed, water and wind can quickly erode it. Plant cover can protect soil from erosion. Plants break the force of falling rain, and plant roots hold the soil together. Wind is another cause of soil loss. Wind erosion is most likely in areas where farming methods are not suited to dry conditions. For example, wind erosion contributed to the Dust Bowl on the Great Plains.

Soil Loss in the Dust Bowl Toward the end of the 1800s, farmers settled the Great Plains. The soil of the Great Plains is fertile. But rainfall decreases steadily from east to west across the Great Plains. The region also has droughts—years when rainfall is scarce. Plowing removed the grass from the Great Plains and exposed the soil. In times of drought, the topsoil quickly dried out, turned to dust, and blew away.

By 1930, almost all of the Great Plains had been turned into farms or ranches. Then, a long drought turned the soil on parts of the Great Plains to dust. The wind blew the soil east in great, black clouds that reached Chicago and New York City. The erosion was most serious in the southern Plains states. This area, shown in Figure 13, was called the **Dust Bowl.** The Dust Bowl helped people appreciate the value of soil. With government support, farmers in the Great Plains and throughout the country began to take better care of their land. They adopted methods of farming that helped save the soil. Some methods were new. Others had been practiced for hundreds of years.

 **Reading Checkpoint** What caused the Dust Bowl?

Soil Conservation

Since the Dust Bowl, farmers have adopted modern methods of soil conservation. **Soil conservation** is the management of soil to prevent its destruction. **Soil can be conserved through contour plowing, conservation plowing, and crop rotation.**

In **contour plowing,** farmers plow their fields along the curves of a slope. This helps slow the runoff of excess rainfall and prevents it from washing the soil away.

In **conservation plowing,** farmers disturb the soil and its plant cover as little as possible. Dead weeds and stalks of the previous year's crop are left in the ground to help return soil nutrients, retain moisture, and hold soil in place. This method is also called low-till or no-till plowing.

In **crop rotation,** a farmer plants different crops in a field each year. Different types of plants absorb different amounts of nutrients from the soil. Some crops, such as corn and cotton, absorb large amounts of nutrients. The year after planting these crops, the farmer plants crops that use fewer soil nutrients, such as oats, barley, or rye. The year after that the farmer sows legumes such as alfalfa or beans to restore the nutrient supply.

✓ **Reading Checkpoint** How does conservation plowing help conserve soil?

FIGURE 14
Soil Conservation Methods
This farm's fields show evidence of contour plowing and crop rotation. **Predicting** *How might contour plowing affect the amount of topsoil?*

Section 3 Assessment

🎯 **Target Reading Skill** Previewing Visuals Compare your questions and answers about Figure 13 with those of a partner.

Reviewing Key Concepts

1. **a. Defining** What is a natural resource?
   b. Explaining Why is soil valuable as a natural resource?
2. **a. Listing** What are two ways in which the value of soil can be reduced?
   b. Explaining Explain how topsoil can be lost.
   c. Relating Cause and Effect What caused the Dust Bowl?
3. **a. Defining** What is soil conservation?
   b. Listing What are three methods by which farmers can conserve soil?
   c. Problem Solving A farmer growing corn wants to maintain soil fertility and reduce erosion. What conservation methods could the farmer try? Explain.

Writing in Science

Public Service Announcement
A severe drought in a farming region threatens to produce another Dust Bowl. Write a paragraph about soil conservation to be read as a public service announcement on radio stations. The announcement should identify the danger of soil loss due to erosion. It should also describe the steps farmers can take to conserve the soil.

1 Rocks and Weathering

Key Concepts

- Weathering and erosion work together continuously to wear down and carry away the rocks at Earth's surface.

- The causes of mechanical weathering include freezing and thawing, release of pressure, plant growth, actions of animals, and abrasion.

- The causes of chemical weathering include the action of water, oxygen, carbon dioxide, living organisms, and acid rain.

- The most important factors that determine the rate at which weathering occurs are the type of rock and the climate.

Key Terms

weathering
erosion
uniformitarianism
mechanical weathering
abrasion
ice wedging
chemical weathering
oxidation
permeable

2 How Soil Forms

Key Concepts

- Soil is a mixture of rock particles, minerals, decayed organic material, water, and air.

- Soil forms as rock is broken down by weathering and mixes with other materials on the surface. Soil is constantly being formed wherever bedrock is exposed.

- Scientists classify the different types of soil into major groups based on climate, plants, and soil composition.

- Some soil organisms make humus, the material that makes soil fertile. Other soil organisms mix the soil and make spaces in it for air and water.

Key Terms

soil
bedrock
humus
fertility
loam
soil horizon
topsoil
subsoil
litter
decomposer

3 Soil Conservation

Key Concepts

- Soil is one of Earth's most valuable natural resources because everything that lives on land, including humans, depends directly or indirectly on soil.

- The value of soil is reduced when soil loses its fertility and when topsoil is lost due to erosion.

- Soil can be conserved through contour plowing, conservation plowing, and crop rotation.

Key Terms

sod
natural resource
Dust Bowl
soil conservation
contour plowing
conservation plowing
crop rotation

Review and Assessment

Go Online
PHSchool.com
For: Self-Assessment
Visit: PHSchool.com
Web Code: cfa-2020

Organizing Information

Sequencing Fill in the flowchart to show how soil horizons form. (For more information on flowcharts, see the Skills Handbook.)

Soil Horizons

Bedrock begins to weather.

↓

a. _____ ?

↓

b. _____ ?

↓

c. _____ ?

Reviewing Key Terms

Choose the letter of the best answer.

1. The process that splits rock through freezing and thawing is called
   a. erosion.
   b. chemical weathering.
   c. ice wedging.
   d. abrasion.

2. Acid rain results in
   a. chemical weathering.
   b. abrasion.
   c. oxidation.
   d. mechanical weathering.

3. Soil that is made up of roughly equal parts of clay, sand, and silt is called
   a. sod.
   b. loam.
   c. tropical soil.
   d. subsoil.

4. The B horizon consists of
   a. subsoil.
   b. topsoil.
   c. litter.
   d. bedrock.

5. The humus in soil is produced by
   a. mechanical weathering.
   b. bedrock.
   c. chemical weathering.
   d. decomposers.

If the statement is true, write *true*. If it is false, change the underlined word or words to make the statement true.

6. <u>Mechanical weathering</u> is the removal of rock particles by gravity, wind, water, or ice.

7. Rock that is <u>permeable</u> weathers easily because it is full of tiny air spaces.

8. The decayed organic material in soil is called <u>loam</u>.

9. The layer of plant remains at the surface of the soil is called <u>litter</u>.

10. In <u>contour plowing</u>, farmers conserve soil fertility by leaving dead stalks and weeds in the ground.

Writing in Science

Journal Entry You are a farmer on the tall grass prairie in the midwestern United States. Write a journal entry describing prairie soil. Include the soil's composition, how it formed, and how animals helped it develop.

Discovery CHANNEL SCHOOL

Weathering and Soil Formation
Video Preview
Video Field Trip
▶ Video Assessment

Review and Assessment

Checking Concepts

11. What is the principle of uniformitarianism?

12. Explain how plants can act as agents of both mechanical and chemical weathering.

13. What is the role of gases such as oxygen and carbon dioxide in chemical weathering?

14. Briefly describe how soil is formed.

15. Which contains more humus, topsoil or subsoil? Which has higher fertility? Explain.

16. What organism does most of the work in mixing humus into soil?

17. What role did grass play in conserving the soil of the prairies?

18. How do conservation plowing and crop rotation contribute to soil conservation?

Thinking Critically

19. **Predicting** If mechanical weathering breaks a rock into pieces, how would this affect the rate at which the rock weathers chemically?

20. **Comparing and Contrasting** Compare the layers in the diagram below in terms of their composition and humus content.

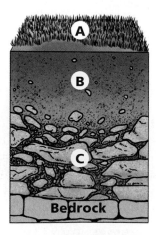

Bedrock

21. **Classifying** Classify as mechanical or chemical weathering: cracks in a sidewalk next to a tree; limestone with holes like Swiss cheese; a rock that slowly turns reddish brown.

Applying Skills

Use the following information to answer Questions 22–24.

You have two samples of soil. One is mostly sand and one is mostly clay.

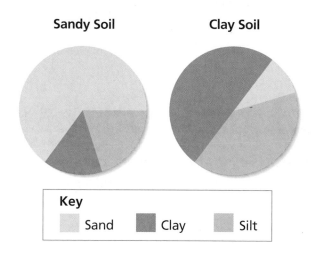

Sandy Soil   Clay Soil

Key
Sand   Clay   Silt

22. **Developing Hypotheses** Which soil sample would lose water more quickly? Why?

23. **Designing Experiments** Design an experiment to test how quickly water passes through each soil sample.

24. **Posing Questions** You are a farmer who wants to grow soybeans in one of these two soils. What questions would you need to answer before choosing where to plant your soybeans?

Lab zone Chapter Project

Performance Assessment You are ready to present your data and conclusions about what type of material is best for growing bean plants. How did your group's results compare with those of the other groups in your class?

In your journal, describe how well the results of your experiment matched your predictions. What have you learned from this project about soil characteristics that help plants to grow? How could you improve your experiment?

ⓘ Standardized Test Practice

Choose the letter of the best answer.

1. Which of the following is a type of mechanical weathering?
  A abrasion
  B freezing and thawing
  C plant growth
  D all of the above

2. You are designing an experiment to test the resistance to weathering of various types of materials. What weathering process could be modeled using sandpaper?
  A acid rain
  B freezing and thawing
  C abrasion
  D all of the above

3. In what type of climate would soil form fastest from limestone bedrock?
  A a cold, dry climate   **B** a cold, wet climate
  C a hot, dry climate   **D** a hot, wet climate

Use the data table below and your knowledge of science to answer Questions 4–5.

Soil Erosion by State			
	tons/acre/year		
State	Water Erosion	Wind Erosion	Total Erosion
Montana	1.08	3.8	4.9
Wyoming	1.57	2.4	3.97
Texas	3.47	14.9	18.4
New Mexico	2.00	11.5	13.5
Colorado	2.5	8.9	11.4
Tennessee	14.12	0.0	14.12
Hawaii	13.71	0.0	13.71

4. Of the states listed in the table, which two have the greatest amount of erosion by water?
  A Texas and Tennessee
  B Texas and Hawaii
  C New Mexico and Colorado
  D Tennessee and Hawaii

5. What state in the table has the greatest soil erosion?
  A Texas
  B Hawaii
  C Tennessee
  D New Mexico

Open-Ended Question

6. Two rocks, each in a different location, have been weathering for the same amount of time. Mature soil has formed from one rock, but only immature soil has formed from the other. What factors might have caused this difference in rate of soil formation? In your answer, include examples of both mechanical and chemical weathering.

Chapter

14

Erosion and Deposition

Academic Standards

This chapter addresses these Indiana standards.

Scientific Thinking

7.2.2 Use formulas to calculate the circumference, area, and volume of various shapes.

7.2.6 Measure length, volume, weight, elapsed time, rates, or temperatures, and choose appropriate units.

The Physical Setting

7.3.18 Describe that waves move at different speeds in different materials.

Common Themes

7.7.1 Explain that the output from one part of a system can become the input to other parts, and that this can control the whole system.

7.7.2 Use different models to represent the same thing, noting that the model's type and complexity depend on its purpose.

7.7.3 Describe how systems usually change until they reach equilibrium, and remain that way unless their surroundings change.

Water erosion formed the Grand Canyon, ▶ viewed here from Toroweap Point.

▶Lab zone™ Chapter **Project**

Design and Build a Dam

Dams on major rivers are among the most spectacular works of engineering. These structures serve many purposes. Dams help to control flooding, generate power, and store water for drinking and watering crops. Dams can be constructed out of a variety of materials—wood, concrete, and even soil.

Your Goal To build a dam using various types of soil. To complete this project, you must

- conduct an experiment to determine the permeability of different soils
- investigate how readily the different soils erode when water passes over them
- design and build a dam
- test the dam and redesign if time allows
- follow the safety guidelines in Appendix A

Plan It! You will use a combination of three different soils to build the dam. First, you will need to test the permeability of each type of soil. Then develop an experiment to test how easily water erodes the soil. The results of the two experiments will provide you with information about the soils you tested. As you design your dam, think about what layers or combinations of materials will make the most effective dam. When you have tested your dam, present your conclusions to your class.

Changing Earth's Surface

Reading Preview

Key Concepts
- What processes wear down and build up Earth's surface?
- What causes the different types of mass movement?

Key Terms
- erosion • sediment
- deposition • gravity
- mass movement

Target Reading Skill
Comparing and Contrasting As you read, compare and contrast the different types of mass movement by completing a table like the one below.

Mass Movement

Type of Mass Movement	Speed	Slope
Landslide		

Lab zone Discover **Activity**

How Does Gravity Affect Materials on a Slope?

1. Place a small board flat on your desk. Place a marble on the board and slowly tip one end of the board up slightly. Observe what happens.
2. Place a block of wood on the board. Slowly lift one end of the board and observe the result.
3. Next, cover the board and the wood block with sandpaper and repeat Step 2.

Think It Over
Developing Hypotheses How do the results of each step compare? Develop a hypothesis to explain the differences in your observations.

The ground you stand on is solid. But under certain conditions, solid earth can quickly change to thick, soupy mud. For example, high rains soaked into the soil and triggered the devastating mudflow in Figure 1. A river of mud raced down the mountainside, burying homes and cars. Several lives were lost. In moments, the mudflow moved a huge volume of soil mixed with water and rock downhill.

Wearing Down and Building Up

A mudflow is a spectacular example of erosion. **Erosion** is the process by which natural forces move weathered rock and soil from one place to another. You may have seen water carrying soil and gravel down a driveway after it rains. That's an example of erosion. A mudflow is a very rapid type of erosion. Other types of erosion move soil and rock more slowly. Gravity, running water, glaciers, waves, and wind are all causes, or agents, of erosion. In geology, an agent is a force or material that causes a change in Earth's surface.

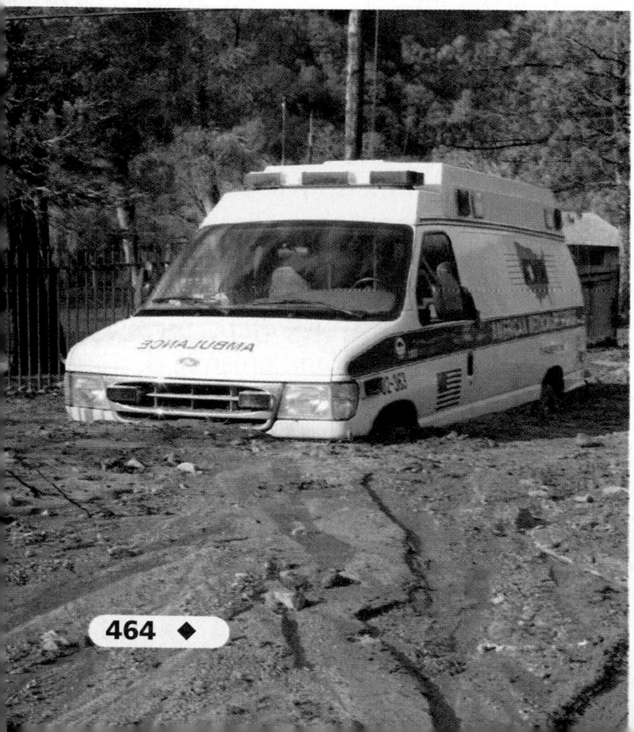

FIGURE 1
Mudflow
A mudflow caused by heavy rains in San Bernardino, California, brought this ambulance to a stop.

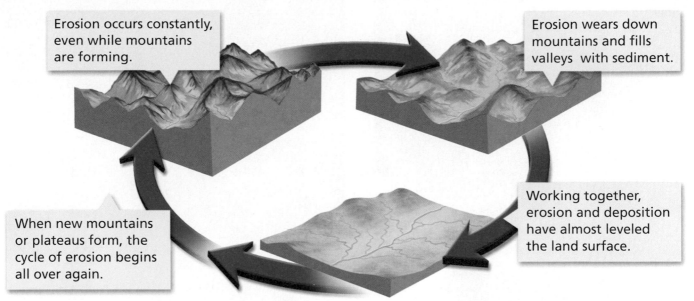

Erosion occurs constantly, even while mountains are forming.

Erosion wears down mountains and fills valleys with sediment.

Working together, erosion and deposition have almost leveled the land surface.

When new mountains or plateaus form, the cycle of erosion begins all over again.

FIGURE 2
Cycle of Erosion and Deposition
Over millions of years, erosion gradually wears away mountains while deposition fills in valleys with sediment.
Predicting *What would happen to the surface of the land if uplift did not occur?*

The material moved by erosion is **sediment.** Sediment may consist of pieces of rock or soil or the remains of plants and animals. Both weathering and erosion produce sediment. **Deposition** occurs where the agents of erosion, deposit, or lay down, sediment. Deposition changes the shape of the land. You may have watched a playing child who picked up several toys, carried them across a room, and then put them down. This child was acting something like an agent of erosion and deposition.

Weathering, erosion, and deposition act together in a cycle that wears down and builds up Earth's surface. Erosion and deposition are at work everywhere on Earth. As a mountain wears down in one place, new landforms build up in other places. The cycle of erosion and deposition is never-ending.

 **Reading Checkpoint** What is sediment?

Mass Movement

Imagine that you are sitting on a bicycle at the top of a hill. With only a slight push, you can coast down the hill. If the slope of the hill is very steep, you will reach a high speed before reaching the bottom. The force that pulls you and your bicycle downward is gravity. Gravity pulls everything toward the center of Earth.

Gravity is the force that moves rock and other materials downhill. Gravity causes **mass movement**, any one of several processes that move sediment downhill. **The different types of mass movement include landslides, mudflows, slump, and creep.** Mass movement can be rapid or slow.

Lab zone **Skills Activity**

Making Models

You can make a model of mass movement. Design a plan to model one of the types of mass movement using sand, pebbles, and water. With your teacher's approval, make and test your model.

How well did your model represent the type of mass movement you chose? How could you improve your model?

Landslide

Slump

FIGURE 3
Mass Movement
In addition to mudflows, types of mass movement include landslides, slump, and creep.
Making Judgments *Which form of mass movement produces the most drastic change in the surface?*

Landslides The most destructive kind of mass movement is a landslide, which occurs when rock and soil slide quickly down a steep slope. Some landslides contain huge masses of rock. But many landslides contain only a small amount of rock and soil. Some landslides occur where road builders have cut highways through hills or mountains. Figure 3 shows an example of a landslide.

Mudflows A mudflow is the rapid downhill movement of a mixture of water, rock, and soil. The amount of water in a mudflow can be as high as 60 percent. Mudflows often occur after heavy rains in a normally dry area. In clay soils with a high water content, mudflows may occur even on very gentle slopes. Under certain conditions, clay soils suddenly turn to liquid and begin to flow. An earthquake can trigger both mudflows and landslides. Mudflows can be very dangerous.

Slump If you slump your shoulders, the entire upper part of your body drops down. In the type of mass movement known as slump, a mass of rock and soil suddenly slips down a slope. Unlike a landslide, the material in a slump moves down in one large mass. It looks as if someone pulled the bottom out from under part of the slope. A slump often occurs when water soaks the bottom of soil that is rich in clay.

Creep

Go Online
active art

For: Mass Movement activity
Visit: PHSchool.com
Web Code: cfp-2031

Creep Creep is the very slow downhill movement of rock and soil. It can even occur on gentle slopes. Creep often results from the freezing and thawing of water in cracked layers of rock beneath the soil. Like the movement of an hour hand on a clock, creep is so slow you can barely notice it. But you can see the effects of creep in objects such as telephone poles, gravestones, and fenceposts. Creep may tilt these objects at spooky angles. Landscapes affected by creep may have the eerie, out-of-kilter look of a funhouse in an amusement park.

 **Reading Checkpoint** What is the main difference between a slump and a landslide?

Section 1 Assessment

Target Reading Skill Comparing and Contrasting Use the information in your table to help you answer Question 2 below.

Reviewing Key Concepts

1. a. Listing What are five agents of erosion?
   b. Defining In your own words, write a definition of *deposition.*
   c. Predicting Over time, how will erosion and deposition affect a mountain range? Explain.
2. a. Listing What are the four types of mass movement?
   b. Relating Cause and Effect What force causes all types of mass movement?
   c. Inferring A fence runs across a steep hillside. The fence is tilted downhill and forms a curve rather than a straight line. What can you infer happened to the fence? Explain.

Lab zone At-Home Activity

Evidence of Erosion After a rainstorm, take a walk with an adult family member around your neighborhood. Look for evidence of erosion. Try to find areas where there is loose soil, sand, gravel, or rock. **CAUTION:** *Stay away from any large pile of loose sand or soil—it may slide without warning.* Which areas have the most erosion? The least erosion? How does the slope of the ground affect the amount of erosion? Sketch or take photographs of the areas showing evidence of erosion.

Sand Hills

Problem

What is the relationship between the height and width of a sand hill?

Skills

developing hypotheses, interpreting data, predicting

Materials

- dry sand, 500 mL • cardboard tube
- tray (about 15 cm × 45 cm × 60 cm)
- wooden barbecue skewer • masking tape
- spoon • ruler • pencil or crayon
- several sheets of white paper

Procedure

1. Begin by observing how gravity causes mass movement. To start, place the cardboard tube vertically in the center of the tray.

2. Using the spoon, fill the cardboard tube with the dry sand. Take care not to spill the sand around the outside of the tube.

3. Carefully lift the sand-filled tube straight up so that all the sand flows out. As you lift the tube, observe the sand's movement.

4. Develop a hypothesis explaining how you think the width of the sand pile is related to its height for different amounts of sand.

5. Empty the sand in the tray back into a container. Then set up your system for measuring the sand hill.

6. Copy the data table into your lab notebook.

7. Following Steps 1 through 3, make a new sand hill.

Data Table					
Test	1	2	3	4	5
Width					
Height					

8. Measure and record the sand hill's height and width for Test 1. (See the instructions on the bottom of the page to help you accurately measure the height and width.)

How to Measure a Sand Hill

1. Cover the bottom of the tray with unlined white paper and tape it firmly in place.

2. Mark off points 0.5 cm apart along one side of the paper in the tray.

3. Carefully draw the sand hill's outline on the paper. The line should go completely around the base of the hill.

4. Now measure the width of the hill against the marks you made along the edge of the paper.

5. Measure the sand hill's height by inserting a barbecue skewer through its center. Make a mark on the skewer at the top of the hill.

6. Remove the skewer and use the ruler to measure how much of the skewer was buried in the hill. Try not to disturb the sand.

9. Now test what happens when you add more sand to the sand hill. Place your cardboard tube vertically at the center of the sand hill. Be careful not to push the tube down into the sand hill! Using the spoon, fill the tube with sand as before.

10. Carefully raise the tube and observe the sand's movement.

11. Measure and record the sand hill's height and width for Test 2.

12. Repeat Steps 9 through 11 at least three more times. After each test, record your results. Be sure to number each test.

Analyze and Conclude

1. **Graphing** Make a graph showing how the sand hill's height and width changed with each test. (Hint: Use the x-axis of the graph for height. Use the y-axis of the graph for width.)

2. **Interpreting Data** What does your graph show about the relationship between the sand hill's height and width?

3. **Drawing Conclusions** Does your graph support your hypothesis about the sand hill's height and width? Why or why not?

4. **Developing Hypotheses** How would you revise your original hypothesis after examining your data? Give reasons for your answer.

5. **Predicting** Predict what would happen if you continued the experiment for five more tests. Extend your graph with a dashed line to show your prediction. How could you test your prediction?

6. **Communicating** Write a paragraph in which you discuss how you measured your sand hill. Did any problems you had in making your measurements affect your results? How did you adjust your measurement technique to solve these problems?

Design an Experiment

Do you think the use of different materials, such as wet sand or gravel, would produce different results from those using dry sand? Make a new hypothesis about the relationship between slope and width in hills made of materials other than dry sand. Design an experiment in which you test how these different materials form hills. *Obtain your teacher's approval before you try the experiment.*

Reading Preview

Key Concepts
- What process is mainly responsible for shaping the surface of the land?
- What features are formed by water erosion and deposition?
- What causes groundwater erosion?

Key Terms
- runoff • rill • gully • stream
- tributary • flood plain
- meander • oxbow lake
- alluvial fan • delta
- groundwater • stalactite
- stalagmite • karst topography

Target Reading Skill

Previewing Visuals Before you read, preview Figure 10. Then write two questions that you have about the illustration in a graphic organizer like the one below. As you read, answer your questions.

The Course of a River

Q.	What features does a river produce by erosion?
A.	
Q.	

Lab zone Discover **Activity**

How Does Moving Water Wear Away Rocks?

1. Obtain two bars of soap that are the same size and brand.
2. Open a faucet just enough to let the water drip out very slowly. How many drops of water does the faucet release per minute?
3. Place one bar of soap in a dry place. Place the other bar of soap under the faucet. Predict the effect of the dripping water droplets on the soap.
4. Let the faucet drip for 10 minutes.
5. Turn off the faucet and observe both bars of soap. What difference do you observe between them?

Think It Over

Predicting What would the bar of soap under the dripping faucet look like if you left it there for another 10 minutes? For an hour? How could you speed up the process? Slow it down?

Walking in the woods in summer, you can hear the racing water of a stream before you see the stream itself. The water roars as it foams over rock ledges and boulders. When you reach the stream, you see water rushing by. Sand and pebbles tumble along the bottom of the stream. As it swirls downstream, the water also carries twigs, leaves, and bits of soil. In sheltered pools, insects such as water striders skim the water's calm surface. Beneath the surface, a rainbow trout swims in the clear water.

In winter, the stream freezes. Chunks of ice scrape and grind away at the stream's bed and banks. In spring, the stream floods. Then the flow of water may be strong enough to move large rocks. But throughout the year, the stream continues to erode its small part of Earth's surface.

▼ A stream in summer

Runoff and Erosion

Moving water is the major agent of the erosion that has shaped Earth's land surface. Erosion by water begins with the splash of rain. Some rainfall sinks into the ground. Some evaporates or is taken up by plants. The force of a falling raindrop can loosen and pick up soil particles. As water moves over the land, it carries these particles with it. This moving water is called runoff. **Runoff** is water that moves over Earth's surface. When runoff flows in a thin layer over the land, it may cause a type of erosion called sheet erosion.

Amount of Runoff The amount of runoff in an area depends on five main factors. The first factor is the amount of rain an area receives. A second factor is vegetation. Grasses, shrubs, and trees reduce runoff by absorbing water and holding soil in place. A third factor is the type of soil. Some types of soils absorb more water than others. A fourth factor is the shape of the land. Land that is steeply sloped has more runoff than flatter land. Finally, a fifth factor is how people use the land. For instance, a paved parking lot absorbs no water, so all the rain that falls on it becomes runoff. Runoff also increases when a farmer cuts down crops, since this removes vegetation from the land.

Generally, more runoff means more erosion. In contrast, factors that reduce runoff will reduce erosion. Even though deserts have little rainfall, they often have high runoff and erosion because they have few plants. In wet areas, runoff and erosion may be low because there are more plants to protect the soil.

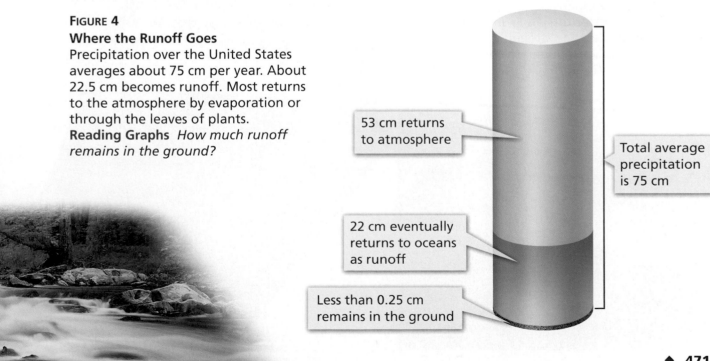

FIGURE 4
Where the Runoff Goes
Precipitation over the United States averages about 75 cm per year. About 22.5 cm becomes runoff. Most returns to the atmosphere by evaporation or through the leaves of plants.
Reading Graphs *How much runoff remains in the ground?*

53 cm returns to atmosphere

Total average precipitation is 75 cm

22 cm eventually returns to oceans as runoff

Less than 0.25 cm remains in the ground

Raindrops Falling

Find out how the force of falling raindrops affects soil.

1. Fill a petri dish with fine-textured soil to a depth of about 1 cm. Make sure the soil has a smooth flat surface, but do not pack it firmly in the dish.

2. Place the dish in the center of a newspaper.

3. Fill a dropper with water. Squeeze a large water drop from a height of 1 m onto the surface of the soil. Repeat 4 times.

4. Use a meter stick to measure the distance the soil splashed from the dish. Record your observations.

5. Repeat Steps 1 through 4, this time from a height of 2 m.

Drawing Conclusions Which test produced the greater amount of erosion? Why?

Rills and Gullies Because of gravity, runoff and the material it contains move downhill. As runoff travels, it forms tiny grooves in the soil called **rills.** As many rills flow into one another, they grow larger, forming gullies. A **gully** is a large groove, or channel, in the soil that carries runoff after a rainstorm. As water flows through gullies, it moves soil and rocks with it, thus enlarging the gullies through erosion. Gullies contain water only after it rains.

Streams and Rivers Gullies join together to form a larger channel called a stream. A **stream** is a channel along which water is continually flowing down a slope. Unlike gullies, streams rarely dry up. Small streams are also called creeks or brooks. As streams flow together, they form larger and larger bodies of flowing water. A large stream is often called a river.

Tributaries A stream grows into a larger stream or river by receiving water from tributaries. A **tributary** is a stream or river that flows into a larger river. For example, the Missouri and Ohio rivers are tributaries of the Mississippi River. A drainage basin, or watershed, is the area from which a river and its tributaries collect their water.

 **Reading Checkpoint** What is a tributary?

FIGURE 5
Runoff, Rills, and Gullies
Water flowing across the land runs together to form rills, gullies, and streams.
Predicting What will happen to the land between the gullies as they grow wider?

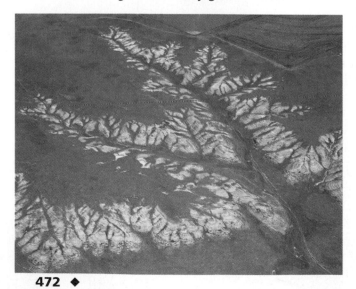

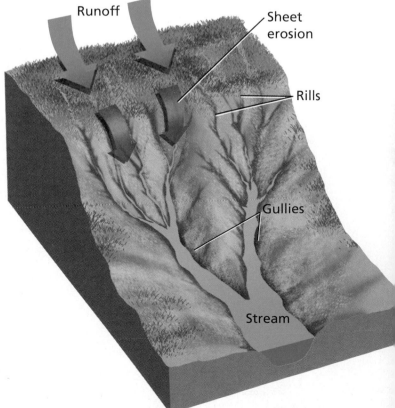

Runoff

Sheet erosion

Rills

Gullies

Stream

Erosion by Rivers

As a river flows from the mountains to the sea, the river forms a variety of features. **Through erosion, a river creates valleys, waterfalls, flood plains, meanders, and oxbow lakes.**

Rivers often form on steep mountain slopes. Near its source, a river is often fast flowing and generally follows a straight, narrow course. The steep slopes along the river erode rapidly. The result is a deep, V-shaped valley.

Waterfalls Waterfalls may occur where a river meets an area of rock that is very hard and erodes slowly. The river flows over this rock and then flows over softer rock downstream. As you can see in Figure 6, the softer rock wears away faster than the harder rock. Eventually a waterfall develops where the softer rock was removed. Areas of rough water called rapids also occur where a river tumbles over hard rock.

Flood Plain Lower down on its course, a river usually flows over more gently sloping land. The river spreads out and erodes the land, forming a wide river valley. The flat, wide area of land along a river is a **flood plain.** A river often covers its flood plain when it overflows its banks during floods. On a wide flood plain, the valley walls may be kilometers away from the river itself.

Go Online
PLANET DIARY

For: More on floods
Visit: PHSchool.com
Web Code: cfd-2032

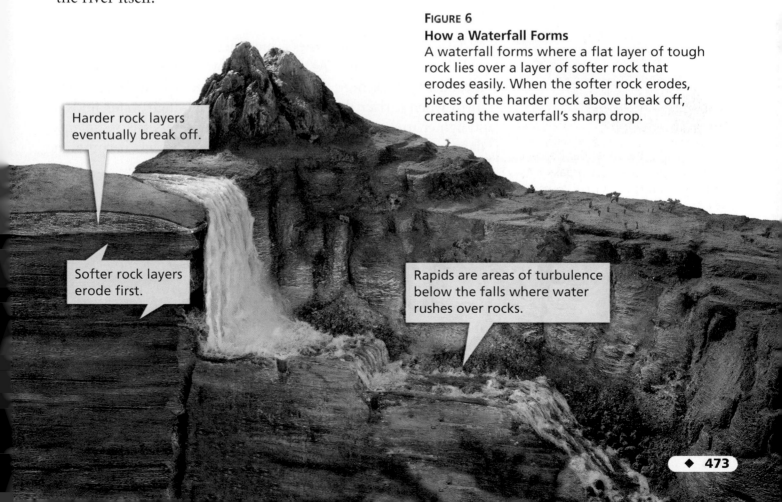

FIGURE 6
How a Waterfall Forms
A waterfall forms where a flat layer of tough rock lies over a layer of softer rock that erodes easily. When the softer rock erodes, pieces of the harder rock above break off, creating the waterfall's sharp drop.

Harder rock layers eventually break off.

Softer rock layers erode first.

Rapids are areas of turbulence below the falls where water rushes over rocks.

FIGURE 7
Meanders and Oxbow Lakes
Erosion often forms meanders and
oxbow lakes where a river winds
across its floodplain.

1 A small obstacle creates a
slight bend in the river.

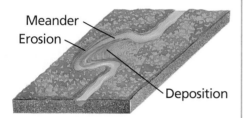

Meander
Erosion
Deposition

2 As water erodes the outer edge
of a meander, the bend becomes
bigger. Deposition occurs along
the inner edge.

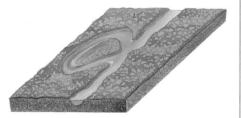

3 Gradually, the meander becomes
more curved. The river breaks
through and takes a new course.

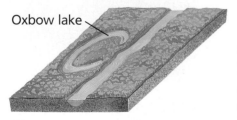

Oxbow lake

4 An oxbow lake remains.

Meanders A river often develops meanders where it flows
through easily eroded rock or sediment. A **meander** is a looplike bend in the course of a river. As the river winds from side
to side, it tends to erode the outer bank and deposit sediment
on the inner bank of a bend. Over time, the meander becomes
more and more curved.

Because of the sediment a river carries, it can erode a very
wide flood plain. Along this part of a river's course, its channel
is deep and wide. Meanders are common. The southern stretch
of the Mississippi River is one example of a river that meanders
on a wide, gently sloping flood plain.

Oxbow Lakes Sometimes a meandering river forms a feature
called an oxbow lake. As Figure 7 shows, an **oxbow lake** is a
meander that has been cut off from the river. An oxbow lake may
form when a river floods. During the flood, high water finds a
straighter route downstream. As the flood waters fall, sediments
dam up the ends of a meander. The meander has become an
oxbow lake.

 **Reading Checkpoint** How does an oxbow lake form?

Deposits by Rivers

As water moves, it carries sediments with it. Any time moving
water slows down, it drops, or deposits, some of the sediment.
As the water slows down, fine particles fall to the river's bed.
Larger stones quit rolling and sliding. **Deposition creates
landforms such as alluvial fans and deltas. It can also add soil
to a river's flood plain.** In Figure 10 on pages 476–477, you can
see these and other features shaped by rivers and streams.

Alluvial Fans Where a stream flows out of a steep, narrow mountain valley, the stream suddenly becomes wider and shallower. The water slows down. Here sediments are deposited in an alluvial fan. An **alluvial fan** is a wide, sloping deposit of sediment formed where a stream leaves a mountain range. As its name suggests, this deposit is shaped like a fan. You can see an alluvial fan in Figure 8.

Deltas A river ends its journey when it flows into a still body of water, such as an ocean or a lake. Because the river water is no longer flowing downhill, the water slows down. At this point, the sediment in the water drops to the bottom. Sediment deposited where a river flows into an ocean or lake builds up a landform called a **delta.** Deltas can be a variety of shapes. Some are arc shaped, others are triangle shaped. The delta of the Mississippi River, shown in Figure 9, is an example of a type of delta called a "bird's foot" delta.

Soil on Flood Plains Deposition can also occur during floods. Then heavy rains or melting snow cause a river to rise above its banks and spread out over its flood plain. When the flood water finally retreats, it deposits sediment as new soil. Deposition of new soil over a flood plain is what makes a river valley fertile. Dense forests can grow in the rich soil of a flood plain. The soil is also perfect for growing crops.

 **Reading Checkpoint** How can a flood be beneficial?

FIGURE 8
Alluvial Fan
This alluvial fan in Death Valley, California, was formed from deposits by streams from the mountains.

FIGURE 9
Mississippi Delta
This satellite image shows the part of the Mississippi River delta where the river empties into the Gulf of Mexico.
Observing *What happens to the Mississippi River as it flows through its delta? Can you find the river's main channel?*

Waterfalls and Rapids
Waterfalls and rapids are common where the river passes over harder rock.

V-Shaped Valley
Near its source, the river flows through a deep, V-shaped valley. As the river flows, it cuts the valley deeper.

Flood Plain
A flood plain forms where the river's power of erosion widens its valley rather than deepening it.

Meanders
Where the river flows across easily eroded sediment, its channel bends from side to side in a series of meanders.

Beaches
Sand carried downstream by the river spreads along the coast to form beaches.

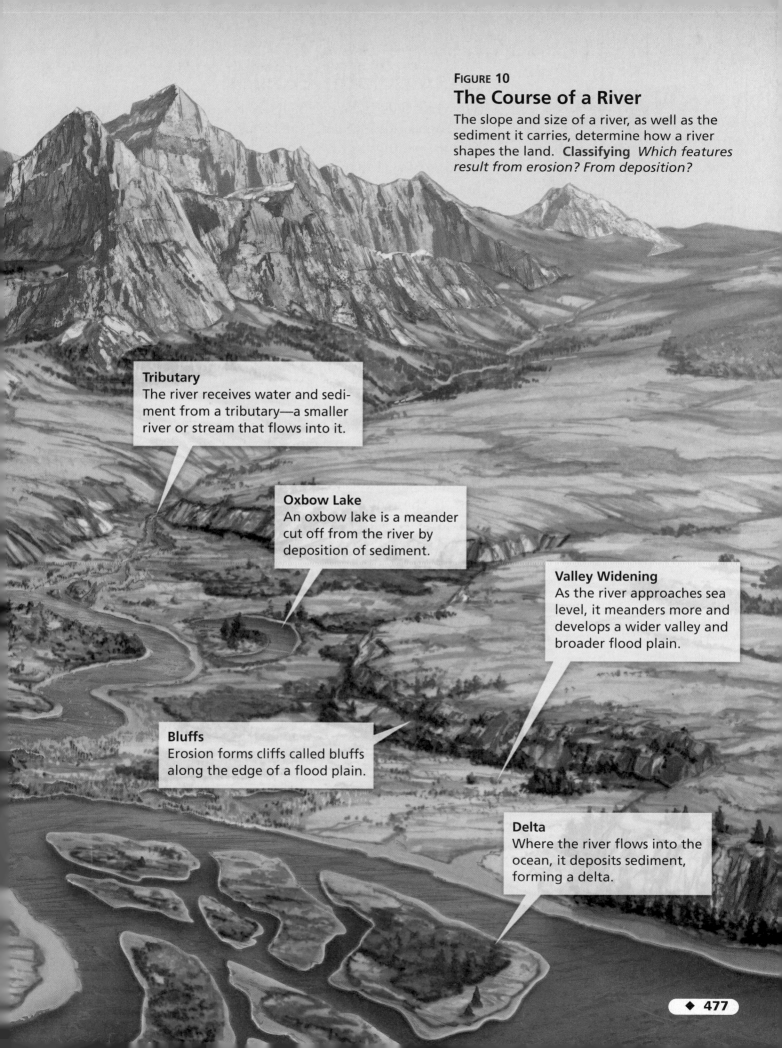

FIGURE 10

The Course of a River

The slope and size of a river, as well as the sediment it carries, determine how a river shapes the land. **Classifying** *Which features result from erosion? From deposition?*

Tributary
The river receives water and sediment from a tributary—a smaller river or stream that flows into it.

Oxbow Lake
An oxbow lake is a meander cut off from the river by deposition of sediment.

Valley Widening
As the river approaches sea level, it meanders more and develops a wider valley and broader flood plain.

Bluffs
Erosion forms cliffs called bluffs along the edge of a flood plain.

Delta
Where the river flows into the ocean, it deposits sediment, forming a delta.

Groundwater Erosion

When rain falls and snow melts, not all of the water evaporates or becomes runoff. Some water soaks into the ground. There it fills the openings in the soil and trickles into cracks and spaces in layers of rock. **Groundwater** is the term geologists use for this underground water. Like running water on the surface, groundwater affects the shape of the land.

Groundwater can cause erosion through a process of chemical weathering. When water sinks into the ground, it combines with carbon dioxide to form a weak acid, called carbonic acid. Carbonic acid can break down limestone. Groundwater containing carbonic acid flows into any cracks in the limestone. Then some of the limestone changes chemically and is carried away in a solution of water. This process gradually hollows out pockets in the rock. Over time, these pockets develop into large holes underground, called caves or caverns.

Cave Formations The action of carbonic acid on limestone can also result in deposition. Inside limestone caves, deposits called stalactites and stalagmites often form. Water containing carbonic acid and calcium from limestone drips from a cave's roof. Carbon dioxide is released from the solution, leaving behind a deposit of calcite. A deposit that hangs like an icicle from the roof of a cave is known as a **stalactite** (stuh LAK tyt). Slow dripping builds up a cone-shaped **stalagmite** (stuh LAG myt) from the cave floor.

Karst Topography In rainy regions where there is a layer of limestone near the surface, groundwater erosion can significantly change the shape of the land. Streams are rare, because water easily sinks down into the weathered limestone. Deep valleys and caverns are common. If the roof of a cave collapses because of the erosion of the underlying limestone, the result is a depression called a sinkhole. This type of landscape is called **karst topography** after a region in Eastern Europe. In the United States, regions of karst topography are found in Florida, Texas, and many other states.

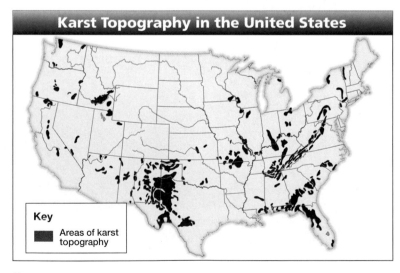

Karst Topography in the United States

Key
■ Areas of karst topography

FIGURE 11
Karst topography is found in many parts of the United States where the bedrock is made up of thick layers of limestone.

 **Reading Checkpoint** How does deposition occur in a limestone cave?

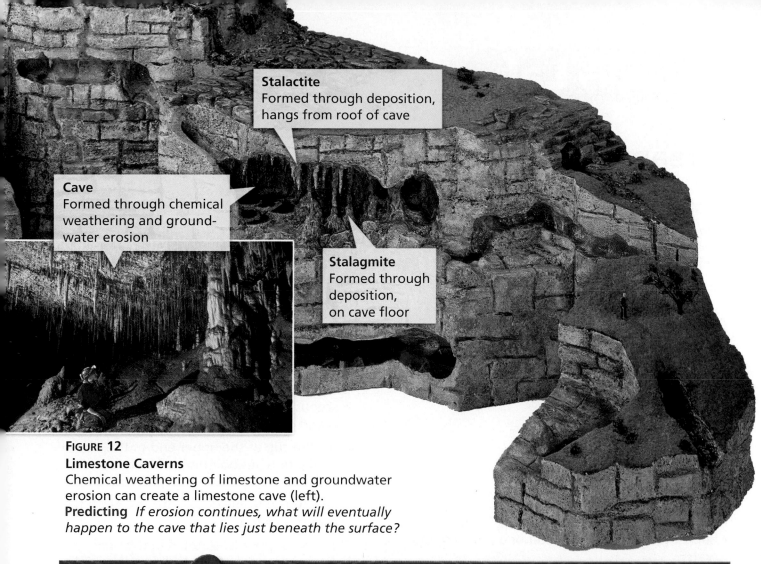

Stalactite
Formed through deposition, hangs from roof of cave

Cave
Formed through chemical weathering and ground-water erosion

Stalagmite
Formed through deposition, on cave floor

FIGURE 12
Limestone Caverns
Chemical weathering of limestone and groundwater erosion can create a limestone cave (left).
Predicting *If erosion continues, what will eventually happen to the cave that lies just beneath the surface?*

Section 2 Assessment

Target Reading Skill Previewing Visuals Refer to your questions and answers about Figure 10 to help you answer Question 2 below.

Reviewing Key Concepts

1. **a. Reviewing** What is the major agent of erosion on Earth's surface?
   b. Sequencing List these in order of size: tributary, stream, rill, gully, runoff, river.
   c. Predicting Where would gullies be more likely to form: a field with plowed soil and no plants, or a field covered with thick grass? Explain.

2. **a. Listing** What are five features that erosion forms along a river?
   b. Listing What are three features that result from deposition along a river?
   c. Relating Cause and Effect Why does a delta often form where a river empties into the ocean?

3. **a. Identifying** What process is the cause of groundwater erosion?
   b. Explaining How do groundwater erosion and deposition produce a limestone cave?

Lab zone **At-Home Activity**

Erosion Cube In a small dish, build a cube out of 27 small sugar cubes. Your cube should be three sugar cubes on a side. Fold a square piece of paper towel to fit the top of the cube. Wet the paper towel, place it on the cube, and let it stand for 15 or 20 minutes. Every few minutes, sprinkle a few drops of water on the paper towel to keep it wet. Then remove the paper towel. What happened to your cube? How is the effect of water on a sugar cube similar to groundwater eroding limestone? How is it different?

Streams in Action

Problem

How do rivers and streams erode the land?

Skills Focus

making models, observing

Materials

- diatomaceous earth
- plastic measuring cup
- spray bottle
- hand lens
- watch or clock
- water
- 1 metal spoon
- plastic foam cup
- blue food coloring
- liquid detergent
- scissors
- 2 wood blocks about 2.5 cm thick
- bucket to hold 2–3 L of water or a source of tap water
- plastic stirrers, 10–12 cm long, with two small holes each
- wire, 13–15 cm long, 20 gauge

Procedure

PART 1 Creating Streams Over Time

1. Your teacher will give you a plastic tub containing diatomaceous earth that has been soaked with water. Place the tub on a level surface. **CAUTION:** *Dry diatomaceous earth produces dust that may be irritating if inhaled.* To keep the diatomaceous earth from drying out, spray it lightly with water.

2. One end of the tub will contain more diatomaceous earth. Use a block of wood to raise this end of the tub 2.5 cm.

3. Place the cup at the upper end of the slope with the notches pointing to the left and right.

4. Press the cup firmly down into the earth to secure its position.

5. Start the dripper (see Step 6 in the box below). Allow the water to drip to the right onto the diatomaceous earth.

6. Allow the dripper to drip for 5 minutes. (*Hint:* When you need to add more water, be careful not to disturb the dripper.)

Making the Dripper

1. Insert the wire into one of the two holes in a plastic stirrer. The ends of the wire should protrude from the stirrer.

2. Gently bend the stirrer into a **U** shape. Be careful not to make any sharp bends. This is the dripper.

3. With scissors, carefully cut two small notches on opposite sides of the top of the foam cup.

4. Fill the cup to just below the notches with water colored with two drops of blue food coloring. Add more food coloring later as you add more water to the cup.

5. Add one drop of detergent to keep air bubbles out of the dripper and increase flow.

6. To start the dripper, fill it with water. Then quickly tip it and place it in one of the notches in the cup, as shown at left.

7. Adjust the flow rate of the dripper to about 2 drips per 1 second. (*Hint:* Bend the dripper into more of a **U** shape to increase flow. Lessen the curve to reduce flow.)

5. Replace the cup and restart the dripper, placing it in the notch on the left side of the cup. Allow the dripper to drip for 5 minutes. Notice any changes in the new stream bed.

6. At the end of 5 minutes, remove the dripper.

7. Draw the new stream bed in your lab notebook. Label it "Increased Angle."

8. Follow your teacher's instructions for cleanup after this activity. Wash your hands when you have finished.

Analyze and Conclude

1. **Observing** Compare the 5-minute stream with the 10-minute stream. How did the length of time that the water flowed affect erosion along the stream bed?

2. **Drawing Conclusions** Were your predictions about the effects of increasing the angle of slope correct? Explain your answer.

3. **Observing** What happened to the eroded material that was carried downstream?

4. **Making Models** What features of streams were you able to observe using your model? How could you modify the model to observe additional features?

5. **Controlling Variables** What other variables besides time and angle of slope might affect the way rivers and streams erode the land?

6. **Communicating** Describe an example of water erosion that you have seen, such as water flowing down a hillside or street after a heavy rain. Include in your answer details such as the slope of the land, the color of the water, and the effects of the erosion.

Design an Experiment

Design an experiment in which you use your model to measure how the amount of sediment carried by a river changes as the volume of flow of the river increases. *Obtain your teacher's approval before you try the experiment.*

7. Observe the flow of water and the changes it makes. Use the hand lens to look closely at the stream bed.

8. After 5 minutes, remove the dripper.

9. In your lab notebook, draw a picture of the resulting stream and label it "5 minutes."

10. Now switch the dripper to the left side of the cup. Restart the dripper and allow it to drip for 10 minutes. Then remove the dripper.

11. Draw a picture and label it "10 minutes."

PART 2 Changing the Angle of Slope

1. Remove the cup from the stream table.

2. Save the stream bed on the right side of the tub. Using the bowl of the spoon, smooth out the diatomaceous earth on the left side.

3. To increase the angle of slope of your stream table, raise the end of the tub another 2.5 cm.

4. In your lab notebook, predict the effects of increasing the angle of slope.

Protecting Homes in Flood Plains

At least ten million American households are located in flood plains. Living near a river is tempting. Riverside land is often flat and easy to build on. Because so many people now live in flood plains, the cost of flood damage has been growing. Communities along rivers want to limit the cost of flooding. They want to know how they can protect the people and buildings already in flood plains. They also want to know how to discourage more people from moving into flood plains.

The Issues

Should the Government Insure People Against Flood Damage?

The United States government offers insurance to households in flood plains. The insurance pays part of the cost of repairs after a flood. Government flood insurance is available only to towns and cities that take steps to reduce flood damage. Cities must allow new building only on high ground. The insurance will not pay to rebuild homes that are badly damaged by flood water. Instead, these people must use the money to find a home somewhere else.

Critics say that insurance just encourages development in areas that flood. Another problem with the insurance is cost. It is very expensive. Most people who live in flood plains don't buy the government insurance. Supporters say insurance rewards towns and cities that make rules to control building on flood plains. Over time, this approach would mean fewer homes and other buildings on flood plains—and less damage from flooding.

▼ Flooded homes in Davenport, Iowa.

Floodwater Rising
Rain from Hurricane Isabel caused this flooding in Alexandria, Virginia in 2003.

How Much of the Flood Plain Should Be Protected?

Government flood insurance is available only in areas where scientists expect flooding at least once in 100 years. But such figures are just estimates. Three floods occurred in only 12 years in a government flood insurance area near Sacramento, California.

Should the Government Tell People Where They Can Live?

Some programs of flood control forbid all new building. Other programs may also encourage people to move to safer areas. The 1997 flood on the Red River in Grand Forks, North Dakota, is one example. After the flood, the city of Grand Forks offered to buy all the damaged buildings near the river. The city wants to build high walls of earth to protect the rest of the town.

The Grand Forks plan might prevent future damage, but is it fair? Supporters say that since the government has to pay for flood damage, it has the right to make people leave flood plains. Critics of such plans say that people should be free to live where they want, even in risky areas.

Who should decide in which neighborhood no new houses can be built? Who decides which people should be asked to move away from a flood plain? Experts disagree over whether local, state, or United States government officials should decide which areas to include. Some believe scientists should make the decision.

You Decide

1. Identify the Problem
In your own words, describe the controversy surrounding flood plains and housing.

2. Analyze the Options
List several steps that could be taken to reduce the damage done to buildings in flood plains. For each step, include who would benefit from the step and who would pay the costs.

3. Find a Solution
Your town has to decide what to do about a neighborhood damaged by the worst flood in 50 years. Write a speech that argues for your solution.

For: More on protecting homes in flood plains
Visit: PHSchool.com
Web Code: cfh-2030

The Force of Moving Water

Reading Preview

Key Concepts
- What enables water to do work?
- How does sediment enter rivers and streams?
- What factors affect a river's ability to erode and carry sediment?

Key Terms
- energy • potential energy
- kinetic energy • abrasion
- load • friction • turbulence

Target Reading Skill
Building Vocabulary A definition states the meaning of a word or phrase by telling about its most important feature or function. Carefully read the definition of each Key Term and also read the neighboring sentences. Then write a definition of each Key Term in your own words.

Lab zone Discover **Activity**

How Are Sediments Deposited?
1. Put on your goggles.
2. Obtain a clear plastic jar or bottle with a top. Fill the jar about two-thirds full with water.
3. Fill a plastic beaker with 200 mL of fine and coarse sand, soil, clay, and small pebbles.
4. Pour the mixture into the jar of water. Screw on the top tightly and shake for two minutes. Be sure to hold onto the jar firmly.
5. Set the jar down and observe it for 10 to 15 minutes.

Think It Over
Inferring In what order are the sediments in the jar deposited? What do you think causes this pattern?

The Merrimack River in New Hampshire and Massachusetts is only 180 kilometers long. But the Merrimack does a great deal of work as it runs from the mountains to the sea. The river's waters fall 82 meters through many rapids and waterfalls. During the 1800s, people harnessed this falling water to run machines that could spin thread and weave cloth.

Work and Energy

A river's water has energy. **Energy** is the ability to do work or cause change. There are two kinds of energy. **Potential energy** is energy that is stored and waiting to be used later. The Merrimack's waters begin with potential energy due to their position above sea level. **Kinetic energy** is the energy an object has due to its motion. **As gravity pulls water down a slope, the water's potential energy changes to kinetic energy that can do work.**

When energy does work, the energy is transferred from one object to another. Along the Merrimack River, the kinetic energy of the moving water was transferred to the spinning machines. It became mechanical energy harnessed for making cloth. But all along a river, moving water has other effects. A river is always moving sediment from the mountains to the sea. At the same time, a river is also eroding its banks and valley.

FIGURE 13
Water Power
Dams like this one on the Merrimack River in Lowell, Massachusetts, help to harness the power of flowing water.

How Water Erodes

Gravity causes the movement of water across Earth's land surface. But how does water cause erosion? In the process of water erosion, water picks up and moves sediment. Sediment includes soil, rock, clay, and sand. Sediment can enter rivers and streams in a number of ways. **Most sediment washes or falls into a river as a result of mass movement and runoff. Other sediment erodes from the bottom or sides of the river.** Wind may also drop sediment into the water.

Abrasion is another process by which a river obtains sediment. **Abrasion** is the wearing away of rock by a grinding action. Abrasion occurs when particles of sediment in flowing water bump into the streambed again and again. Abrasion grinds down sediment particles. For example, boulders become smaller as they are moved down a stream bed. Sediments also grind and chip away at the rock of the stream bed, deepening and widening the stream's channel.

The amount of sediment that a river carries is its **load.** Gravity and the force of the moving water cause the sediment load to move downstream. Most large sediment falls to the bottom and moves by rolling and sliding. Fast-moving water actually lifts sand and other, smaller sediment and carries it downstream. Water dissolves some sediment completely. The river carries these dissolved sediments in solution. Figure 14 shows other ways in which water can carry sediment. For example, grains of sand or small stones can move by bouncing.

> ✓ **Reading Checkpoint**   What causes the sediment in a river to move downstream?

FIGURE 14
Movement of Sediment
Rivers and streams carry sediment in several ways. The salmon at right are swimming upstream through water that looks clear, but contains dissolved sediment. **Predicting** *How would a boulder in a stream be likely to move?*

Direction of flow

Dissolved sediment

Suspended sediment

Larger particles pushed or rolled along streambed

Smaller particles move by bouncing

◆ 485

Erosion and Sediment Load

The power of a river to cause erosion and carry sediment depends on several factors. **A river's slope, volume of flow, and the shape of its stream bed all affect how fast the river flows and how much sediment it can erode.**

A fast-flowing river carries more and larger particles of sediment. When a river slows down, it drops its sediment load. The larger particles of sediment are deposited first.

Slope Generally, if a river's slope increases, the water's speed also increases. A river's slope is the amount the river drops toward sea level over a given distance. If a river's speed increases, its sediment load and power to erode may increase. But other factors are also important in determining how much sediment the river erodes and carries.

Volume of Flow A river's flow is the volume of water that moves past a point on the river in a given time. As more water flows through a river, its speed increases. During a flood, the increased volume of water helps the river to cut more deeply into its banks and bed. When a river floods, its power to erode may increase by a hundredfold. A flooding river can carry huge amounts of sand, soil, and other sediments. It may move giant boulders as if they were pebbles.

✓ **Reading Checkpoint** How does a river's slope affect its speed?

FIGURE 15
The Slope of a River
A river's slope is usually greatest near the river's source. As a river approaches its mouth, its slope lessens. **Inferring** *Where would you expect the water in this river to have the greatest amount of potential energy?*

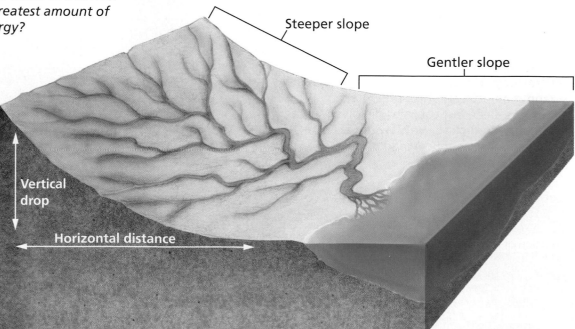

Steeper slope

Gentler slope

Vertical drop

Horizontal distance

Streambed Shape A streambed's shape affects the amount of friction between the water and the streambed. **Friction** is the force that opposes the motion of one surface as it moves across another surface. Friction, in turn, affects a river's speed. Where a river is deep, less water comes in contact with the streambed. The reduced friction allows the river to flow faster. In a shallow river, much of the water comes in contact with the streambed. Therefore friction increases, reducing the river's speed.

A streambed is often full of boulders and other obstacles. This roughness prevents the water from flowing smoothly. Roughness thus increases friction and reduces the river's speed. Instead of moving downstream, the water moves every which way in a type of movement called **turbulence**. For example, a stream on a steep slope may flow at a slower speed than a large river on a gentle slope. Friction and turbulence slow the stream's flow. But a turbulent stream or river may have great power to erode.

FIGURE 16
Turbulence
The turbulent flow of this stream increases the stream's power to cause erosion.

Math ▸ Analyzing Data

Sediment on the Move

The speed, or velocity, of a stream affects the size of the sediment particles the stream can carry. Study the graph, then answer the questions below.

1. **Reading Graphs** What variable is shown on the *x*-axis of the graph?

2. **Reading Graphs** What variable is shown on the *y*-axis of the graph?

3. **Interpreting Data** What is the speed at which a stream can move coarse sand? Small pebbles? Large boulders?

4. **Predicting** A stream's speed increases to about 600 cm per second during a flood. What are the largest particles the stream can move?

5. **Developing Hypotheses** Write a hypothesis that states the relationship between the speed of a stream and the size of the sediment particles it can move.

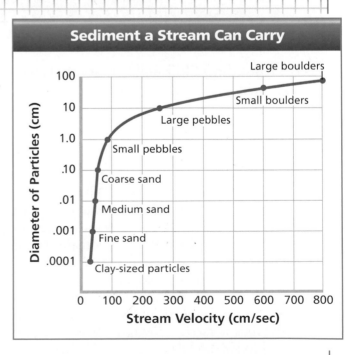

Sediment a Stream Can Carry

Diameter of Particles (cm) — values: 100, 10, 1.0, .10, .01, .001, .0001

Labels: Large boulders, Small boulders, Large pebbles, Small pebbles, Coarse sand, Medium sand, Fine sand, Clay-sized particles

Stream Velocity (cm/sec): 0, 100, 200, 300, 400, 500, 600, 700, 800

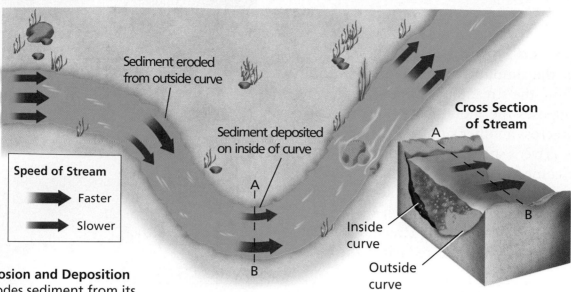

FIGURE 17
Stream Erosion and Deposition
A river erodes sediment from its banks on the outside curve and deposits sediment on the inside curve.
Relating Cause and Effect *Why does a river deposit sediment on the inside of a curve?*

Factors Affecting Erosion and Deposition Whether a river flows in a straight line or a curved line affects the way it erodes and deposits sediment. Where a river flows in a straight line, the water flows faster near the center of the river than along its sides. Deposition occurs along the sides of the river, where the water moves more slowly.

If a river curves, the water moves fastest along the outside of the curve. There, the river tends to cut into its bank, causing erosion. Sediment is deposited on the inside curve, where the water speed is slowest. You can see this process in Figure 17.

Reading Checkpoint Where a stream curves, in what part of the stream does the water flow fastest?

Section 3 Assessment

 **Target Reading Skill Building Vocabulary**
Use your definitions to help answer the questions.

Reviewing Key Concepts

1. a. Defining What is energy?
   b. Explaining How is a river's potential energy changed into kinetic energy?
   c. Relating Cause and Effect What are two effects produced by flowing water in a river?
2. a. Reviewing What are two main sources of the sediment that rivers and streams carry?
   b. Describing Describe a process by which a stream can erode its streambed.
   c. Predicting Near a stream's source, a stream erodes a piece of rock from its streambed. As the rock is carried down the stream, how will its size and shape change? Explain.

3. a. Identifying What three factors affect how fast a river flows?
   b. Interpreting Diagrams Study Figure 17 above. Over time, what will happen to the river's bank at B? Why?

Writing in Science

Comparison Paragraph A river transports different types of sediment particles from its source to its mouth: tiny clay particles, grains of sand, pebbles, and boulders. Write a paragraph that compares clay particles and pebbles in terms of how they move, how fast they travel, and how their potential energy changes during the journey.

Glaciers

Reading Preview

Key Concepts
- What are the two kinds of glaciers?
- How does a valley glacier form and move?
- How do glaciers cause erosion and deposition?

Key Terms
- glacier • continental glacier
- ice age• valley glacier
- plucking • till • moraine • kettle

Target Reading Skill

Asking Questions Before you read, preview the red headings. In a graphic organizer like the one below, ask a *what, how,* or *where* question for each heading. As you read, answer your questions.

Glaciers

Question	Answer
What kinds of glaciers are there?	Valley glaciers and . . .

▼ **The Hubbard Glacier in Alaska**

Lab zone Discover **Activity**

How Do Glaciers Change the Land?

1. Put some sand in a small plastic container.
2. Fill the container with water and place the container in a freezer until the water turns to ice.
3. Remove the block of ice from the container. Hold the ice with a paper towel.
4. Rub the ice, sand side down, over a bar of soap. Observe what happens to the surface of the soap.

Think It Over

Inferring Based on your observations, how do you think moving ice could change the surface of the land?

You are on a boat trip near the coast of Alaska. You sail by vast evergreen forests and snow-capped mountains. Then, as your boat rounds a point of land, you see an amazing sight. A great mass of ice winds like a river between rows of mountains. Suddenly you hear a noise like thunder. Where the ice meets the sea, a giant chunk of ice breaks off and plunges into the water. Carefully, the pilot steers your boat around the iceberg and toward the mass of ice. It towers over your boat. You see that it is made up of solid ice that is deep blue and green as well as white. What is this river of ice?

Huge icebergs form where Antartica's continental glacier meets the ocean.

FIGURE 18
Continental Glaciers
Today, huge icebergs form where a continental glacier (above) meets the ocean. During the last ice age (below), a continental glacier covered most of northern North America.

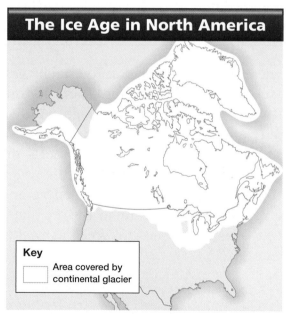

The Ice Age in North America

Key
☐ Area covered by continental glacier

How Glaciers Form and Move

Geologists define a **glacier** as any large mass of ice that moves slowly over land. **There are two kinds of glaciers—continental glaciers and valley glaciers.**

Continental Glaciers A **continental glacier** is a glacier that covers much of a continent or large island. They can spread out over millions of square kilometers. Today, continental glaciers cover about 10 percent of Earth's land. They cover Antarctica and most of Greenland. In places, the glacier covering Antarctica is over 3 kilometers thick. Continental glaciers can flow in all directions as they move. Continental glaciers spread out much as pancake batter spreads out in a frying pan.

Many times in the past, continental glaciers have covered larger parts of Earth's surface. These times are known as **ice ages.** For example, beginning about 2.5 million years ago, continental glaciers covered about one third of Earth's land. The glaciers advanced and retreated, or melted back, several times. They finally retreated about 10,000 years ago.

Valley Glaciers A **valley glacier** is a long, narrow glacier that forms when snow and ice build up high in a mountain valley. The sides of mountains keep these glaciers from spreading out in all directions. Instead, they usually move down valleys that have already been cut by rivers. Valley glaciers are found on many high mountains. Although they are much smaller than continental glaciers, valley glaciers can be tens of kilometers long.

High in mountain valleys, temperatures seldom rise above freezing. Snow builds up year after year. The weight of more and more snow compacts the snow at the bottom into ice. **Glaciers can form only in an area where more snow falls than melts. Once the depth of snow and ice reaches more than 30 to 40 meters, gravity begins to pull the glacier downhill.**

Valley glaciers flow at a rate of a few centimeters to a few meters per day. But sometimes a valley glacier slides down more quickly in what is called a surge. A surging glacier can flow as much as 6 kilometers a year.

 **Reading Checkpoint** On what type of landform are valley glaciers found?

How Glaciers Shape the Land

The movement of a glacier changes the land beneath it. Although glaciers work slowly, they are a major force of erosion. **The two processes by which glaciers erode the land are plucking and abrasion.**

Glacial Erosion As a glacier flows over the land, it picks up rocks in a process called **plucking.** Beneath a glacier, the weight of the ice can break rocks apart. These rock fragments freeze to the bottom of the glacier. When the glacier moves, it carries the rocks with it. Figure 19 shows plucking by a glacier. Plucking can move even huge boulders.

Many rocks remain on the bottom of the glacier, and the glacier drags them across the land. This process, called abrasion, gouges and scratches the bedrock. You can see the results of erosion by glaciers in Figure 19.

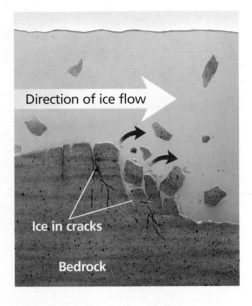

FIGURE 19
Glacial Erosion
As a glacier moves (above), plucking breaks pieces of bedrock from the ground. Erosion by glaciers (below) can carve a mountain peak into a sharp horn and grind out a **V**-shaped valley to form a **U**-shaped valley.
Observing *What other changes did the glacier produce in this landscape?*

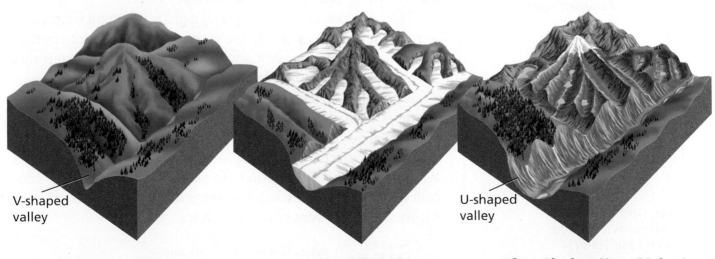

Before Glaciers Form   **During Glaciation**   **After Glaciers Have Melted**

Horn
When glaciers carve away the sides of a mountain, the result is a horn, a sharpened peak.

Cirque
A cirque is a bowl-shaped hollow eroded by a glacier.

Arête
An arête is a sharp ridge separating two cirques.

Fiord
A fiord forms when the level of the sea rises, filling a valley once cut by a glacier.

FIGURE 20
Glacial Landforms
As glaciers advance and retreat, they sculpt the landscape by erosion and deposition.
Classifying *Classify these glacial features according to whether they result from erosion or deposition: drumlin, horn, cirque, moraine, U-shaped valley.*

Go Online
*sci*LINKS™ NSTA

For: Links on glaciers
Visit: www.SciLinks.org
Web Code: scn-0734

Glacial Deposition A glacier gathers a huge amount of rock and soil as it erodes the land in its path. **When a glacier melts, it deposits the sediment it eroded from the land, creating various landforms.** These landforms remain for thousands of years after the glacier has melted. The mixture of sediments that a glacier deposits directly on the surface is called **till.** Till is made up of particles of many different sizes. Clay, silt, sand, gravel, and boulders can all be found in till.

The till deposited at the edges of a glacier forms a ridge called a **moraine.** A terminal moraine is the ridge of till at the farthest point reached by a glacier. Long Island in New York is a terminal moraine from the continental glaciers of the last ice age.

Retreating glaciers also create features called kettles. A **kettle** is a small depression that forms when a chunk of ice is left in glacial till. When the ice melts, the kettle remains. The continental glacier of the last ice age left behind many kettles. Kettles often fill with water, forming small ponds or lakes called kettle lakes. Such lakes are common in areas, such as Minnesota, that were covered with ice.

 **Reading Checkpoint** What is a terminal moraine?

Glacial Lake
Glaciers may leave behind large lakes in long basins.

U-Shaped Valley
A flowing glacier scoops out a U-shaped valley.

Moraine
A moraine forms where a glacier deposits mounds or ridges of till.

Drumlin
A drumlin is a long mound of till that is smoothed in the direction of the glacier's flow.

Kettle Lake
A kettle lake forms when a depression left in till by melting ice fills with water.

Section 4 Assessment

 Target Reading Skill Asking Questions Use the answers to the questions you wrote about the headings to help you answer the questions below.

Reviewing Key Concepts

1. **a. Defining** What is a continental glacier?
   b. Defining What is a valley glacier?
   c. Comparing and Contrasting How are the two types of glaciers similar? How are they different?

2. **a. Reviewing** What condition is necessary for a glacier to form?
   b. Explaining How does a glacier move?
   c. Relating Cause and Effect Why does the snow that forms a glacier change to ice?

3. **a. Identifying** What are two ways in which glaciers erode Earth's surface?
   b. Describing How does glacial deposition occur?

Writing in Science

Travel Brochure A travel agency wants people to go on a tour of a mountain region with many glaciers. Write a paragraph for a travel brochure describing what people will see on the tour. In your answer, include features formed by glacial erosion and deposition.

Reading Preview

Key Concepts
- What gives waves their energy?
- How do waves erode a coast?
- What features result from deposition by waves?

Key Terms
- headland • beach
- longshore drift • spit

Target Reading Skill
Identifying Main Ideas As you read Erosion by Waves, write the main idea in a graphic organizer like the one below. Then write three supporting details that further explain the main idea.

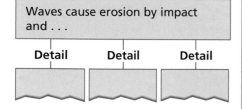

Main Idea

Waves cause erosion by impact and . . .

Detail	Detail	Detail

▼ **Waves on the Oregon coast**

Lab zone Discover Activity

What Is Sand Made Of?

1. Collect a spoonful of sand from each of two different beaches.
2. Examine the first sample of beach sand with a hand lens.
3. Record the properties of the sand grains, for example, color and shape. Are the grains smooth and rounded or angular and rough?
4. Examine the second sample and repeat Step 3. How do the two samples compare?

Think It Over

Posing Questions What questions do you need to answer to understand beach sand? Use what you know about erosion and deposition to help you think of questions.

Ocean waves contain energy—sometimes a great deal of energy. Created by ocean winds, they carry energy vast distances across the Pacific Ocean. Acting like drills or buzz saws, the waves erode the solid rock of the coast into cliffs and caves. Waves also carry sediment that forms features such as beaches.

How Waves Form

The energy in waves comes from wind that blows across the water's surface. As the wind makes contact with the water, some of its energy transfers to the water. Large ocean waves are the result of powerful storms far out at sea. But ordinary breezes can produce waves in lakes or small ponds.

The energy that water picks up from the wind causes water particles to move up and down as the wave goes by. But the water particles themselves don't move forward.

A wave changes as it approaches land. In deep water, a wave only affects the water near the surface. But as it approaches shallow water, the wave begins to drag on the bottom. The friction between the wave and the bottom causes the wave to slow down. Now the water actually does move forward with the wave. This forward-moving water provides the force that shapes the land along the shoreline.

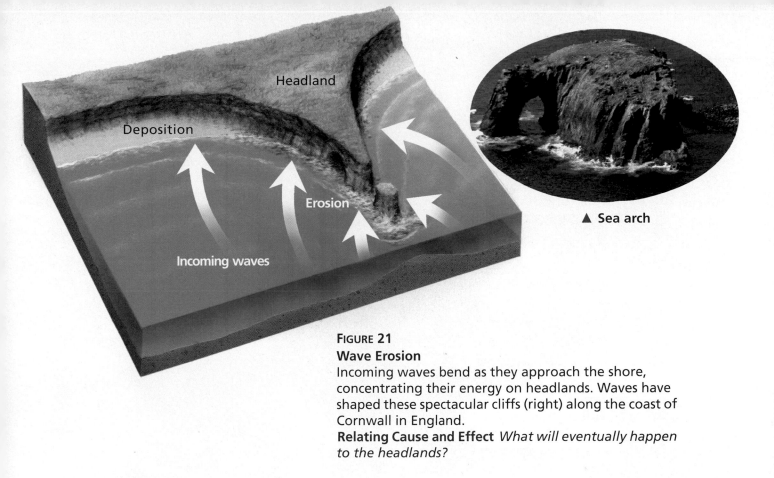

Headland

Deposition

Erosion

Incoming waves

▲ Sea arch

FIGURE 21
Wave Erosion
Incoming waves bend as they approach the shore, concentrating their energy on headlands. Waves have shaped these spectacular cliffs (right) along the coast of Cornwall in England.
Relating Cause and Effect *What will eventually happen to the headlands?*

Erosion by Waves

Waves are the major force of erosion along coasts. **Waves shape the coast through erosion by breaking down rock and transporting sand and other sediment.**

How Waves Erode One way waves erode the land is by impact. Large waves can hit rocks along the shore with great force. This energy in waves can break apart rocks. Over time, waves can make small cracks larger. Eventually, the waves cause pieces of rock to break off.

Waves also erode by abrasion. As a wave approaches shallow water, it picks up sediment, including sand and gravel. This sediment is carried forward by the wave. When the wave hits land, the sediment wears away rock like sandpaper wearing away wood.

Waves coming to shore gradually change direction. The change in direction occurs as different parts of a wave begin to drag on the bottom. Notice how the waves in Figure 21 change direction as they approach the shore. The energy of these waves is concentrated on headlands. A **headland** is a part of the shore that sticks out into the ocean. Headlands stand out from the coast because they are made of harder rock that resists erosion by the waves. But, over time, waves erode the headlands and even out the shoreline.

Go **O**nline
SC*LINKS*™ NSTA

For: Links on waves
Visit: www.SciLinks.org
Web Code: scn-0735

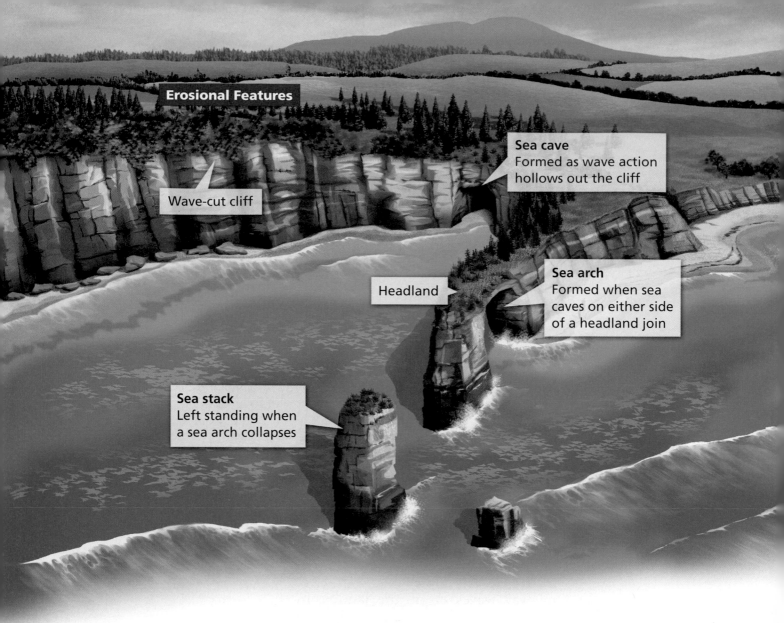

Erosional Features

Wave-cut cliff

Sea cave
Formed as wave action hollows out the cliff

Headland

Sea arch
Formed when sea caves on either side of a headland join

Sea stack
Left standing when a sea arch collapses

FIGURE 22
The Changing Coast

Erosion and deposition create a variety of features along a coast. **Predicting** *What will eventually happen to the sea arch?*

Landforms Created by Wave Erosion When waves hit a steep, rocky coast, they strike the area again and again. Think of an ax striking the trunk of a tree. The cut gets bigger and deeper with each strike of the blade. Finally the tree falls. In a similar way, ocean waves erode the base of the land along a steep coast. Where the rock is softer, the waves erode the land faster. Over time the waves may erode a hollow area in the rock called a sea cave.

Eventually, waves may erode the base of a cliff so much that the rock above collapses. The result is a wave-cut cliff. You can see an example of such a cliff in Figure 22.

Another feature created by wave erosion is a sea arch. A sea arch forms when waves erode a layer of softer rock that underlies a layer of harder rock. If an arch collapses, the result might be a sea stack, a pillar of rock rising above the water.

 Reading Checkpoint **Over a long period of time, what effect do waves have on a steep, rocky coast?**

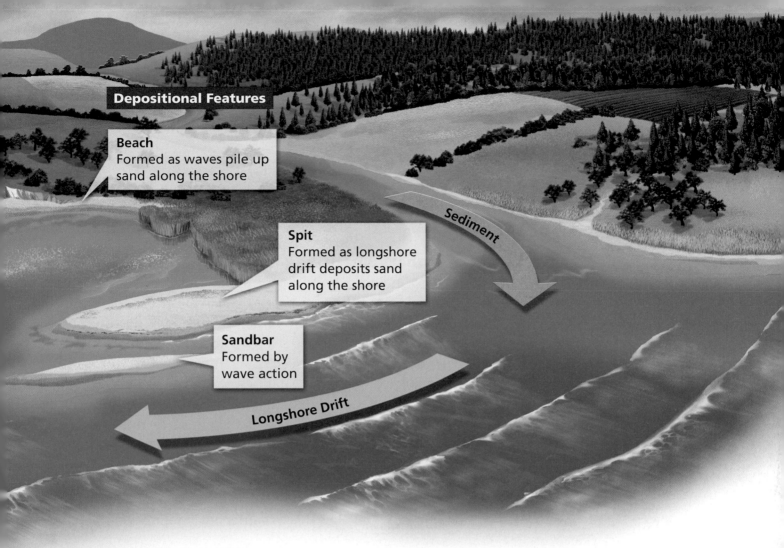

Depositional Features

Beach
Formed as waves pile up sand along the shore

Spit
Formed as longshore drift deposits sand along the shore

Sandbar
Formed by wave action

Sediment

Longshore Drift

Deposits by Waves

Waves shape a coast when they deposit sediment, forming coastal features such as beaches, spits, and barrier beaches. Deposition occurs when waves slow down, causing the water to drop its sediment. This process is similar to the deposition that occurs on a river delta when the river slows down and drops its sediment load.

Beaches As waves reach the shore, they drop the sediment they carry, forming a beach. A **beach** is an area of wave-washed sediment along a coast. The sediment deposited on beaches is usually sand. Most sand comes from rivers that carry eroded particles of rock into the ocean. But not all beaches are made of sand. Some beaches are made of small fragments of coral or sea shells piled up by wave action. Florida has many such beaches.

The sediment on a beach usually moves down the beach after it has been deposited. Waves usually hit the beach at an angle instead of straight on. These angled waves create a current that runs parallel to the coastline. As waves repeatedly hit the beach, some of the beach sediment moves down the beach with the current, in a process called **longshore drift.**

Lab zone **Skills Activity**

Calculating A sandy coast erodes at a rate of 1.25 m per year. But a severe storm can erode an additional 3.75 m from the shore. If 12 severe storms occur during a 50-year period, how much will the coast erode? If you wish, you may use an electronic calculator to find the answer.

Spits One result of longshore drift is the formation of a spit. A **spit** is a beach that projects like a finger out into the water. Spits form as a result of deposition by longshore drift. Spits occur where a headland or other obstacle interrupts longshore drift, or where the coast turns abruptly.

FIGURE 23
Spits
This aerial photograph shows how longshore drift can carry sand and deposit it to form a spit.
Observing *How many spits can you find in this image?*

Sandbars and Barrier Beaches Incoming waves carrying sand may build up sandbars, long ridges of sand parallel to the shore. A barrier beach is similar to a sandbar. A barrier beach forms when storm waves pile up large amounts of sand above sea level forming a long, narrow island parallel to the coast. Barrier beaches are found in many places along the Atlantic coast of the United States, such as the Outer Banks of North Carolina. People have built homes on many of these barrier beaches. But the storm waves that build up the beaches can also wash them away. Barrier beach communities must be prepared for the damage that hurricanes and other storms can bring.

 **Reading Checkpoint** **How does a barrier beach form?**

Section 5 Assessment

Target Reading Skill **Identifying Main Ideas** Use your graphic organizer to help you answer Question 2 below.

Reviewing Key Concepts

1. a. **Explaining** What is the source of the energy in ocean waves?
   b. **Describing** How does an ocean wave change when it reaches shallow water?
   c. **Inferring** Does an ocean wave possess potential energy or kinetic energy? Explain.
2. a. **Identifying** What are two results of wave erosion along a coast?
   b. **Describing** What are two ways in which waves erode rock?
   c. **Sequencing** Place these features in the order in which they would probably form: sea stack, sea cave, headland, cliff, sea arch.

3. a. **Listing** What are three features formed by wave deposition?
   b. **Relating Cause and Effect** Beginning with the source of sand, explain the process by which a spit forms.

Writing in Science

Explaining a Process Suppose that you live in a coastal area that has a barrier beach. Write a paragraph in which you explain the processes that formed the barrier beach. Also describe how the forces might change it over time.

Wind

Reading Preview

Key Concepts
- How does wind cause erosion?
- What features result from deposition by wind?

Key Terms
- sand dune
- deflation
- loess

Target Reading Skill
Sequencing As you read, make a flowchart like the one below that shows the process of wind erosion and deposition. Write each step of the process in a separate box in the flowchart in the order in which it occurs.

Wind Erosion

Wind picks up smallest particles of sediment.

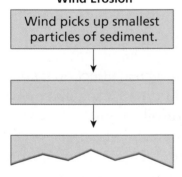

Wind erosion constantly shapes the giant sand dunes in the Namib Desert of southwestern Africa. ▼

Lab zone
Discover Activity

How Does Moving Air Affect Sediment?

1. Cover the bottom of a pan with a flat layer of cornmeal 1–2 cm deep.
2. Gently blow over the layer of cornmeal using a straw to direct your breath. Observe what happens. **CAUTION:** *Do not blow the cornmeal in the direction of another student.*

Think It Over
Observing What changes did the wind you created make in the flat layer of cornmeal?

Imagine a landscape made almost entirely of sand. One such place is the Namib Desert. The desert stretches 1,900 kilometers along the coast of Namibia in Africa. In the southern half of the Namib are rows of giant sand dunes. A **sand dune** is a deposit of wind-blown sand. Some sand dunes in the Namib are more than 200 meters high and 15 kilometers long. Much of the sand in the dunes originally came from the nearby Orange River. Over thousands of years, wind has swept the sand across the desert, piling up huge, ever-changing dunes.

How Wind Causes Erosion

Wind by itself is the weakest agent of erosion. Water, waves, moving ice, and even mass movement have more effect on the land. Yet wind can be a powerful force in shaping the land in areas where there are few plants to hold the soil in place. For example, few plants grow in deserts, so wind can easily move the grains of dry sand. **Wind causes erosion by deflation and abrasion.**

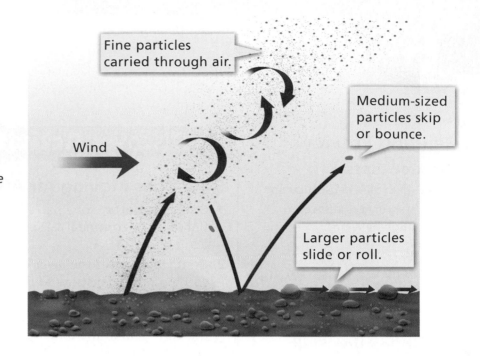

FIGURE 24
Wind Erosion
Wind erosion moves sediment particles of different sizes in the three ways shown at right.
Comparing and Contrasting *Compare the movement of sediment by wind with the movement of sediment by water in Figure 14 on page 87. How are the processes similar? How are they different?*

Fine particles carried through air.

Medium-sized particles skip or bounce.

Wind

Larger particles slide or roll.

FIGURE 25
Desert Pavement
Wind erosion formed this desert pavement in the Arizona desert. Wind-driven sand may polish and shape individual stones.

Deflation The main way that wind causes erosion is by deflation. Geologists define **deflation** as the process by which wind removes surface materials. When wind blows over the land, it picks up the smallest particles of sediment. This sediment is made of bits of clay and silt. The stronger the wind, the larger the particles that it can pick up. Slightly heavier particles, such as sand, might skip or bounce for a short distance. But sand soon falls back to the ground. Strong winds can even roll heavier sediment particles over the ground. Figure 24 shows how wind erodes by deflation.

Deflation does not usually have a great effect on land. However, in parts of the Great Plains in the 1930s, deflation caused the loss of about 1 meter of topsoil in just a few years. In deserts, deflation can sometimes create an area of rock fragments called desert pavement. You can see an area of desert pavement in Figure 25. There, wind has blown away the smaller sediment. All that remains are rocky materials that are too heavy to be moved. Where there is already a slight depression in the ground, deflation can produce a bowl-shaped hollow called a blowout.

Abrasion Abrasion by wind-carried sand can polish rock, but it causes little erosion. At one time, geologists thought that the sediment carried by wind cut the stone shapes seen in deserts. But now evidence shows that most desert landforms are the result of weathering and water erosion.

 **Reading Checkpoint** **Where would you be most likely to see evidence of wind erosion?**

Wind Deposition

All the sediment picked up by wind eventually falls to the ground. This happens when the wind slows down or some obstacle, such as a boulder or a clump of grass, traps the windblown sand sediment. **Wind erosion and deposition may form sand dunes and loess deposits.** When the wind strikes an obstacle, the result is usually a sand dune. Sand dunes can be seen on beaches and in deserts where wind-blown sediment has built up.

Sand Dunes Sand dunes come in many shapes and sizes. Some are long, with parallel ridges, while others are U-shaped. They can also be very small or very large—some sand dunes in China have grown to heights of 500 meters. Sand dunes move over time. Little by little, the sand shifts with the wind from one side of the dune to the other. This process is shown in Figure 26. Sometimes plants begin growing on a dune. Plant roots can help to anchor the dune in one place.

Loess Deposits Sediment that is finer than sand, such as particles of clay and silt, is sometimes deposited in layers far from its source. This fine, wind-deposited sediment is **loess** (LES). Large loess deposits are found in central China and in such states as Nebraska, South Dakota, Iowa, Missouri, and Illinois. Loess helps to form fertile soil. Many areas with thick loess deposits are valuable farmlands.

Crescent-shaped dunes form where the wind usually blows in the same direction.

Star-shaped dunes form where the wind direction changes frequently.

Wind direction

FIGURE 26
Movement of Sand Dunes
Wind direction is one factor that helps determine the shape and size of sand dunes.

Section 6 Assessment

🎯 **Target Reading Skill** Sequencing Refer to your flowchart as you answer the questions below.

Reviewing Key Concepts

1. a. **Reviewing** What are two kinds of wind erosion?
   b. **Explaining** Explain how sediment particles of different sizes move during wind erosion.
   c. **Predicting** In a desert, soil containing a mixture of sand and small rocks is exposed to wind erosion. Over time, how would the land surface change? Explain.

2. a. **Relating Cause and Effect** What causes wind to deposit sand or other sediment?
   b. **Identifying** What are two types of features that result from wind deposition?
   c. **Problem Solving** How could sand dunes be held in place to keep them from drifting onto a parking lot?

Lab zone At-Home **Activity**

Desert Pavement To model desert pavement, put a few coins in a shallow pan. Sprinkle enough flour over the coins to cover them. Then blow air gently through a straw across the surface of the flour. Be careful not to draw in any flour through the straw. Be certain the blown flour will not get in your or anyone else's eyes. Ask your family to predict what would happen if the "wind" blew for a long time.

1 Changing Earth's Surface

Key Concepts

- Weathering, erosion, and deposition act together in a cycle that wears down and builds up Earth's surface.
- Gravity causes mass movement, including landslides, mudflows, slump, and creep.

Key Terms

erosion   gravity
deposition   sediment
mass movement

2 Water Erosion

Key Concepts

- Moving water is the major agent of the erosion that has shaped Earth's land surface.
- Through erosion, a river creates valleys, water-falls, flood plains, meanders, and oxbow lakes.
- Deposition creates alluvial fans and deltas. It can also add soil to a river's flood plain.
- Groundwater can cause erosion through a process of chemical weathering.

Key Terms

- runoff • rill • gully • stream • tributary
- flood plain • meander • oxbow lake
- alluvial fan • delta   groundwater
- stalactite • stalagmite • karst topography

3 The Force of Moving Water

Key Concepts

- As gravity pulls water down a slope, the water's potential energy changes to kinetic energy.
- Most sediment washes or falls into a river as a result of mass movement and runoff.
- A river's slope, volume of flow, and the shape of its stream bed all affect how fast the river flows and how much sediment it can erode.

Key Terms

energy   load
potential energy   friction
kinetic energy   turbulence
abrasion

4 Glaciers

Key Concepts

- There are two kinds of glaciers—continental glaciers and valley glaciers.
- Glaciers can form only in an area where more snow falls than melts.
- The two processes by which glaciers erode the land are plucking and abrasion.
- When a glacier melts, it deposits the sediment it eroded from the land, creating various landforms.

Key Terms

glacier   plucking
continental glacier   till
ice age   moraine
valley glacier   kettle

5 Waves

Key Concepts

- The energy in waves comes from wind that blows across the water's surface.
- Waves shape the coast through erosion by breaking down rock and transporting sand and other sediment.
- Waves shape a coast when they deposit sediment, forming coastal features such as beaches, spits, and barrier beaches.

Key Terms

headland   longshore drift
beach   spit

6 Wind

Key Concepts

- Wind causes erosion by deflation and abrasion.
- Wind erosion and deposition may form sand dunes and loess deposits.

Key Terms

sand dune   deflation   loess

Review and Assessment

Organizing Information

Flowcharts Copy the flowchart about stream formation onto a separate sheet of paper. Then complete it and add a title. (For more on flowcharts, see the Skills Handbook).

Stream Formation

Raindrops strike ground.

↓

Runoff forms.

↓

a. _____ ? _____

↓

b. _____ ? _____

↓

c. _____ ? _____

↓

d. _____ ? _____

Reviewing Key Terms

Choose the letter of the best answer.

1. The eroded materials carried by water or wind are called
   a. stalactites.
   b. desert pavement.
   c. sediment.
   d. moraines.

2. The downhill movement of eroded materials is known as
   a. mass movement.
   b. abrasion.
   c. deposition.
   d. deflation.

3. Where a stream bed is rough, the stream flows more slowly because of
   a. sediment.
   b. friction.
   c. deposition.
   d. potential energy.

4. A mass of rock and soil deposited directly by a glacier is called
   a. load.   b. till.
   c. loess.   d. erosion.

5. The erosion of sediment by wind is
   a. deposition.   b. deflation.
   c. plucking.   d. glaciation.

If the statement is true, write _true_. If it is false, change the underlined word or words to make the statement true.

6. The process by which sediment in water settles in new locations is <u>mass movement</u>.

7. <u>Groundwater</u> that flows in a thin layer over the land causes sheet erosion.

8. Because it is moving, flowing water has a type of energy called <u>kinetic energy</u>.

9. A looplike bend in the river is a <u>meander</u>.

10. The sediment deposited at the edge of a glacier forms a ridge called a <u>kettle</u>.

Writing in Science

Article Suppose that you have just returned from a visit to a limestone cave, such as Mammoth Cave in Kentucky. Write an article describing your visit to the cave. Include how the cave formed, what you saw during your visit, and how features inside the cave developed.

Discovery CHANNEL SCHOOL™

Erosion and Deposition

Video Preview
Video Field Trip
▶ Video Assessment

Review and Assessment

Checking Concepts

11. What agents of erosion are assisted by the force of gravity?

12. How do a river's slope and volume of flow affect the river's sediment load?

13. What is turbulence? How does it affect the speed of a river and the river's power to cause erosion?

14. Where is the speed of the flowing water in a river the slowest? Explain.

15. What are ice ages?

16. How does a kettle lake form?

17. How does a loess deposit form?

Thinking Critically

18. **Comparing and Contrasting** Compare and contrast landslides and mudflows.

19. **Applying Concepts** Under what conditions would you expect abrasion to cause the most erosion of a riverbed?

20. **Making Judgments** A salesperson offers to sell your family a new house right on a riverbank for very little money. Why might your family hesitate to buy this house?

21. **Relating Cause and Effect** What caused the features labeled A, B, and C in the diagram below to form? Explain.

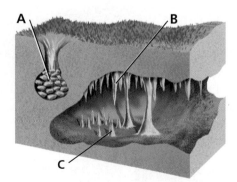

22. **Problem Solving** Suppose you are a geologist studying a valley glacier. What method could you use to tell if it is advancing or retreating?

23. **Inferring** You see a sandy beach along a coastline. Where did the sand come from?

Applying Skills

Use the table below to answer Questions 24–26.

The table shows how a river's volume of flow and sediment load change over six months.

Month	Volume of Flow (cubic meters/second)	Sediment Load (metric tons/day)
January	1.5	200
February	1.7	320
March	2.6	725
April	4.0	1,600
May	3.2	1,100
June	2.8	900

24. **Graphing** Make one graph with the month on the x-axis and the volume of flow on the y-axis. Make a second graph with the sediment load on the y-axis. Compare your two graphs. When were the river's volume of flow and load the greatest? The lowest?

25. **Developing Hypotheses** Use your graphs to develop a hypothesis about the relationship between volume of flow and sediment load.

26. **Relating Cause and Effect** What may have occurred in the river's drainage basin in April to cause the changes in volume of flow and sediment load? Explain.

Lab zone Chapter **Project**

Performance Assessment Now you are ready to present to your class. Explain which types of soil you chose and why you chose them. Discuss the design of your dam, the tests you conducted, and the results. In your journal, write about the easiest and hardest parts of this project. How would you design your dam differently if you did the project again?

⒪Standardized Test Practice

Choose the letter of the best answer.

1. As a stream flows from a mountainous area to a flatter area, what happens to the size of the sediment the stream normally carries?
   A The sediment size does not change.
   B The sediment size carried by the stream increases.
   C The sediment size carried by the stream decreases.
   D The stream drops all the sediment it was carrying.

2. How does wind carry sediment particles?
   A as fine particles carried through the air
   B as particles that bounce along the ground
   C as larger particles that slide or roll along the ground
   D all of the above

Use the diagram below and your knowledge of science to answer Questions 3–4.

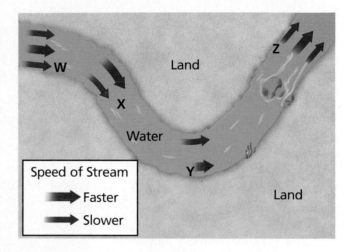

3. What is the erosional feature in the diagram?
   A a meander
   B a delta
   C a flood plain
   D karst topography

4. In the diagram, where is the speed of the stream the greatest?
   A at Y
   B at X
   C at W
   D at Z

5. What is the process by which weathered rock, sediment, and soil is moved from place to place?
   A erosion
   B delta formation
   C running water
   D runoff

Open-Ended Question

6. Describe how gravity is involved in the erosion of Earth's surface by mass movement, running water, and glaciers. Be sure to first explain what erosion is.

Chapter

15 Ocean Motions

▶ Powerful waves have created odd-looking landforms at Cape Kiwanda in Oregon.

Lab zone™ Chapter Project

Design and Build an Erosion-Proof Beach

Waves, tides, and currents move Earth's waters in different ways. These movements change the land. In this project, you will build a model of a shoreline with a lighthouse and use the model to demonstrate how some ocean motions can affect the land along the coast.

Your Goal To design and build a model ocean beach and test methods for preventing shoreline erosion

To complete this project, you must

- build a model beach and use it to demonstrate the effects of wave erosion
- test methods of protecting the lighthouse from damage
- follow the safety guidelines outlined in Appendix A

Plan It! Begin now by previewing the chapter. Find out how engineers protect structures from beach erosion. Begin to design your model ocean beach. Consider what materials you will use for your shoreline and lighthouse. Then develop a plan for protecting your lighthouse.

Wave Action

Reading Preview

Key Concepts
- How does a wave form?
- How do waves change near the shore?
- How do waves affect shorelines and beaches?

Key Terms
- wave • wavelength
- frequency • wave height
- tsunami • longshore drift
- rip current • groin

⟳ Target Reading Skill

Using Prior Knowledge Before you read, look at the section headings and visuals to see what this section is about. Then write what you know about waves in a graphic organizer like the one below. As you read, continue to write in what you learn.

What You Know
1. There are waves in the ocean.
2.

What You Learned
1.
2.

Lab zone Discover **Activity**

How Do Waves Change a Beach?

1. In one end of an aluminum pan, build a "beach" of sand and pebbles. Put a book under that end of the pan to raise it about 5 centimeters.
2. Pour water slowly into the other end of the pan until it covers the edge of the sand, just as water touches the edge of a beach.
3. Place a wooden tongue depressor in the water. Move it back and forth gently in a regular rhythm to make waves in the pan. Continue for about 2 minutes.
4. Once the water has stopped moving, observe what has happened to the beach. Wash your hands after completing this activity.

Think It Over
Observing How has the motion of the water changed the edge of the beach?

Hundreds of years ago, kings and queens ruled the islands of Hawaii. If you could travel back in time, you could watch the royal family engaging in the islands' favorite sport. It wasn't baseball or tennis or polo. Instead, the ancient rulers paddled into the ocean on heavy wooden boards to catch the perfect wave. They were "wave-sliding," a sport we know today as surfing.

If you've ever seen a surfer like the one in Figure 1, you know that they make this difficult sport look almost easy. But even experienced surfers can seldom predict when the next good wave will roll into shore. As you will read in this section, many different forces influence the size, shape, and timing of waves.

What Is a Wave?

When you watch a surfer's wave crash onto a beach, you are seeing the last step in the development of a wave. A **wave** is the movement of energy through a body of water. Wave development usually begins with wind. Without the energy of wind, the surface of the ocean would be as smooth as a mirror. **Most waves form when winds blowing across the water's surface transmit their energy to the water.**

Wave Size Waves start in the open ocean. The size of a wave depends on the strength of the wind and on the length of time it blows. A gentle breeze creates small ripples on the surface of the water. Stronger winds create larger waves.

The size of a wave also depends on the distance over which the wind blows. Winds blowing across longer distances build up bigger waves. Winds blowing across the Pacific Ocean can create bigger waves than winds blowing across the narrower Atlantic Ocean.

Wave Energy Although waves may appear to carry water toward shore, the water does not actually move forward in deep water. If it did, ocean water would eventually pile up on the coasts of every continent! The energy of the wave moves toward shore, but the water itself remains in place. You can test this by floating a cork in a bowl of water. Use a spoon to make a wave in the bowl. As the wave passes, the cork lurches forward a little; then it bobs backward. It ends up in almost the same spot where it started.

FIGURE 1
Wave Energy
A surfer cruises along a cresting wave. The wave's energy moves, but the water mostly stays in one place. **Applying Concepts** *In which direction is the energy of this wave moving?*

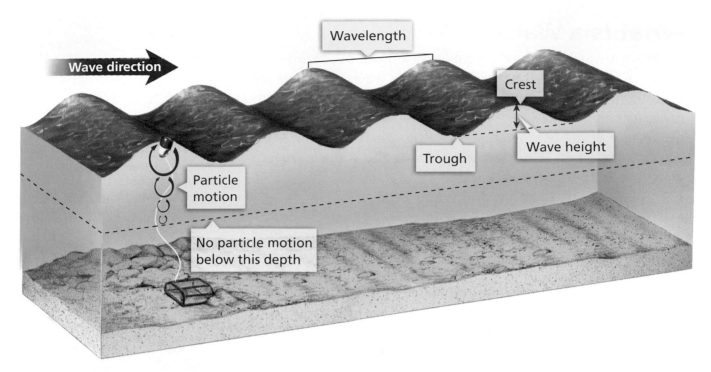

FIGURE 2
Water Motion
As a wave passes, water particles move in a circular motion. The buoy on the surface swings down into the trough of one wave, then back up to the crest of the next. Below the surface, water particles move in smaller circles. At a depth equal to about one half the wavelength, water particles are not affected by the surface wave.

For: Water Motion activity
Visit: PHSchool.com
Web Code: cfp-3031

Water Motion Figure 2 shows what happens to the water as a wave travels along. As the wave passes, water particles move in a circular path. They swing forward and down with the energy of the wave, then back up to their original position.

Notice that the deeper water particles move in smaller circles than those near the surface. The wind affects the water at the surface more than it affects the deep water. Below a certain depth, the water does not move at all as the wave passes. If you were inside a submarine in deep water, you would not be able to tell whether the water above you was rough or calm.

Other Wave Characteristics Scientists have a vocabulary of terms to describe the characteristics of waves. The name for the highest part of a wave is the crest. The horizontal distance between crests is the **wavelength.** Long, rolling waves with lots of space between crests have long wavelengths. Short, choppy waves have shorter wavelengths. Waves are also measured by their **frequency,** the number of waves that pass a point in a certain amount of time.

The lowest part of a wave is the trough. The vertical distance from the crest to the trough is the **wave height.** The energy and strength of a wave depend mainly on its wave height. In the open ocean, most waves are between 2 and 5 meters high. During storms, waves can grow much higher and more powerful.

 **Reading Checkpoint** Which have longer wavelengths—waves that are close together or waves that are far apart?

How Waves Change Near Shore

Have you ever seen an area of ocean water swell, resulting in a wave? Waves begin this way out in the ocean, but as they approach the shore, they change.

Breakers The white-capped waves that crash onto shore are often called "breakers." In deep water, these waves usually travel as long, low waves called swells. As the waves approach the shore, the water becomes shallower. Follow the waves in Figure 3 as they enter the shallow water. The bottoms of the waves begin to touch the sloping ocean floor. Friction between the ocean floor and the water causes the waves to slow down. As the speed of the waves decreases, their shapes change. **Near shore, wave height increases and wavelength decreases.** When the wave reaches a certain height, the crest of the wave topples. The wave breaks onto the shore, forming surf.

As the wave breaks, it continues to move forward. At first the breaker surges up the beach. But gravity soon slows it down, eventually stopping it. The water that had rushed up the beach then flows back out to sea. Have you ever stood at the water's edge and felt the pull of the water rushing back out to the ocean? This pull, often called an undertow, carries shells, seaweed, and sand away from the beach. A strong undertow can be dangerous to swimmers.

Lab zone — Try This **Activity**

Wave Motion
This activity shows how waves that form at the surface affect deeper water.

1. Fill an aquarium about three-quarters full of water.
2. Tie enough metal washers to a cork so that the cork floats about 3 cm from the bottom of the tank.

3. Repeat Step 2 with more corks so that they float 9 cm from the bottom, 15 cm from the bottom, and so on, until the last cork floats on the surface.
4. Make small, steady waves in the tank by moving your hand up and down in the water. Note what happens to each cork.
5. Repeat Step 4, increasing the height of the waves by moving your hand faster.

Observing How does increasing the wave height affect the motion of each cork?

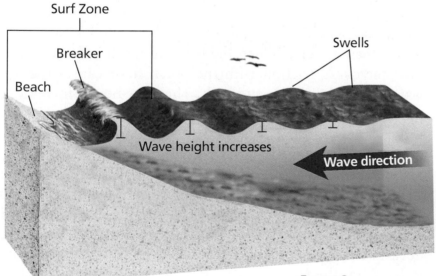

FIGURE 3
How Breakers Change Near Shore
Friction with the ocean floor causes waves to slow down in the shallow water near shore. The wave height increases until the waves break, forming surf.
Comparing and Contrasting *How do swells and breakers differ?*

Motion of ocean floor

FIGURE 4
Tsunamis
At sea, a tsunami travels as a long, low wave. Near shore, the wave height increases suddenly. The wall of water smashes onto land, tossing ships onto the shore and destroying buildings.

Tsunamis So far you have been reading about waves that are caused by the wind. Another kind of wave, shown in Figure 4, forms far below the ocean surface. This type of wave, called a **tsunami,** is usually caused by an earthquake beneath the ocean floor. The abrupt movement of the ocean floor sends pulses of energy through the water above it. When tsunamis reach the coast, they can be as devastating as an earthquake on land, smashing buildings and bridges.

Despite the tremendous amount of energy a tsunami carries, people on a ship at sea may not even realize a tsunami is passing. How is this possible? A tsunami in deep water may have a wavelength of 200 kilometers or more, but a wave height of less than a meter. When the tsunami reaches shallow water near the coast, friction with the ocean floor causes the long wavelength to decrease suddenly. The wave height increases as the water "piles up." The tsunami becomes a towering wall of water. Some tsunamis have reached heights of 20 meters or more—taller than a five-story building!

Tsunamis are most common in the Pacific Ocean, often striking Alaska, Hawaii, and Japan. In 1998, tsunamis in Papua New Guinea killed more than 2,000 people. Governments in areas prone to tsunamis are searching for ways to avoid such devastation. Some Japanese cities have built barriers designed to break up the waves. Scientists also monitor the ocean floor for warnings of earthquakes that may produce tsunamis.

 **Reading Checkpoint** **What usually causes tsunamis?**

How Waves Affect the Shore

What happens on shore as waves pound the beach? Figure 5 shows some of their effects. Because wave direction at sea is determined by the wind, waves usually roll toward shore at an angle. But as they touch bottom, the shallower water slows the shoreward side of the wave first. The rows of waves gradually turn and become more nearly parallel to the shore.

Longshore Drift **As waves come into shore, water washes up the beach at an angle, carrying sand grains. The water and sand then run straight back down the beach.** This movement of sand along the beach is called **longshore drift.** As the waves slow down, they deposit the sand they are carrying on the shallow, underwater slope in a long ridge called a sandbar.

Rip Currents As a sandbar grows, it can trap the water flowing along the shore. In some places, water breaks through the sandbar and begins to flow back down the sloping ocean bottom. This process creates a **rip current,** a rush of water that flows rapidly back to sea through a narrow opening. Rip currents can carry a swimmer out into deep water. Because rip currents are narrow, a strong swimmer can usually escape by swimming across the current, parallel to the beach.

 **Reading Checkpoint** **In what direction does a rip current pull a swimmer?**

Lab zone Skills Activity

Making Models
Half fill an aluminum pan with water. The pan represents the ocean floor. Make the "ocean floor" slope by placing a book or other object under one long end of the pan. Add enough sand in the middle of the pan to create a sandbar. Then pour water from a beaker onto the sand to model a rip current. Use the model to explain why rip currents can be dangerous to swimmers.

FIGURE 5
Longshore Drift
Waves approach the shore at an angle. This results in a gradual movement of sand along the beach. **Interpreting Diagrams** *In which direction is longshore drift moving the sand along this beach?*

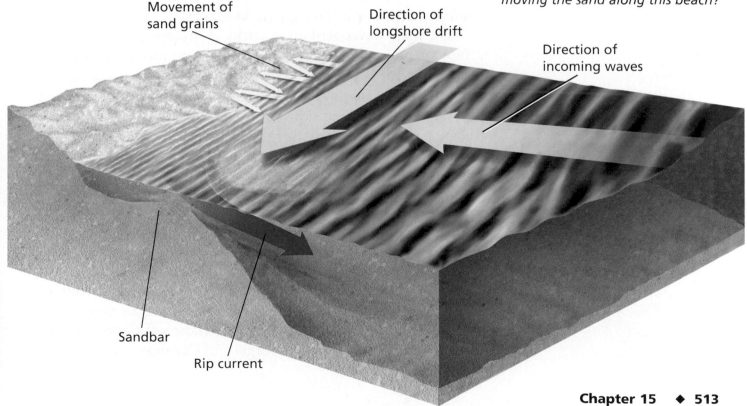

Movement of sand grains

Direction of longshore drift

Direction of incoming waves

Sandbar

Rip current

FIGURE 6

A Barrier Beach
Barrier beaches are sand deposits that form parallel to a shore. Sand dunes are hills of wind-blown sand that help protect the beach. **Interpreting Photographs** *How does a barrier beach protect the mainland from erosion by waves?*

Waves and Beach Erosion

The boundary between land and ocean is always changing shape. If you walk on the same beach every day, you might not notice that it is changing. From day to day, waves remove sand and bring new sand at about the same rate. But if you visit a beach just once each year, you might be startled by what you see. **Waves shape a beach by eroding the shore in some places and building it up in others.**

At first, waves striking a rocky shoreline carve the rocks into tall cliffs and arches. Over many thousands of years, waves break the rocks into pebbles and grains of sand. A wide, sandy beach forms. Then the waves begin to eat away at the exposed beach. The shoreline slowly moves farther inland. Longshore drift carries the sand along the coast and deposits it elsewhere. This process of breaking up rock and carrying it away is known as erosion.

Barrier Beaches A natural landform that protects shorelines from wave action occurs along low-lying beaches. Long sand deposits called barrier beaches form parallel to the shore. Such beaches are separated from the mainland by a shallow lagoon. Waves break against the barrier beach instead of against the land inside. For this reason, people are working to preserve natural barrier beaches like those off Cape Cod, the New Jersey shore, and the Georgia and Carolina coasts.

Sand Dunes Other natural landforms also help protect beaches and reduce erosion, although they can't completely stop the movement of sand. Sand dunes, which are hills of windblown sand, can make a beach more stable and protect the shore from erosion. The strong roots of dune plants, such as beach grass and sea oats, hold the sand in place. These plants help to slow erosion caused by wind and water. But the dunes and plants can be destroyed by cars, bicycles, or even by many people walking over them. Without plants to hold the sand in place, dunes can be easily washed away by wave action.

Groins Many people like to live near the ocean. But over time, erosion can wear away the beach. This threatens the homes and other buildings near the beach. To avoid losing their property, people look for ways to reduce the effect of erosion.

One method of reducing erosion along a stretch of beach is to build a wall of rocks or concrete, called a **groin,** outward from the beach. Sand carried by the water piles up against the groins instead of moving along the shore. Figure 7 shows how groins interrupt the movement of water. However, groins increase the amount of erosion farther down the beach.

Groin

FIGURE 7
Groins
Sand piles up against a series of groins people have built along the New Jersey coast. Building groins to stop longshore drift is one way to reduce beach erosion.

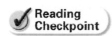 **Reading Checkpoint** Name two natural landforms that help reduce beach erosion.

Section 1 Assessment

Target Reading Skill Using Prior Knowledge Review your graphic organizer and revise it based on what you just learned in the section.

Reviewing Key Concepts

1. a. **Reviewing** How do waves form?
   b. **Explaining** Explain how both a wave's energy and the water in a wave move.
   c. **Applying Concepts** Why does an ocean buoy bob up and down as a wave passes by?

2. a. **Defining** What is the wavelength of a wave? What is wave height?
   b. **Describing** How do wavelength and wave height change as a wave enters shallow water?
   c. **Developing Hypotheses** Using what you know about the wavelength and wave height of tsunamis, propose an explanation of why tsunamis can cause so much damage when they reach the shore.

3. a. **Explaining** What is longshore drift, and how does it affect a shoreline?
   b. **Relating Cause and Effect** Explain how building a groin affects longshore drift. What happens to the beach on each side of the groin?

Lab zone **At-Home Activity**

Wave Model With a family member, make a construction paper model of a wave. Your model should show the wave from the time it develops in the ocean to the time it breaks on the shore. Be sure to label the features of the wave, including crests, troughs, wavelengths, wave heights, swells, and breakers.

Tides

Reading Preview

Key Concepts
- What causes tides?
- What affects the heights of tides?
- How are tides a source of energy?

Key Terms
- tides • spring tide • neap tide

Target Reading Skill

Previewing Visuals Before you read, preview Figure 11. Then write two questions that you have about the diagram in a graphic organizer like the one below. As you read, answer your questions.

Spring and Neap Tides

Q.	When do spring tides occur?
A.	
Q.	

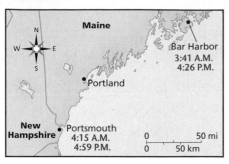

Lab zone Discover Activity

When Is High Tide?

Twice a day, the ocean rises and falls on Earth's coasts. These changes in water level are called tides. The map shows the times of the two high tides in two cities on a specific day.

Maine — Bar Harbor 3:41 A.M. 4:26 P.M.

Portland

New Hampshire • Portsmouth 4:15 A.M. 4:59 P.M.

0   50 mi
0   50 km

1. Calculate the length of time between the two high tides for each city. Remember to consider both hours and minutes.
2. Compare the times of the high tides in Bar Harbor and in Portsmouth. Do you see a pattern?

Think It Over

Predicting Based on the times of the high tides in Bar Harbor and Portsmouth, predict when the high tides will occur in Portland.

You're standing on a riverbank in the town of Saint John, New Brunswick, in Canada. In the distance there's a roaring sound. Suddenly a wall of water twice your height thunders past. The surge of water rushes up the river channel so fast that it almost looks as if the river is flowing backward!

This thundering wall of water is an everyday event at Saint John. The town is located where the Saint John River enters the Bay of Fundy, an arm of the Atlantic Ocean. The Bay of Fundy is famous for its dramatic daily tides. When the tide comes in, fishing boats float on the water near the piers. But once the tide goes out, the boats are stranded on the muddy harbor bottom!

FIGURE 8

Differences in Tides

The Bay of Fundy in Canada is noted for the great differences between its high and low tides. Near the mouth of the bay, boats float at high tide (left). At low tide, the boats are grounded (right).

High Tide

What Causes Tides?

The daily rise and fall of Earth's waters on its coastlines are called **tides.** As the tide comes in, the level of the water on the beach rises gradually. When the water reaches its highest point, it is high tide. Then the tide goes out, flowing back toward the sea. When the water reaches its lowest point, it is low tide. Unlike the surface waves you read about in Section 1, tides happen regularly no matter how the wind blows. Tides occur in all bodies of water, but they are most noticeable in the ocean and large lakes.

Gravity and Tides **Tides are caused by the interaction of Earth, the moon, and the sun.** How can distant objects like the moon and sun influence water on Earth? The answer is gravity. Gravity is the force exerted by an object that pulls other objects toward it. Gravity keeps you and everything around you on Earth's surface. As the distance between objects increases, however, gravity's pull grows weaker.

Figure 9 shows the effect of the moon's gravity on the water on Earth's surface. The moon pulls on the water on the side of Earth closest to it more strongly than it pulls on the center of the Earth. This pull creates a bulge of water, called a tidal bulge, on the side of Earth facing the moon. The water farthest from the moon is pulled toward the moon less strongly than are other parts of Earth. The water farthest from the moon is "left behind," forming a second bulge.

In the places where there are tidal bulges, high tide is occurring along the coastlines. In the places between the bulges, low tide is occurring. Earth's rotation through the tidal bulges causes most coastlines to experience two high tides and two low tides every 25 hours.

Reading Checkpoint What force causes tides to occur on Earth's surface?

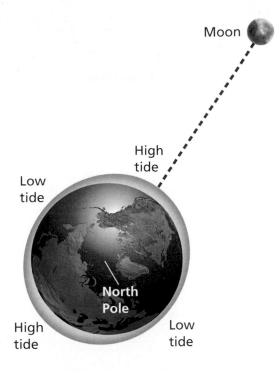

FIGURE 9
How the Moon Causes Tides
The pull of the moon's gravity on Earth's water causes tidal bulges to form on the side closest to the moon and the side farthest from the moon. **Inferring** *Why is the water level high on the side of Earth farthest from the moon?*

Low Tide

FIGURE 10
Sea Turtles and Spring Tides
Some animals are very dependent on tide cycles. Sea turtles can only come to shore to lay their eggs during certain spring tides.

The Daily Tide Cycle As Earth turns completely around once each day, people on or near the shore observe the rise of tides as they reach the area of a tidal bulge. High tides occur about 12 hours and 25 minutes apart in any location. As Earth rotates, easternmost points pass through the area of the tidal bulge before points farther to the west. Therefore, high tide occurs later the farther west you travel along the coast.

In some places, the two high tides and two low tides are easy to observe each day. But in other places, the difference between high tide and low tide is less dramatic. One set of tides may even be so minimal that there appears to be only one high tide and one low tide per day.

Several factors affect the height of a tide in any particular location. For example, certain landforms can interrupt the water's movements. A basin at the mouth of a river can also increase the difference between high and low tide. The speed and depth of moving water increases as it flows into a narrower channel. That is what causes the dramatic tides in the mouth of the Saint John River you read about earlier.

The Monthly Tide Cycle Even though the sun is about 150 million kilometers from Earth, it is so massive that its gravity affects the tides. The sun pulls the water on Earth's surface toward it. In Figure 11, you can follow the positions of Earth, the moon, and the sun at different times during a month. **Changes in the positions of Earth, the moon, and the sun affect the heights of the tides during a month.**

Twice a month, at the new moon and the full moon, the sun and moon are lined up. Their combined gravitational pull produces the greatest difference between the heights of high and low tide, called a **spring tide.** These tides get their name from an Old English word, *springen,* which means "to jump."

At the first and third quarters of the moon, the sun and moon pull at right angles to each other. This arrangement produces a **neap tide,** a tide with the least difference between low and high tide. During a neap tide, the sun's gravity pulls some of the water away from the tidal bulge facing the moon. This acts to "even out" the water level over Earth's surface, decreasing the difference between high and low tides.

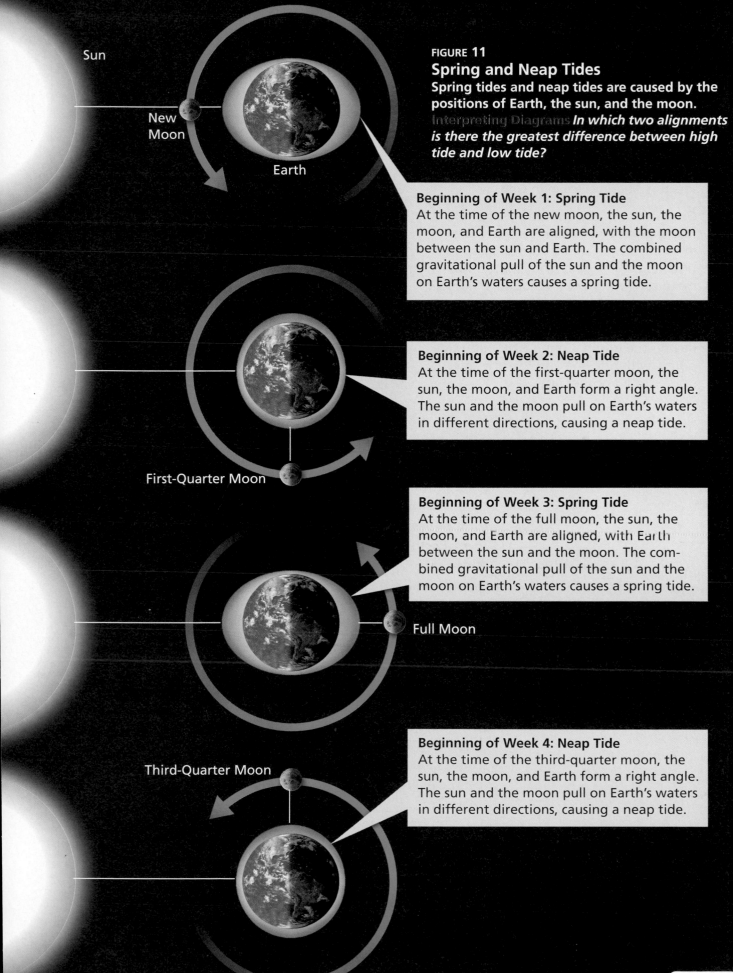

Sun

New Moon

Earth

FIGURE 11
Spring and Neap Tides
Spring tides and neap tides are caused by the positions of Earth, the sun, and the moon.
Interpreting Diagrams *In which two alignments is there the greatest difference between high tide and low tide?*

Beginning of Week 1: Spring Tide
At the time of the new moon, the sun, the moon, and Earth are aligned, with the moon between the sun and Earth. The combined gravitational pull of the sun and the moon on Earth's waters causes a spring tide.

Beginning of Week 2: Neap Tide
At the time of the first-quarter moon, the sun, the moon, and Earth form a right angle. The sun and the moon pull on Earth's waters in different directions, causing a neap tide.

First-Quarter Moon

Beginning of Week 3: Spring Tide
At the time of the full moon, the sun, the moon, and Earth are aligned, with Earth between the sun and the moon. The combined gravitational pull of the sun and the moon on Earth's waters causes a spring tide.

Full Moon

Beginning of Week 4: Neap Tide
At the time of the third-quarter moon, the sun, the moon, and Earth form a right angle. The sun and the moon pull on Earth's waters in different directions, causing a neap tide.

Third-Quarter Moon

Plotting Tides

This table lists the highest high tides and the lowest low tides for one week at the mouth of the Savannah River, where it meets the Atlantic Ocean in Georgia.

1. **Graphing** Use the data in the table to make a graph. On the horizontal axis, mark the days. On the vertical axis, mark tide heights ranging from 3.0 to –1.0 meters. (*Hint:* Mark the negative numbers below the horizontal axis.)

2. **Graphing** Plot the tide heights for each day on the graph. Connect the high tide points with one line and the low tide points with another line.

Tide Table		
Day	Highest High Tide (m)	Lowest Low Tide (m)
1	1.9	0.2
2	2.1	0.1
3	2.3	0.0
4	2.4	–0.2
5	2.5	–0.2
6	2.6	–0.3
7	1.9	0.3

3. **Interpreting Data** How do the high and low tides change during the week?

4. **Inferring** What type of tide might be occurring on Day 6? Explain.

Tide Tables Despite the complex factors affecting tides, scientists can predict tides quite accurately for many locations. They combine knowledge of the movements of the moon and Earth with information about the shape of the coastline and other local conditions. If you live near the coast, your local newspaper probably publishes a tide table. Knowing the times and heights of tides is important to sailors, marine scientists, people who fish, and coastal residents.

 **Reading Checkpoint** What two types of information help scientists predict the times of tides?

Energy From Tides

Look at Figure 12. Can you almost hear the roar of the rushing water? **The movement of huge amounts of water between high and low tide is a source of potential energy—energy that is stored and can be used.** Engineers have designed tidal power plants that capture some of this energy as the tide moves in and out.

The first large-scale tidal power plant was built in 1967 on the Rance River in northwestern France. As high tide swirls up the river, the plant's gates open so that the water flows into a basin. As the tide retreats, the gates shut to trap the water. Gravity pulls the water back to sea through tunnels. The energy of the water moving through the tunnels powers generators that produce electricity, just as in a hydroelectric dam on a river.

Although tidal energy is a clean, renewable source of energy, it has several limitations. Harnessing tidal power is practical only where there is a large difference between high and low tides—at least 4 or 5 meters. There are very few places in the world where such a large difference occurs. Daily tides also may not occur at the time when there is a demand for electricity. However, tidal power can be a useful part of an overall plan to generate electricity that also includes other power sources between tides.

FIGURE 12
Tidal Power
Pulled by the tide, water rushes through this tidal power plant in France.
Making Generalizations
Why are so few locations suitable for tidal power plants?

Reading Checkpoint Under what conditions is it practical to harness tidal power?

Section 2 Assessment

Target Reading Skill Previewing Visuals Refer to your questions and answers about Figure 11 to help you answer Question 2 below.

Reviewing Key Concepts

1. **a. Defining** What is a tide? What causes tides?
   b. Explaining Explain why the moon causes a tidal bulge to form on the side of Earth closest to it.
   c. Inferring The sun is much bigger than the moon. Why doesn't the sun affect tides more than the moon does?
2. **a. Reviewing** Why do the heights of tides change during the course of a month?
   b. Describing Describe the positions of the sun, moon, and Earth during a spring tide and during a neap tide.
   c. Applying Concepts Imagine that you are the captain of a fishing boat. Why would it be helpful to consult a monthly tide table?

3. **a. Reviewing** How can tides be used to generate electricity?
   b. Predicting Do you think that tidal power will ever be a major source of energy worldwide? Why or why not?

Writing in Science

Firsthand Account Imagine that you are fishing on a pier on the Bay of Fundy in Canada. It was high tide when you began fishing. Now it is low tide. Write a firsthand account describing the changes that you observed as the tide went out. Use clear, descriptive language in your writing.

Ocean Water Chemistry

Reading Preview

Key Concepts
- How salty is ocean water?
- How do the temperature and gas content of ocean water vary?
- How do conditions in the ocean change with depth?

Key Terms
- salinity • submersible

Target Reading Skill
Asking Questions Before you read, preview the red headings. In a graphic organizer like the one below, ask a *how* or *what* question for each heading. As you read, answer your questions.

Ocean Water Chemistry

Question	Answer
How salty is the ocean?	One kilogram of ocean water has . . .

Salt storage area ▼

Lab zone Discover **Activity**

Will the Eggs Sink or Float?

1. Fill two beakers or jars with tap water.
2. Add three teaspoons of salt to one beaker. Stir until it dissolves.
3. Place a whole, uncooked egg in each jar. Handle the eggs gently to avoid breakage. Observe what happens to each egg.
4. Wash your hands when you are finished with this activity.

Think It Over
Observing Compare what happens to the two eggs. What does this tell you about the difference between salt water and fresh water?

If you've ever swallowed some water while you were swimming in the ocean, you know that the ocean is salty. Why? According to an old Swedish legend, it's all because of a magic mill. This mill could grind out anything its owner wanted, such as herring, porridge, or even gold. A greedy sea captain once stole the mill and took it away on his ship, but without finding out how to use it. He asked the mill to grind some salt but then could not stop it. The mill ground more and more salt, until the captain's ship sank from its weight. According to the tale, the mill is still at the bottom of the sea, grinding out salt!

The Salty Ocean

Probably no one ever took this legend seriously, even when it was first told. The scientific explanation for the ocean's saltiness begins with the early stages of Earth's history, when the ocean covered much of the surface of the planet. Undersea volcanoes erupted, spewing chemicals into the water. Gradually, the lava from these volcanic eruptions built up areas of land. Rain fell on the bare land, washing more chemicals from the rocks into the ocean. Over time, these dissolved substances built up to the levels present in the ocean today.

Salinity Just how salty is the ocean? If you boiled a kilogram of ocean water in a pot until all the water was gone, there would be about 35 grams of salts left in the pot. **On average, one kilogram of ocean water contains about 35 grams of salts—that is, 35 parts per thousand.** The total amount of dissolved salts in a sample of water is the **salinity** of that sample.

The substance you know as table salt—sodium chloride— is the salt present in the greatest amount in ocean water. When sodium chloride dissolves in water, it separates into sodium and chloride particles called ions. Other salts, such as magnesium chloride, form ions in water in the same way. Together, chloride and sodium make up almost 86 percent of the ions dissolved in ocean water. Ocean water also contains smaller amounts of about a dozen other ions, including magnesium and calcium, and other substances that organisms need, such as nitrogen and phosphorus.

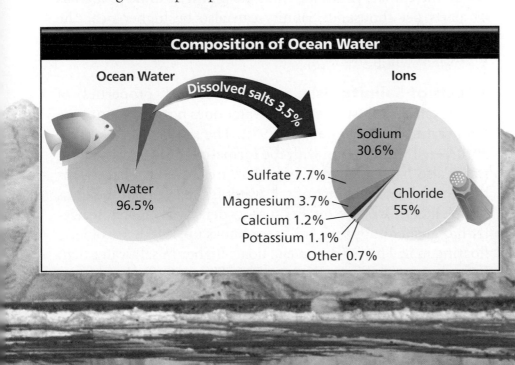

Composition of Ocean Water

Ocean Water

Dissolved salts 3.5%

Ions

Water 96.5%

Sodium 30.6%

Sulfate 7.7%

Magnesium 3.7%

Calcium 1.2%

Potassium 1.1%

Chloride 55%

Other 0.7%

FIGURE 13
Composition of Ocean Water
Ocean water contains many different dissolved salts. When salts dissolve, they separate into particles called ions.
Reading Graphs *Which ion is most common in ocean water?*

FIGURE 14
Salinity and Density
These people are relaxing with the paper while floating in the water! The Dead Sea between Israel and Jordan is so salty that people float easily on its surface.
Relating Cause and Effect
How is the area's hot, dry climate related to the Dead Sea's high salinity?

Math Skills

Calculating Density
To calculate the density of a substance, divide the mass of the substance by its volume.

$$\text{Density} = \frac{\text{Mass}}{\text{Volume}}$$

For example, 1 liter (L) of ocean water has a mass of 1.03 kilograms (kg). Therefore,

$$\text{Density} = \frac{1.03 \text{ kg}}{1.00 \text{ L}}$$

$$\text{Density} = 1.03 \text{ kg/L}$$

Practice Problems A 5-liter sample of one type of crude oil has a mass of 4.10 kg. What is its density? If this oil spilled on the ocean's surface, would it sink or float? Explain your answer in terms of density.

Variations in Salinity In most parts of the ocean, the salinity is between 34 and 37 parts per thousand. But near the ocean's surface, rain, snow, and melting ice add fresh water, lowering the salinity. Salinity is also lower near the mouths of large rivers such as the Amazon or Mississippi. These rivers empty great amounts of fresh water into the ocean. Evaporation, on the other hand, increases salinity, since the salt is left behind as the water evaporates. For example, in the Red Sea, where the climate is hot and dry, the salinity can be as high as 41 parts per thousand. Salinity can also be higher near the poles. As the surface water freezes into ice, the salt is left behind in the remaining water.

Effects of Salinity Salinity affects several properties of ocean water. For instance, ocean water does not freeze until the temperature drops to about −1.9°C. The salt acts as a kind of antifreeze by interfering with the formation of ice crystals. Salt water also has a higher density than fresh water. That means that the mass of one liter of salt water is greater than the mass of one liter of fresh water. Because its density is greater, seawater has greater buoyancy. It lifts, or buoys up, less dense objects floating in it. This is why an egg floats higher in salt water than in fresh water, and why the people in Figure 14 float so effortlessly in the Dead Sea.

Reading Checkpoint Why does salt water have greater buoyancy than fresh water?

Other Ocean Properties

In New England, the news reports on New Year's Day often feature the shivering members of a "Polar Bear Club" taking a dip in the icy Atlantic Ocean. Yet on the same day, people enjoy the warm waters of a Puerto Rico beach. **Like temperatures on land, temperatures at the surface of the ocean vary with location and the seasons. Gases in ocean water vary as well.**

Temperature of Ocean Water Why do surface temperatures of the ocean vary from place to place? The broad surface of the ocean absorbs energy from the sun. Near the equator, surface ocean temperatures often reach 25°C, about room temperature. The temperature drops as you travel away from the equator.

Because warm water is less dense than cold water, warm water forms only a thin layer on the ocean surface. Generally, the deeper you descend into the ocean, the colder and denser the water becomes. When water temperature is lower, the water molecules stay closer together than at higher temperatures. So, a sample of cold water has more water molecules than a sample of warm water of the same volume. The sample of cold water is denser.

Gases in Ocean Water Just as land organisms use gases found in air, ocean organisms use gases found in ocean water. Two gases that ocean organisms use are carbon dioxide and oxygen.

Carbon dioxide is about 60 times as plentiful in the oceans as in the air. Algae need carbon dioxide for photosynthesis. Animals such as corals also use carbon dioxide, which provides the carbon to build their hard skeletons.

Unlike carbon dioxide, oxygen is scarcer in seawater than in air. Oxygen is most plentiful in seawater near the surface. Oxygen in seawater comes from the air and from algae in the ocean, as a product of photosynthesis. The amount of oxygen in seawater is affected by the water temperature. The cold waters in the polar regions contain more oxygen than warm, tropical waters. But there is still enough oxygen in tropical seas to support a variety of organisms.

Reading Checkpoint What are two sources of oxygen in ocean water?

FIGURE 15

Organisms and Ocean Temperatures From the warmest tropical waters to the coldest Antarctic sea, you can find organisms that are adapted to extreme ocean temperatures.

▲ This longfin anthias fish swimming near Hawaii lives in one of the warmest parts of the Pacific Ocean.

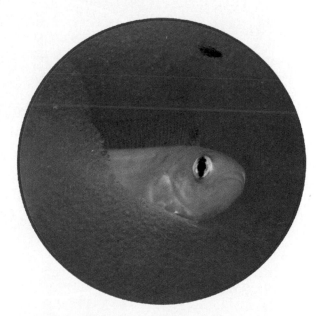

▲ This rockcod is swimming through a hole in an iceberg in near-freezing ocean water.

FIGURE 16

The Water Column

Conditions change as you descend to the ocean floor. **Interpreting Diagrams** *What two factors affect the density of ocean water?*

A scuba diver can descend to about 40 meters.

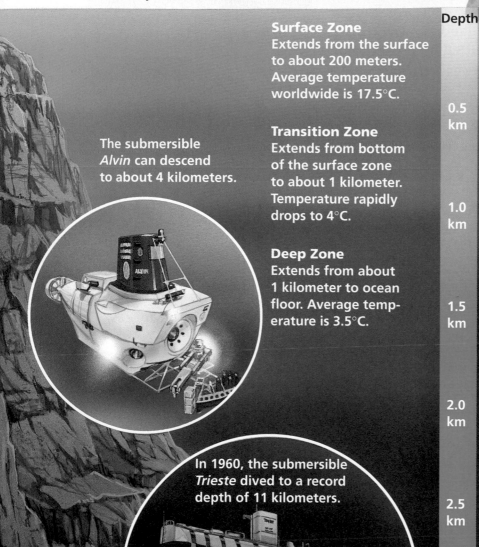

Surface Zone
Extends from the surface to about 200 meters. Average temperature worldwide is 17.5°C.

The submersible *Alvin* can descend to about 4 kilometers.

Transition Zone
Extends from bottom of the surface zone to about 1 kilometer. Temperature rapidly drops to 4°C.

Deep Zone
Extends from about 1 kilometer to ocean floor. Average temperature is 3.5°C.

In 1960, the submersible *Trieste* dived to a record depth of 11 kilometers.

Depth

0.5 km
1.0 km
1.5 km
2.0 km
2.5 km
3.0 km
3.5 km
4.0 km

PRESSURE INCREASES

3.8 km
Average ocean depth

Color and Light
Sunlight penetrates the surface of the ocean. It appears first yellowish, then blue-green, as the water absorbs the red light. No light reaches below about 200 meters.

Temperature
Near the surface, temperature is affected by the weather above. In the transition zone, the temperature drops rapidly. In the deep zone, the water is always extremely cold.

Salinity
Rainfall decreases salinity near the surface, while evaporation increases salinity in warm, dry areas. Below the surface zone, salinity remains fairly constant throughout the water column.

Density
The density of seawater depends on temperature and salinity. The ocean is generally least dense in the surface zone, where it is warmest. However, higher salinity also increases density. The most dense water is found in the cold deep zone.

Pressure
Pressure increases at the rate of 10 times the air pressure at sea level per 100 meters of depth.

Changes With Depth

If you could descend from the ocean's surface to the ocean floor, you would pass through a vertical section of the ocean referred to as the water column. Figure 16 on the previous page shows some of the dramatic changes you would observe.

Decreasing Temperature **As you descend through the ocean, the water temperature decreases.** There are three temperature zones in the water column. The surface zone is the warmest. It typically extends from the surface to between 100 and 500 meters. The transition zone extends from the bottom of the surface zone to about 1 kilometer. Temperatures drop very quickly as you descend through the transition zone, to about 4°C. Below the transition zone is the deep zone. Average temperatures there are 3.5°C in most of the ocean.

Increasing Pressure Water pressure is the force exerted by the weight of water. **Pressure increases continuously with depth in the ocean.** Because of the high pressure in the deep ocean, divers can descend safely only to about 40 meters. To observe the deep ocean, scientists must use a **submersible,** an underwater vehicle built of materials that resist pressure.

Go Online
SciLINKS NSTA

For: Links on ocean water chemistry
Visit: www.SciLinks.org
Web Code: scn-0833

 **Reading Checkpoint**) **What is a submersible?**

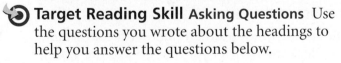
Section 3 Assessment

⊙ **Target Reading Skill** **Asking Questions** Use the questions you wrote about the headings to help you answer the questions below.

Reviewing Key Concepts

1. **a. Defining** What is salinity? What is the average salinity of ocean water?
   b. Describing Describe one factor that increases the salinity of seawater and one factor that decreases its salinity.
   c. Inferring Would you expect the seawater just below the floating ice in the Arctic Ocean to be higher or lower in salinity than the water in the deepest part of the ocean? Explain.
2. **a. Identifying** Where would you find the warmest ocean temperatures on Earth?
   b. Comparing and Contrasting How do carbon dioxide and oxygen levels in the oceans compare to those in the air?

   c. Relating Cause and Effect How does the temperature of ocean water affect oxygen levels in the water?
3. **a. Reviewing** How do temperature and pressure change as you descend in the ocean?
   b. Predicting Where in the water column would you expect to find the following conditions: the highest pressure readings; the densest waters; the warmest temperatures?

Math Practice

4. **Calculating Density** Calculate the density of the following 1-L samples of ocean water. Sample A has a mass of 1.01 kg; Sample B has a mass of 1.06 kg. Which sample would likely have the higher salinity? Explain.

Investigating Changes in Density

Problem

Can you design and build an instrument that can detect differences in density?

Skills Focus

building a prototype, designing a solution, troubleshooting

Materials

• thumbtacks • 250-mL graduated cylinder
• unsharpened pencil with eraser • metric ruler
• fine-point permanent marker • thermometer
• ice • balance • water • spoon • salt
• additional materials provided by your teacher

Procedure

PART 1 Research and Investigate

1. One way to measure the density of a liquid is with a tool called a hydrometer. You can make a simple hydrometer using an unsharpened wooden pencil.

2. Starting at the unsharpened end of a pencil, use a permanent marker to make marks every 2 mm along the side of the pencil. Make longer marks for every whole centimeter. Continue until you have marked off 5 cm.

3. Label each of the long marks, starting at the unsharpened end of the pencil.

4. Insert 3 thumbtacks as weights into the eraser end of the pencil. **CAUTION:** *Be careful not to cut yourself on the sharp points of the thumbtacks.*

5. Fill the graduated cylinder with 250 mL of water at room temperature. Place the pencil in the water, eraser end down.

6. Add or remove thumbtacks and adjust their placement until the pencil floats upright, with about 2 cm sticking up above the surface of the water.

7. In your notebook, record the temperature of the water. Next to that number, record the reading on the pencil hydrometer at the surface of the water.

8. Fill the graduated cylinder with cold water. Place the pencil hydrometer into the water, eraser end down. Then repeat Step 7.

PART 2 Design and Build

9. Using what you learned in Part 1, design and build a hydrometer that can detect density differences among different samples of water. Your hydrometer should
    • be able to measure density differences between hot water and cold water
    • be able to measure density differences between salt water and fresh water
    • be constructed of materials approved by your teacher

10. Sketch your design in your notebook and make a list of the materials you will need. Write a plan for how you will construct your hydrometer. After you have received your teacher's approval for your design, build your hydrometer.

PART 3 **Evaluate and Redesign**

11. Test your hydrometer by using it to measure the density of water at different temperatures. Then test samples of water that have different salinities. Create a data table in which to record your results.

Data Table		
Temperature (°C)	Salinity $\left(\dfrac{g\ salt}{L\ water}\right)$	Hydrometer Reading

12. Based on your tests, decide how you could improve the design of your hydrometer. For example, how could you change your design so your hydrometer is able to detect smaller differences in density? Obtain your teacher's approval, then make the necessary changes, and test how your redesigned hydrometer functions.

Analyze and Conclude

1. **Inferring** Explain why cold water is more dense than hot water. Explain why salt water is more dense than fresh water.

2. **Building a Prototype** How well did the pencil hydrometer you built in Part 1 work? What problems did you encounter with the hydrometer?

3. **Designing a Solution** How did you incorporate what you learned in Part 1 into your hydrometer design in Part 2? For example, how did your hydrometer address the problems you encountered in Part 1?

4. **Troubleshooting** In Part 3, how well did your hydrometer perform when you measured water samples of different densities? How did you redesign your hydrometer to improve its function?

5. **Evaluating the Design** What limitations did factors such as buoyancy, materials, time, costs, or other factors place on the design and function of your hydrometer? Describe how you adapted your design to work within these limitations.

Communicate

Create an informative poster that describes how your hydrometer works. Include illustrations of your hydrometer and any important background information on density.

Currents and Climate

Reading Preview

Key Concepts
- What causes surface currents and how do they affect climate?
- What causes deep currents and what effects do they have?
- How does upwelling affect the distribution of nutrients in the ocean?

Key Terms
- current
- climate
- Coriolis effect
- El Niño
- upwelling

Target Reading Skill
Relating Cause and Effect As you read, identify the main factors that cause surface and deep currents in the oceans. Write the information in graphic organizers like the one below.

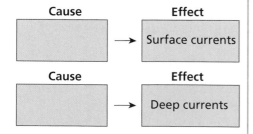

Cause		Effect
	→	Surface currents

Cause		Effect
	→	Deep currents

Which Is More Dense?
1. Fill a plastic container three-quarters full with warm water. Wait for the water to stop moving.
2. Add several drops of food coloring to a cup of ice water and stir.
3. Gently dribble colored water down the inside of the container. Observe.

Think It Over
Inferring Describe what happened to the cold water. Which is more dense, warm water or cold water? Explain.

One spring day, people strolling along a beach in Washington State saw an amazing sight. Hundreds of sneakers of all colors and sizes were washing ashore from the Pacific Ocean! This "sneaker spill" was eventually traced to a cargo ship accident. Containers of sneakers had fallen overboard and now the sneakers were washing ashore.

But the most amazing part of the story is this—scientists could predict where the sneakers would wash up next. And just as the scientists had predicted, sneakers washed up in Oregon, and then thousands of kilometers away in Hawaii!

How did the scientists know that the sneakers would float all the way to Hawaii? The answer lies in a type of ocean movement known as a current. A **current** is a large stream of moving water that flows through the oceans. Unlike waves, currents carry water from one place to another. Some currents move water at the surface of the ocean, while other currents move water deep in the ocean.

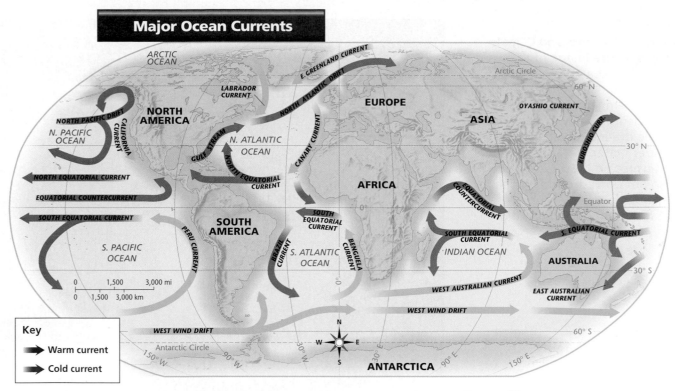

Major Ocean Currents

Key
➡ Warm current
➡ Cold current

Surface Currents

Figure 17 shows the major surface currents in Earth's oceans. **Surface currents, which affect water to a depth of several hundred meters, are driven mainly by winds.** Following Earth's major wind patterns, surface currents move in circular patterns in the five major oceans. Most of the currents flow east or west, and then double back to complete the circle.

Coriolis Effect Why do the currents move in these circular patterns? If Earth were standing still, winds and currents would flow in straight lines between the poles and the equator. But as Earth rotates, the paths of the winds and currents curve. This effect of Earth's rotation on the direction of winds and currents is called the **Coriolis effect** (kawr ee OH lis). In the Northern Hemisphere, the Coriolis effect causes the currents to curve to the right. In the Southern Hemisphere, the Coriolis effect causes the currents to curve to the left.

The largest and most powerful surface current in the North Atlantic Ocean, the Gulf Stream, is caused by strong winds from the west. It is more than 30 kilometers wide and 300 meters deep, and carries a volume of water 100 times greater than the Mississippi River. The Gulf Stream carries warm water from the Gulf of Mexico to the Caribbean Sea, then northward along the coast of the United States. Near Cape Hatteras, North Carolina, it curves eastward across the Atlantic, as a result of the Coriolis effect.

FIGURE 17
Large surface currents generally move in circular patterns in Earth's oceans. **Interpreting Maps** *Name four currents that flow along the coasts of North America. State whether each current is warm or cold.*

Go Online
*sci*LINKS NSTA

For: Links on ocean currents
Visit: www.SciLinks.org
Web Code: scn-0834

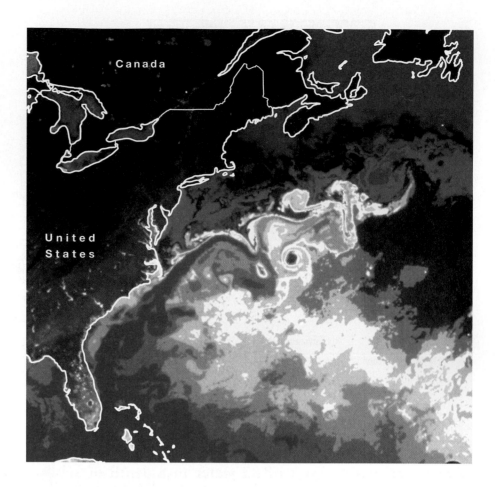

FIGURE 18
Surface Currents and Climate
This satellite image of the Atlantic Ocean has been enhanced with colors that show water temperature. Red and orange indicate warmer water, while green and blue indicate colder water.
Interpreting Maps *The Gulf Stream flows around Florida in the lower left of the map. Is the Gulf Stream a warm or cold current?*

Canada

United States

Lab zone Skills Activity

Drawing Conclusions
Locate the Benguela Current in Figure 17 on the previous page. Near the southern tip of Africa, the winds blow from west to east. Using what you have learned about surface currents and climate, what can you conclude about the impact of this current on the climate of the south–western coast of Africa?

Effects on Climate The Gulf Stream and another warm current, the North Atlantic Drift, are very important to people in the city of Trondheim, Norway. Trondheim is located along Norway's western coast. Although it is very close to the Arctic Circle, winters there are fairly mild. Snow melts soon after it falls. And fortunately for the fishing boats, the local harbors are free of ice most of the winter. The two warm currents bring this area of Norway a mild climate. **Climate** is the pattern of temperature and precipitation typical of an area over a long period of time.

Currents affect climate by moving cold and warm water around the globe. In general, currents carry warm water from the tropics toward the poles and bring cold water back toward the equator. **A surface current warms or cools the air above it, influencing the climate of the land near the coast.**

Winds pick up moisture as they blow across warm-water currents. For example, the warm Kuroshio Current brings mild, rainy weather to the southern islands of Japan. In contrast, cold-water currents cool the air above them. Since cold air holds less moisture than warm air, these currents tend to bring cool, dry weather to the land areas in their path.

El Niño When changes in wind patterns and currents occur, they can have a major impact on the oceans and neighboring land. One example of such changes is **El Niño,** an abnormal climate event that occurs every two to seven years in the Pacific Ocean. El Niño begins when an unusual pattern of winds forms over the western Pacific. This causes a vast sheet of warm water to move eastward toward the South American coast. El Niño conditions can last for one to two years before the usual winds and currents return.

El Niño can have disastrous consequences. It causes shifts in weather patterns around the world, bringing unusual and often severe conditions to different areas. For example, a major El Niño occurred between 1997 and 1998 and caused an especially warm winter in the northeastern United States. However, it was also responsible for heavy rains, flooding, and mudslides in California, as well as a string of deadly tornadoes in Florida.

Although scientists do not fully understand the conditions that cause El Niño, they have been able to predict its occurrence using computer models of world climate. Knowing when El Niño will occur can reduce its impact. Scientists and public officials can plan emergency procedures and make changes to protect people and wildlife.

 **Reading Checkpoint** Why is it helpful to be able to predict when El Niño will occur?

FIGURE 19
El Niño's Impact
El Niño can cause severe weather all around the world.

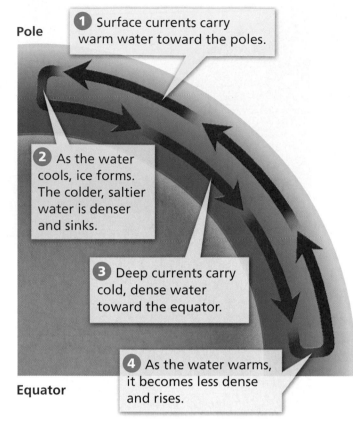

Pole

1 Surface currents carry warm water toward the poles.

2 As the water cools, ice forms. The colder, saltier water is denser and sinks.

3 Deep currents carry cold, dense water toward the equator.

4 As the water warms, it becomes less dense and rises.

Equator

FIGURE 20
Deep Currents
Deep currents are caused by differences in the density of ocean water.

Deep Currents

Deep below the ocean surface, another type of current causes chilly waters to creep slowly across the ocean floor. **These deep currents are caused by differences in the density of ocean water.**

As you read earlier, the density of water depends on its temperature and its salinity. When a warm surface current moves from the equator toward one of the poles, it gradually cools. As ice forms near the poles, the salinity of the water increases from the salt left behind during freezing. As its temperature decreases and its salinity increases, the water becomes denser and sinks. Then, the cold water flows back along the ocean floor as a deep current. Deep currents are affected by the Coriolis effect, which causes them to curve.

Deep currents move and mix water around the world. They carry cold water from the poles toward the equator. Deep currents flow slowly. They may take as long as 1,000 years to flow from the pole to the equator and back again!

Upwelling

In most parts of the ocean, surface waters do not usually mix with deep ocean waters. However, mixing sometimes occurs when winds cause upwelling. **Upwelling** is the movement of cold water upward from the deep ocean. As winds blow away the warm surface water, cold water rises to replace it.

Upwelling brings up tiny ocean organisms, minerals, and other nutrients from the deeper layers of the water. Without this motion, the surface waters of the open ocean would be very scarce in nutrients. Because nutrients are plentiful, zones of upwelling are usually home to huge schools of fish.

One major area of upwelling lies in the Pacific Ocean off the west coast of South America. Many people depend on this rich fishing area for food and jobs. The arrival of El Niño prevents upwelling from occurring. Without the nutrients brought by upwelling, fish die or go elsewhere to find food, reducing the fishing catch that season and hurting people's livelihoods.

 **Reading Checkpoint** What is upwelling?

FIGURE 21
Upwelling
As cold water rises from the deep ocean, it brings a new supply of nutrients to the surface. The nutrients feed enormous schools of fish such as these anchovies.
Relating Cause and Effect *What causes cold water to rise during upwelling?*

Warm surface water

Wind

Upwelling

Section 4 Assessment

Target Reading Skill **Relating Cause and Effect** Refer to your graphic organizer about the causes of ocean currents to answer Questions 1 and 2 below.

Reviewing Key Concepts

1. a. **Defining** What is a current?
   b. **Describing** What causes surface currents to occur? How do surface currents affect the climate of coastal areas?
   c. **Predicting** What type of climate might a coastal area have if nearby currents are cold?
2. a. **Explaining** Explain how deep currents form and move in the ocean.
   b. **Comparing and Contrasting** Compare the causes and effects of deep currents and surface currents.
3. a. **Reviewing** What causes upwelling?

b. **Explaining** Why are huge schools of fish usually found in zones of upwelling?
c. **Applying Concepts** Why would the ability to predict the occurrence of El Niño be important for the fishing industry on the western coast of South America?

Lab zone At-Home **Activity**

Modeling the Coriolis Effect With the help of a family member, use chalk and a globe to model the Coriolis effect. Have your family member slowly rotate the globe in an easterly direction. As the globe rotates, draw a line from the North Pole to the equator. Use your knowledge of the Coriolis effect to explain why the line is curved.

Modeling Ocean Currents

Problem

How can you model the movement of ocean water caused by surface currents?

Skills Focus

making models, observing, inferring

Materials

- rectangular baking tray
- chalk
- modeling clay, 3 sticks
- ruler
- permanent marker
- hole puncher
- newspaper
- construction paper, blue and red
- jointed drinking straws, one per student
- light-reflecting rheoscopic fluid, 400 mL (or water and food coloring)

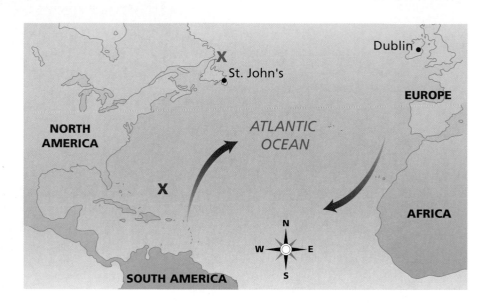

Procedure

1. Cover your work area with newspaper. Place the baking tray on top of the newspaper.

2. Using the map as a guide, draw a chalk outline of the eastern coast of North and South America on the left side of the tray. Draw the outline of the west coast of Europe and Africa on the right side of the tray.

3. Use modeling clay to create the continents, roughly following the chalk outlines you have drawn. Build the continents to a depth of about 3 cm. Press the clay tightly to the pan to form a watertight seal.

4. Fill the ocean area of your model with rheoscopic fluid (or water and food coloring) to a depth of 1 cm.

5. Place 10 blue paper punches in the ocean area marked with a blue X on the map. Place 10 red paper punches in the area marked with a red X.

6. Select a drinking straw and bend it at the joint. Write your initials on the short end of the straw with the marker.

7. With a partner, simulate the pattern of winds that blow in this region of the world. One partner should position his or her straw across the westernmost bulge of Africa and blow toward the west (see arrow on map). The other partner should position his or her straw across the northern end of South America and blow toward the northeast (see arrow on map). Make sure that the straws are bent and that the short ends are parallel to the ocean surface. Both partners should begin blowing gently through the straws at the same time. Try to blow as continuously as possible for one to two minutes.

8. Observe the motion of the fluid and paper punches over the surface of the ocean. Notice what happens when the fluid and punches flow around landmasses.

Analyze and Conclude

1. **Making Models** Draw a map that shows the pattern of ocean currents that was produced in your model. Use red arrows to show the flow of warm water moving north from the equator. Use blue arrows to show the flow of cold water southward from the polar regions.

2. **Classifying** Use Figure 17 to add names to the currents you drew on your map. Which currents are warm-water currents? Which are cold-water currents?

3. **Observing** Based on what you observed with your model, describe the relationship between winds and surface currents in the ocean.

4. **Inferring** Dublin, Ireland, is located at the same latitude as St. John's in Newfoundland, Canada. However, when it's 8°C in Dublin in January, it's usually below 0°C in St. John's. Use your knowledge of ocean currents to explain why the climate in Dublin is different from the climate in St. John's.

5. **Communicating** Suppose you wanted to sail to Europe from the East Coast of the United States. Write a dialogue you might have with a crew member in which you discuss two natural factors that could help speed up the trip.

Design an Experiment

Design an investigation in which you simulate an upwelling off the coast of Africa. (*Hint:* You may use a model similar to the one used in this investigation.) *Obtain your teacher's permission before carrying out your investigation.*

① Wave Action

Key Concepts

- Most waves form when winds blowing across the water's surface transmit their energy to the water.

- Near shore, wave height increases and wavelength decreases.

- As waves come ashore, water washes up the beach at an angle, carrying sand grains. The water and sand then run straight back down the beach. Waves shape a beach by eroding the shore in some places and building it up in others.

Key Terms

wave	tsunami
wavelength	longshore drift
frequency	rip current
wave height	groin

② Tides

Key Concepts

- Tides are caused by the interaction of Earth, the moon, and the sun.

- Changes in the positions of Earth, the moon, and the sun affect the heights of the tides during a month.

- The movement of huge amounts of water between high and low tides is a source of potential energy.

Key Terms

tides	spring tide	neap tide

③ Ocean Water Chemistry

Key Concepts

- On average, one kilogram of ocean water contains about 35 grams of salts.

- Like temperatures on land, temperatures at the surface of the ocean vary with location and the seasons. Gases in ocean water vary as well.

- As you descend through the ocean, the water temperature decreases. Pressure increases continuously with depth in the ocean.

Key Terms

salinity	submersible

④ Currents and Climate

Key Concepts

- Surface currents, which affect water to a depth of several hundred meters, are driven mainly by winds. A surface current warms or cools the air above it, influencing the climate of the land near the coast.

- Deep currents are caused by differences in the density of ocean water. Deep currents move and mix water around the world. They carry cold water from the poles toward the equator.

- Upwelling brings up tiny ocean organisms, minerals, and other nutrients from the deeper layers of the water. Without this motion, the surface waters of the open ocean would be very scarce in nutrients.

Key Terms

current	El Niño
Coriolis effect	upwelling
climate	

Review and Assessment

Go Online
PHSchool.com

For: Self-Assessment
Visit: PHSchool.com
Web Code: cfa-3030

Organizing Information

Sequencing Copy the flowchart about the movement of a wave onto a separate sheet of paper. Then complete it by putting the following three steps in the correct sequence: wave travels as low swell; wave breaks on shore; wavelength decreases and wave height increases. (For more on Sequencing, see the Skills Handbook.)

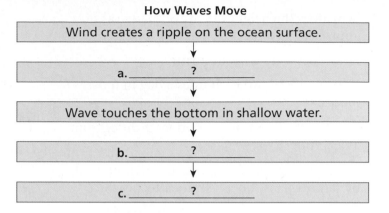

How Waves Move

Wind creates a ripple on the ocean surface.

↓

a. _____ ?

↓

Wave touches the bottom in shallow water.

↓

b. _____ ?

↓

c. _____ ?

Reviewing Key Terms

Choose the letter of the best answer.

1. Rolling waves with a large horizontal distance between crests have a long
   a. wave height.
   b. wavelength.
   c. frequency.
   d. trough.

2. Groins are built to reduce the effect of
   a. tsunamis.
   b. longshore drift.
   c. rip currents.
   d. deep currents.

3. At the full moon, the combined gravitational pulls of the sun and moon produce the biggest difference between low and high tide, called a
   a. surface current.
   b. neap tide.
   c. spring tide.
   d. rip current.

4. Ocean water is more dense than fresh water at the same temperature because of
   a. pressure.
   b. the Coriolis effect.
   c. upwelling.
   d. salinity.

5. Winds and currents move in curved paths because of
   a. the Coriolis effect.
   b. longshore drift.
   c. wave height.
   d. tides.

6. Cold and warm ocean water is carried around the world by
   a. spring tides.
   b. neap tides.
   c. currents.
   d. tsunamis.

Writing in Science

Essay Suppose you were planning to take part in an around-the-world sailing race. Write a short essay about the knowledge of currents that you will need to prepare for the race.

Discovery CHANNEL SCHOOL

Ocean Motions

Video Preview
Video Field Trip
▶ Video Assessment

Review and Assessment

Checking Concepts

7. What factors influence the size of a wave?

8. Why does the height of a wave change as it approaches shore?

9. How does a rip current form?

10. Why are there two high tides a day in most places?

11. What is a spring tide? How does it differ from a neap tide?

12. Name two properties of ocean water affected by salinity. How does salinity affect each?

13. What is the Coriolis effect? How does it influence ocean currents?

14. How do warm-water currents influence climate?

15. What is El Niño? What are some of its effects?

16. Describe the cause and effects of upwelling.

Thinking Critically

17. **Predicting** How will the duck's location change as the wave moves? Explain your answer.

Direction of wave

18. **Applying Concepts** Would you expect the salinity of the ocean to be high or low in a rainy region near the mouth of a river? Why?

19. **Comparing and Contrasting** In what ways is the ocean at 1,000 meters deep different from the ocean at the surface in the same location?

20. **Relating Cause and Effect** How does the movement of ocean currents explain the fact that much of western Europe has a mild, wet climate?

21. **Classifying** Classify the following movements of ocean water by stating whether or not each is caused by winds: waves, tides, surface currents, deep currents, upwelling.

Math Practice

22. **Calculating Density** Two 1-liter samples of water were taken from the ocean, one during the winter, and one during the summer. Sample A has a mass of 1.02 kg. Sample B has a mass of 1.05 kg. Which sample was taken during the winter? Explain your answer.

Applying Skills

Use the data to answer Questions 23–25.

The temperature readings in the table were obtained in the Atlantic Ocean near Bermuda.

Ocean Temperatures

Depth (m)	Temp. (°C)	Depth (m)	Temp. (°C)
0	19	1,000	9
200	18	1,200	5
400	18	1,400	5
600	16	1,600	4
800	12	1,800	4

23. **Graphing** Construct a line graph using the data in the table. Plot depth readings on the horizontal axis and temperature readings on the vertical axis.

24. **Drawing Conclusions** Use your graph to identify the temperature range in the transition zone.

25. **Predicting** Predict how the ocean temperature at depths of 0 meters and at 1,400 meters would change with the seasons in this location. Explain your reasoning.

Lab zone Chapter Project

Performance Assessment Using your model, present your method of shoreline protection to the class. Show your classmates how the method you chose protects the lighthouse from ocean waves and the beach erosion that can result.

◐ Standardized Test Practice

Test-Taking Tip

Interpreting Diagrams

When answering questions about a diagram, examine the diagram carefully, including all the labels. For example, the labels on the diagram below identify the shoreline, a series of groins, and the longshore drift. The arrow labeled *Longshore Drift* shows the direction of the drift. The diagram also has an arrow indicating which way is north on the diagram. Study the diagram and answer the sample question below it.

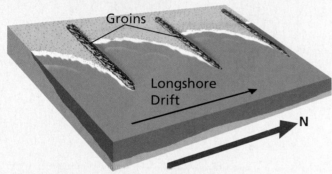

Shoreline

Groins

Longshore Drift

N

Sample Question

Where will sand pile up against the groins shown in the diagram?

    A on the north side of the groins
    B on the west side of the groins
    C on the south side of the groins
    D No sand will pile up against the groins.

Answer

The correct answer is **C**. By looking at the direction of the longshore drift and the north arrow, you can see that sand has begun to pile up on the south side of the groins.

Choose the letter of the best answer.

1. A scientist plans to test the effect temperature has on the density of ocean water. What will the manipulated variable be in her experiment?
    A density   **B** salinity
    C temperature   **D** water depth

2. In which of the following areas would the salinity of the ocean water be the highest?
    A in a hot, dry area
    B near a rainy coastal area close to the equator
    C at the mouth of a large river
    D in cold, deep water, near the ocean bottom

3. A major warm ocean surface current flows along a coastal area. What type of climate would you most likely find in the area influenced by the current?
    A extremely hot and dry
    B cool and dry
    C extremely cool and wet
    D mild and wet

Use the wave diagram below and your knowledge of science to answer Questions 4–5.

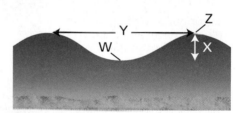

Z

Y

W

X

4. What is the wave feature labeled **W** in the diagram?
    A wave crest
    B wave trough
    C wavelength
    D wave height

5. What is the wave feature labeled **Y** in the diagram?
    A wave crest
    B wave trough
    C wavelength
    D wave height

Open-Ended Question

6. Some people refer to a tsunami as a tidal wave. Explain why this is incorrect. In your answer, describe what a tsunami is and how it forms.

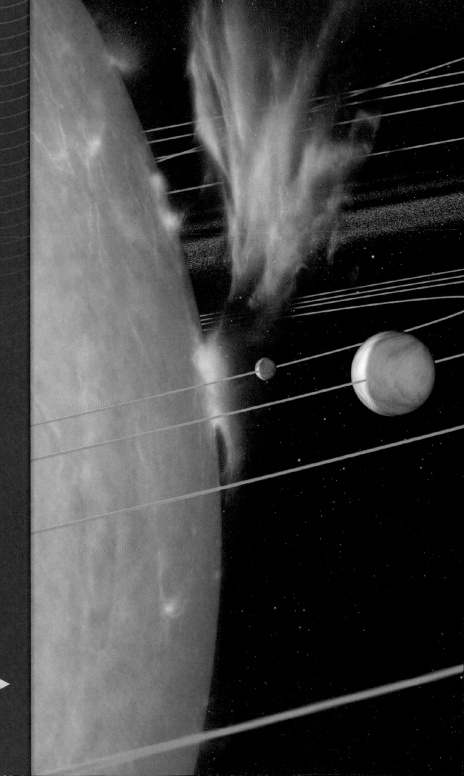

Academic Standards

This chapter addresses these Indiana standards.

The Nature of Science and Technology

7.1.8 Describe some benefits and drawbacks to technology, such as a technology that helps some organisms but hurts others.

7.1.10 Identify ways that technology influences the course of history.

Scientific Thinking

7.2.2 Use formulas to calculate the circumference, area, and volume of various shapes.

The Physical Setting

7.3.2 Recognize that the sun is much closer to Earth than any other star. Sunlight reaches Earth much sooner than the light of other stars.

7.3.11 Explain that the sun loses energy by giving off light. A small part of that light reaches Earth with a wide range of wavelengths.

7.3.17 Investigate how an unbalanced force affects an object's speed and path. If the force always acts toward the same point, the object's path may curve into an orbit.

Interactive Textbook

This illustration shows the planets in orbit around the sun. ▶

Lab zone™ Chapter Project

Build a Model of the Solar System

The solar system is a vast region containing the sun, planets, and many other objects. To help you understand the huge distances involved, you will design three different scale models of the solar system.

Your Goal To design scale models of the solar system

To complete this project, you will

- design a model to show the planets' distances from the sun
- design a model to show the planets' sizes compared to the sun
- test different scales to see if you can use the same scale for both size and distance in one model

Plan It! Begin by previewing the planet tables on pages 561 and 571. With a group of classmates, brainstorm how to build your models. Then design two models—one to show distances and one to show diameters. Next, design a third model that uses the same scale for both size and distance. Try several different scales to find which works best. Prepare a data table to record your calculations.

Observing the Solar System

Reading Preview

Key Concepts
- What are the geocentric and heliocentric systems?
- How did Copernicus, Galileo, and Kepler contribute to our knowledge of the solar system?
- What objects make up the solar system?

Key Terms
- geocentric • heliocentric
- ellipse

Target Reading Skill
Previewing Visuals Preview Figure 2 and Figure 3. Then write two questions that you have about the diagrams in a graphic organizer. As you read, answer your questions.

Models of the Universe

Q.	What is a geocentric model?
A.	
Q.	

Lab zone Discover Activity

What Is at the Center?

1. Stand about 2 meters from a partner who is holding a flashlight. Have your partner shine the flashlight in your direction. Tell your partner not to move the flashlight.
2. Continue facing your partner, but move sideways in a circle, staying about 2 meters away from your partner.
3. Record your observations about your ability to see the light.
4. Repeat the activity, but this time remain stationary and continually face one direction. Have your partner continue to hold the flashlight toward you and move sideways around you, remaining about 2 meters from you.
5. Record your observations about your ability to see the light.

Think It Over
Drawing Conclusions Compare your two sets of observations. If you represent Earth and your partner represents the sun, is it possible, just from your observations, to tell whether Earth or the sun is in the center of the solar system?

Have you ever gazed up at the sky on a starry night? If you watch for several hours, the stars seem to move across the sky. The sky seems to be rotating right over your head. In fact, from the Northern Hemisphere, the sky appears to rotate completely around the North Star once every 24 hours.

Now think about what you see every day. During the day, the sun appears to move across the sky. From here on Earth, it seems as if Earth is stationary and that the sun, moon, and stars are moving around Earth. But is the sky really moving above you? Centuries ago, before there were space shuttles or even telescopes, there was no easy way to find out.

FIGURE 1
Star Trails
This photo was made by exposing the camera film for several hours. Each star appears as part of a circle, and all the stars seem to revolve around the North Star.

Earth at the Center

When the ancient Greeks watched the stars move across the sky, they noticed that the patterns of the stars didn't change. Although the stars seemed to move, they stayed in the same position relative to one another. These patterns of stars, called constellations, kept the same shapes from night to night and from year to year.

Greek Observations As the Greeks observed the sky, they noticed something surprising. Several points of light seemed to wander slowly among the stars. The Greeks called these objects *planets,* from the Greek word meaning "wanderers." The Greeks made careful observations of the motions of the planets that they could see. You know these planets by the names the ancient Romans later gave them: Mercury, Venus, Mars, Jupiter, and Saturn.

Most early Greek astronomers believed the universe to be perfect, with Earth at the center. The Greeks thought that Earth is inside a rotating dome they called the celestial sphere. Since *geo* is the Greek word for "Earth," an Earth-centered model is known as a **geocentric** (jee oh SEN trik) system. **In a geocentric system, Earth is at the center of the revolving planets and stars.**

Ptolemy's Model About A.D. 140, the Greek astronomer Ptolemy (TAHL uh mee) further developed the geocentric model. Like the earlier Greeks, Ptolemy thought that Earth is at the center of a system of planets and stars. In Ptolemy's model, however, the planets move on small circles that move on bigger circles.

Even though Ptolemy's geocentric model was incorrect, it explained the motions observed in the sky fairly accurately. As a result, the geocentric model of the universe was widely accepted for nearly 1,500 years after Ptolemy.

✓ **Reading Checkpoint** What is a geocentric system?

FIGURE 2
Geocentric System
In a geocentric system, the planets and stars are thought to revolve around a stationary Earth. In the 1500s, an astronomy book published the illustration of Ptolemy's geocentric system shown below.
Interpreting Diagrams *Where is Earth located in each illustration?*

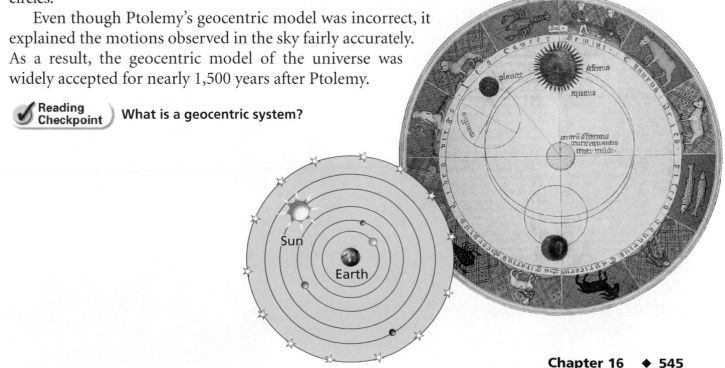

Sun at the Center

Not everybody believed in the geocentric system. An ancient Greek scientist developed another explanation for the motion of the planets. This sun-centered model is called a **heliocentric** (hee lee oh SEN trik) system. *Helios* is Greek for "sun." **In a heliocentric system, Earth and the other planets revolve around the sun.** This model was not well received in ancient times, however, because people could not accept that Earth is not at the center of the universe.

The Copernican Revolution In 1543, the Polish astronomer Nicolaus Copernicus further developed the heliocentric model. **Copernicus was able to work out the arrangement of the known planets and how they move around the sun.** Copernicus's theory would eventually revolutionize the science of astronomy. But at first, many people were unwilling to accept his theory. They needed more evidence to be convinced.

In the 1500s and early 1600s, most people still believed in the geocentric model. However, evidence collected by the Italian scientist Galileo Galilei gradually convinced others that the heliocentric model was correct.

Galileo's Evidence Galileo used the newly invented telescope to make discoveries that supported the heliocentric model. For example, in 1610, Galileo used a telescope to discover four moons revolving around Jupiter. The motion of these moons proved that not everything in the sky revolves around Earth.

FIGURE 3
Heliocentric System
In a heliocentric system, Earth and the other planets revolve around the sun. The illustration by Andreas Cellarius (top) was made in the 1660s.
Interpreting Diagrams *In a heliocentric model, what revolves around Earth?*

Nicolaus Copernicus
1473–1543

Galileo Galilei
1564–1642

▼ A reconstruction of Galileo's telescope

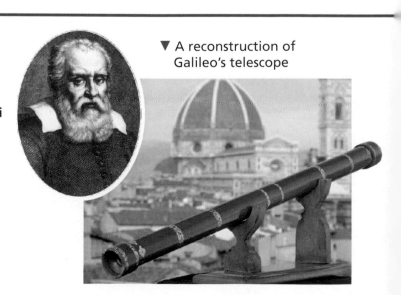

FIGURE 4
Major Figures in the History of Astronomy

Galileo's observations of Venus also supported the heliocentric system. Galileo knew that Venus is always seen near the sun. He discovered that Venus goes through a series of phases similar to those of Earth's moon. But Venus would not have a full set of phases if it circled around Earth. Therefore, Galileo reasoned, the geocentric model must be incorrect.

Tycho Brahe's Observations Copernicus correctly placed the sun at the center of the planets. But he incorrectly assumed that the planets travel in orbits that are perfect circles. Copernicus had based his ideas on observations made by the ancient Greeks.

In the late 1500s, the Danish astronomer Tycho Brahe (TEE koh BRAH uh) and his assistants made much more accurate observations. For more than 20 years, they carefully observed and recorded the positions of the planets. Surprisingly, these observations were made without using a telescope. Telescopes had not yet been invented!

Kepler's Calculations Tycho Brahe died in 1601. His assistant, Johannes Kepler, went to work analyzing the observations. Kepler began by trying to figure out the shape of Mars's orbit. At first, he assumed that the orbit was circular. But his calculations did not fit the observations. Kepler eventually found that Mars's orbit was a slightly flattened circle, or ellipse. An **ellipse** is an oval shape, which may be elongated or nearly circular.

After years of detailed calculations, Kepler reached a remarkable conclusion about the motion of the planets. **Kepler found that the orbit of each planet is an ellipse.** Kepler had used the evidence gathered by Tycho Brahe to disprove the long-held belief that the planets move in perfect circles.

Reading Checkpoint What is an ellipse?

Tycho Brahe
1546–1601

Johannes Kepler
1571–1630

◄ Brahe's observatory on an island between Denmark and Sweden

Mercury 58,000,000 km
Venus 108,000,000 km
Earth 150,000,000 km
Mars 228,000,000 km

Jupiter
779,000,000 km

Saturn
1,434,000,000 km

FIGURE 5

The Sun and Planets
This illustration shows the average distances of the nine planets from the sun. These distances are drawn to scale, but the sizes of the planets are not drawn to the same scale. **Observing** *Which planet is closest to the sun?*

Modern Discoveries

Today, people talk about the "solar system" rather than the "Earth system." This shows that people accept the idea that Earth and the other planets revolve around the sun.

Since Galileo's time, our knowledge of the solar system has increased dramatically. Galileo knew the same planets that the ancient Greeks had known—Mercury, Venus, Earth, Mars, Jupiter, and Saturn. Since Galileo's time, astronomers have discovered three more planets—Uranus, Neptune, and Pluto. Astronomers have also identified many other objects in the solar system, such as comets and asteroids. **Today we know that the solar system consists of the sun, nine planets and their moons, and several kinds of smaller objects that revolve around the sun.**

**Math** Analyzing Data

Planet Speed Versus Distance

Johannes Kepler discovered a relationship between the speed of a planet and its distance from the sun. Use the graph to help discover what Kepler learned.

1. **Reading Graphs** According to the graph, what is Earth's average speed?

2. **Interpreting Data** Which is closer to the sun, Mercury or Mars? Which moves faster?

3. **Drawing Conclusions** What is the general relationship between a planet's speed and its average distance from the sun?

4. **Predicting** The planet Uranus is about 2,900 million km from the sun. Predict whether its speed is greater or less than Jupiter's speed. Explain your answer.

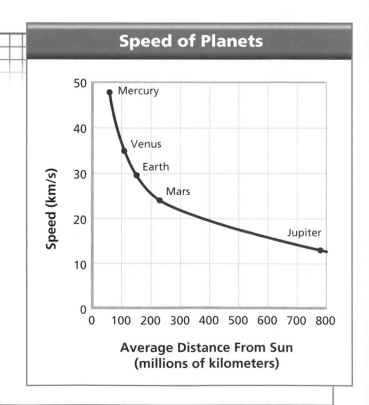

Speed of Planets

Speed (km/s) vs. Average Distance From Sun (millions of kilometers)

Uranus
2,873,000,000 km

Neptune
4,495,000,000 km

Pluto
5,870,000,000 km

Galileo used a telescope to observe the solar system from Earth's surface. Astronomers today still use telescopes located on Earth, but they have also placed telescopes in space to gain a better view of the universe beyond Earth. Scientists have also sent astronauts to the moon and launched numerous space probes to explore the far reaches of the solar system. Our understanding of the solar system continues to grow every day. Who knows what new discoveries will be made in your lifetime!

For: Solar System activity
Visit: PHSchool.com
Web Code: cfp-5031

✓ **Reading Checkpoint** Which six planets were known to the ancient Greeks?

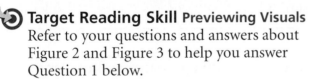

Section 1 Assessment

🎯 **Target Reading Skill** Previewing Visuals Refer to your questions and answers about Figure 2 and Figure 3 to help you answer Question 1 below.

Reviewing Key Concepts

1. a. **Explaining** What are the geocentric and heliocentric systems?
   b. **Comparing and Contrasting** How was Copernicus's model of the universe different from Ptolemy's model?
   c. **Drawing Conclusions** What discoveries by Galileo support the heliocentric model?
   d. **Applying Concepts** People often say the sun rises in the east, crosses the sky, and sets in the west. Is this literally true? Explain.

2. a. **Interpreting Data** How did Kepler use Tycho Brahe's data?
   b. **Describing** What did Kepler discover about the orbits of the planets?
   c. **Inferring** How did Tycho Brahe and Kepler employ the scientific method?

3. a. **Describing** What objects make up the solar system?
   b. **Listing** What are the nine planets, in order of increasing distance from the sun?
   c. **Interpreting Diagrams** Use Figure 5 to find the planet with the closest orbit to Earth.

Writing in Science

Dialogue Write an imaginary conversation between Ptolemy and Galileo about the merits of the geocentric and heliocentric systems. Which system would each scientist favor? What evidence could each offer to support his view? Do you think that one scientist could convince the other to change his mind? Use quotation marks around the comments of each scientist.

Reading Preview

Key Concepts
- What are the three layers of the sun's interior?
- What are the three layers of the sun's atmosphere?
- What features form on or above the sun's surface?

Key Terms
- core
- nuclear fusion
- radiation zone
- convection zone
- photosphere
- chromosphere
- corona
- solar wind
- sunspot
- prominence
- solar flare

Target Reading Skill

Outlining As you read, make an outline about the sun that you can use for review. Use the red headings for main topics and the blue headings for subtopics.

The Sun
I. The sun's interior
A. The core
B.
C.
II. The sun's atmosphere
A. The photosphere

Lab zone Discover Activity

How Can You Safely Observe the Sun?

1. Clamp a pair of binoculars to a ring stand as shown in the photo.
2. Cut a hole in a 20-cm by 28-cm sheet of thin cardboard so that it will fit over the binoculars, as shown in the photo. The cardboard should cover one lens, but allow light through the other lens. Tape the cardboard on securely.
3. Use the binoculars to project an image of the sun onto a sheet of white paper. The cardboard will shade the white paper. Change the focus and move the paper back and forth until you get a sharp image.
   CAUTION: *Never look directly at the sun. You will hurt your eyes if you do. Do not look up through the binoculars.*

Think It Over

Observing Draw what you see on the paper. What do you see on the surface of the sun?

Suppose you are aboard a spaceship approaching the solar system from afar. Your first impression of the solar system might be that it consists of a single star with a few tiny objects orbiting around it. Your first impression wouldn't be that far off. In fact, the sun accounts for 99.8 percent of the solar system's total mass. As a result of its huge mass, the sun exerts a powerful gravitational force throughout the solar system. Although this force decreases rapidly with distance, it is strong enough to hold all the planets and other distant objects in orbit.

FIGURE 6
Active Sun
The sun is a huge, hot ball of glowing gas.

The Sun's Interior

Unlike Earth, the sun does not have a solid surface. Rather, the sun is a ball of glowing gas through and through. About three fourths of the sun's mass is hydrogen and one fourth is helium. There are also small amounts of other elements. Like Earth, the sun has an interior and an atmosphere. **The sun's interior consists of the core, the radiation zone, and the convection zone.**

Go Online
PLANET DIARY

For: More on the sun
Visit: PHSchool.com
Web Code: cfd-5032

The Core The sun produces an enormous amount of energy in its **core,** or central region. This energy is not produced by burning fuel. Rather, the sun's energy comes from nuclear fusion. In the process of **nuclear fusion,** hydrogen atoms join together to form helium. Nuclear fusion occurs only under conditions of extremely high temperature and pressure. The temperature inside the sun's core reaches about 15 million degrees Celsius, high enough for nuclear fusion to take place.

The total mass of the helium produced by nuclear fusion is slightly less than the total mass of the hydrogen that goes into it. What happens to this mass? It is changed into energy. This energy slowly moves outward from the core, eventually escaping into space.

The Radiation Zone The energy produced in the sun's core moves outward through the middle layer of the sun's interior, the radiation zone. The **radiation zone** is a region of very tightly packed gas where energy is transferred mainly in the form of electromagnetic radiation. Because the radiation zone is so dense, energy can take more than 100,000 years to move through it.

The Convection Zone The **convection zone** is the outermost layer of the sun's interior. Hot gases rise from the bottom of the convection zone and gradually cool as they approach the top. Cooler gases sink, forming loops of gas that move energy toward the sun's surface.

Reading Checkpoint What is nuclear fusion?

FIGURE 7
The Sun's Corona
During a total solar eclipse, you can see light from the corona, the outer layer of the sun's atmosphere around the dark disk of the moon.

The Sun's Atmosphere

The sun's atmosphere includes the photosphere, the chromosphere, and the corona. Each layer has unique properties.

The Photosphere The inner layer of the sun's atmosphere is called the **photosphere** (FOH tuh sfeer). The Greek word *photos* means "light," so *photosphere* means the sphere that gives off visible light. The sun does not have a solid surface, but the gases of the photosphere are thick enough to be visible. When you look at an image of the sun, you are looking at the photosphere. It is considered to be the sun's surface layer.

The Chromosphere During a total solar eclipse, the moon blocks light from the photosphere. The photosphere no longer produces the glare that keeps you from seeing the sun's faint, outer layers. At the start and end of a total eclipse, a reddish glow is visible just around the photosphere. This glow comes from the middle layer of the sun's atmosphere, the **chromosphere** (KROH muh sfeer). The Greek word *chroma* means "color," so the chromosphere is the "color sphere."

The Corona During a total solar eclipse an even fainter layer of the sun becomes visible, as you can see in Figure 7. This outer layer, which looks like a white halo around the sun, is called the **corona,** which means "crown" in Latin. The corona extends into space for millions of kilometers. It gradually thins into streams of electrically charged particles called the **solar wind.**

 **Reading Checkpoint** During what event could you see the sun's corona?

Features on the Sun

For hundreds of years, scientists have used telescopes to study the sun. They have spotted a variety of features on the sun's surface. **Features on or just above the sun's surface include sunspots, prominences, and solar flares.**

Sunspots Early observers noticed dark spots on the sun's surface. These became known as sunspots. Sunspots look small. But in fact, they can be larger than Earth. **Sunspots** are areas of gas on the sun's surface that are cooler than the gases around them. Cooler gases don't give off as much light as hotter gases, which is why sunspots look darker than the rest of the photosphere. Sunspots seem to move across the sun's surface, showing that the sun rotates on its axis, just as Earth does. The number of sunspots on the sun varies over a period of about 11 years.

Lab zone Try This **Activity**

Viewing Sunspots

You can observe changes in the number of sunspots.

1. Make a data table to record the number of sunspots you see each day.

2. Decide on a time to study sunspots each day.

3. View the sun's image in the way described in the Discover activity on page 550. **CAUTION:** *Never look directly at the sun. You will hurt your eyes if you do.*

4. Make and record your observations.

Interpreting Data How much did the number of sunspots change from day to day?

FIGURE 8

The Layers of the Sun

The sun has an interior and an atmosphere, each of which consists of several layers. The diameter of the sun (not including the chromosphere and the corona) is about 1.4 million kilometers. *Name the layers of the sun's interior, beginning at its center.*

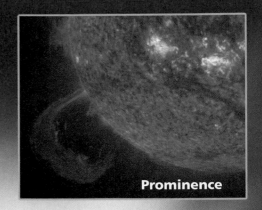

Prominence

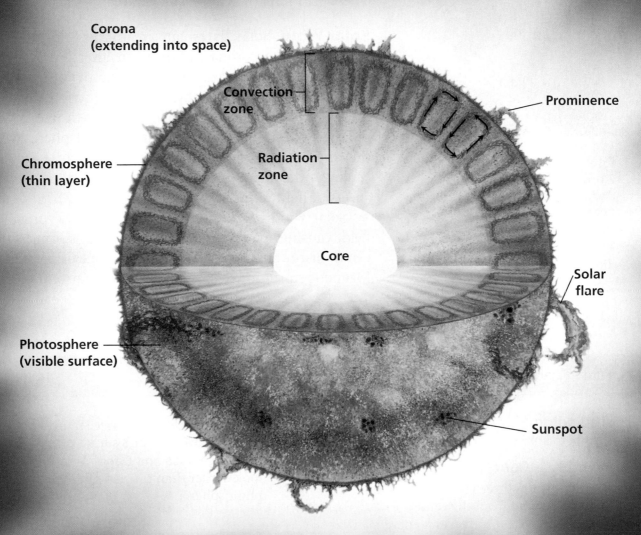

Corona
(extending into space)

Convection
zone

Prominence

Chromosphere
(thin layer)

Radiation
zone

Core

Solar
flare

Photosphere
(visible surface)

Sunspot

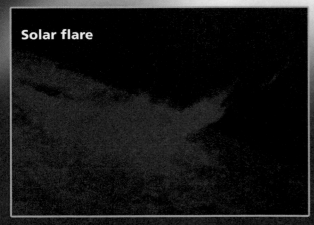

Solar flare

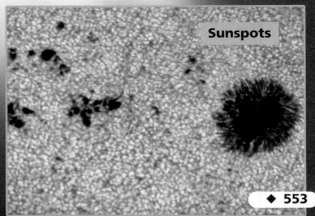

Sunspots

Prominences Sunspots usually occur in groups. Huge, reddish loops of gas called **prominences** often link different parts of sunspot regions. When a group of sunspots is near the edge of the sun as seen from Earth, these loops can be seen extending over the edge of the sun.

Solar Flares Sometimes the loops in sunspot regions suddenly connect, releasing large amounts of magnetic energy. The energy heats gas on the sun to millions of degrees Celsius, causing the gas to erupt into space. These eruptions are called **solar flares.**

Solar Wind Solar flares can greatly increase the solar wind from the corona, resulting in an increase in the number of particles reaching Earth's upper atmosphere. Normally, Earth's atmosphere and magnetic field block these particles. However, near the North and South poles, the particles can enter Earth's atmosphere, where they create powerful electric currents that cause gas molecules in the atmosphere to glow. The result is rippling sheets of light in the sky called auroras.

Solar wind particles can also affect Earth's magnetic field, causing magnetic storms. Magnetic storms sometimes disrupt radio, telephone, and television signals. Magnetic storms can also cause electrical power problems.

FIGURE 9
Auroras
Auroras such as this can occur near Earth's poles when particles of the solar wind strike gas molecules in Earth's upper atmosphere.

 **Reading Checkpoint** **What is a prominence?**

Section 2 Assessment

Target Reading Skill Outlining Use your outline to help answer the questions below.

Reviewing Key Concepts

1. a. **Listing** List the three layers of the sun's interior, starting from the center.
   b. **Explaining** Where is the sun's energy produced?
   c. **Comparing and Contrasting** Compare how energy moves through the radiation zone and the convection zone.
2. a. **Listing** What three layers make up the sun's atmosphere?
   b. **Identifying** Which of the sun's layers produces its visible light?
   c. **Relating Cause and Effect** Why is it usually impossible to see the sun's corona from Earth?

3. a. **Describing** Describe three features found on or just above the sun's surface.
   b. **Relating Cause and Effect** Why do sunspots look darker than the rest of the sun's photosphere?

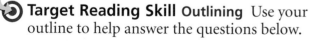 **At-Home Activity**

Sun Symbols As the source of heat and light, the sun is an important symbol in many cultures. With family members, look around your home and neighborhood for illustrations of the sun on signs, flags, clothing, and in artwork. Which parts of the sun's atmosphere do the illustrations show?

Stormy Sunspots

Problem

How are magnetic storms on Earth related to sunspot activity?

Skills Focus

graphing, interpreting data

Materials

• graph paper
• ruler

Procedure

1. Use the data in the table of Annual Sunspot Numbers to make a line graph of sunspot activity between 1972 and 2002.

2. On the graph, label the x-axis "Year." Use a scale with 2-year intervals, from 1972 to 2002.

3. Label the y-axis "Sunspot Number." Use a scale of 0 through 160 in intervals of 10.

4. Graph a point for the Sunspot Number for each year.

5. Complete your graph by drawing lines to connect the points.

Analyze and Conclude

1. **Graphing** Based on your graph, which years had the highest Sunspot Number? The lowest Sunspot Number?

2. **Interpreting Data** How often does the cycle of maximum and minimum activity repeat?

3. **Interpreting Data** When was the most recent maximum sunspot activity? The most recent minimum sunspot activity?

4. **Inferring** Compare your sunspot graph with the magnetic storms graph. What relationship can you infer between periods of high sunspot activity and magnetic storms? Explain.

Annual Sunspot Numbers			
Year	Sunspot Number	Year	Sunspot Number
1972	68.9	1988	100.2
1974	34.5	1990	142.6
1976	12.6	1992	94.3
1978	92.5	1994	29.9
1980	154.6	1996	8.6
1982	115.9	1998	64.3
1984	45.9	2000	119.6
1986	13.4	2002	104.0

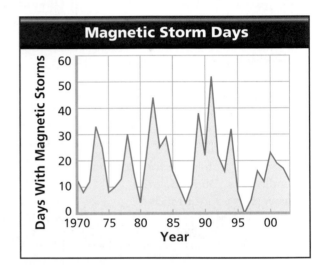

Magnetic Storm Days

5. **Communicating** Suppose you are an engineer working for an electric power company. Write a brief summary of your analysis of sunspot data. Explain the relationship between sunspot number and electrical disturbances on Earth.

More to Explore

Using the pattern of sunspot activity you found, predict the number of peaks you would expect in the next 30 years. Around which years would you expect the peaks to occur?

Gravity and Motion

Reading Preview

Key Concepts

- What determines the strength of the force of gravity between two objects?
- What two factors combine to keep the moon and Earth in orbit?

Key Terms

- force
- gravity
- law of universal gravitation
- mass
- weight
- inertia
- Newton's first law of motion

Target Reading Skill

Asking Questions Before you read, preview the red headings. In a graphic organizer like the one below, ask a question for each heading. As you read, write answers to your questions.

Gravity

Question	Answer
What is gravity?	Gravity is . . .

Lab zone Discover **Activity**

Can You Remove the Bottom Penny?

1. Place 25 or so pennies in a stack on a table.
2. Write down your prediction of what will happen if you attempt to knock the bottom penny out of the stack.
3. Quickly slide a ruler along the surface of the table and strike the bottom penny. Observe what happens to the stack of pennies.
4. Repeat Step 3 several times, knocking more pennies from the bottom of the stack.

Think It Over
Developing Hypotheses Explain what happened to the stack of pennies as the bottom penny was knocked out of the stack.

Earth revolves around the sun in a nearly circular orbit. The moon orbits Earth in the same way. But what keeps Earth and the moon in orbit? Why don't they just fly off into space?

The first person to answer these questions was the English scientist Isaac Newton. Late in his life, Newton told a story of how watching an apple fall from a tree in 1666 had made him think about the moon's orbit. Newton realized that there must be a force acting between Earth and the moon that kept the moon in orbit. A **force** is a push or a pull. Most everyday forces require objects to be in contact. Newton realized that the force that holds the moon in orbit is different in that it acts over long distances between objects that are not in contact.

Gravity

Newton hypothesized that the force that pulls an apple to the ground also pulls the moon toward Earth, keeping it in orbit. This force, called **gravity,** attracts all objects toward each other. In Newton's day, most scientists thought that forces on Earth were different from those elsewhere in the universe. Although Newton did not discover gravity, he was the first person to realize that gravity occurs everywhere. Newton's **law of universal gravitation** states that every object in the universe attracts every other object.

The force of gravity is measured in units called newtons, named after Isaac Newton. **The strength of the force of gravity between two objects depends on two factors: the masses of the objects and the distance between them.**

Gravity, Mass, and Weight According to the law of universal gravitation, all of the objects around you, including Earth and even this book, are pulling on you, just as you are pulling on them. Why don't you notice a pull between you and the book? Because the strength of gravity depends in part on the masses of each of the objects. **Mass** is the amount of matter in an object.

Because Earth is so massive, it exerts a much greater force on you than this book does. Similarly, Earth exerts a gravitational force on the moon, large enough to keep the moon in orbit. The moon also exerts a gravitational force on Earth, as you will learn later in this chapter when you study the tides.

The force of gravity on an object is known as its **weight**. Unlike mass, which doesn't change, an object's weight can change depending on its location. For example, on the moon you would weigh about one sixth of your weight on Earth. This is because the moon is much less massive than Earth, so the pull of the moon's gravity on you would be far less than that of Earth's gravity.

Gravity and Distance The strength of gravity is affected by the distance between two objects as well as their masses. The force of gravity decreases rapidly as distance increases. For example, if the distance between two objects were doubled, the force of gravity between them would decrease to one fourth of its original value.

 **Reading Checkpoint** What is an object's weight?

FIGURE 10
Gravity, Mass, and Distance
The strength of the force of gravity between two objects depends on their masses and the distance between them.
Inferring How would the force of gravity change if the distance between the objects decreased?

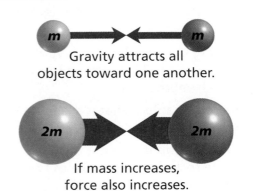

Gravity attracts all objects toward one another.

If mass increases, force also increases.

If distance increases, force decreases.

FIGURE 11
Earth Over the Moon
The force of gravity holds Earth and the moon together.

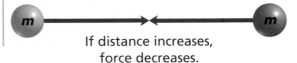

Gravity Versus Distance

As a rocket leaves a planet's surface, the force of gravity between the rocket and the planet changes. Use the graph at the right to answer the questions below.

1. **Reading Graphs** What two variables are being graphed? In what units is each variable measured?

2. **Reading Graphs** What is the force of gravity on the rocket at the planet's surface?

3. **Reading Graphs** What is the force of gravity on the rocket at a distance of two units (twice the planet's radius from its center)?

4. **Making Generalizations** In general, how does the force of gravity pulling on the rocket change as the distance between it and the planet increases?

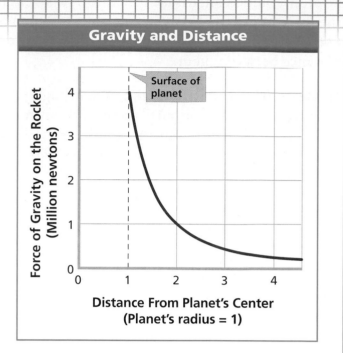

Gravity and Distance

Y-axis: Force of Gravity on the Rocket (Million newtons)

X-axis: Distance From Planet's Center (Planet's radius = 1)

Label: Surface of planet

Go Online

SciLINKS NSTA

For: Links on gravity
Visit: www.SciLinks.org
Web Code: scn-0612

Inertia and Orbital Motion

If the sun and Earth are constantly pulling on one another because of gravity, why doesn't Earth fall into the sun? Similarly, why doesn't the moon crash into Earth? The fact that such collisions have not occurred shows that there must be another factor at work. That factor is called inertia.

Inertia The tendency of an object to resist a change in motion is **inertia.** You feel the effects of inertia every day. When you are riding in a car and it stops suddenly, you keep moving forward. If you didn't have a seat belt on, your inertia could cause you to bump into the car's windshield or the seat in front of you. The more mass an object has, the greater its inertia. An object with greater inertia is more difficult to start or stop.

Isaac Newton stated his ideas about inertia as a scientific law. **Newton's first law of motion** says that an object at rest will stay at rest and an object in motion will stay in motion with a constant speed and direction unless acted on by a force.

 **Reading Checkpoint** What is inertia?

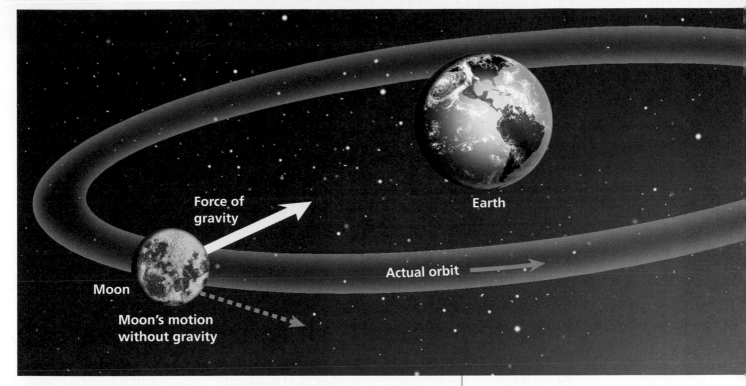

Force of gravity

Earth

Actual orbit

Moon

Moon's motion
without gravity

Orbital Motion Why do Earth and the moon remain in their orbits? **Newton concluded that two factors—inertia and gravity—combine to keep Earth in orbit around the sun and the moon in orbit around Earth.**

As shown in Figure 12, Earth's gravity keeps pulling the moon toward it, preventing the moon from moving in a straight line. At the same time, the moon keeps moving ahead because of its inertia. If not for Earth's gravity, inertia would cause the moon to move off through space in a straight line. In the same way, Earth revolves around the sun because the sun's gravity pulls on it while Earth's inertia keeps it moving ahead.

FIGURE 12
Gravity and Inertia
A combination of gravity and inertia keeps the moon in orbit around Earth. If there were no gravity, inertia would cause the moon to travel in a straight line.
Interpreting Diagrams *What would happen to the moon if it were not moving in orbit?*

Section 3 Assessment

Target Reading Skill Asking Questions
Use your graphic organizer about the headings to help answer the questions below.

Reviewing Key Concepts

1. a. **Summarizing** What is the law of universal gravitation?
   b. **Reviewing** What two factors determine the force of gravity between two objects?
   c. **Predicting** Suppose the moon were closer to Earth. How would the force of gravity between Earth and the moon be different?
2. a. **Identifying** What two factors act together to keep Earth in orbit around the sun?

b. **Applying Concepts** Why doesn't Earth simply fall into the sun?
c. **Predicting** How would Earth move if the sun (including its gravity) suddenly disappeared? Explain your answer.

Writing in Science

Cause and Effect Paragraph Suppose you took a trip to the moon. Write a paragraph describing how and why your weight would change. Would your mass change too?

The Inner Planets

Reading Preview

Key Concepts
- What characteristics do the inner planets have in common?
- What are the main characteristics that distinguish each of the inner planets?

Key Terms
- terrestrial planets
- greenhouse effect

Target Reading Skill
Using Prior Knowledge Look at the section headings and visuals to see what this section is about. Then write what you know about the inner planets in a graphic organizer like the one below. As you read, write what you learn.

What You Know
1. Most of Earth is covered with water.
2.

What You Learned
1.
2.

Discover **Activity**

How Does Mars Look From Earth?

1. Work in pairs. On a sheet of paper, draw a circle 20 cm across to represent Mars. Draw about 100 small lines, each about 1 cm long, at random places inside the circle.

2. Have your partner look at your drawing of Mars from the other side of the room. Your partner should draw what he or she sees.

3. Compare your original drawing with what your partner drew. Then look at your own drawing from across the room.

Think It Over

Observing Did your partner draw any connecting lines that were not actually on your drawing? What can you conclude about the accuracy of descriptions of other planets based on observations from Earth?

Where could you find a planet whose atmosphere has almost entirely leaked away into space? How about a planet whose surface is hot enough to melt lead? And how about a planet with volcanoes higher than any on Earth? Finally, where could you find a planet with oceans of water brimming with fish and other life? These are descriptions of the four planets closest to the sun, known as the inner planets.

Earth and the three other inner planets—Mercury, Venus, and Mars—are more similar to each other than they are to the five outer planets. **The four inner planets are small and dense and have rocky surfaces.** The inner planets are often called the **terrestrial planets,** from the Latin word *terra,* which means "Earth." Figure 13 summarizes data about the inner planets.

Earth

As you can see in Figure 14, Earth has three main layers—a crust, a mantle, and a core. The crust includes the solid, rocky surface. Under the crust is the mantle, a layer of hot molten rock. When volcanoes erupt, this hot material rises to the surface. Earth has a dense core made of mainly iron and nickel. The outer core is liquid, but the inner core is solid.

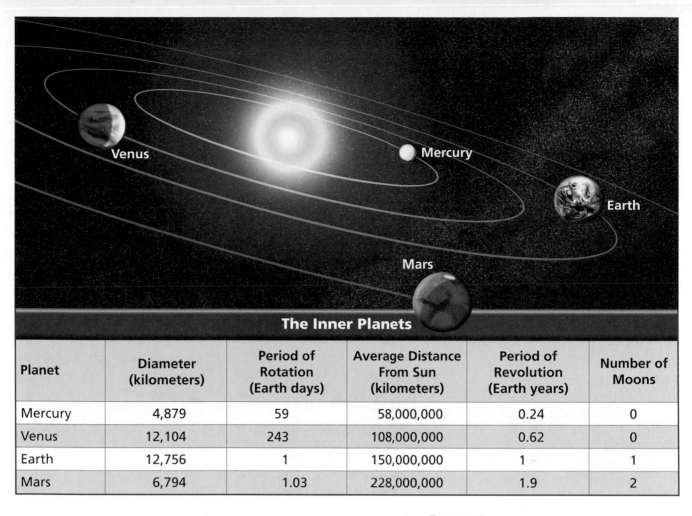

The Inner Planets

Planet	Diameter (kilometers)	Period of Rotation (Earth days)	Average Distance From Sun (kilometers)	Period of Revolution (Earth years)	Number of Moons
Mercury	4,879	59	58,000,000	0.24	0
Venus	12,104	243	108,000,000	0.62	0
Earth	12,756	1	150,000,000	1	1
Mars	6,794	1.03	228,000,000	1.9	2

Water Earth is unique in our solar system in having liquid water at its surface. In fact, most of Earth's surface, about 70 percent, is covered with water. Perhaps our planet should be called "Water" instead of "Earth"! Earth has a suitable temperature range for water to exist as a liquid, gas, or solid. Water is also important in shaping Earth's surface, wearing it down and changing its appearance over time.

Atmosphere Earth has enough gravity to hold on to most gases. These gases make up Earth's atmosphere, which extends more than 100 kilometers above its surface. Other planets in the solar system have atmospheres too, but only Earth has an atmosphere that is rich in oxygen. The oxygen you need to live makes up about 20 percent of Earth's atmosphere. Nearly all the rest is nitrogen, with small amounts of other gases such as argon and carbon dioxide. The atmosphere also includes varying amounts of water in the form of a gas. Water in a gaseous form is called water vapor.

 **Reading Checkpoint** What two gases make up most of Earth's atmosphere?

FIGURE 13
The inner planets take up only a small part of the solar system. Note that sizes and distances are not drawn to scale.

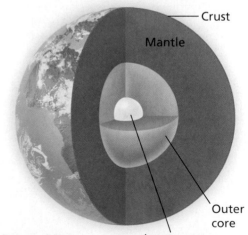

FIGURE 14
Earth's Layers
Earth has a solid, rocky surface.
Interpreting Diagrams *What are Earth's three main layers?*

Crust
Mantle
Outer core
Inner core

Size of Mercury
compared to Earth

FIGURE 15
Mercury
This image of Mercury was
produced by combining a series of
smaller images made by the
Mariner 10 space probe.
Interpreting Photographs *How is
Mercury's surface different from
Earth's?*

Mercury

**Mercury is the smallest terrestrial planet and the planet
closest to the sun.** Mercury is not much larger than Earth's
moon and has no moons of its own. The interior of Mercury is
probably made up mainly of the dense metal iron.

Exploring Mercury Because Mercury is so close to the sun, it
is hard to see from Earth. Much of what astronomers know about
Mercury's surface came from a single probe, *Mariner 10*. It flew
by Mercury three times in 1974 and 1975. Two new missions to
Mercury are planned. The first of these, called *MESSENGER*, is
scheduled to go into orbit around Mercury in 2009.

Mariner 10's photographs show that Mercury has many flat
plains and craters on its surface. The large number of craters
shows that Mercury's surface has changed little for billions of
years. Many of Mercury's craters have been named for artists,
writers, and musicians, such as the composers Bach and Mozart.

Mercury's Atmosphere Mercury has virtually no atmosphere. Mercury's high daytime temperatures cause gas particles to move very fast. Because Mercury's mass is small, its
gravity is weak. Fast-moving gas particles can easily escape into
space. However, astronomers have detected small amounts of
sodium and other gases around Mercury.

Mercury is a planet of extremes, with a greater temperature
range than any other planet in the solar system. It is so close to
the sun that during the day, the side facing the sun reaches
temperatures of 430°C. Because Mercury has almost no atmosphere, at night its heat escapes into space. Then its temperature drops below −170°C.

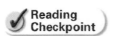 **Reading
Checkpoint** Compare daytime and nighttime temperatures on
Mercury.

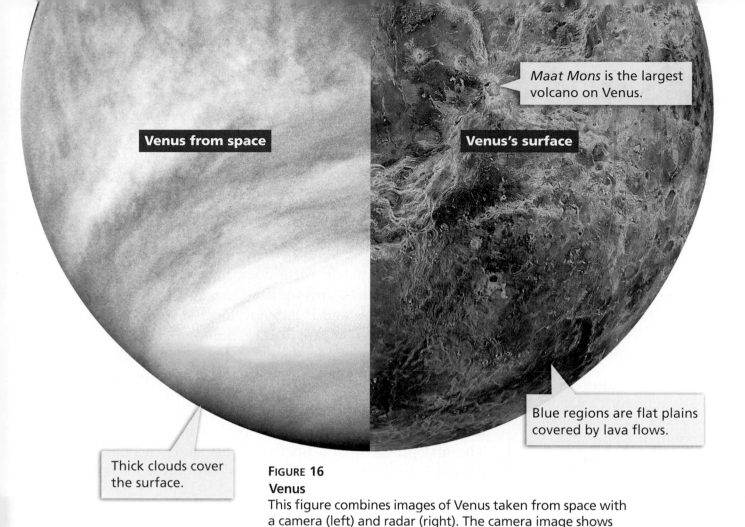

Venus from space

Venus's surface

Maat Mons is the largest volcano on Venus.

Blue regions are flat plains covered by lava flows.

Thick clouds cover the surface.

FIGURE 16
Venus
This figure combines images of Venus taken from space with a camera (left) and radar (right). The camera image shows Venus's thick atmosphere. Radar is able to penetrate Venus's clouds to reveal the surface. Both images are false color.

Venus

You can sometimes see Venus in the west just after sunset. When Venus is visible in that part of the sky, it is known as the "evening star," though of course it really isn't a star at all. At other times, Venus rises before the sun in the morning. Then it is known as the "morning star."

Venus is so similar in size and mass to Earth that it is sometimes called "Earth's twin." **Venus's density and internal structure are similar to Earth's. But, in other ways, Venus and Earth are very different.**

Venus's Rotation Venus takes about 7.5 Earth months to revolve around the sun. It takes about 8 months for Venus to rotate once on its axis. Thus, Venus rotates so slowly that its day is longer than its year! Oddly, Venus rotates from east to west, the opposite direction from most other planets and moons. Astronomers hypothesize that this unusual rotation was caused by a very large object that struck Venus billions of years ago. Such a collision could have caused Venus to change its direction of rotation. Another hypothesis is that Venus's thick atmosphere could have somehow altered its rotation.

Size of Venus compared to Earth

Go Online

SCiLINKS NSTA

For: Links on the planets
Visit: www.SciLinks.org
Web Code: scn-0633

Lab zone Try This Activity

Greenhouse Effect

How can you measure the effect of a closed container on temperature?

1.  Carefully place a thermometer into each of two glass jars. Cover one jar with cellophane. Place both jars either in direct sunlight or under a strong light source.

2. Observe the temperature of both thermometers when you start. Check the temperatures every 5 minutes for a total of 20 minutes. Record your results in a data table.

Inferring Compare how the temperature changed in the uncovered jar and the covered jar. What do you think is the reason for any difference in the temperatures of the two jars? Which jar is a better model of Venus's atmosphere?

Venus's Atmosphere Venus's atmosphere is so thick that it is always cloudy there. From Earth or space, astronomers can see only a smooth cloud cover over Venus. The clouds are made mostly of droplets of sulfuric acid.

If you could stand on Venus's surface, you would quickly be crushed by the weight of its atmosphere. The pressure of Venus's atmosphere is 90 times greater than the pressure of Earth's atmosphere. You couldn't breathe on Venus because its atmosphere is mostly carbon dioxide.

Because Venus is closer to the sun than Earth is, it receives more solar energy than Earth does. Much of this radiation is reflected by Venus's atmosphere. However, some radiation reaches the surface and is later given off as heat. The carbon dioxide in Venus's atmosphere traps heat so well that Venus has the hottest surface of any planet. At 460°C, its average surface temperature is hot enough to melt lead. This trapping of heat by the atmosphere is called the **greenhouse effect**.

Exploring Venus Many space probes have visited Venus. The first probe to land on the surface and send back data, *Venera 7*, landed in 1970. It survived for only a few minutes because of the high temperature and pressure. Later probes were more durable and sent images and data back to Earth.

The *Magellan* probe reached Venus in 1990, carrying radar instruments. Radar works through clouds, so *Magellan* was able to map nearly the entire surface. The *Magellan* data confirmed that Venus is covered with rock. Venus's surface has many volcanoes and broad plains formed by lava flows.

✓ **Reading Checkpoint** What are Venus's clouds made of?

FIGURE 17
Maat Mons
Scientists used radar data to develop this computer image of the giant volcano *Maat Mons*. The height of the mountains is exaggerated to make them stand out.

Mars

Mars is called the "red planet." When you see it in the sky, it has a slightly reddish tinge. This reddish color is due to the breakdown of iron-rich rocks, which creates a rusty dust that covers much of Mars's surface.

Size of Mars compared to Earth

Mars's Atmosphere The atmosphere of Mars is more than 95 percent carbon dioxide. It is similar in composition to Venus's atmosphere, but much thinner. You could walk around on Mars, but you would have to wear an airtight suit and carry your own oxygen, like a scuba diver. Mars has few clouds, and they are very thin compared to clouds on Earth. Mars's transparent atmosphere allows people on Earth to view its surface with a telescope. Temperatures on the surface range from −140°C to 20°C.

Water on Mars In 1877, an Italian astronomer named Giovanni Schiaparelli (sky ah puh REL ee) announced that he had seen long, straight lines on Mars. He called them *canale*, or channels. In the 1890s and early 1900s, Percival Lowell, an American astronomer, convinced many people that these lines were canals that had been built by intelligent Martians to carry water. Astronomers now know that Lowell was mistaken. There are no canals on Mars.

Images of Mars taken from space do show a variety of features that look as if they were made by ancient streams, lakes, or floods. There are huge canyons and features that look like the remains of ancient coastlines. **Scientists think that a large amount of liquid water flowed on Mars's surface in the distant past.** Scientists infer that Mars must have been much warmer and had a thicker atmosphere at that time.

At present, liquid water cannot exist for long on Mars's surface. Mars's atmosphere is so thin that any liquid water would quickly turn into a gas. So where is Mars's water now? Some of it is located in the planet's two polar ice caps, which contain frozen water and carbon dioxide. A small amount also exists as water vapor in Mars's atmosphere. Some water vapor has probably escaped into space. But scientists think that a large amount of water may still be frozen underground.

FIGURE 18
Mars
Because of its thin atmosphere and its distance from the sun, Mars is quite cold. Mars has ice caps at both poles. **Inferring** *Why is it easy to see Mars's surface from space?*

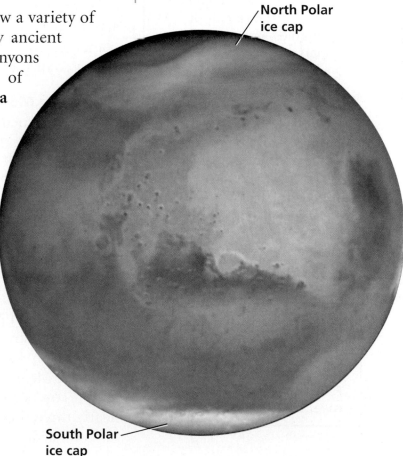

North Polar ice cap

South Polar ice cap

The Solar System

Video Preview
▶ Video Field Trip
Video Assessment

Remote Control

How hard is it to explore another planet by remote control?

1. Tape a piece of paper over the front of a pair of goggles. Have your partner put them on.

2. 🚶 Walk behind your partner and direct him or her to another part of the room. **CAUTION:** *Do not give directions that would cause your partner to walk into a wall or a corner, trip on an obstacle, or bump into anything.*

3. Trade places and repeat Steps 1 and 2.

Drawing Conclusions Which verbal directions worked best? How quickly could you move? How is this activity similar to the way engineers have moved rovers on Mars? How fast do you think such a rover could move?

Seasons on Mars Because Mars has a tilted axis, it has seasons just as Earth does. During the Martian winter, an ice cap grows larger as a layer of frozen carbon dioxide covers it. Because the northern and southern hemispheres have opposite seasons, one ice cap grows while the other one shrinks.

As the seasons change on the dusty surface of Mars, windstorms arise and blow the dust around. Since the dust is blown off some regions, these regions look darker. A hundred years ago, some people thought these regions looked darker because plants were growing there. Astronomers now realize that the darker color is often just the result of windstorms.

Exploring Mars Many space probes have visited Mars. The first ones seemed to show that Mars is barren and covered with craters like the moon. In 2004, two new probes landed on Mars's surface. NASA's *Spirit* and *Opportunity* rovers explored opposite sides of the planet. They examined a variety of rocks and soil samples. At both locations, the rovers found strong evidence that liquid water was once present. The European Space Agency's *Mars Express* probe orbited overhead, finding clear evidence of frozen water (ice). However, the *Mars Express* lander failed.

Volcanoes on Mars Some regions of Mars have giant volcanoes. Astronomers see signs that lava flowed from the volcanoes in the past, but the volcanoes are no longer active. *Olympus Mons* on Mars is the largest volcano in the solar system. It covers a region as large as the state of Missouri and is nearly three times as tall as Mount Everest, the tallest mountain on Earth!

FIGURE 19
Mars's Surface

As the large photo shows, the surface of Mars is rugged and rocky. Mars has many large volcanoes. The volcano *Olympus Mons* (inset) rises about 27 km from the surface. It is the largest volcano in the solar system.

Mars's Moons Mars has two very small moons. Phobos, the larger moon, is only 27 kilometers in diameter, about the distance a car can travel on the highway in 20 minutes. Deimos is even smaller, only 15 kilometers in diameter. Like Earth's moon, Phobos and Deimos are covered with craters. Phobos, which is much closer to Mars than Deimos is, is slowly spiraling down toward Mars. Astronomers predict that Phobos will smash into Mars in about 40 million years.

 **Reading Checkpoint** How many moons does Mars have? What are their names?

Section 4 Assessment

🎯 **Target Reading Skill** Using Prior Knowledge Review your graphic organizer about the inner planets and revise it based on what you just learned in the section.

Reviewing Key Concepts

1. **a. Listing** List the four inner planets in order of size, from smallest to largest.
   b. Comparing and Contrasting How are the four inner planets similar to one another?
2. **a. Describing** Describe an important characteristic of each inner planet.
   b. Comparing and Contrasting Compare the atmospheres of the four inner planets.
   c. Relating Cause and Effect Venus is much farther from the sun than Mercury is. Yet average temperatures on Venus's surface are much higher than those on Mercury. Explain why.

Writing in Science

Travel Brochure Select one of the inner planets other than Earth. Design a travel brochure for your selected planet, including basic facts and descriptions of places of interest. Also include a few sketches or photos to go along with your text.

Space Exploration—
Is It Worth the Cost?

Imagine that your spacecraft has just landed on the moon or on Mars. You've spent years planning for this moment. Canyons, craters, plains, and distant mountains stretch out before you. Perhaps a group of scientists has already begun construction of a permanent outpost. You check your spacesuit and prepare to step out onto the rocky surface.

Is such a trip likely? Would it be worthwhile? How much is space flight really worth to human society? Scientists and public officials have already started to debate such questions. Space exploration can help us learn more about the universe. But exploration can be risky and expensive. Sending people into space costs billions of dollars and risks the lives of astronauts. How can we balance the costs and benefits of space exploration?

▼ **Moon Landing**
A rocket is preparing to dock with a lander on the moon's surface in this imaginative artwork.

The Issues

Should Humans Travel Into Space?

Many Americans think that Neil Armstrong's walk on the moon in 1969 was one of the great moments in history. Learning how to keep people alive in space has led to improvements in everyday life. Safer equipment for firefighters, easier ways to package frozen food, and effective heart monitors have all come from space program research.

What Are the Alternatives?

Space exploration can involve a project to establish a colony on the moon or Mars. It also can involve a more limited use of scientific instruments near Earth, such as the Hubble Space Telescope. Instead of sending people, we could send space probes like *Cassini* to other planets.

◄ Lunar Outpost
A mining operation on the moon is shown in this imaginative artwork. Such a facility may someday harvest oxygen from the moon's soil.

◄ Lunar Module
This artwork shows a futuristic vehicle that may one day be used to explore the moon and Mars. The vehicle serves as a combination lander, rover, and habitat for astronauts.

Is Human Space Exploration Worth the Cost?

Scientists who favor human travel into space say that only people can collect certain kinds of information. They argue that the technologies developed for human space exploration will have many applications on Earth. But no one knows if research in space really provides information more quickly than research that can be done on Earth. Many critics of human space exploration think that other needs are more important. One United States senator said, "Every time you put money into the space station, there is a dime that won't be available for our children's education or for medical research."

You Decide

1. Identify the Problem
In your own words, list the various costs and benefits of space exploration.

2. Analyze the Options
Make a chart of three different approaches to space exploration: sending humans to the moon or another planet, doing only Earth-based research, and one other option. What are the benefits and drawbacks of each of these approaches?

3. Find a Solution
Imagine that you are a member of Congress who has to vote on a new budget. There is a fixed amount of money to spend, so you have to decide which needs are most important. Make a list of your top ten priorities. Explain your decisions.

For: More on space exploration
Visit: PHSchool.com
Web Code: cfh-5030

The Outer Planets

Reading Preview

Key Concepts
- What characteristics do the gas giants have in common?
- What characteristics distinguish each of the outer planets?

Key Terms
- gas giant • ring

Target Reading Skill

Identifying Main Ideas As you read the *Gas Giants and Pluto* section, write the main idea—the biggest or most important idea—in a graphic organizer like the one below. Then write three supporting details that further explain the main idea.

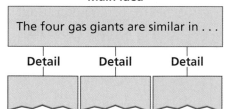

Main Idea

The four gas giants are similar in . . .

Detail	Detail	Detail

Lab zone Discover **Activity**

How Big Are the Planets?

The table shows the diameters of the outer planets compared to Earth. For example, Jupiter's diameter is about 11 times Earth's diameter.

1. Measure the diameter of a quarter in millimeters. Trace the quarter to represent Earth.

2. If Earth were the size of a quarter, calculate how large Jupiter would be. Now draw a circle to represent Jupiter.

3. Repeat Step 2 for each of the other planets in the table.

Think It Over

Classifying List the outer planets in order from largest to smallest. What is the largest outer planet? Which outer planet is much smaller than Earth?

Planet	Diameter (Earth = 1)
Earth	1.0
Jupiter	11.2
Saturn	9.4
Uranus	4.0
Neptune	3.9
Pluto	0.2

Imagine you are in a spaceship approaching Jupiter. You'll quickly discover that Jupiter is very different from the terrestrial planets. The most obvious difference is Jupiter's great size. Jupiter is so large that more than 1,300 Earths could fit within it!

As your spaceship enters Jupiter's atmosphere, you encounter thick, colorful bands of clouds. Next, you sink into a denser and denser mixture of hydrogen and helium gas. Eventually, if the enormous pressure of the atmosphere does not crush your ship, you'll reach an incredibly deep "ocean" of liquid hydrogen and helium. But where exactly is Jupiter's surface? Surprisingly, there isn't a solid surface. Like the other giant planets, Jupiter has no real surface, just a solid core buried deep within the planet.

◄ An illustration of the space probe *Galileo* approaching the cloud-covered atmosphere of Jupiter.

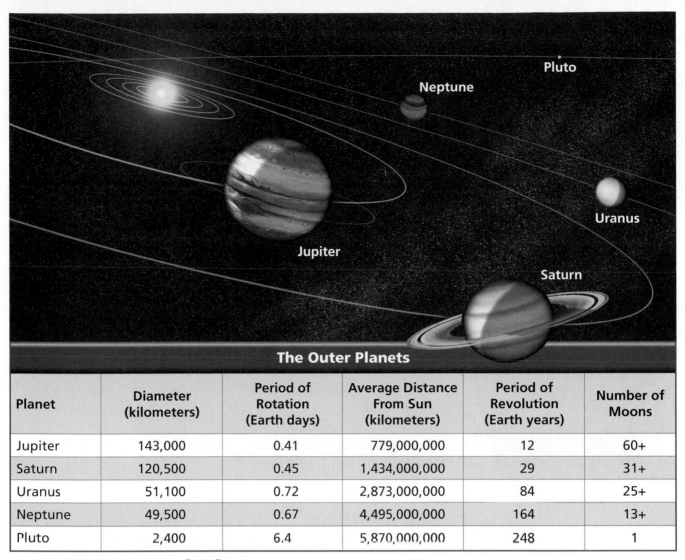

The Outer Planets

Planet	Diameter (kilometers)	Period of Rotation (Earth days)	Average Distance From Sun (kilometers)	Period of Revolution (Earth years)	Number of Moons
Jupiter	143,000	0.41	779,000,000	12	60+
Saturn	120,500	0.45	1,434,000,000	29	31+
Uranus	51,100	0.72	2,873,000,000	84	25+
Neptune	49,500	0.67	4,495,000,000	164	13+
Pluto	2,400	6.4	5,870,000,000	248	1

Gas Giants and Pluto

Jupiter and the other planets farthest from the sun are called the outer planets. **The first four outer planets—Jupiter, Saturn, Uranus, and Neptune—are much larger and more massive than Earth, and they do not have solid surfaces.** Because these four planets are all so large, they are often called the **gas giants.** The fifth outer planet, Pluto, is small and rocky like the terrestrial planets. Figure 20 provides information about these planets.

Like the sun, the gas giants are composed mainly of hydrogen and helium. Because they are so massive, the gas giants exert a much stronger gravitational force than the terrestrial planets. Gravity keeps the giant planets' gases from escaping, so they have thick atmospheres. Despite the name "gas giant," much of the hydrogen and helium is actually in liquid form because of the enormous pressure inside the planets. The outer layers of the gas giants are extremely cold because of their great distance from the sun. Temperatures increase greatly within the planets.

All the gas giants have many moons. In addition, each of the gas giants is surrounded by a set of rings. A **ring** is a thin disk of small particles of ice and rock.

FIGURE 20
The outer planets are much farther apart than the inner planets. Note that planet sizes and distances are not drawn to scale.
Observing *Which outer planet has the most moons?*

For: More on the planets
Visit: PHSchool.com
Web Code: ced-5034

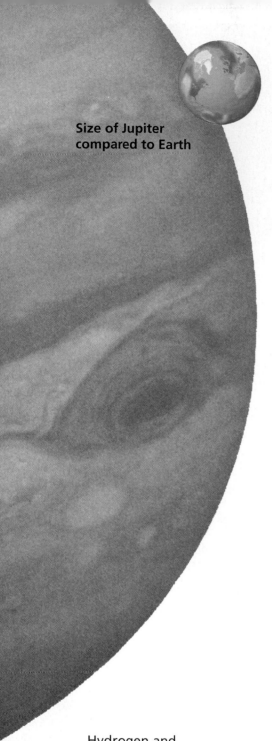

Size of Jupiter compared to Earth

Jupiter

Jupiter is the largest and most massive planet. Jupiter's enormous mass dwarfs the other planets. In fact, its mass is about $2\frac{1}{2}$ times that of all the other planets combined!

Jupiter's Atmosphere Like all of the gas giants, Jupiter has a thick atmosphere made up mainly of hydrogen and helium. An especially interesting feature of Jupiter's atmosphere is its Great Red Spot, a storm that is larger than Earth! The storm's swirling winds blow hundreds of kilometers per hour, similar to a hurricane. But hurricanes on Earth weaken quickly as they pass over land. On Jupiter, there is no land to weaken the huge storm. The Great Red Spot, which was first observed in the mid-1600s, shows no signs of going away soon.

Jupiter's Structure Astronomers think that Jupiter, like the other giant planets, probably has a dense core of rock and iron at its center. As shown in Figure 21, a thick mantle of liquid hydrogen and helium surrounds this core. Because of the crushing weight of Jupiter's atmosphere, the pressure at Jupiter's core is estimated to be about 30 million times greater than the pressure at Earth's surface.

Jupiter's Moons Recall that Galileo discovered Jupiter's four largest moons. These moons, which are highlighted in Figure 22, are named Io (EYE oh), Europa, Ganymede, and Callisto. All four are larger than Earth's own moon. However, they are very different from one another. Since Galileo's time, astronomers have discovered dozens of additional moons orbiting Jupiter. Many of these are small moons that have been found in the last few years thanks to improved technology.

 **Reading Checkpoint** What is Jupiter's atmosphere composed of?

Hydrogen and helium gas

Liquid hydrogen and helium

Liquid "ices" such as water and methane

Rocky core

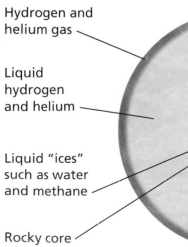

FIGURE 21
Jupiter's Structure
Jupiter is composed mainly of the elements hydrogen and helium. Although Jupiter is often called a "gas giant," much of it is actually liquid.
Comparing and Contrasting *How does the structure of Jupiter differ from that of a terrestrial planet?*

Jupiter's Moons

The astronomer Galileo discovered Jupiter's four largest moons. These images are not shown to scale.
Interpreting Photographs *Which is the largest of Jupiter's moons?*

Callisto's surface is icy and covered with craters. ▼

▲ Io's surface is covered with large, active volcanoes. An eruption of sulfur lava can be seen near the bottom of this photo. Sulfur gives Io its unusual colors.

Ganymede is the largest moon in the solar system. It is larger than either Mercury or Pluto. ▼

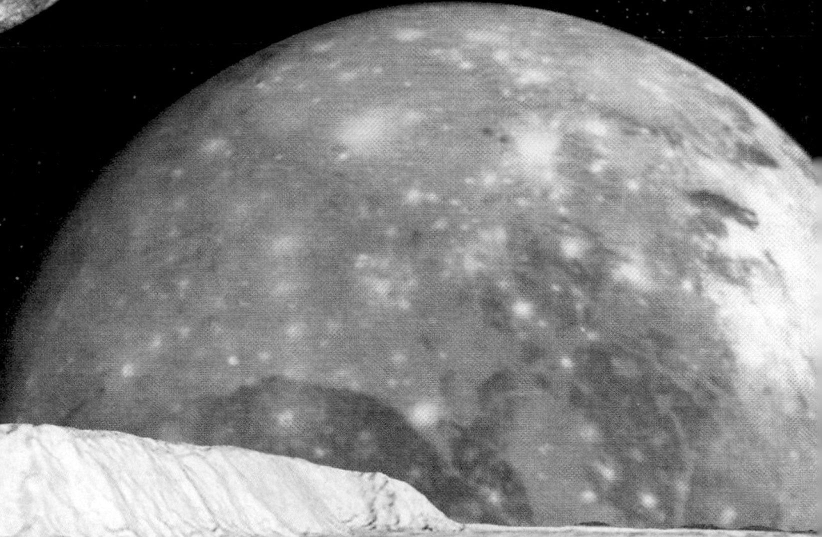

Europa ▼

Astronomers suspect that Europa's icy crust covers an ocean of liquid water underneath. This illustration shows Europa's icy surface.

FIGURE 23
Exploring Saturn
The *Cassini* probe is exploring Saturn and its moons.
Observing *Why might it be hard to see Saturn's rings when their edges are facing Earth?*

Size of Saturn compared to Earth

Lab zone Skills **Activity**

Making Models

1. Use a plastic foam sphere 8 cm in diameter to represent Saturn.

2. Use an overhead transparency to represent Saturn's rings. Cut a circle 18 cm in diameter out of the transparency. Cut a hole 9 cm in diameter out of the center of the circle.

3. Stick five toothpicks into Saturn, spaced equally around its equator. Put the transparency on the toothpicks and tape it to them. Sprinkle baking soda on the transparency.

4. Use a peppercorn to represent Titan. Place the peppercorn 72 cm away from Saturn on the same plane as the rings.

5. What do the particles of baking soda represent?

Saturn

The second-largest planet in the solar system is Saturn. The *Voyager* probes showed that Saturn, like Jupiter, has a thick atmosphere made up mainly of hydrogen and helium. Saturn's atmosphere also contains clouds and storms, but they are less dramatic than those on Jupiter. Saturn is the only planet whose average density is less than that of water.

Saturn's Rings When Galileo first looked at Saturn with a telescope, he could see something sticking out on the sides. But he didn't know what it was. A few decades later, an astronomer using a better telescope discovered that Saturn had rings around it. These rings are made of chunks of ice and rock, each traveling in its own orbit around Saturn.

Saturn has the most spectacular rings of any planet. From Earth, it looks as though Saturn has only a few rings and that they are divided from each other by narrow, dark regions. The *Voyager* spacecraft discovered that each of these obvious rings is divided into many thinner rings. Saturn's rings are broad and thin, like a compact disc.

Saturn's Moons Saturn's largest moon, Titan, is larger than the planet Mercury. Titan was discovered in 1665 but was known only as a point of light until the *Voyager* probes flew by. The probes showed that Titan has an atmosphere so thick that little light can pass through it. Four other moons of Saturn are each over 1,000 kilometers in diameter.

 **Reading Checkpoint** What are Saturn's rings made of?

Size of Uranus
compared to Earth

Uranus

Although the gas giant Uranus (YOOR uh nus) is about four times the diameter of Earth, it is still much smaller than Jupiter and Saturn. Uranus is twice as far from the sun as Saturn, so it is much colder. Uranus looks blue-green because of traces of methane in its atmosphere. Like the other gas giants, Uranus is surrounded by a group of thin, flat rings, although they are much darker than Saturn's rings.

Discovery of Uranus In 1781, Uranus became the first new planet discovered since ancient times. Astronomer William Herschel, in England, found a fuzzy object in the sky that did not look like a star. At first he thought it might be a comet, but it soon proved to be a planet beyond Saturn. The discovery made Herschel famous and started an era of active solar system study.

Exploring Uranus About 200 years after Herschel's discovery, *Voyager 2* arrived at Uranus and sent back close-up views of that planet. Images from *Voyager 2* show only a few clouds on Uranus's surface. But even these few clouds allowed astronomers to calculate that Uranus rotates in about 17 hours.

Uranus's axis of rotation is tilted at an angle of about 90 degrees from the vertical. Viewed from Earth, Uranus is rotating from top to bottom instead of from side to side, the way most of the other planets do. Uranus's rings and moons rotate around this tilted axis. Astronomers think that billions of years ago Uranus was hit by an object that knocked it on its side.

Uranus's Moons Photographs from *Voyager 2* show that Uranus's five largest moons have icy, cratered surfaces. The craters show that rocks from space have hit the moons. Uranus's moons also have lava flows on their surfaces, suggesting that material has erupted from inside each moon. *Voyager 2* images revealed 10 moons that had never been seen before. Recently, astronomers discovered several more moons, for a total of at least 25.

 **Reading Checkpoint** Who discovered Uranus?

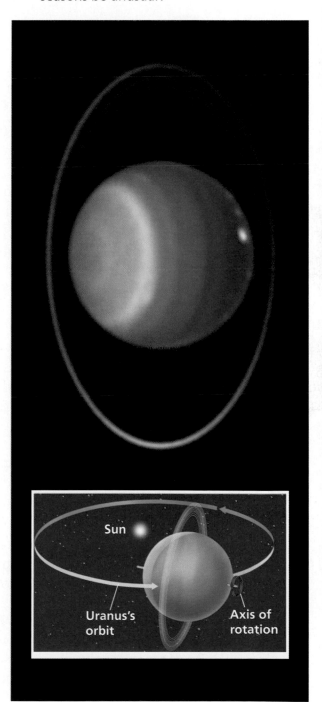

FIGURE 24
Uranus
The false color image of Uranus below was taken by the Hubble Space Telescope. Unlike most other planets, Uranus rotates from top to bottom rather than side to side.
Inferring *How must Uranus's seasons be unusual?*

Sun

Uranus's orbit

Axis of rotation

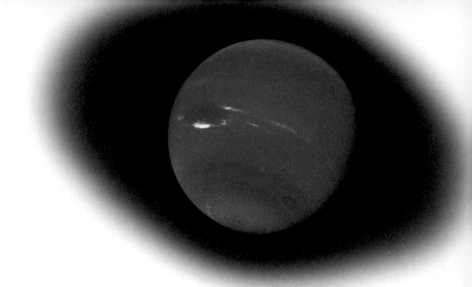

Size of Neptune compared to Earth

Math Skills

Circumference

To calculate the circumference of a circle, use this formula:

$$C = 2\pi r$$

In the formula, $\pi \approx 3.14$, and r is the circle's radius, which is the distance from the center of the circle to its edge. The same formula can be used to calculate the circumference of planets, which are nearly spherical.

Neptune's radius at its equator is about 24,800 km. Calculate its circumference.

$C = 2\pi r$

$= 2.00 \times 3.14 \times 24{,}800 \text{ km}$

$= 156{,}000 \text{ km}$

Practice Problem Saturn's radius is 60,250 km. What is its circumference?

Neptune

Neptune is even farther from the sun than Uranus. In some ways, Uranus and Neptune look like twins. They are similar in size and color. **Neptune is a cold, blue planet. Its atmosphere contains visible clouds.** Scientists think that Neptune, shown in Figure 25, is slowly shrinking, causing its interior to heat up. As this energy rises toward Neptune's surface, it produces clouds and storms in the planet's atmosphere.

Discovery of Neptune Neptune was discovered as a result of a mathematical prediction. Astronomers noted that Uranus was not quite following the orbit predicted for it. They hypothesized that the gravity of an unseen planet was affecting Uranus's orbit. By 1846, mathematicians in England and France had calculated the orbit of this unseen planet. Shortly thereafter, an observer saw an unknown object in the predicted area of the sky. It was the new planet, now called Neptune.

Exploring Neptune In 1989, *Voyager 2* flew by Neptune and photographed a Great Dark Spot about the size of Earth. Like the Great Red Spot on Jupiter, the Great Dark Spot was probably a giant storm. But the storm didn't last long. Images taken five years later showed that the Great Dark Spot was gone. Other, smaller spots and regions of clouds on Neptune also seem to come and go.

Neptune's Moons Astronomers have discovered at least 13 moons orbiting Neptune. The largest moon is Triton, which has a thin atmosphere. The *Voyager* images show that the region near Triton's south pole is covered by nitrogen ice.

 **Reading Checkpoint** Before they could see Neptune, what evidence led scientists to conclude that it existed?

Size of Pluto
compared to Earth

Pluto

Pluto is very different from the gas giants. **Pluto has a solid surface and is much smaller and denser than the other outer planets.** In fact, Pluto is smaller than Earth's moon.

Pluto has a single moon of its own, Charon. Since Charon is more than half the size of Pluto, some astronomers consider them to be a double planet instead of a planet and a moon.

Pluto's Orbit Pluto is so far from the sun that it revolves around the sun only once every 248 Earth years. Pluto's orbit is very elliptical, bringing it closer to the sun than Neptune on part of its orbit.

Is Pluto Really a Planet? Pluto is so small that many astronomers do not think it is worthy of being called a planet at all. Pluto may be merely the largest of tens of thousands of objects made of ice, rock, and dust that revolve around the sun beyond Neptune. If astronomers had found these other objects before they found Pluto, they might not have called Pluto a planet.

 **Reading Checkpoint** How long does it take Pluto to revolve around the sun?

FIGURE 26
Pluto and Charon
The illustration above shows Pluto (lower right) and its moon Charon. **Inferring** *Why do astronomers often call Pluto and Charon a double planet?*

Section 5 Assessment

Target Reading Skill Identifying Main Ideas
Use your graphic organizer about the structure of the gas giants to help you answer Question 1 below.

Reviewing Key Concepts

1. a. **Describing** How are the gas giants similar to one another?
   b. **Explaining** Why do all of the gas giants have thick atmospheres?
   c. **Listing** List the outer planets in order of size, from smallest to largest.
   d. **Comparing and Contrasting** Compare the structure of a typical terrestrial planet with that of a gas giant.

2. a. **Describing** Describe an important characteristic of each outer planet that helps to distinguish it from the other outer planets.
   b. **Comparing and Contrasting** How is Pluto different from the gas giants?
   c. **Classifying** Why do some astronomers think that Pluto should not be classified as a planet?

Math Practice

3. **Circumference** The radius of Jupiter at its equator is about 71,490 km. What is its circumference?

Speeding Around the Sun

Problem

How does a planet's distance from the sun affect its period of revolution?

Skills Focus

making models, developing hypotheses, designing experiments

Materials

- string, 1.5 m   • plastic tube, 6 cm
- meter stick   • weight or several washers
- one-hole rubber stopper
- stopwatch or watch with second hand

Procedure

PART 1   Modeling Planetary Revolution

1. Copy the data table onto a sheet of paper.

Data Table				
Distance (cm)	Period of Revolution			
	Trial 1	Trial 2	Trial 3	Average
20				
40				
60				

2. Make a model of a planet orbiting the sun by threading the string through the rubber stopper hole. Tie the end of the string to the main part of the string. Pull tightly to make sure that the knot will not become untied.

3. Thread the other end of the string through the plastic tube and tie a weight to that end. Have your teacher check both knots.

4. Pull the string so the stopper is 20 cm away from the plastic tube. Hold the plastic tube in your hand above your head. Keeping the length of string constant, swing the rubber stopper in a circle above your head just fast enough to keep the stopper moving. The circle represents a planet's orbit, and the length of string from the rubber stopper to the plastic tube represents the distance from the sun. **CAUTION:** *Stand away from other students. Make sure the swinging stopper will not hit students or objects. Do not let go of the string.*

5. Have your lab partner time how long it takes for the rubber stopper to make ten complete revolutions. Determine the period for one revolution by dividing the measured time by ten. Record the time in the data table.

6. Repeat Step 5 two more times. Be sure to record each trial in a data table. After the third trial, calculate and record the average period of revolution.

PART 2 Designing an Experiment

7. Write your hypothesis for how a planet's period of revolution would be affected by changing its distance from the sun.

8. Design an experiment that will enable you to test your hypothesis. Write the steps you plan to follow to carry out your experiment. As you design your experiment, consider the following factors:
   • What additional materials will you need?
   • What different distances will you test?
   • What variables are involved in your experiment and how will you control them?
   • How many trials will you run for each distance?

9. Have your teacher review your step-by-step plan. After your teacher approves your plan, carry out your experiment.

Analyze and Conclude

1. **Making Models** In your experiment, what represents the planet and what represents the sun?

2. **Developing Hypotheses** How did you decide on the hypothesis you wrote in Step 7? Did your experiment prove or disprove your hypothesis?

3. **Designing Experiments** As you were designing your experiment, which variable was the most difficult to control? How did you design your procedure to control that variable?

4. **Communicating** Write a brief article for a science journal that describes your hypothesis, experiment, and results. Be sure to describe how you controlled the variables.

More to Explore

Develop a hypothesis for how a planet's mass might affect its period of revolution. Then, using a stopper with a different mass, modify the activity to test your hypothesis. Before you swing your stopper, have your teacher check your knots.

Comets, Asteroids, and Meteors

Reading Preview

Key Concepts
- What are the characteristics of comets?
- Where are most asteroids found?
- What are meteoroids and how do they form?

Key Terms
- comet • coma • nucleus
- Kuiper belt • Oort cloud
- asteroid • asteroid belt
- meteoroid • meteor
- meteorite

Target Reading Skill
Comparing and Contrasting
As you read, compare and contrast comets, asteroids, and meteoroids by completing a table like the one below.

Comets, Asteroids, and Meteoroids

Feature	Comets	Asteroids
Origin	Kuiper belt and Oort cloud	
Size		
Composition		

Discover **Activity**

Which Way Do Comet Tails Point?

1. Form a small ball out of modeling clay to represent a comet.
2. Using a pencil point, push three 10-cm lengths of string into the ball. The strings represent the comet's tail. Stick the ball onto the pencil point, as shown.
3. Hold the ball about 1 m in front of a fan. The air from the fan represents the solar wind. Move the ball toward the fan, away from the fan, and from side to side.
CAUTION: *Keep your fingers away from the fan blades.*

Think It Over
Inferring How does moving the ball affect the direction in which the strings point? What determines which way the tail of a comet points?

Imagine watching a cosmic collision! That's exactly what happened in July 1994. The year before, Eugene and Carolyn Shoemaker and David Levy discovered a comet that had previously broken into pieces near Jupiter. When their orbit passed near Jupiter again, the fragments crashed into Jupiter. On Earth, many people were fascinated to view images of the huge explosions—some were as large as Earth!

As this example shows, the sun, planets, and moons aren't the only objects in the solar system. There are also many smaller objects moving through the solar system. These objects are classified as comets, asteroids, or meteoroids.

FIGURE 26
Structure of a Comet
The main parts of a comet are the nucleus, the coma, and the tail. The nucleus is deep within the coma. Most comets have two tails—a bluish gas tail and a white dust tail.

Gas tail

Nucleus

Coma

Dust tail

Comets

One of the most glorious things you can see in the night sky is a comet. But what exactly is a comet? You can think of a **comet** as a "dirty snowball" about the size of a mountain. **Comets are loose collections of ice, dust, and small rocky particles whose orbits are usually very long, narrow ellipses.**

A Comet's Head When a comet gets close enough to the sun, the energy in the sunlight turns the ice into gas, releasing gas and dust. Clouds of gas and dust form a fuzzy outer layer called a **coma.** Figure 26 shows the coma and the **nucleus,** the solid inner core of a comet. The brightest part of a comet, the comet's head, is made up of the nucleus and coma.

A Comet's Tail As a comet approaches the sun and heats up, some of its gas and dust stream outward, forming a tail. The name *comet* means "long-haired star" in Greek. Most comets have two tails—a gas tail and a dust tail. Both tails usually point away from the sun, as shown in Figure 27.

A comet's tail can be more than 100 million kilometers long and stretch across most of the sky. The material is stretched out very thinly, however, so there is little mass in a comet's tail.

Origin of Comets Most comets are found in one of two distant regions of the solar system: the Kuiper belt and the Oort cloud. The **Kuiper belt** is a doughnut-shaped region that extends from beyond Nepune's orbit to about 100 times Earth's distance from the sun. The **Oort cloud** is a spherical region of comets that surrounds the solar system out to more than 1,000 times the distance between Pluto and the sun.

 **Reading Checkpoint** What is the Oort cloud?

FIGURE 27
Comet Orbits
Most comets revolve around the sun in very long, narrow orbits. Gas and dust tails form as the comet approaches the sun. *Observing What shapes a comet's orbit?*

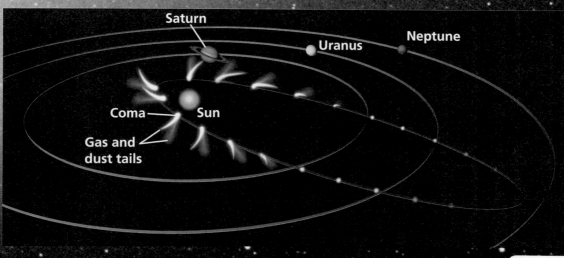

Saturn
Uranus
Neptune
Coma
Sun
Gas and dust tails

Asteroids

Between 1801 and 1807, astronomers discovered four small objects between the orbits of Mars and Jupiter. They named the objects Ceres, Pallas, Juno, and Vesta. Over the next 80 years, astronomers found 300 more. These rocky objects, called **asteroids,** are too small and too numerous to be considered full-fledged planets. **Most asteroids revolve around the sun between the orbits of Mars and Jupiter.** This region of the solar system, shown in Figure 28, is called the **asteroid belt.**

Astronomers have discovered more than 100,000 asteroids, and they are constantly finding more. Most asteroids are small—less than a kilometer in diameter. Only Ceres, Pallas, and Vesta are more than 300 kilometers across. At one time, scientists thought that asteroids were the remains of a shattered planet. However, the combined mass of all the asteroids is too small to support this idea. Scientists now hypothesize that the asteroids are leftover pieces of the early solar system that never came together to form a planet.

Some asteroids have very elliptical orbits that bring them closer to the sun than Earth's orbit. Someday, one of these asteroids could hit Earth. One or more large asteroids did hit Earth about 65 million years ago, filling the atmosphere with dust and smoke and blocking out sunlight around the world. Scientists hypothesize that many species of organisms, including the dinosaurs, became extinct as a result.

✓ **Reading Checkpoint** Name the three largest asteroids.

FIGURE 28
Asteroids
The asteroid belt (right) lies between Mars and Jupiter. Asteroids come in many sizes and shapes. The photo below shows the oddly shaped asteroid Eros.

Meteors

It's a perfect night for stargazing—dark and clear. Suddenly, a streak of light flashes across the sky. For an hour or so, you see a streak at least once a minute. You are watching a meteor shower. Meteor showers happen regularly, several times a year.

Even when there is no meteor shower, you often can see meteors if you are far from city lights and the sky is not cloudy. On average, a meteor streaks overhead every 10 minutes.

A **meteoroid** is a chunk of rock or dust in space. **Meteoroids come from comets or asteroids.** Some meteoroids form when asteroids collide in space. Others form when a comet breaks up and creates a cloud of dust that continues to move through the solar system. When Earth passes through one of these dust clouds, bits of dust enter Earth's atmosphere.

When a meteoroid enters Earth's atmosphere, friction with the air creates heat and produces a streak of light in the sky—a **meteor.** If the meteoroid is large enough, it may not burn up completely. Meteoroids that pass through the atmosphere and hit Earth's surface are called **meteorites.** The craters on the moon were formed by meteoroids.

FIGURE 29
Meteors
Meteoroids make streaks of light called meteors, like the one above, as they burn up in the atmosphere.

 **Reading Checkpoint**) **What is a meteorite?**

Section 5 Assessment

Target Reading Skill Comparing and Contrasting Use the information in your table about comets, asteroids, and meteoroids to help you answer the questions below.

Reviewing Key Concepts

1. **a. Defining** What is a comet?
   b. Listing What are the different parts of a comet?
   c. Relating Cause and Effect How does a comet's appearance change as it approaches the sun? Why do these changes occur?
2. **a. Describing** What is an asteroid?
   b. Explaining Where are most asteroids found?
   c. Summarizing How did the asteroids form?
3. **a. Describing** What is a meteoroid?
   b. Explaining What are the main sources of meteoroids?
   c. Comparing and Contrasting What are the differences between meteoroids, meteors, and meteorites?

Lab zone At-Home Activity

Observing Meteors Meteor showers occur regularly on specific dates. (The Perseid meteor shower, for example, occurs around August 12 each year.) Look in the newspaper, on the Internet, or in an almanac for information about the next meteor shower. With adult family members, go outside on that night and look for meteors. Explain to your family what causes the display.

1 Observing the Solar System

Key Concepts

- In a geocentric system, Earth is perceived to be at the center of the revolving planets and stars. In a heliocentric system, Earth and the other planets revolve around the sun.
- Galileo's discoveries supported the heliocentric model. Kepler found that the orbit of each planet is an ellipse.
- The solar system consists of the sun, nine planets and their moons, and a series of smaller objects that revolve around the sun.

Key Terms

- geocentric • heliocentric • ellipse

2 The Sun

Key Concepts

- The sun's interior consists of the core, radiation zone, and convection zone. The sun's atmosphere consists of the photosphere, chromosphere, and corona.
- Features on or just above the sun's surface include sunspots, prominences, and solar flares.

Key Terms

- core • nuclear fusion • radiation zone
- convection zone • photosphere
- chromosphere • corona • solar wind
- sunspot • prominence • solar flare

4 The Inner Planets

Key Concepts

- The four inner planets are small and dense and have rocky surfaces.
- Earth is unique in our solar system in having liquid water at its surface.
- Mercury is the smallest terrestrial planet.
- Venus's internal structure is similar to Earth's.
- Scientists think that a large amount of liquid water flowed on Mars's surface in the distant past.

Key Terms

- terrestrial planets • greenhouse effect

5 The Outer Planets

Key Concepts

- Jupiter, Saturn, Uranus, and Neptune are much larger and more massive than Earth, and they do not have solid surfaces.
- Jupiter is the largest and most massive planet in the solar system.
- Saturn has the most spectacular rings of any planet.
- Uranus's axis of rotation is tilted at an angle of about 90 degrees from the vertical.
- Neptune is a cold, blue planet. Its atmosphere contains visible clouds.
- Pluto has a solid surface and is much smaller and denser than the other outer planets.

Key Terms

- gas giant • ring

6 Comets, Asteroids, and Meteors

Key Concepts

- Comets are loose collections of ice, dust, and small rocky particles whose orbits are usually very long, narrow ellipses.
- Most asteroids revolve around the sun between the orbits of Mars and Jupiter.
- Meteoroids come from comets or asteroids.

Key Terms

- comet • coma • nucleus • Kuiper belt
- Oort cloud • asteroid • asteroid belt
- meteoroid • meteor • meteorite

Review and Assessment

Organizing Information

aring and Contrasting Fill in the graphic organizer to compare and contrast the geocentric system and the heliocentric system. (For more on Comparing and Contrasting, see the Skills Handbook.)

Feature	Geocentric System	Heliocentric System
Object at center	Earth	a. _____?_____
Objects that move around center	Planets and sun	b. _____?_____
Proposed by	c. _____?_____	Copernicus
Supporters	Ptolemy	d. _____?_____

Reviewing Key Terms

Choose the letter of the best answer.

1. Copernicus thought that the solar system was
   a. an ellipse.
   b. a constellation.
   c. geocentric.
   d. heliocentric.

2. The part of the sun where nuclear fusion occurs is the
   a. photosphere.
   b. core.
   c. chromosphere.
   d. corona.

3. The tendency of an object to resist a change in motion is called
   a. gravity.
   b. intertia.
   c. force.
   d. the law of universal gravitation.

4. The region between Mars and Jupiter where many rocky objects are found is the
   a. asteroid belt.
   b. Oort cloud.
   c. convection zone.
   d. Kuiper belt.

5. A meteoroid that reaches Earth's surface is called a(n)
   a. comet.
   b. meteorite.
   c. meteor.
   d. asteroid.

If the statement is true, write *true*. If it is false, change the underlined word or words to make the statement true.

6. The shape of the orbit of each planet is a(n) <u>ellipse</u>.

7. <u>Prominences</u> are regions of cooler gases on the sun.

8. The trapping of heat by a planet's atmosphere is called <u>nuclear fusion</u>.

9. All the <u>terrestrial planets</u> are surrounded by rings.

10. The solid inner core of a comet is its <u>coma</u>.

Writing in Science

News Report Imagine you are on a mission to explore the solar system. Write a brief news report telling the story of your trip from Earth to another terrestrial planet and to a gas giant. Include a description of each planet.

The Solar System
Video Preview
Video Field Trip
▶ Video Assessment

Review and Assessment

Checking Concepts

11. Describe the contributions Tycho Brahe and Johannes Kepler made to modern astronomy.

12. What is the solar wind?

13. Explain Newton's first law of motion in your own words.

14. Why does Mercury have very little atmosphere?

15. Why can astronomers see the surface of Mars clearly but not the surface of Venus?

Math Practice

16. **Circumference** Mars has a radius of 3,397 km at its equator. Find its circumference.

17. **Circumference** Jupiter has a circumference of about 449,000 km at its equator. Calculate its radius.

Thinking Critically

18. **Applying Concepts** Explain why Venus is hotter than it would be if it had no atmosphere.

19. **Predicting** Do you think astronomers have found all of the moons of the outer planets? Explain.

20. **Comparing and Contrasting** Compare and contrast comets, asteroids, and meteoroids.

21. **Classifying** Look at the diagram below. Do you think it represents the structure of a terrestrial planet or a gas giant? Explain.

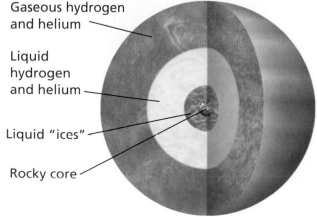

Gaseous hydrogen and helium

Liquid hydrogen and helium

Liquid "ices"

Rocky core

22. **Comparing and Contrasting** How are mass and weight different?

Applying Skills

Use the diagram of an imaginary, newly discovered planetary system around Star X to answer Questions 23–25.

The periods of revolution of planets A, B, and C are 75 Earth days, 200 Earth days, and 300 Earth days.

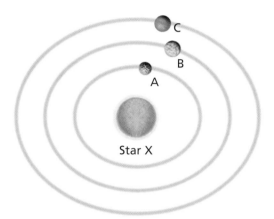

Star X

23. **Interpreting Data** Which planet in this new planetary system revolves around Star X in the shortest amount of time?

24. **Making Models** In 150 days, how far will each planet have revolved around Star X? Copy the diagram and sketch the positions of the three planets to find out. How far will each planet have revolved around Star X in 400 days? Sketch their positions.

25. **Drawing Conclusions** Can Planet C ever be closer to Planet A than to Planet B? Study your drawings to figure this out.

Lab zone Chapter **Project**

Performance Assessment Present your scale models of the solar system. Display your data tables showing how you did the calculations and how you checked them for accuracy.

◊ Standardized Test Practice

Choose the letter of the best answer.

1. What characteristic do all of the inner planets share?

  A They are larger and more massive than the sun.

  B They have thick atmospheres of hydrogen and helium.

  C They have rocky surfaces.

  D They each have many moons.

2. Mercury has a daytime temperature of about 430º C and a nighttime temperature below –170º C. What is the best explanation?

  A Mercury has a greenhouse effect.

  B Global warming is occurring on Mercury.

  C Mercury is the closest planet to the sun.

  D Mercury has no real atmosphere.

The table below shows data for five planets in our solar system. Use the table and your knowledge of science to answer Questions 3–5.

Planet	Period of Rotation (Earth days)	Period of Revolution (Earth years)	Average Distance From the Sun (million km)
Mars	1.03	1.9	228
Jupiter	0.41	12	779
Saturn	0.45	29	1,434
Uranus	0.72	84	2,873
Neptune	0.67	164	4,495

3. Which of these planet's orbits is farthest from Earth's orbit?

  A Mars   **B** Jupiter

  C Uranus   **D** Neptune

4. Which planet has a "day" that is most similar in length to a day on Earth?

  A Mars   **B** Jupiter

  C Uranus   **D** Neptune

5. Light takes about 8 minutes and 20 seconds to travel from the sun to Earth, 150 million kilometers away. About how long does it take light to travel from the sun to Jupiter?

  A 10 minutes   **B** 25 minutes

  C 43 minutes   **D** 112 minutes

Open-Ended Question

6. Describe three major differences between the terrestrial planets and the gas giants.

Chapter
17

Stars, Galaxies, and the Universe

Academic Standards

This chapter addresses these Indiana standards.

The Nature of Science and Technology

7.1.4 Describe how further study can help scientists choose among different explanations for the same evidence.

Scientific Thinking

7.2.4 Express numbers such as 10, 100, and 1,000 as powers of 10.

The Physical Setting

7.3.1 Recognize that the sun is a star located near the edge of a galaxy. The universe contains billions of galaxies. Each galaxy contains billions of stars.

7.3.2 Recognize that the sun is much closer to Earth than any other star. Sunlight reaches Earth much sooner than the light of other stars.

7.3.19 Explain that human eyes see a narrow part of the electromagnetic spectrum.

The dark Horsehead Nebula is visible ▶
against red-glowing hydrogen gas.

Lab zone™ Chapter **Project**

Star Stories

Many years ago, people created stories to explain the patterns of stars they saw in the sky. In your project, you'll learn how the names of these constellations reflect the cultures of the people who named them.

Your Goal To complete the project you will

- learn the star patterns of at least three constellations
- research the myths that gave one constellation its name
- create your own star myth

Plan It! Begin by making a list of constellations that you have heard about. Then use the star charts in Appendix B to locate constellations in the night sky. Make a sketch of the constellations that you locate. Choose one constellation and research the myths that gave it its name. Draw a new picture for the star pattern in your constellation and choose a name for it. Finally, write a story about your constellation. At the end of the chapter, you will present your constellation and a story that explains its name.

• Tech & Design •

Telescopes

Reading Preview

Key Concepts
- What are the regions of the electromagnetic spectrum?
- What are telescopes and how do they work?
- Where are most large telescopes located?

Key Terms
- telescope
- electromagnetic radiation
- visible light
- wavelength
- spectrum
- optical telescope
- refracting telescope
- convex lens
- reflecting telescope
- radio telescope
- observatory

Target Reading Skill
Building Vocabulary Carefully read the definition of each key term. Also read the neighboring sentences. Then write a definition of each key term in your own words.

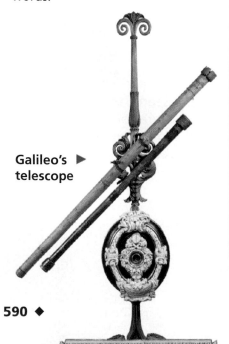

Galileo's ▶
telescope

Lab zone Discover Activity

How Does Distance Affect an Image?

1. Hold a plastic hand lens about 7 cm away from your eye and about 5 cm away from a printed letter on a page. Move the lens slowly back and forth until the letter is in clear focus.
2. Keep the letter about 5 cm from the lens as you move your eye back to about 20 cm from the lens. Then, keeping the distance between your eye and the lens constant, slowly move the object away from the lens.

Think It Over
Observing What did the letter look like through the lens in Step 1 compared with how it looked without the lens? How did the image change in Step 2?

Ancient peoples often gazed up in wonder at the many points of light in the night sky. But they could see few details with their eyes alone. It was not until the invention of the telescope in 1608 that people could observe objects in the sky more closely. Recall that a **telescope** is a device that makes distant objects appear to be closer. The telescope revolutionized astronomy. Scientists now had a tool that allowed them to see many objects in space for the first time.

Although Galileo was not the first to use a telescope, he soon made it famous as he turned his homemade instrument to the sky. With his telescope, Galileo saw things that no one had even dreamed of. He was the first to see sunspots, Saturn's rings, and the four large moons of Jupiter. Galileo could see fine details, such as mountains on the moon, which cannot be seen clearly by the unaided eye.

Since Galileo's time, astronomers have built ever larger and more powerful telescopes. These telescopes have opened up a whole universe of wonders that would have amazed even Galileo.

Electromagnetic Radiation

To understand how telescopes work, it's useful to understand the nature of electromagnetic radiation. Light is a form of **electromagnetic radiation** (ih lek troh mag NET ik), or energy that can travel through space in the form of waves. You can see stars when the light that they produce reaches your eyes.

Forms of Radiation Scientists call the light you can see **visible light.** Visible light is just one of many types of electromagnetic radiation. Many objects give off radiation that you can't see. For example, in addition to their reddish light, the glowing coils of an electric heater give off infrared radiation, which you feel as heat. Radio transmitters produce radio waves that carry signals to radios and televisions. Objects in space give off all types of electromagnetic radiation.

The Electromagnetic Spectrum As shown in Figure 1, the distance between the crest of one wave and the crest of the next wave is called **wavelength.** Visible light has very short wavelengths, less than one millionth of a meter. Some electromagnetic waves have even shorter wavelengths. Other waves have much longer wavelengths, even several meters long.

If you shine white light through a prism, the light spreads out to make a range of different colors with different wavelengths, called a **spectrum.** The spectrum of visible light is made of the colors red, orange, yellow, green, blue, and violet. **The electromagnetic spectrum includes the entire range of radio waves, infrared radiation, visible light, ultraviolet radiation, X-rays, and gamma rays.**

Reading Checkpoint What are two kinds of electromagnetic waves that you might experience every day?

Go Online
SciLINKS
NSTA

For: Links on telescopes
Visit: www.SciLinks.org
Web Code: scn-0641

FIGURE 1
The Electromagnetic Spectrum
The electromagnetic spectrum ranges from long-wavelength radio waves through short-wavelength gamma rays.
Interpreting Diagrams *Are infrared waves longer or shorter than ultraviolet waves?*

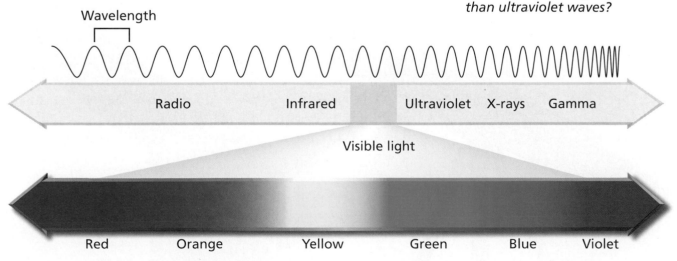

Wavelength

Radio   Infrared   Ultraviolet   X-rays   Gamma

Visible light

Red   Orange   Yellow   Green   Blue   Violet

Types of Telescopes

On a clear night, your eyes can see at most a few thousand stars. But with a telescope, you can see many millions. Why? The light from stars spreads out as it moves through space, and your eyes are too small to gather much light.

Telescopes are instruments that collect and focus light and other forms of electromagnetic radiation. Telescopes make distant objects appear larger and brighter. A telescope that uses lenses or mirrors to collect and focus visible light is called an **optical telescope.** The two major types of optical telescope are refracting telescopes and reflecting telescopes.

Modern astronomy is based on the detection of many forms of electromagnetic radiation besides visible light. Non-optical telescopes collect and focus different types of electromagnetic radiation, just as optical telescopes collect visible light.

Refracting Telescopes A **refracting telescope** uses convex lenses to gather and focus light. A **convex lens** is a piece of transparent glass, curved so that the middle is thicker than the edges.

Figure 2 shows a simple refracting telescope. This telescope has two convex lenses, one at each end of a long tube. Light enters the telescope through the large objective lens at the top. The objective lens focuses the light at a certain distance from the lens. This distance is the focal length of the lens. The larger the objective lens, the more light the telescope can collect. This makes it easier for astronomers to see faint objects.

The smaller lens at the lower end of a refracting telescope is the eyepiece lens. The eyepiece lens magnifies the image produced by the objective lens.

FIGURE 2
Refracting and Reflecting Telescopes
A refracting telescope uses convex lenses to focus light. A reflecting telescope has a curved mirror in place of an objective lens.

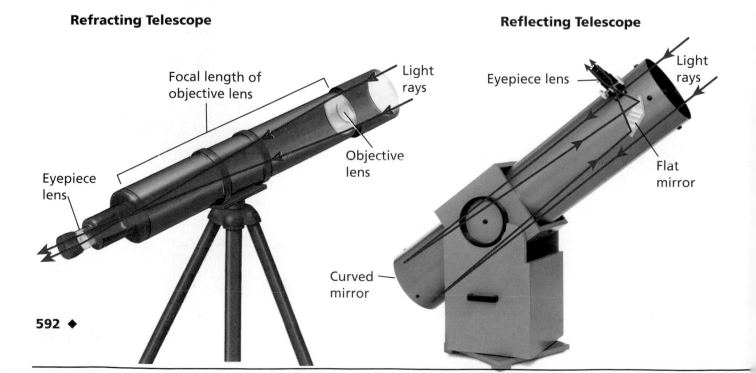

Refracting Telescope

Focal length of objective lens

Light rays

Objective lens

Eyepiece lens

Reflecting Telescope

Eyepiece lens

Light rays

Flat mirror

Curved mirror

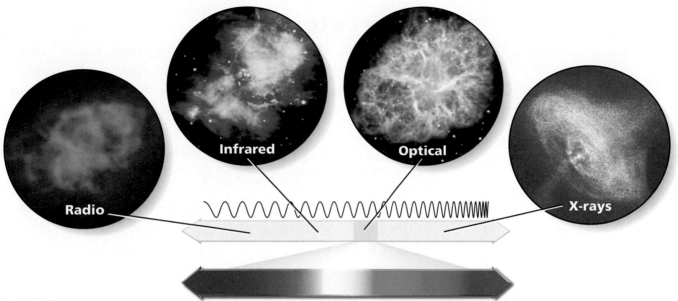

FIGURE 3
Four Views of the Crab Nebula
Different types of telescopes collect electromagnetic radiation at different wavelengths. Astronomers are able to learn a great deal about the Crab Nebula by examining these different images. The images are shown at different scales.

Reflecting Telescopes In 1668, Isaac Newton built the first reflecting telescope. A **reflecting telescope** uses a curved mirror to collect and focus light. Like the objective lens in a refracting telescope, the curved mirror in a reflecting telescope focuses a large amount of light onto a small area. The larger the mirror, the more light the telescope can collect. The largest optical telescopes today are all reflecting telescopes.

Radio Telescopes Devices used to detect radio waves from objects in space are called **radio telescopes.** Most radio telescopes have curved, reflecting surfaces—up to 305 meters in diameter. These surfaces focus radio waves the way the mirror in a reflecting telescope focuses light waves. The surfaces concentrate the faint radio waves from space onto small antennas like those on radios. As with optical telescopes, the larger a radio telescope is, the more radio waves it can collect.

Other Telescopes Some telescopes detect infrared radiation, which has longer wavelengths than visible light but shorter wavelengths than radio waves. There are also telescopes that detect the shortest wavelengths—ultraviolet radiation, X-rays, and gamma rays.

 **Reading Checkpoint** Who built the first reflecting telescope?

Observatories

In general, an **observatory** is a building that contains one or more telescopes. However, some observatories are located in space. **Many large observatories are located on mountaintops or in space.** Why? Earth's atmosphere makes objects in space look blurry. The sky on some mountaintops is clearer than at sea level and is not brightened much by city lights. Unlike optical telescopes, radio telescopes do not need to be located on mountaintops.

One of the best observatory sites on Earth is on the top of Mauna Kea, a dormant volcano on the island of Hawaii. Mauna Kea is so tall—4,200 meters above sea level—that it is above 40 percent of Earth's atmosphere.

• Tech & Design in History •

Development of Modern Telescopes

During the last century, astronomers have built larger telescopes, which can collect more visible light and other types of radiation. Today's astronomers use tools that could not have been imagined 100 years ago.

1897 Yerkes Telescope
The 1-meter-diameter telescope at Yerkes Observatory in Wisconsin is the largest refracting telescope ever built. Because its main lens is so large, the Yerkes telescope can collect more light than any other refracting telescope.

1931 Beginning of Radio Astronomy
Karl Jansky, an American engineer, was trying to find the source of static that was interfering with radio communications. Using a large antenna, he discovered that the static was radio waves given off by objects in space. Jansky's accidental discovery led to the beginning of radio astronomy.

1963 Arecibo Radio Telescope
This radio telescope in Puerto Rico was built in a natural bowl in the ground. It is 305 meters in diameter, the largest radio telescope in existence.

| 1900 | | 1940 | 1960 |

Advanced Telescopes Today, many large optical telescopes are equipped with systems that significantly improve the quality of their images. Optical telescopes on Earth equipped with such systems are able to produce images of small regions of the sky that rival those of optical telescopes based in space.

Some new telescopes are equipped with computer systems that correct images for problems such as telescope movement and changes in air temperature or mirror shape. Other advanced telescopes use lasers to monitor conditions in the atmosphere. The shape of the telescope's mirror is automatically adjusted thousands of times each second in response to changes in the atmosphere.

Writing in Science

Research and Write
Research one of these telescopes or another large telescope. Create a publicity brochure in which you describe the telescope's features, when and where it was built, and what types of research it is used for.

1980 Very Large Array
The Very Large Array is a set of 27 radio telescopes in New Mexico. The telescopes can be moved close together or far apart. The telescopes are linked, so they can be used as if they were one giant radio telescope 25 kilometers in diameter.

1990 Hubble Space Telescope
The Hubble Space Telescope views objects in space from high above the atmosphere. As a result, it can produce extremely sharp images.

2003 Spitzer Space Telescope
The Spitzer Space Telescope is a powerful 0.85-meter diameter telescope that surveys the sky in the infrared range of the spectrum.

1980   **2000**   **2020**

Figure 4
Repairing Hubble
Astronauts have repaired and upgraded the Hubble Space Telescope on several occasions.

Telescopes in Space X-rays, gamma rays, and most ultraviolet radiation are blocked by Earth's atmosphere. To detect these wavelengths, astronomers have placed telescopes in space. Some space telescopes are designed to detect visible light or infrared radiation, since Earth's atmosphere interferes with the transmission of these forms of radiation.

The Hubble Space Telescope is a reflecting telescope with a mirror 2.4 meters in diameter. Because the Hubble telescope orbits Earth above the atmosphere, it can produce very detailed images in visible light. It also collects ultraviolet and infrared radiation. The spectacular Hubble telescope images have changed how astronomers view the universe.

The hottest objects in space give off X-rays. The Chandra X-ray Observatory produces images in the X-ray portion of the spectrum. Chandra's X-ray images are much more detailed than those of earlier X-ray telescopes.

The most recent addition to NASA's lineup of telescopes in space is the Spitzer Space Telescope. Launched in 2003, the Spitzer telescope produces images in the infrared portion of the spectrum.

 **Reading Checkpoint** **What is an observatory?**

Section 1 Assessment

Target Reading Skill Building Vocabulary
Use your definitions to help answer the questions below.

Reviewing Key Concepts

1. a. **Sequencing** List the main types of electromagnetic waves, from longest wavelength to shortest.
   b. **Applying Concepts** Why are images from the Hubble Space Telescope clearer than images from telescopes on Earth?

2. a. **Identifying** What are the two major types of optical telescope?
   b. **Explaining** How does a refracting telescope work?
   c. **Comparing and Contrasting** Use Figure 2 to explain the major differences between reflecting and refracting telescopes.

3. a. **Summarizing** How does the atmosphere affect electromagnetic radiation?
   b. **Explaining** Why are many large optical telescopes located on mountaintops?
   c. **Applying Concepts** Would it make sense to place an X-ray or gamma ray telescope on a mountaintop? Explain why or why not.

Writing in Science

Writing Instructions Write a short explanation of how to build a reflecting telescope for a booklet to be included in a model telescope kit. Be sure to describe the shape and position of each of the lenses or mirrors. You may include drawings.

Design and Build a Telescope

Foam holder

Objective lens
(tape to the
end of tube)

Paper towel
tubes

Eyepiece

Problem

Can you design and build a telescope?

Skills Focus

evaluating the design, redesigning

Materials

• 2 paper towel tubes of slightly different
  diameters • several plastic objective lenses
• several plastic eyepiece lenses • meter stick
• foam holder for eyepiece • transparent tape

Procedure

1. Fit one of the paper towel tubes inside the
   other. Make sure you can move the tubes but
   that they will not slide on their own.

2. Place the large objective lens flat against the
   end of the outer tube. Tape the lens in place.

3. Insert the small eyepiece lens into the opening in the foam holder.

4. Place the foam eyepiece lens holder into the
   inner tube at the end of the telescope opposite to the objective lens.

5. Tape a meter stick to the wall. Look through
   the eyepiece at the meter stick from 5 m
   away. Slide the tubes in and out to focus
   your telescope so that you can
   clearly read the numbers on the
   meter stick. Draw your telescope.
   On the drawing, mark the tube
   position that allows you to read the
   numbers most clearly.

6. Use your telescope to look at other objects at
   different distances, both in your classroom
   and through the window. For each object
   you view, draw your telescope, marking the
   tube position at which you see the object
   most clearly. **CAUTION:** *Do not look at the
   sun. You will damage your eyes.*

7. Design and build a better telescope. Your
   new telescope should make objects appear
   larger than your first model from the same
   observing distance. It should have markings
   on the inner tube to enable you to pre-focus
   the telescope for a given observing distance.

8. Draw a design for your new telescope. List the
   materials you'll need. Obtain your teacher's
   approval. Then build your new model.

Analyze and Conclude

1. **Inferring** Why do you need two tubes?

2. **Observing** If you focus on a nearby object
   and then focus on something farther away,
   do you have to move the tubes together or
   apart?

3. **Evaluating the Design** How could you
   improve on the design of your new telescope? What effects would different lenses
   or tubes have on its performance?

4. **Redesigning** Describe the most important
   factors in redesigning your telescope.

Communicate

Write a product brochure for your new telescope. Be sure to describe in detail why your new
telescope is better than the first telescope.

Characteristics of Stars

Key Concepts

- How are stars classified?
- How do astronomers measure distances to the stars?
- What is an H-R diagram and how do astronomers use it?

Key Terms

- constellation
- spectrograph
- apparent brightness
- absolute brightness
- light-year
- parallax
- Hertzsprung-Russell diagram
- main sequence

Target Reading Skill

Using Prior Knowledge Before you read, write what you know about the characteristics of stars in a graphic organizer like the one below. As you read, write what you learn.

What You Know
1. Stars are bright and hot.
2.

What You Learned
1.
2.

Lab zone Discover Activity

How Does Your Thumb Move?

1. Stand facing a wall, at least an arm's length away. Stretch your arm out with your thumb up and your fingers curled.
2. Close your right eye and look at your thumb with your left eye. Line your thumb up with something on the wall.
3. Now close your left eye and open your right eye. How does your thumb appear to move along the wall?
4. Bring your thumb closer to your eye, about half the distance as before. Repeat Steps 2 and 3.

Think It Over
Observing How does your thumb appear to move in Step 4 compared to Step 3? How are these observations related to how far away your thumb is at each step? How could you use this method to estimate distances?

When ancient observers around the world looked up at the night sky, they imagined that groups of stars formed pictures of people or animals. Today, we call these imaginary patterns of stars **constellations.**

Different cultures gave different names to the constellations. For example, a large constellation in the winter sky is named Orion, the Hunter, after a Greek myth. In this constellation, Orion is seen with a sword in his belt and an upraised arm. The ancient Sumerians thought that the stars in Orion formed the outline of a sheep. In ancient China, this group of stars was called "three," probably because of the three bright stars in Orion's belt.

Astronomers use the patterns of the constellations to locate objects in the night sky. But although the stars in a constellation look as if they are close to one another, they generally are not. They just happen to lie in the same part of the sky as seen from Earth.

Illustration of Orion ▼

Classifying Stars

Like the sun, all stars are huge spheres of glowing gas. They are made up mostly of hydrogen, and they produce energy through the process of nuclear fusion. This energy makes stars shine brightly. Astronomers classify stars according to their physical characteristics. **Characteristics used to classify stars include color, temperature, size, composition, and brightness.**

Color and Temperature If you look at the night sky, you can see slight differences in the colors of the stars. For example, Betelgeuse (BAY tul jooz), the bright star in Orion's shoulder, looks reddish. Rigel, the star in Orion's heel, is blue-white.

Like hot objects on Earth, a star's color reveals its temperature. If you watch a toaster heat up, you can see the wires glow red-hot. The wires inside a light bulb are even hotter and glow white. Similarly, the coolest stars—with a surface temperature of about 3,200 degrees Celsius—appear reddish in the sky. With a surface temperature of about 5,800 degrees Celsius, the sun appears yellow. The hottest stars in the sky, which are over 20,000 degrees Celsius, appear bluish.

Size When you look at stars in the sky, they all appear to be points of light of the same size. Many stars are actually about the size of the sun, which is a medium-sized star. However, some stars are much larger than the sun. Very large stars are called giant stars or supergiant stars. If the supergiant star Betelgeuse were located where our sun is, it would be large enough to fill the solar system as far out as Jupiter.

Most stars are much smaller than the sun. White dwarf stars are about the size of Earth. Neutron stars are even smaller, only about 20 kilometers in diameter.

Go Online
PHSchool.com

For: More on types of stars
Visit: PHSchool.com
Web Code: cfd-5042

FIGURE 5
Star Size
Stars vary greatly in size. Giant stars are typically 10 to 100 times larger than the sun and more than 1,000 times the size of a white dwarf. **Calculating** *Betelgeuse has a diameter of 420 million kilometers. How many times larger is this than the sun, which has a diameter of 1.4 million kilometers?*

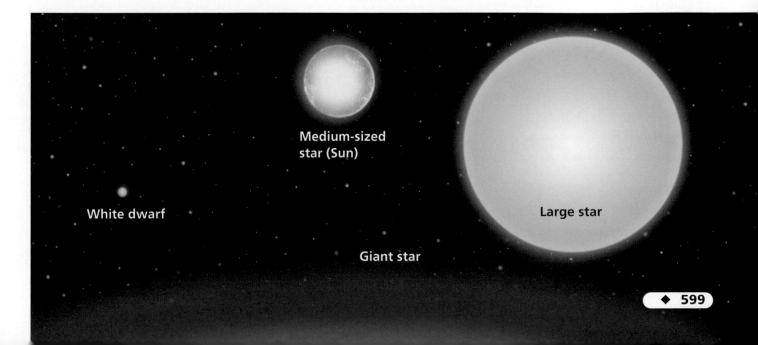

White dwarf

Medium-sized star (Sun)

Giant star

Large star

FIGURE 6
Spectrums of Four Stars
Astronomers can use line spectrums to identify the chemical elements in a star. Each element produces a characteristic pattern of spectral lines.

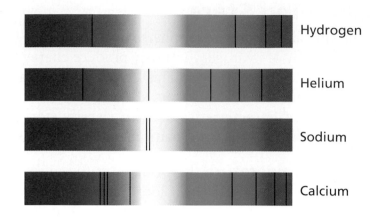

Hydrogen

Helium

Sodium

Calcium

Chemical Composition Stars vary in their chemical composition. The chemical composition of most stars is about 73 percent hydrogen, 25 percent helium, and 2 percent other elements by mass. This is similar to the composition of the sun.

Astronomers use spectrographs to determine the elements found in stars. A **spectrograph** (SPEK truh graf) is a device that breaks light into colors and produces an image of the resulting spectrum. Most large telescopes have spectrographs.

The gases in a star's atmosphere absorb some wavelengths of light produced within the star. When the star's light is seen through a spectrograph, each absorbed wavelength is shown as a dark line on a spectrum. Each chemical element absorbs light at particular wavelengths. Just as each person has a unique set of fingerprints, each element has a unique set of lines for a given temperature. Figure 6 shows the spectral lines of four elements. By comparing a star's spectrum with the spectrums of known elements, astronomers can infer how much of each element is found in the star.

 **Reading Checkpoint** What is a spectrograph?

Brightness of Stars

Stars also differ in brightness, the amount of light they give off. **The brightness of a star depends upon both its size and temperature.** Recall that the photosphere is the layer of a star that gives off light. Betelgeuse is fairly cool, so a square meter of its photosphere doesn't give off much light. But Betelgeuse is very large, so it shines brightly.

Rigel, on the other hand, is very hot, so each square meter of Rigel's photosphere gives off a lot of light. Even though it is smaller than Betelgeuse, Rigel shines more brightly.

Lab zone Skills Activity

Inferring

The lines on the spectrums below are from three different stars. Each of these star spectrums is made up of an overlap of spectrums from the individual elements shown in Figure 6. In star A, which elements have the strongest lines? Which are the strongest in star B? In star C?

A

B

C

How bright a star looks from Earth depends on both its distance from Earth and how bright the star truly is. Because of these two factors, the brightness of a star can be described in two ways: apparent brightness and absolute brightness.

Apparent Brightness A star's **apparent brightness** is its brightness as seen from Earth. Astronomers can measure apparent brightness fairly easily using electronic devices. However, astronomers can't tell how much light a star gives off just from the star's apparent brightness. Just as a flashlight looks brighter the closer it is to you, a star looks brighter the closer it is to Earth. For example, the sun looks very bright. This does not mean that the sun gives off more light than all other stars. The sun looks so bright simply because it is so close. In reality, the sun is a star of only average brightness.

Absolute Brightness A star's **absolute brightness** is the brightness the star would have if it were at a standard distance from Earth. Finding a star's absolute brightness is more complex than finding its apparent brightness. An astronomer must first find out both the star's apparent brightness and its distance from Earth. The astronomer can then calculate the star's absolute brightness.

Astronomers have found that the absolute brightness of stars can vary tremendously. The brightest stars are more than a billion times brighter than the dimmest stars!

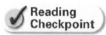 **Reading Checkpoint** What is a star's absolute brightness?

Lab zone Try This Activity

Star Bright
You can compare absolute and apparent brightness.

1. Dim the lights. Put two equally bright flashlights next to each other on a table. Turn them on.
2. Look at the flashlights from the other side of the room. Think of the flashlights as two stars. Then compare them in terms of absolute and apparent brightness.
3. Move one of the flashlights closer to you and repeat Step 2.
4. Replace one of the flashlights with a brighter one. Repeat Steps 1 and 2 with the unequally bright flashlights.

Making Models How could you place the flashlights in Step 4 so that they have the same apparent brightness? Try it.

FIGURE 7
Absolute Brightness
The streetlights in this photo all give off about the same amount of light, and so have about the same absolute brightness.
Applying Concepts *Why do the closer streetlights appear brighter than the more distant lights?*

Measuring Distances to Stars

Imagine that you could travel to the stars at the speed of light. To travel from Earth to the sun would take about 8 minutes, not very much time for such a long trip. The next nearest star, Proxima Centauri, is much farther away. A trip to Proxima Centauri at the speed of light would take 4.2 years!

The Light-Year Distances on Earth's surface are often measured in kilometers. However, distances to the stars are so large that kilometers are not very practical units. **Astronomers use a unit called the light-year to measure distances between the stars.** In space, light travels at a speed of about 300,000 kilometers per second. A **light-year** is the distance that light travels in one year, about 9.5 million million kilometers.

Note that the light-year is a unit of distance, not time. To help you understand this, consider an everyday example. If you bicycle at 10 kilometers per hour, it would take you 1 hour to go to a mall 10 kilometers away. You could say that the mall is "1 bicycle-hour" away.

Parallax Standing on Earth looking up at the sky, it may seem as if there is no way to tell how far away the stars are. However, astronomers have found ways to measure those distances. **Astronomers often use parallax to measure distances to nearby stars.**

Parallax is the apparent change in position of an object when you look at it from different places. For example, imagine that you and a friend have gone to a movie. A woman with a large hat sits down in front of you, as shown in Figure 8. Because you and your friend are sitting in different places, the woman's hat blocks different parts of the screen. If you are sitting on her left, the woman's hat appears to be in front of the large dinosaur. But to your friend on the right, she appears to be in front of the bird.

Have the woman and her hat moved? No. But because you changed your position, she appears to have moved. This apparent movement when you look from two different directions is parallax.

Your view

Your friend's view

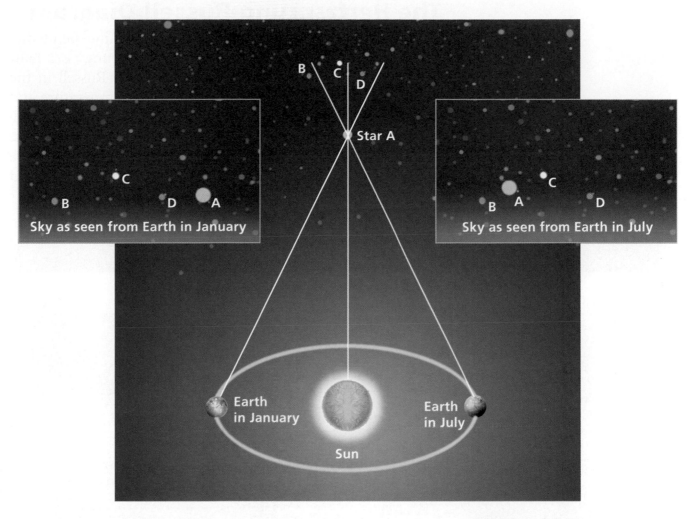

Sky as seen from Earth in January

Sky as seen from Earth in July

Star A

Earth in January

Earth in July

Sun

FIGURE 9
Parallax of Stars
The apparent movement of a star when seen from a different position is called parallax. Astronomers use parallax to calculate the distance to nearby stars. Note that the diagram is not to scale.
Interpreting Diagrams *Why do nearby stars appear to change position between January and July?*

Parallax in Astronomy Astronomers are able to measure the parallax of nearby stars to determine their distances. As shown in Figure 9, astronomers look at a nearby star when Earth is on one side of the sun. Then they look at the same star again six months later, when Earth is on the opposite side of the sun. Astronomers measure how much the nearby star appears to move against a background of stars that are much farther away. They can then use this measurement to calculate the distance to the nearby star. The less the nearby star appears to move, the farther away it is.

Astronomers can use parallax to measure distances up to a few hundred light-years from Earth. The parallax of any star that is farther away is too small to measure accurately.

 **Reading Checkpoint** How is parallax useful in astronomy?

The Hertzsprung-Russell Diagram

About 100 years ago, two scientists working independently made the same discovery. Both Ejnar Hertzsprung (EYE nahr HURT sprung) in Denmark and Henry Norris Russell in the United States made graphs to find out if the temperature and the absolute brightness of stars are related. They plotted the surface temperatures of stars on the *x*-axis and their absolute brightness on the *y*-axis. The points formed a pattern. The graph they made is still used by astronomers today. It is called the **Hertzsprung-Russell diagram,** or H-R diagram.

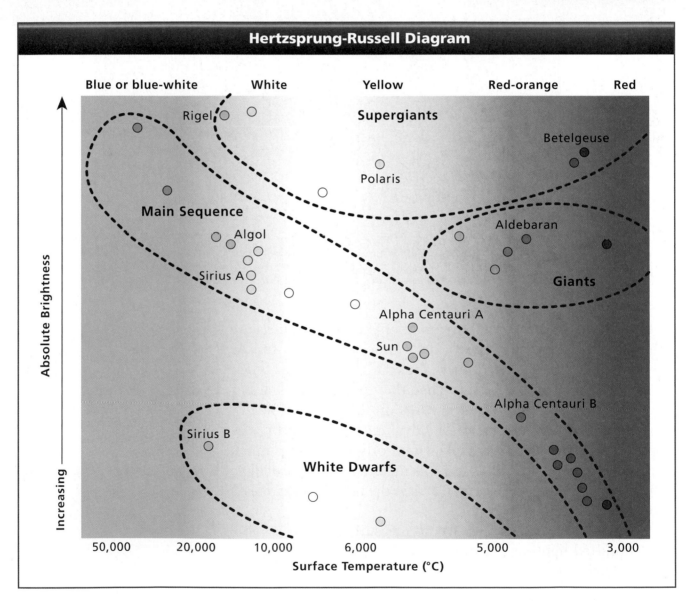

Hertzsprung-Russell Diagram

Blue or blue-white　White　Yellow　Red-orange　Red

Supergiants

Rigel

Betelgeuse

Polaris

Main Sequence

Algol

Aldebaran

Sirius A

Giants

Alpha Centauri A

Sun

Alpha Centauri B

Sirius B

White Dwarfs

Absolute Brightness — Increasing

50,000　20,000　10,000　6,000　5,000　3,000

Surface Temperature (°C)

FIGURE **10**
The Hertzsprung-Russell diagram shows the relationship between the surface temperature and absolute brightness of stars.
Interpreting Diagrams *Which star has a hotter surface: Rigel or Aldebaran?*

Astronomers use H-R diagrams to classify stars and to understand how stars change over time. As you can see in Figure 10, most of the stars in the H-R diagram form a diagonal area called the **main sequence.** More than 90 percent of all stars, including the sun, are main-sequence stars. Within the main sequence, surface temperature increases as absolute brightness increases. Thus, hot bluish stars are located at the left of an H-R diagram and cooler reddish stars are located at the right of the diagram.

The brightest stars are located near the top of an H-R diagram, while the dimmest stars are located at the bottom. Giant and supergiant stars are very bright. They can be found near the top center and right of the diagram. White dwarfs are hot, but not very bright, so they appear at the bottom left or bottom center of the diagram.

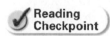 **Reading Checkpoint** What is the main sequence?

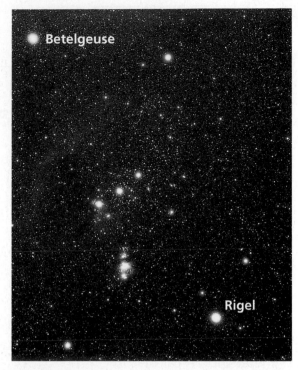

FIGURE 11
Orion
Orion includes the red supergiant Betelgeuse, the blue supergiant Rigel, and many other main sequence and giant stars.

Section 2 Assessment

Target Reading Skill Using Prior Knowledge
Review your graphic organizer and revise it based on what you just learned in the section.

Reviewing Key Concepts

1. a. **Listing** Name three characteristics used to classify stars.
   b. **Comparing and Contrasting** What is the difference between apparent brightness and absolute brightness?
   c. **Applying Concepts** Stars A and B have about the same apparent brightness, but Star A is about twice as far from Earth as Star B. Which star has the greater absolute brightness? Explain your answer.
2. a. **Measuring** What is a light-year?
   b. **Defining** What is parallax?
   c. **Predicting** Vega is 25.3 light-years from Earth and Arcturus is 36.7 light-years away. Which star would have a greater parallax? Explain.

3. a. **Summarizing** What two characteristics of stars are shown in an H-R diagram?
   b. **Identifying** Identify two ways in which astronomers can use an H-R diagram.
   c. **Classifying** The star Procyon B has a surface temperature of 6,600° Celsius and an absolute brightness that is much less than the sun's. What type of star is Procyon B? (*Hint:* Refer to the H-R diagram.)

Lab zone At-Home **Activity**

Observing Orion With adult family members, go outside on a clear, dark night. Determine which way is south. Using the star charts in Appendix B, look for the constellation Orion, which is visible in the evening during winter and spring. Find the stars Betelgeuse and Rigel in Orion and explain to your family why they are different colors.

How Far Is That Star?

Problem

How can parallax be used to determine distances?

Skills Focus

inferring, calculating, predicting

Materials

- masking tape • paper clips • pen
- black and red pencils • metric ruler • paper
- meter stick • calculator
- lamp without a shade, with 100-watt light bulb
- copier paper box (without the lid)
- flat rectangular table, about 1 m wide

Procedure

PART 1 Telescope Model

1. Place the lamp on a table in the middle of the classroom.

2. Carefully use the tip of the pen to make a small hole in the middle of one end of the box. The box represents a telescope.

3. At the front of the classroom, place the box on a flat table so the hole points toward the lamp. Line the left side of the box up with the left edge of the table.

4. Put a small piece of tape on the table below the hole. Use the pen to make a mark on the tape directly below the hole. The mark represents the position of the telescope when Earth is on one side of its orbit.

PART 2 Star 1

5. Label a sheet of paper Star 1 and place it inside the box as shown in the drawing. Hold the paper in place with two paper clips. The paper represents the film in a telescope.

6. Darken the room. Turn on the light to represent the star.

7. With the red pencil, mark the paper where you see a dot of light. Label this dot A. Dot A represents the image of the star on the film.

8. Move the box so the right edge of the box lines up with the right edge of the table. Repeat Step 4. The mark on the tape represents the position of the telescope six months later, when Earth is on the other side of its orbit.

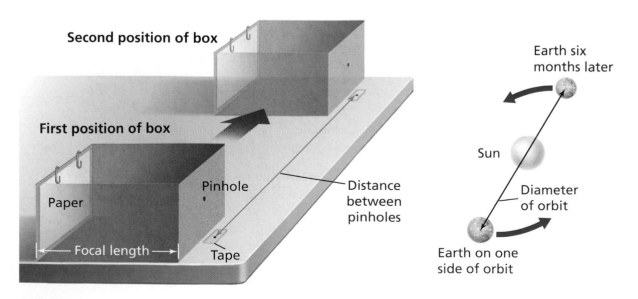

Second position of box

First position of box

Paper

Pinhole

Focal length

Tape

Distance between pinholes

Earth six months later

Sun

Diameter of orbit

Earth on one side of orbit

Data Table						
Star	Parallax Shift (mm)	Focal Length (mm)	Diameter of Orbit (mm)	Calculated Distance to Star (mm)	Calculated Distance to Star (m)	Actual Distance to Star (m)

9. Repeat Step 7, using a black pencil to mark the second dot B. Dot B represents the image of the star as seen 6 months later from the other side of Earth's orbit.

10. Remove the paper. Before you continue, copy the data table into your notebook.

11. Measure and record the distance in millimeters between dots A and B. This distance represents the parallax shift for Star 1.

12. Measure and record the distance from the hole in the box to the lamp. This distance represents the actual distance to the star.

13. Measure and record the distance from the hole (lens) to the back of the box in millimeters. This distance represents the focal length of your telescope.

14. Measure and record the distance in millimeters between the marks on the two pieces of masking tape. This distance represents the diameter of Earth's orbit.

PART 3 Stars 2 and 3

15. Move the lamp away from the table—about half the distance to the back of the room. The bulb now represents Star 2. Predict what you think will happen to the light images on your paper.

16. Repeat Steps 6–12 with a new sheet of paper to find the parallax shift for Star 2.

17. Move the lamp to the back of the classroom. The bulb now represents Star 3. Repeat Steps 6–12 with a new sheet of paper to find the parallax shift for Star 3.

Analyze and Conclude

1. **Inferring** What caused the apparent change in position of the dots of light for each star? Explain.

2. **Calculating** Use the following formula to calculate the distance from the telescope to Star 1.
$$\text{Distance} = \frac{\text{Diameter} \times \text{Focal length}}{\text{Parallax shift}}$$

3. **Calculating** Divide your result from Question 2 by 1,000 to get the distance to the light bulb in meters.

4. **Calculating** Repeat Questions 2 and 3 for Stars 2 and 3.

5. **Predicting** Was your prediction in Step 15 correct? Why or why not?

6. **Interpreting Data** How did your calculation for Star 3 compare with the actual distance? What could you do to improve your results?

7. **Communicating** Write a paragraph that explains how parallax shift varies with distance. Relate each star's parallax shift to its distance from Earth.

Design an Experiment

What would happen if you kept moving the lamp away from the box? Is there a distance at which you can no longer find the distance to the star? Design an experiment to find out.

Lives of Stars

Reading Preview

Key Concepts
- How does a star form?
- What determines how long a star will exist?
- What happens to a star when it runs out of fuel?

Key Terms
- nebula • protostar
- white dwarf • supernova
- neutron star • pulsar
- black hole

Target Reading Skill

Sequencing As you read, make a flowchart like the one below that shows the stages in the life of a star like the sun. Write each step of the process in a separate box in the flowchart in the order that it occurs.

Life Cycle of a Sun-like Star

Protostar forms from a nebula.

↓

A star is born as fusion begins.

↓

Lab zone Discover **Activity**

What Determines How Long Stars Live?

1. This graph shows how the mass of a star is related to its lifetime— how long the star lives before it runs out of fuel.

2. How long does a star with 0.75 times the mass of the sun live? How long does a star with 3 times the mass of the sun live?

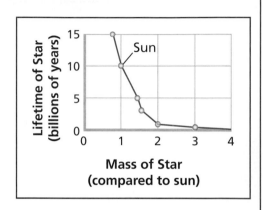

Think It Over

Drawing Conclusions Describe the general relationship between a star's mass and its lifetime.

Imagine that you want to study how people age. You wish you could watch a few people for 50 years, but your project is due next week! You have to study a lot of people for a short time, and classify the people into different age groups. You may come up with groups like *babies, young adults,* and *elderly people.* You don't have time to see a single person go through all these stages, but you know the stages exist.

Astronomers have a similar problem in trying to understand how stars age. They can't watch a single star for billions of years. Instead, they study many stars and other objects in space. Over time, astronomers have figured out that these objects represent different stages in the lives of stars.

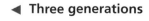

◀ **Three generations**

The Lives of Stars

Stars do not last forever. Each star is born, goes through its life cycle, and eventually dies. (Of course, stars are not really alive. The words *born*, *live*, and *die* are just helpful comparisons.)

A Star Is Born All stars begin their lives as parts of nebulas. A **nebula** is a large cloud of gas and dust spread out in an immense volume. A star, on the other hand, is made up of a large amount of gas in a relatively small volume.

In the densest part of a nebula, gravity pulls gas and dust together. A contracting cloud of gas and dust with enough mass to form a star is called a **protostar.** *Proto* means "earliest" in Greek, so a protostar is the earliest stage of a star's life.

A star is born when the contracting gas and dust from a nebula become so dense and hot that nuclear fusion starts. Recall that nuclear fusion is the process by which atoms combine to form heavier atoms. In the sun, for example, hydrogen atoms combine to form helium. During nuclear fusion, enormous amounts of energy are released.

Lifetimes of Stars **How long a star lives depends on its mass.** You might think that stars with more mass would last longer than stars with less mass. But instead, the reverse is true. You can think of stars as being like cars. A small car has a small gas tank, but it also has a small engine that burns gas slowly. A large car has a larger gas tank, but it also has a larger engine that burns gas rapidly. So the small car might be able to travel farther on a tank of gas than the larger car. Small-mass stars use up their fuel more slowly than large-mass stars, so they have much longer lives.

Generally, stars that have less mass than the sun use their fuel slowly, and can live for up to 200 billion years. Medium-mass stars like the sun live for about 10 billion years. Astronomers think the sun is about 4.6 billion years old, so it is almost halfway through its lifetime.

Stars that have more mass than the sun have shorter lifetimes. A star that is 15 times as massive as the sun may live only about ten million years. That may seem like a long time, but it is only one tenth of one percent of the lifetime of the sun.

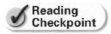 **Reading Checkpoint** How long will a star that is the mass of the sun live?

FIGURE 12
Young Stars
New stars are forming in the nebula on top. The bottom photo shows a protostar in the Orion Nebula. **Applying Concepts** *How do some of the gas and dust in a nebula become a protostar?*

Discovery CHANNEL SCHOOL™

Stars, Galaxies, and the Universe

Video Preview
▶ Video Field Trip
Video Assessment

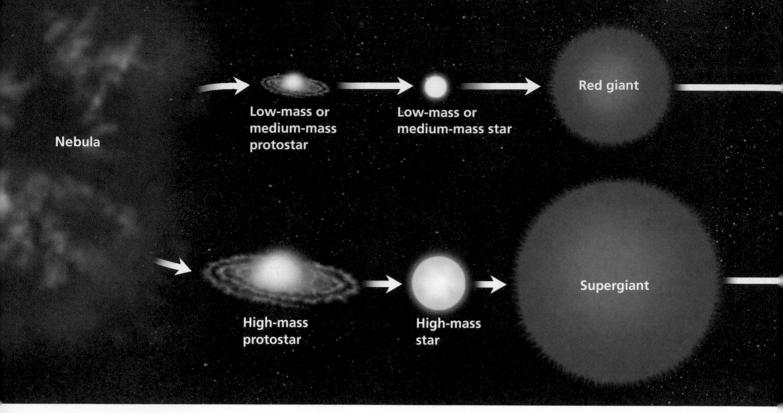

Nebula

Low-mass or medium-mass protostar

Low-mass or medium-mass star

Red giant

High-mass protostar

High-mass star

Supergiant

FIGURE 13
The Lives of Stars
A star's life history depends on its mass. A low-mass main-sequence star uses up its fuel slowly and eventually becomes a white dwarf. A high-mass star uses up its fuel quickly. After its supergiant stage, it will explode as a supernova, producing a neutron star or a black hole.
Interpreting Diagrams *What type of star produces a planetary nebula?*

 **Skills Activity**

Predicting
Find Algol, Sirius B, and Polaris in the H-R diagram on page 132. What type of star is each of these now? Predict what the next stage in each star's life will be.

Deaths of Stars
When a star begins to run out of fuel, its core shrinks and its outer portion expands. Depending on its mass, the star becomes either a red giant or a supergiant. All main-sequence stars eventually become red giants or supergiants. As shown in Figure 13, red giants and supergiants evolve in very different ways. **After a star runs out of fuel, it becomes a white dwarf, a neutron star, or a black hole.**

White Dwarfs Low-mass stars and medium-mass stars like the sun take billions of years to use up their nuclear fuel. As they start to run out of fuel, their outer layers expand, and they become red giants. Eventually, the outer parts grow larger still and drift out into space, forming a glowing cloud of gas called a planetary nebula. The blue-white core of the star that is left behind cools and becomes a **white dwarf.**

White dwarfs are only about the size of Earth, but they have about as much mass as the sun. Since a white dwarf has the same mass as the sun but only one millionth the volume, it is one million times as dense as the sun. A spoonful of material from a white dwarf has as much mass as a large truck. White dwarfs have no fuel, but they glow faintly from leftover energy. After billions of years, a white dwarf eventually stops glowing. Then it is called a black dwarf.

✔ Reading Checkpoint What is a white dwarf?

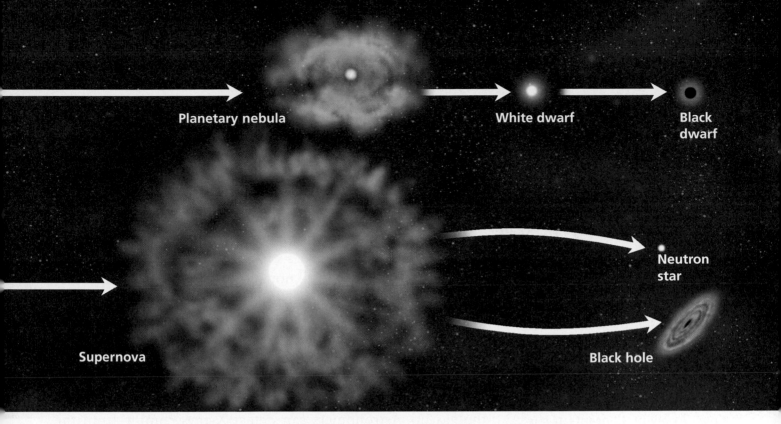

Planetary nebula

White dwarf

Black dwarf

Neutron star

Supernova

Black hole

Supernovas The life cycle of a high-mass star is quite different from the life cycle of a low-mass or medium-mass star. High-mass stars quickly evolve into brilliant supergiants. When a supergiant runs out of fuel, it can explode suddenly. Within hours, the star blazes millions of times brighter. The explosion is called a **supernova.** After a supernova, some of the material from the star expands into space. This material may become part of a nebula. This nebula can then contract to form a new, partly recycled star. Astronomers think the sun began as a nebula that contained material from a supernova.

Neutron Stars After a supergiant explodes, some of the material from the star is left behind. This material may form a neutron star. **Neutron stars** are the remains of high-mass stars. They are even smaller and denser than white dwarfs. A neutron star may contain as much as three times the mass of the sun but be only about 25 kilometers in diameter, the size of a city.

In 1967, Jocelyn Bell, a British astronomy student, detected an object in space that appeared to give off regular pulses of radio waves. Some astronomers hypothesized that the pulses might be a signal from an extraterrestrial civilization. At first, astronomers even named the source LGM, for the "Little Green Men" in early science-fiction stories. Soon, however, astronomers concluded that the source of the radio waves was really a rapidly spinning neutron star. Spinning neutron stars are called **pulsars,** short for pulsating radio sources. Some pulsars spin hundreds of times per second!

Go Online

active art

For: The Lives of Stars activity
Visit: PHSchool.com
Web Code: cfp-5043

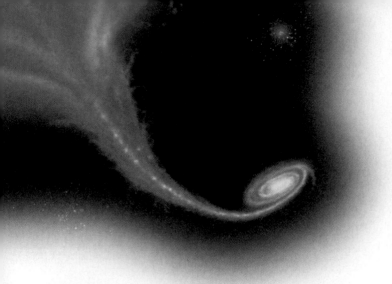

Black Holes The most massive stars—those having more than 40 times the mass of the sun—may become black holes when they die. A **black hole** is an object with gravity so strong that nothing, not even light, can escape. After a very massive star dies in a supernova explosion, more than five times the mass of the sun may be left. The gravity of this mass is so strong that the gas is pulled inward, packing the gas into a smaller and smaller space. The gas becomes so densely packed that its intense gravity will not allow even light to escape. The remains of the star have become a black hole.

No light, radio waves, or any other form of radiation can ever get out of a black hole, so it is not possible to detect a black hole directly. But astronomers can detect black holes indirectly. For example, gas near a black hole is pulled so strongly that it revolves faster and faster around the black hole. Friction heats the gas up. Astronomers can detect X-rays coming from the hot gas and infer that a black hole is present. Similarly, if another star is near a black hole, astronomers can calculate the mass of the black hole from the effect of its gravity on the star. Scientists have detected dozens of star-size black holes with the Chandra X-ray Observatory. They have also detected huge black holes that are millions or billions of times the sun's mass.

FIGURE 14
Black Holes
The remains of the most massive stars collapse into black holes. This artist's impression shows a black hole pulling matter from a companion star. The material glows as it is pulled into the black hole. **Applying Concepts** *If it is impossible to detect a black hole directly, how do astronomers find them?*

 Reading Checkpoint   **What is a black hole?**

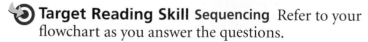

Section 3 Assessment

Target Reading Skill **Sequencing** Refer to your flowchart as you answer the questions.

Reviewing Key Concepts

1. **a. Defining** What is a nebula?
   b. Explaining How does a star form from a nebula?
   c. Comparing and Contrasting How is a protostar different from a star?

2. **a. Identifying** What factor determines how long a star lives?
   b. Applying Concepts A star is twice as massive as the sun. Will its lifespan be longer, shorter, or the same as that of the sun?

3. **a. Comparing and Contrasting** What is a white dwarf? How is it different from a neutron star?

   b. Relating Cause and Effect Why do some stars become white dwarfs and others become neutron stars or black holes?
   c. Predicting What will happen to the sun when it runs out of fuel? Explain.

Writing in Science

Descriptive Paragraph Write a description of one of the stages in the life of a star, such as a nebula, red giant, supernova, or white dwarf. Include information on how it formed and what will happen next in the star's evolution.

Star Systems and Galaxies

Reading Preview

Key Concepts
- What is a star system?
- What are the major types of galaxies?
- How do astronomers describe the scale of the universe?

Key Terms
- binary star
- eclipsing binary • open cluster
- globular cluster • galaxy
- spiral galaxy • elliptical galaxy
- irregular galaxy • quasar
- universe • scientific notation

Target Reading Skill
Building Vocabulary Carefully read the definition of each key term. Also read the neighboring sentences. Then write a definition of each key term in your own words.

Discover **Activity**

Why Does the Milky Way Look Hazy?

1. Using a pencil, carefully poke at least 20 holes close together in a sheet of white paper.
2. Tape the paper to a chalkboard or dark-colored wall.
3. Go to the other side of the room and look at the paper. From the far side of the room, what do the dots look like? Can you see individual dots?

Think It Over
Making Models How is looking at the paper from the far side of the room like trying to see many very distant stars that are close together? How does your model compare to the photograph of the Milky Way below?

On a clear, dark night in the country, you can see a hazy band of light stretched across the sky. This band of stars is called the Milky Way. It looks as if the Milky Way is very far away. Actually, though, Earth is inside the Milky Way! The Milky Way looks milky or hazy from Earth because the stars are too close together for your eyes to see them individually. The dark blotches in the Milky Way are clouds of dust that block light from stars behind them.

The Milky Way

Star Systems and Clusters

Our solar system has only one star, the sun. But this is not the most common situation for stars. **Most stars are members of groups of two or more stars, called star systems.** If you were on a planet in one of these star systems, at times you might see two or more suns in the sky! At other times, one or more of these suns would be below the horizon.

Multiple Star Systems Star systems that have two stars are called double stars or **binary stars.** (The prefix *bi* means "two.") Those with three stars are called triple stars. The nearby star Proxima Centauri may be part of a triple star system. The other two stars in the system, Alpha Centauri A and Alpha Centauri B, form a double star. Scientists are not sure whether Proxima Centauri is really part of the system or is just passing close to the other two stars temporarily.

Often one star in a binary star is much brighter and more massive than the other. Astronomers can sometimes detect a binary star even if only one of the stars can be seen from Earth. Astronomers can often tell that there is a dim star in a binary system by observing the effects of its gravity. As the dim companion star revolves around a bright star, the dim star's gravity causes the bright star to wobble back and forth. Imagine watching a pair of dancers who are twirling each other around. Even if one dancer were invisible, you could tell that the invisible dancer was there from watching the motion of the visible dancer.

Eclipsing Binaries A wobble is not the only clue that a star has a dim companion. A dim star in a binary star may pass in front of a brighter star and eclipse it. From Earth, the binary star would suddenly look much dimmer. A system in which one star periodically blocks the light from another is called an **eclipsing binary.** As Figure 16 shows, the star Algol is actually an eclipsing binary star system.

FIGURE 15
Invisible Partners
If you saw someone dancing but couldn't see a partner, you could infer that the partner was there by watching the dancer you could see. Astronomers use a similar method to detect faint stars in star systems.

FIGURE 16
Eclipsing Binary
Algol is an eclipsing binary star system consisting of a bright star and a dim companion. Each time the dimmer star passes in front of the brighter one, Algol appears less bright.
Interpreting Diagrams *When does Algol appear brighter?*

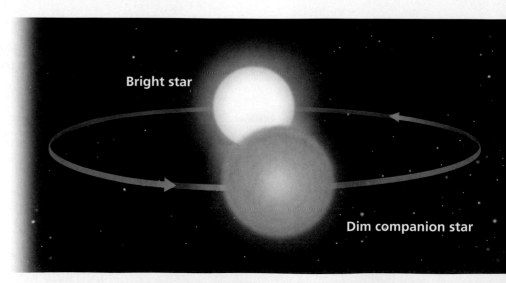

Bright star

Dim companion star

Planets Around Other Stars In 1995, astronomers first discovered a planet revolving around another ordinary star. They used a method similar to the one used in studying binary stars. The astronomers observed that a star was moving slightly toward and away from us. They knew that the invisible object causing the movement didn't have enough mass to be a star. They inferred that it must be a planet.

Since then, astronomers have discovered more than 100 planets around other stars, and new ones are being discovered all of the time. Most of these new planets are very large, with at least half of the mass of Jupiter. A small planet would be hard to detect because it would have little gravitational effect on the star it orbited.

Could there be life on planets in other solar systems? Some scientists think it is possible. A few astronomers are using radio telescopes to search for signals that could not have come from natural sources. Such a signal might be evidence that an extra-terrestrial civilization was sending out radio waves.

Star Clusters Many stars belong to larger groupings called star clusters. All of the stars in a particular cluster formed from the same nebula at about the same time and are about the same distance from Earth.

There are two major types of star clusters: open clusters and globular clusters. **Open clusters** have a loose, disorganized appearance and contain no more than a few thousand stars. They often contain many bright supergiants and much gas and dust. In contrast, **globular clusters** are large groupings of older stars. Globular clusters are round and densely packed with stars—some may contain more than a million stars.

 **Reading Checkpoint** What is a globular cluster?

FIGURE 17
Star Clusters
The stars in a globular cluster (above) are all about the same age and the same distance from Earth. The Pleiades (left), also called the *Seven Sisters*, is an open cluster.

Spiral Galaxy

Elliptical Galaxy

Irregular Galaxy

FIGURE 18
Types of Galaxies
There are three major types of galaxies: spiral, elliptical, and irregular.

Galaxies

A **galaxy** is a huge group of single stars, star systems, star clusters, dust, and gas bound together by gravity. There are billions of galaxies in the universe. The largest galaxies have more than a trillion stars. **Astronomers classify most galaxies into the following types: spiral, elliptical, and irregular.** Figure 18 shows examples of these three.

Spiral Galaxies Some galaxies appear to have a bulge in the middle and arms that spiral outward, like pinwheels. Such galaxies are called **spiral galaxies.** The spiral arms contain many bright, young stars as well as gas and dust. Most new stars in spiral galaxies form in these spiral arms. Relatively few new stars are forming in the central bulge. Some spiral galaxies, called barred-spiral galaxies, have a huge bar-shaped region of stars and gas that passes through their center.

Elliptical Galaxies Not all galaxies have spiral arms. **Elliptical galaxies** look like round or flattened balls. These galaxies contain billions of stars but have little gas and dust between the stars. Because there is little gas or dust, stars are no longer forming. Most elliptical galaxies contain only old stars.

Irregular Galaxies Some galaxies do not have regular shapes. These are known as **irregular galaxies.** Irregular galaxies are typically smaller than other types of galaxies. They generally have many bright, young stars and lots of gas and dust to form new stars.

Quasars In the 1960s, astronomers discovered objects that are very bright, but also very far away. Many of these objects are 10 billion light-years or more away, making them among the most distant objects in the universe. These distant, enormously bright objects looked almost like stars. Since *quasi* means "something like" in Latin, these objects were given the name quasi-stellar objects, or **quasars.**

What could be so bright at such a great distance from Earth? Astronomers have concluded that quasars are active young galaxies with giant black holes at their centers. Each of these black holes has a mass a billion times or more as great as that of the sun. As enormous amounts of gas revolve around the black hole, the gas heats up and shines brightly.

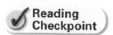 **Reading Checkpoint** What is a quasar?

Side view

Sun's location

Top view

Sun's location

About 100,000 light-years

FIGURE 19
Structure of the Milky Way
From the side, the Milky Way appears to be a narrow disk with a bulge in the middle. The galaxy's spiral structure is visible only from above or below the galaxy.
Interpreting Diagrams *Where in the galaxy is the sun located?*

The Milky Way

Our solar system is located in a spiral galaxy called the Milky Way. As Figure 19 shows, the shape of the Milky Way varies depending on your vantage point. From the side, the Milky Way would look like a narrow disk with a large bulge in the middle. But from the top or bottom, the Milky Way would have a spiral, pinwheel shape. You can't see the spiral shape of the Milky Way from Earth because our solar system is inside the galaxy in one of the spiral arms.

The Milky Way is usually thought of as a standard spiral galaxy. However, some evidence suggests that the Milky Way may be a barred-spiral galaxy instead.

When you see the Milky Way at night during the summer, you are looking toward the center of our galaxy. The center of the galaxy is about 25,000 light-years away, but it is hidden from view by large clouds of dust and gas. However, astronomers can study the center using X-rays, infrared radiation, and radio waves.

 **Reading Checkpoint** How far away is the center of the galaxy?

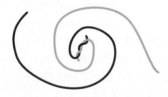

Lab zone Try This Activity

A Spiral Galaxy

You can make a model of our galaxy.

1. Using pipe cleaners, make a pinwheel with two spirals.
2. View the spirals along the surface of the table. Sketch what you see.
3. Next, view the spirals from above the table and sketch them.

Observing The sun is inside a flat spiral galaxy. From Earth's position on the flat surface, is it possible to get a good view of stars in the spiral arms? Why or why not?

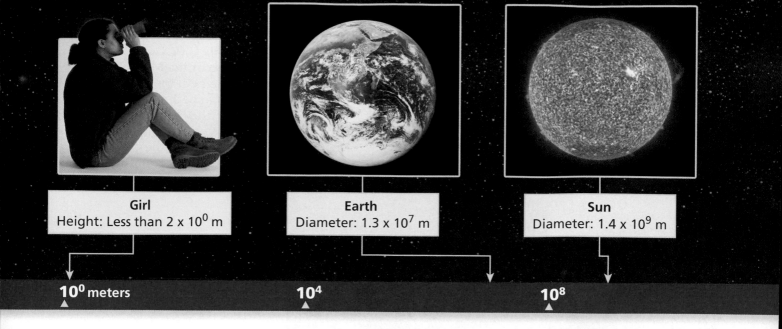

Girl
Height: Less than 2 x 10^0 m

Earth
Diameter: 1.3 x 10^7 m

Sun
Diameter: 1.4 x 10^9 m

10^0 meters

10^4

10^8

The Scale of the Universe

Astronomers define the **universe** as all of space and everything in it. The universe is enormous, almost beyond imagination. Astronomers study objects as close as the moon and as far away as quasars. They study incredibly large objects, such as galaxies that are millions of light-years across. They also study the behavior of tiny particles, such as the atoms within stars. **Since the numbers astronomers use are often very large or very small, they frequently use scientific notation to describe sizes and distances in the universe.**

Scientific Notation **Scientific notation** uses powers of ten to write very large or very small numbers in shorter form. Each number is written as the product of a number between 1 and 10 and a power of 10. For example: 1,200 is written as 1.2×10^3. One light-year is about 9,500,000,000,000,000 meters. Since there are 15 digits after the first digit, in scientific notation this number is written as 9.5×10^{15} meters.

The Immensity of Space The structures in the universe vary greatly in scale. To understand the scale of these structures, imagine that you are going on a journey through the universe. Refer to Figure 20 as you take your imaginary trip. Start at the left with something familiar—a girl looking through binoculars. She is about 1.5 meters tall. Now shift to the right and change the scale by 10,000,000 or 10^7. You're now close to the diameter of Earth, 1.28×10^7 meters. As you move from left to right across Figure 20, the scale increases. The diameter of the sun is about 100 times that of Earth.

Cat's Eye Nebula
Diameter: 3×10^{16} m

Andromeda Galaxy
Diameter: 2×10^{21} m

Virgo Supercluster
Diameter: 9×10^{23} m

10^{16} 10^{20} 10^{24}

Beyond the solar system, the sizes of observable objects become much larger. For example, within our galaxy, the beautiful Cat's Eye Nebula is about 3×10^{16} meters across.

Beyond our galaxy are billions of other galaxies, many of which contain billions of stars. For example, the nearby spiral galaxy Andromeda is about 2×10^{21} meters across. The Milky Way is part of a cluster of 50 or so galaxies called the Local Group. The Local Group is part of the Virgo Supercluster, which contains hundreds of galaxies. The size of the observable universe is about 10^{10} light years, or 10^{26} meters.

FIGURE 20
Scientific Notation
Scientists often use scientific notation to help describe the vast sizes and distances in space.
Calculating *About how many times larger is the Cat's Eye Nebula than Earth?*

Section 4 Assessment

⊙ **Target Reading Skill** Building Vocabulary Use your definitions to help answer the questions.

Reviewing Key Concepts

1. a. **Defining** What is a binary star?
   b. **Classifying** Are all binary stars part of star systems? Explain.
   c. **Applying Concepts** Some binary stars are called eclipsing binaries. Explain why this term is appropriate. (*Hint:* Think about Algol as you write your answer.)
2. a. **Listing** Name the main types of galaxies.
   b. **Classifying** What type of galaxy is the Milky Way?
   c. **Classifying** Suppose astronomers discover a galaxy that contains only old stars. What type of galaxy is it likely to be?

3. a. **Reviewing** What is scientific notation?
   b. **Explaining** How is scientific notation useful to astronomers?
   c. **Calculating** How large is the Cat's Eye Nebula in light-years? (*Hint:* Refer to Figure 20.)

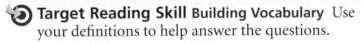

Math Practice

4. **Scientific Notation** The star Betelgeuse has a diameter of 940,000,000 km. Betelgeuse is 427 light-years from Earth. Write each of these figures in scientific notation.

The Expanding Universe

Reading Preview

Key Concepts
- What is the big bang theory?
- How did the solar system form?
- What do astronomers predict about the future of the universe?

Key Terms
- big bang • Hubble's law
- cosmic background radiation
- solar nebula • planetesimal
- dark matter • dark energy

Target Reading Skill
Identifying Supporting Evidence As you read, identify the evidence that supports the big bang theory. Write the evidence in a graphic organizer like the one below.

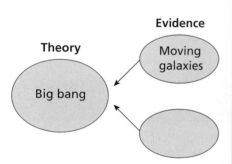

Theory

Big bang

Evidence

Moving galaxies

Discover **Activity**

How Does the Universe Expand?

1. Use a marker to put 10 dots on an empty balloon. The dots represent galaxies.
2. Blow up the balloon. What happens to the distances between galaxies that are close together? Galaxies that are far apart?

Think It Over
Inferring If the universe is expanding, do galaxies that are close together move apart faster or slower than galaxies that are far apart? Explain.

The Andromeda Galaxy is the most distant object that the human eye can see. Light from this galaxy has traveled for about 3 million years before reaching Earth. When that light finally reaches your eye, you are seeing how the galaxy looked 3 million years ago. It is as though you are looking back in time.

Astronomers have photographed galaxies that are billions of light-years away. Light from these galaxies traveled for billions of years before it reached Earth. From these observations, astronomers are able to infer the age of the universe.

How the Universe Formed

Astronomers theorize that the universe began billions of years ago. At that time, the part of the universe we can now see was no larger than the period at the end of this sentence. This tiny universe was incredibly hot and dense. The universe then exploded in what astronomers call the **big bang.**

◀ Nearly every visible object in this image is a distant galaxy.

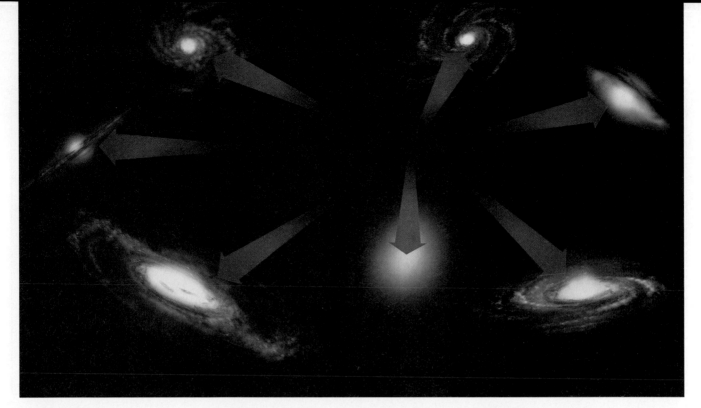

FIGURE 21

Retreating Galaxies
All of the distant galaxies astronomers have observed are moving rapidly away from our galaxy and from each other.

According to the big bang theory, the universe formed in an instant, billions of years ago, in an enormous explosion. Since the big bang, the size of the universe has been increasing rapidly. The universe is billions of times larger now than it was early in its history.

As the universe expanded, it gradually cooled. After a few hundred thousand years, atoms formed. About 200 million years after the big bang, the first stars and galaxies formed.

If the big bang theory is accurate, what evidence might you expect to find in today's universe? You might expect that the matter that had been hurled apart by the big bang would still be moving apart. You might also expect to find evidence of energy left over from the explosion.

Moving Galaxies An American astronomer, Edwin Hubble, discovered important evidence that later helped astronomers to develop the big bang theory. In the 1920s, Hubble studied the spectrums of many galaxies at various distances from Earth. By examining a galaxy's spectrum, Hubble could tell how fast the galaxy is moving and whether it is moving toward our galaxy or away from it.

Hubble discovered that, with the exception of a few nearby galaxies, all galaxies are moving away from us and from each other. Hubble found that there is a relationship between the distance to a galaxy and its speed. **Hubble's law** states that the farther away a galaxy is, the faster it is moving away from us. Hubble's law strongly supports the big bang theory.

Speeding Galaxies

Use the graph to answer the questions below about moving clusters of galaxies.

1. **Reading Graphs** How far away is the Bootes cluster? How fast is it moving?
2. **Reading Graphs** Which galaxy is moving away the fastest? Which galaxy is closest to Earth?
3. **Drawing Conclusions** How are the distance and speed of a galaxy related?
4. **Predicting** Predict the speed of a galaxy that is 80,000 light-years from Earth.

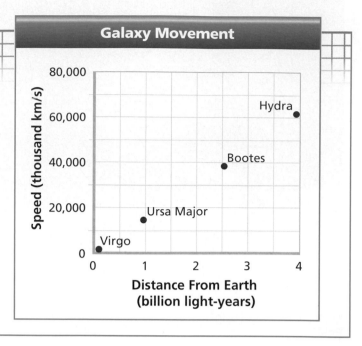

Galaxy Movement

FIGURE 22
Rising Dough
The galaxies in the universe are like the raisins in rising bread dough. **Making Models** *How does rising raisin bread dough resemble the expanding universe?*

To understand how the galaxies are moving, think of raisin bread dough that is rising. If you could shrink yourself to sit on a raisin, you would see all the other raisins moving away from you. The farther a raisin was from you, the faster it would move away, because there would be more bread dough to expand between you and the raisin. No matter which raisin you sat on, all the other raisins would seem to be moving away from you. You could tell that the bread dough was expanding by watching the other raisins.

The universe is like the bread dough. Like the raisins in the dough, the galaxies in the universe are moving away from each other. In the universe, it is space that is expanding, like the dough between the raisins.

Cosmic Background Radiation In 1965, two American physicists, Arno Penzias and Robert Wilson, accidentally detected faint radiation on their radio telescope. This mysterious glow was coming from all directions in space. Scientists later concluded that this glow, now called **cosmic background radiation,** is the leftover thermal energy from the big bang. This energy was distributed in every direction as the universe expanded.

Age of the Universe Since astronomers can measure approximately how fast the universe is expanding now, they can infer how long it has been expanding. Based on careful measurements of how fast distant galaxies are moving away from us and the cosmic background radiation, astronomers estimate that the universe is about 13.7 billion years old.

Formation of the Solar System

After the big bang, matter in the universe separated into galaxies. Gas and dust spread throughout space. Where the solar system is now, there was only cold, dark gas and dust. How did the solar system form? The leading hypothesis is explained below.

The Solar Nebula **About five billion years ago, a giant cloud of gas and dust collapsed to form our solar system.** A large cloud of gas and dust such as the one that formed our solar system is called a **solar nebula.** Slowly, gravity began to pull the solar nebula together. As the solar nebula shrank, it spun faster and faster. The solar nebula flattened, forming a rotating disk. Gravity pulled most of the gas into the center of the disk, where the gas eventually became hot and dense enough for nuclear fusion to begin. The sun was born.

Planetesimals Meanwhile, in the outer parts of the disk, gas and dust formed small asteroid-like bodies called **planetesimals.** These formed the building blocks of the planets. Planetesimals collided and grew larger by sticking together, eventually combining to form the planets.

The Inner Planets When the solar system formed, temperatures were very high. It was so hot close to the sun that most water and other ice-forming materials simply vaporized. Most gases escaped the gravity of the planets that were forming in this region. As a result, the inner planets, Mercury, Venus, Earth, and Mars, are relatively small and rocky.

The Outer Planets In contrast, farther from the sun it was much cooler. As the planets in this region grew, their gravity increased and they were able to capture much of the hydrogen and helium gas in the surrounding space. As a result, the planets Jupiter, Saturn, Uranus, and Neptune became very large. Beyond these gas giants, a huge disk of ice and other substances formed, with a cloud of such substances farther out. This disk and cloud are the main sources of comets. Pluto also formed in this region as part of the icy outer disk.

 **Reading Checkpoint** What is a solar nebula?

A cloud of gas and dust formed a spinning disk.

Gas in the center of the disk collapsed to form the sun.

The remaining gas and dust formed the planets.

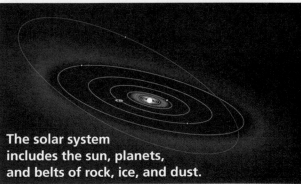
The solar system includes the sun, planets, and belts of rock, ice, and dust.

FIGURE 23
How the Solar System Formed
The solar system formed from a collapsing cloud of gas and dust.

FIGURE 24
Vera Rubin
Astronomer Vera Rubin's observations proved the existence of dark matter.

The Future of the Universe

What will happen to the universe in the future? One possibility is that the universe will continue to expand, as it is doing now. All of the stars will eventually run out of fuel and burn out, and the universe will be cold and dark. Another possibility is that the force of gravity will begin to pull the galaxies back together. The result would be a reverse big bang, or "big crunch." All of the matter in the universe would be crushed into an enormous black hole.

Which of these possibilities is more likely? Recent discoveries have produced a surprising new view of the universe that is still not well understood. **New observations lead many astronomers to conclude that the universe will likely expand forever.**

Dark Matter Until fairly recently, astronomers assumed that the universe consisted solely of the matter they could observe directly. But this idea was disproved by the American astronomer Vera Rubin. Rubin made detailed observations of the rotation of spiral galaxies. She discovered that the matter that astronomers can see, such as stars and nebulas, makes up as little as ten percent of the mass in galaxies. The remaining mass exists in the form of dark matter.

Dark matter is matter that does not give off electromagnetic radiation. Dark matter cannot be seen directly. However, its presence can be inferred by observing the effect of its gravity on visible objects, such as stars, or on light.

Astronomers still don't know much about dark matter—what it is made of or all of the places where it is found. But astronomers estimate that about 23 percent of the universe's mass is made of dark matter.

An Accelerating Expansion In the late 1990s, astronomers observed that the expansion of the universe appears be accelerating. That is, galaxies seem to be moving apart at a faster rate now than in the past. This observation was puzzling, as no known force could account for it. Astronomers infer that a mysterious new force, which they call **dark energy,** is causing the expansion of the universe to accelerate. Current estimates indicate that most of the universe is made of dark energy and dark matter.

Astronomy is one of the oldest sciences, but there are still many discoveries to be made and puzzles to be solved about this universe of ours!

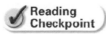 **Reading Checkpoint** What is the effect of dark energy?

FIGURE 25
Dark Matter
Astronomers measured the effect of gravity on light to produce this computer image of how dark matter (in blue) is distributed across a cluster of galaxies.

Section 5 Assessment

Target Reading Skill Identifying Supporting Evidence Refer to your graphic organizer about the big bang theory as you answer Question 1 below.

Reviewing Key Concepts

1. **a. Defining** What was the big bang?
   b. Summarizing When did the big bang occur?
   c. Describing Describe two pieces of evidence that support the big bang theory.
2. **a. Summarizing** How old is the solar system?
   b. Relating Cause and Effect What force caused the solar system to form?
   c. Sequencing Place the following events in the proper order: planets form; planetesimals form; solar nebula shrinks; nuclear fusion begins in the sun.
3. **a. Defining** What is dark matter?
   b. Explaining How do scientists know that dark matter exists?
   c. Predicting What evidence has led scientists to predict that the universe will continue to expand forever?

Lab zone At-Home **Activity**

Stargazing Plan an evening of stargazing with adult family members. Choose a dark, clear night. Use binoculars if available and the star charts in Appendix B to locate the Milky Way and some interesting stars that you have learned about. Explain to your family what you know about the Milky Way and each constellation that you observe.

1 Telescopes

Key Concepts

- The electromagnetic spectrum includes radio waves, infrared radiation, visible light, ultraviolet radiation, X-rays, and gamma rays.
- Telescopes are instruments that collect and focus light and other forms of electromagnetic radiation.
- Many large observatories are located on mountaintops or in space.

Key Terms

- telescope
- visible light
- wavelength
- spectrum
- optical telescope
- electromagnetic radiation
- refracting telescope
- convex lens
- reflecting telescope
- radio telescope
- observatory

2 Characteristics of Stars

Key Concepts

- Characteristics used to classify stars include color, temperature, size, composition, and brightness.
- The brightness of a star depends upon both its size and temperature.
- Astronomers use a unit called the light-year to measure distances between the stars.
- Astronomers often use parallax to measure distances to nearby stars.
- Astronomers use H-R diagrams to classify stars and to understand how stars change over time.

Key Terms

- constellation • spectrograph
- apparent brightness • absolute brightness
- light-year • parallax
- Hertzsprung-Russell diagram
- main sequence

3 Lives of Stars

Key Concepts

- A star is born when the contracting gas and dust from a nebula become so dense and hot that nuclear fusion starts.
- How long a star lives depends on its mass.
- After a star runs out of fuel, it becomes a white dwarf, a neutron star, or a black hole.

Key Terms

- nebula • protostar • white dwarf
- supernova • neutron star • pulsar
- black hole

4 Star Systems and Galaxies

Key Concepts

- Most stars are members of groups of two or more stars called star systems.
- Astronomers classify most galaxies into the following types: spiral, elliptical, and irregular.
- Our solar system is located in a spiral galaxy called the Milky Way.
- Astronomers often use scientific notation to describe sizes and distances in the universe.

Key Terms

- binary star • eclipsing binary • open cluster
- globular cluster • galaxy • spiral galaxy
- elliptical galaxy • irregular galaxy
- quasar • universe • scientific notation

5 The Expanding Universe

Key Concepts

- According to the big bang theory, the universe formed in an instant, billions of years ago, in an enormous explosion.
- About five billion years ago, a giant cloud of gas and dust collapsed to form our solar system.
- New observations lead astronomers to conclude that the universe will likely expand forever.

Key Terms

- big bang • Hubble's law
- cosmic background radiation • solar nebula
- planetesimal • dark matter • dark energy

Review and Assessment

Organizing Information

Concept Mapping Copy the concept map about telescopes onto a separate sheet of paper. Then complete it and add a title. (For more on Concept Mapping, see the Skills Handbook.)

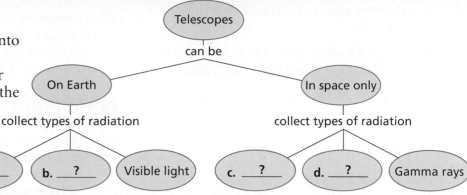

Telescopes — can be — On Earth / In space only
On Earth — collect types of radiation — a. ___?___ , b. ___?___ , Visible light
In space only — collect types of radiation — c. ___?___ , d. ___?___ , Gamma rays

Reviewing Key Terms

Choose the letter of the best answer.

1. Visible light is a form of
   a. spectrum.
   b. electromagnetic radiation.
   c. wavelength.
   d. cosmic background radiation.

2. An H-R diagram is a graph of stars' temperature and
   a. apparent brightness.
   b. main sequence.
   c. absolute brightness.
   d. parallax.

3. A low-mass main sequence star will eventually evolve into a
   a. white dwarf.   **b.** protostar.
   c. black hole.   **d.** nebula.

4. A star system in which one star blocks the light from another is called a(n)
   a. open cluster.
   b. quasar.
   c. binary star.
   d. eclipsing binary.

5. Astronomers theorize that the universe began in an enormous explosion called the
   a. solar nebula.
   b. supernova.
   c. big bang.
   d. big crunch.

If the statement is true, write *true*. If it is false, change the underlined word or words to make the statement true.

6. A <u>reflecting telescope</u> uses convex lenses to gather and focus light.

7. Astronomers use <u>spectrographs</u> to determine the chemical composition of stars.

8. Pulsars are a kind of <u>neutron star</u>.

9. A galaxy shaped like a ball and containing only older stars is most likely a <u>spiral galaxy</u>.

10. <u>Globular clusters</u> are small asteroid-like bodies that formed the building blocks of the planets.

Writing in Science

News Article Imagine that you are a journalist covering current research in astronomy, including stars and black holes. Write an article explaining what black holes are, how they form, and how they can be detected.

Discovery CHANNEL SCHOOL™

Stars, Galaxies, and the Universe
Video Preview
Video Field Trip
▶ Video Assessment

Review and Assessment

Checking Concepts

11. Is a light-year a unit of distance or a unit of time? Explain.

12. Why can't astronomers measure the parallax of a star that is a million light-years away?

13. At what point in the evolution of a star is the star actually born?

14. Where in our galaxy does most star formation take place?

15. What is Hubble's law?

16. How can astronomers detect dark matter if they cannot observe it directly?

Math Practice

17. **Calculating** The bright star Spica is 262 light-years from our solar system. How many kilometers is this?

18. **Scientific Notation** The star Antares is approximately 604 light-years from Earth. Write this distance in scientific notation.

Thinking Critically

19. **Inferring** What advantage might there be to locating a telescope, such as the one shown below, on the moon?

20. **Applying Concepts** Describe a real-world situation involving absolute and apparent brightness. (*Hint:* Think about riding in a car at night.)

21. **Relating Cause and Effect** How does a star's mass affect its lifetime?

22. **Comparing and Contrasting** Compare the conditions that led to the formation of the terrestrial planets with those that led to the formation of the gas giants.

Applying Skills

Use the data in the H-R diagram below to answer Questions 23–26.

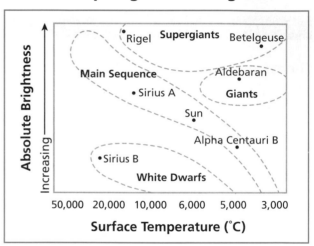

Hertzsprung-Russell Diagram

23. **Interpreting Diagrams** Which star has a greater absolute brightness, Aldebaran or Sirius B?

24. **Interpreting Diagrams** Which stars have higher surface temperatures than Sirius A?

25. **Applying Concepts** Which star is most likely to be red: Rigel, Sirius B, or Betelgeuse?

26. **Comparing and Contrasting** Compare Aldebaran and the sun in terms of size, temperature, and absolute brightness.

Lab zone Chapter Project

Performance Assessment Check the final draft of your constellation story for correct spelling, grammar, punctuation, and usage. Then decide how you will present your story. For example, you could make a poster, read your story aloud, or perform it as a skit or a play.

Ⓞ Standardized Test Practice

Choose the letter of the best answer.

1. The most common chemical element in most stars is
   - **A** oxygen.
   - **B** hydrogen
   - **C** helium.
   - **D** nitrogen.

2. The main factor that affects the evolution of a star is its
   - **A** color.
   - **B** apparent brightness.
   - **C** mass.
   - **D** parallax.

3. The color of a star is related to its temperature. Which of the following color sequences correctly identifies the temperatures of stars in order from hottest to coldest?
   - **A** red, red-orange, yellow, white, blue
   - **B** yellow, white, blue, red, red-orange
   - **C** blue, yellow, red-orange, red, white
   - **D** blue, white, yellow, red-orange, red

The table below gives an estimate of the distribution of stars in the Milky Way galaxy. Use the table and your knowledge of science to answer Questions 4 and 5.

Type of Star	Percentage of Total
Main sequence	90.75%
Red Giant	0.50%
Supergiant	< 0.0001%
White Dwarf	8.75%

4. According to the table, the most common type of stars in the Milky Way is
   - **A** main-sequence stars.
   - **B** red giants.
   - **C** supergiants.
   - **D** white dwarfs.

5. If there are a total of 400 billion stars in the Milky Way, about how many white dwarfs are there in the galaxy?
   - **A** 8.75 billion
   - **B** 35 billion
   - **C** 87.5 billion
   - **D** 3,500 billion

Open-Ended Question

6. Describe the appearance of the Milky Way as you would see it both from Earth and from a point directly above or below the galaxy. Why does the galaxy look different from different vantage points?

Journey to Mars

The six-wheeled rover inched onto the surface of Mars. Scientists on Earth held their breaths. Then, *Spirit* hummed into action.

Spirit was the first star of the 2004 Mars mission. Engineers at the Jet Propulsion Laboratory in Pasadena, California, guided the rover from Earth by remote control. *Spirit* carried a high-tech microscope, cameras, and geologic instruments. Within hours of landing in Gusev Crater, *Spirit* was beaming images of the rocks and red soil back to Earth. Engineers on Earth "drove" *Spirit* to its first target, a large rock that they named "Adirondack."

A major goal of the Mars Exploration Mission was to look for evidence of past liquid water on Mars. Earlier photos of the red planet lead scientists to believe that Gusev Crater was once a dried-up lake bed. The presence of water increases the likelihood that life may have once existed on Mars.

Just three weeks later, another rover called *Opportunity* landed on the opposite side of Mars in a strange, flat landscape. It sent back images of a shallow red crater with bedrock in the distance.

Spirit Rover
The artwork below shows *Spirit* exploring Mars. The image of the Martian landscape at right was taken by *Spirit*.

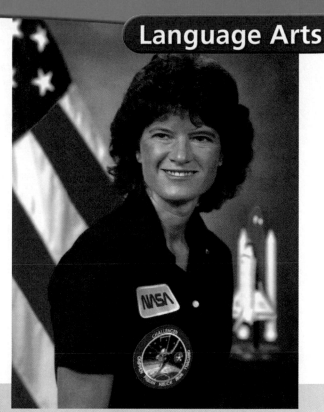

When People Go to Mars

In 1983, Sally Ride became the first American woman in space as a crew member on the space shuttle *Challenger*. Since retiring from NASA in 1987, she has encouraged young people to explore their interests in science, math, and technology. Sally continues to dream of future achievements in space. The following passage is from *The Mystery of Mars*, a book Sally Ride co-wrote with Tam O'Shaughnessy.

Dr. Sally Ride at NASA

When the first astronauts visit Mars, what will they find? Though an astronaut could not survive without a spacesuit, she would feel more at home on Mars than anywhere else in the solar system. She could stand on a rocky surface, scoop up a gloveful of dirt, and explore extinct volcanoes and ancient canyons.

She would need the spacesuit to protect her from the thin Martian air and the extreme cold. The spacesuit would be bulky, but not heavy. Because Mars is smaller than Earth, the pull of gravity on its surface is lower. She and her spacesuit would weigh about one-third what they weighed on Earth.

As the astronaut hiked across the rugged, rocky terrain, her boots would leave deep footprints in the dusty red soil. Fine red dust would cling to her spacesuit. Even on days when the wind was calm, she would look up at a pink sky loaded with red dust. As she headed back to the warmth of her spacecraft at the end of the day, she would look past the silhouettes of crater rims at a dimmer setting sun.

The planet she was exploring would seem strangely familiar. But it would be missing the air and water that make Earth habitable, and the plants and animals that share her home world.

Language Arts Activity

Suppose you are a member of the team that has sent Sally Ride's imaginary astronaut to Mars. What is your job? Did you design the spacesuit or outfit the spacecraft? Were you a scientist or an engineer or a different team member? Write a description of your job. Include as many details as you can.

Mathematics

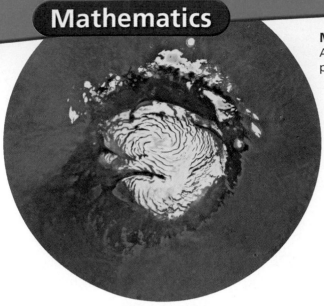

Mars Polar Cap
An ice cap covers the northern polar region of Mars.

Sols of Mars

Mars is the planet most like Earth. But its smaller size, greater distance from the sun, and different orbit cause some immense differences. A Martian day, called a sol, is only about 40 minutes longer than an Earth day. The Martian year, however, is much longer—669 sols.

Mars, like Earth, tilts on its axis, so it has seasons. Each Martian season lasts longer than an Earth season because the Martian year is longer. The shape of Mars's orbit makes the seasons unequal in length (see the table at right).

The climate in the southern hemisphere is more extreme than in the northern hemisphere. Winters in the south are longer and colder, while summers are shorter and warmer. Winter in the south, for instance, lasts 177 sols. In the northern hemisphere, winter lasts only 156 sols.

Seasonal changes affect Mars's north and south poles, which are covered with polar ice caps made of water and carbon dioxide. During winter in the southern hemisphere, the polar cap covers almost half the hemisphere. Here the ice cap is mainly frozen carbon dioxide—like dry ice. In spring, the ice cap partially melts, releasing carbon dioxide into the air. In a similar way, when spring comes in the northern hemisphere, the north polar cap melts. But in the north, the frozen core is made mainly of water ice.

Math Activity

There are 669 sols (Martian days) in a Martian year. Knowing the number of sols in a season, you can figure the percent of the year that is winter. For example, winter in the northern hemisphere is 156 sols ÷ 669 sols ≈ 0.233 ≈ 23%.

Martian Seasons in Sols (Martian Days)		
	Northern Hemisphere	**Southern Hemisphere**
Winter	156	177
Spring	194	142
Summer	177	156
Fall	142	194

Northern Hemisphere   Southern Hemisphere

Northern Hemisphere: 23%, ?, 27%, ?
Southern Hemisphere: 27%, ?, 23%, ?

■ Winter   ■ Spring   ■ Summer   ■ Fall

- Use the table and circle graphs above to figure out what percent of the Martian year in each hemisphere is spring and fall. Round to the nearest hundredth.

- Make two circle graphs like those shown here. Label, color, and write the percent for each season in the northern and southern hemispheres.

- Choose a different color for each.

If you had a choice, which hemisphere would you choose to live in?

Partners in Space

Many engineers and scientists are sure that humans will travel to Mars sometime in the next 20 years. Meanwhile, people have gotten a preview of a space voyage from astronauts and cosmonauts traveling on space shuttles, on *Mir* (Russia's space station), and most recently, aboard the International Space Station.

For years, the United States and the Soviet Union competed in the race to send missions into space. Now the race has become a cooperative effort. On *Mir*, astronauts worked with cosmonauts to solve problems, make repairs, take space walks, and run the ship's computers. Since 2000, cosmonauts and astronauts have lived and worked together on the International Space Station, which is in orbit about 354 kilometers above the surface of Earth.

What's it like for crew members from different backgrounds to live and work together in a cramped spacecraft? Besides having cultural and language differences, Russian and American crews have different training and different equipment. Still, it seems they have learned how to get along. They even celebrated the first-ever space wedding together in August of 2003!

This experience of living and working together and solving problems will be invaluable should we ever send a manned expedition to Mars.

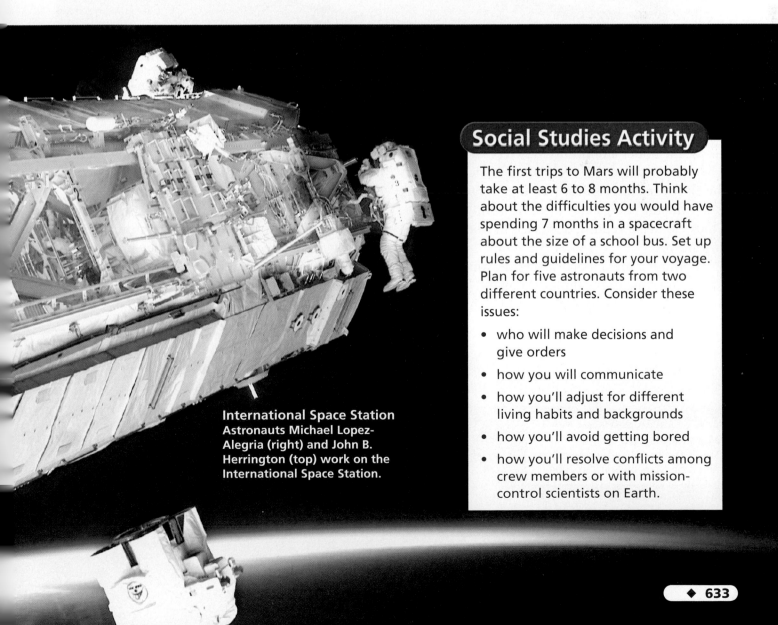

International Space Station
Astronauts Michael Lopez-Alegria (right) and John B. Herrington (top) work on the International Space Station.

Social Studies Activity

The first trips to Mars will probably take at least 6 to 8 months. Think about the difficulties you would have spending 7 months in a spacecraft about the size of a school bus. Set up rules and guidelines for your voyage. Plan for five astronauts from two different countries. Consider these issues:

- who will make decisions and give orders
- how you will communicate
- how you'll adjust for different living habits and backgrounds
- how you'll avoid getting bored
- how you'll resolve conflicts among crew members or with mission-control scientists on Earth.

Future Space Colony
In this painting, an artist imagines a human colony on another planet.

Essentials for Survival

You step out of your spacecraft onto a dusty red landscape under a pinkish-red sky. Now you know why Mars is called the "red planet." Water vapor in the air forms thin clouds, even fog. Because the air is so thin, the sun glares down. It's windy, too. Thick clouds of reddish dust, rich in iron, blow around you.

Without a pressurized spacesuit, you would not survive for long in the thin Martian air. Unlike the thick layers of atmosphere around Earth, this atmosphere gives almost no protection against harmful ultraviolet radiation. You also must carry oxygen. Martian air is about 95 percent carbon dioxide, which humans can't breathe.

Your spacesuit must keep you warm. Even at the Martian equator, daytime temperatures are generally below freezing. At night they plunge as low as −140°C. Walk carefully, too, because Martian gravity is weak. You'll feel only 38 percent of your Earth weight!

Mars Landscape
This is the first 360-degree image taken on Mars by *Spirit* in 2004.

Any human settlement on Mars would have to grow some of its own food. Experiment with a method called hydroponics—growing plants mainly in water, without soil. Set up two plant containers to grow tomatoes or peppers.

- Decide what variables to control.

- In one container, use just water and plant food, with a wire mesh support.

- In the other, add sand or gravel to root plants; add water and plant food.

- Record the rate of growth and strength of each plant over a two-to three-week period.

Which technique worked best? How do you think hydroponics would work on Mars?

Plant Grown in Water

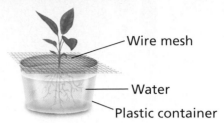

Wire mesh

Water

Plastic container

Plant Grown in Gravel

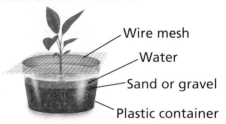

Wire mesh

Water

Sand or gravel

Plastic container

Tie It Together

Plan a Martian Station

At last, you will be going to Mars to set up the first human research station. For an expedition this long, good planning is essential. Review the major problems that Mars presents to humans, such as a thin atmosphere, a lack of oxygen, and extreme temperatures.

Remember that it's too expensive to send most supplies to Mars. Work in groups to make a plan for setting up Earth's research station. Include maps and drawings. As you make your plan, consider questions such as these:

- How will you supply oxygen? Water? Fuel?

- What site will you choose for your settlement? Consider the landscape and climate on Mars.

- What supplies will you bring with you?

- What will you use for building materials?

- What kinds of food will you get? How will you get food?

Rocky Plains of Mars
This painting shows a future scene in which humans walk on Mars.

Chapter

18

Solids, Liquids, and Gases

Academic Standards

This chapter addresses these Indiana standards.

Scientific Thinking

7.2.2 Use formulas to calculate the circumference, area, and volume of various shapes.

7.2.6 Measure length, volume, weight, elapsed time, rates, or temperatures, and choose appropriate units.

7.2.7 Use graphs, diagrams, and symbols in writing to provide evidence for conclusions.

Common Themes

7.7.4 Use equations to show a change over time or in response to changes in other variables.

This Japanese macaque soaks in a hot spring. In and around the spring, water exists as a liquid, solid, and gas.

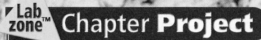

Chapter Project

A Story of Changes in Matter

In this chapter, you will learn how particles of matter change from a solid to a liquid to a gas. As you read this chapter, you will build a model that shows these changes.

Your Goal To create a skit or cartoon that demonstrates how particles of matter behave as they change from a solid to a liquid to a gas and then from a gas to a liquid to a solid

To complete the project, you must

● describe what happens to the particles during each change of state

● outline your skit or cartoon in a storyboard format

● illustrate your cartoon or produce your skit

Plan It! With a group of classmates, brainstorm a list of the properties of solids, liquids, and gases. You'll be working on this project as you study this chapter. When you finish Section 2, describe the particles in solids, liquids, and gases, and begin preparing a storyboard. Add information when you finish Section 3, and complete your cartoon or skit at the end of the chapter. Finally, present your completed skit or cartoon to the class.

States of Matter

Reading Preview

Key Concepts
- What are the characteristics of a solid?
- What are the characteristics of a liquid?
- What are the characteristics of a gas?

Key Terms
- solid • crystalline solid
- amorphous solid • liquid
- fluid • surface tension
- viscosity • gas

Target Reading Skill
Building Vocabulary A definition states the meaning of a word or phrase by telling about its most important feature or function. After you read the section, reread the paragraphs that contain definitions of Key Terms. Use all the information you have learned to write a definition of each Key Term in your own words.

Lab zone **Discover Activity**

What Are Solids, Liquids, and Gases?

1. Break an antacid tablet (fizzing type) into three or four pieces. Place them inside a large, uninflated balloon.
2. Fill a 1-liter plastic bottle about halfway with water. Stretch the mouth of the balloon over the top of the bottle, taking care to keep the tablet pieces inside the balloon.
3. Jiggle the balloon so that the pieces fall into the bottle. Observe what happens for about two minutes.
4. Remove the balloon and examine its contents.

Think It Over
Forming Operational Definitions Identify examples of the different states of matter—solids, liquids, and gases—that you observed in this activity. Define each of the three states in your own words.

It's a bitter cold January afternoon. You are practicing ice hockey moves on a frozen pond. Relaxing later, you close your eyes and recall the pond in July, when you and your friends jumped into the refreshing water on a scorching hot day. Was the water in July made of the same water you skated on this afternoon? Perhaps, but you're absolutely certain that solid water and liquid water do not look or feel the same. Just imagine trying to swim in an ice-covered pond in January or play hockey on liquid water in July!

FIGURE 1
A Wintry Solid
As a solid, water makes a great surface for ice hockey.
Observing *What useful property does the frozen water have here?*

Your everyday world is full of substances that can be classified as solids, liquids, or gases. (You will read about a less familiar form of matter, called plasma, in Chapter 19.) Solids, liquids, and gases may be elements, compounds, or mixtures. Gold is an element. Water is a compound you've seen as both a solid and a liquid. Air is a mixture of gases. Although it's easy to list examples of these three states of matter, defining them is more difficult. To define solids, liquids, and gases, you need to examine their properties. The familiar states of matter are defined not by what they are made of but mainly by whether or not they hold their volume and shape.

Solids

What would happen if you were to pick up a solid object, such as a pen or a comb, and move it from place to place around the room? What would you observe? Would the object ever change in size or shape as you moved it? Would a pen become larger if you put it in a bowl? Would a comb become flatter if you placed it on a table-top? Of course not. A **solid** has a definite shape and a definite volume. If your pen has a cylindrical shape and a volume of 6 cubic centimeters, then it will keep that shape and volume in any position and in any container.

FIGURE 2
Liquid Lava, Solid Rock
Hot, liquid lava flows from a volcano. When it cools to a solid, new rock will be formed.

FIGURE 3
Behavior of Solid Particles
Particles of a solid vibrate back
and forth but stay in place.

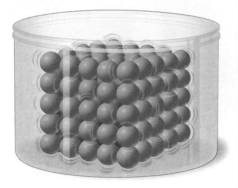

Particles in a Solid The particles that make up a solid are packed very closely together. In addition, each particle is tightly fixed in one position. **This fixed, closely packed arrangement of particles causes a solid to have a definite shape and volume.**

Are the particles in a solid completely motionless? No, not really. The particles vibrate, meaning that they move back and forth slightly. This motion is similar to a group of people running in place. The particles that make up a solid stay in about the same position, but they vibrate in place.

Types of Solids In many solids, the particles form a regular, repeating pattern. These patterns create crystals. Solids that are made up of crystals are called **crystalline solids** (KRIS tuh lin). Salt, sugar, and snow are examples of crystalline solids. When a crystalline solid is heated, it melts at a specific temperature.

In **amorphous solids** (uh MAWR fus), the particles are not arranged in a regular pattern. Plastics, rubber, and glass are amorphous solids. Unlike a crystalline solid, an amorphous solid does not melt at a distinct temperature. Instead, it may become softer and softer or change into other substances.

 **Reading Checkpoint** How do crystalline and amorphous solids differ?

FIGURE 4
Types of Solids
Solids are either crystalline
or amorphous.

◄ Quartz is a crystalline solid. Its particles are arranged in a regular pattern.

◄ Butter is an amorphous solid. Its particles are not arranged in a regular pattern.

Liquids

A **liquid** has a definite volume but no shape of its own. Without a container, a liquid spreads into a wide, shallow puddle. Like a solid, however, a liquid does have a constant volume. If you gently tried to squeeze a water-filled plastic bag, for example, the water might change shape, but its volume would not decrease or increase. Suppose that you have 100 milliliters of milk in a pitcher. If you pour it into a tall glass, you still have 100 milliliters. The milk has the same volume no matter what shape its container has.

Particles in a Liquid In general, the particles in a liquid are packed almost as closely as in a solid. However, the particles in a liquid move around one another freely. You can compare this movement to the way you might move a group of marbles around in your hand. In this comparison, the solid marbles serve as models for the particles of a liquid. The marbles slide around one another but stay in contact. **Because its particles are free to move, a liquid has no definite shape. However, it does have a definite volume.** These freely moving particles allow a liquid to flow from place to place. For this reason, a liquid is also called a **fluid,** meaning "a substance that flows."

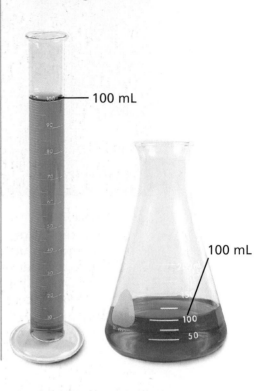

FIGURE 5
Equivalent Volumes
A liquid takes the shape of its container but its volume does not change.

100 mL

100 mL

FIGURE 6
Behavior of Liquid Particles
Particles in a liquid are packed close together but move freely, allowing liquids to flow.
Comparing and Contrasting *How are liquids and solids alike? How do they differ?*

FIGURE 7
Surface Tension
Water beads up on a leaf due to attractions between the water molecules. Surface tension in water is strong enough to support the weight of an insect.

Lab zone Try This **Activity**

As Thick as Honey

You can compare the viscosity of two liquids.

1. Place on a table a clear plastic jar almost filled with honey and another clear plastic jar almost filled with vegetable oil. Make sure that the tops of both jars are tightly closed.

2. Turn the jars upside down at the same time. Observe what happens.

3. Turn the two jars right-side up and again watch what happens.

Drawing Conclusions Which fluid has a greater viscosity? What evidence leads you to this conclusion?

Properties of Liquids One characteristic property of liquids is surface tension. **Surface tension** is the result of an inward pull among the molecules of a liquid that brings the molecules on the surface closer together. Perhaps you have noticed that water forms droplets and can bead up on many surfaces, such as the leaf shown in Figure 7. That's because water molecules attract one another strongly. These attractions cause molecules at the water's surface to be pulled slightly toward the water molecules beneath the surface.

Due to surface tension, the surface of water can act like a sort of skin. For example, a sewing needle floats when you place it gently on the surface of a glass of water, but it quickly sinks if you push it below the surface. Surface tension enables the water strider in Figure 7 to "walk" on the calm surface of a pond.

Another property of liquids is **viscosity** (vis KAHS uh tee)—a liquid's resistance to flowing. A liquid's viscosity depends on the size and shape of its particles and the attractions between the particles. Some liquids flow more easily than others. Liquids with high viscosity flow slowly. Honey is an example of a liquid with a particularly high viscosity. Liquids with low viscosity flow quickly. Water and vinegar have relatively low viscosities.

 **Reading Checkpoint** What property of liquids causes water to form droplets?

Gases

Like a liquid, a gas is a fluid. Unlike a liquid, however, a **gas** can change volume very easily. If you put a gas in a closed container, the gas particles will either spread apart or be squeezed together as they fill that container. Take a deep breath. Your chest expands, and your lungs fill with air. Air is a mixture of gases that acts as one gas. When you breathe in, air moves from your mouth to your windpipe to your lungs. In each place, the air has a different shape. When you breathe out, the changes happen in reverse.

What about the volume of the air? If you could see the particles that make up a gas, you would see them moving in all directions. The particles are no longer limited by the space in your body, so they move throughout the room. **As they move, gas particles spread apart, filling all the space available. Thus, a gas has neither definite shape nor definite volume.** You will read more about the behavior of gases in Section 3.

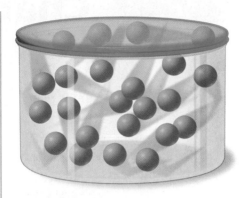

FIGURE 8
Modeling Gas Particles
The particles of a gas can be squeezed into a small volume.
Predicting *What will happen if the container lid is removed?*

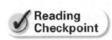 **Reading Checkpoint** How does breathing demonstrate that gases are fluids?

Section 1 Assessment

Target Reading Skill
Building Vocabulary Use your definitions to help answer the questions below.

Reviewing Key Concepts

1. **a. Listing** What are the general characteristics of solids?
   b. Comparing and Contrasting How do crystalline solids differ from amorphous solids?
   c. Drawing Conclusions A glass blower can bend and shape a piece of glass that has been heated. Is glass a crystalline or an amorphous solid? Explain.

2. **a. Describing** How may liquids be described in terms of shape and volume?
   b. Explaining How do the positions and movements of particles in a liquid help to explain the shape and volume of the liquid?
   c. Relating Cause and Effect Explain why a sewing needle can float on the surface of water in a glass.

3. **a. Reviewing** What determines the shape and volume of a gas inside a container?
   b. Applying Concepts Use what you know about the particles in a gas to explain why a gas has no definite shape and no definite volume.

Lab zone **At-Home Activity**

Squeezing Liquids and Gases Show your family how liquids and gases differ. Fill the bulb and cylinder of a turkey baster with water. Seal the end with your finger and hold it over the sink. Have a family member squeeze the bulb. Now empty the turkey baster. Again, seal the end with your finger and have a family member squeeze the bulb. Did the person notice any difference? Use what you know about liquids and gases to explain your observations.

Changes of State

Reading Preview

Key Concepts
- What happens to a substance during changes between solid and liquid?
- What happens to a substance during changes between liquid and gas?
- What happens to a substance during changes between solid and gas?

Key Terms
- melting   • melting point
- freezing   • vaporization
- evaporation   • boiling
- boiling point   • condensation
- sublimation

🎯 Target Reading Skill
Outlining As you read, make an outline about changes of state. Use the red headings for the main ideas and the blue headings for the supporting ideas.

Changes in State
I. Changes Between Solid and Liquid
A. Melting
B.
II. Changes Between Liquid and Gas

Lab zone Discover **Activity**

What Happens When You Breathe on a Mirror?
1. Obtain a hand mirror. Clean it with a dry cloth. Describe the mirror's surface.
2. Hold the mirror about 15 cm away from your face. Try to breathe against the mirror's surface.
3. Reduce the distance until breathing on the mirror produces a visible change. Record what you observe.

Think It Over
Developing Hypotheses What did you observe when you breathed on the mirror held close to your mouth? How can you explain that observation? Why did you get different results when the mirror was at greater distances from your face?

Picture an ice cream cone on a hot summer day. The ice cream quickly starts to drip onto your hand. You're not surprised. You know that ice cream melts if it's not kept cold. But why does the ice cream melt?

Particles of a substance at a warmer temperature have more thermal energy than particles of that same substance at a cooler temperature. Remember from Chapter 8 that thermal energy always flows as heat from a warmer substance to a cooler substance. So, when you take ice cream outside on a hot summer day, it absorbs thermal energy from the air and your hand. The added energy changes the ice cream from a solid to a liquid.

▶ **Increased thermal energy turns an ice cream cone into a gooey mess!**

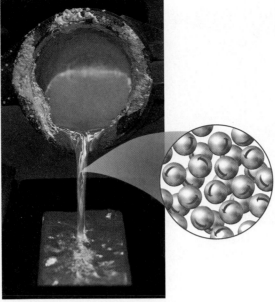

Solid silver

Liquid silver

FIGURE 9
Solid to Liquid
In solid silver, atoms are in a regular, cubic pattern. Atoms in liquid (molten) silver have no regular arrangement.
Applying Concepts *How can a jewelry maker take advantage of changes in the state of silver?*

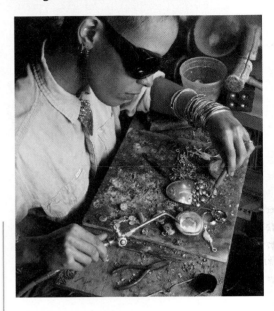

Changes Between Solid and Liquid

How does the physical state of a substance relate to its thermal energy? Particles of a liquid have more thermal energy than particles of the same substance in solid form. As a gas, the particles of this same substance have even more thermal energy. A substance changes state when its thermal energy increases or decreases sufficiently. A change from solid to liquid involves an increase in thermal energy. As you can guess, a change from liquid to solid is just the opposite: It involves a decrease in thermal energy.

Melting The change in state from a solid to a liquid is called **melting.** In most pure substances, melting occurs at a specific temperature, called the **melting point.** Because melting point is a characteristic property of a substance, chemists often compare melting points when trying to identify an unknown material. The melting point of pure water, for example, is 0°C.

What happens to the particles of a substance as it melts? Think of an ice cube taken from the freezer. The energy to melt the ice comes mostly from the air in the room. At first, the added thermal energy makes the water molecules vibrate faster, raising their temperature. **At its melting point, the particles of a solid substance are vibrating so fast that they break free from their fixed positions.** At 0°C, the temperature of the ice stops increasing. Any added energy continues to change the arrangement of the water molecules from ice crystals into liquid water. The ice melts.

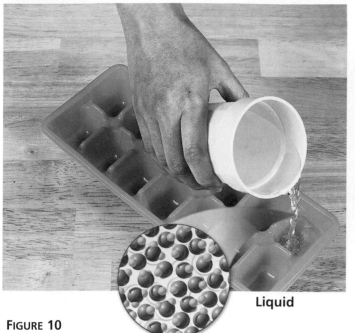

Liquid

Solid

FIGURE 10
Liquid to Solid
Just a few hours in a freezer will change liquid water into a solid.

Lab zone Try This **Activity**

Keeping Cool

1. Wrap the bulbs of two alcohol thermometers with equal amounts of gauze.

2. Lay the thermometers on a paper towel on a table.

3. Use a medicine dropper to put 10 drops of water on the gauze surrounding the bulb of one thermometer.

4. Using rubbing alcohol rather than water, repeat step 3 with the second thermometer.

5. Read the temperatures on the two thermometers for several minutes.

Interpreting Data Which liquid evaporates faster? Explain your answer.

Freezing The change of state from liquid to solid is called **freezing.** It is just the reverse of melting. **At its freezing temperature, the particles of a liquid are moving so slowly that they begin to form regular patterns.**

When you put liquid water into a freezer, for example, the water loses energy to the cold air in the freezer. The water molecules move more and more slowly as they lose energy. Over time, the water becomes solid ice. When water begins to freeze, its temperature remains at 0°C until freezing is complete. The freezing point of water, 0°C, is the same as its melting point.

Reading Checkpoint What happens to the particles of a liquid as they lose more and more energy?

Changes Between Liquid and Gas

Have you ever wondered how clouds form, or why rain falls from clouds? And why do puddles dry up after a rain shower? To answer these questions, you need to look at what happens when changes occur between the liquid and gas states.

The change from a liquid to a gas is called **vaporization** (vay puhr ih ZAY shun). **Vaporization takes place when the particles in a liquid gain enough energy to form a gas.** There are two main types of vaporization—evaporation and boiling.

Evaporation Vaporization that takes place only on the surface of a liquid is called **evaporation** (ee vap uh RAY shun). A shrinking puddle is an example. Water in the puddle gains energy from the ground, the air, or the sun. The added energy enables some of the water molecules on the surface of the puddle to escape into the air, or evaporate.

Boiling Another kind of vaporization is called boiling. **Boiling** occurs when a liquid changes to a gas below its surface as well as at the surface. You see the results of this process when the boiling liquid bubbles. The temperature at which a liquid boils is called its **boiling point.** As with melting points, chemists use boiling points to help identify an unknown substance.

Boiling Point and Air Pressure The boiling point of a substance depends on the pressure of the air above it. The lower the pressure, the less energy needed for the particles of the liquid to escape into the air. In places close to sea level, the boiling point of water is 100°C. In the mountains, however, air pressure is lower and so is water's boiling point. In Denver, Colorado, where the elevation is 1,600 meters above sea level, water boils at 95°C.

FIGURE 11
Evaporation and Boiling
Liquids can vaporize in two ways.
Interpreting Diagrams *How do these processes differ?*

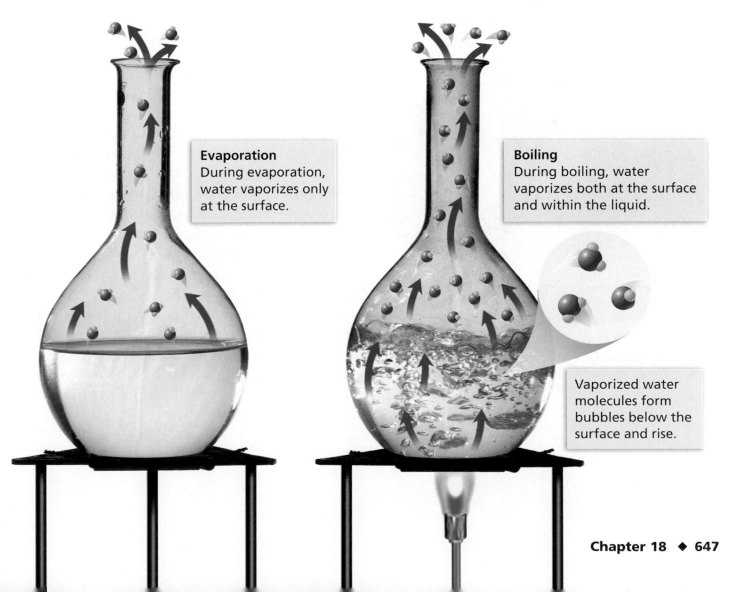

Evaporation
During evaporation, water vaporizes only at the surface.

Boiling
During boiling, water vaporizes both at the surface and within the liquid.

Vaporized water molecules form bubbles below the surface and rise.

Temperature and Changes of State

A beaker of ice at −10°C was slowly heated to 110°C. The changes in the temperature of the water over time were recorded. The data were plotted on the graph shown here.

1. **Reading Graphs** What two variables are plotted on the graph?

2. **Reading Graphs** What is happening to the temperature of the water during segment C of the graph?

3. **Interpreting Data** What does the temperature value for segment B represent? For segment D?

4. **Drawing Conclusions** What change of state is occurring during segment B of the graph? During segment D?

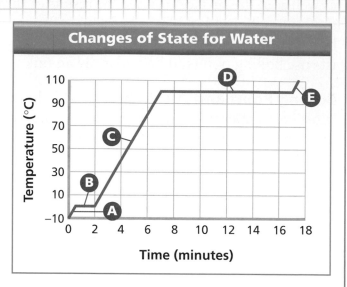

Changes of State for Water

5. **Inferring** In which segment, A or E, do the water molecules have more thermal energy? Explain your reasoning.

FIGURE 12
Condensation of Water
Water vapor from a hot shower contacts the cool surface of a bathroom mirror and condenses into a liquid.

Condensation The opposite of vaporization is called **condensation.** One way you can observe condensation is by breathing onto a mirror. When warm water vapor in your breath reaches the cooler surface of the mirror, the water vapor condenses into liquid droplets. **Condensation occurs when particles in a gas lose enough thermal energy to form a liquid.** For example, clouds typically form when water vapor in the atmosphere condenses into liquid droplets. When the droplets get heavy enough, they fall to the ground as rain.

You cannot see water vapor. Water vapor is a colorless gas that is impossible to see. The steam you see above a kettle of boiling water is not water vapor, and neither are clouds or fog. What you see in those cases are tiny droplets of liquid water suspended in air.

 Reading Checkpoint How do clouds typically form?

Changes Between Solid and Gas

If you live where the winters are cold, you may have noticed that snow seems to disappear even when the temperature stays well below freezing. This change is the result of sublimation. **Sublimation** occurs when the surface particles of a solid gain enough energy that they form a gas. **During sublimation, particles of a solid do not pass through the liquid state as they form a gas.**

One example of sublimation occurs with dry ice. Dry ice is the common name for solid carbon dioxide. At ordinary atmospheric pressures, carbon dioxide cannot exist as a liquid. So instead of melting, solid carbon dioxide changes directly into a gas. As it changes state, the carbon dioxide absorbs thermal energy. This property helps keep materials near dry ice cold and dry. For this reason, using dry ice is a way to keep temperature low when a refrigerator is not available. When dry ice becomes a gas, it cools water vapor in the nearby air. The water vapor then condenses into a liquid, forming fog around the dry ice.

FIGURE 13
Dry Ice
When solid carbon dioxide, called "dry ice," sublimates, it changes directly into a gas. **Predicting** *If you allowed the dry ice to stand at room temperature for several hours, what would be left in the glass dish? Explain.*

 **Reading Checkpoint** **What physical state is skipped during the sublimation of a substance?**

Section 2 Assessment

Target Reading Skill Outlining Use the information in your outline about changes of state to help you answer the questions below.

Reviewing Key Concepts

1. **a. Reviewing** What happens to the particles of a solid as it becomes a liquid?
   b. Applying Concepts How does the thermal energy of solid water change as it melts?
   c. Making Judgments You are stranded in a blizzard. You need water to drink, and you're trying to stay warm. Should you melt snow and then drink it, or just eat snow? Explain.
2. **a. Describing** What is vaporization?
   b. Comparing and Contrasting Name the two types of vaporization. Tell how they are similar and how they differ.
   c. Relating Cause and Effect Why does the evaporation of sweat cool your body on a warm day?

3. **a. Identifying** What process occurs as pieces of dry ice gradually get smaller?
   b. Interpreting Photos What is the fog you see in the air around the dry ice in Figure 13? Why does the fog form?

Writing in Science

Using Analogies Write a short essay in which you create an analogy to describe particle motion. Compare the movements and positions of people dancing with the motions of water molecules in liquid water and in water vapor.

Go Online
PHSchool.com

For: Data Sharing
Visit: PHSchool.com
Web Code: cgd-1022

Melting Ice

Problem

How does the temperature of the surroundings affect the rate at which ice melts?

Skills Focus

predicting, interpreting data, inferring

Materials

- stopwatch or timer
- thermometer or temperature probe
- 2 plastic cups, about 200 mL each
- 2 stirring rods, preferably plastic
- ice cubes, about 2 cm on each side
- warm water, about 40°C–45°C
- water at room temperature, about 20°C–25°C

Procedure

1. Read Steps 1–8. Based on your own experience, predict which ice cube will melt faster.

2. In your notebook, make a data table like the one below.

3. Fill a cup halfway with warm water (about 40°C to 45°C). Fill a second cup to the same depth with water at room temperature.

4. Record the exact temperature of the water in each cup. If you are using a temperature probe, see your teacher for instructions.

5. Obtain two ice cubes that are as close to the same size as possible.

6. Place one ice cube in each cup. Begin timing with a stopwatch. Gently stir each cup with a stirring rod until the ice has completely melted.

7. Observe both ice cubes carefully. At the moment one of the ice cubes is completely melted, record the time and the temperature of the water in the cup.

8. Wait for the second ice cube to melt. Record its melting time and the water temperature.

Analyze and Conclude

1. **Predicting** Was your prediction in Step 1 supported by the results of the experiment? Explain why or why not.

2. **Interpreting Data** In which cup did the water temperature change the most? Explain.

3. **Inferring** When the ice melted, its molecules gained enough energy to overcome the forces holding them together as solid ice. What is the source of that energy?

4. **Communicating** Write a paragraph describing how errors in measurement could have affected your conclusions in this experiment. Tell what you would do differently if you repeated the procedure. (*Hint*: How well were you able to time the exact moment that each ice cube completely melted?)

Design an Experiment

When a lake freezes in winter, only the top turns to ice. Design an experiment to model the melting of a frozen lake during the spring. *Obtain your teacher's permission before carrying out your investigation.* Be prepared to share your results with the class.

Data Table			
Cup	Beginning Temperature (°C)	Time to Melt (s)	Final Temperature (°C)
1			
2			

Reading Preview

Key Concepts
- What types of measurements are useful when working with gases?
- How are the volume, temperature, and pressure of a gas related?

Key Terms
- pressure • Boyle's law
- Charles's law

Target Reading Skill
Asking Questions Before you read, preview the red headings. In a graphic organizer like the one below, ask a *what* or *how* question for each heading. As you read, write the answers to your questions.

Gases

Question	Answer
What measurements are useful in studying gases?	Measurements useful in studying gases include . . .

Before a flight, a hot-air ▶ balloon is filled with air.

Lab zone **Discover Activity**

How Can Air Keep Chalk From Breaking?

1. Stand on a chair and drop a piece of chalk onto a hard floor. Observe what happens to the chalk.

2. Wrap a second piece of chalk in wax paper or plastic food wrap. Drop the chalk from the same height used in Step 1. Observe the results.

3. Wrap a third piece of chalk in plastic bubble wrap. Drop the chalk from the same height used in Step 1. Observe the results.

Think It Over

Inferring Compare the results from Steps 1, 2, and 3. What properties of the air in the bubble wrap accounted for the results in Step 3?

How do you prepare a hot-air balloon for a morning ride? First, you inflate the balloon, using powerful air fans. Then you heat the air inside with propane gas burners. But the balloon and its cargo won't begin to rise until the warmer air inside is less dense than the air outside the balloon. How does this change occur? How can you keep the balloon floating safely through the atmosphere? How can you make it descend when you are ready to land? To answer these and other questions, you would need to understand the relationships between the temperature, pressure, and volume of a gas.

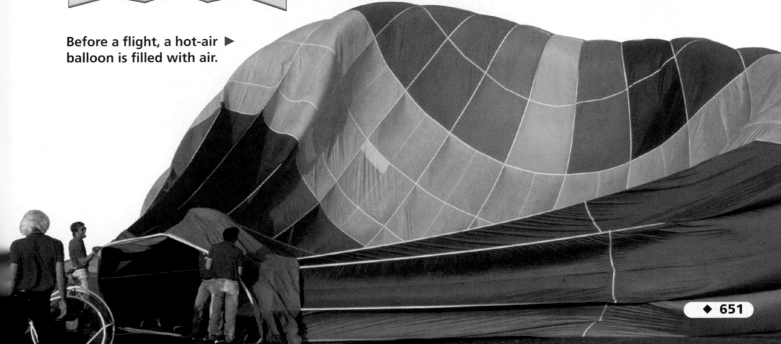

Measuring Gases

How much helium is in the tank in Figure 14? If you don't know the mass of the helium, you may think that measuring the volume of the tank will give you an answer. But gases easily contract or expand. To fill the tank, helium was compressed—or pressed together tightly—to decrease its volume. When you use the helium to fill balloons, it fills a total volume of inflated balloons much greater than the volume of the tank. The actual volume of helium you get, however, depends on the temperature and air pressure that day. **When working with a gas, it is helpful to know its volume, temperature, and pressure.** So what exactly do these measurements mean?

Volume From Chapter 1, you know that volume is the amount of space that matter fills. Volume is measured in cubic centimeters (cm^3), milliliters (mL), liters (L), and other units. Because gas particles move and fill the space available, the volume of a gas is the same as the volume of its container.

Temperature Hot soup, warm hands, cool breezes—you are familiar with matter at different temperatures. But what does temperature tell you? Recall that the particles within any substance are constantly moving. Temperature is a measure of the average energy of random motion of the particles of a substance. The faster the particles are moving, the greater their energy and the higher the temperature. You might think of a thermometer as a speedometer for molecules.

Even at ordinary temperatures, the average speed of particles in a gas is very fast. At room temperature, or about 20°C, the particles in a typical gas travel about 500 meters per second—more than twice the cruising speed of a jet plane!

FIGURE 14
How Much Helium?
A helium tank the height of this girl can fill over 500 balloons!
Interpreting Photos *How is the helium in the tank different from the helium in the balloons?*

Pressure Gas particles constantly collide with one another and with the walls of their container. As a result, the gas pushes on the walls of the container. The **pressure** of the gas is the force of its outward push divided by the area of the walls of the container. Pressure is measured in units of pascals (Pa) or kilopascals (kPa). (1 kPa = 1,000 Pa.)

$$\text{Pressure} = \frac{\text{Force}}{\text{Area}}$$

The firmness of a gas-filled object comes from the pressure of the gas. For example, the air inside a fully pumped basketball has a higher pressure than the air outside. This higher pressure is due to a greater concentration of gas particles inside the ball than in the surrounding air. (Concentration is the number of particles in a given unit of volume.)

When air leaks out of a basketball, the pressure decreases and the ball becomes softer. Why does a ball leak even when it has a tiny hole? The higher pressure inside the ball results in gas particles hitting the inner surface of the ball more often. Therefore, gas particles inside the ball reach the hole and escape more often than gas particles outside the ball reach the hole and enter. Thus, many more particles go out than in. The pressure inside drops until it is equal to the pressure outside.

 **Reading Checkpoint** What units are used to measure pressure?

FIGURE 15
A Change in Pressure
A punctured basketball deflates as the gas particles begin to escape.

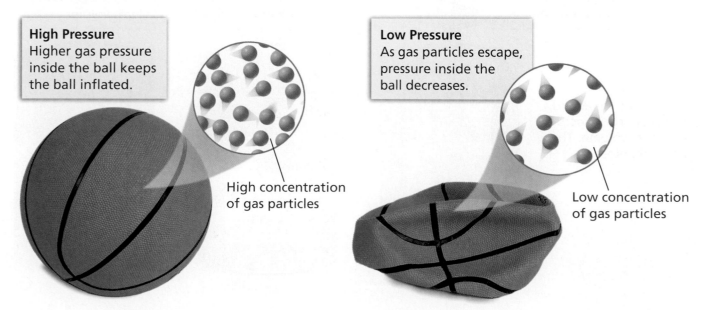

High Pressure
Higher gas pressure inside the ball keeps the ball inflated.

High concentration of gas particles

Low Pressure
As gas particles escape, pressure inside the ball decreases.

Low concentration of gas particles

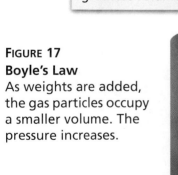

Pressure and Volume

Suppose you are using a bicycle pump. By pressing down on the plunger, you force the gas inside the pump through the rubber tube and out the nozzle into the tire. What will happen if you close the nozzle and then push down on the plunger?

Boyle's Law The answer to this question comes from experiments done by the scientist Robert Boyle in an effort to improve air pumps. In the 1600s, Boyle measured the volumes of gases at different pressures. **Boyle found that when the pressure of a gas at constant temperature is increased, the volume of the gas decreases. When the pressure is decreased, the volume increases.** This relationship between the pressure and the volume of a gas is called **Boyle's law.**

Boyle's Law in Action Boyle's law plays a role in research using high-altitude balloons. Researchers fill the balloons with only a small fraction of the helium gas that the balloons can hold. As a balloon rises through the atmosphere, the air pressure around it decreases and the balloon expands. If the balloon were fully filled at takeoff, it would burst before it got very high.

Boyle's law also applies to situations in which the *volume* of a gas is changed. Then the *pressure* changes in the opposite way. A bicycle pump works this way. As you push on the plunger, the volume of air inside the pump cylinder gets smaller and the pressure increases, forcing air into the tire.

FIGURE 16
Inflating a Tire
A bicycle pump makes use of the relationship between the volume and pressure of a gas.

✓ **Reading Checkpoint** What could cause a helium balloon to burst as it rises in the atmosphere?

FIGURE 17
Boyle's Law
As weights are added, the gas particles occupy a smaller volume. The pressure increases.

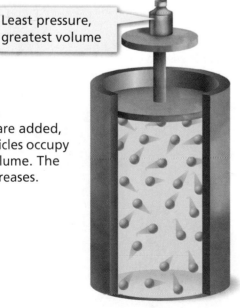

Least pressure, greatest volume

Increasing pressure, decreasing volume

Greatest pressure, least volume

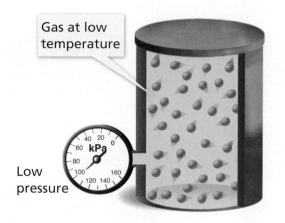
Gas at low temperature

Low pressure

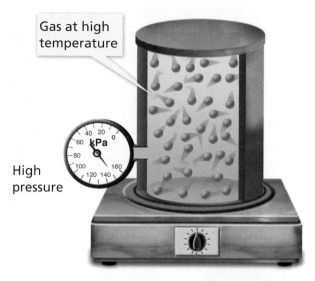
Gas at high temperature

High pressure

FIGURE 18
Gas Pressure and Temperature
When a gas is heated, the particles move faster and collide more with each other and with the walls of their container. The pressure of the gas increases.

Pressure and Temperature

If you dropped a few grains of sand onto your hand, you would hardly feel them. But what if you were caught in a sandstorm? Ouch! The sand grains fly around very fast, and they would sting if they hit you. The faster the grains travel, the harder they hit your skin.

Although gas particles are much smaller than sand grains, a sandstorm is a good model for gas behavior. Like grains of sand in a sandstorm, gas particles travel individually and at high speeds (but randomly). The faster the gas particles move, the more frequently they collide with the walls of their container and the greater the force of the collisions.

Increasing Temperature Raises Pressure Recall from Section 2 that the higher the temperature of a substance, the faster its particles are moving. Now you can state a relationship between temperature and pressure. **When the temperature of a gas at constant volume is increased, the pressure of the gas increases. When the temperature is decreased, the pressure of the gas decreases.** (*Constant volume* means that the gas is in a closed, rigid container.)

Pressure and Temperature in Action Have you ever looked at the tires of an 18-wheel truck? Because the tires need to support a lot of weight, they are large, heavy, and stiff. The inside volume of these tires doesn't vary much. On long trips, especially in the summer, a truck's tires can become very hot. As the temperature increases, so does the pressure of the air inside the tire. If the pressure becomes greater than the tire can hold, the tire will burst. For this reason, truck drivers need to monitor and adjust tire pressure on long trips.

Go **Online**
active art
For: Gas Laws activity
Visit: PHSchool.com
Web Code: cgp-1023

Discovery
CHANNEL
SCHOOL

Solids, Liquids, and Gases

Video Preview
▶ Video Field Trip
Video Assessment

FIGURE 19

Charles's Law

Changing the temperature of a gas at constant pressure changes its volume in a similar way.
Inferring *What happens to the gas particles in the balloon as the gas is warmed?*

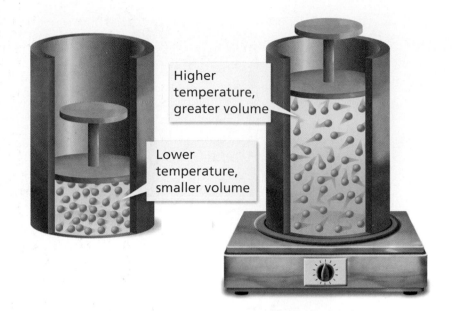

Higher temperature, greater volume

Lower temperature, smaller volume

▲ A gas-filled balloon is at room temperature.

▲ The balloon is lowered into liquid nitrogen at −196°C.

▲ The balloon shrinks as gas volume decreases.

Volume and Temperature

In the late 1700s, French scientist Jacques Charles helped start a new sport. He and others took to the skies in the first hydrogen balloons. Charles's interest in balloon rides led him to discover how gas temperature and volume are related.

Charles's Law Jacques Charles examined the relationship between the temperature and volume of a gas that is kept at a constant pressure. He measured the volume of a gas at various temperatures in a container that could change volume. (A changeable volume allows the pressure to remain constant.) **Charles found that when the temperature of a gas is increased at constant pressure, its volume increases. When the temperature of a gas is decreased at constant pressure, its volume decreases.** This principle is called **Charles's law.**

Charles's Law in Action In Figure 19, you can see the effects of Charles's law demonstrated with a simple party balloon. Time-lapse photos show a balloon as it is slowly lowered into liquid nitrogen at nearly −200°C, then removed. The changes to the balloon's volume result from changes in the temperature of the air inside the balloon. The pressure remains more or less constant because the air is in a flexible container.

▲ When removed from the nitrogen, the gas warms and the balloon expands.

▲ The balloon is at room temperature again.

Now think again about a hot-air balloon. Heating causes the air inside the balloon to expand. Some of the warm air leaves through the bottom opening of the balloon, keeping the pressure constant. But now, the air inside is less dense than the air outside the balloon, so the balloon begins to rise. If the pilot allows the air in the balloon to cool, the reverse happens. The air in the balloon contracts, and more air enters through the opening. The density of the air inside increases, and the balloon starts downward.

Boyle, Charles, and others often described the behavior of gases by focusing on only two factors that vary at a time. In everyday life, however, gases can show the effects of changes in pressure, temperature, and volume all at once. People who work with gases, such as tire manufacturers and balloonists, must consider these combined effects.

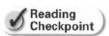 **Reading Checkpoint** **What factor is kept unchanged when demonstrating Charles's law?**

FIGURE 20
Hot-Air Balloon
Balloonists often use a propane burner to heat the air in a balloon.

Section 3 Assessment

Target Reading Skill **Asking Questions** Use the answers to the questions you wrote about the headings to help you answer the questions below.

Reviewing Key Concepts

1. **a. Defining** How is gas pressure defined?
   b. Describing Describe how the motions of gas particles are related to the pressure exerted by the gas.
   c. Relating Cause and Effect Why does pumping more air into a basketball increase the pressure inside the ball?
2. **a. Reviewing** How does Boyle's law describe the relationship between gas pressure and volume?
   b. Explaining Explain why increasing the temperature of a gas in a closed, rigid container causes the pressure in the container to increase.

c. Applying Concepts Suppose it is the night before a big parade, and you are in charge of inflating the parade balloons. You just learned that the temperature will rise 15°C between early morning and the time the parade starts. How will this information affect the way you inflate the balloons?

Math **Practice**

3. **Using Formulas** Suppose the atmosphere exerts a force of 124,500 N on a kitchen table with an area of 1.5m². What is the pressure in pascals of the atmosphere on the table?

Graphing Gas Behavior

Reading Preview

Key Concepts
- What type of relationship does the graph for Charles's law show?
- What type of relationship does the graph for Boyle's law show?

Key Terms
- graph
- origin
- directly proportional
- vary inversely

Target Reading Skill

Previewing Visuals Before you read, preview Figure 23. In a graphic organizer like the one below, write questions that you have about the diagram. As you read, answer your questions.

Graphing Charles's Law

Q.	What is the relationship between gas volume and temperature?
A.	
Q.	

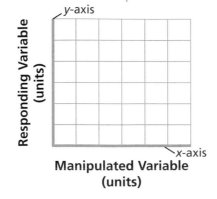

Responding Variable (units)

y-axis

x-axis

Manipulated Variable (units)

FIGURE 21
Making a Graph
The *x*-axis (horizontal) and the *y*-axis (vertical) form the "backbone" of a graph.

Lab zone **Discover Activity**

Can You Graph Gas Behavior?

Temperature (°C)	Pressure (kPa)
0	8
5	11
10	14
15	17
20	20
25	23

1. In an experiment, the temperature of a gas at a constant volume was varied. Gas pressure was measured after each 5°C change. Use the data in this table and follow Steps 2–4 to make a graph.
2. Show temperature on the horizontal axis with a scale from 0°C to 25°C. Show pressure on the vertical axis with a scale from 0 kPa to 25 kPa. (1 kPa = 1,000 Pa.)
3. For each pair of measurements, draw a point on the graph.
4. Draw a line to connect the points.

Think It Over
Drawing Conclusions What happens to the pressure of a gas when the temperature is increased at constant volume?

Graphs are a way to tell a story with data. A **graph** is a diagram that tells how two variables, or factors that change, are related. If you did the activity above, you made a graph that helped you understand how the pressure of a gas changes when its temperature is changed. In this section, you will learn how to make and interpret graphs that relate these and other properties of gases.

A graph consists of a grid set up by two lines, one horizontal and one vertical. Each line, or axis, is divided into equal units. The horizontal axis, or *x*-axis, shows the manipulated variable. The vertical axis, or *y*-axis, shows the responding variable. Each axis is labeled with the name of the variable, the unit of measurement, and a range of values.

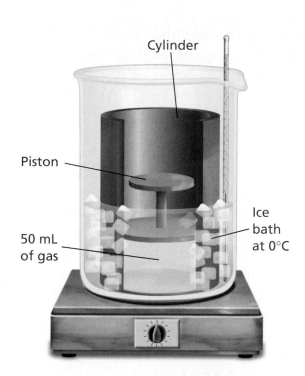

Cylinder

Piston

50 mL
of gas

Ice
bath
at 0°C

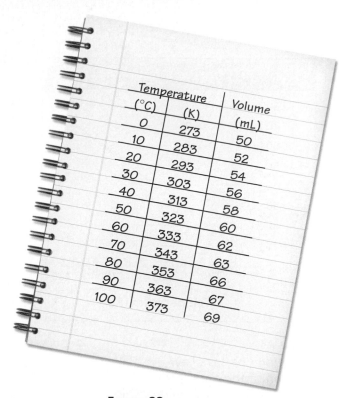

| Temperature | | Volume |
(°C)	(K)	(mL)
0	273	50
10	283	52
20	293	54
30	303	56
40	313	58
50	323	60
60	333	62
70	343	63
80	353	66
90	363	67
100	373	69

FIGURE 22
Temperature and Gas Volume
As the temperature of the water bath increases, the gas inside the cylinder is warmed by the water. The data from the experiment are recorded in the notebook table.
Calculating *How do you convert Celsius degrees to kelvins?*

Temperature and Volume

Recall that Charles's law relates the temperature and volume of a gas that is kept at a constant pressure. You can explore this relationship by doing an experiment in which you change the temperature of a gas and measure its volume. Then you can graph the data you have recorded and interpret the results.

Collecting Data As you can see from the cutaway view in Figure 22, the gas in the experiment is in a cylinder that has a movable piston. The piston moves up and down freely, which allows the gas to change volume and keep the same pressure. To control the temperature of the gas, the cylinder is placed in a water bath.

The experiment begins with an ice-water bath at 0°C and the gas volume at 50 mL. Then the water bath is slowly heated. Gradually, the temperature increases from 0°C to 100°C. Each time the temperature increases by 10°C, the volume of the gas in the cylinder is recorded.

You'll notice a second set of temperatures listed in the table in Figure 22. Scientists often work with gas temperatures in units called kelvins. To convert from Celsius degrees to kelvins (K), add 273. The kelvin temperatures will be used to graph the data.

 **Reading Checkpoint** What units do scientists use to measure gas temperatures?

Go Online

SciLINKS NSTA

For: Links on gases
Visit: www.SciLinks.org
Web Code: scn-1124

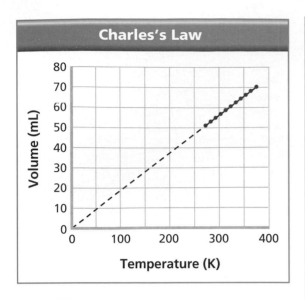

FIGURE 23
Graphing Charles's Law
A graph of the data from Figure 22 shows the relationship known as Charles's law. The dotted line predicts how the graph would look if the gas could be cooled further.

Graphing the Results Look at the graph in Figure 23. It appears as if the line would continue downward if data could be collected for lower temperatures. Such a line would pass through the point (0, 0), called the **origin.** When a graph of two variables is a straight line passing through the origin, the variables are said to be **directly proportional** to each other. **The graph of Charles's law shows that the volume of a gas is directly proportional to its kelvin temperature under constant pressure.**

In reality, the line on the graph cannot be extended as far as the origin. Remember that if a gas is cooled enough, it will condense into a liquid. After that, the volume would no longer change much. However, the line that results from the data represents a relationship that is directly proportional.

Pressure and Volume

A different experiment can show how gas pressure and volume are related when temperature is kept constant. Recall that this relationship is called Boyle's law.

Collecting Data The gas in this experiment is also contained in a cylinder with a movable piston. A gauge indicates the pressure of the gas inside the cylinder. The experiment begins with the volume of the gas at 300 mL. The pressure of the gas is 20 kPa. Next, the piston is pushed into the cylinder, making the gas volume smaller. The pressure of the gas is recorded after each 50-mL change in volume. Temperature remains constant.

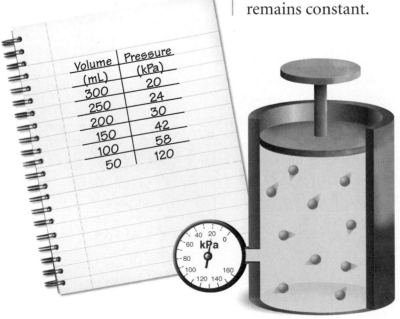

Volume (mL)	Pressure (kPa)
300	20
250	24
200	30
150	42
100	58
50	120

FIGURE 24
Pushing on the top of the piston decreases the volume of the gas. The pressure of the gas increases. The data from the experiment are recorded in the notebook table.
Predicting *What would happen if you pulled up on the piston?*

Graphing the Results In this pressure-volume experiment, the manipulated variable is volume. Volume is shown on the scale of the horizontal axis from 0 mL to 300 mL. The responding variable is pressure. Pressure is shown on the scale of the vertical axis from 0 kPa to 120 kPa.

As you can see in Figure 25, the plotted points lie on a curve. Notice that the curve slopes downward from left to right. Also notice that the curve is steep at lower volumes and becomes less steep as volume increases. When a graph of two variables forms this kind of curve, the variables are said to **vary inversely** with one another. Such a relationship means that when one variable goes up, the other variable goes down in a regular way. **The graph for Boyle's law shows that the pressure of a gas varies inversely with its volume at constant temperature.**

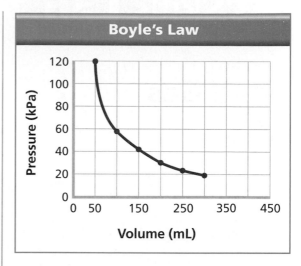

FIGURE 25
This graph of the data from Figure 24 shows the relationship between pressure and volume known as Boyle's law.

 **Reading Checkpoint** What is the manipulated variable in the pressure-volume experiment?

Section 4 Assessment

Target Reading Skill Previewing Visuals Refer to your questions and answers about Figure 23 to help you answer Question 1 below.

Reviewing Key Concepts

1. **a. Classifying** What term describes the relationship illustrated by the graph in Figure 23?
   b. Relating Cause and Effect How does the volume of a gas change when its temperature is increased at constant pressure?
   c. Predicting Suppose the temperature of the gas is increased to 400 kelvins (127°C). Use Figure 23 to predict the volume of the gas at this temperature.
2. **a. Classifying** What is the relationship between the pressure and the volume of a gas?
   b. Estimating Use the graph in Figure 25 to estimate the gas pressure when the gas volume is 125 mL.
   c. Comparing and Contrasting Compare and contrast the Charles's law and Boyle's law graphs. How can you tell the difference between a graph in which one variable is directly proportional to another and a graph in which two variables vary inversely?

Lab zone **At-Home Activity**

Finding Graphs Look for graphs in your newspaper or in magazines. Point out to members of your family which variable is the manipulated variable and which is the responding variable for each graph. Then compare any line graphs you have found to the graphs in this section. Which of your graphs show two variables that are directly proportional to each other? Do any show variables that vary inversely?

It's a Gas

Problem

How does the pressure you exert on a syringe affect the volume of the air inside it?

Skills Focus

graphing, predicting, interpreting data, drawing conclusions

Materials

• strong plastic syringe (with no needle), at least 35-cm^3 capacity
• modeling clay
• 4 books of uniform weight

Procedure

1. Make a data table in your notebook like the one below.

2. Lift the plunger of the syringe as high as it will move without going off scale. The volume inside the syringe will then be as large as possible.

3. Seal the small opening of the syringe with a piece of clay. The seal must be airtight.

4. Hold the syringe upright with the clay end on the table. With the help of a partner, place one book on top of the plunger. Steady the book carefully so it does not fall.

5. With the book positioned on the plunger, read the volume shown by the plunger and record it in your data table.

6. Predict what will happen as more books are placed on top of the plunger.

7. Place another book on top of the first book resting on the plunger. Read the new volume and record it in your data table.

8. One by one, place each of the remaining books on top of the plunger. After you add each book, record the volume of the syringe in your data table.

9. Predict what will happen as books are removed from the plunger one by one.

10. Remove the books one at a time. Record the volume of the syringe in your data table after you remove each book.

Data Table			
Adding Books		Removing Books	
Number of Books	Volume (cm³)	Number of Books	Volume (cm³)
0		4	
1		3	
2		2	
3		1	
4		0	

Analyze and Conclude

1. **Graphing** Make a line graph of the data obtained from Steps 5, 7, and 8. Show volume in cubic centimeters (cm^3) on the vertical axis and number of books on the horizontal axis. Title this Graph 1.

2. **Graphing** Make a second line graph of the data obtained from Step 10. Title this Graph 2.

3. **Predicting** Did the results you obtained support your predictions in Steps 6 and 9? Explain.

4. **Interpreting Data** Compare Graph 2 with Graph 1. How can you explain any differences in the two graphs?

5. **Drawing Conclusions** What does Graph 1 tell you about how the volume of a gas changes with increasing pressure?

6. **Communicating** Write a paragraph explaining how the volume of the gas changed as books were added one by one. Base your explanation on what was happening to the gas particles in the syringe.

Design an Experiment

How could you use ice and warm water to show how the temperature and volume of a gas are related? Design an experiment to test the effect on the volume of a gas when you change its temperature. *Obtain your teacher's permission before carrying out your investigation.*

① States of Matter

Key Concepts

- A fixed, closely packed arrangement of particles causes a solid to have a definite shape and volume.

- Because its particles are free to move, a liquid has no definite shape. However, it does have a definite volume.

- As they move, gas particles spread apart, filling the space available. Thus, a gas has neither definite shape nor definite volume.

Key Terms

solid
crystalline solid
amorphous solid
liquid
fluid
surface tension
viscosity
gas

② Changes of State

Key Concepts

- At its melting point, the particles of a solid substance are vibrating so fast that they break free from their fixed positions.

- At its freezing temperature, the particles of a liquid are moving so slowly that they begin to form regular patterns.

- Vaporization takes place when the particles in a liquid gain enough energy to form a gas.

- Condensation occurs when particles in a gas lose enough thermal energy to form a liquid.

- During sublimation, particles of a solid do not pass through the liquid state as they form a gas.

Key Terms

melting	boiling
melting point	boiling point
freezing	condensation
vaporization	sublimation
evaporation	

③ Gas Behavior

Key Concepts

- When working with a gas, it is helpful to know its volume, temperature, and pressure.

- $\text{Pressure} = \dfrac{\text{Force}}{\text{Area}}$

- Boyle found that when the pressure of a gas at constant temperature is increased, the volume of the gas decreases. When the pressure is decreased, the volume increases.

- When the temperature of a gas at constant volume is increased, the pressure of the gas increases. When the temperature is decreased, the pressure of the gas decreases.

- Charles found that when the temperature of a gas is increased at constant pressure, its volume increases. When the temperature of a gas is decreased at constant pressure, its volume decreases.

Key Terms

pressure
Boyle's law
Charles's law

④ Graphing Gas Behavior

Key Concepts

- A graph of Charles's law shows that the volume of a gas is directly proportional to its kelvin temperature under constant pressure.

- A graph of Boyle's law shows that the pressure of a gas varies inversely with its volume at constant temperature.

Key Terms

graph
origin
directly proportional
vary inversely

Review and Assessment

Go Online
PHSchool.com

For: Self-Assessment
Visit: PHSchool.com
Web Code: cga-1020

Organizing Information

Comparing and Contrasting Copy the graphic organizer about solids, liquids, and gases onto a separate piece of paper. Complete the table and add a title. (For more on Comparing and Contrasting, see the Skills Handbook.)

State of Matter	Shape	Volume	Example (at room temperature)
a. ___?___	Definite	b. ___?___	Diamond
Liquid	c. ___?___	Definite	d. ___?___
Gas	e. ___?___	Not definite	f. ___?___

Reviewing Key Terms

Choose the letter of the best answer.

1. A substance with a definite volume but no definite shape is a(n)
   a. crystalline solid.
   b. liquid.
   c. gas.
   d. amorphous solid.

2. Unlike solids and liquids, a gas will
   a. keep its volume in different containers.
   b. keep its shape in different containers.
   c. expand to fill the space available to it.
   d. have its volume decrease when the temperature rises.

3. The process in which a gas cools and becomes a liquid is called
   a. evaporation.
   b. sublimation.
   c. boiling.
   d. condensation.

4. According to Boyle's law, the volume of a gas increases when its
   a. pressure increases.
   b. pressure decreases.
   c. temperature falls.
   d. temperature rises.

5. The vertical axis of a graph shows the
   a. responding variable.
   b. manipulated variable.
   c. constant factors.
   d. same variable as the *x*-axis.

If the statement is true, write *true*. If it is false, change the underlined word or words to make the statement true.

6. Rubber and glass, which become softer as they are heated, are examples of <u>crystalline solids</u>.

7. When you see steam, fog, or clouds, you are seeing water in the <u>liquid</u> state.

8. A substance changes from a solid to a liquid at its <u>boiling point</u>.

9. The <u>volume</u> of a gas is the force of its outward push divided by the area of the walls of the container.

10. According to <u>Boyle's law</u>, the volume of a gas varies invesley with its pressure.

Writing in Science

Explanation Write an introduction to a safety manual for deep-sea divers who use compressed air (scuba) tanks. Explain what air pressure is and what happens to gas molecules when air is compressed.

Discovery CHANNEL SCHOOL™

Solids, Liquids, and Gases
Video Preview
Video Field Trip
▶ Video Assessment

Review and Assessment

Checking Concepts

11. Describe the motion of particles in a solid.

12. Why are both liquids and gases called fluids?

13. Compare and contrast liquids with high and low viscosities.

14. How is the thermal energy of a substance related to its physical state?

15. Describe four examples of changes in state.

16. What happens to water molecules when water is heated from 90°C to 110°C?

17. What happens to the gas particles when the air in an inflated ball leaks out?

18. How does heating a gas in a rigid container change its pressure?

Math Practice

19. **Using Formulas** A skier exerts a force of 660 N on the snow. The surface area of the skis contacting the snow is about 0.20 m². What is the pressure in Pa of the skier on the snow?

Thinking Critically

20. **Relating Cause and Effect** Explain why placing a dented table-tennis ball in boiling water is one way to remove the dent in the ball. (Assume the ball has no holes.)

21. **Applying Concepts** When you open a solid room air freshener, the solid slowly loses mass and volume. How do you think this happens?

22. **Interpreting Data** Use the table below that shows the volume and pressure of a gas to predict how a graph of the data would look.

Volume (cm³)	Pressure (kPa)
15	222
21	159
31	108
50	6/

Applying Skills

Use the table to answer Questions 23–25.

The data table tells how much mass of a compound dissolves in 100 mL of water as the temperature of the water is increased. Use the data to construct and interpret a graph.

Temperature (°C)	Mass of Compound Dissolved (g)
0	37
10	47
20	56
30	66
40	75

23. **Graphing** Label each axis of your graph with the appropriate variable, units, and range of values. Then plot the data in a line graph.

24. **Interpreting Data** What does the graph show about the effect of temperature on the amount of the compound that will dissolve in water?

25. **Predicting** Assume the amount of the compound dissolved continues to increase as the water is heated. Predict how many grams will dissolve at 50°C.

Lab zone Chapter **Project**

Performance Assessment If you prepared a cartoon, read the captions to the class and discuss the illustrations. If you prepared a skit, perform the skit in front of the class. After you finish your presentation, invite the class to ask questions about your project. Be prepared to share the decisions you made in creating your presentation.

⚓ Standardized Test Practice

Choose the letter of the best answer.

1. A wet towel is hanging on a clothesline in the sun. The towel dries by the process of

   A boiling.   **B** condensation.
   C evaporation.   **D** sublimation.

2. The pressure of a confined gas equals the force pushing on the surface divided by the area of the surface.

$$\text{Pressure} = \frac{\text{Force}}{\text{Area}}$$

   What is the pressure if a force of 1,000 N acts on an area of 5.0 m^2?
   A 200 Pa   **B** 500 Pa
   C 2,000 Pa   **D** 5,000 Pa

3. The graph below shows changes in 1 kg of a solid as energy is added.

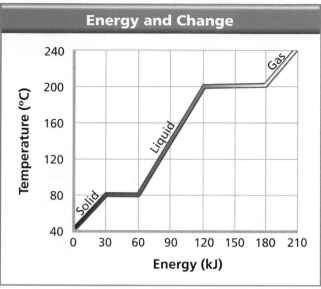

Based on the graph, what is the total amount of energy absorbed by the substance as it changes from a solid at 40°C to a gas?
   A 30 kJ
   B 60 kJ
   C 120 kJ
   D 180 kJ

4. A gas at constant temperature is confined to a cylinder with a movable piston. The piston is slowly pushed into the cylinder, decreasing the volume of the gas. The pressure increases. What are the variables in this experiment?
   A temperature and time
   B time and volume
   C volume and pressure
   D pressure and temperature

Open-Ended Question

5. Spray cans filled with gas usually have a warning printed on their labels that say, "Store in a cool place." Explain the danger in storing the can near a source of heat. Describe the motion of the gas molecules in the can when they gain thermal energy.

 Academic Standards

This chapter addresses these Indiana standards.

The Nature of Science and Technology

7.1.5 Identify important contributions to science, mathematics, and technology by people of different cultures and times.

Common Themes

7.7.2 Use different models to represent the same thing, noting that the model's type and complexity depend on its purpose.

Just as each spice in this Turkish bazaar has its own bin, every element has its own place in the periodic table.

Discovery CHANNEL **SCHOOL**™

Elements and the
Periodic Table
▶ Video Preview
Video Field Trip
Video Assessment

Lab zone™ Chapter **Project**

Survey Properties of Metals

Chemists have a system for organizing the elements. There are more than 100 elements, and as you will learn in this chapter, about 80 of them are classified as metals. In this project, you will examine more closely the physical and chemical properties of metals.

Your Goal To survey the properties of several samples of metallic elements

To complete the project, you must

● interpret what the periodic table tells you about your samples

● design and conduct experiments that will allow you to test at least three properties of your metals

● compare and contrast the properties of your sample metals

● follow the safety guidelines in Appendix A

Plan It! Study the periodic table in Section 2 to determine which elements are metals. Brainstorm with your classmates about the properties of metals. What properties allow you to recognize a metal? How do you think metals differ from nonmetals? Your teacher will assign samples of metals to your group. You will be observing their properties in this project.

Introduction to Atoms

Reading Preview

Key Concepts
- What is the structure of an atom?
- How are elements described in terms of their atoms?
- Why are models useful for understanding atoms?

Key Terms
- nucleus • proton
- neutron • electron
- atomic number • isotope
- mass number • model

Target Reading Skill

Previewing Visuals Before you read, preview Figure 2. Then write two questions you have about the diagram in a graphic organizer like the one below. As you read, answer your questions.

Structure of an Atom

Q.	What particles are in the center of an atom?
A.	
Q.	

Discover Activity

What's in the Box?

1. Your teacher will give you a sealed box that contains an object. Without opening the box, move the box around to find out as much as you can about the object.
2. Make a list of your observations about the object. For example, does the object slide or roll? Is it heavy or light? Is it soft or hard? Is the object round or flat?
3. Think about familiar objects that could give you clues about what's inside the box.

Think It Over
Inferring Make a sketch showing what you think the object looks like. Tell how you inferred the properties of the object from indirect observations.

Glance at the painting below and you see people enjoying an afternoon in the park. Now look closely at the circled detail of the painting. There you'll discover that the artist used thousands of small spots of color to create these images of people and the park.

Are you surprised that such a rich painting can be created from lots of small spots? Matter is like that, too. The properties of matter that you can observe result from the properties of tiny objects that you cannot see. As you learned in Chapter 1, the tiny objects that make up all matter are atoms.

FIGURE 1
Sunday Afternoon on the Island of La Grande Jatte
This painting by artist Georges Seurat, which is made from tiny dots of paint, gives you a simple model for thinking about how matter is made of atoms.

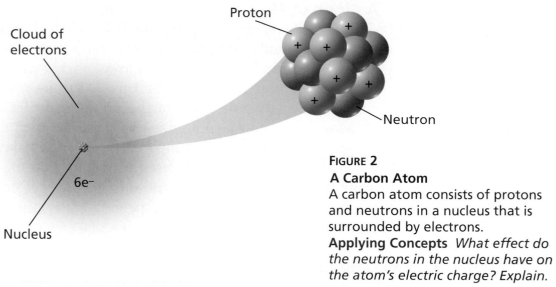

Cloud of electrons

Proton

Nucleus

6e⁻

Neutron

FIGURE 2
A Carbon Atom
A carbon atom consists of protons and neutrons in a nucleus that is surrounded by electrons.
Applying Concepts *What effect do the neutrons in the nucleus have on the atom's electric charge? Explain.*

Structure of an Atom

If you could look into a single atom, what might you see? Figuring out what atoms are made of hasn't been easy. Theories about their shape and structure have changed many times and continue to be improved even now. Until about 100 years ago, scientists thought atoms were the smallest particles of matter. Now, scientists know more. **Atoms are made of even smaller particles called protons, neutrons, and electrons.** Understanding the structure of atoms will help you understand the properties of matter.

Particles in Atoms An atom consists of a nucleus surrounded by one or more electrons. The **nucleus** (NOO klee us) (plural *nuclei*) is the very small center core of an atom. The nucleus is a group of smaller particles called protons and neutrons. **Protons** have a positive electric charge (indicated by a plus symbol, +). **Neutrons** have no charge. They are neutral. The third type of particle in an atom moves in the space outside the nucleus. **Electrons** move rapidly around the nucleus and have a negative electric charge. An electron is shown by the symbol e⁻.

Look at the model of a carbon atom in Figure 2. If you count the number of protons and electrons, you'll see there are six of each. In an atom, the number of protons equals the number of electrons. As a result, the positive charge from the protons equals the negative charge from the electrons. The charges balance, making the atom neutral.

 **Reading Checkpoint** What kind of charge does a proton have?

Go Online
PHSchool.com

For: More on atoms
Visit: PHSchool.com
Web Code: cgd-1031

A Cloud of Electrons Electrons move within a sphere-shaped region surrounding the nucleus. Scientists depict this region as a cloud of negative charge because electrons may be anywhere within it. Electrons with lower energy usually move in the space near the atom's nucleus. Electrons with higher energy move within the space farther from the nucleus.

Most of an atom's volume is the space in which electrons move. That space is huge compared to the space taken up by the nucleus. To picture the difference, imagine holding a pencil while standing at the pitcher's mound in a baseball stadium. If the nucleus were the size of the pencil's eraser, the electrons could be as far away as the top row of seats!

Science and **History**

Models of Atoms

For over two centuries, scientists have created models of atoms in an effort to understand why matter behaves as it does. As scientists have learned more, the model of the atom has changed.

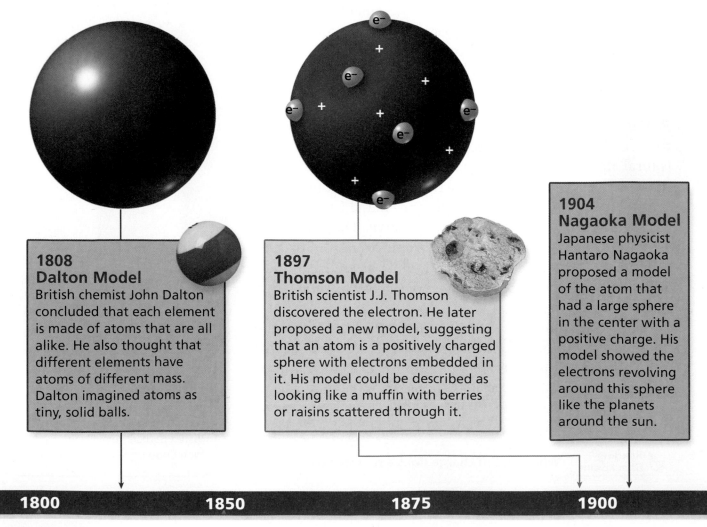

1808
Dalton Model
British chemist John Dalton concluded that each element is made of atoms that are all alike. He also thought that different elements have atoms of different mass. Dalton imagined atoms as tiny, solid balls.

1897
Thomson Model
British scientist J.J. Thomson discovered the electron. He later proposed a new model, suggesting that an atom is a positively charged sphere with electrons embedded in it. His model could be described as looking like a muffin with berries or raisins scattered through it.

1904
Nagaoka Model
Japanese physicist Hantaro Nagaoka proposed a model of the atom that had a large sphere in the center with a positive charge. His model showed the electrons revolving around this sphere like the planets around the sun.

1800   1850   1875   1900

Comparing Particle Masses Although electrons occupy most of an atom's volume, they don't account for much of its mass. It takes almost 2,000 electrons to equal the mass of just one proton. On the other hand, a proton and a neutron are about equal in mass. Together, the protons and neutrons make up nearly all the mass of an atom.

Atoms are too small to be measured in everyday units of mass, such as grams or kilograms. Instead, scientists use units known as atomic mass units (amu). A proton or a neutron has a mass equal to about one amu. The mass of an electron is about 1/2,000 amu.

Writing in Science

Research and Write Find out more about one of the scientists who worked on models of the atom. Write an imaginary interview with this person in which you discuss his work with him.

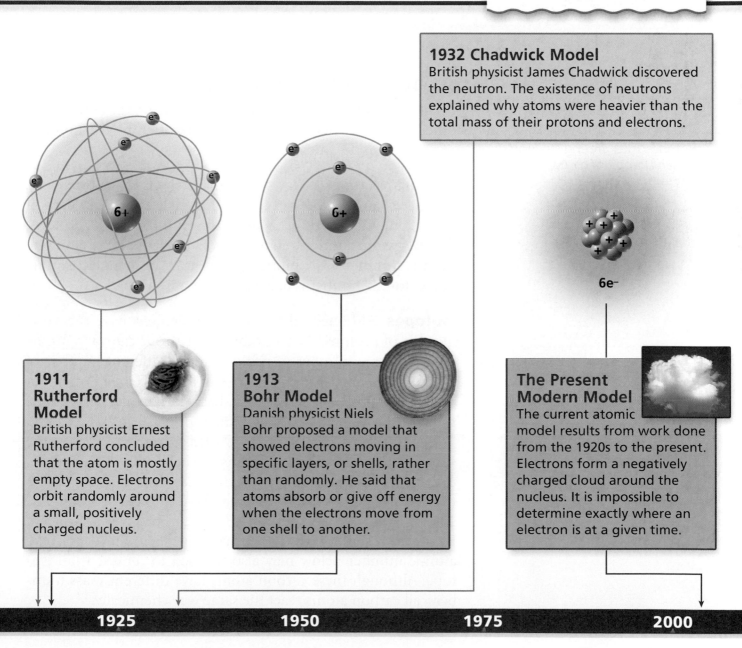

1932 Chadwick Model
British physicist James Chadwick discovered the neutron. The existence of neutrons explained why atoms were heavier than the total mass of their protons and electrons.

1911 Rutherford Model
British physicist Ernest Rutherford concluded that the atom is mostly empty space. Electrons orbit randomly around a small, positively charged nucleus.

1913 Bohr Model
Danish physicist Niels Bohr proposed a model that showed electrons moving in specific layers, or shells, rather than randomly. He said that atoms absorb or give off energy when the electrons move from one shell to another.

The Present Modern Model
The current atomic model results from work done from the 1920s to the present. Electrons form a negatively charged cloud around the nucleus. It is impossible to determine exactly where an electron is at a given time.

1925   1950   1975   2000

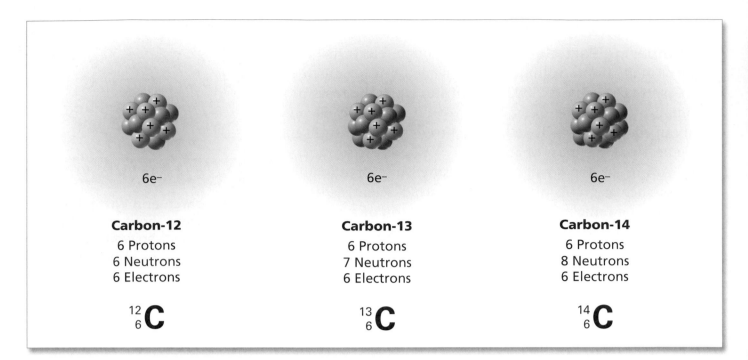

Carbon-12
6 Protons
6 Neutrons
6 Electrons

$${}^{12}_{6}\text{C}$$

6e⁻

Carbon-13
6 Protons
7 Neutrons
6 Electrons

$${}^{13}_{6}\text{C}$$

6e⁻

Carbon-14
6 Protons
8 Neutrons
6 Electrons

$${}^{14}_{6}\text{C}$$

6e⁻

FIGURE 3
Isotopes
Atoms of all isotopes of carbon contain 6 protons, but they differ in their number of neutrons. Carbon-12 is the most common isotope. **Interpreting Diagrams** *Which isotope of carbon has the largest mass number?*

Atoms and Elements

Each element consists of atoms that differ from the atoms of all other elements. **An element can be identified by the number of protons in the nucleus of its atoms.**

Atomic Number Every atom of an element has the same number of protons. For example, the nucleus of every carbon atom contains 6 protons. Every oxygen atom has 8 protons, and every iron atom has 26 protons. Each element has a unique **atomic number**—the number of protons in its nucleus. Carbon's atomic number is 6, oxygen's is 8, and iron's is 26.

Isotopes Although all atoms of an element have the same number of protons, their number of neutrons can vary. Atoms with the same number of protons and a different number of neutrons are called **isotopes** (EYE suh tohps). Three isotopes of carbon are illustrated in Figure 3. Each carbon atom has 6 protons, but you can see that the number of neutrons is 6, 7, or 8.

An isotope is identified by its **mass number,** which is the sum of the protons and neutrons in the nucleus of an atom. The most common isotope of carbon has a mass number of 12 (6 protons + 6 neutrons) and may be written as "carbon-12." Two other isotopes are carbon-13 and carbon-14. As shown in Figure 3, a symbol with the mass number above and the atomic number below may also be used to represent an isotope. Although these carbon atoms have different mass numbers, all carbon atoms react the same way chemically.

Modeling Atoms

Atoms are hard to study because they are amazingly small. The smallest visible speck of dust may contain 10 million billion atoms! Even a sheet of paper is about 10,000 atoms thick. Powerful microscopes can give a glimpse of atoms, such as the one shown in Figure 4. But they do not show the structure of atoms or how they might work.

Because atoms are so small, scientists create models to describe them. In science, a **model** may be a diagram, a mental picture, a mathematical statement, or an object that helps explain ideas about the natural world. Scientists use models to study objects and events that are too small, too large, too slow, too fast, too dangerous, or too far away to see. These models are used to make and test predictions. For example, you may know that engineers use crash-test dummies to test the safety of new car designs. The dummies serve as models for live human beings. In chemistry, models of atoms are used to explain how matter behaves. The modern atomic model explains why most elements react with other elements, while a few elements hardly react at all.

FIGURE 4
Imaging Atoms
This image was made by a scanning tunneling microscope. It shows a zigzag chain of cesium atoms (red) on a background of gallium and arsenic atoms (blue). The colors were added to the image.

 **Reading Checkpoint** What are three types of situations for which models can be useful?

Section 1 Assessment

Target Reading Skill Previewing Visuals Compare your questions and answers about Figure 2 with those of a partner.

Reviewing Key Concepts

1. **a. Reviewing** What are the three main particles in an atom?
   b. Comparing and Contrasting How do the particles of an atom differ in electric charge?
   c. Relating Cause and Effect Why do atoms have no electric charge even though most of their particles have charges?
2. **a. Defining** What is the atomic number of an element?
   b. Explaining How can atomic numbers be used to distinguish one element from another?
   c. Applying Concepts The atomic number of the isotope nitrogen-15 is 7. How many protons, neutrons, and electrons make up an atom of nitrogen-15?

3. **a. Reviewing** What is the main reason that scientists use models to study atoms?
   b. Making Generalizations What kind of information do scientists seek when using models to study atoms?

Lab zone **At-Home Activity**

Modeling Atoms Build a three-dimensional model of an atom to show to your family. The model could be made of beads, cotton, small candies, clay, plastic foam, and other simple materials. Describe how the mass of the nucleus compares to the mass of the electrons. Explain what makes atoms of different elements different from one another. Emphasize that everything in your home is made of atoms in different combinations.

Organizing the Elements

Reading Preview

Key Concepts
- How did Mendeleev discover the pattern that led to the periodic table?
- What data about elements is found in the periodic table?
- How is the organization of the periodic table useful for predicting the properties of elements?

Key Terms
- atomic mass • periodic table
- chemical symbol • period
- group

Target Reading Skill

Asking Questions Before you read, preview the red headings. In a graphic organizer like the one below, ask a *what* or *how* question for each heading. As you read, write the answers to your questions.

Patterns in the Elements

Question	Answer
What pattern of elements did Mendeleev discover?	Patterns appeared when . . .

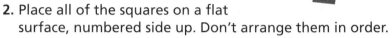

Lab zone Discover **Activity**

Which Is Easier?

1. Make 4 sets of 10 paper squares, using a different color for each set. Number the squares in each set from 1 through 10.
2. Place all of the squares on a flat surface, numbered side up. Don't arrange them in order.
3. Ask your partner to name a square by color and number. Have your partner time how long it takes you to find this square.
4. Repeat Step 3 twice, choosing different squares each time. Calculate the average value of the three times.
5. Rearrange the squares into four rows, one for each color. Order the squares in each row from 1 to 10.
6. Repeat Step 3 three times. Calculate an average time.
7. Trade places with your partner and repeat Steps 2 through 6.

Think It Over
Inferring Which average time was shorter, the one produced in Step 4 or Step 6? Why do you think the times were different?

You wake up, jump out of bed, and start to get dressed for school. Then you ask yourself a question: Is there school today? To find out, you check the calendar. There's no school today because it's Saturday.

The calendar arranges the days of the month into horizontal periods called weeks and vertical groups called days of the week. This arrangement follows a repeating pattern that makes it easy to keep track of which day it is. The chemical elements can also be organized into something like a calendar. The name of the "chemists' calendar" is the periodic table.

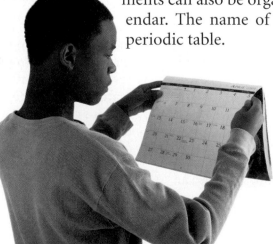

◄ A calendar organizes the days of the week into a useful, repeating pattern.

Patterns in the Elements

By 1869, a total of 63 elements had been discovered. These elements had a wide variety of properties. A few were gases. Two were liquids. Most were solid metals. Some reacted explosively as they formed compounds. Others reacted more slowly. Scientists wondered if the properties of elements followed any sort of pattern. A Russian scientist, Dmitri Mendeleev (men duh LAY ef), discovered a set of patterns that applied to all the elements.

Mendeleev's Work Mendeleev knew that some elements have similar chemical and physical properties. For example, both fluorine and chlorine are gases that irritate the lungs and form similar compounds. Silver and copper, shown in Figure 5, are both shiny metals that tarnish if exposed to air. Mendeleev thought these similarities were important clues to a hidden pattern.

To try to find that pattern, Mendeleev wrote each element's melting point (M.P.), density, and color on individual cards. He also included the element's atomic mass and the number of chemical bonds it could form. The **atomic mass** of an element is the average mass of all the isotopes of that element. Mendeleev tried various arrangements of cards. **He noticed that a pattern of properties appeared when he arranged the elements in order of increasing atomic mass.**

Mendeleev's Periodic Table Mendeleev found that the properties of elements repeated. After fluorine (F), for instance, the next heaviest element he knew was sodium (Na). (Neon had not yet been discovered.) Sodium reacted with water the same way that lithium (Li) and potassium (K) did. So he placed the cards for these elements into a group. He did the same with other similar elements.

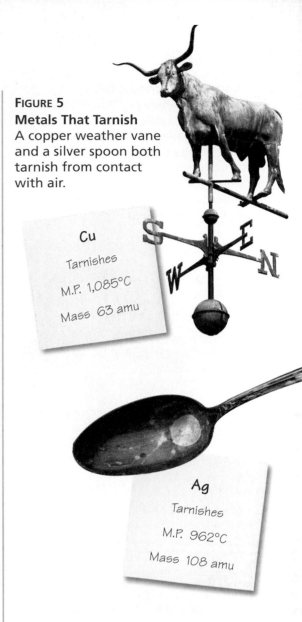

FIGURE 5
Metals That Tarnish
A copper weather vane and a silver spoon both tarnish from contact with air.

Cu
Tarnishes
M.P. 1,085°C
Mass 63 amu

Ag
Tarnishes
M.P. 962°C
Mass 108 amu

FIGURE 6
Metals That React With Water
Lithium and sodium both react with water. **Interpreting Photographs** *Which metal reacts more vigorously with water?*

Na
Reacts with water
M.P. 98°C
Mass 23 amu

Li
Reacts with water
M.P. 180°C
Mass 7 amu

FIGURE 7

Mendeleev's Periodic Table
When Mendeleev published his
first periodic table, he left
question marks in some places.
Based on the properties and
atomic masses of surrounding
elements, he predicted that new
elements with specific properties
would be discovered.

				Ti = 50	Zr = 90	? = 180.
				V = 51	Nb = 94	Ta = 182.
				Cr = 52	Mo = 96	W = 186.
				Mn = 55	Rh = 104,4	Pt = 197,4
				Fe = 56	Ru = 104,4	Ir = 198.
			Ni = Co = 59		Pl = 106₆,	Os = 199.
H = 1			Cu = 63,4		Ag = 108	Hg = 200.
	Be = 9,4	Mg = 24	Zn = 65,2		Cd = 112	
	B = 11	Al = 27,4	? = 68		Ur = 116	Au = 197?
	C = 12	Si = 28	? = 70		Sn = 118	
	N = 14	P = 31	As = 75		Sb = 122	Bi = 210
	O = 16	S = 32	Se = 79,4		Te = 128?	
	F = 19	Cl = 35,5	Br = 80		I = 127	
Li = 7	Na = 23	K = 39	Rb = 85,4		Cs = 133	Tl = 204
		Ca = 40	Sr = 57,6		Ba = 137	Pb = 207.
		? = 45	Ce = 92			
		?Er = 56	La = 94			
		?Yt = 60	Di = 95			
		?In = 75,6	Th = 118?			

Predicting New Elements Mendeleev found that arranging the known elements strictly by increasing atomic mass did not always group similar elements together. So, he moved a few of his element cards into groups where the elements did have similar properties. After arranging all 63 elements, three blank spaces were left. Mendeleev predicted that the blank spaces would be filled by elements that had not yet been discovered. He even predicted the properties of those new elements.

In 1869, Mendeleev published the first periodic table. It looked something like the one shown in Figure 7. Within 16 years, chemists discovered the three missing elements—scandium, gallium, and germanium. Their properties are close to those that Mendeleev had predicted.

The Modern Periodic Table In the **periodic table** used today, the properties of the elements repeat in each period—or row—of the table. (The word *periodic* means "in a regular, repeated pattern.") The periodic table has changed a little since Mendeleev's time. New elements were added as they were discovered. Also, an important change occurred in the early 1900s. In 1913, Henry Moseley, a British scientist, discovered a way to measure the positive charge on an atom's nucleus—in other words, the atomic number. Not long after, the table was rearranged in order of atomic number, not atomic mass. As a result, a few of the elements shifted position, and some of the patterns of properties became more regular. An up-to-date version of the table appears on pages 84 and 85.

Lab zone **Skills Activity**

Classifying

Choose any ten elements and assign them letters from *A* to *J*. On an index card for each element, write the letter for the element and list some of its properties. You may list properties that you learn about in this chapter or properties presented in another reference source.

Exchange cards with a classmate. Can you identify each element? Can you identify elements that have similar properties? Which properties are most helpful in identifying elements?

Finding Data on Elements

The periodic table has one square for each element. **In this book, each square includes the element's atomic number, chemical symbol, name, and atomic mass.**

Atomic Number Look at the periodic table on the next two pages and find the square for iron. That square is reproduced below in Figure 8. The first entry in the square is the number 26, the atomic number of iron. From Section 1, you know that the atomic number tells you that every iron atom has 26 protons in its nucleus. Because it has 26 protons, an iron atom also has 26 electrons.

Chemical Symbols and Names Just below the atomic number are the letters Fe—the **chemical symbol** for iron. Most chemical symbols contain either one or two letters. Often, an element's symbol is an abbreviation of the element's name in English. For example, zinc's symbol is Zn, the symbol for calcium is Ca, and the symbol for silicon is Si. Other elements, especially those that were known in ancient times, have symbols that are abbreviations of their Latin names. For example, the Latin name of sodium is *natrium*, so its symbol is Na. The Latin name of potassium is *kalium*, so its symbol is K. The symbol Au for gold stands for *aurum*. Fe for iron stands for *ferrum*, and Pb for lead stands for *plumbum*.

Average Atomic Mass The last number in the square is the average atomic mass. For iron, this value is 55.847 amu. The atomic mass is an average because most elements consist of a mixture of isotopes. For example, iron is a mixture of four isotopes. About 92 percent of iron atoms are iron-56 (having 30 neutrons). The rest are a mixture of iron-54, iron-57, and iron-58. The average atomic mass of iron is determined from the combined percentages of all its isotopes.

 **Reading Checkpoint** Why is the atomic mass of an element an average?

Atomic number —————— 26

Element symbol —————— **Fe**

Element name —————— Iron

Atomic mass —————— **55.847**

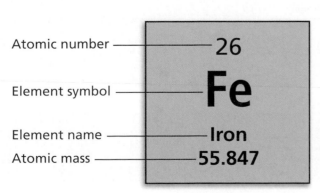

FIGURE 8
Iron
Bok choy is a green, leafy vegetable used in Asian cooking. It is rich in iron.
Interpreting Diagrams *What does atomic number 26 in the square tell you about iron?*

FIGURE 9
Periodic Table of the Elements

The periodic table includes over 100 elements. Many of the properties of an element can be predicted by its position in the table.

For: Periodic Table activity
Visit: PHSchool.com
Web Code: cgp-1032

Key

C	Solid
Br	Liquid
H	Gas
T̶c̶	Not found in nature

Symbol
One- or two-letter symbols identify most elements. Some periodic tables also list the names of the elements.

Period

Group

Period	1	2	3	4	5	6	7	8	9
1	1 **H** Hydrogen 1.0079								
2	3 **Li** Lithium 6.941	4 **Be** Beryllium 9.0122							
3	11 **Na** Sodium 22.990	12 **Mg** Magnesium 24.305							
4	19 **K** Potassium 39.098	20 **Ca** Calcium 40.08	21 **Sc** Scandium 44.956	22 **Ti** Titanium 47.90	23 **V** Vanadium 50.941	24 **Cr** Chromium 51.996	25 **Mn** Manganese 54.938	26 **Fe** Iron 55.847	27 **Co** Cobalt 58.933
5	37 **Rb** Rubidium 85.468	38 **Sr** Strontium 87.62	39 **Y** Yttrium 88.906	40 **Zr** Zirconium 91.22	41 **Nb** Niobium 92.906	42 **Mo** Molybdenum 95.94	43 **Tc** Technetium (98)	44 **Ru** Ruthenium 101.07	45 **Rh** Rhodium 102.91
6	55 **Cs** Cesium 132.91	56 **Ba** Barium 137.33	71 **Lu** Lutetium 174.97	72 **Hf** Hafnium 178.49	73 **Ta** Tantalum 180.95	74 **W** Tungsten 183.85	75 **Re** Rhenium 186.21	76 **Os** Osmium 190.2	77 **Ir** Iridium 192.22
7	87 **Fr** Francium (223)	88 **Ra** Radium (226)	103 **Lr** Lawrencium (262)	104 **Rf** Rutherfordium (261)	105 **Db** Dubnium (262)	106 **Sg** Seaborgium (263)	107 **Bh** Bohrium (264)	108 **Hs** Hassium (265)	109 **Mt** Meitnerium (268)

Lanthanides

57 **La** Lanthanum 138.91	58 **Ce** Cerium 140.12	59 **Pr** Praseodymium 140.91	60 **Nd** Neodymium 144.24	61 **Pm** Promethium (145)	62 **Sm** Samarium 150.4

To make the table easier to read, the lanthanides and the actinides are printed below the rest of the elements. Follow the blue shading to see how they fit in the table.

Actinides

89 **Ac** Actinium (227)	90 **Th** Thorium 232.04	91 **Pa** Protactinium 231.04	92 **U** Uranium 238.03	93 **Np** Neptunium (237)	94 **Pu** Plutonium (244)

Key

- **Metal**
- **Metalloid**
- **Nonmetal**
- **Properties not established**

Atomic Number
The atomic number is the number of protons in an atom's nucleus.

Atomic Mass
Atomic mass is the average mass of an element's atoms. Atomic masses in parentheses are those of the most stable isotope.

Many periodic tables include a zigzag line that separates the metals from the nonmetals.

18

| 2 He Helium 4.0026 |

13

| 5 B Boron 10.81 |

14

| 6 C Carbon 12.011 |

15

| 7 N Nitrogen 14.007 |

16

| 8 O Oxygen 15.999 |

17

| 9 F Fluorine 18.998 |

| 10 Ne Neon 20.179 |

| 13 Al Aluminum 26.982 | 14 Si Silicon 28.086 | 15 P Phosphorus 30.974 | 16 S Sulfur 32.06 | 17 Cl Chlorine 35.453 | 18 Ar Argon 39.948 |

10   **11**   **12**

| 28 Ni Nickel 58.71 | 29 Cu Copper 63.546 | 30 Zn Zinc 65.38 | 31 Ga Gallium 69.72 | 32 Ge Germanium 72.59 | 33 As Arsenic 74.922 | 34 Se Selenium 78.96 | 35 Br Bromine 79.904 | 36 Kr Krypton 83.80 |

| 46 Pd Palladium 106.4 | 47 Ag Silver 107.87 | 48 Cd Cadmium 112.41 | 49 In Indium 114.82 | 50 Sn Tin 118.69 | 51 Sb Antimony 121.75 | 52 Te Tellurium 127.60 | 53 I Iodine 126.90 | 54 Xe Xenon 131.30 |

| 78 Pt Platinum 195.09 | 79 Au Gold 196.97 | 80 Hg Mercury 200.59 | 81 Tl Thallium 204.37 | 82 Pb Lead 207.2 | 83 Bi Bismuth 208.98 | 84 Po Polonium (209) | 85 At Astatine (210) | 86 Rn Radon (222) |

| 110 Ds Darmstadtium (269) | 111 *Uuu Unununium (272) | 112 *Uub Ununbium (277) | | 114 *Uuq Ununquadium | |

*Name not officially assigned

| 63 Eu Europium 151.96 | 64 Gd Gadolinium 157.25 | 65 Tb Terbium 158.93 | 66 Dy Dysprosium 162.50 | 67 Ho Holmium 164.93 | 68 Er Erbium 167.26 | 69 Tm Thulium 168.93 | 70 Yb Ytterbium 173.04 |

| 95 Am Americium (243) | 96 Cm Curium (247) | 97 Bk Berkelium (247) | 98 Cf Californium (251) | 99 Es Einsteinium (252) | 100 Fm Fermium (257) | 101 Md Mendelevium (258) | 102 No Nobelium (259) |

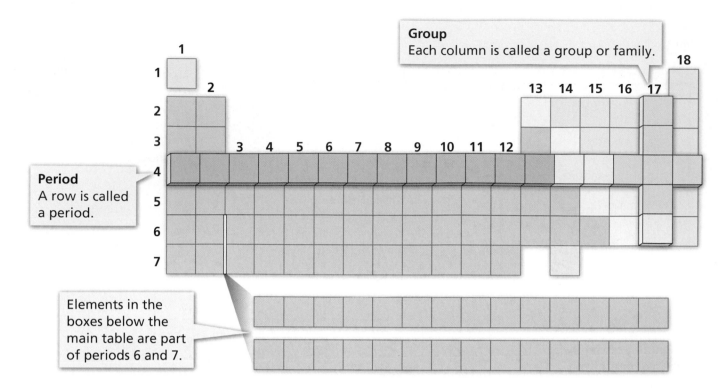

Group
Each column is called a group or family.

Period
A row is called a period.

Elements in the boxes below the main table are part of periods 6 and 7.

FIGURE 10
Periods and Groups
The 18 columns of the periodic table reflect a repeating pattern of properties that generally occur across a period. **Interpreting Tables** *How many periods are in the periodic table?*

Organization of the Periodic Table

Remember that the periodic table is arranged by atomic number. Look over the entire table, starting at the top left with hydrogen (H), which has atomic number 1. Follow the atomic numbers as they increase from left to right, and read across each row.

The properties of an element can be predicted from its location in the periodic table. As you look at elements across a row, the elements' properties change in a predictable way. This predictability is the reason that the periodic table is so useful to chemists.

Periods The table is arranged in horizontal rows called **periods.** A period contains a series of different elements, just as a week on a calendar has a series of seven days. As you move across a period from left to right, properties of the elements change according to a pattern.

As an example, look at the fourth period of the periodic table in Figure 10. The elements on the left of this period are highly reactive metals, such as potassium (K) and calcium (Ca). Elements in the center of the period are relatively unreactive metals, such as nickel (Ni) and copper (Cu). Elements to the right of these include metalloids such as arsenic (As) and the nonmetals selenium (Se) and bromine (Br). The last element in a period is always a very unreactive gas. In this period, that element is krypton (Kr).

Groups The modern periodic table has 7 periods, which form 18 vertical columns. The elements in a column are called a **group**. Groups are also known as families. The groups are numbered, from Group 1 on the left of the table to Group 18 on the right. Group 17 is highlighted in Figure 10. Most groups are named for the first element in the column. Group 14, for example, is the carbon family. Group 15 is the nitrogen family.

Because the pattern of properties of elements repeats in each new period, the elements in each group have similar characteristics. The elements in Group 1 are all metals that react violently with water, while the metals in Group 2 all react with water slowly or not at all. Group 17 elements react violently with elements from Group 1. Group 18 elements rarely react at all.

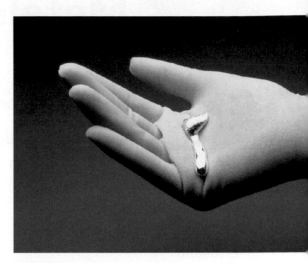

FIGURE 11
Group 13 Element
This sample of gallium metal is an element in Group 13.

 **Reading Checkpoint** **How many groups are in the modern periodic table?**

Section 2 Assessment

Target Reading Skill Asking Questions Use your graphic organizer about the section headings to help you answer the questions below.

Reviewing Key Concepts

1. a. **Reviewing** In what order did Mendeleev arrange the elements in the first periodic table?
   b. **Explaining** What pattern did Mendeleev discover when he arranged the elements?
   c. **Comparing and Contrasting** Describe two differences between Mendeleev's periodic table and the modern periodic table.

2. a. **Identifying** List three kinds of information about an element that can be found in a square of the periodic table.
   b. **Interpreting Tables** What element has 47 protons in its nucleus?
   c. **Making Generalizations** Why aren't the atomic masses of most elements whole numbers?

3. a. **Describing** What does an element's location in the periodic table tell you about that element?
   b. **Predicting** Use the periodic table to name two elements that you would expect to have properties very much like those of calcium.

Writing in Science

Advertisement Write an advertisement that you could use to sell copies of Mendeleev's periodic table to chemists in 1869. Be sure to emphasize the benefits of the table to the chemical profession. Remember, the chemists have never seen such a table.

Metals

Lab zone | Discover Activity

Why Use Aluminum?

1. Examine several objects made from aluminum, including a can, a disposable pie plate, heavy-duty aluminum foil, foil-covered wrapping paper, and aluminum wire.
2. Compare the shape, thickness, and general appearance of the objects.
3. Observe what happens if you try to bend and unbend each object.
4. For what purpose is each object used?

Think It Over

Inferring Use your observations to list as many properties of aluminum as you can. Based on your list of properties, infer why aluminum was used to make each object. Explain your answer.

Metals are all around you. The cars and buses you ride in are made of steel, which is mostly iron. Airplanes are covered in aluminum. A penny is made of zinc coated with copper. Copper wires carry electricity into lamps, stereos, and computers. It's hard to imagine modern life without metals.

Properties of Metals

What is a metal? Take a moment to describe a familiar metal, such as iron, copper, gold, or silver. What words did you use— *hard, shiny, smooth*? Chemists classify an element as a **metal** based on its properties. Look again at the periodic table in Section 2. All of the elements in blue-tinted squares to the left of the zigzag line are metals.

Physical Properties The physical properties of metals include shininess, malleability, ductility, and conductivity. A **malleable** (MAL ee uh bul) material is one that can be hammered or rolled into flat sheets and other shapes. A **ductile** material is one that can be pulled out, or drawn, into a long wire. For example, copper can be made into thin sheets and wire because it is malleable and ductile.

Conductivity is the ability of an object to transfer heat or electricity to another object. Most metals are good conductors. In addition, a few metals are magnetic. For example, iron (Fe), cobalt (Co), and nickel (Ni) are attracted to magnets and can be made into magnets like the one in Figure 12. Most metals are also solids at room temperature. However, one metal—mercury (Hg)—is a liquid at room temperature.

Chemical Properties The ease and speed with which an element combines, or reacts, with other elements and compounds is called its **reactivity.** Metals usually react by losing electrons to other atoms. Some metals are very reactive. For example, you read in Section 2 that sodium (Na) reacts strongly when exposed to air or water. To prevent a reaction, sodium and metals like it must be stored under oil in sealed containers. By comparison, gold (Au) and platinum (Pt) are valued for their *lack* of reactivity and because they are rare.

The reactivities of other metals fall somewhere between those of sodium and gold. Iron, for example, reacts slowly with oxygen in the air, forming iron oxide, or rust. If iron is not protected by paint or plated with another metal, it will slowly turn to reddish-brown rust. The destruction of a metal through this process is called **corrosion.**

 **Reading Checkpoint** **What are three physical properties of metals?**

FIGURE 12
Properties of Metals

Metals have certain physical and chemical properties. **Classifying** *Categorize each of the properties of metals that are shown as either physical or chemical.*

▼ **Malleability**
Gold can be pounded into coins.

Magnetism ▲
Many metals are attracted to magnets.

Reactivity ▶
This iron chain is coated with rust after being exposed to air.

◄ Potassium is highly reactive with air, so it is stored in oil.

Bananas are a good source of potassium in a healthful diet. ▶

▲ The reactions of some compounds containing potassium help get fireworks off the ground.

2
3 **Li** Lithium
11 **Na** Sodium
19 **K** Potassium
37 **Rb** Rubidium
55 **Cs** Cesium
87 **Fr** Francium

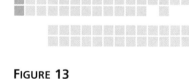

FIGURE 13
Alkali Metals

Potassium is an alkali metal.
Making Generalizations *What characteristics do other Group 1 elements share with potassium?*

Metals in the Periodic Table

The metals in a group, or family, have similar properties, and these family properties change gradually as you move across the table. **The reactivity of metals tends to decrease as you move from left to right across the periodic table.**

Alkali Metals The metals in Group 1, from lithium to francium, are called the **alkali metals.** Alkali metals react with other elements by losing one electron. These metals are so reactive that they are never found as uncombined elements in nature. Instead, they are found only in compounds. In the laboratory, scientists have been able to isolate alkali metals from their compounds. As pure, uncombined elements, some of the alkali metals are shiny and so soft that you can cut them with a plastic knife.

The two most important alkali metals are sodium and potassium. Examples of potassium are shown in Figure 13. Sodium compounds are found in large amounts in seawater and salt beds. Your diet includes foods that contain compounds of sodium and potassium, elements important for life. Another alkali metal, lithium, is used in batteries and some medicines.

Alkaline Earth Metals Group 2 of the periodic table contains the **alkaline earth metals.** Each is fairly hard, gray-white, and a good conductor of electricity. Alkaline earth metals react by losing two electrons. These elements are not as reactive as the metals in Group 1, but they are more reactive than most other metals. Like the Group 1 metals, the Group 2 metals are never found uncombined in nature.

The two most common alkaline earth metals are magnesium and calcium. Mixing magnesium and a small amount of aluminum makes a strong but lightweight material used in ladders, airplane parts, automobile wheels, and other products. Calcium compounds are an essential part of teeth and bones. Calcium also helps muscles work properly. You get calcium compounds from milk and other dairy products, as well as from green, leafy vegetables.

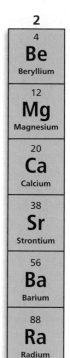

▲ Without calcium, muscles and bones cannot grow and function.

FIGURE 14
Alkaline Earth Metals
Calcium is one of the Group 2 elements.

Math → Analyzing Data

Melting Points in a Group of Elements
The properties of elements within a single group in the periodic table often vary in a certain pattern. The following graph shows the melting points of Group 1 elements (alkali metals) from lithium to francium.

1. **Reading Graphs** As you look at Group 1 from lithium to francium, describe how the melting points of the alkali metals change.

2. **Predicting** If element number 119 were synthesized, it would fall below francium in Group 1 of the periodic table. Predict the approximate melting point of new element 119.

3. **Interpreting Data** Room temperature is usually about 22°C. Human body temperature is 37°C. Which of the alkali metals are liquids at room temperature? Which might melt if you could hold them in your hand?

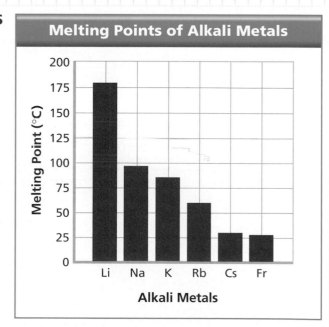

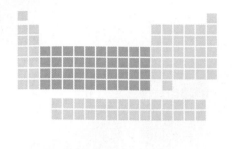

Transition Metals The elements in Groups 3 through 12 are called the **transition metals.** The transition metals include most of the familiar metals, such as iron, copper, nickel, silver, and gold. Most of the transition metals are hard and shiny. All of the transition metals are good conductors of electricity. Many of these metals form colorful compounds.

The transition metals are less reactive than the metals in Groups 1 and 2. This lack of reactivity is the reason ancient gold coins and jewelry are as beautiful and detailed today as they were thousands of years ago. Even when iron reacts with air and water, forming rust, it sometimes takes many years to react completely. Some transition metals are important to your health. For example, you would not survive without iron. It forms the core of a large molecule called hemoglobin, which carries oxygen in your bloodstream.

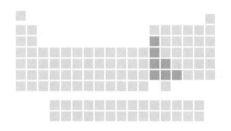

Metals in Mixed Groups Only some of the elements in Groups 13 through 15 of the periodic table are metals. These metals are not nearly as reactive as those on the left side of the table. The most familiar of these metals are aluminum, tin, and lead. Aluminum is the lightweight metal used in beverage cans and airplane bodies. A thin coating of tin protects steel from corrosion in some cans of food. Lead was once used in paints and water pipes. But lead is poisonous, so it is no longer used for these purposes. Now, its most common uses are in automobile batteries and weights for balancing tires.

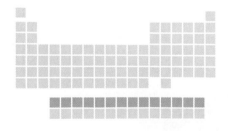

Lanthanides Two rows of elements are placed below the main part of the periodic table. This makes the table more compact. The elements in the top row are called the lanthanides (LAN thuh nydz). Lanthanides are soft, malleable, shiny metals with high conductivity. They are mixed with more common metals to make alloys. An **alloy** is a mixture of a metal with at least one other element, usually another metal. (You will read more about alloys in Chapter 4.) Different lanthanides are usually found together in nature. They are difficult to separate from one another because they all share very similar properties.

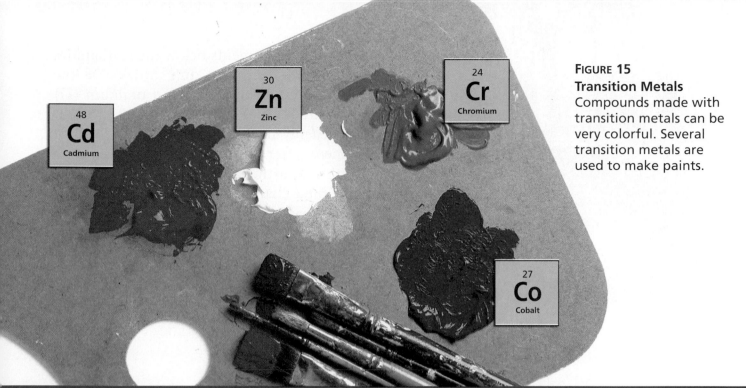

FIGURE 15
Transition Metals
Compounds made with transition metals can be very colorful. Several transition metals are used to make paints.

FIGURE 16
Metals in Groups 13, 14, and 15
Lead can be used in the borders around the glass sections in stained glass objects. Tin can be fashioned into artistic objects, such as picture frames.

FIGURE 17
Lanthanides
Neodymium is used in manufacturing the tiny speakers inside stereo headphones.

Actinides The elements below the lanthanides are called actinides (AK tuh nydz). Of the actinides, only thorium (Th) and uranium (U) occur naturally on Earth. Uranium is used to produce energy in nuclear power plants. All of the elements after uranium in the periodic table were created artificially in laboratories. The nuclei of these elements are very unstable, meaning that they break apart very quickly into smaller nuclei. In fact, many of these elements are so unstable that they last for only a fraction of a second after they are made.

 **Reading Checkpoint** Where are the actinides located in the periodic table?

FIGURE 18

Mars Exploration Rover
Curium, one of the actinide elements, is used as a source of high-energy particles that heat and provide power for certain scientific equipment aboard the Mars Exploration Rover.
Posing Questions *Based on this information, write a question about curium.*

Synthetic Elements

Elements with atomic numbers higher than 92 are sometimes described as synthetic elements because they are not found naturally on Earth. **Instead, elements that follow uranium are made—or synthesized—when nuclear particles are forced to crash into one another.** For example, plutonium is made by bombarding nuclei of uranium-238 with neutrons in a nuclear reactor. Americium-241 (Am-241) is made by bombarding plutonium nuclei with neutrons.

To make even heavier elements (with atomic numbers above 95), scientists use powerful machines called particle accelerators. **Particle accelerators** move atomic nuclei faster and faster until they have reached very high speeds. If these fast-moving nuclei crash into the nuclei of other elements with enough energy, the particles can sometimes combine into a single nucleus. Curium (Cm) was the first synthetic element to be made by colliding nuclei. In 1940, scientists in Chicago synthesized curium by colliding helium nuclei with plutonium nuclei.

In general, the difficulty of synthesizing new elements increases with atomic number. So, new elements have been synthesized only as more powerful particle accelerators have been built. For example, German scientists synthesized element 112 in 1996 by accelerating zinc nuclei and crashing them into lead. Element 112, like other elements with three-letter symbols, has been given a temporary name and symbol. In the future, scientists around the world will agree on permanent names and symbols for these elements.

 **Reading Checkpoint** Which elements are described as synthetic elements and why?

Americium-241 is produced in nuclear reactors. It is widely used in smoke detectors.

FIGURE 19
Synthetic Elements
Synthetic elements are not found naturally on Earth.

The heaviest synthetic elements are synthesized in particle accelerators.

Section 3 Assessment

Target Reading Skill Using Prior Knowledge
Review your graphic organizer about metals and revise it based on what you learned in the section.

Reviewing Key Concepts

1. **a. Defining** What properties of metals do the terms *conductivity* and *ductility* describe?
   b. Classifying Give an example of how the ductility of metal can be useful.
   c. Inferring What property of metals led to the use of plastic or wood handles on many metal cooking utensils? Explain.
2. **a. Identifying** What family of elements in the periodic table contains the most reactive metals?
   b. Applying Concepts What area of the periodic table is the best place to look for a metal that could be used to coat another metal to protect it from corrosion?

   c. Predicting If scientists could produce element 120, what predictions would you make about its reactivity?
3. **a. Describing** Describe the general process by which new elements are synthesized.
   b. Applying Concepts How is plutonium made?

Lab zone At-Home **Activity**

Everyday Metals Make a survey of compounds in your home that contain metals. Look at labels on foods, cooking ingredients, dietary supplements, medicines, and cosmetics. Also look for examples of how metals are used in your home, such as in cookware and wiring. Identify for your family the ways that the properties of metals make them useful in daily life.

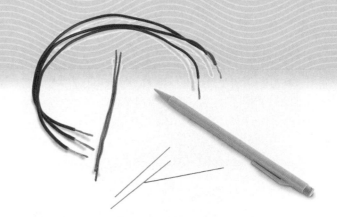

Copper or Carbon? That Is the Question

Problem

Materials scientists work to find the best materials for different products. In this lab, you will look for an answer to the following problem: How do the properties of copper and graphite determine their uses? You will compare the properties of a copper wire and a pencil lead. Pencil lead is made mostly of graphite, a form of the nonmetal element carbon.

Skills Focus

observing, classifying, controlling variables, drawing conclusions

Materials

- 1.5-V dry cell battery
- 250-mL beaker • stopwatch
- flashlight bulb and socket
- 3 lengths of insulated wire
- thin copper wire with no insulation, about 5–6 cm long
- 2 graphite samples (lead from a mechanical pencil), each about 5–6 cm long
- hot plate
- water

Procedure 🐾 💊 🧪

1. Fill a 250-mL beaker about three-fourths full with water. Heat it slowly on a hot plate. Let the water continue to heat as you complete Part 1 and Part 2 of the investigation.

PART 1 Physical Properties

2. Compare the shininess and color of your copper and graphite samples. Record your observations.

3. Bend the copper wire as far as possible. Next, bend one of the graphite samples as far as possible. Record the results of each test.

PART 2 Electrical Conductivity

4. Place a bulb into a lamp socket. Use a piece of insulated wire to connect one pole of a dry cell battery to the socket, as shown in the photo below.

5. Attach the end of a second piece of insulated wire to the other pole of the dry cell battery. Leave the other end of this wire free.

6. Attach the end of a third piece of insulated wire to the other pole of the lamp socket. Leave the other end of this wire free.

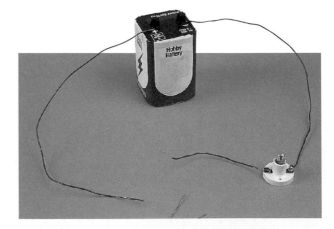

7. Touch the free ends of the insulated wire to the ends of the copper wire. Record your observations of the bulb.

8. Repeat Step 7 using a graphite sample instead of the copper wire.

PART 3 Heat Conductivity

9. Turn off the hot plate.

10. Hold one end of a graphite sample between the fingertips of one hand. Hold one end of the copper wire between the fingertips of the other hand. **CAUTION:** *Be careful not to touch the beaker.*

11. Dip both the graphite and copper wire into the hot water at the same time. Allow only about 1 cm of each piece to reach under the water's surface. From your fingertips to the water, the lengths of both the graphite sample and copper wire should be approximately equal.

12. Time how long it takes to feel the heat in the fingertips of each hand. Record your observations.

Analyze and Conclude

1. **Observing** Compare the physical properties of copper and graphite that you observed.

2. **Classifying** Based on the observations you made in this lab, explain why copper is classified as a metal.

3. **Controlling Variables** In Step 11, why was it important to use equal lengths of copper wire and graphite?

4. **Drawing Conclusions** Which of the two materials, graphite or copper, would work better to cover the handle of a frying pan? Explain your choice.

5. **Communicating** Write a paragraph explaining why copper is better than graphite for electrical wiring. Include supporting evidence from your observations in this lab.

More to Explore

Research other uses of copper in the home and in industry. For each use, list the physical properties that make the material a good choice.

Nonmetals and Metalloids

Reading Preview

Key Concepts
- What are the properties of nonmetals?
- How are the metalloids useful?

Key Terms
- nonmetal
- diatomic molecule • halogen
- noble gas • metalloid
- semiconductor

Target Reading Skill
Using Prior Knowledge Before you read, write what you know about the properties of nonmetals and metalloids in a graphic organizer like the one below. As you read, write what you learn.

What You Know
1. Nonmetals are not shiny.
2.

What You Learned
1.
2.

What Are the Properties of Charcoal?

1. Break off a piece of charcoal and roll it between your fingers. Record your observations.
2. Rub the charcoal on a piece of paper. Describe what happens.
3. Strike the charcoal sharply with the blunt end of a fork. Describe what happens.
4. When you are finished with your investigation, return the charcoal to your teacher and wash your hands.

Think It Over
Classifying Charcoal is a form of the element carbon. Would you classify carbon as a metal or a nonmetal? Use your observations from this activity to explain your answer.

Life on Earth depends on certain nonmetal elements. The air you and other animals breathe contains several nonmetals, including oxygen. And all living organisms are made from compounds of the nonmetal carbon. Yet, while many compounds containing nonmetals are useful to life, some nonmetals by themselves are poisonous and highly reactive. Still other nonmetals are completely unreactive. Compared to metals, nonmetals have a much wider variety of properties. However, nonmetals do have several properties in common.

These bears, the grass behind them, and all life on Earth is based on carbon, a nonmetal. ▶

FIGURE 20
**Physical Properties
of Nonmetals**
Nonmetals have properties
that are the opposite of metals.
Comparing and Contrasting
*Contrast the properties of these
nonmetals with those of metals.*

▲ The helium filling this
blimp is a gas at room
temperature.

◄ Sulfur crumbles
into a powder.

Nonmetals are good
insulators. Carbon
compounds are found
in the plastic insulating
these copper wires. ▶

Properties of Nonmetals

A **nonmetal** is an element that lacks most of the properties of a
metal. **Most nonmetals are poor conductors of electricity and
heat and are reactive with other elements. Solid nonmetals
are dull and brittle.** Look at the periodic table in Section 2. All
of the elements in green-tinted boxes are nonmetals. Many of
the nonmetals are common elements on Earth.

Physical Properties Ten of the 16 nonmetals are gases at
room temperature. The air you breathe is mostly a mixture of
two nonmetals, nitrogen (N) and oxygen (O). Other nonmetal
elements, such as carbon (C), iodine (I), and sulfur (S), are solids at room temperature. Bromine (Br) is the only nonmetal
that is liquid at room temperature.

Look at examples of nonmetals in Figure 20. In general, the
physical properties of nonmetals are the opposite of those of the
metals. Solid nonmetals are dull, meaning not shiny, and brittle, meaning not malleable or ductile. If you hit most solid nonmetals with a hammer, they break or crumble into a powder.
Nonmetals usually have lower densities than metals. And nonmetals are also poor conductors of heat and electricity.

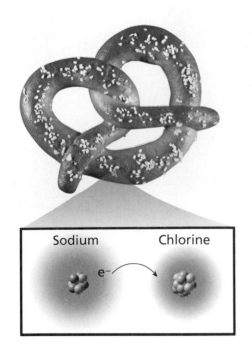

FIGURE 21
Reactions of Nonmetals
The table salt on a pretzel is mined from deposits found on Earth. The same compound can also be formed from a reaction between the metal sodium and the nonmetal chlorine.

14
6 **C** Carbon
14 **Si** Silicon
32 **Ge** Germanium
50 **Sn** Tin
82 **Pb** Lead

Chemical Properties Most nonmetals are reactive, so they readily form compounds. In fact, fluorine (F) is the most reactive element known. Yet, Group 18 elements hardly ever form compounds.

Atoms of nonmetals usually gain or share electrons when they react with other atoms. When nonmetals and metals react, electrons move from the metal atoms to the nonmetal atoms, as shown by the formation of salt, shown in Figure 21. Another example is rust—a compound made of iron and oxygen (Fe_2O_3). It's the reddish, flaky coating you might see on an old piece of steel or an iron nail.

Many nonmetals can also form compounds with other nonmetals. The atoms share electrons and become bonded together into molecules.

✓ **Reading Checkpoint** In which portion of the periodic table do you find nonmetals?

Families of Nonmetals

Look again at the periodic table. Notice that only Group 18 contains elements that are all nonmetals. In Groups 14 through 17, there is a mix of nonmetals and other kinds of elements.

The Carbon Family Each element in the carbon family has atoms that can gain, lose, or share four electrons when reacting with other elements. In Group 14, only carbon is a nonmetal. What makes carbon especially important is its role in the chemistry of life. Compounds made of molecules containing long chains of carbon atoms are found in all living things.

Most of the fuels that are burned to yield energy contain carbon. Coal, for example, is mostly the element carbon. Gasoline is made from crude oil, a mixture of carbon compounds with chains of 5 to 50 or more carbon atoms in their molecules.

FIGURE 22
Carbon
Charcoal is one form of carbon, the only nonmetal in Group 14.

The Nitrogen Family Group 15, the nitrogen family, contains two nonmetals, nitrogen and phosphorus. These nonmetals usually gain or share three electrons when reacting with other elements. To introduce yourself to nitrogen, take a deep breath. The atmosphere is almost 80 percent nitrogen gas (N_2). Nitrogen does not readily react with other elements, so you breathe out as much nitrogen as you breathe in.

Nitrogen is an example of an element that occurs in nature in the form of diatomic molecules, as N_2. A **diatomic molecule** consists of two atoms. In this form, nitrogen is not very reactive. Although living things need nitrogen, most of them are unable to use nitrogen from the air. However, certain kinds of bacteria can use this nitrogen to form compounds. This process is called nitrogen fixation. Plants can then take up these nitrogen compounds formed in the soil by the bacteria. Farmers also add nitrogen compounds to the soil in the form of fertilizers. Like all animals, you get the nitrogen you need from the food you eat—from plants, or from animals that ate plants.

Phosphorus is the other nonmetal in the nitrogen family. Phosphorus is much more reactive than nitrogen, so phosphorus in nature is always found in compounds. A compound containing phosphorus is used to make matches, because it can react with oxygen in the air.

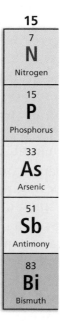

15
7
N
Nitrogen
15
P
Phosphorus
33
As
Arsenic
51
Sb
Antimony
83
Bi
Bismuth

FIGURE 23
The Nitrogen Family
Nitrogen and phosphorus are grouped in the same family of the periodic table, Group 15. **Making Generalizations** *How do atoms of both these elements change when they react?*

▼ Nitrogen is a key ingredient of fertilizers.

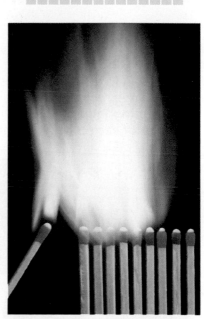

▲ Match heads contain a highly reactive phosphorus compound that ignites easily.

Show Me the Oxygen

How can you test for the presence of oxygen?

1. Pour about a 3-cm depth of hydrogen peroxide (H_2O_2) into a test tube.

2. Add a pea-sized amount of manganese dioxide (MnO_2) to the test tube.

3. Observe the test tube for about 1 minute.

4. When instructed by your teacher, set a wooden splint on fire.

5. Blow the splint out after 5 seconds and immediately plunge the glowing splint into the mouth of the test tube. Avoid getting the splint wet.

Observing Describe the change in matter that occurred in the test tube. What evidence indicates that oxygen was produced?

The Oxygen Family Group 16, the oxygen family, contains three nonmetals—oxygen, sulfur, and selenium. These elements usually gain or share two electrons when reacting with other elements.

You are using oxygen right now. With every breath, oxygen travels into your lungs. There, it is absorbed into your bloodstream, which distributes it all over your body. You could not live without a steady supply of oxygen. Like nitrogen, the oxygen you breathe is a diatomic molecule (O_2). In addition, oxygen sometimes forms a triatomic (three-atom) molecule, which is called ozone (O_3). Ozone collects in a layer in the upper atmosphere, where it screens out harmful radiation from the sun. However, ozone is a dangerous pollutant at ground level because it is highly reactive.

Because oxygen is highly reactive, it can combine with almost every other element. It also is the most abundant element in Earth's crust and the second-most abundant element in the atmosphere. (The first is nitrogen.)

Sulfur is the other common nonmetal in the oxygen family. If you have ever smelled the odor of a rotten egg, then you are already familiar with the smell of some sulfur compounds. Sulfur is used in the manufacture of rubber for rubber bands and automobile tires. Most sulfur is used to make sulfuric acid (H_2SO_4), one of the most important chemicals used in industry.

FIGURE 24

The Oxygen Family

Oxygen and sulfur are the most common of the three nonmetals in Group 16.
Interpreting Tables *What is the atomic number of each Group 16 element?*

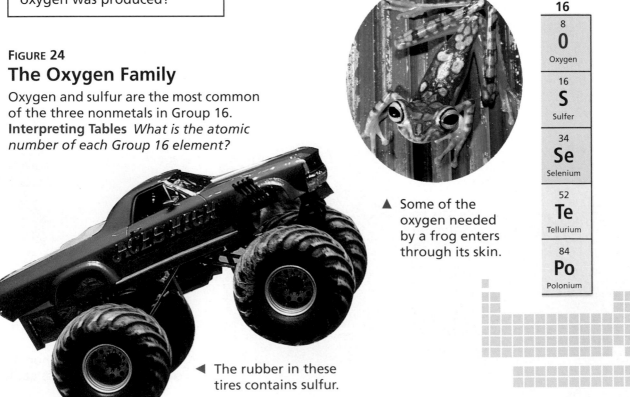

▲ Some of the oxygen needed by a frog enters through its skin.

16
8 **O** Oxygen
16 **S** Sulfer
34 **Se** Selenium
52 **Te** Tellurium
84 **Po** Polonium

◄ The rubber in these tires contains sulfur.

The Halogen Family Group 17 contains fluorine, chlorine, bromine, iodine, and astatine. These elements are also known as the **halogens,** which means "salt forming." All but astatine are nonmetals, and all share similar properties. A halogen atom typically gains or shares one electron when it reacts with other elements.

All of the halogens are very reactive, and the uncombined elements are dangerous to humans. Fluorine is so reactive that it reacts with almost every other known substance. Even water and powdered glass will burn in fluorine. Chlorine gas is extremely dangerous, but it is used in small amounts to kill bacteria in water supplies.

Even though the halogen elements are dangerous, many of the compounds that halogens form are quite useful. Compounds of carbon and fluorine make up the nonstick coating on cookware. Small amounts of fluorine compounds are added to the water supply to help prevent tooth decay. Chlorine is one of the two elements in ordinary table salt (the other is sodium). Another salt of chlorine is calcium chloride, which is used to help melt snow. Bromine reacts with silver to form silver bromide, which is used in photographic film.

Go Online
SciLINKS NSTA

For: Links on nonmetals
Visit: www.SciLinks.org
Web Code: scn-1134

FIGURE 25

The Halogens

The Group 17 elements are the most reactive nonmetals. Atoms of these elements easily form compounds by sharing or gaining one electron with atoms of other elements.

17	
9 **F** Fluorine	
17 **Cl** Chlorine	
35 **Br** Bromine	
53 **I** Iodine	
85 **At** Astatine	

◄ Bromine is highly reactive, and will burn skin on contact.

▲ Fluorine-containing compounds are found in toothpaste.

FIGURE 26
The Noble Gases
Electricity makes the Group 18 elements glow brightly inside glass tubes. **Applying Concepts** *Why are neon and the other noble gases so unreactive?*

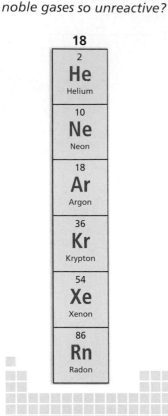

The Noble Gases The elements in Group 18 are known as the **noble gases.** They do not ordinarily form compounds because atoms of noble gases do not usually gain, lose, or share electrons. As a result, the noble gases are usually unreactive. Even so, scientists have been able to form some compounds of the heavy noble gases (Kr, Xe) in the laboratory.

All the noble gases exist in Earth's atmosphere, but only in small amounts. Because they are so unreactive, the noble gases were not discovered until the late 1800s. Helium was discovered by a scientist who was studying not the atmosphere but the sun.

Have you made use of a noble gas? You have if you have ever purchased a floating balloon filled with helium. Noble gases are also used in glowing electric lights. These lights are commonly called neon lights, even though they are often filled with argon, xenon, or other noble gases.

Hydrogen Alone in the upper left corner of the periodic table is hydrogen—the element with the simplest and smallest atoms. Each hydrogen atom has one proton and one electron. Some hydrogen atoms also have neutrons. Because the chemical properties of hydrogen differ very much from those of the other elements, it really cannot be grouped into a family. Although hydrogen makes up more than 90 percent of the atoms in the universe, it makes up only 1 percent of the mass of Earth's crust, oceans, and atmosphere. Hydrogen is rarely found on Earth as a pure element. Most hydrogen is combined with oxygen in water (H_2O).

✓ **Reading Checkpoint** Why were the noble gases undiscovered until the late 1800s?

FIGURE 27
Importance of Hydrogen
Water is a compound of hydrogen and oxygen. Without liquid water, life on Earth would be impossible.

The Metalloids

Along the border between the metals and the nonmetals are seven elements called metalloids. These elements are shown in the purple squares in the periodic table in Section 2. The **metalloids** have some characteristics of both metals and nonmetals. All are solids at room temperature. They are brittle, hard, and somewhat reactive.

The most common metalloid is silicon (Si). Silicon combines with oxygen to form silicon dioxide (SiO_2). Ordinary sand, which is mostly SiO_2, is the main component of glass. A compound of boron (B) and oxygen is added during the process of glassmaking to make heat-resistant glass. Compounds of boron are also used in some cleaning materials.

The most useful property of the metalloids is their varying ability to conduct electricity. Whether or not a metalloid conducts electricity can depend on temperature, exposure to light, or the presence of small amounts of impurities. For this reason, metalloids such as silicon, germanium (Ge), and arsenic (As) are used to make semiconductors. **Semiconductors** are substances that can conduct electricity under some conditions but not under other conditions. Semiconductors are used to make computer chips, transistors, and lasers.

FIGURE 28
Silicon
A silicon computer chip is dwarfed by an ant, but the chip's properties as a semiconductor make it a powerful part of modern computers.

 **Reading Checkpoint** What is the most common metalloid, and where is it found?

Section 4 Assessment

Target Reading Skill Using Prior Knowledge Review your graphic organizer about nonmetals and metalloids, and revise it based on what you learned in the section.

Reviewing Key Concepts

1. a. **Reviewing** What physical and chemical properties are found among the nonmetals?
   b. **Making Generalizations** What happens to the atoms of most nonmetals when they react with other elements?
   c. **Comparing and Contrasting** How do the physical and chemical properties of the halogens compare with those of the noble gases?
2. a. **Identifying** Where in the periodic table are the metalloids found?
   b. **Describing** What are three uses of metalloids?
   c. **Applying Concepts** What property makes certain metalloids useful as "switches" to turn a small electric current on and off?

Lab zone At-Home **Activity**

Halogen Hunt Identify compounds in your home that contain halogens. Look at labels on foods, cooking ingredients, cleaning materials, medicines, and cosmetics. The presence of a halogen is often indicated by the words *fluoride*, *chloride*, *bromide*, and *iodide* or the prefixes *fluoro-*, *chloro-*, *bromo-*, and *iodo-*. Show your family these examples and describe properties of the halogens.

Alien Periodic Table

Problem

Imagine that inhabitants of another planet send a message to Earth that contains information about 30 elements. However, the message contains different names and symbols for these elements than those used on Earth. Which elements on the periodic table do these "alien" names represent?

Skills Focus

drawing conclusions, classifying, interpreting data, inferring

Materials

• ruler
• periodic table from text for reference

Procedure

1. Copy the blank periodic table on page 107 into your notebook.

2. Listed below are data on the chemical and physical properties of the 30 elements. Place the elements in their proper position in the blank periodic table.

Alien Elements

The noble gases are **bombal** (Bo), **wobble** (Wo), **jeptum** (J), and **logon** (L). Among these gases, wobble has the greatest atomic mass and bombal the least. Logon is lighter than jeptum.

The most reactive group of metals are **xtalt** (X), **byyou** (By), **chow** (Ch), and **quackzil** (Q). Of these metals, chow has the lowest atomic mass. Quackzil is in the same period as wobble.

Apstrom (A), **vulcania** (V), and **kratt** (Kt) are nonmetals whose atoms typically gain or share one electron. Vulcania is in the same period as quackzil and wobble.

The metalloids are **ernst** (E), **highho** (Hi), **terriblum** (T), and **sississ** (Ss). Sississ is the metalloid with the greatest atomic mass. Ernst is the metalloid with the lowest atomic mass. Highho and terriblum are in Group 14. Terriblum has more protons than highho. **Yazzer** (Yz) touches the zigzag line, but it's a metal, not a metalloid.

The lightest element of all is called **pfsst** (Pf). The heaviest element in the group of 30 elements is **eldorado** (El). The most chemically active nonmetal is apstrom. Kratt reacts with byyou to form table salt.

The element **doggone** (D) has only 4 protons in its atoms.

Floxxit (Fx) is important in the chemistry of life. It forms compounds made of long chains of atoms. **Rhaatrap** (R) and **doadeer** (Do) are metals in the fourth period, but rhaatrap is less reactive than doadeer.

Magnificon (M), **goldy** (G), and sississ are all members of Group 15. Goldy has fewer electrons than magnificon.

Urrp (Up), **oz** (Oz), and **nuutye** (Nu) all gain 2 electrons when they react. Nuutye is found as a diatomic molecule and has the same properties as a gas found in Earth's atmosphere. Oz has a lower atomic number than urrp.

The element **anatom** (An) has atoms with a total of 49 electrons. **Zapper** (Z) and **pie** (Pi) lose two electrons when they react. Zapper is used to make lightweight alloys.

Alien Periodic Table

	1			13	14	15	16	17	18
1		2							
2									
3									
4									
5									

Analyze and Conclude

1. **Drawing Conclusions** List the Earth names for the 30 alien elements in order of atomic number.

2. **Classifying** Were you able to place some elements within the periodic table with just a single clue? Explain using examples.

3. **Interpreting Data** Why did you need two or more clues to place other elements? Explain using examples.

4. **Inferring** Why could you use clues about atomic mass to place elements, even though the table is now based on atomic numbers?

5. **Communicating** Write a paragraph describing which groups of elements are not included in the alien periodic table. Explain whether or not you think it is likely that an alien planet would lack these elements.

More to Explore

Notice that Period 5 is incomplete on the alien periodic table. Create names and symbols for each of the missing elements. Then, compose a series of clues that would allow another student to identify these elements. Make your clues as precise as possible.

▼ **Radio telescopes in New Mexico**

Elements From Stardust

Reading Preview

Key Concepts
- How are elements created in stars?
- What are the results of fusion in large stars?

Key Terms
- plasma • nuclear fusion
- nebula • supernova

Target Reading Skill
Sequencing As you read, make a flowchart like the one below that shows how elements are formed in stars. Write the steps in separate boxes in the flowchart in the order in which they occur.

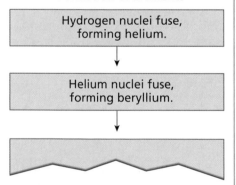

Formation of Elements

Hydrogen nuclei fuse, forming helium.

↓

Helium nuclei fuse, forming beryllium.

↓

Lab zone Discover **Activity**

Can Helium Be Made From Hydrogen?

1. A hydrogen atom has a nucleus of 1 proton surrounded by an electron. Most hydrogen nuclei do not contain neutrons, but one isotope of hydrogen contains 1 neutron, and another isotope contains 2 neutrons. Draw models of each of the three isotopes of hydrogen.

2. All helium atoms have 2 protons and 2 electrons, and almost all have 2 neutrons. Draw a model of a typical helium atom.

Think It Over
Developing Hypotheses How might the hydrogen atoms you drew combine to form a helium atom? Draw a diagram to illustrate your hypothesis. Why would hydrogen nuclei with neutrons be important for this process?

Have you wondered where the elements come from, or why some elements are common here on Earth, while others are much more rare? To answer questions such as these, scientists have looked in a place that might surprise you: stars. They have looked not only at distant stars, but also at the nearest star, the sun. By studying the sun and other stars, scientists have formed some interesting models of how the stars shine and theories about the origins of matter here on Earth.

How Elements Form in Stars

Like many other stars, the sun is made mostly of one element—hydrogen. This hydrogen exists at tremendously high pressures and hot temperatures. How hot is it? The temperature in the sun's core is about 15 million degrees Celsius.

FIGURE 29
The Sun
Hot plasma streams into space from the surface of the sun.

Plasma At the extreme temperatures found in the sun and other stars, matter does not exist as a solid, a liquid, or a gas. Instead, it exists in a state called plasma. The **plasma** state of matter consists of a gas-like mixture of free electrons and atoms stripped of electrons. Plasmas don't exist just in stars. A comet's tail is made partly of plasma. Plasmas also can be produced by high-voltage electricity or even an electric spark. A plasma forms inside a fluorescent light when it is switched on. Plasmas are also used to generate light inside flat-panel TV screens that you can hang on a wall. The difference between a plasma in a fluorescent light and plasma in the sun is that the sun's plasma is under extremely high pressure.

When Nuclei Combine Remember that atomic nuclei contain protons, which means that nuclei are positively charged. Usually, positively charged nuclei repel one another. But in stars, the pressure is so high that nuclei are squeezed close together and collide with one another.

As in particle accelerators, when colliding nuclei have enough energy, they can join together, as shown in Figure 31. **Nuclear fusion** is a process in which two atomic nuclei combine to form a larger nucleus, releasing huge amounts of energy in the process. **Nuclear fusion, which occurs in stars on a huge scale, combines smaller nuclei into larger nuclei, creating heavier elements.**

Figure 30
Plasma in Comets
The glowing tail of a comet consists partly of plasma that forms as the comet comes closer to the sun.

FIGURE 31
Nuclear Fusion
During nuclear fusion, two atomic nuclei collide and fuse. **Applying Concepts** *Why does nuclear fusion result in the production of a different element?*

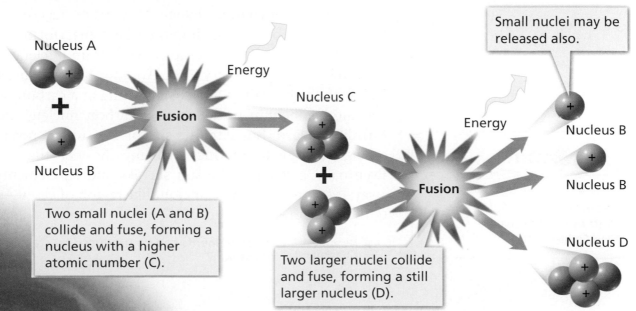

Nucleus A

Energy

Nucleus C

Small nuclei may be released also.

Nucleus B

Fusion

Energy

Nucleus B

Fusion

Nucleus B

Two small nuclei (A and B) collide and fuse, forming a nucleus with a higher atomic number (C).

Two larger nuclei collide and fuse, forming a still larger nucleus (D).

Nucleus D

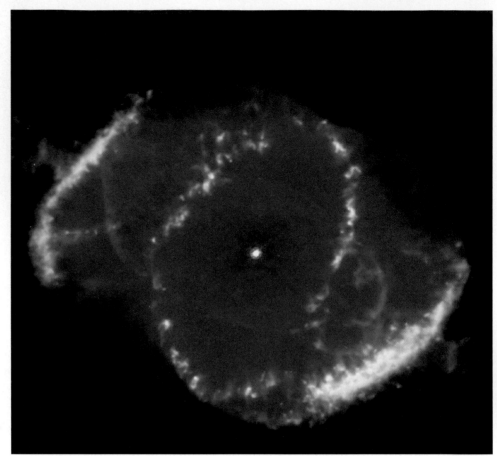

FIGURE 32
Planetary Nebula
The Cat's Eye Nebula is the remains of a star similar to the sun. Energy from the star causes the gases to glow.

New Elements From Fusion What are the steps of nuclear fusion in the sun and other stars? In the sun, different isotopes of hydrogen fuse, producing nuclei of helium. This reaction produces a huge amount of energy and is the most important source of the energy in the sun. In other words, hydrogen is the fuel that powers the sun. Scientists estimate that the sun has enough hydrogen to last another 5 billion years.

As more and more helium builds up in the core, the sun's temperature and volume change. New fusion reactions occur. Over time, two or more helium nuclei can fuse, forming nuclei of heavier elements. For example, two helium nuclei combine, forming a nucleus of beryllium. Another helium nucleus can fuse with the beryllium nucleus, resulting in a carbon nucleus. Yet another helium nucleus and a carbon nucleus can fuse, forming oxygen. But stars the size of the sun do not contain enough energy to produce elements heavier than oxygen. Eventually, a star like the sun shrinks and its elements blow away. It forms a **nebula**—or cloudlike region of gases—similar to the one shown in Figure 32.

 **Reading Checkpoint** What elements can be produced by stars the size of the sun?

Elements From Large Stars

As they age, larger stars become even hotter than the sun. These stars have enough energy to produce heavier elements, such as magnesium and silicon. In more massive stars, fusion continues until the core is almost all iron.

Find iron on the periodic table in Section 2. You can see that there are many other elements heavier than iron. How are elements heavier than iron produced? In the final hours of the most massive stars, scientists have observed an event called a supernova. A **supernova** is a huge explosion that breaks apart a massive star, producing temperatures up to 1 billion degrees Celsius. **A supernova provides enough energy for the nuclear fusion reactions that create the heaviest elements.** The elements are blown off into space as the star burns out.

Most astronomers agree that the matter in the sun and the planets around it, including Earth, originally came from a gigantic supernova that occurred billions of years ago. If so, this means that the matter all around you was created in a star, and all matter on Earth is a form of stardust.

 **Reading Checkpoint** Where are elements heavier than iron produced?

FIGURE 33
Supernova
The Crab Nebula is the supernova of a massive star first observed on Earth in the year 1054 by Chinese astronomers.
Making Generalizations *What elements may have formed in this supernova that would not have formed in a smaller star?*

Section 5 Assessment

Target Reading Skill Sequencing Refer to your flowchart about the formation of elements in stars as you answer Question 1.

Reviewing Key Concepts

1. **a. Identifying** What is the process that produces elements in stars?
   b. Explaining How are the elements beryllium, carbon, and oxygen produced in stars like the sun?
   c. Applying Concepts Why can elements be produced in the sun but not in Earth's atmosphere?
2. **a. Defining** What is a supernova?
   b. Describing What conditions of a supernova cause elements that are heavier than iron to form?
   c. Developing Hypotheses Earth has abundant amounts of iron, but also has many elements heavier than iron. Form a hypothesis to explain the presence of these heavier elements.

Writing in Science

How-to Paragraph Suppose you are the science officer on a spaceship. Your mission is to collect and analyze samples of matter from various sites as the ship travels around the Milky Way Galaxy. You and your assistants are able to identify the elements present in a sample. You want to know whether the sample could have come from a star like the sun, a more massive star, or a supernova. Write a set of instructions telling your assistants how to decide on the origin of the samples.

1 Introduction to Atoms

Key Concepts

- Atoms are made of even smaller particles called protons, neutrons, and electrons.
- An element can be identified by the number of protons in the nucleus of its atoms.
- Because atoms are so small, scientists create models to describe them.

Key Terms

nucleus
proton
neutron
electron
atomic number
isotope
mass number
model

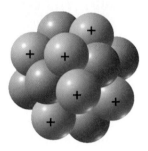

2 Organizing the Elements

Key Concepts

- Mendeleev noticed that a pattern of properties appeared when he arranged the elements in order of increasing atomic mass.
- Each square in the periodic table includes the element's atomic number, chemical symbol, name, and atomic mass.
- The properties of an element can be predicted from its location in the periodic table.

Key Terms

atomic mass	period
periodic table	group
chemical symbol	

3 Metals

Key Concepts

- The physical properties of metals include shininess, malleability, ductility, and conductivity.
- The reactivity of metals tends to decrease as you move from left to right across the periodic table.
- Elements that follow uranium in the periodic table are made—or synthesized—when nuclear particles are forced to crash into one another.

Key Terms

metal	alkali metal
malleable	alkaline earth metal
ductile	transition metal
conductivity	alloy
reactivity	particle accelerator
corrosion	

4 Nonmetals and Metalloids

Key Concepts

- Most nonmetals are poor conductors of heat and electricity and are reactive with other elements. Solid nonmetals are dull and brittle.
- The most useful property of the metalloids is their varying ability to conduct electricity.

Key Terms

nonmetal	noble gas
diatomic molecule	metalloid
halogen	semiconductor

5 Elements From Stardust

Key Concepts

- Nuclear fusion, which occurs in stars on a huge scale, combines smaller nuclei into larger nuclei, creating heavier elements.
- A supernova provides enough energy for the nuclear fusion reactions that create the heaviest elements.

Key Terms

plasma	nebula
nuclear fusion	supernova

Review and Assessment

Go Online
PHSchool.com
For: Self-Assessment
Visit: PHSchool.com
Web Code: cga-1030

Organizing Information

Concept Mapping Copy the concept map about the periodic table onto a sheet of paper. Then complete it and add a title. (For more on Concept Mapping, see the Skills Handbook.)

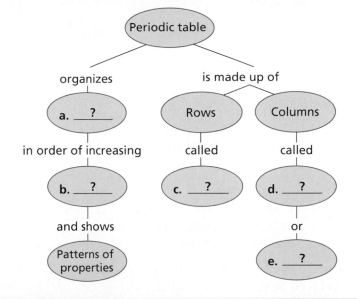

Reviewing Key Terms

Choose the letter of the best answer.

1. The atomic number of an atom is determined by the number of
   a. protons.
   b. electrons.
   c. neutrons.
   d. isotopes.

2. In the modern periodic table, elements are arranged
   a. according to atomic mass.
   b. according to atomic number.
   c. in alphabetical order.
   d. according to the number of neutrons in their nuclei.

3. Of the following, the group that contains elements that are the most reactive is the
   a. alkali metals.
   b. alkaline earth metals.
   c. carbon family.
   d. noble gases.

4. Unlike metals, many nonmetals are
   a. good conductors of heat and electricity.
   b. malleable and ductile.
   c. gases at room temperature.
   d. shiny.

5. At the hot temperatures of stars, electrons are stripped away from nuclei. This process forms a state of matter called
   a. a heavy element.
   b. liquid.
   c. plasma.
   d. supernova.

6. Inside the sun, nuclear fusion creates helium nuclei from
   a. oxygen nuclei.
   b. beryllium nuclei.
   c. carbon nuclei.
   d. hydrogen nuclei.

Writing in Science

News Report Imagine you are writing an article for a space magazine about the life cycle of a star. Which elements are produced in a star at different stages? How are these elements distributed into space?

Elements and the Periodic Table
Video Preview
Video Field Trip
▶ Video Assessment

Review and Assessment

Checking Concepts

7. How do two isotopes of an element differ from one another?

8. What element has an average atomic mass nearest to 31?

9. Use the periodic table to name two elements that have properties similar to those of chlorine (Cl).

10. Which two elements in Group 14 on the periodic table are most likely to be malleable and good conductors of electricity?

11. Of the elements oxygen (O), zinc (Zn), and iodine (I), which one would you predict to be a poor conductor of electricity and a brittle solid at room temperature?

12. Why are elements heavier than oxygen *not* produced in stars like the sun?

Thinking Critically

13. Comparing and Contrasting List the three kinds of particles that make up atoms, and compare their masses and their locations in an atom.

14. Applying Concepts Below is a square taken from the periodic table. Identify the type of information given by each labeled item.

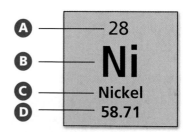

15. Applying Concepts Explain how particle accelerators are used to synthesize elements with atomic numbers above 95.

16. Inferring What property of the materials used in computer chips makes them useful as switches that turn electricity on and off?

17. Relating Cause and Effect Why is extremely high pressure required to cause atomic nuclei to crash into one another in stars?

Applying Skills

Use the table to answer Questions 18–22.

The table below lists properties of five elements.

Element	Appearance	Atomic Mass	Conducts Electricity
A	Invisible gas	14.007	No
B	Invisible gas	39.948	No
C	Hard, silvery solid	40.08	Yes
D	Silvery liquid	200.59	Yes
E	Shiny, bluish-white solid	207.2	Slightly

18. Classifying Classify each element in the table as a metal or a nonmetal. Explain your answers.

19. Inferring Both elements B and C have an atomic mass close to 40. How is this similarity possible?

20. Drawing Conclusions Use the periodic table to identify the five elements.

21. Predicting Would you expect elements A and B to have similar chemical properties? Why or why not?

22. Predicting Would you expect to find element C uncombined in nature? Explain.

Lab zone Chapter **Project**

Performance Assessment Display the chart showing the metals you studied. Be ready to discuss which properties are common to all metals. Describe other properties of metals you could not test. List all the properties that could be used to find out whether an unknown element is a metal.

Standardized Test Practice

Choose the letter of the best answer.

1. Elements that are gases at room temperature are likely to be classified as which of the following?
   - **A** metals
   - **B** nonmetals
   - **C** metalloids
   - **D** unreactive

2. Which property of aluminum makes it a suitable metal for soft drink cans?
   - **A** It has good electrical conductivity.
   - **B** It can be hammered into a thin sheet (malleability).
   - **C** It can be drawn into long wires (ductility).
   - **D** It can reflect light (shininess).

Use the table below to answer Questions 3–5.

8	9	10
O	**F**	**Ne**
Oxygen 15.999	Fluorine 18.998	Neon 20.179
16	17	18
S	**Cl**	**Ar**
Sulfur 32.06	Chlorine 35.453	Argon 39.948

3. Which element has an atomic number of 18?
   - **A** hydrogen
   - **B** oxygen
   - **C** fluorine
   - **D** argon

4. An atom of fluorine has 10 neutrons. What is the total number of other subatomic particles in this atom?
   - **A** 9 protons and 9 electrons
   - **B** 9 protons and 19 electrons
   - **C** 10 protons and 10 electrons
   - **D** 19 protons and 19 electrons

5. Which combination of elements represents part of a group, or family, of the periodic table?
   - **A** oxygen, fluorine, and neon
   - **B** sulfur, chlorine, and argon
   - **C** fluorine and chlorine
   - **D** oxygen and chlorine

Open-Ended Question

6. Describe the modern model of the atom. Your discussion should include the three main types of particles that make up an atom and the charge and location of each. Include an explanation of the overall charge on an atom.

Chapter 20

Exploring Materials

Academic Standards

This chapter addresses these Indiana standards.

The Nature of Science and Technology

7.1.5 Identify important contributions to science, mathematics, and technology by people of different cultures and times.

7.1.10 Identify ways that technology influences the course of history.

The Living Environment

7.4.10 Describe how technologies used in food production, sanitation, and disease prevention have changed how people live and the growth of human population.

Interactive Textbook

Navajo women weave wool, a natural polymer. ▶

Lab zone™ Chapter **Project**

Material Profiles

In this chapter, you will explore the properties of different types of materials. As you read this chapter, you will survey different materials found around you.

Your Goal To collect and investigate different materials found around you

To complete the project, you must

- collect at least eight material samples from at least three different locations
- identify several properties of each material
- create an informative display about these materials
- follow the safety guidelines in Appendix A

Plan It! With a group of classmates, brainstorm a list of the properties of various materials and how you might test these properties. You'll be working on this project as you study this chapter. When you finish Section 1, describe some polymers and composites you chose to collect and begin preparing a showcase. Add information when you finish Section 2, and complete your list of materials at the end of the chapter. Finally, present your completed showcase to the class.

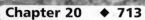

Polymers and Composites

Reading Preview

Key Concepts
- How do polymers form?
- What are composites made of?
- What benefits and problems relate to the use of synthetic polymers?

Key Terms
- polymer • monomer • plastic
- composite

🎯 Target Reading Skill
Asking Questions Before you read, preview the red headings. In a graphic organizer like the one below, ask a *how* or *why* question for each heading. As you read, write the answers to your questions.

Question	Answer
How do polymers form?	Polymers form when chemical bonds link . . .

Lab zone Discover **Activity**

What Did You Make?

1. Look at a sample of borax solution and write down the properties you observe. Do the same with white glue.
2. Put about 2 tablespoons of borax solution into a paper cup.
3. Stir the solution as you add about 1 tablespoon of white glue.
4. After 2 minutes, record the properties of the material in the cup. Wash your hands when you are finished.

Think It Over
Observing What evidence of a chemical reaction did you observe? How did the materials change? What do you think you made?

Delectable foods and many other interesting materials surround you every day. Have you ever wondered what makes up these foods and materials? You might be surprised to learn that many are partly or wholly polymers. A **polymer** (PAHL uh mur) is a large, complex molecule built from smaller molecules joined together in a repeating pattern.

The starches in pancakes and the proteins in meats and eggs are natural polymers. Many other polymers, however, are manufactured or synthetic. These synthetic polymers include polyester and nylon clothing, and plastics. Whether synthetic or natural, most polymers rely on the element carbon for their fundamental structures.

FIGURE 1
Polymers
The clothing, boots, goggles, and helmet worn by this climber are all made of polymers.

Forming Polymers

Food materials, living things, and plastic have something in common. All are made of carbon compounds. Carbon compounds contain atoms of carbon bonded to each other and to other kinds of atoms. Carbon is present in several million known compounds, and more carbon-containing compounds are being discovered or invented every day.

Carbon's Chains and Rings Carbon's unique ability to form so many compounds comes from two properties. First, carbon atoms can form four covalent bonds. Second, they can bond to each other in straight and branched chains and ring-shaped groups, as you can see in Figure 2. These structures form the "backbones" to which other atoms attach.

Hydrogen is the most common element found in compounds with carbon. Other elements include oxygen, nitrogen, phosphorus, sulfur, and the halogens—especially chlorine.

Carbon Compounds and Polymers Molecules of some carbon compounds can bond together, forming larger molecules, such as polymers. The smaller molecules from which polymers are built are called **monomers** (MAHN uh murz). **Polymers form when chemical bonds link large numbers of monomers in a repeating pattern.** A polymer may consist of hundreds or even thousands of monomers.

Many polymers consist of a single kind of monomer that repeats over and over again. You could think of these monomers as linked like the identical cars of a long passenger train. In other cases, two or three monomers may join in an alternating pattern. Sometimes links between monomer chains occur, forming large webs or netlike molecules. The chemical properties of a polymer depend on the monomers from which it is made.

> **Reading Checkpoint** What are the patterns in which monomers come together to form polymers?

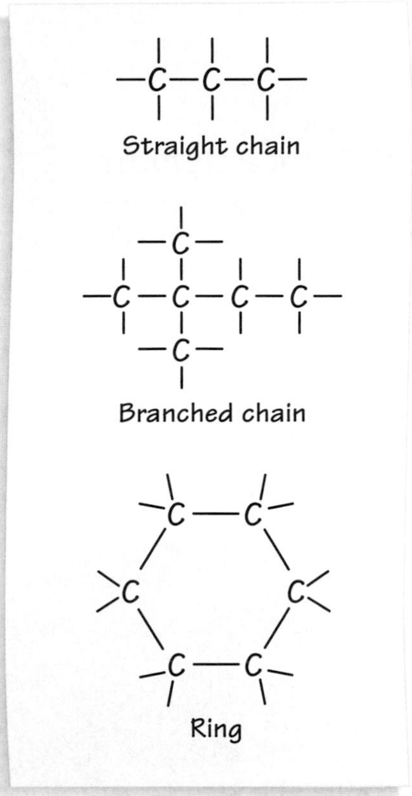

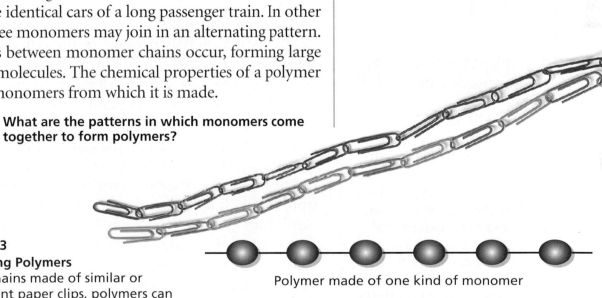

FIGURE 2
Carbon's Bonds
Carbon atoms can form structures like those shown above. In these drawings, lines represent covalent bonds. **Interpreting Diagrams** *How many covalent bonds are shown for each carbon atom?*

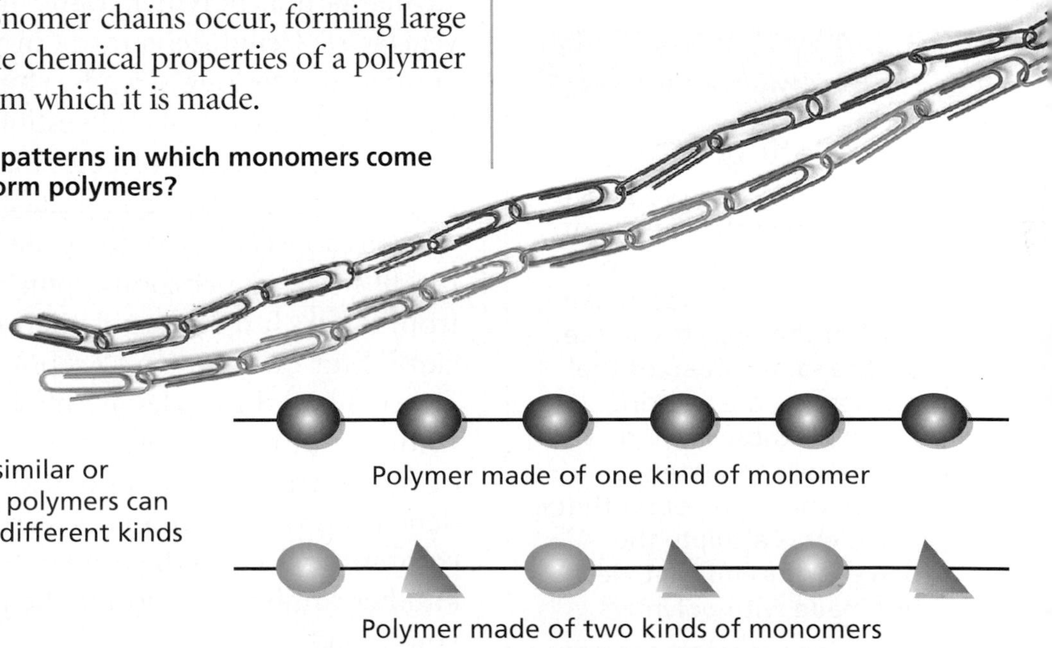

FIGURE 3
Building Polymers
Like chains made of similar or different paper clips, polymers can form from similar or different kinds of monomers.

Polymer made of one kind of monomer

Polymer made of two kinds of monomers

FIGURE 4
Natural Polymers

Cellulose, the proteins in snake venom, and spider's silk are three examples of natural polymers.

▲ The cellulose in fruits and vegetables serves as dietary fiber that keeps the human digestive system healthy.

A spider's web is a silken polymer that is one of the strongest materials known. ▶

▲ Snake venom is a mixture containing approximately 90 percent proteins.

Lab zone Skills **Activity**

Calculating

Sit or stand where you have a clear view of the room you are in. Slowly sweep the room with your eyes, making a list of the objects you see. Do the same sweep of the clothes you are wearing. Check off those items on your list made (completely or partly) of natural or synthetic polymers. Calculate the percent of items that were *not* made with polymers.

Polymers and Composites

Polymers have been around as long as life on Earth. Plants, animals, and other living things produce many natural materials made of large polymer molecules.

Natural Polymers Cellulose (SEL yoo lohs) is a flexible but strong natural polymer found in the cell walls of fruits and vegetables. Cellulose is made in plants when sugar molecules are joined into long strands. Humans cannot digest cellulose. But plants also make digestible polymers called starches, formed from sugar molecules that are connected in a different way. Starches are found in pastas, breads, and many vegetables.

You can wear polymers made by animals. Silk is made from the fibers of the cocoons spun by silkworms. Wool is made from sheep's fur. These polymers can be woven into thread and cloth. Your own body makes polymers, too. For example, your fingernails and muscles are made of polymers called proteins. Within your body, proteins are assembled from combinations of monomers called amino acids. The properties of a protein depend on which amino acids are used and in what order. One combination builds the protein that forms your fingernails. Yet another combination forms the protein that carries oxygen in your blood.

Synthetic Polymers Many polymers you use every day are synthesized—or made—from simpler materials. The starting materials for many synthetic polymers come from coal or oil. **Plastics**, which are synthetic polymers that can be molded or shaped, are the most common products. But there are many others. Carpets, clothing, glue, and even chewing gum can be made of synthetic polymers.

Figure 5 lists just a few of the hundreds of polymers people use. Although the names seem like tongue twisters, see how many you recognize. You may be able to identify some polymers by their initials printed on the bottoms of plastic bottles.

Compare the uses of polymers shown in the figure with their characteristics. Notice that many products require materials that are flexible, yet strong. Others must be hard or lightweight. When chemical engineers develop a new product, they have to think about how it will be used. Then they synthesize a polymer with properties to match.

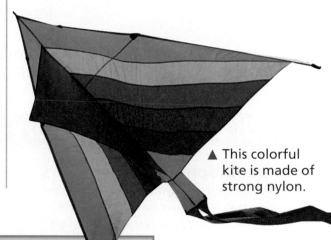

▲ This colorful kite is made of strong nylon.

Some Synthetic Polymers You Use		
Name	**Properties**	**Uses**
Low-density polyethylene (LDPE)	Flexible, soft, melts easily	Plastic bags, squeeze bottles, electric wire insulation
High-density polyethylene (HDPE)	Stronger than LDPE; higher melting temperatures	Detergent bottles, gas cans, toys, milk jugs
Polypropylene (PP)	Hard, keeps its shape	Toys, car parts, bottle caps
Polyvinyl chloride (PVC)	Tough, flexible	Garden hoses, imitation leather, piping
Polystyrene (PS)	Lightweight, can be made into foam	Foam drinking cups, insulation, furniture, "peanut" packing material
Nylon	Strong, can be drawn into flexible thread	Stockings, parachutes, fishing line, fabric
Teflon (polytetrafluoroethylene)	Nonreactive, low friction	Nonstick coating for cooking pans

FIGURE 5
The properties of synthetic polymers make them ideal starting materials for many common objects.
Applying Concepts
Which synthetic polymer would you use to make a cover for a picnic table?

Exploring Materials

Video Preview
▶Video Field Trip
Video Assessment

Comparing Polymers Synthetic polymers are often used in place of natural materials that are too expensive or wear out too quickly. Polyester and nylon fabrics, for example, are frequently used instead of wool, silk, and cotton to make clothes. Laminated countertops and vinyl floors replace wood in many kitchens. Other synthetic polymers have uses for which there is no suitable natural material. Compact discs, computer parts, artificial heart valves, and even bicycle tires couldn't exist without synthetic polymers.

Composites Every substance has its desirable and undesirable properties. What would happen if you could take the best properties of two substances and put them together? A **composite** combines two or more substances in a new material with different properties.

• Tech & Design in History •

The Development of Polymers

The first synthetic polymers were made by changing natural polymers in some way. Later, crude oil and coal became the starting materials. Now, new polymers are designed regularly in laboratories.

**1839
Synthetic Rubber**
Charles Goodyear invented a process that turned natural rubber into a hard, stretchable polymer. It did not get sticky and soft when heated or become brittle when cold, as natural rubber does. Bicycle tires were an early use.

**1869
Celluloid**
Made using cellulose, celluloid became a substitute for ivory in billiard balls and combs and brushes. It was later used to make movie film. Because celluloid is very flammable, other materials have replaced it for almost all purposes.

**1909
Bakelite**
Bakelite was the first commercial polymer made from compounds in coal tar. Bakelite doesn't get soft when heated, and it doesn't conduct electricity. These properties made it useful for handles of pots and pans, for telephones, and for parts in electrical outlets.

1800   1850   1900

By combining the useful properties of two or more substances in a composite, chemists can make a new material that works better than either one alone. **Many composite materials include one or more polymers.** The idea of putting two different materials together to get the advantages of both was inspired by the natural world. Many synthetic composites are designed to imitate a common natural composite—wood.

Wood is made of long fibers of cellulose, held together by another plant polymer called lignin. Cellulose fibers are flexible and can't support much weight. Lignin is brittle and would crack under the weight of the tree branches. But the combination of the two polymers makes a strong tree trunk.

Reading Checkpoint) Why is wood a composite?

Writing in Science

Research and Write Find out more about the invention of one of these polymers. Write a newspaper headline announcing the invention. Then write the first paragraph of the news report telling how the invention will change people's lives.

**1934
Nylon**
A giant breakthrough came with a synthetic fiber that imitates silk. Nylon replaced expensive silk in women's stockings and fabric for parachutes and clothing. It can also be molded to make objects like buttons, gears, and zippers.

**1971
Kevlar**
Kevlar is five times stronger than steel. Kevlar is tough enough to substitute for steel ropes and cables in offshore oil rigs but light enough to use in spacecraft parts. It is also used in protective clothing for firefighters and police officers.

**2002
Light-Emitting Polymers**
Discovered accidentally in 1990, light-emitting polymers (LEPs) are used commercially in products such as MP3 audio players and electric shavers with display screens. LEPs give off light when exposed to low-voltage electricity. Newer, more colorful LEPs may be useful as flexible monitors for computers, TV screens, and watch-sized phones.

| 1950 | 2000 | 2050 |

FIGURE 6
Synthetic Composites
The composites in the fishing rod above make it flexible so that it will not break when reeling in a fish. Fiberglass makes the snowboard at right both lightweight and strong.

Uses of Composites The idea of combining the properties of two substances to make a more useful one has led to many new products. Fiberglass composites are one example. Strands of glass fiber are woven together and strengthened with a liquid plastic that sets like glue. The combination makes a strong, hard solid that can be molded around a form to give it shape. These composites are lightweight but strong enough to be used as a boat hull or car body. Also, fiberglass will not rust as metal does.

Many other useful composites are made from strong polymers combined with lightweight ones. Bicycles, automobiles, and airplanes built from such composites are much lighter than the same vehicles built from steel or aluminum. Some composites are used to make fishing rods, tennis rackets, and other sports equipment that needs to be flexible but strong.

 **Reading Checkpoint** **What are two examples of composites?**

Too Many Polymers?

You can hardly look around without seeing something made of synthetic polymers. They have replaced many natural materials for several reasons. **Synthetic polymers are inexpensive to make, strong, and last a long time.**

But synthetic polymers have caused some problems, too. Many of the disadvantages of using plastics come from the same properties that make them so useful. **For example, it is often cheaper to throw plastics away and make new ones than it is to reuse them. As a result, plastics increase the volume of trash.**

Go Online
PHSchool.com

For: More on polymers
Visit: PHSchool.com
Web Code: cgd-1041

One of the reasons that plastics last so long is that most plastics don't react very easily with other substances. As a result, plastics don't break down—or degrade—into simpler materials in the environment. In contrast, natural polymers do. Some plastics are expected to last thousands of years. How do you get rid of something that lasts that long?

Is there a way to solve these problems? One solution is to use waste plastics as raw material for making new plastic products. You know this idea as recycling. Recycling has led to industries that create new products from discarded plastics. Bottles, fabrics for clothing, and parts for new cars are just some of the many items that can come from waste plastics. A pile of empty soda bottles can even be turned into synthetic wood. Look around your neighborhood. You may see park benches or "wooden" fences made from recycled plastics. Through recycling, the disposal problem is eased and new, useful items are created.

FIGURE 7
Recycling Plastics
Plastics can be recycled to make many useful products. This boardwalk, for example, is made of recycled plastics. **Making Judgments** *What advantages or disadvantages does this material have compared to wood?*

 **Reading Checkpoint** Why do plastic materials often increase the volume of trash?

Section 1 Assessment

Target Reading Skill Asking Questions Use your graphic organizer about the section headings to help answer the questions below.

Reviewing Key Concepts

1. a. **Defining** What are polymers made of?
   b. **Identifying** What properties enable carbon atoms to form polymers and so many other compounds?
   c. **Interpreting Diagrams** How do the two kinds of polymers modeled in Figure 3 differ?
2. a. **Reviewing** Distinguish between natural polymers, synthetic polymers, and composites.
   b. **Classifying** Make a list of polymers you can find in your home. Classify them as natural or synthetic.
   c. **Drawing Conclusions** Why are composites often more useful than the individual materials from which they are made?

3. a. **Listing** List two benefits and two problems associated with the use of synthetic polymers.
   b. **Making Judgments** Think of something plastic that you have used today. Is there some other material that would be better than plastic for this use?

Writing in Science

Advertisement You are a chemist. You invent a polymer that can be a substitute for a natural material such as wood, cotton, or leather. Write an advertisement for your polymer, explaining why you think it is a good replacement for the natural material.

Technology Lab
· Tech & Design ·

Design and Build a Polymer Package

Problem

Can you design and build packaging made of polymers that is suitable for mailing a breakable object to a friend?

Design Skills

designing a solution, building a prototype, evaluating the design

Materials

- water
- hand lens
- weights (or books)
- scissors
- packaging tape
- thermometer
- balance
- clock or timer
- containers (20 beakers, trays, or plastic cups)
- iodine solution, 1% solution (10 mL)
- cookies or hard-boiled eggs
- polymers used in packaging (paper, Tyvek, plastic foam, ecofoam, cardboard, fabric, popcorn, sawdust, wood shavings, plastic)

Procedure 🥽 🧤

PART 1 Research and Investigate

1. Make a list of all the ways you can think of to test the properties of polymers. Think about properties including:
   - ability to protect a fragile object
   - reaction to water • appearance
   - heat insulation • strength
   - reaction to iodine • mass

   Note: Iodine turns a dark blue-black color when starch is present. (Starch may attract insects or other pests.)

2. Select a property you wish to test. Choose a method that you think would be the best way to test that property.

3. Design a step-by-step procedure for the test. Do the same for each of the other properties you decide to investigate. Be sure that you change only one variable at a time. Include any safety directions in your procedure.

4. Predict which polymers you think will perform best in each test you plan.

5. After your teacher has approved your procedure, perform the tests on each polymer.

6. Record your observations in a table similar to the one shown.

Data Table				
Polymer	Brief Description of Test 1	Brief Description of Test 2	Brief Description of Test 3	Brief Description of Test 4
A				
B				
C				

PART 2 Design and Build

7. Using what you learned in Part 1, design packaging that
   - could be used to completely enclose a hard-boiled egg or cookie.
   - can drop a distance of 1.5 m without breaking the egg or cookie.
   - is strong and inexpensive to make.

8. Sketch your design on a sheet of paper, and list the materials you will need. Design an experiment to test the packaging.

9. Obtain your teacher's approval for your design. Then construct the packaging.

PART 3 Evaluate and Redesign

10. Test your packaging to evaluate how well the packaging meets the criteria in Step 7.

11. Based on the results of your tests, decide how you could improve your packaging. Then make any needed changes and test how the packaging performs again.

Analyze and Conclude

1. **Building a Prototype** What properties of polymers that you identified in Part 1 proved most useful when you designed your prototype in Part 2?

2. **Evaluating the Design** Did your packaging protect the object inside? What characteristics of your design do you think led to this result?

3. **Designing a Solution** How did your testing and evaluation of your prototype help you to redesign it?

4. **Evaluating the Impact on Society** How might people change their behavior if stronger and cheaper packaging material becomes available?

5. **Working With Design Constraints** Suppose the constraints on your design are changed. Now, your packaging must also be able to support a 10-kilogram weight. How would this affect your choice of materials and your design?

Communicate

Write an advertisement to market your packaging. In your ad, explain why your packaging does the best job of protecting the objects inside.

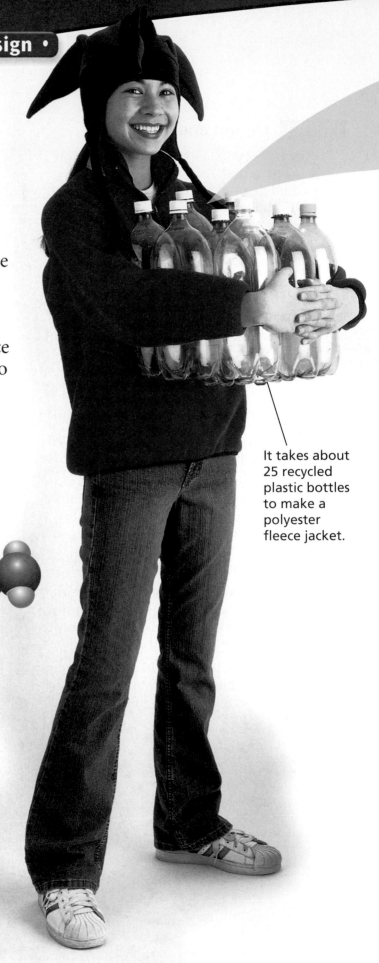

Polyester Fleece

Would you go hiking in the freezing Antarctic wearing a bunch of plastic beverage bottles? If you are like most serious hikers, you would. Polyester fleece is a lightweight, warm fabric made from plastic, including recycled soda bottles. The warmth of the fabric is due to its ability to trap and hold air. Polyester fleece is easy to wash and requires less energy to dry than wool or goose down.

It takes about 25 recycled plastic bottles to make a polyester fleece jacket.

Molecular Model
A simplified molecular model of the polymer used to create polyester fleece is shown here. The molecules form long, straight chains.

Making Polyester Fleece

Polyethylene terephthalate, or PET, is the polymer that is used to make polyester fleece. The first step in the process is creating the polyester fiber or thread. It can be made from raw materials or recycled PET plastic. The thread is then knit into fabric, which can be dyed or printed. It is then dried and "napped." In the napping process, the fibers are first raised and then clipped to an even height. This process increases the amount of air the fabric can hold, which helps keep you warm in cold weather.

Properties of Polyester Fleece

Fleece Fabric
Similar to yarn in a sweater, fleece fibers are knit together to create a stretchy, dense fabric that is soft, lightweight, and durable.

Air pockets between fibers trap body heat.

Moisture from the body passes through the fabric.

Polyester Fleece and the Environment

Making polyester fleece fabric uses water and energy, like other fabric-making processes. Using recycled materials to create polyester fleece saves energy and reduces wastes. One trade-off involves the safety of workers in the fleece factories. The clipping process creates dust particles in the air that workers then breathe. Some companies that produce fleece are developing technology that should reduce dust in the workplace, as well as technologies that conserve and reuse energy and water.

Plastic Bottle Granules
PET plastic bottles are chipped to create granules like those shown here. The granules can be used in making polyester fleece.

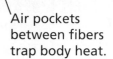

Weigh the Impact

1. Identify the Need
What are some benefits of using polyester fleece to make clothing and blankets?

2. Research
Use the Internet to find companies that make or sell polyester fleece made from recycled plastic. Identify ways in which this form of recycling helps the environment.

3. Write
Create a pamphlet to encourage your classmates to recycle plastics. Describe how PET plastic can be used to create polyester fleece.

For: More on polyester fleece
Visit: PHSchool.com
Web Code: cgh-1040

Metals and Alloys

Reading Preview

Key Concepts
- How do the properties of metals and alloys compare?
- How are steels and other alloys made and used?

Key Term
- alloy

Target Reading Skill
Outlining As you read, make an outline about metals and alloys that you can use for review. Use the red section headings for the main topics and the blue headings for the subtopics.

Metals and Alloys
I. Comparing metals and alloys
A. Properties of metals
B.
II. Making and using alloys
A.

Lab zone — Discover Activity

Are They "Steel" the Same?

1. Wrap a cut nail (low-carbon steel), a wire nail (high-carbon steel), and a stainless steel bolt together in a paper towel.
2. Place the towel in a plastic bag. Add about 250 mL of salt water and seal the bag.
3. After one or two days, remove the nails and bolt. Note any changes in the metals.

Think It Over
Developing Hypotheses What happened to the three types of steel? Which one changed the most, and which one changed the least? What do you think accounts for the difference?

More than 6,000 years ago, people learned to make copper tools that were sharper than stone tools. Later, people also used tin for tools. But copper and tin are soft, so they bend easily and are hard to keep sharp. About 5,000 years ago, metal makers discovered a way to make better tools.

Comparing Metals and Alloys

Copper and tin mixed together in the right amounts make a stronger, harder metal that keeps its sharp edge after long use. This discovery marked the beginning of the Bronze Age. It also was the invention of the first alloy. An **alloy** is a mixture made of two or more elements that has the properties of metal. In every alloy, at least one of the elements is a metal.

Properties of Metals You know a piece of metal when you see it. It's usually hard and shiny. At room temperature, all metallic elements (except mercury) are solids. Metals share other properties, too. You learned in Chapter 3 that metals can conduct electricity. They are ductile—that is, they can be drawn out into thin wire. For example, copper made into wire carries electric current to the outlets in your home. Metals are also malleable—that is, they can be hammered into a sheet. Aluminum, rolled flat, makes aluminum foil.

▲ A brass euphonium

Properties of Alloys The properties of an alloy can differ greatly from those of its individual elements. Pure gold, for example, is soft and easily bent. For that reason, gold jewelry and coins are made of an alloy of gold with another metal, such as copper or silver. These gold alloys are much harder than pure gold but still let its beauty show. Even after thousands of years, objects made of gold alloys do not change. They still look exactly the same as when they were first made.

Alloys are used much more than pure metals because they are generally stronger and less likely to react with air or water. Iron, for example, is often alloyed with one or more other elements to make steel. And steel is used in many tools because of its superior strength and hardness. You have seen iron objects rust when they are exposed to air and water. But forks and spoons made of stainless steel can be washed over and over again without rusting. That's because stainless steel—an alloy of iron, carbon, nickel, and chromium—does not react with air and water as iron does.

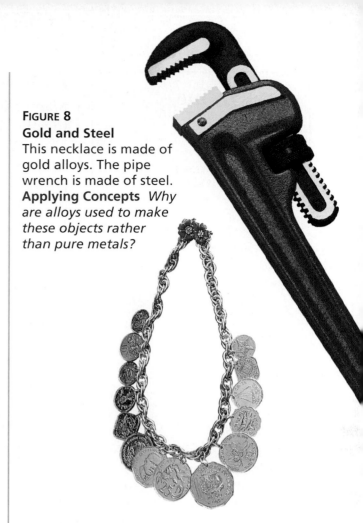

FIGURE 8
Gold and Steel
This necklace is made of gold alloys. The pipe wrench is made of steel.
Applying Concepts *Why are alloys used to make these objects rather than pure metals?*

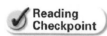 **Reading Checkpoint** **Why is most jewelry made of gold alloys rather than pure gold?**

Math ➤ **Analyzing Data**

Calculating Karat Value

Gold is often alloyed with other metals, such as silver, to improve its hardness and durability. The mass percent of gold in such an alloy is usually expressed by its karat value. Gold karat values and mass percent data are plotted on the graph shown here.

1. **Reading Graphs** Which axis has values that describe the mass of gold relative to the mass of the alloy?

2. **Reading Graphs** How does the mass percent of gold change as the karat value increases?

3. **Interpreting Data** What is the mass percent of gold for a 14-karat gold alloy?

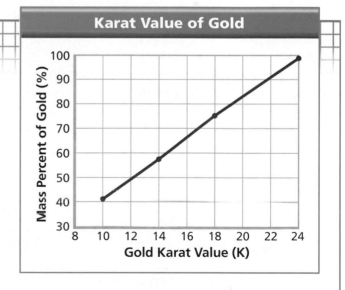

Karat Value of Gold

(graph: x-axis "Gold Karat Value (K)" from 8 to 24; y-axis "Mass Percent of Gold (%)" from 30 to 100)

4. **Creating Data Tables** Create a data table that gives the approximate mass percent of gold for alloys with karat values of 10, 12, 14, 16, 18, 20, 22, and 24.

Making and Using Alloys

Many alloys are made by melting metals and mixing them together in carefully measured amounts. Since the beginning of the Bronze Age, this technique has been used to make copper alloys. Some modern alloys are made by mixing the elements as powders and then heating them under high pressure. This process uses less energy because the metal powders blend at lower temperatures. The material then can be molded into the desired shape immediately. Using a more recent technique, titanium may be bombarded with nitrogen ions to make a strong alloy for artificial joints.

Steels When you want to describe something very hard or tough, you may use the expression "hard as steel." Steel is an alloy of iron with other elements. It is used for its strength, hardness, and resistance to corrosion. Without steel, automobiles, suspension bridges, skyscrapers, and surgical knives would not exist.

Not all steels are alike. Their properties depend on which elements are added to iron and in what amounts. Carbon steels are stronger and harder than wrought iron, which is almost pure iron.

FIGURE 9
Alloys have a wide variety of uses. **Making Generalizations** *How do the properties of bronze make it well-suited for its uses?*

Common Alloys			
Alloy	**Elements**	**Properties**	**Uses**
Brass	Copper, zinc	Strong, resists corrosion, polishes well	Musical instruments, faucets, decorative hardware, jewelry
Bronze	Copper, tin	Hard, resists corrosion	Marine hardware, screws, grillwork
Stainless steel	Iron, carbon, nickel, chromium	Strong, resists corrosion	Tableware, cookware, surgical instruments
Carbon steel	Iron, carbon	Inexpensive, strong	Tools, auto bodies, machinery, steel girders, rails
Plumber's solder	Lead, tin	Low melting point	Sealer for joints and leaks in metal plumbing
Sterling silver	Silver, copper	Shiny, harder than pure silver	Jewelry, tableware
Dental amalgam	Mercury, silver, tin, copper, zinc	Low melting point, easily shaped	Dental fillings
Pewter	Tin, antimony, copper; sometimes lead*	Bright or satin finish, resists tarnish	Tableware, decorative objects
Wood's metal	Bismuth, lead, tin, cadmium	Low melting point	Fire sprinklers, electric fuses

*Pewter containing lead cannot be used with food.

FIGURE 10
Alloys in Daily Life
Solder is used by plumbers to seal leaking pipes. Brass is found in decorative objects, such as this door knocker. Stainless steel is often found in cookware, and pewter is used in some tableware.

Solder

▲ Brass

▲ Stainless steel

▲ Pewter

High-carbon steels contain 0.6 to 1.5 percent carbon. Tools, knives, and springs are just some of the uses for high-carbon steels. Low-carbon steels, with less than 0.2 percent carbon, are ductile and malleable and are used for nails, cables, and chains.

There are hundreds of different types of steels. Usually carbon is added to the iron plus one or more of the following metals: chromium, manganese, molybdenum, nickel, tungsten, and vanadium. Steels made with these metals are generally stronger, harder, and more corrosion-resistant than carbon steel. Depending on their properties, these steels may become bicycle frames, train rails, steel tubing, or construction equipment.

Other Alloys Bronze, brass, sterling silver, and solder (SAHD ur) are just a few examples of other kinds of alloys. Alloys are used to make items ranging from plumbing materials and sprinkler systems to tableware and doorknobs. Even your dentist uses alloys. Have you ever had a cavity in a tooth? A mixture of mercury with silver or gold (called an amalgam) makes a pasty solid. It hardens quickly, filling a hole in the tooth. Look at Figure 9 and see how many of the examples listed in the table are alloys you have seen or used.

 **Reading Checkpoint** Name three uses of high-carbon steels.

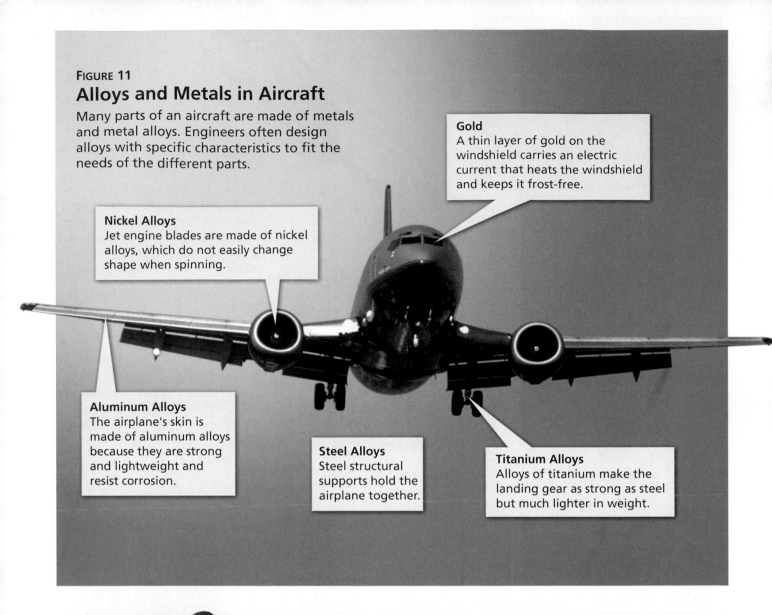

FIGURE 11
Alloys and Metals in Aircraft
Many parts of an aircraft are made of metals and metal alloys. Engineers often design alloys with specific characteristics to fit the needs of the different parts.

Gold
A thin layer of gold on the windshield carries an electric current that heats the windshield and keeps it frost-free.

Nickel Alloys
Jet engine blades are made of nickel alloys, which do not easily change shape when spinning.

Aluminum Alloys
The airplane's skin is made of aluminum alloys because they are strong and lightweight and resist corrosion.

Steel Alloys
Steel structural supports hold the airplane together.

Titanium Alloys
Alloys of titanium make the landing gear as strong as steel but much lighter in weight.

Section 2 Assessment

Target Reading Skill Outlining Use the information in your outline about metals and alloys to answer the questions.

Reviewing Key Concepts

1. a. **Listing** List three properties you would expect a pure metal object to have.
   b. **Reviewing** From what pure metals is bronze made?
   c. **Comparing and Contrasting** Compare and contrast the general properties of alloys and pure metals.
2. a. **Describing** Describe one way in which alloys are made.
   b. **Inferring** A steel suitable for making nails is malleable and ductile. What can you infer about the probable carbon content of the steel?
   c. **Interpreting Tables** Look at the table in Figure 9. What metal may be alloyed with silver to make tableware that is shiny and harder than pure silver?

Lab zone At-Home **Activity**

Finding Alloys Find items in your home that are made from metals or alloys. Look for cooking utensils, tools, toys, sports equipment, appliances, and other household items that are made with these materials. Discuss with members of your family how properties of the metals or alloys relate to the uses of the objects.

3 Ceramics and Glass

Reading Preview

Key Concepts
- What are the properties of ceramics?
- What are the properties of glass?

Key Terms
- ceramic • glass
- optical fiber

Target Reading Skill
Identifying Main Ideas As you read about ceramics, write the main idea in a graphic organizer like the one below. Then write three supporting details that give examples of the main idea.

Main Idea

Ceramics are useful because they resist moisture.

Detail	**Detail**	**Detail**

Discover **Activity**

Does It Get Wet?
1. Find the masses of a glazed pottery flowerpot and an unglazed one of similar size. Record both values.
2. Place both pots in a basin of water for ten minutes.
3. Remove the pots from the water and gently blot dry with paper towels.
4. Find and record the masses of both flowerpots again.
5. Calculate the percent of change in mass for each pot.

Think It Over
Inferring Which pot gained the most mass? What can you infer about the effect that glazing has on the pot?

Have you ever heard the phrase "a bull in a china shop"? Imagine the damage! The phrase comes from the fact that ceramics and glass are brittle and can shatter when struck. In spite of this property, archaeologists have uncovered many ceramic and glass artifacts used by the Romans and other ancient civilizations. Because ceramics and glass resist moisture and don't react readily, some of these ancient objects remain in excellent condition even today.

Ceramics

Ceramics are hard, crystalline solids made by heating clay and other mineral materials to high temperatures. Clay is made of water and very small mineral particles containing mostly silicon, aluminum, and oxygen. Clay forms when the minerals in rock break down.

FIGURE 12
Homes Made of Clay
These homes in New Mexico were built with clay bricks hundreds of years ago.

Making Ceramics When a clay object is heated above 1,000°C, much of the water present in the clay evaporates, and the particles of clay stick together. This process forms hard ceramics such as bricks and flowerpots. These ceramics have tiny spaces in their structure that absorb and hold water. However, potters can cover a ceramic with a thin layer of silicon dioxide and heat it again. This process forms a glassy, waterproof coating called a glaze. You might see glazed pottery used to serve or store food. Potters often use colorful glazes to create artistic designs on their work.

Properties and Uses of Ceramics Despite their tendency to break, ceramics have several properties that make them useful. **Ceramics resist moisture, do not conduct electricity, and can withstand temperatures that would cause metals to melt.**

Ceramic pottery has been used for thousands of years to store food, protecting it from moisture and animals. Roofing tiles, bricks, and sewer pipes are all long-standing uses of ceramics. Ceramics also are used as insulators in electric equipment and light fixtures.

New uses for ceramics continue to be developed. Surgeons use bioceramic materials, for example, to replace human hips, knees, and other body parts. The catalytic converters in modern cars and trucks contain ceramics that help convert harmful exhaust gases to harmless carbon dioxide and water.

✓ **Reading Checkpoint** **What are some uses of ceramics?**

FIGURE 13
Making and Using Ceramics
Colorful glazes were used to decorate the ceramic plates below. **Predicting** *What will happen to the clay, right, when the potter heats it in a kiln, or hot oven?*

Glass

Thousands of years ago, people learned that sand mixed with limestone can be melted into a thick, hot liquid that flows like molasses. If this liquid cools quickly, it forms a clear, solid material with no crystal structure, called **glass**.

Making Glass Early glassmakers added calcium (in the form of limestone) and sodium (in the form of sodium carbonate) to the melting sand. This mixture melts at a lower temperature than sand alone, so it is easier to work with. Window glass, bottles, and jars are still made with this type of glass.

More than 2,000 years ago, glassmakers in ancient Syria invented glassblowing. A glassmaker would put a blob of melted glass on the end of an iron pipe. By blowing air through the pipe, the glassmaker could produce a hollow glass vessel. If the glass was blown inside a wooden mold, jars and vases in beautiful patterns and shapes could be created.

Properties and Uses of Glass Like ceramics, glass is brittle and can shatter when struck. Nonetheless, it has many useful properties. **Glass is clear, can be made in many shapes and colors, and can't be penetrated by liquids.**

Different materials may be added to glass to make it useful for particular purposes. Substituting lead oxide for limestone makes a glass that bends light in useful ways. This kind of glass is used to make lenses for eyeglasses, telescopes, and microscopes. Adding boron oxide creates a glass that resists heat better than ordinary glass. This type of glass is used for cookware and laboratory glassware that must be heated.

Lab zone Try This **Activity**

A Bright Idea
Model communication through glass.

1. Construct a barrier between you and a partner so that you cannot see each other.
2. Run a plastic optical fiber past the barrier. (Plastic fibers work similarly to glass fibers.)
3. Bring the bulb of a penlight flashlight close to your end of the fiber.
4. Using a single flash for "yes" and two flashes for "no," send your partner a message by responding to a series of yes and no questions he or she asks.
5. Change roles so that your partner has a chance to send signals in response to your questions.

Observing What happened when you and your partner sent signals to each other?

FIGURE 15
Light in Optical Fibers
Even if optical fibers are twisted into a loop, the light moves within the fibers.

Communication Through Glass There's a good chance that the next time you make a phone call, your message will travel through glass. An **optical fiber** is a threadlike piece of glass (or plastic) that can be used for transmitting light. When you speak into a telephone, the signal created by your voice is converted to light signals that travel through the glass fiber. At the other end, the light may be converted into electronic signals that can then be converted to sound.

A pair of optical fibers, each the thickness of a human hair, can carry 625,000 phone calls at one time. One quarter pound of glass fiber can replace more than 2 tons of copper wire. This difference is a big advantage when installing long lines like those that carry messages under the ocean. Another benefit of glass fiber is its stability. Since the glass does not corrode as metals do, the lines are easier to maintain.

✔ **Reading Checkpoint** In what form is a signal transmitted through an optical fiber?

Section 3 Assessment

⊙ **Target Reading Skill** Identifying Main Ideas Use your graphic organizer about ceramics to help you answer Question 1 below.

Reviewing Key Concepts

1. a. **Listing** What are the general properties of ceramics?
   b. **Explaining** Why are ceramics used in the manufacture of spark plugs and many other electrical devices?
   c. **Inferring** Before ceramics were invented, people stored food in containers such as baskets, leather bags, and wooden bowls. Why were ceramics an improvement as containers for food?
2. a. **Reviewing** What is the principal material used in making glass?
   b. **Describing** Describe how the composition of glass may be changed in order to make it useful in lenses.
   c. **Applying Concepts** What properties of glass make it particularly useful for communication via optical fibers?

Writing in Science

Letter It's Upper Egypt and the year is about 5000 B.C. You notice something strange that happens when your pottery furnace overheats. The presence of limestone containing sand and soda produces shiny coatings on your ceramic pots. Amazingly, the coatings render the pots waterproof! Write a letter to a relative describing your discovery.

High-Tech Glass

You may be familiar with some types of high-tech glass, such as those used for flat screen computer monitors or flat screen televisions, but can you picture a high-tech glass house?

In Park City, Utah there is an amazing house with some windows that are computer monitors, television sets, or speakers. This house is filled with high-tech glass that is lighter, stronger, smoother, and thinner than ever before. This allows glass to be used for advanced applications.

Some windows in the Park City house contain a microfiber LCD screen. This screen allows the windows to change from clear to opaque or to display a television image. The computer monitor windows are touch screens, so you could just touch your window to hop on the Internet. Or, if you wanted to, you could push a button to make all the windows clear for a see-through house!

Weigh the Impact

1. Identify the Uses
List four ways high-tech glass would be beneficial in the classroom setting.

2. Analyze
Research information about high-tech glass and determine whether it is currently practical for use in a school. Consider its affordability as well.

3. Evaluate
Using the information you collect, write a summary that explains what you have learned through your research.

① Polymers and Composites

Key Concepts

- Polymers form when chemical bonds link large numbers of monomers in a repeating pattern.
- Many composite materials include one or more polymers.
- Synthetic polymers are strong, inexpensive to make, and last a long time.
- It is often cheaper to throw plastics away and make new ones than it is to reuse them. As a result, plastics increase the volume of trash.

Key Terms

polymer
monomer
plastic
composite

② Metals and Alloys

Key Concepts

- Alloys are used much more than pure metals because they are generally stronger and less likely to react with air or water.
- Many alloys are made by melting metals and mixing them together in carefully measured amounts.

Key Term

alloy

③ Ceramics and Glass

Key Concepts

- Ceramics resist moisture, do not conduct electricity, and can withstand temperatures that would cause metals to melt.
- Glass is clear, can be made in many shapes and colors, and can't be penetrated by liquids.

Key Terms

ceramic
glass
optical fiber

Review and Assessment

Organizing Information

Comparing and Contrasting Copy the table about polymers, alloys, ceramics, and glass onto a separate sheet of paper. Then fill in the empty spaces and add a title. (For more on Comparing and Contrasting tables, see the Skills Handbook.)

Material	Made From	How Made	How Used
Polymers	Monomers (carbon compounds)	a. ____?____	b. ____?____
Alloys	c. ____?____	Metals heated and mixed	d. ____?____
Ceramics	Clay; other materials	e. ____?____	f. ____?____
Glass	g. ____?____	Melted, then cooled in desired shapes	h. ____?____

Reviewing Key Terms

Choose the letter of the best answer.

1. Any large molecule made of many monomers is called a
   a. plastic.
   b. polymer.
   c. protein.
   d. chain.

2. Fiberglass is a type of
   a. polymer.
   b. alloy.
   c. ceramic.
   d. composite.

3. The properties of alloys most resemble those of
   a. ceramics.
   b. glass.
   c. metals.
   d. polymers.

4. Clean sand is heated to its melting point to make
   a. ceramics.
   b. glass.
   c. alloys.
   d. composites.

5. A threadlike piece of glass that can be used for transmitting light is a(n)
   a. optical ceramic
   b. optical fiber
   c. polymer ceramic
   d. polymer fiber

If the statement is true, write *true*. If it is false, change the underlined word or words to make the statement true.

6. <u>Oxygen</u> is the element that forms the backbone of most polymers.

7. Cellulose is an example of a <u>synthetic</u> polymer.

8. A useful alloy of copper and tin is <u>steel</u>.

9. Roofing tiles and bricks are made with <u>ceramics</u>.

10. <u>Plastic</u> is clear and can't be penetrated by liquids, but it is also brittle and shatters easily.

Writing in Science

Comparison Paragraph Write a paragraph comparing and contrasting natural and synthetic polymers. Give two examples of each.

Discovery CHANNEL SCHOOL

Exploring Materials

Video Preview
Video Field Trip
▶ Video Assessment

Review and Assessment

Checking Concepts

11. Name some polymers that are produced in nature. Tell where they come from.

12. Explain why some advantages of using synthetic polymers can become disadvantages.

13. Why is gold mixed with other metals to make jewelry?

14. What are three uses of high-carbon steels? What are three uses of low-carbon steels?

15. Describe the process that changes clay into ceramics.

16. Why are glass fibers advantageous over copper wire when installing long telephone lines?

Thinking Critically

17. **Comparing and Contrasting** Explain which material—steel, glass, or polystyrene foam—would be the best choice for each of the following uses: a hammer, the wall of a saltwater aquarium, an egg carton.

18. **Calculating** A pair of optical fibers can carry 625,000 phone calls at one time. How many pairs of optical fibers would be needed to carry 5,250,000 calls at one time?

19. **Interpreting Diagrams** One carbon atom can form four covalent bonds. Carbon compounds, the base of many polymers, can form structures like those shown below. Which type of carbon structure has 18 covalent bonds?

Straight chain

Ring

Branched chain

Applying Skills

Use the diagram to answer the questions.

The table below shows the composition of four different alloys.

Percentage of Pure Metals in Alloy

Pure Metal Ingredient	Alloy 1	Alloy 2	Alloy 3	Alloy 4
Lead	50	20	10	60
Tin	10	50	45	10
Zinc	40	30	45	30

20. **Interpreting Data** Which alloy has lead for more than half of its composition? Which alloy is 45 percent zinc?

21. **Classifying** Which common alloy could all four of the above alloys be used to produce?

22. **Calculating** Which two of the above alloys could you combine to produce a new alloy that was 40 percent lead, 30 percent tin, and 30 percent zinc?

23. **Inferring** Lead can be poisonous to people. Which of the above alloys would you not want to use to make an eating utensil?

▸ Lab zone Chapter **Project**

Performance Assessment Prepare a chart or poster to display the polymers you examined. Provide a sample of each polymer and include information such as its name, where it was found, what monomers it is made of (if known), and significant physical and chemical properties that you determined. Be prepared to compare the polymers with other types of materials such as glass, ceramics, and metals.

⓪ Standardized Test Practice

Test-Taking Tip

Interpreting a Data Table

When answering a question related to a data table, read the title of the table to see what type of data it contains. Next look at the headings of the columns and rows to see how the data are organized. For example, the data table below shows the parts gold to alloy in different karats of gold. Finally, read the question to determine which data you will need to answer the question.

Sample Question

Based on the data table below, how does the percentage of gold change as the karats increase by 4 units?

Karat	Parts Gold to Alloy	Percentage	Fineness
10K	10/24	41.67%	417
14K	14/24	58.33%	583
18K	18/24	75.00%	750
22K	22/24	91.66%	917

A It stays the same.
B It increases by 170.
C It increases by approximately 17%.
D It increases by 4 parts.

Answer

The correct answer is **C**. The percentage of gold in a 14K gold alloy increases by 16.66% from a 10K gold alloy. This trend continues as karat increases. Answer **A** is not correct since the percentage of gold varies by karat. Answer **B** refers to the increase in fineness. Answer **D** refers to parts gold to alloy.

Choose the letter of the best answer.

1. Which of the following is *not* an example of an alloy?
   A brass
   B bronze
   C stainless steel
   D iron

Use the information and data table below to answer Questions 2–3.

Polymer Identification			
Test	**Cotton**	**Wool**	**Polyester**
Texture	Smooth	Rough	Smooth
Near flame	Does not bend or melt	Curls away from heat	Melts
In flame	Burns; smells like paper burning	Burns; smells like hair burning	Melts

2. A student has two pieces of fabric—one blue and one green. The student performs an investigation to identify the fabrics. What can the student conclude if the texture of both pieces of fabric is smooth?
   A Both fabrics must be cotton.
   B Both fabrics must be polyester.
   C One fabric must be cotton and the other must be polyester.
   D Neither piece is wool.

3. What should the student do before testing either piece of fabric near or in a flame?
   A Put on safety goggles and an apron and tie back long hair.
   B Crumple the fabric to make it burn more easily.
   C Wash his or her hands.
   D Determine the mass of the fabric

4. Radioactive isotopes give off radiation that can be detected. This property makes them useful in which of the following ways?
   A as tracers in chemical reactions
   B in detecting leaks in oil pipelines
   C in diagnosing certain medical problems
   D all of the above

Open-Ended Question

5. You are considering using either glass or disposable plastic to serve soft drinks at a party. Discuss how the beverage containers are similar and how they are different.

◀ A gold crown is a symbol of royalty.

Gold—The Noble Metal

You can find it —

on people's wrists, in your computer, on dinner plates, satellites, and in spacesuits

Because gold is both rare and beautiful, people have prized it since ancient times. Gold was so valuable that it was used to make crowns for rulers and coins for trade. In some cultures, people wear gold bracelets and necklaces to show their wealth.

In spite of its many uses, gold is scarce. For every 23,000 metric tons of rock and minerals from the Earth's crust, you could produce only about 14 grams of gold, enough to make a small ring. Today, gold is found in many parts of the world. But even rich gold fields produce only small amounts of gold. In fact, if all the gold mined over the years were gathered and melted down, you would have a cube only about 15 meters on a side—about the size of a four-story square building.

Wearing Gold
This woman from Ghana in Africa displays her wealth in gold jewelry.

Gold Nugget
A nugget is gold in one of its natural forms.

Properties of Gold

Why is gold used for everything from bracelets to space helmets to medicine? You'll find the answers in this precious metal's unusual chemical and physical properties. Gold is deep yellow in color and so shiny, or lustrous, that its Latin name, *aurum,* means "glowing dawn." Gold's chemical symbol—Au—comes from that Latin word. Gold is very heavy—one of the densest metals.

Gold is very soft and malleable. That is, it's easy to bend or hammer into shapes without breaking. It can be pounded into very thin sheets called gold leaf. Gold is also the most ductile metal. You can draw out 30 grams of gold into a fine thread as long as 8 kilometers without breaking it.

Gold is very stable. Unlike iron, gold doesn't rust. It also doesn't tarnish in air as silver does. Ancient chemists thought that gold was superior to other metals. They classified it as one of the "noble" metals.

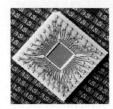

Ductile
Because gold is so ductile, it can be made into fine wires like the ones in this computer chip.

Malleable
A Korean delicacy is dried fish coated with gold leaf.

Stable and Lustrous
Hundreds of years ago, traders used these gold doubloons as money.

Science Activity

The gold hunters who flocked to California during the Gold Rush of 1849 were searching for gold in streams and rivers. Although they had very simple equipment, their technique worked because gold is so dense. Using pans, miners washed gold-bearing gravel in running water. Try your own gold panning.

Set up your own model of gold panning, using a large pan, a gravel mixture, and a very dense material as a substitute for gold. Use a sink trap. Under running water, shake and swirl the pan until the lighter materials wash away. What's left is your "gold."

- Why is "gold" left in the pan while other materials are washed away?

Golden Trade Routes

In West Africa nearly 1,000 years ago, salt was said to be worth its weight in gold. It may be hard to imagine how valuable this mineral was to people. But if you lived in a very hot, dry climate, you would need salt. It would be as valuable to you as gold. In West Africa, salt and gold were the most important goods traded.

Camel caravans crossed the desert going south, carrying slabs of salt from mines in the desert to trade centers, such as Jenne and Timbuktu. But several hundred kilometers south in the Kingdom of Ghana, salt was scarce and gold was plentiful. Salt traders from the north traveled into the forests of Ghana to trade salt for gold.

Around 1100, Arab travelers in Africa wrote about the fabulous wealth of the Kingdom of Ghana. The most popular tale was that the salt traders and gold miners never met, as a way of keeping secret the location of gold mines. Traders from the north left slabs of salt in an agreed-upon trading place, pounded their drums to indicate a trade, and then withdrew. Miners from the south arrived, left an amount of gold that seemed fair, and withdrew. The salt traders returned. If they thought the trade was fair, they took the gold and left. If they were not satisfied, the silent trade continued.

Salt Caravan
Camels carrying salt slabs
travel to Timbuktu.

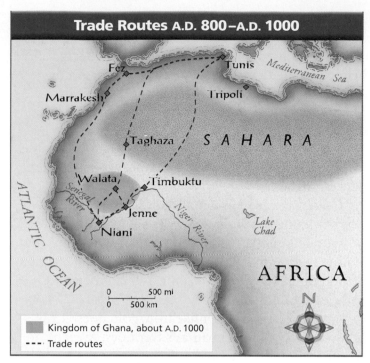

Trade Routes A.D. 800–A.D. 1000

Kingdom of Ghana, about A.D. 1000
- - - Trade routes

Gold Trade Routes
The map shows the busy north-south trade routes in West Africa about 1,000 years ago.

Social Studies Activity

How would you succeed as a gold or salt trader? Find out by carrying out your own silent trade. Work in teams of Salt Traders and Gold Miners. Before trading, each team should decide how much a bag of gold or a block of salt is worth. Then, for each silent trade, make up a situation that would change the value of gold or salt, such as, "Demand for gold in Europe increases."

- Suppose you are selling a product today. How would the supply of the product affect the value or sale price of the product?

Go for the Gold

What do these sayings have in common?

> "It's worth its weight in gold."

> "Speech is silver, silence is golden."

> "All that glitters is not gold."

> "Go for the gold!"

All of these sayings use gold as a symbol of excellence, richness, and perfection—things that people want and search for. When writers use *gold* or *golden,* they are referring to something desirable, of value or worth. These words may also represent the beauty of gold.

In literature, writers and poets often use *gold* to make a comparison in a simile or metaphor. Similes and metaphors are figures of speech.

- A simile makes a comparison between two things, using *like* or *as* in the comparison. Here's an example: "An honest person's promise is as good as gold."

- A metaphor is a comparison without the use of like or as, such as, "When you're in trouble, true friends are golden."

Look for similes and metaphors in the poem by Florence Converse. What similes or metaphors has Converse made? What would this poem be like without the comparisons?

Rune of Riches*

I have a golden ball,
A big, bright, shining one,
Pure gold; and it is all
Mine—It is the sun.

I have a silver ball
A white and glistening stone
That other people call
The moon;—my very own!

The jewel things that prick
My cushion's soft blue cover
Are mine,—my stars, thick, thick,
Scattered the sky all over.

And everything that's mine
Is yours, and yours, and yours,—
The shimmer and the shine!—
Let's lock our wealth out-doors!

———Florence Converse

*A rune is a song or poem.

Language Arts Activity

What does gold symbolize for you? Think of some comparisons of your own in which you use gold in a simile or metaphor. After jotting down all of your ideas, choose one (or more) and decide what comparison you will make. Write a short saying, a proverb, or a short poem that includes your own simile or metaphor.

- How does your comparison make your saying or poem more interesting?

Measuring Gold

People often say that something is "worth its weight in gold." But modern-day jewelry is seldom made of pure gold. Because gold is so soft, it is usually mixed with another metal to form an alloy—a mixture of two or more metals. Most commonly the other metal in a gold alloy is copper, although alloys of gold can also contain silver, zinc, or other metals.

Suppose you are shopping for a gold chain. You see two chains that look the same and are exactly the same size. How do you decide which one to buy? If you look closely at the gold jewelry, you'll probably see in small print the numbers "20K," "18K," "14K," or "12K." The "K" is the abbreviation for karat, which is the measure of how pure an alloy of gold is. Pure gold is 24 karat. Gold that is 50 percent pure is $\frac{12}{24}$ gold, or 12 karat. The greater the amount of gold in a piece of jewelry, the higher the value.

You look again at the two gold chains and decide that your favorite is the 18-karat gold chain. It has copper in it. What percent of the 18 K gold chain is gold? What percent is copper?

Weighing Gold
A worker in the Federal Reserve Bank of the United States weighs dense ingots, or bars, of pure gold.

❶ Read and Understand

You know that pure gold is $\frac{24}{24}$ gold,

and an 18 karat chain is $\frac{18}{24}$ gold.

❷ Plan and Solve

In order to find out what percent of an 18 K chain is gold, you need to write a proportion.

$$\frac{\text{Number of gold parts}}{\text{Number of parts in the whole}} \rightarrow \frac{18}{24}$$

Then simplify the fraction and convert it to a percentage.

$$\frac{18}{24} = \frac{3}{4} = 75\%$$

❸ Look Back and Check

If 75% of the chain is gold, then 25% of the chain must be copper.

Math Activity

How would you choose a gold ring? To decide, you might determine what percent of each ring is gold.

- What percent of a 14 K gold ring is gold? What percent is another metal? Round decimals to the nearest hundredth.

- What percent of a 12 K ring is gold? What percent of the 20 K ring is gold?

- Which ring would you like to own—the 12 K or the 20 K? Why?

Gold Mask
This gold mask was found in the tomb of a ruler of Mycenae, a city in ancient Greece. The mask is about 3,500 years old.

Tie It Together

Gold Producers

South Africa	United States	Russia
Australia	Canada	China

A Treasure Hunt

Work in small groups to make a World Treasure Map of one of the countries where gold is mined today. Use the library to learn about the gold-producing countries listed above.

On a large map of the world, use push pins to mark the locations of the gold sites. In the United States and Canada, mark the states and provinces that are the largest producers. Make up fact sheets to answer questions such as:

- Where are gold sites located in each country?

- When was gold first discovered there?

- Did a gold rush influence the history of that area?

If possible, collect photographs to illustrate gold products in each country. Post your pictures and fact sheets at the side of the World Treasure Map.

Indiana Science Standards Refresher Grade 7

Use the following pages to help you master the Indiana Academic Standards for Science. First, read each science standard. Then study the Review section until you are sure that you understand the standard. Check your understanding by answering the Reading Checkpoint questions in the longer Review sections. Then answer the Practice questions. You'll find the answers to the Reading Checkpoint and Practice questions on page 788.

Note to Parents

The Indiana Science Standards Refresher is a short, efficient study guide to the science knowledge and skills that all Indiana middle-school students are expected to master in Grade 7. Your middle-school student can use the Standards Refresher to prepare for a final science exam. Review the Indiana Science Standards with your child to help him or her prepare for these exams.

Contents

1 The Nature of Science and Technology

The Scientific View of the World

Indicator 7.1.1 Recognize that when similar experiments give different results, more research may be needed.

Review

Results May Differ At times, scientists may get different results from the same experiment. The scientific challenge is to decide if the differences are trivial or significant. When an experiment is repeated, minor differences may occur. As a result, the same experiment will give slightly different results each time it is performed. Usually these differences are considered trivial and normal. If it is determined that the differing results are not the result of a normal laboratory error, additional study and experimentation may be required. The scientists may need to form a new hypothesis and design new experiments. This process will repeat until the scientists are satisfied with the results.

In Your Book Chapter 1, Sections 1, 3

Practice

1. A trivial difference between two results is _____.
   A unacceptable
   B acceptable
   C correct
   D wrong

2. Kathy and Robert each performed an experiment to find the boiling point of a salt solution. Kathy's boiling point was 105°C and Robert's was 107°C for the same solution. The accuracy of the thermometers is ±2°C. Are these differing results trivial or significant? Explain.

Differing Results Inaccurate laboratory equipment could cause different results when duplicating an experiment.

Academic Standards

INDIANA

Indicator 7.1.2 Explain that what people expect to observe often affects what they do observe.

Review

Bias in Science Science is based on facts, not opinions. It is important that all observations and results in the field of science are based on facts. When someone bases a decision upon an opinion instead of facts, it is called bias.

There are several ways to avoid bias in science. One way is to take careful and accurate measurements. Another way is to write down everything that is observed, even things that may not seem important at the time. To avoid bias when taking a survey, it is important to use a random sample of people. In taking a survey that compares items, all labels should be concealed so that all items look the same.

Reading Checkpoint

3. What is bias?

Drawing Conclusions Eliminating bias while collecting data is very important. However, it is just as important to eliminate bias when drawing conclusions. Collected data should be studied very carefully. All decisions should be based on the available data, not on opinion or what is expected to occur.

Reading Checkpoint

4. How can you avoid bias when drawing conclusions?

Accurate Measurements Scientists should take careful and accurate measurements in their experiments in order to eliminate bias.

Practice

5. In science, conclusions should be based on _____.
   A collected data
   B the opinion of the scientist
   C what is expected to occur
   D a combination of opinions and surveys

6. Which of the following statements is an opinion?
   A Earth has one moon.
   B The glass rod is 3 cm long.
   C The chemical is a white powder.
   D Blue is a beautiful color.

7. How can you avoid bias in surveys?

8. Malcolm wants to find out which soft drink is preferred by his classmates. What should he do to eliminate bias in the survey?

Indicator 7.1.3 Explain the importance of keeping honest, clear, and accurate records.

Review

Honesty in Science Dishonesty in science, though rare, has occurred. For example, in 1999, a team of scientists at a well-known university claimed to have created two new elements. This announcement brought fame to the university and to the science team. Other scientists around the world tried to duplicate the results, but they were unable to do so. Scientists began to suspect that something was wrong since no one could successfully repeat the experiment. An investigation determined that someone on the team made up the data and misled the other team members. Instead of fame, the dishonest scientist and the other team members lost their good reputation in the scientific community.

9. How was one of the scientists dishonest?

Clear and Accurate Records Despite the fact that one of the scientists was dishonest, the team did keep clear and accurate records of all their experiments. After a careful evaluation of the original data, it became clear that the new elements had not been created as was originally claimed. Had the team kept sloppy records, other scientists would not have been able to repeat the experiment to test the results. Scientists would have had no way to verify that the data could be duplicated.

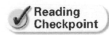

10. What was used to prove that the new elements had not been created?

Accurate Records Honest, clear, and accurate records are essential for all successful experiments.

Practice

11. What was the first indication that something was wrong with the claim that new elements were created?
   A The science team had a bad reputation.
   B An investigation found that data was made up.
   C Other scientists could not duplicate the results.
   D The dishonest scientist left the university.

12. Why is it important to keep clear and accurate records?
   A Other scientists may have to read and interpret the records.
   B Scientists who are sloppy may be dishonest.
   C Clear and accurate records indicate truth in science.
   D Sloppy records are an indication of wrong results.

13. What could happen if a scientist made up data about a new drug that was supposed to cure a disease?

14. Why is it important for scientists to be able to duplicate experiments?

Academic Standards

Indicator 7.1.4 Describe how further study can help scientists choose among different explanations for the same evidence.

Review

Different Explanations Sometimes more than one explanation can be given for the same evidence. It is not always possible to tell which explanation is correct without further study. For example, the explanation of how a human hand can warm a cool spoon has changed over the years. Before the nineteenth century, it was widely believed that a liquid called caloric was transferred from your hand to the spoon. This seemed like a reasonable explanation because something was being transferred that was not visible to the human eye. It was not until the mid-nineteenth century that a new, scientific explanation was found. Scientists were able to demonstrate that it was a form of energy, not a liquid, that was being transferred from the hand to the spoon.

In Your Book Chapter 1, Section 1; Chapter 16, Section 1; Chapter 17, Section 5

Practice

15. Before the nineteenth century, what was the accepted explanation about how a hand warmed a cool spoon?

A Energy was transferred from a hand to the spoon.

B A substance called caloric was transferred between a hand and the spoon.

C There were many widely accepted theories at this time.

D Scientists believed that it was impossible to explain because it could not be seen.

16. If more than one explanation is possible, how do scientists determine which one is correct?

The Scientific Enterprise

Indicator 7.1.5 Identify important contributions to science, mathematics, and technology by people of different cultures and times.

Review

An Accumulation of Knowledge

The body of scientific, mathematical, and technological knowledge is an accumulation of work over thousands of years from many cultures. For example, one of the first computers, an abacus, was used by the Babylonians around 2400 B.C. The widespread use of the abacus resulted in the idea of the number zero. The first known use of zero was in India around 876 B.C. Zero was not a number initially but served as a position marker on an abacus. Without using a place holder, numbers such as 123, 1,023, 1,203, and 1,230 were easily confused. The use of zero is now a vital part of mathematics.

Another more recent example of an accumulation of knowledge is the Human Genome Project. The Human Genome Project began in the United States in 1990. Other scientists from Japan, the United Kingdom, Italy, France, and Russia have joined in the goal to identify the location of every human gene. The information gathered from this project is expected to lead to great advancements in the study of biology, disease, and medicine.

In Your Book Chapter 4, Section 4; Chapter 10, Section 3; Chapter 12, Section 2; Chapter 16, Section 1; Chapter 19, Section 1

Practice

17. One of the first computers, the abacus, was used in _____ in 2400 B.C.

A Babylonia

B China

C India

D Russia

18. Explain why science is an accumulation of knowledge from many cultures.

Indicator 7.1.6 Provide examples of people who overcame adversity to excel in the fields of science.

Review

Overcoming Poverty Dmitri Mendeleev (1834–1907) was a bright, but poor student, who was encouraged by his mother to pursue his scientific interests. Because of political and social unrest in Russia, Dmitri was rejected at the university in Moscow since he was not from Moscow. After the death of his parents, Mendeleev eventually entered the University of St. Petersburg as a student and later became a teacher there. He soon became known throughout Russia as a chemist whose work benefited farmers and workers. Mendeleev's greatest accomplishment was creating the periodic table—a table organizing all the known elements. Some scientists at the time scoffed at Mendeleev because he used the table to predict the existence of three undiscovered elements. Other scientists took him seriously a few years later, after the discovery of those elements: gallium, scandium, and germanium.

19. Why did other scientists eventually take Mendeleev seriously?

Overcoming Adversity Lise Meitner (1878–1968) was an Austrian-born physicist. Meitner faced much discrimination because she was Jewish and living in Nazi Germany, and also because she was a woman working in a male-dominated field. Meitner published the first paper about nuclear fission in 1939. She predicted that during nuclear fission, a chain reaction would occur. This early research led to the development of the atomic bomb. Meitner fled Germany after Adolph Hitler came to power and lived in exile in Sweden. Meitner had to battle prejudice throughout her lifetime, yet she made lasting contributions to science.

Meitner was denied the Nobel Prize for her work in nuclear fission, but element 109, meitnerium, was named in her honor in 1997.

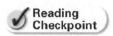

20. What field of science did Lise Meitner study?

Lise Meitner Austrian-born physicist Lise Meitner succeeded in her field of science despite prejudice.

Practice

21. Dmitri Mendeleev developed the _____.
    A periodic table
    B laws of nature
    C elements
    D atomic number

22. What was the topic of Lise Meitner's paper that was published in 1939?
    A atomic bombs
    B German Jews
    C nuclear fission
    D element 109

23. Why was Mendeleev known by the people of Russia?

24. Why was Meitner's gender an obstacle to her success as a scientist?

Academic Standards

INDIANA

Technology and Science

Indicator 7.1.7 Explain how people use science to solve practical problems in design and technology.

Review

Solving Practical Problems Science and technology are useful in solving practical problems. For example, in the early 1900s, polio was a dreaded disease worldwide. An estimated 21,000 children and young adults were paralyzed each year from polio. Dr. Jonas Salk, a physician, developed the first vaccine to protect children and young adults. Today this crippling disease has been almost eliminated in the United States and Canada. Some parts of the world, such as Africa, the Middle East, and South Asia, still have large numbers of children affected by polio. It is hoped that one day polio will be eliminated worldwide.

In Your Book Chapter 1, Section 5; Chapter 2, Section 3; Chapter 12, Section 3; Chapter 17, Section 1; Chapter 20

Practice

25. Dr. Jonas Salk developed the first vaccine for _____.
  A crippling diseases
  B diseases
  C paralysis
  D polio

26. Give another example of how scientific knowledge has solved practical problems.

Indicator 7.1.8 Describe some benefits and drawbacks to technology, such as technology that helps some organisms but hurts others.

Review

Benefits and Drawbacks Sometimes technology solves one problem but creates new ones. For example, some early pesticides were very effective in controlling insects, but they also killed many other organisms. The bald eagle was almost driven to extinction because of a pesticide called DDT. Another example of a technological advance that had benefits and drawbacks was the use of chlorofluorocarbons, or CFCs. CFCs are compounds that were widely used in refrigerators, freezers, air conditioners, heat pumps, and aerosols. During the 1970s, CFCs were linked to the destruction of the Earth's ozone layer. CFCs that are released into the atmosphere rise to the ozone layer. Once they reach the ozone layer, strong ultraviolet radiation breaks down the CFC molecules. The chlorine in the CFC molecules then reacts with the ozone molecules. A single chlorine atom from a CFC can destroy as many as 100,000 ozone molecules. Manufacturing CFCs is now banned in most countries.

In Your Book Chapter 1, Section 4; Chapter 20, Section 1

Practice

27. What nearly drove the bald eagle to extinction?
  A aerosols
  B DDT
  C CFCs
  D the ozone layer

28. Describe another type of technology that has both benefits and drawbacks.

Indicator 7.1.9 Explain how societies influence what types of technology are developed and used.

Review

Responding to Public Demand Society often influences the types of technologies that are developed. Since cars and trucks are used in many parts of the world, a great deal of emphasis is placed on their development. As a result, engineers and scientists are trying to develop new cars that create less pollution, which has led to the development of the fuel cell. Unlike cars powered by fossil fuels—which pollute the air with their waste products—the only waste product of cars powered by fuel cells is water.

In Your Book Chapter 1, Section 4; Chapter 2, Section 3; Chapter 4, Section 5; Chapter 9, Section 3; Chapter 17, Section 1

Practice

29. What is the waste product from a fuel cell?

A carbon

B hydrogen

C oxygen

D water

30. Give an example of how scientists have responded to public demand when developing new technologies.

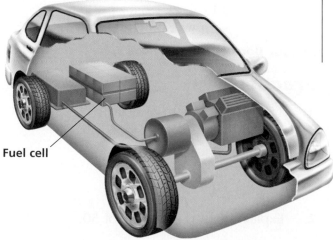

Fuel cell

Indicator 7.1.10 Identify ways that technology influences the course of history.

Review

Technology and History Technology has influenced the course of history many times and in many ways. For example, during the Industrial Revolution many people who lived on farms moved into cities to work in factories. This population shift had a great effect on social and political systems. Another example of technology influencing history is the development of nuclear fission. During World War II, technology in nuclear fission progressed rapidly. Nuclear bombs were used for the first time in conflict during this war. The threat of nuclear war kept the United States and the United Soviet Socialist Republic in a stand-off called the Cold War for decades after World War II.

In Your Book Chapter 1, Section 4; Chapter 6, Sections 1, 3; Chapter 12, Section 2; Chapter 16, Section 1; Chapter 17, Section 1

Practice

31. During the Industrial Revolution, _____.

A people moved into cities to work in factories

B the United States and the United Soviet Socialist Republic were in a stand-off

C global communications became very fast

D technology in nuclear fission progressed rapidly

32. Give another example of how technology has strongly influenced the course of history.

Alternative-Fuel Vehicle Cars that use fuel cells are an example of public demand influencing the development of technology.

Academic Standards

753

Indicator 7.1.11 Illustrate how numbers can be represented by sequences of only two symbols and how that affects the storage of information.

Review

Binary System The binary system is a number system that uses only two numbers, 0 and 1. Numbers are written differently in this system. The number 2 is written as 10 because that is the next number that can be made using only 0's and 1's. The numbers 3 through 9 are written as 11, 100, 101, 110, 111, 1000, 1001.

Computers use the binary system to store information by using switches that are either "on" or "off." The 1's correspond to the "on" position and the 0's correspond to the "off" position.

In Your Book Chapter 12, Section 3

Practice

33. What does a computer use to store information?
A on-off switches
B magnetic dots
C pits and bumps
D laser light

34. Explain why the binary representation for 5 is 101.

2 Scientific Thinking

Computation and Estimation

Indicator 7.2.1 Find what percentage one number is of another. Find any percentage of any number.

Review

Finding Percentages You can find what percent one number is of another. For example, 27 is what percent of 60? First, write a fraction for the numbers. There are 27 out of 60 parts or $\frac{27}{60}$. Then divide: $27 \div 60 = 0.45$.

Next, write 0.45 as a percent:

$$0.45 = \frac{45}{100} = 45\%$$

So, 27 is 45% of 60.

You can also find the percentage of a number. For example, what is

$$12\% \text{ of } 32?$$

First write 12% as a decimal.

$$12\% = \frac{12}{100} = 0.12$$

Then multiply 0.12 by 32:

$$0.12 \times 32 = 3.84$$

So, 12% of 32 is 3.84.

In Your Book *Skills Handbook*

Practice

1. 15 is what percent of 60?
A 2.5%
B 15%
C 25%
D 75%

2. Explain how to find 20% of 50.

Indicator 7.2.2 Use formulas to calculate the circumference, area, and volume of various shapes.

Indicator 7.2.3 Use the precision of original data to determine the precision and significant digits of a calculated value.

Review

Using Formulas A formula is a rule written as an equation with symbols or variables that describe the relationship between quantities. Formulas can be used to calculate the circumference, area, or volume of various figures. Here are some formulas.

> **Circumference of a Circle**
> $C = 2 \times \pi \times r$, or $C = 2\pi r$
>
> **Area of a Rectangle**
> $A = l \times w$, or $A = lw$
>
> **Area of a Square**
> $A = s \times s$, or $A = s^2$
>
> **Area of a Circle**
> $A = \pi \times r \times r$, or $A = \pi r^2$
>
> **Volume of a Rectangular Object**
> $V = l \times w \times h$, or $V = lwh$
>
> **Volume of a Cylinder**
> $V = (\pi r^2)h$

In Your Book *Skills Handbook*

Practice

3. What is the area of a rectangle with a length of 12 centimeters and a width of 6 centimeters?

A 18 cm²

B 48 cm²

C 60 cm²

D 72 cm²

4. What formula could you use to find the volume of a shoe box?

Review

Precision and Significant Digits

Scientists report numerical values using decimal places and significant digits. A temperature of 30.6°C is rounded to one decimal place and has 3 significant digits.

When you add or subtract measurements, the answer can only be as accurate as the measurement with the least number of decimal places. For example, if you add 1.31 cm (2 decimal places) and 4.9 cm (1 decimal place), the answer is 6.21 cm. You should round the answer to 6.2 cm (1 decimal place).

When you multipy or divide measurements, the answer can only be as accurate as the measurement with the least number of significant digits. For example, if you multiply 2.19 cm (3 significant digits) by 7.33cm (3 significant digits), the answer is 16.0527 cm². You should round the answer to 16.1 cm² (3 significant digits).

In Your Book *Skills Handbook*

Practice

5. Rhonda cut 1.5 centimeters from a string 6.89 centimeters long. What is the new length of the string? Round your answer to the correct number of significant digits.

A 5.39 cm

B 5.40 cm

C 5.3 cm

D 5.4 cm

6. Find 3.2 m × 1.09 m. Round your answer to the correct number of significant digits.

Academic Standards

Indicator 7.2.4 Express numbers such as 10, 100, and 1,000 as powers of 10.

Review

Powers of Ten You can use powers of ten to express numbers such as 10, 100, and 1,000. The power of ten is written as an exponent of the number 10. The exponent indicates how many times 10 is used as a factor. Here are some examples.

$$10^1 = 10$$
$$10^2 = 10 \times 10 = 100$$
$$10^3 = 10 \times 10 \times 10 = 1,000$$
$$10^4 = 10 \times 10 \times 10 \times 10 = 10,000$$

In Your Book Chapter 17, Section 4; *Skills Handbook*

Practice

7. $10^3 = $ _____

A $10 \times 10 \times 10 = 1,000$

B $10 \times 10 = 100$

C 10

D 1

8. A microscope magnifies objects 100 times. How is 100 written as a power of 10?

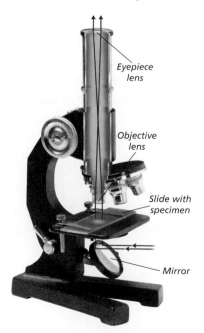

Eyepiece lens

Objective lens

Slide with specimen

Mirror

100x This microscope magnifies objects up to 100 times.

Indicator 7.2.5 Estimate probabilities of outcomes based on experience or the number of possible outcomes.

Review

Probability Probability is the chance that an event will occur. The following formula can be used to find the probability of an event.

$$P(\text{event}) = \frac{\text{Number of times the event can occur}}{\text{Total number of possible events}}$$

You can write probability as a ratio, fraction, or percent. For example, suppose you spin a spinner divided into four equal sections labeled 1–4. Here is how to find and write the probability of spinning a 3.

$$P(3) = \frac{1 \text{ section labeled 3}}{4 \text{ sections total}}$$
$$P(3) = \frac{1}{4} = \frac{25}{100} = 25\%$$

In Your Book *Skills Handbook*

Practice

9. There are 2 black rabbits, 1 white rabbit, 3 gray rabbits, and 1 spotted rabbit in a hutch. If you picked 1 rabbit without looking, what is the probability of picking a gray rabbit?

A $\frac{2}{7}$

B $\frac{3}{5}$

C $\frac{1}{3}$

D $\frac{3}{7}$

10. How can probability be expressed?

Manipulation and Observation

Indicator 7.2.6 Measure length, volume, weight, elapsed time, rates, or temperatures and choose appropriate units.

Review

Making Measurements Scientists use instruments to measure length, mass, capacity, time, rate, and temperature. Using measurements, they can compare two or more objects. For example, length is the distance between two points. Length can be measured and compared using millimeters, centimeters, meters, or kilometers. Mass is the amount of matter in an object. Mass can be measured and compared using grams or kilograms. When you measure, it is important to use the appropriate units. If you were measuring the distance from your home to school, you would not use centimeters because the number would be too great and it would be difficult to measure. Kilometers would be a more appropriate unit of measure.

In Your Book Chapter 4, Section 2; Chapter 10, Section 1 and Chapter Project; Chapter 13, Chapter Project; Chapter 15, Section 3

Practice

11. What would be the appropriate unit of measure for the mass of four beans?

    A millimeters

    B grams

    C kiloliters

    D meters

12. What are some metric units used to measure length?

Communication Skills

Indicator 7.2.7 Use graphs, diagrams, and symbols in writing to provide evidence for conclusions.

Review

Data Displays Scientists use graphs, diagrams, and symbols to present data clearly and help them draw conclusions from the data. Graphs are organized, visual representations of data. Graphs can be used to compare data, to show change over time, and to show data as a part of the whole.

A diagram is a drawing that is a visual picture of a topic. Diagrams are useful in showing at a glance how concepts are related. In science, there are many complex situations that are clarified by using diagrams.

Symbols are used widely in science. They are used to represent elements, concepts, and processes. The letters or drawings that make up symbols often reflect some aspect of its meaning.

In Your Book Chapter 1, Section 3; Chapter 3, Chapter Project; Chapter 9, Section 4; Chapter 12, Section 2; *Skills Handbook*

Practice

13. To show change over time, use a _____.

    A symbol

    B graph

    C diagram of the body

    D letters and numbers

14. Why are symbols, graphs, and diagrams used in science?

Academic Standards

INDIANA

Critical Response Skills

Indicator 7.2.8 Question claims based on statements that are vague or made by people speaking outside their area of expertise.

Review

Critical Viewing You may have seen advertisements on TV or in magazines that show a celebrity talking about products such as gum or face cream, making claims about their ability to have some positive scientific effect on you. It is important to look at these advertisements critically and question whether the claims are reasonable. Even though a celebrity says a juice drink is healthy, it does not mean that there is scientific evidence to back up that claim. Celebrities are not usually science experts. They are often paid to make statements about a product.

One way to check a claim's validity is to see if the claim is endorsed by a government agency. For example, if the Food and Drug Administration (FDA) endorses a product in an ad, you can be sure that any scientific claims in the ad are valid.

In Your Book Chapter 1, Section 1; *Skills Handbook*

Practice

15. You can trust a claim that is _____.
    A unclear or vague
    B approved by the FDA
    C endorsed by a famous athlete
    D scientific sounding

16. A television commercial made the following claim, "According to professional athletes, Brand X Sports Drink provides more energy than the other brands." Explain why you might question this statement.

Question Claims Reading food labels and viewing advertisements critically can help people make informed choices about products.

3 The Physical Setting

The Universe

Indicator 7.3.1 Recognize that the sun is a star located near the edge of a galaxy. The universe contains billions of galaxies. Each galaxy contains billions of stars.

Review

Medium-Sized Star The Universe is made up of billions of galaxies, each of which contains billions of stars, as well as clouds of dust and gas. Astronomers have divided galaxies into four main types according to their shapes: spiral, barred spiral, elliptical, and irregular.

Stars, which consist of extremely hot gas, radiate light and heat. They vary widely in size, color, brightness, temperature, and mass. Our sun is a medium-sized star on the edge of a spiral galaxy called the Milky Way. From Earth we see our spiral galaxy from the side, so the Milky Way looks like a band of light across the night sky.

In Your Book Chapter 16, Section 2; Chapter 17

Practice

1. What is the sun?
    A a large-sized planet
    B a barred spiral galaxy
    C a star in the center of the Milky Way
    D a medium-sized star on the edge of the Milky Way

2. A galaxy is _____.
    A a massive group of planets
    B a vast collection of stars
    C a medium-sized star
    D bigger than the Universe

Our Sun The sun lies on the edge of the Milky Way.

Academic Standards

Indicator 7.3.2 Recognize that the sun is much closer to Earth than any other star. Sunlight reaches Earth much sooner than the light of other stars.

Review

Closer, Brighter, Hotter Our sun is a star and the center of our solar system. All the planets, including Earth, revolve, or travel in an orbit, around it.

Like the sun, all stars are huge balls of extremely hot gas that radiate light and heat into space. Stars vary in size and temperature. Some stars are huge with a diameter as large as 700,000,000 km. The surface temperatures of some stars can reach over 20,000°C. Our sun, with a diameter of 1.4 million km, is a medium-sized star, and its surface temperature reaches only about 5,800°C. Yet it provides more light and heat to Earth than any other star because it is the star closest to us. At a distance of about 150 million km, the sun is many thousands of times closer to Earth than any other star. Its light reaches Earth in a few minutes while light from the next closest star takes 4.3 years to arrive.

In Your Book Chapter 16, Section 2; Chapter 17

Practice

3. Why does light from the sun reach Earth faster than from any other star?
  A The sun is closer than other stars.
  B The sun is farther away than other stars.
  C The sun is larger than other stars.
  D The sun is hotter than other stars.

4. All stars are _____.
  A smaller than the sun
  B closer than the sun
  C huge balls of gas
  D the same distance from Earth

Earth and the Processes That Shape It

Indicator 7.3.3 Describe how changes in Earth's crust sometimes changed climates abruptly.

Review

Climate Change Climate is the average weather conditions, such as amounts of precipitation and ranges of temperature, in a certain place over a period of decades. In the past, there have been abrupt changes in climates due to changes in the Earth's crust.

There is evidence that huge volcanic eruptions changed climates by sending dust and ash into the atmosphere. The ash and dust blocked sunlight from reaching Earth's surface, causing lower temperatures. Climatic changes caused by volcanoes can be sudden, and can last for a short time or for years.

Asteroids, or rocks from space, have also changed the climate. In the past, when a huge asteroid hit Earth's crust, fine particles were sent into the atmosphere, blocking sunlight and lowering the atmosphere's temperature abruptly. Fine particles can stay suspended in the atmosphere for long periods of time, changing the climate for years.

In Your Book Chapter 8, Sections 3, 4

Practice

5. When a volcano erupts, what happens that causes changes in Earth's climate?
  A The volcano spews lava.
  B The lava hardens on the surface.
  C The volcano ejects huge rocks into space.
  D The volcano emits ash and dust that block sunlight.

6. How can asteroids affect the climate on Earth?

Indicator 7.3.4 Explain how heat flow and movement within Earth cause earthquakes and volcanic eruptions and create mountains and ocean basins.

Review

Making Mountains Earth's surface may appear calm but within its crust, huge plates are moving and red-hot melted rock or magma is flowing and rising. When a volcano erupts, magma rises to the surface through a vent or weak spot in Earth's crust. Magma that escapes is called lava. Volcanoes can erupt, expelling lava, ash, and chunks of rock. Mountains form as layers of these materials build up.

Mountains can also be formed by earthquakes. Earth's crust is made up of huge plates that meet at fault lines, or cracks in the crust. Movement of these plates can cause earthquakes. When plates collide, rock is pressed together and can be forced upward, creating a mountain. When plates move apart, a block of crust between fault lines drops down, creating a basin. When two oceanic plates move apart, lava rises and cools, forming the floor of an ocean basin.

In Your Book *Careers In Science,* pages 1–3; Chapter 8; Chapter 9

Practice

7. What forms a new ocean floor?
    A a weak spot in an oceanic plate
    B oceanic plates moving together
    C oceanic plates moving apart
    D magma in the oceanic plates

8. Describe how mountains are formed by volcanoes.

Indicator 7.3.5 Explain how heat carried by ocean currents influences climate.

Review

Warm and Cool Currents Many variables, including ocean currents, can affect a climate. An ocean current is a massive stream of water that moves through the ocean. Currents can have cooler or warmer water than the surrounding ocean. Generally, currents carry warm water from the equator to the poles and cold water from the poles back to the equator. Warm surface currents heat the air above them, and cold currents cool the air. Sea-surface temperatures, which are affected by ocean currents, affect the amount of rainfall, air pressure, and wind temperatures in regions near these currents. Because oceans store a large amount of heat, even small changes in ocean currents can strongly affect coastal and global climates.

In Your Book Chapter 15, Section 4

Practice

9. The climate would be warmer in a place _____.
    A near a current flowing from one of the poles to the equator
    B near a current flowing from the equator to one of the poles
    C near a surface ocean current
    D near a current deep within the ocean

10. Explain how surface currents can affect the climate.

Indicator 7.3.6 Describe how gas and dust from volcanoes change the atmosphere.

Review

Cooling and Warming Effects When a volcano erupts, much more than lava escapes. Gases, steam, and rock fragments explode from the volcano, creating a cloud. Like lava, gases and other emissions affect our environment. The ash, dust, and fragments in a volcanic cloud can disperse into the atmosphere and spread around the globe. This large cloud can block light and heat from the sun and cool the climate over large areas of Earth. Volcanoes also release sulfur dioxide into the atmosphere. This gas reflects solar heat away from Earth, contributing to global cooling. Sulfur dioxide from volcanoes also leads to acid rain.

Other emitted gases, like carbon dioxide, contribute to global warming. Carbon dioxide is one of the gases contributing to the "Greenhouse Effect," which traps the sun's heat in Earth's atmosphere and warms temperatures on Earth. The size and duration of a volcanic eruption determine how long these emitted gases will affect the environment.

In Your Book Chapter 9, Section 5

Practice

11. How do clouds of ash and dust from volcanoes affect the atmosphere?
    A They make it rain.
    B They magnify heat from the sun.
    C They block light from the sun.
    D They warm the atmosphere.

12. Explain how volcanoes can contribute to the Greenhouse Effect.

Indicator 7.3.7 Give examples of abrupt and very slow changes in Earth's surface.

Review

Dynamic Earth Earth is constantly changing in many different ways. Some changes are immediate and obvious, like volcanoes and earthquakes. When a volcano erupts, lava, ash, gases, and rock fragments are expelled into the environment. Lava changes the landscape, destroying every living thing in its path. Gases released by volcanoes can warm or cool the climate almost immediately. Earthquakes, which occur when plates in Earth's crust slowly grind together or pull apart, can level cities, buildings, and highways.

While earthquakes occur suddenly, other changes in Earth's surface can take place very slowly over large periods of time. Erosion, the process of carrying away rock particles by water, wind, or ice, gradually wears down the surfaces of land masses over time. Glacial erosion took place during past ice ages when huge, slow-moving rivers of ice covered large parts of Earth's surface. The glaciers carried boulders and rocks across Earth's surface, reshaping it as they passed.

In Your Book *Careers in Science,* pages 1–3; Chapter 8; Chapter 9; Chapter 11, Section 6; Chapter 14

Practice

13. Which cause slow changes in Earth's surface?
    A volcanoes and glaciers
    B erosion and earthquakes
    C erosion and glaciers
    D earthquakes and volcanoes

14. Explain how glaciers change Earth's surface.

Indicator 7.3.8 Describe how sediments are buried and bonded together by dissolved minerals to form solid rock.

Review

Rock to Sediment to Rock Erosion wears down and carries away particles of rock and creates sediment. Sediment consists of small particles of rocks and once-living organisms. Sedimentary rock is created by particles of sediment being joined together.

Four processes are at work in the formation of most sedimentary rocks—erosion, deposition, compaction, and cementation. In deposition, the agents of erosion—water, wind, or ice—deposit sediment. During compaction, sediment builds up in thick layers over millions of years. The increasing weight of the layers on top presses the lower layers tightly together. Cementation takes place when water carries finely ground minerals into the compacted layers of sediment. The dissolved minerals act as a glue, spreading between sediment particles and binding them together until they set and harden into solid sedimentary rock.

In Your Book Chapter 11, Sections 3, 6; Chapter 14, Section 2

Practice

15. Which shows the correct order of the processes of sediment becoming rock?

  A erosion, deposition, compaction, cementation

  B cementation, compaction, erosion, deposition

  C compaction, cementation, erosion, deposition

  D erosion, cementation, deposition, compaction

16. What particles form sediment?

Indicator 7.3.9 Explain that pressure and heat can change deeply buried sedimentary rock. These rock layers may become land surface, and subsequently erode.

Review

Full Cycle Rocks can change in composition over time. Sedimentary rocks are formed by a series of processes that join particles. After sedimentary rock has formed, it can change again into a new type of rock, called metamorphic rock. This change takes place underground and is caused by pressure, intense heat, or both. Sedimentary rock heats when magma rises up through the crust or when Earth's plates collide and push rock down toward the heat of the mantle. The movement of plates can apply intense pressure to rock. Heat and pressure change the minerals in the rock to other types of minerals, creating metamorphic rock.

Metamorphic rock may also change. During earthquakes, rock below the surface can be pushed up above Earth's crust to form mountains. Rock in the newly formed mountains is exposed to the agents of erosion—water, wind, and ice—that wear rock away and break it down into particles. In time, metamorphic rock can be reduced to sediment again.

In Your Book Chapter 11; Chapter 14

Practice

17. What happens when sedimentary rock changes to metamorphic rock?

  A The minerals in the rock change.

  B The rock is eroded, forming sediment.

  C Colliding plates push the rock upward.

  D The rock turns into red-hot magma.

18. Explain how heat and pressure change sedimentary rock to metamorphic rock.

Academic Standards

Indicator 7.3.10 Explain how layers of sedimentary rock can show the history of the Earth's surface and life forms. The youngest layers are not always found on top.

Review

Layers of History Sedimentary rock is formed when layers of sediment—particles of rock and once-living things—join together and harden. The layers of sediment remain visible and reveal to geologists past changes in the Earth's crust. When layers of sedimentary rock are horizontal, the oldest layers are generally those near the bottom. Those near the top, having settled last over earlier layers, are usually the youngest. However, changes in Earth's crust can disturb the chronological order of the layers. Along faults—breaks in Earth's crust—blocks of rock may slide and layers can shift, changing the original order. Below the surface, magma—a molten mixture of rock-forming substances, gases, and water—can squeeze up through rock. When it cools, magma hardens, creating an intrusion between rock layers. In addition, forces below Earth's surface can fold or tilt layers of sedimentary rock. Different kinds of rocks that were formed in different time periods, and sometimes fossils, appear in these layers. Scientists often know when certain life forms existed on Earth, so their fossils embedded in rock can help scientists to identify the age of rock layers.

In Your Book Chapter 11, Sections 3, 6

Practice

19. Fossils found in rock help scientists find _____.
    A the location of an intrusion
    B the age of layers of rock
    C a fault in Earth's crust
    D new sedimentary rock

20. What changes the order of horizontal layers of sedimentary rock?

Matter and Energy

Indicator 7.3.11 Explain that the sun loses energy by giving off light. A small part of that light reaches Earth with a wide range of wavelengths.

Review

Light Energy From the Sun The sun is a star—a massive ball of hot gas. At its core, the process of nuclear fusion produces energy by joining hydrogen atoms together to form helium. During fusion, some of the matter is changed into energy, including light and heat. This released energy escapes into space, and a small fraction of the light reaches the Earth, making life on our planet possible. Light travels as a wave and moves extremely fast. Light waves have a wide range of wavelengths, but only some can be seen, and they are called visible light. We see visible light when it reflects off of something. The other wavelengths of light—radio, infrared, ultraviolet, X-rays, and gamma—are present on Earth even though we cannot see them.

In Your Book Chapter 16, Section 2; Chapter 17, Sections 1, 3

Practice

21. Light is energy lost from the sun during _____.
    A the rotation of the sun
    B chemical reactions
    C nuclear fusion
    D intense fire

22. How does energy from the sun travel to Earth?

Indicator 7.3.12 Investigate how the temperature and acidity of a solution influence reaction rates.

Review

Reaction Rates How quickly a chemical reaction happens depends on how easily the particles of the starting materials, or reactants, can come together. When you heat something, its particles move faster. Faster-moving particles come in contact with each other more often and with greater energy. This energy helps to start a reaction. As a result, most chemical reactions occur more quickly when reactants are heated.

Many chemical reactions involve the exchange of hydrogen ions, which are produced by acids. These reactions occur more quickly in a strongly acidic solution. Many of the chemical reactions involved in the spoilage of food occur most quickly under warm, slightly acidic conditions. Keeping food cold can slow down spoilage.

In Your Book Chapter 3, Section 3

Practice

23. Most chemical reactions, including food spoilage, occur faster at _____.
   A high temperatures
   B refrigerated temperatures
   C freezing temperatures
   D all temperatures

24. What happens in a strongly acidic solution?
   A Chemical reactions begin.
   B Chemical reactions stop.
   C Chemical reactions happen more quickly.
   D Chemical reactions happen more slowly.

Indicator 7.3.13 Explain that many substances dissolve in water. These substances can affect the rates of reactions in the water.

Review

Solvents and Changing Reactions
A solvent is something that dissolves other substances. Water dissolves many substances so it often is used as a solvent. Sugar dissolves in water, making it taste sweet, and carbon dioxide dissolves in water, making it bubbly. The substances that dissolve are called solutes. Solutes affect the rates of reactions in water. For example, substances dissolved in water can lower its freezing point and raise its boiling point. When salt is dissolved in water, the water temperature must drop below the normal freezing point before it will freeze. Similarly, salt water must be heated above the normal boiling point of water before it will boil. The rates of reaction have been changed by the presence of the solute.

In Your Book Chapter 15, Section 3

Practice

25. A solvent _____.
   A dissolves in water
   B dissolves other substances
   C is the same as a solute
   D makes water sweeter

26. How can a solute affect the boiling point of water?

INDIANA

Indicator 7.3.14 Explain that heat is almost always one of the products of an energy transformation.

Review

Transforming Energy Energy is the ability to do work or cause a change. Blowing wind, splashing waves, racing horses, and speeding cars are some of the many forms of energy that we know. The change from one type of energy into another type is called energy transformation. When you climb a hill, energy in your food is transformed into muscle power for motion. When water is heated on a stove, energy from the burner is transformed into heat energy.

27. What are some forms of energy?

Generating Heat Heat is a type of energy, and it is one of the most common products of energy transformations. When you use energy to rub your hands together, heat is given off, warming your hands. When energy inside of wood or gas is transformed by burning, heat is given off. When your body transforms food energy so that you can run, heat is generated.

28. Give an example of heat as a product of an energy transformation.

Generating Heat The spinning top gives off heat as it spins.

Practice

29. An energy transformation occurs when _____.
    A energy turns into matter
    B electricity is turned off
    C energy changes forms
    D energy is used for movement

30. Heat is generated when _____.
    A energy is transformed
    B energy is stored
    C energy is wasted
    D energy is lost

31. What is energy? Give some examples.

32. Why does a marathon runner eat a lot of pasta the night before the race and sweat profusely during the race?

Indicator 7.3.15 Describe various ways that electrical energy can be produced and transformed into other forms of energy.

Review

Many Sources Electrical energy is formed when moving electrical charges produce electricity. It can also be produced from a variety of sources. Solar power plants capture the sun's rays to heat a tank of water. When water boils, the steam is used to generate electrical energy. Fuels, heat from magma in Earth, or geothermal energy, can be used in a similar way. Nuclear power plants harness the power of nuclear fission by creating heat, producing steam from boiling water, and generating electricity.

Moving water and wind can also be used to produce electrical energy. Water, controlled by a dam, is released through tunnels. The water turns turbines in the tunnels that are connected to generators, which create electrical energy. Windmills work in a similar way. Blowing wind turns turbines that are connected to energy generators.

33. Name a source that produces electrical energy.

Many Uses Electrical energy is accessible in power lines, electrical lines, and batteries. It can be transformed into heat, light, and mechanical energy for many purposes, including lighting and heating homes, powering computers, and running trains. We use electrical energy every day in many ways.

34. List two uses of electrical energy.

Water Power This dam in Arizona uses water as a source of energy to generate power.

Practice

35. Moving electric charges produce _____.
   A solar energy
   B electrical energy
   C wind energy
   D fuel energy

36. What is one way electrical energy reaches us?
   A through water
   B through wind
   C through power lines
   D through light

37. How does solar power create electrical energy?

38. Which is one way to use electrical energy?
   A riding a bike
   B running water
   C riding a motorcycle
   D running a computer

Academic Standards

INDIANA

Indicator 7.3.16 Recognize that different ways of obtaining, transforming, and distributing energy have different impacts on the environment.

Review

Nonrenewable Resources There are many different ways of obtaining, transforming, and distributing energy. Some have a lasting effect on the environment. Most energy comes from fossil fuels. Fossil fuels are energy-rich substances formed from the remains of organisms that lived hundreds of millions of years ago. Coal, oil, and natural gas are the major fossil fuels. Fossil fuels are converted into energy in a process called combustion, which releases heat and light. The combustion of fossil fuels provides more energy than does the combustion of the same amount of other fuels. However, fossil fuels take hundreds of millions of years to form, so they are considered nonrenewable resources. Once they have been used, they can't be replaced in any foreseeable future. Extracting fuels also damages the environment. The use of these fuels in cars and factories creates smog, acid rain, and "greenhouse gases" that contribute to the "Greenhouse Effect" warming Earth's atmosphere.

 Reading Checkpoint

39. What are nonrenewable resources?

Oil Production Oil rigs pump crude oil out of the ground.

Renewable Sources of Energy Renewable energy comes from sources that are constantly being created, such as sunlight, wind, and magma. Power plants convert these sources into elec-tricity, heat, and fuel. These sources do not deplete the environment or produce smog, but they do have some negative environmental effects. Windmills occupy lots of land, destroying habitats and encouraging erosion. Dams for water-powered plants also dramatically change the environment around them, sometimes flooding areas and impacting plants, animals, and people. Geothermal plants require drilling deeply into the ground.

 Reading Checkpoint

40. What are renewable energy sources?

Practice

41. What are two sources of renewable energy and how are they transformed into easily accessible energy?

42. What are some of the negative side effects of using fossil fuels for energy?
   A They create acid rain and greenhouse gases.
   B Dams disturb the environment around rivers.
   C They cause erosion around power plants.
   D They are constantly renewed.

43. Why is it a problem that fossil fuels are nonrenewable?

44. Give an example of negative impact of a renewable source of energy.

Forces of Nature

Indicator 7.3.17 Investigate how an unbalanced force affects an object's speed and path. If the force always acts toward the same point, the object's path may curve into an orbit.

Review

Forces at Work A force is a push or a pull and is described by its strength and by the direction of its action on an object. For example, when you push on a window to open it, you are exerting a force on it. More than one force can act on an object at the same time. The combination of all forces acting on an object at one time is called the net force. Unbalanced forces acting on an object result in a net force that can cause an object to start moving, stop moving, or change direction of its movement.

The motion of an object depends on the force applied and whether the object is already in motion when that force is applied. For example, a satellite orbiting Earth is pulled toward Earth by the force of gravity. However, its forward motion is fast enough that it does not fall to the ground. Instead, it goes into orbit. If a force always acts toward a constant center as an object moves, the object's path may curve into an orbit around that center.

In Your Book Chapter 16, Section 3 and Chapter Project

Practice

45. Unbalanced forces acting on an object _____.

  A cause a change in the object's motion

  B have a net force of zero

  C do not change an object's motion

  D are equal forces applied in opposite directions

46. Why don't satellites fall to Earth?

Indicator 7.3.18 Describe that waves move at different speeds in different materials.

Review

Traveling Through Mediums Waves transfer energy from one place to another. Sound, light, and water all travel in waves. Some kinds of waves need to travel through a medium such as a gas, liquid, or solid. For example, sound can travel through air when you talk to someone next to you, or it can pass through wood when you knock on a door. Light can travel through air, from a light source to your eyes or it can travel through water.

Waves travel through different mediums at different speeds. The rate at which sound waves travel depends on the elasticity, density, and temperature of the medium. The more elasticity—the ability of a material to bounce back after being disturbed—that a medium has, the faster sound travels through it. Sound travels more slowly through liquid than air because liquid is less elastic. Sound also travels more slowly through a denser medium and at lower temperatures. For example, sound would travel more slowly through lead than through water because lead is a denser medium. Sound also travels faster in warmer air than in cold air.

In Your Book Chapter 7, Section 3

Practice

47. Waves _____ from one place to another.

  A transfer liquids

  B carry a medium

  C transfer energy

  D carry air

48. What affects the speed that sound waves travel?

Academic Standards

769

Indicator 7.3.19 Explain that human eyes see a narrow part of the electromagnetic spectrum.

Review

Visible Light Electromagnetic radiation is energy that can travel through space in the form of waves. There are many forms of electromagnetic radiation, including visible light. Electromagnetic radiation has a range of different wavelengths. A wavelength is the distance between the crest of one wave and the crest of the next wave. The electromagnetic spectrum includes the entire range of radio waves, infrared radiation, visible light, ultraviolet radiation, X-rays, and gamma rays. Some types of electromagnetic energy, like radio waves, have longer wavelengths than visible light, and we cannot see them. Some wavelengths, like those of ultraviolet waves, are shorter, and we cannot see them either. Visible light occupies a narrow band in the middle of the electromagnetic spectrum. The visible light spectrum that our eyes can see includes the colors of red, orange, yellow, green, blue, indigo and violet.

In Your Book Chapter 7, Section 3; Chapter 17, Section 1

Practice

49. What is the visible light spectrum?
 A the waves with shorter wavelengths
 B the waves that you cannot see
 C the range of colors you can see
 D the waves with longer wavelengths

50. Describe the part of the electromagnetic spectrum that the human eye can see.

Indicator 7.3.20 Describe that seeing occurs when light waves enter the eye, just as sound is heard when sound waves enter the ear.

Review

Sight and Sound Light rays reflect off of objects. Eyes take in these light rays and focus them to create a picture. From this image, billions of nerve impulses are sent to the brain. The brain uses these impulses to create the image that we see. For example, if you look at a wall that is painted yellow, yellow wavelengths are reflected off the wall into your eye where the color yellow is perceived by your eye and brain.

Ears are the sense organs that respond to the stimulus of sound. Sound waves travel through the air to the ear, enter the ear, and travel to the eardrum. The eardrum transmits them to structures in the middle ear, causing the structures to vibrate. Next, the vibrations go to the inner ear. From there, nerve impulses travel to the brain through the auditory nerve. Your brain interprets these nerve impulses as the specific sound that you hear.

In Your Book Chapter 7, Section 3

Practice

51. How do vibrations get from the inner ear to the brain?
 A through the eardrum
 B through the outer ear
 C through the middle ear
 D as nerve impulses

52. A wall is painted blue. Why do you see it as blue?

4 The Living Environment

Diversity of Life

Indicator 7.4.1 Explain that similarities among organisms in anatomy and at the cellular level are used to classify organisms.

Review

Classifying Organisms Scientists organize living things into groups based on their similarities. This helps scientists to identify and study organisms. Organisms are classified by many different types of characteristics, such as physical appearance, cell structure, body chemistry, and evolutionary history. For example, bears and cheetahs have body hair, a four-chambered heart, and give birth to live young. Bears and cheetahs are both classified as mammals. In another example, frogs and salamanders have smooth, moist skin and webbed feet, and they lay eggs in water. Frogs and salamanders are both classified as amphibians.

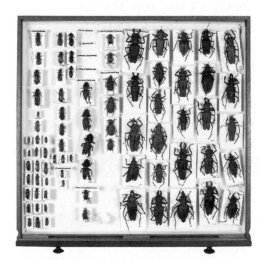

Classification These beetles can be classified according to the characteristics they have.

Reading Checkpoint

1. What do bears and cheetahs have in common?

Cellular Level Scientists also classify organisms based on similarities at the cellular level. Some organisms are grouped together based on how many cells they have. For example, members of the Monera Kingdom have one cell, while members of the Animal Kingdom have many cells. Some organisms are classified by characteristics of their cells. For example, plant cells have a cell wall, while animal cells do not have a cell wall. Organisms are also grouped together based on whether or not each of their cells has a nucleus.

Reading Checkpoint

2. What type of cells have cell walls?

Practice

3. Animal Kingdom members have _____.
   A many cells
   B no cells
   C a cell wall
   D only one cell

4. Where do frogs and salamanders lay their eggs?
   A on land
   B in trees
   C in water
   D underground

5. How do scientists classify organisms on the cellular level?

6. What are some of the characteristics that scientists use to classify organisms?

Academic Standards

INDIANA

Indicator 7.4.2 Describe that all organisms are part of and depend on the ocean food web or the land food web.

Review

Interconnected Food Chains A food chain is a series of events in which one organism eats another and obtains energy. For example, a grasshopper eats the grass, a frog eats the grasshopper, and then a hawk eats the frog. In this way, each animal obtains energy from the organism it eats. The many overlapping food chains in an ecosystem make up a food web. Food webs are made up of many different types of organisms including scavengers, parasites, and decomposers. Food webs include environmental factors as well, such as ocean currents and the sun.

 **Reading Checkpoint**

7. What is a food web?

Global Food Web There are two main food webs—the land food web and the ocean food web. The land food web concerns the relationships among all organisms that live on land, and the ocean food web concerns the relationships among all organisms that live in the ocean. The two webs are interconnected, with some organisms that are a part of both. Together, they make up the global food web. All organisms are part of the global food web.

 **Reading Checkpoint**

8. What are the two main food webs?

Energy Flow This barn owl and rat are part of a food chain and the global food web.

Practice

9. Which organism would most likely be part of both the land food web and the ocean food web?
   A a mouse
   B a fox
   C a seagull
   D a shark

10. How are food webs related to food chains?
    A Food webs are found on land, and food chains are found in the ocean.
    B Many overlapping food chains make up a food web.
    C Food webs only include plants, and food chains only include animals.
    D Food webs are found in warmer climates, and food chains are found in colder climates.

11. Write an example of a food chain involving three organisms.

12. Explain how an organism can be part of both the land food web and the ocean food web.

Indicator 7.4.3 Describe how a fertilized egg carries genetic information from each parent and forms a new organism.

Review

Fertilization and Genes In reproduction, a female egg cell joins with a male sperm cell in a process called fertilization. The result of this joining is a fertilized egg. When two cells combine in this manner, they each bring an equal number of genes to the new cell. Genes control traits, such as eye color, hair color, and height. Traits are passed on from parents to children through these genes.

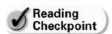
Reading Checkpoint

13. What are some examples of traits?

Cell Division After the egg cell is fertilized, it undergoes a series of cell divisions. The single cell divides, becoming two cells; then those cells divide again, becoming four cells, then eight cells, and so on. Cell division can occur in some organisms until there are trillions of cells. Eventually, these cells specialize, forming all the different types of cells needed to form a new organism.

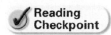
Reading Checkpoint

14. What happens to an egg cell after it is fertilized?

Practice

15. The joining of a female egg cell with a male sperm cell is called _____.
  A fertilization
  B genes
  C trait
  D cell division

16. A fertilized egg receives _____.
  A half its genes from the male sperm cell and half from the female egg cell
  B one third of its genes from the sperm cell and one third from the egg cell
  C a varying amount of genes from the sperm cell and the egg cell
  D no genes from the sperm cell and the egg cell

17. What happens during cell division?

18. What must happen to an egg cell before it can undergo cell division?

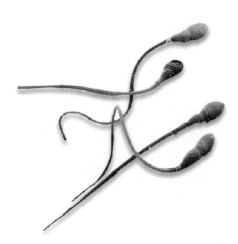
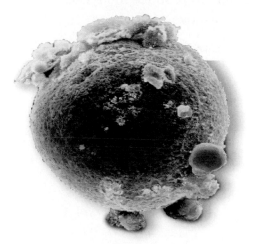

Sex Cells Sperm are male sex cells, and eggs are female sex cells.

Indicator 7.4.4 Explain that cells constantly divide to make more cells for growth and repair. Various organs and tissues provide cells with food, air, and waste removal.

Review

Cell Reproduction Cells are constantly dividing, or reproducing, to create more cells. In humans, what starts out as one fertilized egg cell eventually becomes trillions of cells. This is how organisms grow. Cell reproduction also repairs damage to an organism. For example, if you accidentally scrape your knee, your cells will divide to create new skin cells. These new cells will replace the damaged cells.

Cells are only able to carry out their functions, such as cell reproduction, with the support of the body's tissues and organs. Tissues and organs are made up of cells. They help bring food and oxygen to cells, as well as help remove waste from them.

In Your Book Chapter 2; Chapter 6, Section 2

Practice

19. Growth and healing occur because _____.
    A cells are continually getting stronger
    B cells get bigger and bigger each day
    C cells divide to produce more cells
    D cells never move

20. What is the function of tissues and organs?

Indicator 7.4.5 Explain that the basic functions of all organisms occur within cells in similar ways.

Review

Cell Similarities The basic functions of organisms occur within cells. The cells in all organisms function in a similar manner. For example, cells in different organisms contain genetic information, reproduce, take in food, transport materials, and remove waste. Not all cells are exactly the same, however. Plant cells and animal cells are similar in structure and function, but they do have a few differences. One difference is that plant cells have cell walls, while animal cells do not have cell walls.

In Your Book Chapter 2

Practice

21. Plant cells and animal cells are _____.
    A exactly the same
    B completely different
    C similar
    D found in every organism

22. What basic functions of organisms do cells carry out?

Interdependence of Life and Evolution

Indicator 7.4.6 Explain how food provides fuel and the building material for all organisms.

Review

Food Energy Food provides energy to all organisms for growth, activity, and tissue repair by supplying the cells with nutrients. Nutrients are substances in food that provide raw materials that the body needs. Carbohydrates, fats, proteins, vitamins, and minerals are all examples of nutrients that animals, including humans, need to survive. When food is consumed, the food's nutrients are broken down and carried to the cells, where they are absorbed and used.

In Your Book Chapter 3

Practice

23. Nutrients are substances in food that _____.
   A provide raw materials the body needs
   B are a waste result from cell activity
   C absorb energy from the body
   D absorb raw materials from the body

24. What does food provide to all organisms?

Indicator 7.4.7 Describe how plants make their own food.

Review

Photosynthesis Like all organisms, plants need food to grow, develop, and reproduce. Plants make their own food in a process called photosynthesis, which takes place in the green parts of plants. During photosynthesis, carbon dioxide from the air and water from the soil combine in the presence of light energy (usually from the sun), to produce oxygen and a form of sugar. The sugar is a nutrient used by the plant as its food, and oxygen is a waste product that the plant releases.

 **Reading Checkpoint**

25. What is produced through photosynthesis?

Food Use and Storage The plant immediately uses some of the sugar food to provide it with the nutrients it needs to survive. In addition, some of the food is stored in the energy-rich structures of the plant. Plants store this food in their fruits, stems, or roots. For example, an apple tree stores some of its food in the apples, and a carrot plant stores some of its food in its carrots.

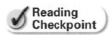 **Reading Checkpoint**

26. Where do plants store their food?

A Plant's Food When you eat cucumbers, tomatoes, and other plant products, you are eating food made and stored by plants.

Practice

27. What is combined in the process of photosynthesis?
   A sugar, oxygen, and soil
   B carbon dioxide, light, and water
   C fruit, leaves, and stems
   D cells, chloroplasts, and sugar

28. Plants can store the food they make _____.
   A in water molecules
   B in the soil
   C in their roots or fruits
   D in carbon dioxide

29. Why do plants need food?

30. How do plants create their own food?

INDIANA

Indicator 7.4.8 Describe how plant-eating organisms break down plant structures to obtain the materials and energy that they need. These organisms are consumed by other organisms.

Review

Energy from Plants When an organism eats a plant, the organism's digestive system breaks down the plant structure into molecules that can be used for energy. For example, when a fish eats a plant, the digestive system of the fish breaks down the plant into molecules it can use. These molecules are then absorbed into the blood and carried to the cells. By digesting the plant, the fish gains energy for growth and life functions.

If the fish is eaten by a seagull, the process remains the same. This seagull breaks down the fish through the digestive process to gain needed energy for its own functioning. In this way, the seagull gains energy from the plant that was originally eaten by the fish.

In Your Book Chapter 3, Sections 1, 3, 5

Practice

31. What happens during digestion?
   A Food is created.
   B Food is broken down.
   C Plants are created.
   D Plants create energy.

32. How is it possible to get energy from a plant without actually eating it?

Indicator 7.4.9 Understand that one or more environmental factors control population growth.

Review

Population Growth All the members of a species that live in one area make up a population. Scientists study populations to see how they grow and change. If a population has good living conditions, such as adequate shelter, food, and water, the population usually grows. However, as a population grows, there are environmental factors that limit its growth. Some factors may even cause a population to decrease.

33. Why do scientists study populations?

Limiting Factors Some limiting factors that can affect population size are disease, attack by predators, and lack of food, water, or land. These limiting factors can affect both plants and animals. Human development may also affect the population size of some organisms by greatly decreasing the amount of land available to those organisms for food, shelter, and water. For example, if a new building is constructed and trees are cut down, large amounts of food and shelter provided by the trees are lost.

34. What are some limiting factors that can affect population size?

Fighting Jackals These jackals are fighting over the limited food available to them.

Practice

35. All the members of a species that live in one area make up _____.

  A an environmental factor
  B a genetic factor
  C a development
  D a population

36. Adequate food, water, and land are some examples of _____.

  A limiting factors
  B predator factors
  C limiting living conditions
  D good living conditions

37. What is one factor that would limit the growth of a population of lemon trees?

38. How might human development limit the population growth of some organisms?

Human Identity

Indicator 7.4.10 Describe how technologies used in food production, sanitation, and disease prevention have changed how people live and the growth of human population.

Review

Population Explosion The human population has grown dramatically in the last 3,000 years, from about 50 million people to over 6 billion people. The population has grown especially quickly over the past 300 to 400 years as a result of many improvements in medicine, sanitation, and food production.

Some of the greatest improvements have come in the field of medicine. Some diseases that were once deadly are now treatable with new medicines, surgical procedures, medical equipment, and medical technologies.

Agricultural technology has also been improved, and has greatly increased the amount of food available to humans. There have also been technological improvements in human waste disposal. In the past, the disposal of waste contributed to the spread of many diseases through the contamination of local water supplies. This led to an increase in the number of disease-carrying pests. Today, however, there are sophisticated systems for disposing of and treating human waste in order to prevent environmental contamination and the spread of disease.

In Your Book Chapter 1, Section 4; Chapter 6, Section 5

Sewage Treatment Riverbank State Park in New York City is a huge recreational complex built over a sewage treatment plant that treats household waste.

Practice

39. Improvements in medicine, sanitation, and food production have _____.

  A decreased the human population
  B increased the human population
  C not affected the human population
  D resulted in most people living shorter lives

40. How has improved technology for human waste disposal affected population growth?

INDIANA

Indicator 7.4.11 Explain that the amount of food energy a person needs depends on weight, age, sex, activity, and efficiency. Exercise is important to health.

Review

Food and Exercise Food provides your body with the energy it needs to grow, maintain overall health, and perform daily activities. Everyone needs to receive a certain amount of food energy each day. This amount is measured in calories. The number of calories needed varies among individuals and depends on many factors. Some of these factors include size, age, sex, activity level, and natural body efficiency. Larger people need more calories than smaller people, and men usually need more calories than women. Taking in excess calories leads to weight gain, but taking in the right number of calories for your body is important to maintaining overall health. Exercise is also important for good health because it helps maintain ideal weight and strengthens the bones, heart, and other muscles.

In Your Book Chapter 2, Section 2; Chapter 3, Section 1; Chapter 4, Section 4

Practice

41. Eating the right number of calories each day _____.

A leads to weight gain

B is the same for everyone

C depletes energy for daily activities

D is important for overall health

42. What are some reasons that exercise is important for overall health?

Indicator 7.4.12 Explain that parasites can cause disease. A person can catch a cold many times because there are many different cold viruses.

Review

Disease Certain organisms cause disease when they infect the human body. Four major types of these organisms are bacteria, viruses, fungi, and parasites. The common cold is caused by a group of viruses. When you have a cold, your immune system gets rid of the cold by disabling the virus. Even after the virus has been disabled, your immune system continues to develop the same antibodies that were used to fight that particular virus. Because of this, you are less likely to become ill from the same kind of cold virus again. However, because there are more than 200 different kinds of cold viruses, you can catch a cold many times.

In Your Book Chapter 6, Sections 1, 3

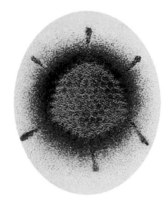

Adenovirus When you have a cough and a sore throat, this round-shaped virus, called an adenovirus, may be to blame.

Practice

43. The common cold is caused by _____.

A having wet hair

B having open windows

C a virus

D a fungus

44. Why is it unlikely that you would catch the common cold from the same virus soon after getting better?

Indicator 7.4.13 Explain that white blood cells fight invaders. Antibodies produced by white blood cells can fight off subsequent invaders of the same kind.

Review

White Blood Cells When a disease-causing organism gets inside your body, white blood cells are one of your body's main defenses against the disease. One type of white blood cell destroys the invading organism by engulfing it and breaking it down. Another type of white blood cell creates antibodies, which attach to the disease-causing organism and mark it to be destroyed by another type of cell. The antibodies that were created to fight this particular disease-causing organism continue to be created for some time. These antibodies can fight off the same kind of organism if it invades the body again.

In Your Book Chapter 4, Section 3; Chapter 6, Sections 2, 3

Practice

45. White blood cells are _____.
  A a main defense against disease-causing organisms
  B a type of antibody that causes disease
  C a type of cell that causes disease
  D not actually cells

46. How do antibodies fight against disease?

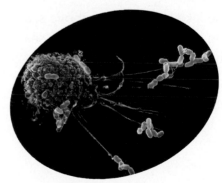

White Blood Cells White blood cells destroy bacteria.

Indicator 7.4.14 Explain that the environment may contain dangerous levels of harmful substances. Public health requires monitoring the soil, air, and water quality.

Review

Environmental Dangers Harmful substances that cause disease in humans and other organisms can exist in the air, water, and soil. As a result, the quality of the environment needs to be monitored regularly to ensure there is no risk to the health of humans and other organisms. Organizations such as the Environmental Protection Agency monitor the air, water, and soil to determine if the environment is safe for humans and other organisms. If a dangerous contaminant is found, the agency will clean up the area.

In Your Book Chapter 5, Section 2; Chapter 6, Sections 4, 5

Cleaning Up Organizations clean up contaminated parts of the environment to make it safer.

Practice

47. Harmful substances that can cause disease in humans and other organisms _____
  A can exist in air, water, and soil
  B do not exist in air, water, and soil
  C are not a problem
  D are created by the Environmental Protection Agency

48. How can harmful substances in the water, air, or soil be a problem for people and other organisms?

Academic Standards

5 The Mathematical World

Numbers

Indicator 7.5.1 Demonstrate how negative numbers are shown and used on a number line.

Review

Negative Numbers A number line can be used to show positive and negative numbers. On a number line, positive numbers are to the right of zero, and negative numbers are to the left of zero. A negative number is indicated by a negative symbol placed to the left of the number. For example, negative ten is written as –10. On a number line, the value of the numbers increases as you move from left to right. So, –4 is greater than –6.

 **Reading Checkpoint**

1. How is negative eight written?

Uses of Negative Numbers Scientists often need to use negative numbers. A weather forecaster uses negative numbers to indicate temperatures below zero. A forecaster reports a temperature of –15°C as "fifteen degrees below zero Celsius." A geographer indicates elevations that are below sea level by using negative numbers. The elevation of the Dead Sea, for example, is 411 meters below sea level or –411 meters.

 **Reading Checkpoint**

2. How would a scientist represent an elevation of 86 meters below sea level?

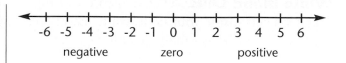

-6 -5 -4 -3 -2 -1 0 1 2 3 4 5 6
negative   zero   positive

Number Line Negative numbers are shown to the left of zero on a number line.

Practice

3. Which number is greater than –2?
   A –8
   B –5
   C –3
   D –1

4. Which is a true statement about the temperatures –10°C and 10°C?
   A 10°C is less than –10°C.
   B –10°C is less than 10°C.
   C The temperatures are the same.
   D –10°C is greater than 10°C.

5. The elevation of a lake is reported as –20 meters. What does this mean?
   A The lake is 20 meters below the horizon.
   B The lake is 20 meters above sea level.
   C The lake is 20 meters below sea level.
   D The temperature of the lake is –20°C.

6. How does a scientist use negative numbers when recording elevations?

Shapes and Symbolic Relationships

Indicator 7.5.2 Illustrate parallel, perpendicular, or oblique lines.

Review

Lines A line lies in a plane and continues without end in opposite directions. A line has no thickness. Two points determine the position of a line. A line can be named by using two points shown on the line. For example, the line that goes through points A and B is denoted as $\overrightarrow{AB}$.

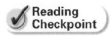

7. What does $\overrightarrow{MN}$ indicate?

Parallel, Perpendicular, and Oblique

Lines Lines that lie in the same plane may be parallel or they may intersect. When two lines intersect, they intersect at one point. Parallel lines do not intersect. Lines that intersect may be perpendicular lines or oblique lines. Perpendicular lines intersect at right angles. Oblique lines intersect and create acute and obtuse angles where they intersect.

8. What name is used to describe two lines that do not intersect?

Practice

9. Perpendicular lines are lines that _____.
  A never intersect
  B intersect at right angles
  C intersect at acute angles
  D intersect at obtuse angles

10. Which statement about parallel lines is true?
  A They never intersect.
  B They intersect at right angles.
  C They intersect at acute angles.
  D They intersect at obtuse angles.

11. Line *PQ* intersects line *RS* at right angles. Which statement is true?
  A $\overrightarrow{PQ}$ and $\overrightarrow{RS}$ are parallel.
  B $\overrightarrow{PQ}$ and $\overrightarrow{RS}$ are perpendicular.
  C $\overrightarrow{PQ}$ and $\overrightarrow{RS}$ are oblique.
  D $\overrightarrow{PQ}$ and $\overrightarrow{RS}$ intersect at two points.

12. Compare and contrast perpendicular lines and oblique lines.

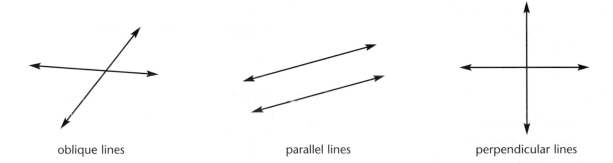

oblique lines   parallel lines   perpendicular lines

Lines The pairs of lines are parallel, perpendicular, and oblique.

Academic Standards

INDIANA

Indicator 7.5.3 Demonstrate how the scale of a graph or drawing affects its interpretation.

Review

Interpret Graphs Scientists use graphs to present information in a visual format. This allows them to compare data or see patterns in data more easily. Bar graphs and line graphs use a scale to represent numerical values. The interval chosen for the scale affects the way the graph looks. For example, the bar graph below shows the number of Lyme disease cases in different age groups. The vertical scale has an interval of 50. If the interval were changed to 25, the bars on the graph would be taller. The difference between the number of cases occurring in the 10–19 age group and the 20–29 age group would appear greater.

In Your Book Chapter 12, Section 2; Chapter 16, Section 5; Chapter 17, Section 4

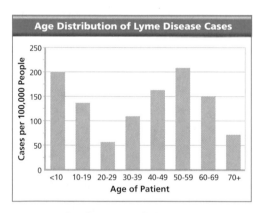

Bar Graph The interval chosen for the scale of a graph affects the interpretation of the data.

Practice

13. How would the height of the bars on the graph be affected if the interval on the vertical scale changed from 50 to 100?
   A The bars would be taller.
   B The bars would be shorter.
   C The bars would remain the same.
   D Some bars would be taller and some would be shorter.

14. One plant grew 2 inches in 1 week, and a second plant grew 6 inches in the same week. A bar graph showing the growth of the plants uses a scale with an interval of 3 inches. Describe how the bars on the graph would be affected if the interval on the scale were changed to 1 inch.

Reasoning and Uncertainty

Indicator 7.5.4 Describe that large, well-chosen samples can accurately represent the whole.

Review

Samples A scientist might want to find how many types of one plant exist in a large area. Because it would be impossible to count each and every plant in the area, the scientist counts the plants in a small area and uses this information to estimate the number of plants in the larger area. This technique is called sampling. The number of plants in the small area is called the sample. When using samples, it is important to pick a large enough sample so that it accurately represents the whole. It is also important to choose a sample that is varied enough to represent the whole. This is called a representative sample. Choosing two different areas from which to sample plants would also ensure that the sample would better represent the whole.

In Your Book Chapter 1, Section 1

Practice

15. A representative sample _____.
   A represents the whole
   B is the whole
   C gives the results you want
   D is not very large

16. A student took a survey to find how many students named blue as their favorite color. There are 400 students in the school. He asked 14 of his friends. Is this survey likely to give him accurate results? Why?

6 Historical Perspectives

Indicator 7.6.1 Describe old explanations for disease and the discovery that diseases are caused by microorganisms.

Review

Spirits and Microorganisms Throughout history, people have created explanations for disease. Some believed that evil spirits caused disease. Others believed that illness resulted from an imbalance in body fluids. In the 1860s, a surgeon named Joseph Lister hypothesized that microorganisms caused disease. He began cleaning all his instruments and bandages to kill microorganisms. The results were remarkable; far fewer patients died after surgery. Around the same time, Louis Pasteur showed that killing microorganisms could prevent the spread of certain diseases. Years later, a German doctor named Robert Koch linked different pathogens to specific diseases. These doctors and scientists helped pioneer the study of what we know today: diseases are caused by pathogens such as bacteria, viruses, yeasts, and parasites.

In Your Book Chapter 6, Section 1

Practice

1. In the past, some people believed incorrectly that disease was caused by _____.
   A pathogens
   B surgery
   C evil spirits
   D viruses

2. What type of pathogens cause disease?

Indicator 7.6.2 Explain how Louis Pasteur discovered that microorganisms can spoil food or cause diseases. Microorganisms can also be useful. Specific kinds of germs cause specific diseases.

Review

Spoilage and Diseases Louis Pasteur, a French scientist who lived in the 1800s, discovered that microorganisms cause wine and milk to spoil. He found that microorganisms, entering from the air, multiplied rapidly and created waste products, causing wine to ferment and milk to spoil. While fermentation was a positive effect, milk spoilage was not. To avoid spoilage, Pasteur showed that microorganisms needed to be kept out or destroyed with heat. The process of destroying microorganisms with heat is called pasteurization.

Pasteur also discovered that microorganisms caused many diseases in animals. Later, other doctors were able to prove that specific pathogens cause specific diseases, paving the way for the discovery of how to protect against those diseases.

In Your Book Chapter 6, Section 1

Practice

3. Which of the following did Louis Pasteur discover?
   A microorganisms exist in heat
   B vaccines cure disease
   C microorganisms spoil milk
   D animals have diseases

4. What is pasteurization?

Academic Standards

INDIANA

Indicator 7.6.3 Explain that Louis Pasteur found that infection causes immunity to future infection by the same organism, and that a vaccine can provide immunity without causing disease.

Review

Using Germs to Protect In the nineteenth century, scientists found that pathogens (harmful microorganisms, also called germs) caused infectious disease by getting inside the body and causing harm. Louis Pasteur worked with animals to find a way to protect against infectious disease. Pasteur found that when an animal had already had such a disease, it was immune from getting it again. Based on this idea and following the work of an English doctor, Edward Jenner, Pasteur protected animals against infectious disease by injecting them with weakened pathogens. This process is called vaccination. A vaccine usually consists of pathogens that have been weakened or killed but can still trigger the immune system into action to protect against disease. Eventually, vaccinations were applied to people and are widely used today.

In Your Book Chapter 6, Section 3

Practice

5. What did Pasteur notice about some animals that had a disease?

A They died quickly.

B They were immune to the disease later.

C They got the disease again later.

D They were weakened by the disease later.

6. How does a vaccine protect against infectious disease?

Indicator 7.6.4 Describe how the germ theory of disease led to sanitation, pasteurization of milk, quarantine, clean surgery, vaccination, and antibiotics.

Review

Disease Prevention In the nineteenth century, scientists discovered that germs lead to infectious disease. Before that, people believed that evil spirits, swamp air, and body fluid imbalances caused disease. People thought that cures included appeals to supernatural powers, bloodletting, cutting patients to let out diseased blood, and vomiting to rid the body of the illness.

With the discovery that germs cause disease, protection against disease changed. Surgeons started sterilizing all of their instruments and far fewer patients died following surgery. Hospitals began to quarantine, or isolate, patients with diseases that could be passed from person to person. Germ theory also led to the pasteurization of milk, which prevented it from spoiling. Several other food and water safety processes were developed to prevent people from getting sick. The development of antibiotics, chemicals that kill bacteria or slow their growth without harming body cells, was another important discovery for disease prevention.

In Your Book Chapter 6

Practice

7. What happened in the nineteenth century when surgeons started protecting patients against germs?

A far fewer patients lived

B far more patients got diseases

C far more patients needed antibiotics

D far fewer patients died

8. What were some ways diseases were treated before the acceptance of a germ theory?

7 Common Themes

Systems

Indicator 7.7.1 Explain that the output from one part of a system can become the input to other parts, and that this can control the whole system.

Review

Input and Output The different parts of any system are connected. The output from one part of a system might be the input for another part of the system. A bicycle is an example of a system. The pedals of a bicycle are connected to the gears and chain. Moving the gears and chain of a bicycle causes the wheels to turn. The input to the system is pushing the pedals. The output is the gears moving and the chain turning. The movement of the gears and chain serves as the input to turn the wheels.

In Your Book Chapter 3, Sections 1, 3, 4; Chapter 5, Section 3; Chapter 7, Section 3

Practice

1. Output from one part of a system may become _____.
   A input for another part of the system
   B input for a different system
   C output for many systems
   D output for a different system

2. Describe how a bicycle is an example of an input and output system.

Bicycling A bicycle is an example of a system.

Academic Standards

785

INDIANA

Models and Scale

Indicator 7.7.2 Use different models to represent the same thing, noting that the model's type and complexity depend on its purpose.

Review

Models A model is a picture, diagram, or other representation of an object or process. Different types of models can be used to represent the same object. Models may be three-dimensional, two-dimensional, or symbolic. Different models of the same object are used to demonstrate different features of the object.

For example, different models of a molecule illustrate different characteristics of the molecule. A three-dimensional model of a molecule might be composed of table tennis balls and toothpicks. This model accurately shows the spatial relationship of the atoms in the molecule. Electron dot diagrams and written notations, such as NaCl for sodium chloride, are symbolic ways to model a molecule. These models accurately name the type of atoms in the molecule.

In Your Book Chapter 8, Chapter Project; Chapter 9, Section 4; *Skills Handbook*, Inquiry Skills

Practice

3. Different models may be used to represent the same object because _____.

   A each model shows the same characteristics of the object

   B each model shows different characteristics of the object

   C each model is a symbolic representation of the object

   D each model shows spatial relationships in the object

4. Which type of model would best represent Earth and its interior? Explain.

Constancy and Change

Indicator 7.7.3 Describe how systems usually change until they reach equilibrium, and remain that way unless their surroundings change.

Review

Reaching a Balance Physical and biological systems tend to change until they arrive at a balance, or equilibrium. For example, the systems inside the human body work together to maintain a balance called homeostasis. The regulation of body temperature is controlled by the mechanism of homeostasis. Body temperature remains constant at about 37°C despite variations in temperature in the environment. Internal systems work to maintain this body temperature whether the external temperature is cold or hot. The human body responds to a colder external temperature by shivering, which warms the body. It responds to a warmer external temperature by sweating, which cools the body.

In Your Book Chapter 2, Section 1; Chapter 5, Section 3; Chapter 15, Section 3

Practice

5. The process by which the human body maintains a constant internal temperature is called _____.

   A growth

   B homogenization

   C photosynthesis

   D homeostasis

6. Explain what is meant when a system is said to be at equilibrium.

Indicator 7.7.4 Use equations to show a change over time or in response to changes in other variables.

Review

Equations Equations show relationships between quantities. Scientists use equations to show how a change in one variable affects other variables. The equation that shows the relationship between distance, speed, and time is *Distance = Speed × Time*, or $D = S \times T$. If scientists know the speed at which something travels and the amount of time it travels, they can use the equation to find the distance traveled.

For example, a biologist might observe that an eagle flies 600 meters per minute for 10 minutes. To find the distance flown, the biologist substitutes the numbers in the equation.

$$D = 600 \times 10, \text{ or } D = 6,000$$

The eagle flew 6,000 meters. If the eagle flew for twice that amount of time, it would have flown for 20 minutes at 600 meters per minute.

$$D = 600 \times 20, \text{ or } D = 12,000$$

The eagle would have flown 12,000 meters.

In Your Book Chapter 1, Sections 1, 3; Chapter 18, Sections 2–4; *Skills Handbook*

Practice

7. A cheetah runs 3 meters per second for 30 seconds. How far does the cheetah run?
    A 9 meters
    B 10 meters
    C 90 meters
    D 900 meters

8. How would the distance change if the cheetah ran for the same amount of time but at half the speed?

Calculating Distance The distance an eagle flies is the product of its speed and the amount of time it flies.

Standards Refresher
Answers to Questions

The Nature of Science and Technology

1. B
2. The difference in results is trivial because it is probably an error due to the accuracy of the thermometers.
3. Bias occurs when a decision is based on an opinion instead of facts.
4. by basing all conclusions on data, not on opinion
5. A
6. D
7. using a random sample of people; making sure labels are concealed; making sure all samples look the same
8. He should make sure that all the soft drinks are in identical cups.
9. The scientist made up new data and claimed to have made two new elements.
10. the original data
11. C
12. A
13. The drug could harm or kill patients.
14. Scientists duplicate experiments to test the results.
15. B
16. further study; observation; experimentation
17. A
18. When people learn new things or invent new ways of doing things, they share their ideas with others. As people travel, these new ideas are then shared with others. Over time, there is an accumulation of knowledge.
19. His predictions were found to be true.
20. physics
21. A
22. C
23. because his work benefited farmers and workers
24. because Meitner lived during a time when women were not considered equal, and their contributions were not thought of as important or relevant
25. D
26. Refrigerators were invented to protect food from spoilage.

27. B
28. vehicles that use fossil fuels; factories that produce goods using coal; nuclear power plants; power plants that use fossil fuels to produce electricity
29. D
30. There is a demand for a nonpolluting car that does not use fossil fuels, so scientists are developing fuel cells.
31. A
32. Advances in medical technology allow people to live longer and healthier lives.
33. A
34. 101 is the fifth number that can be made using the digits 1 and 0.

Scientific Thinking

1. C
2. First write 20% as a decimal, 0.2. Then multiply 50 by 0.2, $0.2 \times 50 = 10$. So, 20% of 50 is 10.
3. D
4. $V = lwh$
5. D
6. 3.5 m^2
7. A
8. 10^2
9. D
10. Probability can be expressed as a fraction, percent, or ratio.
11. B
12. millimeters, centimeters, meters, kilometers
13. B
14. Symbols, graphs, and diagrams are used in science to represent data and concepts in an organized format, making it easier to draw conclusions from the data.
15. B
16. Professional athletes are not experts in the medical field or the sports drink business. It is probable that the athletes are paid to endorse the sports drink.

STANDARDS REFRESHER

The Physical Setting

1. D
2. B
3. A
4. C
5. D
6. When a large asteroid collides with Earth's crust, particles are sent into the atmosphere. The resulting decrease in sunlight lowers atmospheric temperature. These effects can last for a long time.
7. C
8. When a volcano erupts, it sends out lava, ash, and rock. The lava flows out of and around the volcano and combines with the ash. When they cool, the lava and ash form layers of hardened lava. These layers build up and create a mountain.
9. B
10. Surface currents carry warm water from the equator to the poles and cold water from the poles to the equator, warming or cooling the atmosphere near them. These temperature changes can affect rainfall, air pressure, and wind temperature.
11. C
12. During a volcanic eruption, carbon dioxide is released into the atmosphere, where it traps heat and contributes to global warming.
13. C
14. Glaciers are huge, slow-moving rivers of ice that carry boulders and rocks across Earth's surface as they move, slowly wearing down and reshaping the surface.
15. A
16. particles of rock and once-living things
17. A
18. Heat from the mantle and rising magma, as well as pressure from colliding plates and layers of rock above, change the mineral content of sedimentary rock to transform it into metamorphic rock.
19. B
20. Blocks of rock along faults can slide and layers can shift, changing the layers' original order. Forces below Earth's surface can also fold or tilt layers of rock.
21. C
22. Energy from the sun travels to Earth in the form of light waves. It comes in a range of different wavelengths.
23. A
24. C
25. B
26. A solute in water can raise the temperature at which the water would boil.
27. heat; mechanical; electromagnetic
28. Heat is produced when electrical energy is transformed into light.
29. C
30. A
31. Energy is the ability to do work or cause a change. Some examples are wind, sunlight, gasoline, and moving water.
32. The pasta contains potential energy, which is changed into mechanical energy and heat. The heat causes the runner to sweat.
33. nuclear power plants
34. producing light and running a computer
35. B
36. C
37. Solar power plants capture the sun's rays, which heat a tank of water. When the water boils, it creates steam that turns a turbine and generates electrical energy.
38. D
39. energy sources that cannot be replaced in the near future
40. energy sources that are constantly being created
41. Wind energy can move blades on a windmill. Solar energy can heat water.
42. A
43. They may run out.
44. Dams drastically change the landscape.
45. A
46. Satellites around Earth are pulled toward Earth by the force of gravity. However, because their forward motion is fast enough, they go into orbit rather than falling toward Earth.
47. C
48. the elasticity, density, and temperature of the medium through which the waves travel
49. C
50. The human eye can see visible light, which includes red, orange, yellow, green, blue, indigo, and violet.
51. D
52. Blue wavelengths are reflected off the wall and enter the eye. The eye focuses and transforms the light waves and transmits them to the brain as nerve impulses.

The Living Environment

1. both are mammals, have body hair, have four-chambered hearts, and give birth to live young
2. plant cells

INDIANA

3. A

4. C

5. Scientists group organisms based on the number of cells, whether they have a cell wall, or whether each cell has a nucleus.

6. Organisms are classified by characteristics such as physical appearance, cell structure, body chemistry, and evolutionary history.

7. A food web is a group of interconnected food chains in an ecosystem.

8. The two main food webs are the ocean and land food webs.

9. C

10. B

11. A fish eats a plant and a bird eats the fish.

12. If an organism eats animals on the land and in the ocean, it is part of both food webs.

13. Traits include eye color, hair color, and height.

14. It undergoes a series of cell divisions.

15. A

16. A

17. A single cell divides, to become two cells; those cells divide to become four cells; and so on. In this way, one cell becomes many cells.

18. A male sperm cell must join with the female egg cell to fertilize the egg.

19. C

20. Tissues and organs help to bring food and oxygen to the cells, and help to remove waste from the cells.

21. C

22. Cells contain genetic information; reproduce; take in food; transport materials, and remove waste.

23. A

24. Food provides energy for all organisms for growth, activity, and tissue repair.

25. sugar and oxygen

26. in their roots, stems, and fruits

27. B

28. C

29. Plants need food to grow, develop, and reproduce.

30. Plants use water from the soil, carbon dioxide from the air, and light energy to create sugar and oxygen. Sugar is their food source.

31. B

32. by eating another organism that has eaten the plant

33. Scientists study populations to see how they grow and change.

34. Factors include disease, attack by predators, and lack of food, water, or land.

35. D

36. A

37. Acceptable answers include inadequate rainfall.

38. Human development might limit the population growth of some organisms by greatly decreasing the amount of land available to those organisms for food, shelter, and water.

39. B

40. Better sanitation has prevented the spread of disease and supported population growth.

41. D

42. Exercise is important for overall health because it helps maintain ideal weight and strengthens the heart, other muscles, and bones.

43. C

44. Once the virus has been disabled, your immune system continues to produce the same antibodies that were used to disable that virus.

45. A

46. Antibodies attach to disease-causing organisms and mark them to be destroyed by cells of the immune system.

47. A

48. When harmful substances exist in water, air, and soil, they can cause health problems in humans and other organisms.

The Mathematical World

1. -8

2. -86 m

3. D

4. B

5. C

6. A scientist uses a negative number to describe an elevation below sea level.

7. It names the line that goes through points M and N.

8. parallel lines

9. B

10. A

11. B

12. Perpendicular lines and oblique lines both intersect; perpendicular lines intersect to form four right angles, while oblique lines intersect to form a pair of acute angles and a pair of obtuse angles.

13. B

14. On the graph with 1-inch intervals, the bars would be taller and the difference between the bars would be greater than on the graph with 3-inch intervals.

15. A

16. No. He should ask more people because his friends are a small group and they may share the same opinion.

Historical Perspectives

1. C
2. bacteria, viruses, yeasts, and parasites
3. C
4. the process of destroying microorganisms with heat
5. B
6. A vaccine usually consists of pathogenss that have been weakened or killed but can still trigger the immune system to protect against a disease.
7. D
8. Before the germ theory, diseases were treated by appealing to supernatural powers, blood letting, and vomiting.

Common Themes

1. A
2. The output of moving the gears and chain becomes the input to turn the wheels.
3. B
4. A cross section of a three-dimensional model would show the different layers of Earth.
5. D
6. The system is in balance.
7. C
8. The cheetah would run half the distance.

Academic Standards

Think Like a Scientist

Scientists have a particular way of looking at the world, or scientific habits of mind. Whenever you ask a question and explore possible answers, you use many of the same skills that scientists do. Some of these skills are described on this page.

Observing

When you use one or more of your five senses to gather information about the world, you are **observing.** Hearing a dog bark, counting twelve green seeds, and smelling smoke are all observations. To increase the power of their senses, scientists sometimes use microscopes, telescopes, or other instruments that help them make more detailed observations.

An observation must be an accurate report of what your senses detect. It is important to keep careful records of your observations in science class by writing or drawing in a notebook. The information collected through observations is called evidence, or data.

Inferring

When you interpret an observation, you are **inferring,** or making an inference. For example, if you hear your dog barking, you may infer that someone is at your front door. To make this inference, you combine the evidence—the barking dog—and your experience or knowledge—you know that your dog barks when strangers approach—to reach a logical conclusion.

Notice that an inference is not a fact; it is only one of many possible interpretations for an observation. For example, your dog may be barking because it wants to go for a walk. An inference may turn out to be incorrect even if it is based on accurate observations and logical reasoning. The only way to find out if an inference is correct is to investigate further.

Predicting

When you listen to the weather forecast, you hear many predictions about the next day's weather—what the temperature will be, whether it will rain, and how windy it will be. Weather forecasters use observations and knowledge of weather patterns to predict the weather. The skill of **predicting** involves making an inference about a future event based on current evidence or past experience.

Because a prediction is an inference, it may prove to be false. In science class, you can test some of your predictions by doing experiments. For example, suppose you predict that larger paper airplanes can fly farther than smaller airplanes. How could you test your prediction?

Activity

Use the photograph to answer the questions below.

Observing Look closely at the photograph. List at least three observations.

Inferring Use your observations to make an inference about what has happened. What experience or knowledge did you use to make the inference?

Predicting Predict what will happen next. On what evidence or experience do you base your prediction?

Classifying

Could you imagine searching for a book in the library if the books were shelved in no particular order? Your trip to the library would be an all-day event! Luckily, librarians group together books on similar topics or by the same author. Grouping together items that are alike in some way is called **classifying.** You can classify items in many ways: by size, by shape, by use, and by other important characteristics.

Like librarians, scientists use the skill of classifying to organize information and objects. When things are sorted into groups, the relationships among them become easier to understand.

> **Activity**
>
> Classify the objects in the photograph into two groups based on any characteristic you choose. Then use another characteristic to classify the objects into three groups.

> **Activity**
>
> This student is using a model to demonstrate what causes day and night on Earth. What do the flashlight and the tennis ball in the model represent?

Making Models

Have you ever drawn a picture to help someone understand what you were saying? Such a drawing is one type of model. A model is a picture, diagram, computer image, or other representation of a complex object or process. **Making models** helps people understand things that they cannot observe directly.

Scientists often use models to represent things that are either very large or very small, such as the planets in the solar system, or the parts of a cell. Such models are physical models—drawings or three-dimensional structures that look like the real thing. Other models are mental models—mathematical equations or words that describe how something works.

Communicating

Whenever you talk on the phone, write a report, or listen to your teacher at school, you are communicating. **Communicating** is the process of sharing ideas and information with other people. Communicating effectively requires many skills, including writing, reading, speaking, listening, and making models.

Scientists communicate to share results, information, and opinions. Scientists often communicate about their work in journals, over the telephone, in letters, and on the Internet.

They also attend scientific meetings where they share their ideas with one another in person.

> **Activity**
>
> On a sheet of paper, write out clear, detailed directions for tying your shoe. Then exchange directions with a partner. Follow your partner's directions exactly. How successful were you at tying your shoe? How could your partner have communicated more clearly?

Making Measurements

**By measuring, scientists can express their observations more precisely
and communicate more information about what they observe.**

Measuring in SI

The standard system of measurement used by
scientists around the world is known as the
International System of Units, which is abbreviated as SI (**Système International d'Unités,** in
French). SI units are easy to use because they are
based on multiples of 10. Each unit is ten times
larger than the next smallest unit and one tenth
the size of the next largest unit. The table lists the
prefixes used to name the most common SI units.

Common SI Prefixes		
Prefix	Symbol	Meaning
kilo-	k	1,000
hecto-	h	100
deka-	da	10
deci-	d	0.1 (one tenth)
centi-	c	0.01 (one hundredth)
milli-	m	0.001 (one thousandth)

Length To measure length, or the distance
between two points, the unit of measure is the
meter (m). The distance from the floor to a doorknob is approximately one meter. Long distances,
such as the distance be-
tween two cities, are
measured in kilometers
(km). Small lengths are
measured in centimeters
(cm) or millimeters
(mm). Scientists use
metric rulers and meter
sticks to measure length.

Common Conversions		
1 km	=	1,000 m
1 m	=	100 cm
1 m	=	1,000 mm
1 cm	=	10 mm

Activity

The larger lines on the metric ruler in the
picture show centimeter divisions, while
the smaller, unnumbered lines show millimeter divisions. How many centimeters
long is the shell? How many millimeters
long is it?

Liquid Volume To measure the volume of a
liquid, or the amount of space it takes up, you
will use a unit of measure known as the
liter (L). One liter is the approximate volume of
a medium-size carton of milk. Smaller volumes
are measured in milliliters (mL). Scientists use
graduated cylinders to measure liquid volume.

Activity

The graduated cylinder in
the picture is marked in
milliliter divisions. Notice
that the water in the
cylinder has a curved
surface. This curved
surface is called the
meniscus. To measure
the volume, you must
read the level at the
lowest point of the
meniscus. What is the
volume of water in this
graduated cylinder?

Common Conversion
1 L = 1,000 mL

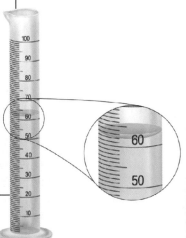

Mass To measure mass, or the amount of matter in an object, you will use a unit of measure known as the **gram (g).** One gram is approximately the mass of a paper clip. Larger masses are measured in kilograms (kg). Scientists use a balance to find the mass of an object.

Common Conversion

1 kg = 1,000 g

Activity

The mass of the potato in the picture is measured in kilograms. What is the mass of the potato? Suppose a recipe for potato salad called for one kilogram of potatoes. About how many potatoes would you need?

0.25 KG

Temperature To measure the temperature of a substance, you will use the **Celsius scale.** Temperature is measured in degrees Celsius (°C) using a Celsius thermometer. Water freezes at 0°C and boils at 100°C.

Time The unit scientists use to measure time is the **second (s).**

Activity

What is the temperature of the liquid in degrees Celsius?

Converting SI Units

To use the SI system, you must know how to convert between units. Converting from one unit to another involves the skill of **calculating,** or using mathematical operations. Converting between SI units is similar to converting between dollars and dimes because both systems are based on multiples of ten.

Suppose you want to convert a length of 80 centimeters to meters. Follow these steps to convert between units.

1. Begin by writing down the measurement you want to convert—in this example, 80 centimeters.

2. Write a conversion factor that represents the relationship between the two units you are converting. In this example, the relationship is 1 meter = 100 centimeters. Write this conversion factor as a fraction, making sure to place the units you are converting from (centimeters, in this example) in the denominator.

3. Multiply the measurement you want to convert by the fraction. When you do this, the units in the first measurement will cancel out with the units in the denominator. Your answer will be in the units you are converting to (meters, in this example).

Example

80 centimeters = ■ meters

$$80 \text{ centimeters} \times \frac{1 \text{ meter}}{100 \text{ centimeters}} = \frac{80 \text{ meters}}{100}$$

$$= 0.8 \text{ meters}$$

Activity

Convert between the following units.
1. 600 millimeters = ■ meters
2. 0.35 liters = ■ milliliters
3. 1,050 grams = ■ kilograms

Conducting a Scientific Investigation

In some ways, scientists are like detectives, piecing together clues to learn about a process or event. One way that scientists gather clues is by carrying out experiments. An experiment tests an idea in a careful, orderly manner. Although experiments do not all follow the same steps in the same order, many follow a pattern similar to the one described here.

Posing Questions

Experiments begin by asking a scientific question. A scientific question is one that can be answered by gathering evidence. For example, the question "Which freezes faster—fresh water or salt water?" is a scientific question because you can carry out an investigation and gather information to answer the question.

Developing a Hypothesis

The next step is to form a hypothesis. A **hypothesis** is a possible explanation for a set of observations or answer to a scientific question. In science, a hypothesis must be something that can be tested. A hypothesis can be worded as an *If . . . then . . .* statement. For example, a hypothesis might be *"If I add salt to fresh water, then the water will take longer to freeze."* A hypothesis worded this way serves as a rough outline of the experiment you should perform.

Designing an Experiment

Next you need to plan a way to test your hypothesis. Your plan should be written out as a step-by-step procedure and should describe the observations or measurements you will make.

Two important steps involved in designing an experiment are controlling variables and forming operational definitions.

Controlling Variables In a well-designed experiment, you need to keep all variables the same except for one. A **variable** is any factor that can change in an experiment. The factor that you change is called the **manipulated variable.** In this experiment, the manipulated variable is the amount of salt added to the water. Other factors, such as the amount of water or the starting temperature, are kept constant.

The factor that changes as a result of the manipulated variable is called the **responding variable.** The responding variable is what you measure or observe to obtain your results. In this experiment, the responding variable is how long the water takes to freeze.

An experiment in which all factors except one are kept constant is called a **controlled experiment.** Most controlled experiments include a test called the control. In this experiment, Container 3 is the control. Because no salt is added to Container 3, you can compare the results from the other containers to it. Any difference in results must be due to the addition of salt alone.

Forming Operational Definitions Another important aspect of a well-designed experiment is having clear operational definitions. An **operational definition** is a statement that describes how a particular variable is to be measured or how a term is to be defined. For example, in this experiment, how will you determine if the water has frozen? You might decide to insert a stick in each container at the start of the experiment. Your operational definition of "frozen" would be the time at which the stick can no longer move.

Experimental Procedure
1. Fill 3 containers with 300 milliliters of cold tap water.
2. Add 10 grams of salt to Container 1; stir. Add 20 grams of salt to Container 2; stir. Add no salt to Container 3.
3. Place the 3 containers in a freezer.
4. Check the containers every 15 minutes. Record your observations.

Interpreting Data

The observations and measurements you make in an experiment are called **data.** At the end of an experiment, you need to analyze the data to look for any patterns or trends. Patterns often become clear if you organize your data in a data table or graph. Then think through what the data reveal. Do they support your hypothesis? Do they point out a flaw in your experiment? Do you need to collect more data?

Drawing Conclusions

A **conclusion** is a statement that sums up what you have learned from an experiment. When you draw a conclusion, you need to decide whether the data you collected support your hypothesis or not. You may need to repeat an experiment several times before you can draw any conclusions from it. Conclusions often lead you to pose new questions and plan new experiments to answer them.

Activity

Is a ball's bounce affected by the height from which it is dropped? Using the steps just described, plan a controlled experiment to investigate this problem.

Technology Design Skills

Engineers are people who use scientific and technological knowledge to solve practical problems. To design new products, engineers usually follow the process described here, even though they may not follow these steps in the exact order. As you read the steps, think about how you might apply them in technology labs.

Identify a Need

Before engineers begin designing a new product, they must first identify the need they are trying to meet. For example, suppose you are a member of a design team in a company that makes toys. Your team has identified a need: a toy boat that is inexpensive and easy to assemble.

Research the Problem

Engineers often begin by gathering information that will help them with their new design. This research may include finding articles in books, magazines, or on the Internet. It may also include talking to other engineers who have solved similar problems. Engineers often perform experiments related to the product they want to design.

For your toy boat, you could look at toys that are similar to the one you want to design. You might do research on the Internet. You could also test some materials to see whether they will work well in a toy boat.

Drawing for a boat design ▼

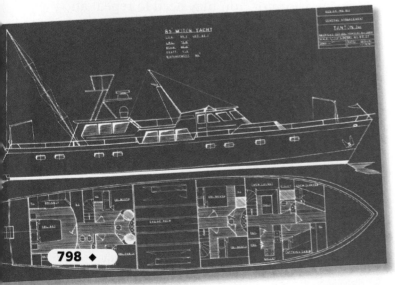

Design a Solution

Research gives engineers information that helps them design a product. When engineers design new products, they usually work in teams.

Generating Ideas Often design teams hold brainstorming meetings in which any team member can contribute ideas. **Brainstorming** is a creative process in which one team member's suggestions often spark ideas in other group members. Brainstorming can lead to new approaches to solving a design problem.

Evaluating Constraints During brainstorming, a design team will often come up with several possible designs. The team must then evaluate each one.

As part of their evaluation, engineers consider constraints. **Constraints** are factors that limit or restrict a product design. Physical characteristics, such as the properties of materials used to make your toy boat, are constraints. Money and time are also constraints. If the materials in a product cost a lot, or if the product takes a long time to make, the design may be impractical.

Making Trade-offs Design teams usually need to make trade-offs. In a **trade-off,** engineers give up one benefit of a proposed design in order to obtain another. In designing your toy boat, you will have to make trade-offs. For example, suppose one material is sturdy but not fully waterproof. Another material is more waterproof, but breakable. You may decide to give up the benefit of sturdiness in order to obtain the benefit of waterproofing.

Build and Evaluate a Prototype

Once the team has chosen a design plan, the engineers build a prototype of the product. A **prototype** is a working model used to test a design. Engineers evaluate the prototype to see whether it works well, is easy to operate, is safe to use, and holds up to repeated use.

Think of your toy boat. What would the prototype be like? Of what materials would it be made? How would you test it?

Troubleshoot and Redesign

Few prototypes work perfectly, which is why they need to be tested. Once a design team has tested a prototype, the members analyze the results and identify any problems. The team then tries to **troubleshoot,** or fix the design problems. For example, if your toy boat leaks or wobbles, the boat should be redesigned to eliminate those problems.

Communicate the Solution

A team needs to communicate the final design to the people who will manufacture and use the product. To do this, teams may use sketches, detailed drawings, computer simulations, and word descriptions.

Activity

You can use the technology design process to design and build a toy boat.

Research and Investigate

1. Visit the library or go online to research toy boats.
2. Investigate how a toy boat can be powered, including wind, rubber bands, or baking soda and vinegar.
3. Brainstorm materials, shapes, and steering for your boat.

Design and Build

4. Based on your research, design a toy boat that
   - is made of readily available materials
   - is no larger than 15 cm long and 10 cm wide
   - includes a power system, a rudder, and an area for cargo
   - travels 2 meters in a straight line carrying a load of 20 pennies
5. Sketch your design and write a step-by-step plan for building your boat. After your teacher approves your plan, build your boat.

Evaluate and Redesign

6. Test your boat, evaluate the results, and troubleshoot any problems.
7. Based on your evaluation, redesign your toy boat so it performs better.

Creating Data Tables and Graphs

How can you make sense of the data in a science experiment?
The first step is to organize the data to help you understand them.
Data tables and graphs are helpful tools for organizing data.

Data Tables

You have gathered your materials and set up your experiment. But before you start, you need to plan a way to record what happens during the experiment. By creating a data table, you can record your observations and measurements in an orderly way.

Suppose, for example, that a scientist conducted an experiment to find out how many Calories people of different body masses burn while doing various activities. The data table shows the results.

Notice in this data table that the manipulated variable (body mass) is the heading of one column. The responding variable (for

Calories Burned in 30 Minutes			
Body Mass	Experiment 1: Bicycling	Experiment 2: Playing Basketball	Experiment 3: Watching Television
30 kg	60 Calories	120 Calories	21 Calories
40 kg	77 Calories	164 Calories	27 Calories
50 kg	95 Calories	206 Calories	33 Calories
60 kg	114 Calories	248 Calories	38 Calories

Experiment 1, the number of Calories burned while bicycling) is the heading of the next column. Additional columns were added for related experiments.

Bar Graphs

To compare how many Calories a person burns doing various activities, you could create a bar graph. A bar graph is used to display data in a number of separate, or distinct, categories. In this example, bicycling, playing basketball, and watching television are the three categories.

To create a bar graph, follow these steps.

1. On graph paper, draw a horizontal, or *x*-, axis and a vertical, or *y*-, axis.

2. Write the names of the categories to be graphed along the horizontal axis. Include an overall label for the axis as well.

3. Label the vertical axis with the name of the responding variable. Include units of measurement. Then create a scale along the axis by marking off equally spaced numbers that cover the range of the data collected.

4. For each category, draw a solid bar using the scale on the vertical axis to determine the height. Make all the bars the same width.

5. Add a title that describes the graph.

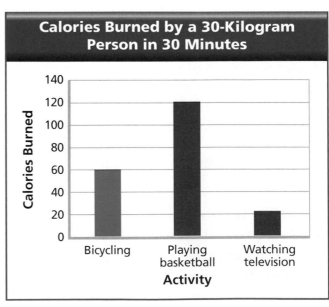

Calories Burned by a 30-Kilogram Person in 30 Minutes

Line Graphs

To see whether a relationship exists between body mass and the number of Calories burned while bicycling, you could create a line graph. A line graph is used to display data that show how one variable (the responding variable) changes in response to another variable (the manipulated variable). You can use a line graph when your manipulated variable is **continuous,** that is, when there are other points between the ones that you tested. In this example, body mass is a continuous variable because there are other body masses between 30 and 40 kilograms (for example, 31 kilograms). Time is another example of a continuous variable.

Line graphs are powerful tools because they allow you to estimate values for conditions that you did not test in the experiment. For example, you can use the line graph to estimate that a 35-kilogram person would burn 68 Calories while bicycling.

To create a line graph, follow these steps.

1. On graph paper, draw a horizontal, or *x*-, axis and a vertical, or *y*-, axis.

2. Label the horizontal axis with the name of the manipulated variable. Label the vertical axis with the name of the responding variable. Include units of measurement.

3. Create a scale on each axis by marking off equally spaced numbers that cover the range of the data collected.

4. Plot a point on the graph for each piece of data. In the line graph above, the dotted lines show how to plot the first data point (30 kilograms and 60 Calories). Follow an imaginary vertical line extending up from the horizontal axis at the 30-kilogram mark. Then follow an imaginary horizontal line extending across from the vertical axis at the 60-Calorie mark. Plot the point where the two lines intersect.

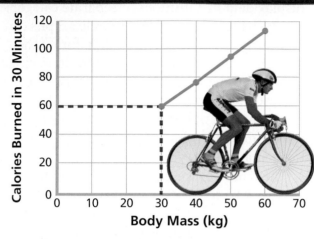

Effect of Body Mass on Calories Burned While Bicycling

5. Connect the plotted points with a solid line. (In some cases, it may be more appropriate to draw a line that shows the general trend of the plotted points. In those cases, some of the points may fall above or below the line. Also, not all graphs are linear. It may be more appropriate to draw a curve to connect the points.)

6. Add a title that identifies the variables or relationship in the graph.

Activity

Create line graphs to display the data from Experiment 2 and Experiment 3 in the data table.

Activity

You read in the newspaper that a total of 4 centimeters of rain fell in your area in June, 2.5 centimeters fell in July, and 1.5 centimeters fell in August. What type of graph would you use to display these data? Use graph paper to create the graph.

Circle Graphs

Like bar graphs, circle graphs can be used to display data in a number of separate categories. Unlike bar graphs, however, circle graphs can only be used when you have data for *all* the categories that make up a given topic. A circle graph is sometimes called a pie chart. The pie represents the entire topic, while the slices represent the individual categories. The size of a slice indicates what percentage of the whole a particular category makes up.

The data table below shows the results of a survey in which 24 teenagers were asked to identify their favorite sport. The data were then used to create the circle graph at the right.

Favorite Sports	
Sport	Students
Soccer	8
Basketball	6
Bicycling	6
Swimming	4

To create a circle graph, follow these steps.

1. Use a compass to draw a circle. Mark the center with a point. Then draw a line from the center point to the top of the circle.

2. Determine the size of each "slice" by setting up a proportion where *x* equals the number of degrees in a slice. (*Note:* A circle contains 360 degrees.) For example, to find the number of degrees in the "soccer" slice, set up the following proportion:

$$\frac{\text{Students who prefer soccer}}{\text{Total number of students}} = \frac{x}{\text{Total number of degrees in a circle}}$$

$$\frac{8}{24} = \frac{x}{360}$$

Cross-multiply and solve for x.

$$24x = 8 \times 360$$
$$x = 120$$

The "soccer" slice should contain 120 degrees.

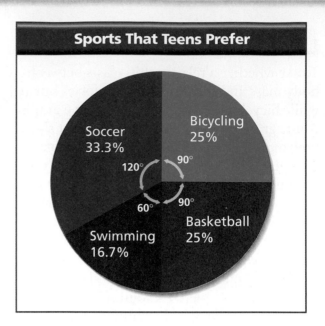

Sports That Teens Prefer

3. Use a protractor to measure the angle of the first slice, using the line you drew to the top of the circle as the 0° line. Draw a line from the center of the circle to the edge for the angle you measured.

4. Continue around the circle by measuring the size of each slice with the protractor. Start measuring from the edge of the previous slice so the wedges do not overlap. When you are done, the entire circle should be filled in.

5. Determine the percentage of the whole circle that each slice represents. To do this, divide the number of degrees in a slice by the total number of degrees in a circle (360), and multiply by 100%. For the "soccer" slice, you can find the percentage as follows:

$$\frac{120}{360} \times 100\% = 33.3\%$$

6. Use a different color for each slice. Label each slice with the category and with the percentage of the whole it represents.

7. Add a title to the circle graph.

Activity

In a class of 28 students, 12 students take the bus to school, 10 students walk, and 6 students ride their bicycles. Create a circle graph to display these data.

Math Review

Scientists use math to organize, analyze, and present data. This appendix will help you review some basic math skills.

Mean, Median, and Mode

The **mean** is the average, or the sum of the data divided by the number of data items. The middle number in a set of ordered data is called the **median**. The **mode** is the number that appears most often in a set of data.

Example

A scientist counted the number of distinct songs sung by seven different male birds and collected the data shown below.

Male Bird Songs							
Bird	A	B	C	D	E	F	G
Number of Songs	36	29	40	35	28	36	27

To determine the mean number of songs, add the total number of songs and divide by the number of data items—in this case, the number of male birds.

$$\text{Mean} = \frac{231}{7} = 33 \text{ songs}$$

To find the median number of songs, arrange the data in numerical order and find the number in the middle of the series.

27 28 29 35 36 36 40

The number in the middle is 35, so the median number of songs is 35.

The mode is the value that appears most frequently. In the data, 36 appears twice, while each other item appears only once. Therefore, 36 songs is the mode.

Practice

Find out how many minutes it takes each student in your class to get to school. Then find the mean, median, and mode for the data.

Probability

Probability is the chance that an event will occur. Probability can be expressed as a ratio, a fraction, or a percentage. For example, when you flip a coin, the probability that the coin will land heads up is 1 in 2, or $\frac{1}{2}$, or 50 percent.

The probability that an event will happen can be expressed in the following formula.

$$P(\text{event}) = \frac{\text{Number of times the event can occur}}{\text{Total number of possible events}}$$

Example

A paper bag contains 25 blue marbles, 5 green marbles, 5 orange marbles, and 15 yellow marbles. If you close your eyes and pick a marble from the bag, what is the probability that it will be yellow?

$$P(\text{yellow marbles}) = \frac{15 \text{ yellow marbles}}{50 \text{ marbles total}}$$

$$P = \frac{15}{50}, \text{ or } \frac{3}{10}, \text{ or } 30\%$$

Practice

Each side of a cube has a letter on it. Two sides have *A*, three sides have *B*, and one side has *C*. If you roll the cube, what is the probability that *A* will land on top?

Area

The **area** of a surface is the number of square units that cover it. The front cover of your textbook has an area of about 600 cm².

Area of a Rectangle and a Square To find the area of a rectangle, multiply its length times its width. The formula for the area of a rectangle is

$$A = \ell \times w, \text{ or } A = \ell w$$

Since all four sides of a square have the same length, the area of a square is the length of one side multiplied by itself, or squared.

$$A = s \times s, \text{ or } A = s^2$$

Example

A scientist is studying the plants in a field that measures 75 m × 45 m. What is the area of the field?

$$A = \ell \times w$$
$$A = 75 \text{ m} \times 45 \text{ m}$$
$$A = 3,375 \text{ m}^2$$

Area of a Circle The formula for the area of a circle is

$$A = \pi \times r \times r, \text{ or } A = \pi r^2$$

The length of the radius is represented by r, and the value of π is approximately $\frac{22}{7}$.

Example

Find the area of a circle with a radius of 14 cm.

$$A = \pi r^2$$
$$A = 14 \times 14 \times \frac{22}{7}$$
$$A = 616 \text{ cm}^2$$

Practice

Find the area of a circle that has a radius of 21 m.

Circumference

The distance around a circle is called the circumference. The formula for finding the circumference of a circle is

$$C = 2 \times \pi \times r, \text{ or } C = 2\pi r$$

Example

The radius of a circle is 35 cm. What is its circumference?

$$C = 2\pi r$$
$$C = 2 \times 35 \times \frac{22}{7}$$
$$C = 220 \text{ cm}$$

Practice

What is the circumference of a circle with a radius of 28 m?

Volume

The volume of an object is the number of cubic units it contains. The volume of a wastebasket, for example, might be about 26,000 cm³.

Volume of a Rectangular Object To find the volume of a rectangular object, multiply the object's length times its width times its height.

$$V = \ell \times w \times h, \text{ or } V = \ell w h$$

Example

Find the volume of a box with length 24 cm, width 12 cm, and height 9 cm.

$$V = \ell w h$$
$$V = 24 \text{ cm} \times 12 \text{ cm} \times 9 \text{ cm}$$
$$V = 2,592 \text{ cm}^3$$

Practice

What is the volume of a rectangular object with length 17 cm, width 11 cm, and height 6 cm?

Fractions

A **fraction** is a way to express a part of a whole. In the fraction $\frac{4}{7}$, 4 is the numerator and 7 is the denominator.

Adding and Subtracting Fractions To add or subtract two or more fractions that have a common denominator, first add or subtract the numerators. Then write the sum or difference over the common denominator.

To find the sum or difference of fractions with different denominators, first find the least common multiple of the denominators. This is known as the least common denominator. Then convert each fraction to equivalent fractions with the least common denominator. Add or subtract the numerators. Then write the sum or difference over the common denominator.

Example

$$\frac{5}{6} - \frac{3}{4} = \frac{10}{12} - \frac{9}{12} = \frac{10 - 9}{12} = \frac{1}{12}$$

Multiplying Fractions To multiply two fractions, first multiply the two numerators, then multiply the two denominators.

Example

$$\frac{5}{6} \times \frac{2}{3} = \frac{5 \times 2}{6 \times 3} = \frac{10}{18} = \frac{5}{9}$$

Dividing Fractions Dividing by a fraction is the same as multiplying by its reciprocal. Reciprocals are numbers whose numerators and denominators have been switched. To divide one fraction by another, first invert the fraction you are dividing by—in other words, turn it upside down. Then multiply the two fractions.

Example

$$\frac{2}{5} \div \frac{7}{8} = \frac{2}{5} \times \frac{8}{7} = \frac{2 \times 8}{5 \times 7} = \frac{16}{35}$$

Practice

Solve the following: $\frac{3}{7} \div \frac{4}{5}$.

Decimals

Fractions whose denominators are 10, 100, or some other power of 10 are often expressed as decimals. For example, the fraction $\frac{9}{10}$ can be expressed as the decimal 0.9, and the fraction $\frac{7}{100}$ can be written as 0.07.

Adding and Subtracting With Decimals To add or subtract decimals, line up the decimal points before you carry out the operation.

Example

```
   27.4          278.635
 + 6.19        − 191.4
 ------        ---------
  33.59          87.235
```

Multiplying With Decimals When you multiply two numbers with decimals, the number of decimal places in the product is equal to the total number of decimal places in each number being multiplied.

Example

```
   46.2   (one decimal place)
 × 2.37   (two decimal places)
 --------
 109.494  (three decimal places)
```

Dividing With Decimals To divide a decimal by a whole number, put the decimal point in the quotient above the decimal point in the dividend.

Example

$$15.5 \div 5$$

```
     3.1
  5)15.5
```

To divide a decimal by a decimal, you need to rewrite the divisor as a whole number. Do this by multiplying both the divisor and dividend by the same multiple of 10.

Example

$$1.68 \div 4.2 = 16.8 \div 42$$

```
     0.4
  42)16.8
```

Practice

Multiply 6.21 by 8.5.

Ratio and Proportion

A **ratio** compares two numbers by division. For example, suppose a scientist counts 800 wolves and 1,200 moose on an island. The ratio of wolves to moose can be written as a fraction, $\frac{800}{1,200}$, which can be reduced to $\frac{2}{3}$. The same ratio can also be expressed as 2 to 3 or 2 : 3.

A **proportion** is a mathematical sentence saying that two ratios are equivalent. For example, a proportion could state that $\frac{800 \text{ wolves}}{1,200 \text{ moose}} = \frac{2 \text{ wolves}}{3 \text{ moose}}$. You can sometimes set up a proportion to determine or estimate an unknown quantity. For example, suppose a scientist counts 25 beetles in an area of 10 square meters. The scientist wants to estimate the number of beetles in 100 square meters.

Example

1. Express the relationship between beetles and area as a ratio: $\frac{25}{10}$, simplified to $\frac{5}{2}$.

2. Set up a proportion, with x representing the number of beetles. The proportion can be stated as $\frac{5}{2} = \frac{x}{100}$.

3. Begin by cross-multiplying. In other words, multiply each fraction's numerator by the other fraction's denominator.

$$5 \times 100 = 2 \times x, \text{ or } 500 = 2x$$

4. To find the value of x, divide both sides by 2. The result is 250, or 250 beetles in 100 square meters.

Practice

Find the value of x in the following proportion: $\frac{6}{7} = \frac{x}{49}$.

Percentage

A **percentage** is a ratio that compares a number to 100. For example, there are 37 granite rocks in a collection that consists of 100 rocks. The ratio $\frac{37}{100}$ can be written as 37%. Granite rocks make up 37% of the rock collection.

You can calculate percentages of numbers other than 100 by setting up a proportion.

Example

Rain falls on 9 days out of 30 in June. What percentage of the days in June were rainy?

$$\frac{9 \text{ days}}{30 \text{ days}} = \frac{d\%}{100\%}$$

To find the value of d, begin by cross-multiplying, as for any proportion:

$$9 \times 100 = 30 \times d \qquad d = \frac{900}{30} \qquad d = 30$$

Practice

There are 300 marbles in a jar, and 42 of those marbles are blue. What percentage of the marbles are blue?

Significant Figures

The **precision** of a measurement depends on the instrument you use to take the measurement. For example, if the smallest unit on the ruler is millimeters, then the most precise measurement you can make will be in millimeters.

The sum or difference of measurements can only be as precise as the least precise measurement being added or subtracted. Round your answer so that it has the same number of digits after the decimal as the least precise measurement. Round up if the last digit is 5 or more, and round down if the last digit is 4 or less.

> **Example**
>
> Subtract a temperature of 5.2°C from the temperature 75.46°C.
>
> **75.46 − 5.2 = 70.26**
>
> 5.2 has the fewest digits after the decimal, so it is the least precise measurement. Since the last digit of the answer is 6, round up to 3. The most precise difference between the measurements is 70.3°C.

> **Practice**
>
> Add 26.4 m to 8.37 m. Round your answer according to the precision of the measurements.

Significant figures are the number of nonzero digits in a measurement. Zeroes between nonzero digits are also significant. For example, the measurements 12,500 L, 0.125 cm, and 2.05 kg all have three significant figures. When you multiply and divide measurements, the one with the fewest significant figures determines the number of significant figures in your answer.

> **Example**
>
> Multiply 110 g by 5.75 g.
>
> **110 × 5.75 = 632.5**
>
> Because 110 has only two significant figures, round the answer to 630 g.

Scientific Notation

A **factor** is a number that divides into another number with no remainder. In the example, the number 3 is used as a factor four times.

An **exponent** tells how many times a number is used as a factor. For example, $3 \times 3 \times 3 \times 3$ can be written as 3^4. The exponent 4 indicates that the number 3 is used as a factor four times. Another way of expressing this is to say that 81 is equal to 3 to the fourth power.

> **Example**
>
> $$3^4 = 3 \times 3 \times 3 \times 3 = 81$$

Scientific notation uses exponents and powers of ten to write very large or very small numbers in shorter form. When you write a number in scientific notation, you write the number as two factors. The first factor is any number between 1 and 10. The second factor is a power of 10, such as 10^3 or 10^6.

> **Example**
>
> The average distance between the planet Mercury and the sun is 58,000,000 km. To write the first factor in scientific notation, insert a decimal point in the original number so that you have a number between 1 and 10. In the case of 58,000,000, the number is 5.8.
>
> To determine the power of 10, count the number of places that the decimal point moved. In this case, it moved 7 places.
>
> **58,000,000 km = 5.8 × 10^7 km**

> **Practice**
>
> Express 6,590,000 in scientific notation.

Reading Comprehension Skills

Your textbook is an important source of science information. As you read your science textbook, you will find that the book has been written to assist you in understanding the science concepts.

Learning From Science Textbooks

As you study science in school, you will learn science concepts in a variety of ways. Sometimes you will do interesting activities and experiments to explore science ideas. To fully understand what you observe in experiments and activities, you will need to read your science textbook. To help you read, some of the important ideas are highlighted so that you can easily recognize what they are. In addition, a target reading skill in each section will help you understand what you read.

By using the target reading skills, you will improve your reading comprehension—that is, you will improve your ability to understand what you read. As you learn science, you will build knowledge that will help you understand even more of what you read. This knowledge will help you learn about all the topics presented in this textbook.

And—guess what?—these reading skills can be useful whenever you are reading. Reading to learn is important for your entire life. You have an opportunity to begin that process now.

The target reading skills that will improve your reading comprehension are described below.

Building Vocabulary

To understand the science concepts taught in this textbook, you need to remember the meanings of the Key Terms. One strategy consists of writing the definitions of these terms in your own words. You can also practice using the terms in sentences and make lists of words or phrases you associate with each term.

Using Prior Knowledge

Your prior knowledge is what you already know before you begin to read about a topic. Building on what you already know gives you a head start on learning new information. Before you begin a new assignment, think about what you know. You might page through your reading assignment, looking at the headings and the visuals to spark your memory. You can list what you know in the graphic organizer provided in the section opener. Then, as you read, consider questions like the ones below to connect what you learn to what you already know.

- How does what you learn relate to what you know?
- How did something you already know help you learn something new?
- Did your original ideas agree with what you have just learned? If not, how would you revise your original ideas?

Asking Questions

Asking yourself questions is an excellent way to focus on and remember new information in your textbook. You can learn how to ask good questions.

One way is to turn the text headings into questions. Then your questions can guide you to identify and remember the important information as you read. Look at these examples:

Heading: Using Seismographic Data
Question: How are seismographic data used?
Heading: Kinds of Faults
Question: What are the kinds of faults?

You do not have to limit your questions to the text headings. Ask questions about anything that you need to clarify or that will help you understand the content. *What* and *how* are probably the most common question words, but you may also ask *why, who, when,* or *where* questions. Here is an example:

Properties of Waves

Question	Answer
What is amplitude?	Amplitude is . . .

Previewing Visuals

Visuals are photographs, graphs, tables, diagrams, and illustrations. Visuals, such as this diagram of a normal fault, contain important information. Look at visuals and their captions before you read. This will help you prepare for what you will be reading about.

Often you will be asked what you want to learn about a visual. For example, after you look at the normal fault diagram, you might ask: What is the movement along a normal fault? Questions about visuals give you a purpose for reading—to answer your questions. Previewing visuals also helps you see what you already know.

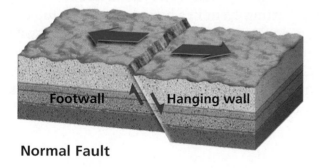

Footwall **Hanging wall**

Normal Fault

Outlining

An outline shows the relationship between main ideas and supporting ideas. An outline has a formal structure. You write the main ideas, called topics, next to Roman numerals. The supporting ideas, sometimes called subtopics, are written under the main ideas and labeled A, B, C, and so on. An outline looks like this:

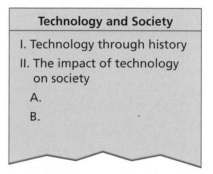

Technology and Society

I. Technology through history

II. The impact of technology on society

  A.

  B.

When you have completed an outline like this, you can see at a glance the structure of the section. You can use this outline as a study tool.

Identifying Main Ideas

When you are reading, it is important to try to understand the ideas and concepts that are in a passage. As you read science material, you will recognize that each paragraph has a lot of information and detail. Good readers try to identify the most important—or biggest—idea in every paragraph or section. That's the main idea. The other information in the paragraph supports or further explains the main idea.

Sometimes main ideas are stated directly. In this book, some main ideas are identified for you as key concepts. These are printed in boldface type. However, you must identify other main ideas yourself. In order to do this, you must identify all the ideas within a paragraph or section. Then ask yourself which idea is big enough to include all the other ideas.

Comparing and Contrasting

When you compare and contrast, you examine the similarities and differences between things. You can compare and contrast in a Venn diagram or in a table. Your completed diagram or table shows you how the items are alike and how they are different.

Venn Diagram A Venn diagram consists of two overlapping circles. In the space where the circles overlap, you write the characteristics that the two items have in common. In one of the circles outside the area of overlap, you write the differing features or characteristics of one of the items. In the other circle outside the area of overlap, you write the differing characteristics of the other item.

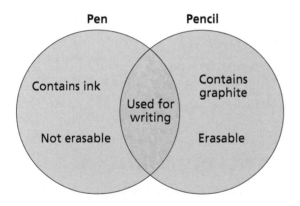

Table In a compare/contrast table, you list the items to be compared across the top of the table. Then list the characteristics or features to be compared in the left column. Complete the table by filling in information about each characteristic or feature.

Blood Vessel	Function	Structure of Wall
Artery	Carries blood away from heart	
Capillary		
Vein		

Sequencing

A sequence is the order in which a series of events occurs. Recognizing and remembering the sequence of events is important to understanding many processes in science. Sometimes the text uses words like *first, next, during,* and *after* to signal a sequence. A flowchart or a cycle diagram can help you visualize a sequence.

Flowchart To make a flowchart, write a brief description of each step or event in a box. Place the boxes in order, with the first event at the top of the page. Then draw an arrow to connect each step or event to the next.

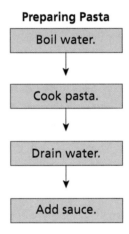

Cycle Diagram A cycle diagram shows a sequence that is continuous, or cyclical. A continuous sequence does not have an end because when the final event is over, the first event begins again. To create a cycle diagram, write the starting event in a box placed at the top of a page in the center. Then, moving in a clockwise direction around an imaginary circle, write each event in a box in its proper sequence. Draw arrows that connect each event to the one that occurs next, forming a continuous circle.

Identifying Supporting Evidence

A hypothesis is a possible explanation for observations made by scientists or an answer to a scientific question. A hypothesis is tested over and over again. The tests may produce evidence that supports the hypothesis. When enough supporting evidence is collected, a hypothesis may become a theory.

Identifying the supporting evidence for a hypothesis or theory can help you understand the hypothesis or theory. Evidence consists of facts—information whose accuracy can be confirmed by testing or observation.

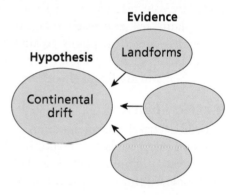

Relating Cause and Effect

Identifying causes and effects helps you understand relationships among events. A cause makes something happen. An effect is what happens. When you recognize that one event causes another, you are relating cause and effect. Words like *cause, because, effect, affect,* and *result* often signal a cause or an effect.

Sometimes an effect can have more than one cause, or a cause can produce several effects. For example, car exhaust and smoke from industrial plants are two causes of air pollution. Some effects of air pollution include breathing difficulties for some people, death of plants along some highways, and damage to some building surfaces.

Science involves many cause-and-effect relationships. Seeing and understanding these relationships helps you understand science processes.

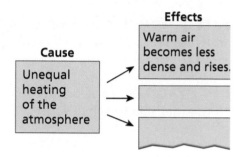

Concept Mapping

Concept maps are useful tools for organizing information on any topic. A concept map begins with a main idea or core concept and shows how the idea can be subdivided into related subconcepts or smaller ideas. In this way, relationships between concepts become clearer and easier to understand.

You construct a concept map by placing concepts (usually nouns) in ovals and connecting them with linking words. The biggest concept or idea is placed in an oval at the top of the map. Related concepts are arranged in ovals below the big idea. The linking words are often verbs and verb phrases and are written on the lines that connect the ovals.

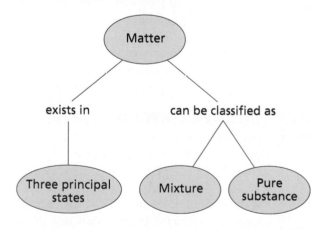

Safety Symbols

These symbols warn of possible dangers in the laboratory and remind you to work carefully.

 Safety Goggles Wear safety goggles to protect your eyes in any activity involving chemicals, flames or heating, or glassware.

 Lab Apron Wear a laboratory apron to protect your skin and clothing from damage.

 Breakage Handle breakable materials, such as glassware, with care. Do not touch broken glassware.

 Heat-Resistant Gloves Use an oven mitt or other hand protection when handling hot materials such as hot plates or hot glassware.

 Plastic Gloves Wear disposable plastic gloves when working with harmful chemicals and organisms. Keep your hands away from your face, and dispose of the gloves according to your teacher's instructions.

 Heating Use a clamp or tongs to pick up hot glassware. Do not touch hot objects with your bare hands.

 Flames Before you work with flames, tie back loose hair and clothing. Follow instructions from your teacher about lighting and extinguishing flames.

 No Flames When using flammable materials, make sure there are no flames, sparks, or other exposed heat sources present.

 Corrosive Chemical Avoid getting acid or other corrosive chemicals on your skin or clothing or in your eyes. Do not inhale the vapors. Wash your hands after the activity.

 Poison Do not let any poisonous chemical come into contact with your skin, and do not inhale its vapors. Wash your hands when you are finished with the activity.

 Fumes Work in a ventilated area when harmful vapors may be involved. Avoid inhaling vapors directly. Only test an odor when directed to do so by your teacher, and use a wafting motion to direct the vapor toward your nose.

 Sharp Object Scissors, scalpels, knives, needles, pins, and tacks can cut your skin. Always direct a sharp edge or point away from yourself and others.

 Animal Safety Treat live or preserved animals or animal parts with care to avoid harming the animals or yourself. Wash your hands when you are finished with the activity.

 Plant Safety Handle plants only as directed by your teacher. If you are allergic to certain plants, tell your teacher; do not do an activity involving those plants. Avoid touching harmful plants such as poison ivy. Wash your hands when you are finished with the activity.

 Electric Shock To avoid electric shock, never use electrical equipment around water, or when the equipment is wet or your hands are wet. Be sure cords are untangled and cannot trip anyone. Unplug equipment not in use.

 Physical Safety When an experiment involves physical activity, avoid injuring yourself or others. Alert your teacher if there is any reason you should not participate.

 Disposal Dispose of chemicals and other laboratory materials safely. Follow the instructions from your teacher.

 Hand Washing Wash your hands thoroughly when finished with the activity. Use antibacterial soap and warm water. Rinse well.

 General Safety Awareness When this symbol appears, follow the instructions provided. When you are asked to develop your own procedure in a lab, have your teacher approve your plan before you go further.

Science Safety Rules

General Precautions

Follow all instructions. Never perform activities without the approval and supervision of your teacher. Do not engage in horseplay. Never eat or drink in the laboratory. Keep work areas clean and uncluttered.

Dress Code

Wear safety goggles whenever you work with chemicals, glassware, heat sources such as burners, or any substance that might get into your eyes. If you wear contact lenses, notify your teacher.

Wear a lab apron or coat whenever you work with corrosive chemicals or substances that can stain. Wear disposable plastic gloves when working with organisms and harmful chemicals. Tie back long hair. Remove or tie back any article of clothing or jewelry that can hang down and touch chemicals, flames, or equipment. Roll up long sleeves. Never wear open shoes or sandals.

First Aid

Report all accidents, injuries, or fires to your teacher, no matter how minor. Be aware of the location of the first-aid kit, emergency equipment such as the fire extinguisher and fire blanket, and the nearest telephone. Know whom to contact in an emergency.

Heating and Fire Safety

Keep all combustible materials away from flames. When heating a substance in a test tube, make sure that the mouth of the tube is not pointed at you or anyone else. Never heat a liquid in a closed container. Use an oven mitt to pick up a container that has been heated.

Using Chemicals Safely

Never put your face near the mouth of a container that holds chemicals. Never touch, taste, or smell a chemical unless your teacher tells you to.

Use only those chemicals needed in the activity. Keep all containers closed when chemicals are not being used. Pour all chemicals over the sink or a container, not over your work surface. Dispose of excess chemicals as instructed by your teacher.

Be extra careful when working with acids or bases. When mixing an acid and water, always pour the water into the container first and then add the acid to the water. Never pour water into an acid. Wash chemical spills and splashes immediately with plenty of water.

Using Glassware Safely

If glassware is broken or chipped, notify your teacher immediately. Never handle broken or chipped glass with your bare hands.

Never force glass tubing or thermometers into a rubber stopper or rubber tubing. Have your teacher insert the glass tubing or thermometer if required for an activity.

Using Sharp Instruments

Handle sharp instruments with extreme care. Never cut material toward you; cut away from you.

Animal and Plant Safety

Never perform experiments that cause pain, discomfort, or harm to animals. Only handle animals if absolutely necessary. If you know that you are allergic to certain plants, molds, or animals, tell your teacher before doing an activity in which these are used. Wash your hands thoroughly after any activity involving animals, animal parts, plants, plant parts, or soil.

During field work, wear long pants, long sleeves, socks, and closed shoes. Avoid poisonous plants and fungi as well as plants with thorns.

End-of-Experiment Rules

Unplug all electrical equipment. Clean up your work area. Dispose of waste materials as instructed by your teacher. Wash your hands after every experiment.

The microscope is an essential tool in the study of life science. It allows you to see things that are too small to be seen with the unaided eye.

You will probably use a compound microscope like the one you see here. The compound microscope has more than one lens that magnifies the object you view.

Typically, a compound microscope has one lens in the eyepiece, the part you look through. The eyepiece lens usually magnifies 10 ×. Any object you view through this lens would appear 10 times larger than it is.

The compound microscope may contain one or two other lenses called objective lenses. If there are two objective lenses, they are called the low-power and high-power objective lenses. The low-power objective lens usually magnifies 10 ×. The high-power objective lens usually magnifies 40 ×.

To calculate the total magnification with which you are viewing an object, multiply the magnification of the eyepiece lens by the magnification of the objective lens you are using. For example, the eyepiece's magnification of 10 × multiplied by the low-power objective's magnification of 10 × equals a total magnification of 100 ×.

Use the photo of the compound microscope to become familiar with the parts of the microscope and their functions.

The Parts of a Compound Microscope

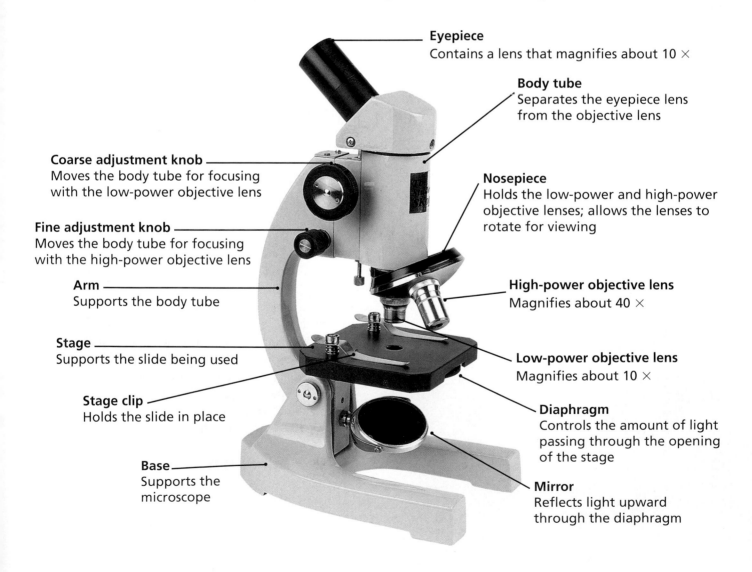

Eyepiece
Contains a lens that magnifies about 10 ×

Body tube
Separates the eyepiece lens from the objective lens

Coarse adjustment knob
Moves the body tube for focusing with the low-power objective lens

Nosepiece
Holds the low-power and high-power objective lenses; allows the lenses to rotate for viewing

Fine adjustment knob
Moves the body tube for focusing with the high-power objective lens

Arm
Supports the body tube

High-power objective lens
Magnifies about 40 ×

Stage
Supports the slide being used

Low-power objective lens
Magnifies about 10 ×

Stage clip
Holds the slide in place

Diaphragm
Controls the amount of light passing through the opening of the stage

Base
Supports the microscope

Mirror
Reflects light upward through the diaphragm

Using the Microscope

Use the following procedures when you are working with a microscope.

1. To carry the microscope, grasp the microscope's arm with one hand. Place your other hand under the base.
2. Place the microscope on a table with the arm toward you.
3. Turn the coarse adjustment knob to raise the body tube.
4. Revolve the nosepiece until the low-power objective lens clicks into place.
5. Adjust the diaphragm. While looking through the eyepiece, also adjust the mirror until you see a bright white circle of light. **CAUTION:** *Never use direct sunlight as a light source.*
6. Place a slide on the stage. Center the specimen over the opening on the stage. Use the stage clips to hold the slide in place. **CAUTION:** *Glass slides are fragile.*
7. Look at the stage from the side. Carefully turn the coarse adjustment knob to lower the body tube until the low-power objective almost touches the slide.
8. Looking through the eyepiece, very slowly turn the coarse adjustment knob until the specimen comes into focus.
9. To switch to the high-power objective lens, look at the microscope from the side. Carefully revolve the nosepiece until the high-power objective lens clicks into place. Make sure the lens does not hit the slide.
10. Looking through the eyepiece, turn the fine adjustment knob until the specimen comes into focus.

Making a Wet-Mount Slide

Use the following procedures to make a wet-mount slide of a specimen.

1. Obtain a clean microscope slide and a coverslip. **CAUTION:** *Glass slides and coverslips are fragile.*
2. Place the specimen on the slide. The specimen must be thin enough for light to pass through it.
3. Using a plastic dropper, place a drop of water on the specimen.
4. Gently place one edge of the coverslip against the slide so that it touches the edge of the water drop at a 45° angle. Slowly lower the coverslip over the specimen. If air bubbles are trapped beneath the coverslip, tap the coverslip gently with the eraser end of a pencil.
5. Remove any excess water at the edge of the coverslip with a paper towel.

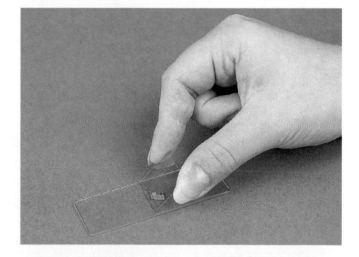

Group 1: Metallic Luster, Mostly Dark-Colored

Mineral/ Formula	Hardness	Density (g/cm³)	Luster	Streak	Color	Other Properties/Remarks
Pyrite FeS_2	6–6.5	5.0	Metallic	Greenish, brownish black	Light yellow	Called "fool's gold," but harder than gold and very brittle
Magnetite Fe_3O_4	6	5.2	Metallic	Black	Iron black	Very magnetic; important iron ore; some varieties known as "lodestone"
Hematite Fe_2O_3	5.5–6.5	4.9–5.3	Metallic or earthy	Red or red brown	Reddish brown to black	Most important ore of iron; used as red pigment in paint
Pyrrhotite FeS	4	4.6	Metallic	Gray black	Brownish bronze	Less hard than pyrite; slightly magnetic
Sphalerite ZnS	3.5–4	3.9–4.1	Resinous	Brown to light yellow	Brown to yellow	Most important zinc ore
Chalcopyrite $CuFeS_2$	3.5–4	4.1–4.3	Metallic	Greenish black	Golden yellow, often tarnished	Most important copper ore; softer than pyrite and more yellow
Copper Cu	2.5–3	8.9	Metallic	Copper red	Copper red to black	Used in making electrical wires, coins, pipes
Gold Au	2.5–3	19.3	Metallic	Yellow	Rich yellow	High density; does not tarnish; used in jewelry, coins, dental fillings
Silver Ag	2.5–3	10.0–11.0	Metallic	Silver to light gray	Silver white (tarnishes)	Used in jewelry, coins, electrical wire, photography
Galena PbS	2.5	7.4–7.6	Metallic	Lead gray	Lead gray	Main ore of lead; used in shields against radiation
Graphite C	1–2	2.3	Metallic to dull	Black	Black	Feels greasy; very soft; used as pencil "lead" and as a lubricant

Group 2: Nonmetallic Luster, Mostly Dark-Colored

Mineral/ Formula	Hardness	Density (g/cm³)	Luster	Streak	Color	Other Properties/Remarks
Corundum Al_2O_3	9	3.9–4.1	Brilliant to glassy	White	Usually brown	Very hard; used as an abrasive; transparent crystals used as "ruby" (red) and "sapphire" (blue) gems
Garnet $(Ca,Mg,Fe)_3$ $(Al,Fe,Cr)_2$ $(SiO_4)_3$	7–7.5	3.5–4.3	Glassy to resinous	White, light brown	Red, brown, black, green	A group of minerals used in jewelry, as a birthstone, and as an abrasive
Olivine $(Mg,Fe)_2SiO_4$	6.5–7	3.3–3.4	Glassy	White or gray	Olive green	Found in igneous rocks; sometimes used as a gem
Augite $Ca(Mg,Fe,Al)$ $(Al,Si)_2O_6$	5–6	3.2–3.4	Glassy	Greenish gray	Dark green to black	Found in igneous rocks
Hornblende $NaCa_2$ $(Mg,Fe,Al)_5$ $(Si,Al)_8O_{22}(OH)_2$	5–6	3.0–3.4	Glassy, silky	White to gray	Dark green, brown, black	Found in igneous and metamorphic rocks

Group 2: Nonmetallic Luster, Mostly Dark-Colored

Mineral/Formula	Hardness	Density (g/cm³)	Luster	Streak	Color	Other Properties/Remarks
Apatite $Ca_5(PO_4)_3F$	5	3.1–3.2	Glassy	White	Green, brown, red, blue	Sometimes used as a gem; source of the phosphorus needed by plants
Azurite $Cu_3(CO_3)_2(OH)_2$	3.5–4	3.8	Glassy to dull	Pale blue	Intense blue	Ore of copper; used as a gem
Biotite $K(Mg,Fe)_3$ $AlSiO_{10}(OH)_2$	2.5–3	2.8–3.4	Glassy or pearly	White to gray	Dark green, brown, or black	A type of mica; sometimes used as a lubricant
Serpentine $Mg_6Si_4O_{10}(OH)_8$	2–5	2.2–2.6	Greasy, waxy, silky	White	Usually green	Once used in insulation but found to cause cancer; used in fireproofing; can be in the form of asbestos
Bauxite aluminum oxides	1–3	2.0–2.5	Dull to earthy	Colorless to gray	Brown, yellow, gray, white	Ore of aluminum, smells like clay when wet; a mixture, not strictly a mineral

Group 3: Nonmetallic Luster, Mostly Light-Colored

Mineral/Formula	Hardness	Density (g/cm³)	Luster	Streak	Color	Other Properties/Remarks
Diamond C	10	3.5	Brilliant	White	Colorless and varied	Hardest substance; used in jewelry, abrasives, cutting tools
Topaz $Al_2SiO_4(F,OH)_2$	8	3.5–3.6	Glassy	White	Straw yellow, pink, bluish	Valuable gem
Quartz SiO_2	7	2.6	Glassy, greasy	White	Colorless, white; any color when not pure	The second most abundant mineral; many varieties are gems (amethyst, jasper); used in making glass
Feldspar (K,Na,Ca) $(AlSi_3O_8)$	6	2.6	Glassy	Colorless, white	Colorless, white; various colors	As a family, the most abundant of all minerals; the feldspars make up over 60 percent of Earth's crust
Fluorite CaF_2	4	3.0–3.3	Glassy	Colorless	Purple, light green, yellow, bluish green	Some types are fluorescent (glow in ultraviolet light); used in making steel
Calcite $CaCO_3$	3	2.7	Glassy	White to grayish	Colorless, white	Easily scratched; bubbles in dilute hydrochloric acid; frequently fluorescent
Halite $NaCl$	2.5	2.1–2.6	Glassy	White	Colorless	Perfect cubic crystals; has salty taste
Gypsum $CaSO_4 \cdot 2H_2O$	2	2.3	Glassy, pearly	White	Colorless, white	Very soft; used in plaster of Paris; form known as alabaster used for statues
Sulfur S	2	2.0–2.1	Resinous to greasy	White	Yellow to brown	Used in medicines, in production of sulfuric acid, and in vulcanizing rubber
Talc $Mg_3Si_4O_{10}(OH)_2$	1	2.7–2.8	Pearly to greasy	White	Gray, white, greenish	Very soft; used in talcum powder; also called "soapstone"

The laboratory balance is an important tool in scientific investigations. You can use a balance to determine the masses of materials that you study or experiment with in the laboratory.

Different kinds of balances are used in the laboratory. One kind of balance is the triple-beam balance. The balance that you may use in your science class is probably similar to the balance illustrated in this Appendix. To use the balance properly, you should learn the name, location, and function of each part of the balance you are using. What kind of balance do you have in your science class?

The Triple-Beam Balance

The triple-beam balance is a single-pan balance with three beams calibrated in grams. The back, or 100-gram, beam is divided into ten units of 10 grams each. The middle, or 500-gram, beam is divided into five units of 100 grams each. The front, or 10-gram, beam is divided into ten major units of 1 gram each. Each of these units is further divided into units of 0.1 gram. What is the largest mass you could find with a triple-beam balance?

The following procedure can be used to find the mass of an object with a triple-beam balance:

1. Place the object on the pan.
2. Move the rider on the middle beam notch by notch until the horizontal pointer drops below zero. Move the rider back one notch.
3. Move the rider on the back beam notch by notch until the pointer again drops below zero. Move the rider back one notch.
4. Slowly slide the rider along the front beam until the pointer stops at the zero point.
5. The mass of the object is equal to the sum of the readings on the three beams.

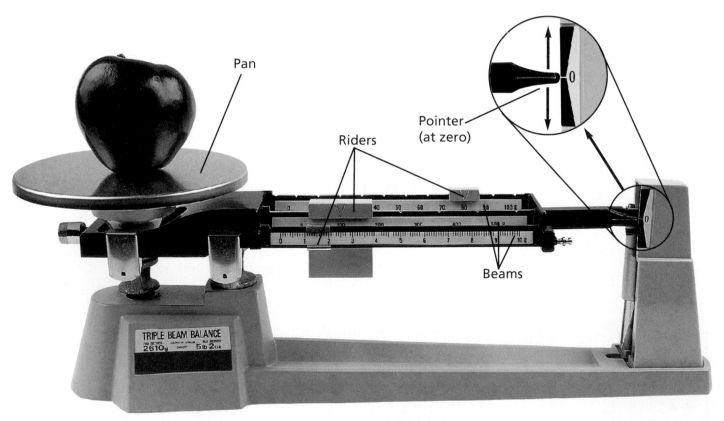

Triple-Beam Balance

Name	Symbol	Atomic Number	Atomic Mass[†]
Actinium	Ac	89	(227)
Aluminum	Al	13	26.982
Americium	Am	95	(243)
Antimony	Sb	51	121.75
Argon	Ar	18	39.948
Arsenic	As	33	74.922
Astatine	At	85	(210)
Barium	Ba	56	137.327
Berkelium	Bk	97	(247)
Beryllium	Be	4	9.012
Bismuth	Bi	83	208.980
Bohrium	Bh	107	(264)
Boron	B	5	10.811
Bromine	Br	35	79.904
Cadmium	Cd	48	112.411
Calcium	Ca	20	40.078
Californium	Cf	98	(251)
Carbon	C	6	12.011
Cerium	Ce	58	140.115
Cesium	Cs	55	132.905
Chlorine	Cl	17	35.453
Chromium	Cr	24	51.996
Cobalt	Co	27	58.933
Copper	Cu	29	63.546
Curium	Cm	96	(247)
Darmstadtium	Ds	110	(269)
Dubnium	Db	105	(262)
Dysprosium	Dy	66	162.50
Einsteinium	Es	99	(252)
Erbium	Er	68	167.26
Europium	Eu	63	151.965
Fermium	Fm	100	(257)
Fluorine	F	9	18.998
Francium	Fr	87	(223)
Gadolinium	Gd	64	157.25
Gallium	Ga	31	69.723
Germanium	Ge	32	72.61
Gold	Au	79	196.967
Hafnium	Hf	72	178.49
Hassium	Hs	108	(265)
Helium	He	2	4.003
Holmium	Ho	67	164.930
Hydrogen	H	1	1.008
Indium	In	49	114.818
Iodine	I	53	126.904
Iridium	Ir	77	192.22
Iron	Fe	26	55.847
Krypton	Kr	36	83.80
Lanthanum	La	57	138.906
Lawrencium	Lr	103	(262)
Lead	Pb	82	207.2
Lithium	Li	3	6.941
Lutetium	Lu	71	174.967
Magnesium	Mg	12	24.305
Manganese	Mn	25	54.938
Meitnerium	Mt	109	(268)
Mendelevium	Md	101	(258)

Name	Symbol	Atomic Number	Atomic Mass[†]
Mercury	Hg	80	200.659
Molybdenum	Mo	42	95.94
Neodymium	Nd	60	144.2
Neon	Ne	10	20.180
Neptunium	Np	93	(237)
Nickel	Ni	28	58.69
Niobium	Nb	41	92.906
Nitrogen	N	7	14.007
Nobelium	No	102	(259)
Osmium	Os	76	190.23
Oxygen	O	8	15.999
Palladium	Pd	46	106.42
Phosphorus	P	15	30.974
Platinum	Pt	78	195.08
Plutonium	Pu	94	(244)
Polonium	Po	84	(209)
Potassium	K	19	39.098
Praseodymium	Pr	59	140.908
Promethium	Pm	61	(145)
Protactinium	Pa	91	231.036
Radium	Ra	88	(226)
Radon	Rn	86	(222)
Rhenium	Re	75	186.207
Rhodium	Rh	45	102.906
Rubidium	Rb	37	85.468
Ruthenium	Ru	44	101.07
Rutherfordium	Rf	104	(261)
Samarium	Sm	62	150.36
Scandium	Sc	21	44.956
Seaborgium	Sg	106	(263)
Selenium	Se	34	78.96
Silicon	Si	14	28.086
Silver	Ag	47	107.868
Sodium	Na	11	22.990
Strontium	Sr	38	87.62
Sulfur	S	16	32.066
Tantalum	Ta	73	180.948
Technetium	Tc	43	(98)
Tellurium	Te	52	127.60
Terbium	Tb	65	158.925
Thallium	Tl	81	204.383
Thorium	Th	90	232.038
Thulium	Tm	69	168.934
Tin	Sn	50	118.710
Titanium	Ti	22	47.88
Tungsten	W	74	183.85
Ununbium	Uub	112	(277)
Ununquadium	Uuq	114	*
Unununium	Uuu	111	(272)
Uranium	U	92	238.029
Vanadium	V	23	50.942
Xenon	Xe	54	131.29
Ytterbium	Yb	70	173.04
Yttrium	Y	39	88.906
Zinc	Zn	30	65.39
Zirconium	Zr	40	91.224

[†] Numbers in parentheses give the mass number of the most stable isotope.

*Newly discovered

Appendix F Periodic Table of the Elements

Key

C	Solid
Br	Liquid
H	Gas
Tc	Not found in nature

	1	2	3	4	5	6	7	8	9
1	1 H Hydrogen 1.0079								
2	3 Li Lithium 6.941	4 Be Beryllium 9.0122							
3	11 Na Sodium 22.990	12 Mg Magnesium 24.305							
4	19 K Potassium 39.098	20 Ca Calcium 40.08	21 Sc Scandium 44.956	22 Ti Titanium 47.90	23 V Vanadium 50.941	24 Cr Chromium 51.996	25 Mn Manganese 54.938	26 Fe Iron 55.847	27 Co Cobalt 58.933
5	37 Rb Rubidium 85.468	38 Sr Strontium 87.62	39 Y Yttrium 88.906	40 Zr Zirconium 91.22	41 Nb Niobium 92.906	42 Mo Molybdenum 95.94	43 Tc Technetium (98)	44 Ru Ruthenium 101.07	45 Rh Rhodium 102.91
6	55 Cs Cesium 132.91	56 Ba Barium 137.33	71 Lu Lutetium 174.97	72 Hf Hafnium 178.49	73 Ta Tantalum 180.95	74 W Tungsten 183.85	75 Re Rhenium 186.21	76 Os Osmium 190.2	77 Ir Iridium 192.22
7	87 Fr Francium (223)	88 Ra Radium (226)	103 Lr Lawrencium (262)	104 Rf Rutherfordium (261)	105 Db Dubnium (262)	106 Sg Seaborgium (263)	107 Bh Bohrium (264)	108 Hs Hassium (265)	109 Mt Meitnerium (268)

Lanthanides

57 La Lanthanum 138.91	58 Ce Cerium 140.12	59 Pr Praseodymium 140.91	60 Nd Neodymium 144.24	61 Pm Promethium (145)	62 Sm Samarium 150.4

Actinides

89 Ac Actinium (227)	90 Th Thorium 232.04	91 Pa Protactinium 231.04	92 U Uranium 238.03	93 Np Neptunium (237)	94 Pu Plutonium (244)

Key

■	Metal
□	Metalloid
■	Nonmetal
■	Properties not established

18

| 2 | He | Helium | 4.0026 |

13

| 5 | B | Boron | 10.81 |

14

| 6 | C | Carbon | 12.011 |

15

| 7 | N | Nitrogen | 14.007 |

16

| 8 | O | Oxygen | 15.999 |

17

| 9 | F | Fluorine | 18.998 |

| 10 | Ne | Neon | 20.179 |

13	Al	Aluminum	26.982
14	Si	Silicon	28.086
15	P	Phosphorus	30.974
16	S	Sulfur	32.06
17	Cl	Chlorine	35.453
18	Ar	Argon	39.948

10 **11** **12**

28	Ni	Nickel	58.71
29	Cu	Copper	63.546
30	Zn	Zinc	65.38
31	Ga	Gallium	69.72
32	Ge	Germanium	72.59
33	As	Arsenic	74.922
34	Se	Selenium	78.96
35	Br	Bromine	79.904
36	Kr	Krypton	83.80

46	Pd	Palladium	106.4
47	Ag	Silver	107.87
48	Cd	Cadmium	112.41
49	In	Indium	114.82
50	Sn	Tin	118.69
51	Sb	Antimony	121.75
52	Te	Tellurium	127.60
53	I	Iodine	126.90
54	Xe	Xenon	131.30

78	Pt	Platinum	195.09
79	Au	Gold	196.97
80	Hg	Mercury	200.59
81	Tl	Thallium	204.37
82	Pb	Lead	207.2
83	Bi	Bismuth	208.98
84	Po	Polonium	(209)
85	At	Astatine	(210)
86	Rn	Radon	(222)

110	Ds	Darmstadtium	(269)
111	*Uuu	Unununium	(272)
112	*Uub	Ununbium	(277)
114	*Uuq	Ununquadium

*Name not officially assigned
(Atomic masses in parentheses are those of the most stable isotope.)

63	Eu	Europium	151.96
64	Gd	Gadolinium	157.25
65	Tb	Terbium	158.93
66	Dy	Dysprosium	162.50
67	Ho	Holmium	164.93
68	Er	Erbium	167.26
69	Tm	Thulium	168.93
70	Yb	Ytterbium	173.04

95	Am	Americium	(243)
96	Cm	Curium	(247)
97	Bk	Berkelium	(247)
98	Cf	Californium	(251)
99	Es	Einsteinium	(252)
100	Fm	Fermium	(257)
101	Md	Mendelevium	(258)
102	No	Nobelium	(259)

English and Spanish Glossary

abrasion The grinding away of rock by other rock particles carried in water, ice, or wind. (p. 439), (p. 485)
abrasión Desgaste de la roca por otras partículas de roca llevadas por el agua, el viento o el hielo.

absolute brightness The brightness of a star if it were at a standard distance from Earth. (p. 601)
magnitud absoluta Brillo que tendría una estrella si estuviera a una distancia estándar de la Tierra.

absorption The process by which nutrient molecules pass through the wall of the digestive system into the blood. (p. 101)
absorción Proceso por el cual las moléculas de nutrientes pasan a través de la pared del sistema digestivo a la sangre.

active immunity Immunity that occurs when a person's own immune system produces antibodies in response to the presence of a pathogen. (p. 194)
inmunidad activa Inmunidad que ocurre cuando el sistema inmunológico de una persona produce anticuerpos en respuesta a la presencia de un patógeno.

addiction A physical dependence on a substance. (p. 163), (p. 243)
adicción Dependencia física de una sustancia.

AIDS (acquired immunodeficiency syndrome) A disease caused by a virus that attacks the immune system. (p. 190)
SIDA (Síndrome de inmunodeficiencia adquirida) Enfermedad causada por un virus que ataca el sistema inmunológico.

alcoholism A disease in which a person is both physically addicted to and emotionally dependent on alcohol. (p. 247)
alcoholismo Enfermedad en la que una persona es adicta físicamente y dependiente emocionalmente del alcohol.

alkali metal An element in Group 1 of the periodic table. (p. 686)
metal alcalino Elemento en el Grupo 1 de la tabla periódica.

alkaline earth metal An element in Group 2 of the periodic table. (p. 687)
metal alcalinotérreo Elemento en el Grupo 2 de la tabla periódica.

allergen A substance that causes an allergy. (p. 200)
alergeno Sustancia que causa la alergia.

allergy A disorder in which the immune system is overly sensitive to a foreign substance. (p. 200)
alergia Desorden fisiológico en el cual el sistema inmunológico es extremadamente sensible a las sustancias externas.

alloy A mixture of two or more elements, one of which is a metal. (p. 365), (p. 688), (p. 726)
aleación Mezcla de dos o más elementos, uno de los cuales es el metal.

alluvial fan A wide, sloping deposit of sediment formed where a stream leaves a mountain range. (p. 475)
abanico aluvial Depósito ancho de sedimento en declive, que se forma donde un arroyo sale de una cordillera.

alveoli Tiny sacs of lung tissue specialized for the movement of gases between air and blood. (p. 156)
alveolos Sacos diminutos de tejido pulmonar especializados en el movimiento de gases entre el aire y la sangre.

amino acids Small units that are linked together chemically to form large protein molecules. (p. 89)
aminoácidos Pequeñas unidades que están unidas químicamente entre ellas para formar grandes moléculas de proteínas.

amorphous solid A solid made up of particles that are not arranged in a regular pattern. (p. 640)
sólido amorfo Sólido constituido por partículas que no están dispuestas en un patrón regular.

anabolic steroids Synthetic chemicals that are similar to hormones produced in the body. (p. 244)
esteroides anabólicos Sustancias químicas sintéticas que son semejantes a las hormonas producidas por el cuerpo.

antibiotic A chemical that kills bacteria or slows their growth without harming body cells. (p. 196)
antibiótico Sustancia química que mata las bacterias o frena su crecimiento sin dañar las células del cuerpo humano.

antibody A protein produced by a B cell of the immune system that destroys pathogens. (p. 188)
anticuerpo Proteína producida por una célula B del sistema inmunológico que destruye un tipo específico de patógeno.

anticline An upward fold in rock formed by compression of Earth's crust. (p. 304)
anticlinal Pliegue de la roca hacia arriba ocasionado por compresión de la corteza terrestre.

antigen A molecule that the immune system recognizes either as part of the body or as coming from outside the body. (p. 188)

antígeno Molécula en una célula que puede reconocer el sistema inmunológico como parte del cuerpo o como un agente extraño.

anus A muscular opening at the end of the rectum through which waste material is eliminated from the body. (p. 111)
ano Abertura muscular al final del recto a través de la cual se elimina el material de desecho digestivo del cuerpo.

aorta The largest artery in the body; receives blood from the left ventricle. (p. 124)
aorta La arteria más grande del cuerpo; recibe la sangre del ventrículo izquierdo.

apparent brightness The brightness of a star as seen from Earth. (p. 601)
magnitud aparente Brillo de una estrella visto desde la Tierra.

artery A blood vessel that carries blood away from the heart. (p. 122)
arteria Vaso sanguíneo que transporta la sangre que sale del corazón.

arthritis A disease of the joints that makes movement painful. (p. 63)
artritis Enfermedad de las articulaciones que hace que el movimiento sea doloroso.

arthroscope A slim, tube-shaped, surgical instrument that doctors use to diagnose a problem in a joint. (p. 63)
artroscopía Instrumento de cirugía con forma de tubo delgado que usan los doctores para diagnosticar un problema en una articulación.

asteroid Rocky objects revolving around the sun that are too small and numerous to be considered planets. (p. 582)
asteroides Objetos rocosos que se mueven alrededor del Sol y que son demasiado pequeños y numerosos como para ser considerados planetas.

asteroid belt The region of the solar system between the orbits of Mars and Jupiter, where many asteroids are found. (p. 582)
cinturón de asteroides Región del sistema solar entre las órbitas de Marte y Júpiter, donde se encuentran muchos asteroides.

asthenosphere The soft layer of the mantle on which the lithosphere floats. (p. 267)
astenosfera Capa suave del manto en la que flota la litosfera.

asthma A disorder in which the respiratory passages narrow significantly. (p. 201)
asma Desorden fisiológico por el cual las vías respiratorias se estrechan considerablemente.

atherosclerosis A condition in which an artery wall thickens as a result of the buildup of fatty materials. (p. 139)
arteriosclerosis Condición en la que la pared de una arteria se hace más gruesa debido a la acumulación de materiales grasos.

atomic mass The average mass of all the isotopes of an element. (p. 677)
masa atómica Promedio de la masa de todos los isótopos de un elemento.

atomic number The number of protons in the nucleus of an atom. (p. 674)
número atómico Número de protones en el núcleo de un átomo.

atrium Each of the two upper chambers of the heart that receives blood that comes into the heart. (p. 121)
aurícula Cada una de las dos cámaras superiores del corazón que reciben la sangre que entra en el corazón.

autonomic nervous system The group of nerves in the peripheral nervous system that controls involuntary actions. (p. 227)
sistema nervioso autónomo Grupo de nervios en el sistema nervioso periférico que controla las acciones involuntarias.

axon A threadlike extension of a neuron that carries nerve impulses away from the cell body. (p. 218)
axón Extensión con forma de hilo de una neurona que saca los impulsos nerviosos del cuerpo de la célula.

B

B cell A lymphocyte that produces proteins that help destroy pathogens. (p. 188)
célula B Linfocito que produce proteínas que ayudan a destruir un tipo específico de patógeno.

basalt A dark, dense, igneous rock with a fine texture, found in oceanic crust. (p. 266), (p. 375)
basalto Roca ígnea, oscura y densa, de textura fina, que se encuentra en la corteza oceánica.

beach Wave-washed sediment along a coast. (p. 497)
playa Sedimento depositado por las olas a lo largo de una costa.

bedrock The solid layer of rock beneath the soil. (p. 446)
lecho rocoso Capa sólida de roca debajo del suelo.

big bang The initial explosion that resulted in the formation and expansion of the universe. (p. 620)

big bang Explosión inicial que dio como resultado la formación y expansión del universo.

bile A substance produced by the liver that breaks up fat particles. (p. 109)
bilis Sustancia producida por el hígado que rompe las partículas de grasa.

binary star A star system with two stars. (p. 614)
estrella binaria Sistema de estrellas con dos estrellas.

black hole An object whose gravity is so strong that nothing, not even light, can escape. (p. 612)
agujero negro Objeto cuya gravedad es tan fuerte que nada, ni siquiera la luz, puede escapar.

blood pressure (p. 125) The pressure that is exerted by the blood against the walls of blood vessels. (p. 128)
presión arterial Presión que ejerce la sangre contra las paredes de los vasos sanguíneos.

boiling The process that occurs when vaporization takes place inside a liquid as well as on the surface. (p. 647)
ebullición Proceso que se da cuando la vaporización se efectúa dentro de un líquido, además de en la superficie.

boiling point The temperature at which a substance changes from a liquid to a gas; the same as the condensation point, or temperature at which a gas changes to a liquid. (p. 647)
punto de ebullición Temperatura a la que una sustancia cambia de líquido a gas; es lo mismo que el punto de condensación (la temperatura a la que un gas se vuelve líquido).

Boyle's law A principle that describes the relationship between the pressure and volume of a gas at constant temperature. (p. 654)
ley de Boyle Principio que describe la relación entre la presión y el volumen de un gas a temperatura constante.

brain The part of the central nervous system that is located in the skull and controls most functions in the body. (p. 223)
encéfalo Parte del sistema nervioso central que está ubicado en el cráneo y controla la mayoría de las funciones del cuerpo.

brainstem The part of the brain that lies between the cerebellum and spinal cord and controls the body's involuntary actions. (p. 224)
tronco encefálico Parte del encéfalo que se encuentra entre el cerebelo y la médula espinal, y controla las acciones involuntarias del cuerpo.

brainstorming A process in which group members freely suggest any creative solutions that come to mind. (p. 37)
lluvia de ideas Proceso mediante el cual los miembros de un grupo sugieren libremente cualquier solución creativa que se les ocurre.

bronchi The passages that direct air into the lungs. (p. 156)
bronquios Conductos que dirigen el aire hacia los pulmones.

bronchitis An irritation of the breathing passages in which the small passages become narrower than normal and may be clogged with mucus. (p. 164)
bronquitis Irritación de los conductos respiratorios en la que los conductos pequeños se hacen más estrechos de lo normal y se pueden obstruir con mucosidad.

C

calorie The amount of energy needed to raise the temperature of one gram of water by one degree Celsius. (p. 85)
caloría Cantidad de energía que se necesita para elevar la temperatura de un gramo de agua un grado Celsius.

cancer A disease in which some body cells divide uncontrollably. (p. 75)
cáncer Enfermedad en la que algunas células del cuerpo se dividen descontroladamente.

capillary A tiny blood vessel where substances are exchanged between the blood and the body cells. (p. 122)
capilar Vaso sanguíneo minúsculo donde se intercambian las sustancias de la sangre y las células del cuerpo.

carbohydrate Nutrient composed of carbon, oxygen, and hydrogen that is a major source of energy. (p. 86)
carbohidratos Nutrientes compuestos de carbono, oxígeno e hidrógeno que son la fuente de energía principal y proveen la materia prima necesaria para la formación de algunas partes de las células.

carbon monoxide A colorless, odorless gas produced when substances—including tobacco—are burned. (p. 163)
monóxido de carbono Gas incoloro e inodoro producido cuando se queman algunas sustancias, incluido el tabaco.

carcinogen A substance or a factor in the environment that can cause cancer. (p. 202)

carcinógeno Sustancia o factor en el ambiente que puede causar cáncer.

cardiac muscle Muscle tissue found only in the heart. (p. 67)
músculo cardiaco Tejido muscular que sólo se encuentra en el corazón.

cardiovascular system The body system that consists of the heart, blood vessels, and blood; also called the circulatory system. (p. 118)
sistema cardiovascular Sistema corporal que está formado por el corazón, los vasos sanguíneos y la sangre, y que transporta las sustancias que las células necesitan y recoge de ellas los productos de desecho.

cartilage A connective tissue that is more flexible than bone and that protects the ends of bones and keeps them from rubbing together. (p. 55)
cartílago Tejido conectivo que es más flexible que el hueso y que protege los extremos de los huesos y evita que se rocen.

cell The basic unit of structure and function in living things. (p. 47)
célula Unidad básica de estructura y función de los seres vivos.

cell membrane The outside boundary of a cell. (p. 47)
membrana celular Borde externo de la célula.

cementation The process by which dissolved minerals crystallize and glue particles of sediment together into one mass. (p. 383)
cementación Proceso mediante el cual minerales disueltos se cristalizan, y adhieren partículas de sedimento formando una masa.

central nervous system The division of the nervous system consisting of the brain and spinal cord. (p. 222)
sistema nervioso central División del sistema nervioso formado por el encéfalo y en la médula espinal.

ceramic A hard, crystalline solid made by heating clay and other mineral materials to high temperatures. (p. 731)
cerámica Sólido cristalino duro hecho al calentar a altas temperaturas arcilla y otros materiales minerales.

cerebellum The part of the brain that coordinates the actions of the muscles and helps maintain balance. (p. 224)
cerebelo Parte del encéfalo que coordina las acciones de los músculos y ayuda a mantener el equilibrio.

cerebrum The part of the brain that interprets input from the senses, controls movement, and carries out complex mental processes. (p. 224)
cerebro Parte del encéfalo que interpreta los estímulos de los sentidos, controla el movimiento y realiza procesos mentales complejos.

Charles's law A principle that describes the relationship between the temperature and volume of a gas at constant pressure. (p. 656)
ley de Charles Principio que describe la relación entre la temperatura y el volumen de un gas a presión constante.

chemical rock Sedimentary rock that forms when minerals crystallize from a solution. (p. 385)
roca química Roca sedimentaria que se forma cuando los minerales en una solución se cristalizan.

chemical symbol A one- or two-letter representation of an element. (p. 679)
símbolo químico Representación con una o dos letras de un elemento.

chemical weathering The process that breaks down rock through chemical changes. (p. 440)
desgaste químico Proceso que erosiona la roca mediante cambios químicos.

chromosphere The middle layer of the sun's atmosphere. (p. 552)
cromosfera Capa central en la atmósfera del Sol.

cilia Tiny hairlike extensions that move together in a sweeping motion. (p. 155)
cilios Extensiones minúsculas de las células que tienen forma de pelo y se mueven como látigo.

clastic rock Sedimentary rock that forms when rock fragments are squeezed together under high pressure. (p. 384)
roca clástica Roca sedimentaria que se forma cuando fragmentos de roca se unen baja a una gran presión.

cleavage A mineral's ability to split easily along flat surfaces. (p. 350)
exfoliación La facilidad con la que un mineral se divide en capas planas.

climate The pattern of temperature and precipitation typical of an area over a long period of time. (p. 532)
clima Patrón de temperatura y precipitación típico de un área a lo largo de mucho tiempo.

cochlea A snail-shaped tube in the inner ear that is lined with receptor cells that respond to sound. (p. 237)

cóclea Tubo en forma de caracol en el oído interno que está recubierto de células receptoras que responden al sonido.

coma The fuzzy outer layer of a comet. (p. 581)
coma Capa exterior y difusa de un cometa.

comet A loose collection of ice, dust and small rocky particles, typically with a long, narrow orbit. (p. 581)
cometa Conjunto no compacto de hielo, polvo y partículas rocosas pequeñas, que normalmente tiene una órbita larga y estrecha.

communicating The process of sharing ideas with others through writing and speaking. (p. 10)
comunicar Proceso de compartir ideas con otras personas a través de la escritura o el lenguage hablado.

compact bone Hard, dense bone tissue that is beneath the outer membrane of a bone. (p. 56)
hueso compacto Tejido de hueso denso y duro que se encuentra debajo de la membrana externa de un hueso.

compaction The process by which sediments are pressed together under their own weight. (p. 383)
compactación Proceso mediante el cual los sedimentos se unen por la presión de su propio peso.

composite A combination of two or more substances that creates a new material with different properties. (p. 718)
compuesto Combinación de dos o más sustancias que crea un nuevo material con propiedades diferentes.

compression Stress that squeezes rock until it folds or breaks. (p. 301)
compresión Esfuerzo que oprime una roca hasta que ésta se pliega o rompe.

concussion A bruiselike injury of the brain that occurs when the soft tissue of the brain collides against the skull. (p. 229)
contusión Magulladura en el encéfalo que ocurre cuando el tejido suave del encéfalo choca contra el cráneo.

condensation The change of state from a gas to a liquid. (p. 648)
condensación Cambio del estado gaseoso a líquido.

conduction The transfer of heat from one particle of matter to another. (p. 271), (p. 685)
conducción Transferencia de calor desde una partícula de materia a otra.

connective tissue A body tissue that provides support for the body and connects all of its parts. (p. 48)
tejido conectivo Tejido que da soporte al cuerpo y conecta todas sus partes.

conservation plowing Soil conservation method in which the dead stalks from the previous year's crop are left in the ground to hold the soil in place. (p. 457)
arada de conservación Método de conservación del suelo en el cual los tallos muertos de la cosecha del año anterior se dejan en la tierra para que sujeten el suelo en su lugar.

constellation An imaginary pattern of stars in the sky. (p. 598)
constelación Patrón imaginario de estrellas en el cielo.

constraint Any factor that limits or restricts a design. (p. 37)
restricción Cualquier factor que limita o restringe un diseño.

continental drift The hypothesis that the continents slowly move across Earth's surface. (p. 275)
deriva continental Hipótesis según la cual los continentes se desplazan lentamente en la superficie de la Tierra.

continental glacier A glacier that covers much of a continent or large island. (p. 490)
glaciar continental Glaciar que cubre gran parte de un continente o una isla grande.

contour interval The difference in elevation from one contour line to the next. (p. 425)
intervalo entre curvas de nivel Diferencia de elevación de una curva de nivel a otra.

contour line A line on a topographic map that connects points of equal elevation. (p. 425)
curva de nivel Línea en un mapa topográfico que conecta puntos de igual elevación.

contour plowing Plowing fields along the curves of a slope to prevent soil loss. (p. 457)
arada en contarno Arar los campos siguiendo las curvas de una pendiente para evitar que el suelo se suelte.

controlled experiment An experiment in which only one variable is manipulated at a time. (p. 8)
experimento controlado Experimento en el cual sólo una variable es manipulada a la vez.

convection The transfer of heat by movement of a fluid. (p. 272)
convección Transferencia de calor mediante el movimiento de un líquido.

convection current The movement of a fluid, caused by differences in temperature, that transfers heat from one part of the fluid to another. (p. 272)
corriente de convección Movimiento de un líquido ocasionado por diferencias en la temperatura, que transfiere calor de un punto del líquido a otro.

convection zone The outermost layer of the sun's interior. (p. 551)
zona de convección Capa más superficial del interior del Sol.

convergent boundary A plate boundary where two plates move toward each other. (p. 291)
borde convergente Borde de placa donde dos placas se deslizan una hacia la otra.

convex lens A piece of transparent glass curved so that the middle is thicker than the edges. (p. 592)
lente convexa Trozo de cristal transparente curvado de tal manera que el centro es más grueso que los extremos.

coordinate A pair of numbers used to determine the position of a point on a graph. (p. 23)
coordinada Par de números que se usa para determinar la posición de un punto en una gráfica.

coral reef A structure of calcite skeletons built up by coral animals in warm, shallow ocean water. (p. 388)
arrecife coralino Estructura de esqueletos calcáreos formada por corales en aguas oceánicas templadas y poco profundas.

core The central region of the sun, where nuclear fusion takes place. (p. 551)
núcleo Región central del Sol, donde ocurre la fusión nuclear.

Coriolis effect The effect of Earth's rotation on the direction of winds and currents. (p. 531)
efecto Coriolis Efecto de la rotación terrestre sobre la dirección de los vientos y las corrientes.

cornea The clear tissue that covers the front of the eye. (p. 233)
córnea Tejido transparente que cubre el frente del ojo.

corona The outer layer of the sun's atmosphere. (p. 552)
corona Capa externa de la atmósfera del Sol.

coronary artery An artery that supplies blood to the heart itself. (p. 126)
arteria coronaria Arteria que lleva sangre al corazón en sí.

corrosion The gradual wearing away of a metal element due to a chemical reaction. (p. 685)

corrosión Desgaste gradual de un elemento metal debido a una reacción química.

cosmic background radiation The electromagnetic radiation left over from the big bang. (p. 622)
radiación cósmica de fondo Radiación electromagnética que quedó del big bang.

crater A bowl-shaped area that forms around a volcano's central opening. (p. 330)
cráter Área en forma de tazón que se forma alrededor de la entrada central de un volcán.

crop rotation The planting of different crops in a field each year to maintain the soil's fertility. (p. 457)
rotación de las cosechas Plantación de cosechas diferentes en un campo cada año para mantener la fertilidad del suelo.

crust The layer of rock that forms Earth's outer surface. (p. 266)
corteza Capa de rocas que forma la superficie externa de la Tierra.

crystal A solid in which the atoms are arranged in a pattern that repeats again and again. (p. 345)
cristal Sólido en el que los átomos están dispuestos en un patrón que se repite una y otra vez.

crystalline solid A solid that is made up of crystals in which particles are arranged in a regular, repeating pattern. (p. 640)
sólido cristalino Sólido constituido por cristales en los que las partículas están dispuestas en un patrón regular repetitivo.

crystallization The process by which atoms are arranged to form a material with a crystal structure. (p. 354)
cristalización Proceso mediante el cual los átomos se organizan para formar materiales con estructura cristalina.

current A large stream of moving water that flows through the oceans. (p. 530)
corriente Un gran volumen de agua que fluye por los océanos.

cytoplasm The material within a cell apart from the nucleus. (p. 47)
citoplasma Material que hay en una célula, pero fuera del núcleo.

D

dark energy A mysterious force that appears to be causing the expansion of the universe to accelerate. (p. 624)

energía negra Misteriosa fuerza que parece acelerar la expansión del universo.

dark matter Matter that does not give off electromagnetic radiation but appears to be quite abundant in the universe. (p. 624)
materia negra Materia que no despide radiación electromagnética, pero que es muy abundante en el universo.

data Facts, figures, and other evidence gathered through observations. (p. 8)
dato Hecho, cifra u otra evidencia reunida por medio de las observaciones.

data point A point on a graph showing the location of a piece of data. (p. 23)
punto de dato Punto en una gráfica que muestra la ubicación de parte de los datos.

decomposer Soil organism that breaks down the remains of organisms and digests them. (p. 451)
descomponedor Organismo del suelo que desintegra los restos de organismos y los digiere.

deep-ocean trench A deep valley along the ocean floor beneath which oceanic crust slowly sinks toward the mantle. (p. 284)
fosa oceánica profunda Valle profundo a lo largo del suelo oceánico debajo del cual la corteza oceánica se hunde lentamente hacia el manto.

deflation Wind erosion that removes surface materials. (p. 500)
deflación Erosión por viento que se lleva materiales superficiales.

degree A unit used to measure distances around a circle. One degree equals 1/360 of a full circle. (p. 411)
grado Unidad usada para medir distancias alrededor de un círculo. Un grado es igual a 1/360 de un círculo completo.

delta A landform made of sediment that is deposited where a river flows into an ocean or lake. (p. 475)
delta Accidente geográfico formado por sedimentos que se depositan en la desembocadura de un río en un océano o lago.

dendrite A threadlike extension of a neuron that carries nerve impulses toward the cell body. (p. 218)
dendrita Extensión en forma de hilo de una neurona que lleva los impulsos nerviosos hacia el cuerpo de las células.

density The amount of mass in a given space; mass per unit volume. (p. 17), (p. 272)
densidad Cantidad de masa en un espacio dado; masa por unidad de volumen.

deposition The process by which sediment settles out of the water or wind that is carrying it. (p. 383), (p. 465)
sedimentación Proceso mediante el cual el sedimento es depositado por el agua o el viento que lo transporta.

depressant A drug that slows down the activity of the central nervous system. (p. 244)
depresora Droga que disminuye la velocidad de la actividad del sistema nervioso central.

dermis The inner layer of the skin. (p. 73)
dermis Capa más interna de la piel.

diabetes A condition in which either the pancreas fails to produce enough insulin or the body's cells can't use it properly. (p. 201)
diabetes Condición en la que el páncreas no puede producir suficiente insulina o las células del cuerpo no la pueden usar adecuadamente.

diaphragm A large, dome-shaped muscle that plays an important role in breathing. (p. 158)
diafragma Músculo grande con forma de cúpula localizado en la base de los pulmones, que juega un papel muy importante en la respiración.

diatomic molecule A molecule consisting of two atoms. (p. 697)
molécula diatómica Molécula que tiene dos átomos.

Dietary Reference Intakes (DRIs) Guidelines that show the amounts of nutrients needed everyday. (p. 99)
Ingesta de referencia dietética Pautas que muestran la cantidad de nutrientes que se necesitan diariamente.

diffusion The process by which molecules move from an area of higher concentration to an area of lower concentration. (p. 127)
difusión Proceso por el cual las moléculas se mueven de un área de mayor concentración a un área de menor concentración.

digestion The process by which the body breaks down food into small nutrient molecules. (p. 101)
digestión Proceso por el cual el cuerpo descompone la comida en pequeñas moléculas de nutrientes.

digitizing Converting information to numbers for use by a computer. (p. 419)
digitalizar Convertir información a números para que pueda ser usada por una computadora.

directly proportional A term used to describe the relationship between two variables whose graph is

a straight line passing through the point (0, 0). (p. 660)
directamente proporcional Término empleado para describir la relación entre dos variables cuya gráfica forma una línea recta que pasa por elpunto (0, 0).

dislocation An injury in which a bone comes out of its joint. (p. 60)
dislocación Lesión en la que un hueso se sale de su articulación.

divergent boundary A plate boundary where two plates move away from each other. (p. 290)
borde divergente Borde de placa donde dos placas se separan.

dormant A volcano that is not currently active, but that may become active in the future. (p. 335)
inactivo Volcán que en la actualidad no está activo, pero que puede volver a ser activo en el futuro.

drug Any chemical taken into the body that causes changes in a person's body or behavior. (p. 241)
droga Cualquier sustancia química que se incorpora al cuerpo, que causa cambios en el cuerpo o comportamiento de una persona.

drug abuse The deliberate misuse of drugs for purposes other than medical. (p. 241)
abuso de drogas Uso indebido deliberado de drogas para fines no médicos.

ductile A term used to describe a material that can be pulled out into a long wire. (p. 684)
dúctil Término usado para describir un material que se puede estirar hasta convertirlo en un alambre largo.

Dust Bowl The area of the Great Plains where wind erosion caused soil loss during the 1930s. (p. 456)
Cuenca del polvo Área de las Grandes Llanuras donde la erosión por el viento causó la pérdida de suelo durante la década de 1930.

E

eardrum The membrane that separates the outer ear from the middle ear, and that vibrates when sound waves strike it. (p. 237)
tímpano Membrana que separa el oído externo del oído medio, y que vibra cuando le llegan ondas sonoras.

earthquake The shaking that results from the movement of rock beneath Earth's surface. (p. 307)
terremoto Temblor que resulta del movimiento de la roca debajo de la superficie de la Tierra.

eclipsing binary A binary star system in which one star periodically blocks the light from another. (p. 614)
eclipse binario Sistema de estrella binaria en el que una estrella bloquea periódicamente la luz de la otra.

El Niño An abnormal climate event that occurs every two to seven years in the Pacific Ocean, causing changes in winds, currents, and weather patterns for one to two years. (p. 533)
El Niño Suceso climático anormal que se presenta cada dos a siete años en el océano Pacífico y que causa cambios en los vientos, corrientes y patrones meteorológicos que duran uno o dos años.

electromagnetic radiation Energy that travels through space in the form of waves. (p. 591)
radiación electromagnética Energía que viaja a través del espacio en forma de ondas.

electron A tiny, negatively charged particle that moves around the nucleus of an atom. (p. 671)
electrón Partícula diminuta cargada negativamente, que se mueve alrededor del núcleo de un átomo.

elevation Height above sea level. (p. 405)
elevación Altura sobre el nivel del mar.

ellipse An oval shape, which may be elongated or nearly circular. (p. 547)
elipse Círculo alargado de forma ovalada.

elliptical galaxy A galaxy shaped like a round or flattened ball, generally ball, generally containing only old stars. (p. 616)
galaxia elíptica Galaxia con forma de pelota aplastada, que generalmente está formada sólo de estrellas viejas.

emphysema A serious disease that destroys lung tissue and causes breathing difficulties. (p. 165)
enfisema Enfermedad grave que destruye el tejido pulmonar y causa dificultades respiratorias.

energy The ability to do work or cause change. (p. 484)
energía Capacidad para realizar un trabajo o producir cambios.

engineer A person who is trained to use both technological and scientific knowledge to solve practical problems. (p. 35)
ingeniero Persona capacitada para usar conocimientos tecnológicos y científicos para resolver problemas prácticos.

enzyme A protein that speeds up chemical reactions in the body. (p. 103)

enzima Proteina que acelera las reacciones químicas en el cuerpo.

epicenter The point on Earth's surface directly above an earthquake's focus. (p. 307)
epicentro Punto en la superficie de la Tierra directamente sobre el foco de un terremoto.

epidermis The outer layer of the skin. (p. 72)
epidermis Capa más externa de la piel.

epiglottis A flap of tissue that seals off the windpipe and prevents food from entering. (p. 103)
epiglotis Extensión de tejido que sella la entrada de la tráquea impidiendo la entrada del alimento.

epithelial tissue A body tissue that covers the surfaces of the body, inside and out. (p. 48)
tejido epitelial Tejido corporal que cubre la superficie del cuerpo, por dentro y por fuera.

equator An imaginary line that circles Earth halfway between the North and South poles. (p. 412)
ecuador Línea imaginaria que rodea la Tierra por el centro, entre los polos Norte y Sur.

erosion The process by which water, ice, wind, or gravity moves weathered rock and soil. (p. 383), (p. 437), (p. 464)
erosión Proceso por el cual el agua, el hielo, el viento o la gravedad desplazan rocas meteorizadas y suelo.

esophagus A muscular tube that connects the mouth to the stomach. (p. 103)
esófago Tubo muscular que conecta la boca con el estómago.

evaporation The process that occurs when vaporization takes place only on the surface of a liquid. (p. 646)
evaporación Proceso que se da cuando la vaporización se efectúa únicamente en la superficie de un líquido.

excretion The process by which wastes are removed from the body. (p. 167)
excreción Proceso por el cual se eliminan los desechos del cuerpo.

extinct A volcano that is no longer active and is unlikely to erupt again. (p. 335)
extinto Volcán que ya no es activo y es poco probable que haga erupción otra vez.

extrusive rock Igneous rock that forms from lava on Earth's surface. (p. 378)
roca extrusiva Roca ígnea que se forma de la lava en la superficie de la Tierra.

F

farsightedness The condition in which a person can see distant objects clearly. (p. 235)
hipermetropía Condición en la que una persona puede ver claramente los objetos distantes.

fat Energy-containing nutrients that are composed of carbon, oxygen. (p. 87)
grasas Nutrientes que contienen energía y están compuestos de carbono, oxígeno e hidrógeno.

fault A break in Earth's crust where masses of rock slip past each other. (p. 290)
falla Fractura en la corteza de la Tierra que ocurre cuando grandes placas de roca se deslizan una con respecto a la otra.

feedback The information a technological system uses to monitor the input, process, and output so that the system can adjust itself to meet the goal. (p. 29)
retroalimentación Información que usa un sistema tecnológico para comprobar la entrada, proceso y salida para autoajustarse con el fin de conseguir un objetivo.

fertility A measure of how well soil supports plant growth. (p. 447)
fertilidad Medida de lo apropiado de un suelo para mantener el crecimiento de las plantas.

flood plain Wide valley through which a river flows. (p. 473)
llanura de aluvión Valle ancho por el cual fluye un río.

fluid Any substance that can flow. (p. 641)
fluid Cualquier sustancia que puede fluir.

focus The point beneath Earth's surface where rock breaks under stress and causes an earthquake. (p. 307)
foco Punto debajo de la superficie de la Tierra en el que la roca se rompe a raíz del esfuerzo, y causa un terremoto.

foliated Term used to describe metamorphic rocks that have grains arranged in parallel layers or bands. (p. 391)
foliación Término usado para describir las rocas metamórficas que tienen granos dispuestos en capas paralelas o bandas.

follicle Structure in the dermis of the skin from which a strand of hair grows. (p. 73)
folículos Estructura en la dermis de la piel de donde crece un pelo.

Food Guide Pyramid A diagram that classifies foods into six groups to help people plan a healthy diet. (p. 96)
Pirámide guía de los alimentos Diagrama que clasifica los alimentos en seis grupos para ayudar a la gente a planear una dieta sana.

footwall The block of rock that forms the lower half of a fault. (p. 302)
labio inferior Bloque de roca que constituye la mitad inferior de una falla.

force A push or a pull exerted on an object. (p. 556)
fuerza Empuje o atracción ejercida sobre un objeto.

fossil A trace of an ancient organism that has been preserved in rock or other substance. (p. 276)
fósil Vestigio de un organismo de la antigüedad que se ha preservado en la roca.

fracture A break in a bone. (p. 60); The way a mineral looks when it breaks apart in an irregular way. (p. 351)
fractura Rotura de un hueso; Apariencia de un mineral cuando se rompe irregularmente.

freezing The change in state from a liquid to a solid. (p. 646)
congelación Cambio del estado líquido al sólido.

frequency The number of waves that pass a specific point in a given amount of time. (p. 510)
frecuencia Número de ondas u olas que pasan por un punto dado en cierto tiempo.

friction The force that opposes the motion of one surface as it moves across another surface. (p. 320), (p. 487)
fricción Fuerza que se opone al movimiento de una superficie a medida que se mueve a través de otra superficie.

G

galaxy A huge group of single stars, star systems, star clusters, dust, and gas bound together by gravity. (p. 616)
galaxia Enorme grupo de estrellas individuales, sistemas de estrellas, cúmulos de estrellas, polvo y gas unidos por la gravedad.

gallbladder The organ that stores bile after it is produced by the liver. (p. 109)
vesícula Órgano que almacena la bilis después de ser producida por el hígado.

gas A state of matter with no definite shape or volume. (p. 643)

gas Estado de la materia sin forma ni volumen definidos.

gas giant The name often given to the first four outer planets; Jupiter, Saturn, Uranus, and Neptune. (p. 571)
gigantes gaseosos Nombre que normalmente se da a los cuatro primeros planetas exteriores; Júpiter, Saturno, Urano y Neptuno.

gemstone A hard, colorful mineral that has a brilliant or glassy luster and is valued for its appearance. (p. 361)
gema Mineral duro y colorido, con lustre brillante o vidrioso.

geocentric A model of the universe in which Earth is at the center of the revolving planets and stars. (p. 545)
geocéntrico Modelo del universo en el que la Tierra es el centro de los planetas y estrellas que giran alrededor de ella.

geode A hollow rock inside which mineral crystals have grown. (p. 354)
geoda (p. 354) Roca hueca dentro de la que se forman cristales minerales.

glacier A large mass of moving ice and snow on land. (p. 490)
glaciar Gran masa de hielo y nieve que se mantiene en movimiento sobre la tierra.

glass A clear, solid material with no crystal structure, created by heating sand to a very high temperature. (p. 733)
vidrio Material sólido y transparente que no tiene estructura de cristal, creado al calentar arena a temperaturas muy altas.

Global Positioning System A method of finding latitude and longitude using a network of satellites. (p. 421)
Sistema de posicionamiento global Método para hallar la latitud y longitud usando una red de satélites.

globe A sphere that represents Earth's entire surface. (p. 410)
globo terráqueo Esfera que representa toda la superficie de la Tierra.

globular cluster A large, round, densely-packed grouping of older stars. (p. 615)
cúmulo globular Conjunto grande y redondo de estrellas viejas densamente apretadas.

glucose A sugar that is the major source of energy for the body's cells. (p. 86)
glucosa Azúcar que es la principal fuente de energía de las células del cuerpo.

goal The overall purpose of a technological system. (p. 29)
objetivo El propósito general de un sistema tecnológico.

grains The particles of minerals or other rocks that give a rock its texture. (p. 376)
granos Partículas de minerales o de otras rocas que dan la textura a una roca.

granite A usually light-colored igneous rock that is found in continental crust. (p. 266), (p. 375)
granito Roca usualmente de color claro que se encuentra en la corteza continental.

graph A diagram that shows how two variables are related. (p. 22), (p. 658)
gráfica Diagrama que muestra la relación entre dos variables.

gravity The attractive force between objects; its strength depends on their masses and the distance between them. (p. 465), (p. 556)
gravedad Fuerza de atracción entre los objetos; su fuerza depende de sus masas y de la distancia que les separa.

greenhouse effect The trapping of heat by a planet's atmosphere. (p. 564)
efecto invernadero Acumulación de calor en la atmósfera de un planeta.

groin A wall made of rocks or concrete that is built outward from a beach to reduce erosion. (p. 515)
escollera Pared de piedra o concreto que se construye perpendicularmente a una playa para reducir la erosión.

groundwater Water that fills the cracks and spaces in underground soil and rock layers. (p. 478)
aguas freáticas Agua que llena las grietas y huecos de las capas subterráneas de tierra y roca.

group Elements in the same vertical column of the periodic table; also called family. (p. 683)
grupo Elementos en la misma columna vertical de la tabla periódica; también llamado familia.

gully A large channel in soil formed by erosion. (p. 472)
barranco Canal grande en el suelo, formado por la erosión.

halogen An element found in Group 17 of the periodic table. (p. 699)
halógeno Elemento que se encuentra en el Grupo 17 de la tabla periódica.

hanging wall The block of rock that forms the upper half of a fault. (p. 302)
labio superior Bloque de roca que constituye la mitad superior de una falla.

headland A part of the shore that sticks out into the ocean. (p. 495)
promontorio Parte de la costa que se interna en el mar.

heart A hollow, muscular organ that pumps blood throughout the body. (p. 120)
corazón Órgano muscular hueco que bombea sangre a todo el cuerpo.

heart attack A condition in which blood flow to part of the heart muscle is blocked, causing heart cells to die. (p. 139)
infarto cardiaco Condición en la que se obstruye el flujo de sangre a una parte del músculo cardiaco, lo que causa la muerte de las células cardiacas.

heliocentric A model of the solar system in which Earth and the other planets revolve around the sun. (p. 546)
heliocéntrico Modelo del sistema solar en el que la Tierra y otros planetas giran alrededor del Sol.

hemisphere One half of the sphere that makes up Earth's surface. (p. 412)
hemisferio La mitad de la esfera que forma la superficie de la Tierra.

hemoglobin An iron-containing protein that binds chemically to oxygen molecules; makes up most of red blood cells. (p. 132)
hemoglobina Proteína que contiene hierro, y que se enlaza químicamente a las moléculas de oxígeno; forma la mayoría de los glóbulos rojos. (p. 132)

Hertzsprung-Russell diagram A graph relating the surface temperatures and absolute brightnesses of stars. (p. 604)
diagrama Hertzsprung-Russel Gráfica que muestra la relación entre las temperaturas en la superficie de las estrellas y su magnitud absoluta.

histamine A chemical that is responsible for the symptoms of an allergy. (p. 200)
histamina Sustancia química responsable de los síntomas de una alergia.

HIV (human immunodeficiency virus) The virus that causes AIDS. (p. 190)
VIH (Virus de la inmunodeficiencia humana) Virus que causa el SIDA.

homeostasis The process by which an organism's internal environment is kept stable in spite of changes in the external environment. (p. 50)

homeostasis Tendencia del cuerpo a mantener un equilibrio interno, a pesar de los cambios en el ambiente externo.

horizontal axis (or x-axis) A line that runs left to right along the bottom of a graph, on which the manipulated variable (or independent variable) is labeled. (p. 23)
eje horizontal (o eje x) A line that runs left to right along the bottom of a graph, on which the manipulated variable (or independent variable) is labeled.

hot spot An area where magma from deep within the mantle melts through the crust above it. (p. 327)
punto caliente Área por donde el magma de las profundidades del manto atraviesa la corteza.

Hubble's law The observation that the farther away a galaxy is, the faster it is moving away. (p. 621)
ley de Hubble Observación que enuncia que mientras más lejos de nosotros se encuentra una galaxia, más rápido se está alejando.

humus Dark-colored organic material in soil. (p. 447)
humus Material orgánico de color oscuro en el suelo.

hypertension A disorder in which a person's blood pressure is consistently higher than normal; also called high blood pressure. (p. 140)
hipertensión Transtorno en el que la presión arterial de una persona es constantemente más alta de lo normal.

hypothesis A possible explanation for a set of observations or answer to a scientific question; must be testable. (p. 7)
hipótesis Explicación posible a un conjunto de observaciones o respuesta a una pregunta científica; debe ser verificable.

ice age Times in the past when continental glaciers covered large parts of Earth's surface. (p. 490)
glaciación Épocas del pasado en las que glaciares continentales cubrieron grandes extensiones de la superficie terrestre.

ice wedging Process that splits rock when water seeps into cracks, then freezes and expands. (p. 439)
calza de hielo Proceso que parte la roca cuando el agua penetra en las grietas, y luego se congela y expande.

igneous rock A type of rock that forms from the cooling of molten rock at or below the surface. (p. 377)
roca ígnea Tipo de roca que se forma cuando se enfrían las rocas fundidas en la superficie o debajo de la superficie.

immune response Part of the body's defense against pathogens in which cells of the immune system react to each kind of pathogen with a defense targeted specifically at that pathogen. (p. 188)
reacción inmunológica Parte de la defensa del cuerpo contra los patógenos en la que las células del sistema inmunológico reaccionan a cada tipo de patógeno con una defensa específica.

immunity The body's ability to destroy pathogens before they can cause disease. (p. 194)
inmunidad Capacidad del cuerpo para destruir los patógenos antes de que causen enfermedades.

index contours On a topographic map, a heavier contour line that is labeled with elevation of that contour line in round units. (p. 425)
curva de nivel índice En un mapa topográfico, una curva de nivel más gruesa que lleva rotulada la elevación de esa curva de nivel en unidades redondeadas.

inertia The tendency of an object to resist a change in motion. (p. 558)
inercia Tendencia de un objeto a resistir un cambio en su movimiento.

infectious disease A disease caused by the presence of a living thing in the body. (p. 181)
enfermedad infecciosa Enfermedad causada por la presencia de un ser vivo en el cuerpo.

inflammatory response Part of the body's defense against pathogens, in which fluid and white blood cells leak from blood vessels into tissues and destroys pathogens by breaking them down. (p. 187)
reacción inflamatoria Parte de la defensa del cuerpo contra los patógenos en la cual los fluidos y los glóbulos blancos salen de los vasos sanguíneos hacia los tejidos; los glóbulos blancos destruyen los patógenos descomponiéndolos.

inner core A dense sphere of solid iron and nickel at the center of Earth. (p. 268)
núcleo interno Densa esfera de hierro y níquel situada en el centro de la Tierra.

inorganic Not formed from living things or the remains of living things. (p. 345)
inorgánic Que no está formado de seres vivos o los restos de seres vivos.

input Something that is put into a technological system in order to achieve a goal. (p. 29)
entrada Algo que se agrega a un sistema tecnológico para conseguir un propósito.

insulin A chemical produced in the pancreas that enables the body's cells to take in glucose from the blood and use it for energy. (p. 201)
insulina Sustancia química que se produce en el páncreas, que permite que las células del cuerpo absorban glucosa de la sangre y la usen como energía.

interneuron A neuron that carries nerve impulses from one neuron to another. (p. 219)
interneurona Neurona que lleva los impulsos nerviosos de una neurona a otra.

intrusive rock Igneous rock that forms when magma hardens beneath Earth's surface. (p. 379)
roca intrusiva Roca ígnea que se forma cuando el magma se endurece bajo la superficie de la Tierra.

involuntary muscle A muscle that is not under conscious control. (p. 64)
músculos involuntarios Músculo que no se puede controlar conscientemente.

iris The circular structure that surrounds the pupil and regulates the amount of light entering the eye. (p. 233)
iris Estructura circular que rodea la pupila y regula la cantidad de luz que entra en el ojo.

irregular galaxy A galaxy that does not have a regular shape. (p. 616)
galaxia irregular Galaxia que no tiene una forma regular.

island arc A string of islands formed by the volcanoes along a deep ocean trench. (p. 326)
arco de islas Cadena de islas formadas por los volcanes que se encuentran a lo largo de una fosa oceánica profunda.

isotope An atom with the same number of protons and a different number of neutrons from other atoms of the same element. (p. 674)
isótopo Átomo con el mismo número de protones y un número diferente de neutrones que otros átomos del mismo elemento.

joint A place in the body where two bones come together. (p. 54)
articulación Lugar en el cuerpo en donde se unen dos huesos.

karst topography A region in which a layer of limestone close to the surface creates deep valleys, caverns and sinkholes. (p. 478)
topografía kárstica Tipo de terreno de regiones lluviosas en las que hay piedra caliza cerca de la superficie; se caracteriza por tener grutas, pozas hundidas y valles.

kettle A small depression that forms when a chunk of ice is left in glacial till. (p. 492)
cazuela Pequeña depresión que se forma cuando queda un trozo de hielo en arcilla glaciárica.

key A list of the symbols used on a map. (p. 410)
clave Lista de símbolos usados en un mapa.

kidney A major organ of the excretory system which removes urea and other wastes from the blood. (p. 168)
riñón Órgano principal del sistema excretor que elimina la urea, el exceso de agua y otros materiales de desecho del cuerpo.

Kinetic energy kinetic energy The energy an object has due to its motion. (p. 484)
energía cinética Energía que tiene un objeto por el hecho de estar en movimiento.

Kuiper belt A doughnut-shaped region that stretches from around Pluto's orbit to about 100 times Earth's distance from the sun. (p. 581)
cinturón de Kuiper Región en forma de disco que se extiende desde la órbita de Plutón hasta alrededor de 100 veces la distancia de la Tierra al Sol.

landform A feature of topography formed by the processes that shape Earth's surface. (p. 405)
accidente geográfico Característica de la topografía creada por los procesos de formación de la superficie terrestre.

landform region A large area of land where the topography is similar. (p. 408)
región con accidentes geográficos Gran extensión de tierra con topografía y estructura generales similares.

large intestine The last section of the digestive system, where water is absorbed into the bloodstream and the remaining material is eliminated from the body. (p. 111)
intestino grueso Última sección del sistema digestivo, donde se absorbe el agua hacia el torrente

sanguíneo y los materiales restantes son eliminados del cuerpo.

larynx The voice box; located in the top part of the trachea, underneath the epiglottis. (p. 160)
laringe Caja de la voz localizada en la parte superior de la tráquea por debajo de la epiglotis.

latitude The distance in degrees north or south of the equator. (p. 414)
latitud Distancia en grados al norte o al sur del ecuador.

lava Liquid magma that reaches the surface; also the rock formed when liquid lava hardens. (p. 324)
lava Magma líquida que sale a la superficie ; también, la roca que se forma cuando la lava líquida se solidifica.

lava flow The area covered by lava as it pours out of a volcano's vent. (p. 330)
colada de lava Área cubierta de lava a medida que ésta sale por la boca del volcán.

law of universal gravitation The scientific law that states that every object in the universe attracts every other object. (p. 556)
ley de gravitación universal Ley científica que establece que todos los objetos del universo se atraen entre ellos.

lens The flexible structure that focuses light that has entered the eye. (p. 233)
cristalino Estructura flexible que enfoca la luz que entra en el ojo.

ligament Strong connective tissue that holds bones together in movable joints. (p. 55)
ligamentos Tejido conectivo resistente que une dos huesos en las articulaciones móviles.

light-year The distance that light travels in one year, about 9.5 million million kilometers. (p. 602)
año luz Distancia a la que viaja la luz en un año; alrededor de 9.5 millones de millones de kilómetros.

line of best fit A smooth line that reflects the general pattern in a graph. (p. 24)
recta de mayor aproximación Recta que refleja el patrón general en una gráfica.

linear graph A line graph in which the data points yield a straight line. (p. 24)
gráfica lineal Gráfica en la cual los puntos de los datos forman una línea recta.

liquid A state of matter that has no definite shape but has a definite volume. (p. 641)
líquido Estado de la materia que no tiene forma definida pero sí volumen definido.

lithosphere A rigid layer made up of the uppermost part of the mantle and the crust. (p. 267)
litosfera Capa rígida constituida por la parte superior del manto y la corteza.

litter The loose layer of dead plant leaves and stems on the surface of the soil. (p. 450)
hojarasca Capa suelta de hojas y tallos de plantas muertas en la superficie del suelo.

liver The largest organ in the body; it plays a role in many body processes. (p. 109)
hígado Órgano más grande del cuerpo; produce bilis, descompone las medicinas y elimina el nitrógeno del cuerpo.

load The amount of sediment that a river or stream carries. (p. 485)
carga La cantidad de sedimento que lleva un río o arroyo.

loam Rich, fertile soil that is made up of about equal parts of clay, sand, and silt. (p. 447)
marga Suelo rico y fértil que está formado por partes casi iguales de arcilla, arena y cieno.

loess A wind-formed deposit made of fine particles of clay and silt. (p. 501)
loes Depósito de partículas finas de arcilla y limo arrastradas por el viento.

longitude The distance in degrees east or west of the prime meridian. (p. 414)
longitud Distancia en grados al este o al oeste del primer meridiano.

longshore drift The movement of sand along a beach. (p. 497), (p. 513)
deriva litoral Movimiento de arena a lo largo de una playa.

lungs The main organs of the respiratory system. (p. 156)
pulmones Órganos principales del sistema respiratorio.

luster The way a mineral reflects light from its surface. (p. 347)
lustre La manera en la que un mineral refleja la luz en su superficie.

lymph The fluid that the lymphatic system collects and returns to the bloodstream. (p. 137)
linfa Fluido que recoge el sistema linfático y devuelve al torrente sanguíneo.

lymph node A small knob of tissue in the lymphatic system that filters lymph, trapping bacteria and other microorganisms that cause disease. (p. 137)
ganglio linfático Pequeña prominencia de tejido en el sistema linfático que filtra la linfa, atrapando

las bacterias y otros microorganismos que causan enfermedades.

lymphatic system A network of veinlike vessels that returns the fluid that leaks out of blood vessels to the bloodstream. (p. 136)
sistema linfático Red de vasos semejantes a venas que devuelve al torrente sanguíneo el fluido que sale de los vasos sanguíneos.

lymphocyte White blood cell that distinguishes between each kind of pathogen. (p. 188)
linfocito Glóbulo blanco que reacciona a cada tipo de patógeno con una defensa específica.

magma The molten mixture of rock-forming substances, gases, and water from the mantle. (p. 324)
magma Mezcla fundida de las sustancias que forman las rocas, gases y agua, proveniente del manto.

magma chamber (p. 330) The pocket beneath a volcano where magma collects. (p. 330)
cámara magmática Bolsa debajo de un volcán en la que se acumula el magma.

magnetic resonance imaging A method for taking images of both the bones and soft tissues of the body. (p. 62)
imágenes por resonancia magnética Método que se usa para tomar imágenes claras de los huesos y de los tejidos blandos del cuerpo.

magnitude The measurement of an earthquake's strength based on seismic waves and movement along faults. (p. 310)
magnitud Medida de la fuerza de un sismo basada en las ondas sísmicas y en el movimiento que ocurre a lo largo de las fallas.

main sequence A diagonal area on an H-R diagram which includes more than 90 percent of all stars. (p. 605)
secuencia principal Área diagonal en un diagrama de H-R que incluye más del 90 por ciento de todas las estrellas.

malleable A term used to describe material that can be pounded into shapes. (p. 684)
maleable Término usado para describir el material al que se le puede dar forma.

manipulated variable The one factor that a scientist changes during an experiment; also called independent variable. (p. 8)
variable manipulada Único factor que un científico cambia durante un experimento; también llamada variable independiente.

mantle The layer of hot, solid material between Earth's crust and core. (p. 267)
manto Capa de material caliente y sólido entre la corteza terrestre y el núcleo.

map A flat model of all or part of Earth's surface as seen from above. (p. 410)
mapa Modelo plano de toda la superficie de la Tierra o parte de ella tal y como se ve desde arriba.

map projection A framework of lines that helps to show landmasses on a flat surface. (p. 416)
proyección de mapa Sistema de líneas que ayuda a mostrar volúmenes de tierra en una superficie plana.

marrow The soft connective tissue that fills the internal spaces in bone. (p. 56)
médula ósea Tejido conectivo suave que rellena los espacios internos de un hueso.

mass A measure of the amount of matter an object contains. (p. 16)
masa Medida de la cantidad de materia que contiene un objeto.

mass The amount of matter in an object. (p. 557)
masa Cantidad de materia que hay en un objeto.

mass movement Any one of several processes by which gravity moves sediment downhill. (p. 465)
movimiento masivo Cualquiera de varios procesos por los cuales la gravedad desplaza sedimentos cuesta abajo.

mass number The sum of protons and neutrons in the nucleus of an atom. (p. 674)
número de masa Suma de protones y neutrones en el núcleo de un átomo.

meander A looplike bend in the course of a river. (p. 474)
meandro Curva muy pronunciada en el curso de un río.

mechanical weathering The type of weathering in which rock is physically broken into smaller pieces. (p. 438)
desgaste mecánico Tipo de desgaste en el cual una roca se rompe físicamente en trozos más pequeños.

melanin A pigment that gives the skin its color. (p. 73)
melanina Pigmento que da color a la piel.

melting The change in state from a solid to a liquid. (p. 645)
fusión Cambio del estado sólido a líquido.

melting point The temperature at which a substance changes from a solid to a liquid; the same as

the freezing point, or temperature at which a liquid changes to a solid. (p. 645)

punto de fusión Temperatura a la que una sustancia cambia de estado sólido a líquido; es lo mismo que el punto de congelación (la temperatura a la que un líquido se vuelve sólido).

meniscus The curved upper surface of a liquid in a column of liquid. (p. 17)

menisco Superficie superior curvada de un líquido en una columna de líquido.

Mercalli scale A scale that rates earthquakes according to their intensity and how much damage they cause. (p. 310)

escala de Mercalli (p. 309) Escala con la que se miden los sismos basándose en la intensidad y el daño que ocasionan.

metal A class of elements characterized by physical properties that include shininess, malleability, ductility, and conductivity. (p. 684)

metal Clase de elementos caracterizados por las propiedades físicas que incluye brillo, maleabilidad, ductilidad y conductividad.

metalloid An element that has some characteristics of both metals and nonmetals. (p. 701)

metaloide Elemento que tiene algunas características de metales y de no metales.

metamorphic rock A type of rock that forms from an existing rock that is changed by heat, pressure, or chemical reactions. (p. 377)

roca metamórfica Tipo de roca que se forma cuando una roca es transformada por el calor, presión o reacciones químicas.

meteor A streak of light in the sky produced by the burning of a meteoroid in Earth's atmosphere. (p. 583)

meteoro Rayo de luz en el cielo producido por el incendio de un meteoroide en la atmósfera de la Tierra.

meteorite A meteoroid that passes through the atmosphere and hits Earth's surface. (p. 583)

meteorito Meteoroide que pasa por la atmósfera y golpea la superficie de la Tierra.

meteoroid A chunk of rock or dust in space. (p. 583)

meteoroide Pedazo de roca o polvo en el espacio.

metric system A system of measurement based on the number 10. (p. 14)

sistema métrico Sistema de medida basado en el número 10.

mid-ocean ridge An undersea mountain chain where new ocean floor is produced; a divergent plate boundary. (p. 280)

cordillera oceánica central Cadena montañosa submarina donde se produce el nuevo suelo oceánico; borde de placa divergente.

mineral A naturally occurring, inorganic solid that has a crystal structure and a definite chemical composition. (p. 344); Nutrients that are needed by the body in small amounts and are not made by living things. (p. 92)

mineral Sólido inorgánico que ocurre en la naturaleza, de estructura cristalina y composición química definida; Nutrientes que el cuerpo necesita en pequeñas cantidades y que no producen los seres vivos.

model In science, a diagram, a mental picture, a mathematical statement, or an object that helps explain ideas about the natural world. (p. 675)

modelo En ciencias, un diagrama, una imagen mental, un enunciado matemático o un objeto que ayuda a explicar ideas sobre el mundo natural.

Mohs hardness scale A scale ranking ten minerals from softest to hardest; used in testing the hardness of minerals. (p. 348)

escala de dureza de Mohs Escala en la que se clasifican diez minerales del más blando al más duro; se usa para probar la dureza de los minerales.

moment magnitude scale A scale that rates earthquakes by estimating the total energy released by an earthquake. (p. 311)

escala de magnitud de momento Escala con la que se miden los sismos estimando la cantidad total de energía liberada por un terremoto.

monomer One of the smaller molecules from which polymers are built. (p. 715)

monómero Una de las moléculas más pequeñas que componen un polímero.

moraine A ridge formed by the till deposited at the edge of a glacier. (p. 492)

morrena Montículo formado por la arcilla glaciárica depositada en el borde de un glaciar.

motor neuron A neuron that sends an impulse to a muscle or gland, causing the muscle or gland to react. (p. 218)

neurona motora Neurona que envía un impulso a un músculo o glándula, haciendo que el músculo o la glándula reaccione.

mountain A landform with high elevation and high relief. (p. 407)

montaña Accidente geográfico con una elevación alta y un relieve alto.

mountain range A series of mountains that have the same general shape and structure. (p. 407)

cordillera Serie de montañas que tienen la misma forma y estructura general.

mucus A thick, slippery substance produced by the body. (p. 103)
mucosidad Sustancia espesa y lubricante que produce el cuerpo.

muscle tissue A body tissue that contracts or shortens, making body parts move. (p. 48)
tejido muscular Tejido corporal que se contrae o acorta, permitiendo así que se muevan las partes del cuerpo.

N

natural resource Anything in the environment that humans use. (p. 455)
recurso natural Cualquier cosa de la naturaleza que usan los humanos.

neap tide A tide with the least difference between low and high tide that occurs when the sun and moon pull at right angles to each other at the first and third quarters of the moon. (p. 518)
marea muerta Marea con la mínima diferencia entre pleamar y bajamar; se presenta cuando el Sol y la Luna ejercen su atracción en direcciones que forman un ángulo recto, durante los cuartos creciente y menguante de la Luna.

nearsightedness The condition in which a person can see nearby objects clearly. (p. 235)
miopía Condición en la que una persona puede ver claramente los objetos cercanos.

nebula A large cloud of gas and dust in space, spread out in an immense volume. (p. 609), (p. 706)
nebulosa Gran nube de gas y polvo en el espacio, expandida en un volumen inmenso.

nephron Small filtering structure found in the kidneys that removes wastes from blood and produces urine. (p. 168)
nefrón Una de los millones de estructuras diminutas de filtración que hay en los riñones, que elimina los desechos de la sangre y que produce la orina.

nerve A bundle of nerve fibers. (p. 218)
nervio Conjunto de fibras nerviosas.

nerve impulse The message carried by a neuron. (p. 218)
impulso nervioso Mensaje que lleva una neurona.

nervous tissue A body tissue that carries electrical messages back and forth between the brain and every other part of the body. (p. 48)

tejido nervioso Tejido corporal que lleva mensajes eléctricos entre el cerebro y todas las demás partes del cuerpo y viceversa.

neuron A cell that carries information through the nervous system. (p. 218)
neurona Célula que lleva información a través del sistema nervioso.

neutron A small particle in the nucleus of the atom, with no electrical charge. (p. 671)
neutrón Partícula pequeña en el núcleo del átomo, que no tiene carga eléctrica.

neutron star The small, dense remains of a high-mass star after a supernova. (p. 611)
estrella de neutrones Restos pequeños y densos de una estrella de gran masa después de una supernova.

Newton's first law of motion The scientific law that states that an object at rest will stay at rest and an object in motion will stay in motion with a constant speed and direction unless acted on by a force. (p. 558)
Primera ley de movimiento de Newton Ley científica que establece que un objeto en reposo se mantendrá en reposo y un objeto en movimiento se mantendrá en movimiento con una velocidad y dirección constante a menos que se ejerza una fuerza sobre él.

nicotine A stimulant drug in tobacco that increases the activities of the nervous system, heart, and other organs. (p. 163)
nicotina Sustancia química en el tabaco que acelera la actividad del sistema nervioso, corazón y otros órganos.

noble gas An element in Group 18 of the periodic table. (p. 700)
gas noble Elemento del Grupo 18 de la tabla periódica.

noninfectious disease A disease that is not caused by a pathogen. (p. 199)
enfermedad no infecciosa Enfermedad que no es causada por un patógeno.

nonlinear graph A line graph in which the data points do not fall along a straight line. (p. 25)
gráfica no lineal Gráfica lineal en la que los puntos de los datos no forman una línea recta.

nonmetal An element that lacks most of the properties of a metal. (p. 695)
no metal Elemento que carece de la mayoría de las propiedades de un metal.

normal fault A type of fault where the hanging wall slides downward (p. 302)

falla normal Tipo de falla en la cual el labio superior se desliza hacia abajo como resultado de la tensión en la corteza.

nuclear fusion The process in which two atomic nuclei combine to form a larger nucleus, forming a heavier element and releasing huge amounts of energy. (p. 551), (p. 705)
fusión nuclear Proceso en el cual dos núcleos atómicos se combinan para formar un núcleo mayor; forman un elemento más pesado y liberan grandes cantidades de energía.

nucleus The control center of a cell that directs the cell's activities and contains the information that determines the cell's form and function. (p. 47); The solid inner core of a comet. (p. 581); The central core of an atom containing protons and usually neutrons. (p. 671)
núcleo Centro de control de la célula que dirige las actividades de la célula y que contiene información que determina la forma y función de la célula; Centro interno sólido de un cometa; Parte central del átomo que contiene protones y normalmente neutrones.

nutrients Substances in food that provide the raw materials and energy the body needs to carry out all its essential processes. (p. 84)
nutrientes Sustancias que contienen los alimentos que proveen la materia prima y la energía que necesita el cuerpo para realizar los procesos elementales.

O

observatory A building that contains one or more telescopes. (p. 594)
observatorio Edificio que contiene uno o más telescopios.

obsolete No longer in use. (p. 28)
obsoleto Que ya no está en uso.

Oort cloud A spherical region of comets that surrounds the solar system. (p. 581)
nube de Oort Región esférica de cometas que rodea el sistema solar.

open cluster A star cluster that has a loose, disorganized appearance and contains no more than a few thousand stars. (p. 615)
cúmulo abierto Cúmulo de estrellas que tiene una apariencia no compacta y desorganizada, y que no contiene más de unas pocos miles de estrellas.

operational definition A statement that describes how to measure a particular variable or how to define a particular term. (p. 8)

definición operativa Enunciado que describe cómo medir una variable determinada o cómo definir un término determinado.

optical fiber A threadlike piece of glass (or plastic) that can be used for transmitting messages in the form of light. (p. 734)
fibra óptica Pieza de vidrio (o plástico) parecido a hilo que se puede usar para transmitir mensajes en forma de luz.

optical telescope A telescope that uses lenses or mirrors to collect and focus visible light. (p. 592)
telescopio óptico Telescopio que usa lentes o espejos para captar y enfocar la luz visible.

ore Rock that contains a metal or economically useful mineral. (p. 362)
mena Rocaque contiene un metal o un mineral de importancia económica.

organ A structure in the body that is composed of different kinds of tissue. (p. 48)
órgano Estructura del cuerpo compuesta de diferentes tipos de tejidos.

organ system A group of organs that work together to perform a major function in the body. (p. 48)
sistema de órganos Grupo de órganos que trabajan juntos para realizar una función importante del cuerpo.

organic rock Sedimentary rock that forms from remains of organisms deposited in thick layers. (p. 384)
roca orgánica Roca sedimentaria que se forma cuando los restos de organismos se depositan en capas gruesas.

origin The point where the x-axis and y-axis cross on a graph. (p. 23), (p. 660)
origen Punto en donde el eje x y el eje y se cruzan en una gráfica.

osteoporosis A condition in which the body's bones become weak and break easily. (p. 59)
osteoporosis condición en la cual los huesos del cuerpo se debilitan y se rompen fácilmente.

outer core A layer of molten iron and nickel that surrounds the inner core of Earth. (p. 268)
núcleo externo Capa de hierro y níquel fundidos que rodea el núcleo interno de la Tierra.

output The result or product from the operation of a technological system. (p. 29)
salida Resultado o producto de la operación de un sistema tecnológico.

oxbow lake A meander cut off from a river. (p. 474)
lago de recodo Meandro que ha quedado aislado de un río.

oxidation A chemical change in which a substance combines with oxygen, as when iron oxidizes, forming rust. (p. 441)
oxidación Cambio químico en el cual una sustancia se combina con el oxígeno, como cuando el hierro se oxida y se forma herrumbre.

P wave A type of seismic wave that compresses and expands the ground. (p. 309)
onda P Tipo de onda sísmica que comprime y expande el suelo.

pacemaker A group of cells located in the right atrium that sends out signals that make the heart muscle contract and that regulates heartbeat rate. (p. 122)
marcapasos Grupo de células ubicado en la aurícula derecha que envía señales para que el músculo cardiaco se contraiga, y que regula el ritmo cardiaco.

pancreas A triangular organ that lies between the stomach and first part of the small intestine. (p. 110)
páncreas Órgano triangular que produce enzimas que fluyen al intestino delgado.

Pangaea The name of the single landmass that broke apart 200 million years ago and gave rise to today's continents. (p. 275)
Pangea Nombre de la masa terrestre única que se dividió hace 200 millones de años, dando origen a los continentes actuales.

parallax The apparent change in position of an object when seen from different places. (p. 602)
paralaje Cambio aparente en la posición de un objeto cuando es visto desde diferentes lugares.

particle accelerator A machine that moves atomic nuclei at higher and higher speeds until they crash into one another, sometimes forming heavier elements. (p. 690)
acelerador de partículas Máquina que mueve los núcleos atómicos a velocidades cada vez más altas hasta que chocan entre ellas, a veces forman elementos más pesados.

passive immunity Immunity in which antibodies are given to a person rather than produced within the person's own body. (p. 198)
inmunidad pasiva Inmunidad en la que los anticuerpos que luchan contra un patógeno vienen de otro organismo y no del cuerpo de la propia persona.

patent A legal document issued by the government that gives an inventor exclusive rights to make, use, or sell an invention for a limited time. (p. 39)
patente Documento legal emitido por el gobierno que otorga a un inventor los derechos exclusivos de hacer, usar o vender un invento por un tiempo limitado.

pathogen An organism that causes disease. (p. 181)
patógeno Organismo que causa enfermedades.

Percent Daily Value A value that shows how the nutritional content of one serving of food fits into the diet of a person who consumes 2,000 calories a day. (p. 98)
Porcentaje de valor diario Valor que muestra cómo el contenido nutricional de una porción de alimento se corresponde con la dieta de una persona que consume 2,000 Calorías al día.

period A horizontal row of elements in the periodic table. (p. 682)
período Fila horizontal de los elementos en la tabla periódica.

periodic table A chart of the elements showing the repeating pattern of their properties. (p. 678)
tabla periódica Tabla de los elementos que muestra el patrón repetido de sus propiedades.

peripheral nervous system The division of the nervous system consisting of all of the nerves located outside the central nervous system. (p. 222)
sistema nervioso periférico División del sistema nervioso formada por todos los nervios ubicados fuera del sistema central nervioso.

peristalsis Involuntary waves of muscle contraction that keep food moving along in one direction through the digestive system. (p. 103)
peristalsis Ondulaciones involuntarias de contracción muscular que empujan el alimento en una dirección a través del sistema digestivo.

permeable Characteristic of a material that is full of tiny, connected air spaces that water can seep through. (p. 442)
permeable Característica de un material que está lleno de diminutos espacios de aire conectados entre sí, por los que puede penetrar el agua.

phagocyte A white blood cell that destroys pathogens by engulfing them and breaking them down. (p. 187)
fagocito Glóbulo blanco que destruye los patógenos envolviéndolos y descomponiéndolos.

pharynx The throat; part of both the respiratory and digestive systems. (p. 155)
faringe Garganta; parte de los sistemas respiratorio y digestivo.

English and Spanish Glossary

photosphere The inner layer of the sun's atmosphere that gives off its visible light; the sun's surface. (p. 552)
fotosfera Capa más interna de la atmósfera del Sol que provoca la luz que vemos; superficie del Sol.

pipe A long tube through which magma moves from the magma chamber to Earth's surface. (p. 330)
chimenea Largo tubo por el que el magma sube desde la cámara magmática hasta la superficie

pixels The tiny dots in a satellite image. (p. 420)
pixels Puntos diminutos en una imagen de satélite.

plain A landform made up of flat or gently rolling land with low relief. (p. 406)
llanura Accidente geográfico que consiste en un terreno plano o ligeramente ondulado con un relieve bajo.

planetesimal One of the small asteroid-like bodies that formed the building blocks of the planets. (p. 623)
planetesimal Uno de los cuerpos pequeños parecidos a asteroides que dieron origen a los planetas.

plasma The liquid part of blood. (p. 131); A gas-like state of matter consisting of a mixture of free electrons and atoms that are stripped of their electrons. (p. 705)
plasma Parte líquida de la sangre; Estado de la materia similar al gas que consiste en la mezcla de electrones libres y átomos que son desprovistos de sus electrones.

plastic A synthetic polymer that can be molded or shaped. (p. 717)
plástico Polímero sintético que se puede moldear o se le puede dar forma.

plate A section of the lithosphere that slowly moves over the asthenosphere, carrying pieces of continental and oceanic crust. (p. 288)
placa Sección de la litosfera que se desplaza lentamente sobre la astenosfera, llevando consigo trozos de la corteza continental y de la oceánica.

plate tectonics The theory that pieces of Earth's lithosphere are in constant motion, driven by convection currents in the mantle. (p. 289)
tectónica de placas Teoría según la cual las partes de la litosfera de la Tierra están en continuo movimiento, impulsadas por las corrientes de convección del manto.

plateau A landform that has high elevation and a more or less level surface. (p. 306), (p. 407)

meseta Accidente geográfico que tiene una elevación alta y cuya superficie está más o menos nivelada.

platelet A cell fragment that plays an important part in forming blood clots. (p. 134)
plaqueta Fragmento de célula que juega un papel muy importante en la formación de coágulos sanguíneos.

plucking The process by which a glacier picks up rocks as it flows over the land. (p. 491)
extracción Proceso por el cual un glaciar arranca rocas al fluir sobre la tierra.

polymer A large complex molecule built from smaller molecules joined together in a repeating pattern. (p. 714)
polímero Molécula grande y compleja formada por moléculas más pequeñas que se unen en un patrón que se repite.

pore An opening through which sweat reaches the surface of the skin. (p. 73)
poros Aberturas a través de las cuales el sudor sale a la superficie de la piel.

potential energy Energy that is stored and available to be used later. (p. 484)
energía potencial Energía que se encuentra almacenada y puede utilizarse posteriormente.

pressure The force pushing on a surface divided by the area of that surface. (p. 265), (p. 653)
presión Fuerza que actúa contra una superficie, dividida entre el área de esa superficie.

prime meridian The line that makes a half circle from the North Pole to the South Pole and that passes through Greenwich, England. (p. 413)
primer meridiano Línea que forma medio círculo desde el Polo Norte al Polo Sur y que pasa por Greenwich, Inglaterra.

probability A number that describes how likely it is that an event will occur. (P. 803)
Probabilidad Número que describe la posibilidad de que ocurra un suceso.

process A sequence of actions that a technological system undergoes to produce an output. (p. 29)
proceso Secuencia de acciones que experimenta un sistema tecnológico para producir un resultado.

prominence A huge, reddish loop of gas that protrudes from the sun's surface, linking parts of sunspot regions. (p. 554)
prominencia Enorme burbuja rojiza de gas que sobresale de la superfice del Sol, que une partes de las regiones de las manchas solares.

protein Nutrient that contains nitrogen as well as carbon, hydrogen, and oxygen; they are needed for tissue growth and repair and play a part in chemical reactions within cells. (p. 89)
proteínas Nutrientes que contienen nitrógeno, carbono, hidrógeno y oxígeno; son necesarios para el crecimiento y reparación del tejido, y juegan un papel muy importante en las reacciones químicas de las células.

proton A small, positively charged particle in the nucleus of the atom. (p. 671)
protón Partícula pequeña cargada positivamente, que se encuentra en el núcleo del átomo.

protostar A contracting cloud of gas and dust with enough mass to form a star. (p. 609)
protoestrella Nube de gas y polvo que se contrae, con suficiente masa como para formar una estrella.

prototype A working model used to test a design. (p. 38)
prototipo Modelo funcional usado para probar un diseño.

pulsar A rapidly spinning neutron star that produces radio waves. (p. 611)
púlsar Estrella de neutrones que gira rápidamente y produce ondas de radio.

pulse The alternating expansion and relaxation of an artery wall as blood travels through an artery. (p. 126)
pulso Expansión y relajación alternada de una pared arterial a medida que la sangre viaja por la arteria.

pupil The opening through which light enters the eye. (p. 233)
pupila Abertura por la que entra la luz al ojo.

quasar An enormously bright, distant galaxy with a giant black hole at its center. (p. 616)
quásar Galaxia extraordinariamente luminosa y distante con un agujero negro gigante en el centro.

radiation The direct transfer of energy by electromagnetic waves. (p. 271)
radiación Transferencia directa de energía por ondas electromagnéticas.

radiation zone A region of very tightly packed gas in the sun's interior where energy is transferred mainly in the form of light. (p. 551)

zona radioactiva Región de gases estrechamente comprimidos en el interior del Sol en donde se transfiere la energía principalmente en forma de luz.

radio telescope A device used to detect radio waves from objects in space. (p. 593)
radiotelescopio Aparato usado para detectar ondas de radio de los objetos en el espacio.

reactivity The ease and speed with which an element combines, or reacts, with other elements and compounds. (p. 685)
reactividad Facilidad y rapidez con las que un elemento se combina, o reacciona, con otros elementos y compuestos.

rectum The end of the large intestine where waste material is compressed into a solid form before being eliminated. (p. 111)
recto Tubo corto al final del intestino grueso, donde el material de desecho se comprime a una forma sólida antes de ser eliminado.

red blood cell A cell in the blood that takes up oxygen in the lungs and delivers it to cells elsewhere in the body. (p. 132)
glóbulo rojo Célula de la sangre que capta el oxígeno en los pulmones y lo lleva a las células de todo el cuerpo.

reflecting telescope A telescope that uses a curved mirror to collect and focus light. (p. 593)
telescopio de reflexión Telescopio que usa un espejo curvado para captar y enfocar la luz.

reflex An automatic response that occurs rapidly and without conscious control. (p. 227)
reflejo Respuesta automática que ocurre muy rápidamente y sin control consciente.

refracting telescope A telescope that uses convex lenses to gather and focus light. (p. 592)
telescopio de refracción Telescopio que usa lentes convexas para captar y enfocar la luz.

relief The difference in elevation between the highest and lowest parts of an area. (p. 405)
relieve Diferencia en la elevación entre las partes más altas y más bajas en un área.

respiration The process in which oxygen and glucose undergo a complex series of chemical reactions inside cells; also called cellular respiration. (p. 153)
respiración celular Proceso en el cual el oxígeno y la glucosa sufren una compleja serie de reacciones químicas en las células; también se llama respiración celular.

responding variable The factor that changes as a result of changes to the manipulated, or independent, variable in an experiment; also called dependent variable. (p. 8)
variable de respuesta Factor que cambia como resultado del cambio de la variable manipulada, o independiente, en un experimento; también llamada variable dependiente.

response What the body does in reaction to a stimulus. (p. 217)
respuesta Lo que hace el cuerpo como reacción a un estímulo.

retina The layer of receptor cells at the back of the eye on which an image is focused. (p. 234)
retina Capa de células receptoras en la parte posterior del ojo donde se enfoca una imagen.

reverse fault A type of fault where the hanging wall slides upward; caused by compression in the crust. (p. 302)
falla inversa Tipo de falla en la cual el labio superior se desliza hacia arriba como resultado de compresión en la corteza.

Richter scale A scale that rates seismic waves as measured by a particular type of mechanical seismograph. (p. 310)
escala de Richter Escala con la que se miden las ondas sísmicas utilizando un tipo especial de sismógrafo mecánico.

rift valley A deep valley that forms where two plates move apart. (p. 290)
valle de fisura Valle profundo que se forma cuando dos placas se separan.

rill A tiny groove in soil made by flowing water. (p. 472)
arroyuelo Pequeño surco en el suelo que deja el agua al fluir.

ring A thin disk of small ice and rock particles surrounding a planet. (p. 571)
anillo Disco fino de pequeñas partículas de hielo y roca que rodea un planeta.

Ring of Fire A major belt of volcanoes that rims the Pacific Ocean. (p. 325)
Cinturón de Fuego Gran cadena de volcanes que rodea el océano Pacífico.

rip current A rush of water that flows rapidly back to sea through a narrow opening in a sandbar. (p. 513)
corriente de resaca Torrente de agua que fluye con fuerza desde una playa hacia mar adentro por un canal estrecho en un banco de arena.

risk-benefit analysis The process of evaluating the possible problems of a technology compared to the expected advantages. (p. 32)
análisis de riesgo y beneficios Proceso por el cual se evalúan los posibles problemas de una tecnología y se compara con las ventajas deseadas.

rock-forming minerals One of the common minerals that make up most of the rocks of Earth's crust. (p. 375)
minerales formadores de rocas Uno de los minerales comunes de los que están compuestas la mayoría de las rocas de la corteza de la Tierra.

runoff Water that flows over the ground surface rather than soaking into the ground. (p. 471)
escurrimiento Agua que fluye sobre la superficie del suelo en lugar de ser absorbida por éste.

S wave A type of seismic wave that moves the ground up and down or side to side. (p. 309)
onda S Tipo de onda sísmica que hace que el suelo se mueva de arriba abajo, o de lado a lado.

salinity The total amount of dissolved salts in a water sample. (p. 523)
salinidad Cantidad total de sales disueltas en una muestra de agua.

saliva The fluid released when the mouth waters that plays an important role in both mechanical and chemical digestion. (p. 102)
saliva Líquido liberado por la boca que juega un papel muy importante en la digestión química y mecánica.

sand dune A deposit of wind-blown sand. (p. 499)
duna de arena Depósito de arena arrastrada por el viento.

satellite images Pictures of the land surface based on computer data collected from satellites. (p. 420)
imágenes satelitales Fotografías de la superficie terrestre basadas en información computarizada reunida por satélites.

scale Used to compare distance on a map or globe to distance on Earth's surface. (p. 410)
escala Se usa para comparar la distancia en un mapa o globo terráqueo con la distancia en la superficie de la Tierra.

scientific inquiry The ongoing process of discovery in science; the diverse ways in which scientists study the natural world and propose explanations based on evidence they gather. (p. 6)
investigación científica Proceso continuo de descubrimiento en la ciencia; diversidad de méto-

dos con los que los científicos estudian el mundo natural y proponen explicaciones del mismo basadas en la evidencia que reúnen.

scientific law A statement that describes what scientists expect to happen every time under a particular set of conditions. (p. 10)
ley científica Enunciado que describe lo que los científicos esperan que suceda cada vez que se da una serie de condiciones determinadas.

scientific literacy The knowledge and understanding of scientific terms and principles required for evaluating information, making personal decisions, and taking part in public affairs. (p. 11)
alfabetismo científico Conocimiento y comprensión de los términos y principios científicos necesarios para evaluar información, tomar decisiones personales y participar en actividades públicas.

scientific notation A mathematical method of writing numbers using powers of ten. (p. 618)
notación científica Método matemático de escritura de números que usa la potencia de diez.

scientific theory A well-tested explanation for a wide range of observations or experimental results. (p. 10), (p. 288)
teoría científica Explicación comprobada de una gran variedad de observaciones o resultados de experimentos.

sea-floor spreading The process by which molten material adds new oceanic crust to the ocean floor. (p. 281)
despliegue del suelo oceánico Proceso mediante el cual la materia fundida añade nueva corteza oceánica al suelo oceánico.

sediment Small, solid pieces of material that come from rocks or organisms. (p. 382), (p. 465)
sedimento Partículas sólidas de materiales que provienen de rocas u organismos.

sedimentary rock A type of rock that forms when particles from other rocks or the remains of plants and animals are pressed and cemented together. (p. 377)
roca sedimentaria Tipo de roca que se forma cuando las partículas de otras rocas o los restos de plantas y animales son presionados y cementados.

seismic waves Vibrations that travel through Earth carrying the energy released during an earthquake. (p. 264)
ondas sísmicas Vibraciónes que se desplazan por la Tierra, llevando la energía liberada durante un terremoto.

seismogram The record of an earthquake's seismic waves produced by a seismograph. (p. 310), (p. 317)
sismograma Registro producido por un sismógrafo de las ondas sísmicas de un terremoto.

seismograph A device that records ground movements caused by seismic waves as they move through Earth. (p. 310)
sismógrafo Aparato con el que se registran los movimientos del suelo ocasionados por las ondas sísmicas a medida que éstas se desplazan por la Tierra.

semicircular canals Structures in the inner ear that are responsible for the sense of balance. (p. 238)
canales semicirculares Estructuras en el oído interno responsables del sentido del equilibrio.

semiconductor A material that conducts current under certain conditions. (p. 701)
semiconductor Material que conduce la corriente bajo ciertas condiciones.

sensory neuron A neuron that picks up stimuli from the internal or external environment and converts each stimulus into a nerve impulse. (p. 218)
neurona sensorial Neurona que recoge los estímulos del medio ambiente interno o externo y convierte cada estímulo en un impulso nervioso.

shearing Stress that pushes a mass of rock in opposite directions. (p. 301)
cizallamiento Esfuerzo que presiona masas de roca en sentidos opuestos.

significant figures All the digits in a measurement that have been measured exactly, plus one digit whose value has been estimated. (p. 807)
cifras significativas Todos los dígitos en una medida que se han medido con exactitud, más un dígito cuyo valor se ha estimado.

SI (Système International d'Unités) International System of Units; a version of the metric system used by scientists all over the world. (p. 14)
SI (Sistema Internacional de Unidades) Sistema Internacional de Unidades; versión del sistema métrico usado por científicos de todo el mundo.

skeletal muscle A muscle that is attached to the bones of the skeleton and provides the force that moves the bones. (p. 66)
músculos esqueléticos Músculo que está unido a los huesos del esqueleto y que proporciona la fuerza para que los huesos se muevan.

skeleton The inner framework made of all the bones of the body. (p. 52)

esqueleto Estructura formada por todos los huesos del cuerpo.

slope The steepness of a graph line; the ratio of the vertical change (the rise) to the horizontal change (the run). (p. 24)
pendiente Inclinación de una gráfica lineal; la razón del cambio vertical (el ascenso) al cambio horizontal (el avance).

small intestine The part of the digestive system in which most chemical digestion takes place. (p. 108)
intestino delgado Parte del sistema digestivo en la cual se produce la mayoría de la digestión química.

smelting The process by which ore is melted to separate the useful metal from other elements. (p. 364)
fundición Proceso mediante el que una mena se funde para separar el mineral útil de otros elementos.

smooth muscle Involuntary muscle found inside many internal organs of the body. (p. 66)
músculos lisos Músculo involuntario que se encuentra dentro de muchos órganos internos del cuerpo.

sod A thick mass of grass roots and soil. (p. 454)
tepe Masa gruesa de raíces de hierbas y suelo.

soil The loose, weathered material on Earth's surface in which plants can grow. (p. 446)
suelo Material suelto y desgastado sobre la superficie de la Tierra en donde crecen las plantas.

soil conservation The management of soil to prevent its destruction. (p. 457)
conservación del suelo Cuidado del suelo para prevenir su destrucción.

soil horizon The layer of soil that differs in color and texture from the layers above or below it. (p. 448)
horizonte de suelo Capa de suelo que se diferencia en color y textura de las capas que tiene encima o debajo.

solar flare An eruption of gas from the sun's surface that occurs when the loops in sunspot regions suddenly connect. (p. 554)
destello solar Erupción de gas desde la superficie del Sol que ocurre cuando las burbujas en las regiones de las manchas solares se unen repentinamente.

solar nebula A large cloud of gas and dust such as the one that formed our solar system. (p. 623)
nebulosa solar Gran nube de gas y polvo como la que forma nuestro sistema solar.

solar wind A stream of electrically charged particles that emanate from the sun's corona. (p. 552)
viento solar Flujo de partículas cargadas eléctricamente que emanan de la corona del Sol.

solid A state of matter that has a definite shape and a definite volume. (p. 639)
sólido Estado de la materia con forma y volumen definidos.

solution A mixture in which one substance is dissolved in another. (p. 355)
solución Mezcla en la que una substancia se halla disuelta en otra.

somatic nervous system The group of nerves in the peripheral nervous system that controls voluntary actions. (p. 227)
sistema nervioso somático Grupo de nervios en el sistema nervioso periférico que controla las acciones voluntarias.

sonar A device that determines the distance of an object under water by recording echoes of sound waves. (p. 280)
sona sonar Aparato con el cual se determina la distancia de un objeto sumergido en el agua mediante el registro del eco de las ondas sonoras.

spectrograph An instrument that separates light into colors and makes an image of the resulting spectrum. (p. 600)
espectrógrafo Instrumento que separa la luz en colores y crea una imagen del espectro resultante.

spectrum The range of wavelengths of electromagnetic waves. (p. 591)
espectro Abanico de longitudes de ondas electromagnéticas.

spinal cord The thick column of nerve tissue that links the brain to most of the nerves in the peripheral nervous system. (p. 223)
médula espinal Columna gruesa de tejido nervioso que une el encéfalo con la mayoría de los nervios en el sistema nervioso periférico.

spiral galaxy A galaxy with a bulge in the middle and arms that spiral outward in a pinwheel pattern. (p. 616)
galaxia espiral Galaxia con una protuberancia en el centro y brazos que giran en espiral hacia el exterior, como un remolino.

spit A beach formed by longshore drift that projects like a finger out into the water. (p. 498)
banco de arena Playa formada por la deriva litoral; se proyecta como un dedo agua adentro.

English and Spanish Glossary

spongy bone Layer of bone tissue having many small spaces and found just inside the layer of compact bone. (p. 56)
hueso esponjoso Capa de tejido de un hueso que tiene muchos espacios pequeños y se encuentra justo dentro de la capa del hueso compacto.

sprain An injury in which the ligaments holding bones together are stretched too far and tear. (p. 61)
esguince Lesión en la que los ligamentos se estiran demasiado y se rompen.

spring tide A tide with the greatest difference between high and low tide that occurs when the sun and the moon are aligned with Earth at the new moon and the full moon. (p. 518)
marea viva Marea que presenta la mayor diferencia entre pleamar y bajamar; se presenta cuando el Sol y la Luna están alineados con la Tierra en la luna nueva y la luna llena.

stalactite A calcite deposit that hangs from the roof of a cave. (p. 478)
estalactita Depósito de calcita que cuelga del techo de una gruta.

stalagmite A cone-shaped calcite deposite that builds up from the floor of a cave. (p. 478)
estalagmita Depósito cónico de calcita que se forma en el piso de una gruta

stimulant A drug that speeds up body processes. (p. 244)
estimulante Droga que acelera los procesos del cuerpo.

stimulus Any change or signal in the environment that can make an organism react in some way. (p. 217)
estímulo Cualquier cambio o señal en el medio ambiente que puede hacer que un organismo reaccione de alguna manera.

stomach A J-shaped, muscular pouch located in the abdomen. (p. 104)
estómago Bolsa muscular con forma de J localizada en el abdomen, que se expande para albergar toda la comida que se ingiere.

streak The color of a mineral's powder. (p. 347)
raya El color del polvo de un mineral.

stream A channel through which water is continually flowing downhill. (p. 472)
arroyo Canal por el cual fluye continuamente agua cuesta abajo.

stress The reaction of a person's body to potentially threatening, challenging, or disturbing events.

(p. 51); A force that acts on rock to change its shape or volume. (p. 300)
estrés Reacción del cuerpo de un individuo a amenazas, retos o sucesos molestos potenciales; Fuerza que al actuar sobre una roca cambia su forma o volumen.

striated muscle A muscle that appears banded; also called skeletal muscle. (p. 66)
músculo estriado Músculo con forma de franjas; también se llama músculo esquelético.

strike-slip fault A type of fault where rocks on either side move past each other sideways with little up-or-down motion. (p. 303)
falla transcurrente su fuerza depende de sus masas y de la distancia que les separa.

subduction The process by which oceanic crust sinks beneath a deep-ocean trench and back into the mantle at a convergent plate boundary. (p. 284)
subducción Proceso mediante el cual la corteza oceánica se hunde debajo de una fosa oceánica profunda y vuelve al manto por el borde de una placa convergente.

sublimation The change in state from a solid directly to a gas without passing through the liquid state. (p. 649)
sublimación Cambio del estado sólido directamente a gas, sin pasar por el estado líquido.

submersible An underwater vehicle built of strong materials to resist pressure. (p. 527)
sumergible Vehículo submarino de materiales fuertes para resistir la presión.

subsoil The layer of soil beneath the topsoil that contains mostly clay and other minerals. (p. 448)
subsuelo Capa del suelo bajo el mantillo que contiene principalmente arcilla y otros minerales.

sunspot A dark area of gas on the sun's surface that is cooler than surrounding gases. (p. 552)
mancha solar Área oscura de gas en la superficie del Sol, que está más fría que los gases que la rodean.

supernova The brilliant explosion of a dying supergiant star. (p. 611); (p. 707)
supernova Explosión brillante de una estrella supergigante en extinción.

surface tension The result of an inward pull among the molecules of a liquid that brings the molecules on the surface closer together; causes the surface to act as if it has a thin skin. (p. 642)
tensión superficial Resultado de la atracción hacia el centro entre las moléculas de un líquido, que hace que las moléculas de la superficie se

junten más, y la superficie actúe como si tuviera una piel delgada.

surface wave A type of seismic wave that forms when P waves and S waves reach Earth's surface. (p. 309)
onda superficial Tipo de onda sísmica que se forma cuando las ondas P y las ondas S llegan a la superficie de la Tierra.

surveying The process of gathering data for a map by using instruments and the principles of geometry to determine distance and elevations. (p. 419)
agrimensura Proceso de reunir información para un mapa usando instrumentos y los principios de geometría para determinar distancias y elevaciones.

symbol On a map, pictures used by mapmakers to stand for features on Earth's surface. (p. 410)
símbolos En un mapa, los dibujos que usan los cartógrafos para representar características de la superficie de la Tierra.

synapse The junction where one neuron can transfer an impulse to the next structure. (p. 220)
sinapsis Unión donde una neurona puede transferir un impulso a la siguiente estructura.

syncline A downward fold in rock formed by compression in Earth's crust. (p. 304)
sinclinal Pliegue de la roca hacia abajo ocasionado por la compresión de la corteza terrestre.

system A group of related parts that work together. (p. 29)
sistema Grupo de partes relacionadas que funcionan en conjunto.

T

T cell A lymphocyte that identifies pathogens and distinguishes one pathogen from another. (p. 188)
célula T Linfocito que identifica los patógenos y distingue un patógeno de otro.

tar A dark, sticky substance that forms when tobacco burns. (p. 163)
alquitrán Sustancia oscura y pegajosa producida cuando se quema tabaco.

technology How people modify the world around them to meet their needs or to solve practical problems. (p. 28)
tecnología Cómo la gente modifica el mundo que la rodea para satisfacer sus necesidades o para solucionar problemas prácticos.

telescope A device built to observe distant objects by making them appear closer. (p. 590)

telescopio Aparato construido para observar objetos distantes que hace que aparezcan más cercanos.

tendon Strong connective tissue that attaches muscle to bone. (p. 66)
tendón Tejido conectivo resistente que une un músculo a un hueso.

tension Stress that stretches rock so that it becomes thinner in the middle. (p. 301)
tensión Esfuerzo que estira una roca, haciéndola más delgada en el centro.

terrestrial planets The name often given to the four inner planets; Mercury, Venus, Earth, and Mars. (p. 560)
planetas telúricos Nombre dado normalmente a los cuatro planetas interiores; Mercurio, Venus, Tierra y Marte.

texture The look and feel of a rock's surface, determined by the size, shape, and pattern of a rock's grains. (p. 376)
textura Apariencia y sensación producida por la superficie de una roca, determinadas por el tamaño, forma y patrón de los granos de la roca.

tides The daily rise and fall of Earth's waters on its coastlines. (p. 517)
mareas Ascenso y descenso diario de las aguas de la Tierra en las costas.

till The sediments deposited directly by a glacier. (p. 492)
arcilla glaciárica Sedimentos depositados directamente por un glaciar.

tissue A group of similar cells that perform the same function. (p. 48)
tejido Grupo de células semejantes que realizan la misma función.

tolerance A state in which a drug user needs larger amounts of the drug to produce the same effect on the body. (p. 242)
tolerancia Estado en el que un consumidor de drogas necesita mayores cantidades de la droga para que produzca el mismo efecto en el cuerpo.

topographic map A map that shows the surface features of an area. (p. 425)
mapa topográfico Mapa que muestra los accidentes geográficos de la superficie terrestre de un área.

topography (taw puh gra fee) The shape of the land determined by elevation, relief, and landforms. (p. 404)
topografía Forma del terreno determinada por la elevación, el relieve y los accidentes geográficos.

topsoil Mixture of humus, clay, and other minerals that forms the crumbly, topmost layer of soil. (p. 448)
mantillo Mezcla de humus, arcilla y otros minerales que forman la capa superior y suelta del suelo.

toxin A poison produced by bacterial pathogens that damages cells. (p. 182)
toxina Veneno producido por patógenos bacteriales y que daña las células.

trachea The windpipe; a passage through which air moves in the respiratory system. (p. 156)
tráquea Conducto a través del cual se mueve el aire en el sistema respiratorio.

trade-off An exchange in which one benefit is given up in order to obtain another. (p. 37)
intercambio Intercambio en el cual se renuncia a un beneficio para obtener otro.

transform boundary A plate boundary where two plates move past each other in opposite directions. (p. 291)
borde de transformación Borde de una placa cuando dos placas se deslizan una respecto a la otra, pero en sentidos opuestos.

transition metal One of the elements in Groups 3 through 12 of the periodic table. (p. 688)
metal de transición Uno de los elementos en los Grupos 3 a 12 de la tabla periódica.

tributary A stream that flows into a larger stream. (p. 472)
afluente Arroyo que desemboca en una corriente de agua más grande.

troubleshooting The process of analyzing a design problem and finding a way to fix it. (p. 38)
solución de problemas Proceso por el cual se analiza un problema de diseño y se halla una forma de solucionarlo.

tsunami A giant wave usually caused by an earthquake beneath the ocean floor. (p. 512)
tsunami Ola gigantesca, casi siempre causada por un sismo bajo la cuenca oceánica.

tumor An abnormal tissue mass that results from the rapid division of cells. (p. 202)
tumor Masa de tejido anormal que resulta de la rápida división de las células cancerosas.

turbulence A type of movement of water in which, rather than moving downstream, the water moves every which way. (p. 487)
turbulencia Tipo de movimiento del agua en el que, en vez de moverse corriente abajo, el agua se mueve en todas direcciones.

U

uniformitarianism The geologic principle that the same geologic processes that operate today operated in the past to change Earth's surface. (p. 437)
uniformitarianismo Principio geológico que enuncia que los mismos procesos geológicos que cambian la superficie de la Tierra en la actualidad, ocurrían en el pasado.

universe All of space and everything in it. (p. 618)
universo Todo el espacio y todo lo que hay en él.

upwelling The movement of cold water upward from the deep ocean that is caused by wind. (p. 534)
corriente de ascenso Movimiento ascendente de aguas frías desde las profundidades del mar, causado por los vientos.

urea A chemical that comes from the breakdown of proteins. (p. 168)
urea Sustancia química que viene de la descomposición de proteínas y que elimina el cuerpo a través del sistema excretor.

ureter A narrow tube that carries urine from one of the kidneys to the urinary bladder. (p. 168)
ureter Conducto estrecho que lleva la orina desde cada uno de los riñones a la vejiga urinaria.

urethra A small tube through which urine flows from the body. (p. 168)
uretra Pequeño conducto a través del cual fluye la orina desde el cuerpo.

urinary bladder A sacklike muscular organ that stores urine until it is eliminated from the body. (p. 168)
Vejiga urinaria Órgano muscular con forma de saco que almacena la orina hasta que es eliminada del cuerpo.

urine A watery fluid produced by the kidneys that contains urea and other wastes. (p. 168)
orina Fluido acuoso producido por los riñones que contiene urea y otros materiales de desecho.

V

vaccination The process by which harmless antigens are deliberately introduced into a person's body to produce active immunity; also called immunization. (p. 195)
vacunación Proceso por el cual antígenos inocuos se introducen deliberadamente en el cuerpo de una persona para producir inmunidad activa; también se llama inmunizacíon.

vaccine A substance used in a vaccination that consists of pathogens that have been weakened or killed but can still trigger the immune system into action. (p. 195)
vacuna Sustancia usada en una vacunación que está formada por patógenos que han sido debilitados o muertos pero que todavía pueden activar el sistema inmunológico.

valley glacier A long, narrow glacier that forms when snow and ice build up in a mountain valley. (p. 490)
glaciar de valle Glaciar largo y angosto que se forma por acumulación de hielo y nieve en un valle de montaña.

valve A flap of tissue in the heart or a vein that prevents blood from flowing backward. (p. 121)
válvula Tapa de tejido en el corazón o en un vena que impide que la sangre fluya hacia atrás.

vaporization The change of state from a liquid to a gas. (p. 646)
vaporización Cambio del estado de líquido a gas.

variable A factor that can change in an experiment. (p. 8)
variable Factor que puede cambiar en un experimento.

vary inversely A term used to describe the relationship between two variables whose graph forms a curve that slopes downward. (p. 661)
variar inversamente Término empleado para describir la relación entre dos variables cuya gráfica forma una curva con pendiente hacia abajo.

vein A blood vessel that carries blood back to the heart. (p. 122); A narrow deposit of a mineral that is sharply different from the surrounding rock. (p. 356)
vena Vaso sanguíneo que transporta la sangre de vuelta al corazón; Placa delgada de un mineral que es marcadamente distinto de la roca que lo rodea.

vent The opening through which molten rock and gas leave a volcano. (p. 330)
boca Abertura a través de la que la roca en fusión y los gases salen de un volcán.

ventricle Each of the two lower chambers of the heart that pumps blood out of the heart. (p. 121)
ventrículo Cada una de las dos cámaras inferiores del corazón que bombean la sangre hacia afuera del corazón.

vertebra The 26 small bones that make up the backbone. (p. 53)
vértebras Los 26 huesecillos que forman la columna vertebral.

vertical axis (or y-axis) A line that runs up and down along the side of a graph, on which the responding variable (or dependent variable) is labeled. (p. 23)
eje vertical (o eje y) A line that runs up and down along the side of a graph, on which the responding variable (or dependent variable) is labeled.

villi Tiny finger-shaped structures that cover the inner surface of the small intestine and provide a large surface area through which digested food is absorbed. (p. 110)
vellosidades Pequeñas estructuras con forma de dedo que cubren la superficie interna del intestino delgado y proporcionan una amplia superficie a través de la cual se absorbe el alimento digerido.

viscosity A liquid's resistance to flowing. (p. 642)
viscosidad Resistencia a fluir que presenta un líquido.

visible light Electromagnetic radiation that can be seen with the unaided eye. (p. 591)
luz visible Radiación electromagnética que se puede ver a simple vista.

vitamins Molecules that act as helpers in a variety of chemical reactions within the body. (p. 90)
vitaminas Moléculas que actúan como ayudantes en gran variedad de reacciones químicas que se producen en el cuerpo.

vocal cords Folds of connective tissue that stretch across the opening of the larynx and produce a person's voice. (p. 160)
Cuerdas vocales Pliegues de tejido conectivo que se extienden a lo largo de la abertura de la laringe y producen la voz de la persona.

volcano A weak spot in the crust where magma has come to the surface. (p. 324)
volcán Punto débil en la corteza por donde el magma escapa hacia la superficie.

volume The amount of space an object takes up. (p. 16)
volumen Cantidad de espacio que ocupa un objeto.

voluntary muscle A muscle that is under conscious control. (p. 65)
músculos voluntarios Músculo que se puede controlar conscientemente.

wave The movement of energy through a body of water. (p. 509)

ola Movimiento de energía a través de un cuerpo de agua.

wave height The vertical distance from the crest of a wave to the trough. (p. 510)
altura de una ola Distancia vertical desde la cresta de una ola hasta el valle.

wavelength The distance between the crest of one wave and the crest of the next wave. (p. 510), (p. 591)
longitud de onda Distancia entre la cresta de una onda y la cresta de la siguiente onda.

weathering The chemical and physical processes that break down rock at Earth's surface. (p. 437)
desgaste Procesos químicos y físicos que rompen la roca de la superficie de la Tierra.

weight The force of gravity on an object. (p. 16), (p. 557)
peso Fuerza de la gravedad que actúa sobre un objeto.

white blood cell A blood cell that fights disease. (p. 133)
glóbulos blancos Célula de la sangre que protege al organismo de las enfermedades.

white dwarf The blue-white hot core of a star that is left behind after its outer layers have expanded and drifted out into space. (p. 610)
enana blanca Núcleo caliente azul blanquecino de una estrella, que queda después de que sus capas externas se han expandido y viajan por el espacio.

withdrawal A period of adjustment that occurs when a drug-dependant person stops taking the drug. (p. 243)
síndrome de abstinencia Período de ajuste que ocurre cuando una persona adicta a las drogas deja de consumirlas.

X-rays A form of energy that travels in waves. (p. 61)
rayos X Forma de energía que viaja en ondas.

Index

Page numbers for key terms are printed in **boldface** type.
Page numbers for illustrations, maps, and charts are printed in *italics*.

breccia, 384
bromine, 699
bronchi (bronchus), 156
bronchitis, 164
bronze, 362, 728, 729

C

caffeine, 248–249
calcite, 349, 353, 478
calcium, 687
calculating skill, 795
Callisto, 572, 573
calories, 85
cancer, 75
 causes of, 202
 environmental causes, 206–209
 how it develops, 202
 lung, 165
 preventing, 203
 treatment, 203
 types of, 202
capillaries, 122, 127
carbohydrates, 86–87
carbon, 692–693, 696
 chains and rings, 716
 compounds and polymers, 716
carbon dioxide
 breathing and removing, 154
 chemical weathering and, 441
 in ocean water, 525
carbonic acid, 441, 478
carbon monoxide, 163
carcinogens, 202, 203
 environmental causes, 206–209
cardiac muscles, 65, 67
cardiovascular diseases
 atherosclerosis, 139
 hypertension, 140–141
cardiovascular (circulatory) system, 49
 blood, 131–136
 blood flow, 122, 123–124, 126–128
 blood pressure, 128–129
 blood vessels, 122, 125–128
 functions of, 118
 heart, 120–122
 keeping healthy, 142
cartilage, 55
Carver, George Washington, 455
Cassini, 568, 574
Cat's Eye Nebula, 619, 706
caves
 formation of, 478, 479
 sea, 496
CCA in wood products, 209
Celsius temperature scale, 18, 795
cells
 defined, 47
 functions of, 47
 membrane, 47
 structures of, 47
celluloid, 718
cellulose, 715, 718
cementation, 383

centimeter (cm), 15
central nervous system, 222, 223–226
ceramics, 731–732
cerebellum, 224, 225
cerebrum, 224, 225
Ceres, 582
Chadwick, James, 673
Chadwick model, 673
chalcopyrite, 347
Chandra X-ray Observatory, 596, 612
charcoal, 696
Charles, Jacques, 656
Charles's law, 656, 659, 660
Charon, 577
charts, portolan navigation, 412
chemical composition of minerals, 346
chemical rocks, 385
chemical symbol, 679
chemical weathering, 440–441, 478
chlorine, 699, 716
cholera, 183
cholesterol, 88, 139
chromosphere, 552, 553
chronic bronchitis, 164
chronometers, 413
cilia, 155, 156
circulatory system. *See* **cardiovascular system**
cirque, 492
Clark, William, 404
classifying skill, 793
clastic rocks, 384
clay, 731–732
cleavage, 351, 352
cliffs, wave-cut, 496
climate
 affected by currents, 532–533
 evidence from, 277
 rate of weathering and, 442–443
coal, 385
cocaine, 244, 245
cochlea, 237
color
 of minerals, 347
 of rocks, 375
Colorado Plateau, 306
Columbia Plateau, 407
coma, 581
comets, 548
 head, 581
 origin of, 581
 tail, 581
communicating, 10, 38, 793
compact bone, 56
compaction, 383
complex carbohydrates, 86
composites, 718–720
composition, soil, 447
compression, 301
computer mapping, 419–421
conclusions, drawing, 9, 797
concussions, 229
condensation, 648
conduction, 271

conductivity, 684, 685
conglomerate, 384
conic projection, 417
connective tissue, 48
conservation plowing, 457
constellations, 545, 589, 598
constraint, 37
continental drift, 275–278
continental glaciers, 490
continental shelf, mining of minerals from, 358–359
contour interval, 425
contour lines, 425, 427
contour plowing, 457
controlled experiments, 8
convection, 272
convection currents, 272–273, 289, 293
convection zone, 551
convergent boundaries, 291
converging boundaries, formation of volcanoes along, 326
convex lens, 592
coordinates, 23
Copernicus, Nicolaus, 546, 547
copper, 362, 692–693, 726
coral reefs, 388–389
core
 Earth's, 268–269, 560, 561
 Jupiter's, 572
 Sun's, 551
Coriolis effect, 531
cornea, 233
corona, 552, 553
coronary arteries, 126
corrosion, 685
corundum, 350
Cosmic background radiation, 622
Crab Nebula, 593, 707
crater, 330
creep, 467
creep meters, 318, 319
crest, wave, 510
crop rotation, 457
crust. *See* **Earth's crust**
crystal, 346
crystal garden, growing a, 344
crystalline solids, 640
crystallization, 354
crystal systems, 351
currents
 climate affected by, 532–533
 Coriolis effect, 531
 deep, 534
 defined, 530
 El Niño, 533
 major ocean, 531
 modeling, 536–537
 rip, 513
 surface, 531–533
 upwelling, 534–535
cytoplasm, 47

Index

Index

Page numbers for key terms are printed in **boldface** type.
Page numbers for illustrations, maps, and charts are printed in *italics*.

Index

Page numbers for key terms are printed in **boldface** type.
Page numbers for illustrations, maps, and charts are printed in *italics*.

Index

Page numbers for key terms are printed in **boldface** type.
Page numbers for illustrations, maps, and charts are printed in *italics*.

Index

Page numbers for key terms are printed in **boldface** type.
Page numbers for illustrations, maps, and charts are printed in *italics*.

Acknowledgments

Excerpt on page 631 is from *The Mystery of Mars* by Sally Ride and Tam O'Shaughnessy. Copyright © by Sally K. Ride and Tam E. O'Shaughnessy. Used by permission of Crown Publishers, an imprint of Random House Children's Books, a division of Random House, Inc.

Acknowledgment for page 743: "Rune of Riches" by Florence Converse from *Sung Under the Silver Umbrella: Poems for Young Children.* Copyright © 1937 by The Macmillan Company. Reprinted by permission of the Association for Childhood Education International.

Staff Credits

Diane Alimena, Scott Andrews, Michele Angelucci, Jennifer Angel, Carolyn Belanger, Barbara A. Bertell, Suzanne Biron, Peggy Bliss, Stephanie Bradley, James Brady, Anne M. Bray, Sarah M. Carroll, Kerry Cashman, Jonathan Cheney, Joshua D. Clapper, Lisa J. Clark, Bob Craton, Patricia Cully, Patricia M. Dambry, Kathy Dempsey, Emily Ellen, Leanne Esterly, Thomas Ferreira, Jonathan Fisher, Patricia Fromkin, Paul Gagnon, Kathy Gavilanes, Joel Gendler, Holly Gordon, Robert Graham, Ellen Granter, Diane Grossman, Barbara Hollingdale, Linda Johnson, Anne Jones, John Judge, Kevin Keane, Kelly Kelliher, Toby Klang, Sue Langan, Russ Lappa, Carolyn Lock, Rebecca Loveys, Constance J. McCarty, Carolyn B. McGuire, Ranida Touranont McKneally, Anne McLaughlin, Eve Melnechuk, Natania Mlawer, Janet Morris, Karyl Murray, Francine Neumann, Baljit Nijjar, Marie Opera, Jill Ort, Kim Ortell, Joan Paley, Dorothy Preston, Maureen Raymond, Laura Ross, Rashid Ross, Siri Schwartzman, Melissa Shustyk, Laurel Smith, Emily Soltanoff, Jennifer A. Teece, Elizabeth Torjussen, Diane Walsh, Amanda M. Watters, Merce Wilczek, Amy Winchester, Char Lyn Yeakley.

Additional Credits Allen Gold, Andrea Golden, Etta Jacobs, Meg Montgomery, Kim Schmidt, Adam Teller, Joan Tobin.

Illustration

Articulate Graphics: 350, 351; **Carol Barber:** 271, 272; **Morgan Cain & Associates:** 187, 194, 202, 215, 218, 223, 226r, 228, 264, 267r, 269r, 273, 281, 282, 296, 377, 379, 383, 395, 400, 447, 450, 451, 466, 467, 488, 500, 505, 548–549, 553, 557, 559, 561, 571, 572, 602, 603, 610–611, 612, 614, 617, 622, 623, 635, 640, 641, 643, 645–646, 647, 654–656, 659–660, 670–671, 674, 696, 705, 715, 725; **Kerry Cashman:** 54–55, 95, 99–106, 274, 275, 292, 320, 345, 371, 433, 442, 562–563, 565, 574–575, 577, 580, 589, 592, 618–619; **John Ceballos:** 181; **David Corrente:** 541; **John Edwards and Associates:** 164, 182, 190, 199, 201, 210, 217, 226l, 412t, 414, 415t, 425, 442, 485, 486, 491r, 493, 513; **Forge FX:** 308, 309; **Chris Forsey:** 284, 290, 291, 327; **GeoSystems Global Corporation:** 405b, 408, 453, 456, 475, 490; **Andria Golden:** 2; **Biruta Hansen:** 64–65; **Robert Hynes:** 51, 356, 357, 368; **Kevin Jones Associates:** 58t, 73, 74–75, 89, 91–92, 207, 358, 359, 406, 407, 438, 439, 465, 472, 491b, 496, 497, 501, 504; **Dorling Kindersley:** 266, 267l; **Martucci Design:** 340r, 426; **Richard McMahon:** 594; **Karen Minot:** 130, 137, 471; **Matthew Pippin:** 364, 449, 476, 477, 492, 493; **Pond and Giles:** 78, 133; **Brucie Rosch:** 285; **J/B Woolsey Associates:** 52, 114, 195, 305, 340l, 341l, 460; **XNR Productions:** 126–127, 160, 276, 277, 280, 289, 313, 315, 325, 410, 411, 415b, 416, 417, 427, 478. **All charts and graphs by Matt Mayerchak and Joe Paterno.**

Photography

Photo Research: Sue McDermott, John Judge, Paula Wehde

Cover Image top, Jeff Greenberg/Omni-Photo Communications, Inc.; **bottom,** Dimitr Iundt/CORBIS

Page IN14, Richard Haynes; **IN36,** Douglas Peebles/Corbis; **1,** Ben Hankins/USGS; **2,** Kaj R. Svensson/ SPL/Photo Researchers, Inc.; **2–3,** C. Heliker/USGS.

Chapter 1
Pages 4–5, Flip Nicklin/Minden Pictures; **5 inset,** Richard Haynes; **6t,** Richard Haynes; **6b,** M. T. Frazier/Photo Researchers, Inc.; **7,** Richard Haynes; **b** Richard Haynes; **9 all** Richard Haynes; **11,** Fisher/Thatcher/Getty Images, Inc.; **12,** Russ Lappa; **13,** David Young-Wolf//Photo Edit; **14,** Richard Haynes; **15,** Richard Haynes; **16,** Richard Haynes; **17 both,** Richard Haynes; **18,** Richard Haynes; **20,** Richard Haynes; **27tl,** Getty Images, Inc.; **27tm,** Casio, Inc.; **27tml,** Corbis; **27tmr,** Corbis; **27tr,** Dorling; Kindersley; **27ml,** Advertising Archives; **27br,** The Granger Collection; **29,** David Young-Wolf//Photo Edit; **30l,** John Jenkins/AmericanMuseum of Radio & Electricity; **30r,** Science Photo Library; **31l,** AP/Wide World Photos; **31m,** David Ducros/Science Photo Library/Photo Researchers, Inc.; **31r,** Tony Freeman Photographs; **34, both** Russ Lappa; **36l,** Spencer Family Archives; **36r,** Grant Heilman Photography; **37,** Tim Flach/Getty Images, Inc.; **38,** Advertising Archive/The Picture Desk, Inc.; **38,** U.S. Patent Office.

Chapter 2
Pages 44–45, Getty Images, Inc.; **45 inset,** Richard Haynes; **46t,** Tom Lazar/Animals Animals/Earth Scenes; **46b,** C.K. Lorenz/Photo Researchers, Inc.; **47,** C.W. Schwartz/ Animals Animals/Earth Scenes; **48t,** Konrad Wothe/Minden Pictures; **48m,** Christoph Burki/Getty Images, Inc.; **48b,** John Cancalosi/Tom Stack & Associates; **49,** Breck P. Kent/Animals Animals/Earth Scenes; **53,** Frans Lanting/Minden Pictures; **54l,** Fred Bruemmer/Peter Arnold, Inc.; **54r,** C. Allan Morgan/DRK Photo; **55l,** Thomas Mangelsen/Minden Pictures; **55r,** Wallace J. Nichols; **57t,** Alan D. Carey/Photo Researchers, Inc.; **57b,** Leonard Lee Rue III/Photo Researchers, Inc.; **58,** Kenneth W. Fink/Photo Researchers, Inc.; **59t,** Anthony Bannister/Animals Animals/Earth Scenes; **59b,** Tony Craddock/Getty Images, Inc.; **60,** Tom & Pat Leeson/Photo Researchers, Inc.; **61,** Dave King/Dorling Kindersley; **62–63t,** Gary Griffen/Animals Animals/Earth Scenes; **62b,** Raymond Gehman/Corbis; **66tl,** Ron Willocks/Animals Animals/Earth Scenes; **66ml,** Patti Murray/Animals Animals/Earth Scenes; **66bl,** Rob Simpson/Visuals Unlimited; **66r,** Wally Eberhart/Visuals Unlimited; **67,** F. Stuart Westmorland/Photo Researchers, Inc.; **68,** S. Dalton/OSF/Animals Animals/Earth Scenes; **69tl,** Leroy Simon/ Visuals Unlimited; **69tr,** Dante Fenolio/Photo Researchers, Inc.; **69mr,** Nigel J. Dennis/Photo Researchers. Inc.; **69bl,** Art Wolfe; **69br,** Brian Rogers/Visuals Unlimited; **70,** Daryl Balfour/Getty Images, Inc.; **71t,** Volker Steiger/SPL/Photo Researchers, Inc.; **71b,** Richard Haynes; **72 both,** Tom & Pat Leeson/Photo Researchers, Inc.

Chapter 3
Pages 80–81, Daniel J. Cox/Getty Images, Inc.; **81 inset,** Richard Haynes; **82–83,** Kent Foster/Photo Researchers, Inc.; **83t inset,** David Northcott/DRK Photo; **83m inset,** Adam Jones/Photo Researchers, Inc.; **83b inset,** S. Nielsen/DRK Photo; **86t,** Frank Greenaway/Dorling Kindersley; **86tm,** Kim Taylor & Jane Burton/Dorling Kindersley; **86bm,** Dorling Kindersley; **86bm,** Frank Greenaway/Dorling Kindersley Media Library; **86b,** Kim Taylor & Jane Burton/Dorling Kindersley; **87,** Andy Rouse/DRK Photo; **88,** Richard Haynes; **90,** Asa C. Thoresen/Photo Researchers, Inc.; **93,** E. R. Degginger/Photo Researchers, Inc.; **94t,** Richard Haynes; **94b,** Penny Tweedie/Getty Images, Inc.; **96l,** Gregory K. Scott/Photo Researchers, Inc.; **96m,** Kenneth H. Thomas/Photo Researchers, Inc.; **96r,** Runk/Schoenberger/Grant Heilman, Inc.; **99,** Jim Zipp/Photo Researchers, Inc.; **99l inset,** David Young Wolff/PhotoEdit; **99r inset,** Jack Clark/Animals Animals/Earth Scenes; **100l,** Frans Lanting/Minden Pictures; **100m,** Renee Lynn/Getty Images, Inc.; **100r,** Michael & Patricia Fogden/Minden Pictures; **101,** Barbara Gerlach/DRK Photo; **101 inset,** Maslowski/Photo Researchers, Inc.; **102,** Art Wolfe/Getty Images, Inc.; **102 inset,** Gerry Ellis/Minden Pictures; **103,** Carr Clifton/Minden Pictures; **103t inset,** Nick Bergkessel/Photo Researchers, Inc.; **103b inset,** Stephen J. Krasemann/DRK Photo; **104l,** Stephen J. Krasemann/DRK Photo; **104r,** Jeff Lepore/Photo Researchers, Inc.; **105,** Michio Hoshino/Minden Pictures; **105 inset,** Yva Momotiuk/John Eastcott /Minden Pictures; **106,** Douglas E. Walker/Masterfile Corporation; **106 inset,** Frans Lanting/Minden Pictures; **109,** Richard Haynes; **110t,** Tom & Pat Leeson/Photo Researchers, Inc.; **110b,** Bill Kamin/Visuals Unlimited; **110b inset,** Kim Heacox/DRK Photo; **111,** David Weintraub/Photo Researchers, Inc.; **111 inset,** Steven David Miller/Animals Animals/Earth Scenes; **112,** Michele Burgess/Corbis; **115,** Russ Lappa; **116t,** Andy Rouse/DRK Photo; **116b,** Kim Heacox/DRK Photo.

Chapter 4
Pages 120–121, Animals Animals/Earth Scenes; **121 inset,** Russ Lappa; **122–123,** Key Sanders/Getty Images, Inc.; **124l,** Corbis; **124m,** Corbis; **124r,** UPI/Corbis-Bettmann; **125l,** Erich Hartmann/Magnum Photos; **125m,** Kevin Fleming/Corbis; **125r,** William Campbell/Peter Arnold, Inc.; **126t,** Corbis; **126b,** Warren Morgan/Corbis; **127t,** Ariel Skelley/Corbis; **127b,** Marc Epstein/DRK Photo; **128–129,** Richard Haynes; **131,** Inga Spence/Visuals Unlimited; **132,** G.R. Robinson/Visuals Unlimited; **133,** Greg Vaughn/Tom Stack & Associates; **134,** Russ Lappa; **135,** Richard Haynes; **136t,** C Squared Studios /Getty Images, Inc.; **136b,** Frans Lanting/Minden Pictures; **137t,** David Wrobel/Visuals Unlimited; **137b,** Stephen J. Krasemann/DRK Photo; **138t,** Wayne Lynch/DRK Photo; **138b,** Fred Bavendam/Minden Pictures; **139,** D. Cavagnaro/DRK Photo; **140tl,** David Sieren/Visuals Unlimited; **140tr,** David Dennis/Animals Animals/Earth Scenes; **140b,** Jeff Lepore/Photo Researchers, Inc.; **141t,** Stephen J. Krasemann/DRK Photo; **141bl,** David Liebman; **141bm,** Marilyn Kazmers/Peter Arnold, Inc.; **141br,** Ken Lucas/Visuals Unlimited; **142,** Kent Gilbert/AP/Wide World Photos; **143,** James H. Robinson/Animals Animals/Earth Scenes; **144t,** Roy Toft/Tom Stack & Associates; **144b,** Tom Uhlman/AP/Wide World Photos; **145,** James H. Robinson/Animals Animals/Earth Scenes; **146,** Doug Perrine/DRK Photo; **147l,** Walter H. Hodge/Peter Arnold, Inc.; **147m,** Doug Perrine/DRK Photo; **147r,** Ed Reschke/Peter Arnold, Inc.; **148t,** Greg Vaughn/Tom Stack & Associates; **148b,** Bill Greenblatt/Getty Images, Inc.; **149,** G. Payne/Liaison/Getty Images, Inc.; **150t,** David Dennis/Animals Animals/Earth Scenes; **150bl,** Greg Vaughn/Tom Stack & Associates; **150br,** Walter H. Hodge/Peter Arnold, Inc.

Chapter 5
Pages 154–155, Jim Wark/Airphoto; **155 inset,** Richard Haynes, **156t,** Richard Haynes; **156b,** Corbis; **157,** David Zalubowski/AP/Wide World Photos; **158l,** Peter Griffiths/Dorling Kindersley Media Library; **158t inset,** Michael Habicht/Animals Animals; **158m inset,** S.L. Rose/Visuals Unlimited; **158b inset,** Gilbert S. Grant/Photo Researchers, Inc.; **159l,** Martin Benjamin/The Image Works; **159r,** Tom

Bean 1994/DRK Photo; **160l,** Peter Johnson/Corbis; **160r,** Walt Anderson/Visuals Unlimited; **161 both,** Department of Environmental Protection, Commonwealth of Pennsylvania/Mineral Information Institute; **162–163,** Nick Vedros, Vedros & Assoc./ Getty Images, Inc.; **165,** David Joel/Getty Images, Inc.; **166l,** Richard Haynes; **166r,** Randy Faris/Corbis; **167t,** Larry Lefever/Grant Heilman Photography, Inc.; **167b,** Rosemary Mayer/Holt Studios/Photo Researchers, Inc.; **168 all,** Russ Lappa; **169 all,** Russ Lappa; **170,** Russ Lappa; **171,** Russ Lappa; **172–173,** Richard Berenholtz/ Corbis; **173t,** Richard Hutchings/Photo Researchers, Inc.; **173b,** Michael S. Yamashita/ Corbis; **175,** Dorling Kindersley; **176,** Norman McGrath; **177,** Armando Franca/ AP/Wide World Photos; **178t,** Russ Lappa; **178b,** Derek Trask/Corbis; **179,** P. Baeza/ Publiphoto/Photo Researchers, Inc.; **180,** Richard Megna/Fundamental Photographs; **182,** Eric Pearle/Getty Images, Inc.; **183,** Ed Pritchard/Getty Images, Inc.; **185,** Richard Haynes; **186 both,** Richard Haynes; **188,** NASA/Goddard Space Flight Center Scientific Visualization Studio; **189 all,** NASA/Goddard Space Flight Center Scientific Visualization Studio; **191,** NASA Goddard Space Flight Center.

Chapter 6
Pages 196–197, Didier Dorval/Masterfile Corporation; **197 inset,** Visuals Unlimited; **198t,** E.R. Degginger; **198b,** Toby Talbot/AP/Wide World Photos; **201t,** Colin Keates/Dorling Kindersley; **201m,** Andreas Einsiedel/Dorling Kindersley; **201b,** Andreas Einsiedel /Dorling Kindersley; **202,** Bill Ross/Corbis; **203,** Roger Ball/Corbis; **204,** Owen Franken/Corbis; **205,** Lawrence Migdale/Photo Researchers, Inc.; **206,** Nadia MacKenzie/Getty Images, Inc.; **208t,** Tom Bean/DRK Photo; **208b,** Doug Sokell/ Tom Stack & Associates; **209t,** Daniel Putterman/Stock Boston, Inc./PictureQuest; **209b,** Brian Branch-Price/AP/Wide World Photos; **211,** NASA; **212,** Richard Haynes; **213,** Richard Haynes.

Chapter 7
Page 214t, Russ Lappa; **214b,** Bettmann-Corbis; **216t,** Joseph Sohm/ChromoSohm, Inc./Corbis; **216b,** E.R. Degginger; **219,** Richard Haynes; **220l,** Mitch Kezar/Getty Images, Inc.; **220m,** Tony Freeman/PhotoEdit; **220r,** Scott Olson/Getty Images, Inc.; **221l,** Anthony Meshkinyar/Getty Images, Inc.; **221m,** Yves Marcoux/Getty Images, Inc.; **221r,** Mike Fiala/Getty Images, Inc.; **222l,** Michael Newman/Photo Edit; **222r,** David Young-Wolff/Photo Edit; **230,** Devez/CNRS/Photo Researchers, Inc.; **231b,**Tom Brakefield/DRK Photo; **231ml,** Mc Donald Wildlife Photography/Animals Animals/Earth Scenes; **231mr,** Peter Steyn/Ardea London, Ltd.; **231t,** M.C. Chamberlain/DRK Photo; **232–233,** Chinch Gryniewicz/Ecoscene/Corbis; **233b,** Jose Anzel/Aurora Photos; **233t,** Christie's Images; **234t,** Corbis-Bettmann; **234–235,** M. Harvey/DRK Photo; **235bl,** Wolfgang Kaehler/Corbis; **235bm,** Frans Lanting/Minden Pictures; **235br,** Tim Davis/Photo Researchers, Inc.; **235t,** Neil Lucas/Nature Picture Library; **236,** Tony Freeman/ PhotoEdit; **237b,** Russ Lappa; **237m,** Richard Haynes; **237t,** Russ Lappa; **238,** Richard Haynes; **240,** Richard Haynes; **242,** Morton Beebe/Corbis; **243,** Catherine Karnow/Corbis; **245b,** Richard Haynes; **245t,** Dorling Kindersley.

Chapter 8
Pages 260–261, Mats Wibe Lund; **261 inset,** Richard Haynes; **262–263,** David Briscoe/AP/Wide World Photos; **263l,** Jeff Greenberg/PhotoEdit; **263r,** Michael Nichols/Magnum; **264,** DGGS, Alaska Department of Natural Resources; **265,** Tracy Frankel/Getty Images, Inc.; **266,** Dorling Kindersley; **267,** Getty Images, Inc.; **269,** Runk/Schoenberger/Grant Heilman Photography, Inc.; **270,** Richard Haynes; **271,** Richard Haynes; **272,** Randy Faris/Corbis; **274,** Dorling Kindersley/Stephen Oliver; **277,** Ken Lucas/Visuals Unlimited; **278,** Bettmann/Corbis; **279,** Jeffrey L. Rotman/ Corbis; **283,** SIO Archives/UCSD; **286 all,** Richard Haynes; **287,** Richard Haynes; **288,** Russ Lappa; **293,** Russ Lappa.

Chapter 9
Pages 298–299, AP/Wide World Photos; **299 inset,** Richard Haynes; **300b,** Wang Yuan-Mao/AP/Wide World Photos; **300t,** Russ Lappa; **302b,** Tom & Susan Bean Inc.; **303l,** Martin Miller/Visuals Unlimited; **303r,** W. Kenneth Hamblin; **304,** E.R. Degginger/Animals Animals/Earth Scenes; **305,** Jim Wark/Airphoto; **306,** Tom Bean; **307,** Richard Haynes; **308–309,** Wesley K. Wallace/Geophysical Institute, University of Alaska Fairbanks; **310br,** AP/Wide World Photos; **310m,** Tim Crosby/Getty Images, Inc.; **310t,** Lauren McFalls/AP/Wide World Photos; **311,** Dorling Kindersley/Peter Griffiths; **312,** Roger Ressmeyer/Corbis; **314b,** Richard Haynes; **314t,** Russ Lappa; **316b,** Michael Holford; **316t,** Russ Lappa; **321,** Reuters NewMedia Inc./Corbis; **322,** Richard Haynes; **323,** Richard Haynes; **324,** Bettmann/Corbis; **329b,** Dorling Kindersley; **329m,** E.R. Degginger/Color Pic, Inc.; **329t,** Breck P. Kent; **330,** G. Brad Lewis/Getty Images, Inc.; **331,** Dorling Kindersley; **332 inset,** P. Lipman/U.S. Geological Survey/Geologic Inquiries Group; **332–333,** Richard Thom/Visuals Unlimited; **334l,** North Wind Picture Archives; **334m,** Robert Fried Photography; **334r,** Kim Heacox/Peter Arnold, Inc.; **335bl,** Alberto Garcia/Saba Press; **335m,** Alberto Garcia/Saba Press; **335ml,** Alberto Garcia/Saba Press; **335r,** Fabrizio Villa/AP/Wide World Photos; **335tl,** Alberto Garcia/Saba Press; **336,** Roger Ressmeyer/Corbis; **337tr,** JPL/NASA; **337bl,** Corbis.

Chapter 10
Pages 342–343, Kevin Downey; **343 inset,** Richard Haynes; **344t,** Richard Haynes; **344b,** Anthony Bannister/Gallo Images/Corbis; **345t,** Tim Wright/Corbis; **345b,** Dorling Kindersley; **346tl,** Dorling Kindersley/Colin Keates; **346tm,** Breck P. Kent; **346tr,** Breck P. Kent; **346b,** AFP/Corbis; **347t,** Russ Lappa; **347ml,** Breck P. Kent; **347m,** Charles D. Winters/Photo Researchers, Inc.; **347mr,** Charles D. Winters/Photo Researchers, Inc.; **347bl,** Ken Lucas/Visuals Unlimited; **347bm,** Breck P. Kent; **347br,** Barry Runk/Grant Heilman Photography, Inc.; **348 all,** Dorling Kindersley; **349l,** Dorling Kindersley; **349ml,** Dorling Kindersley; **349m,** Charles D. Winters/Photo Researchers, Inc.; **349mr,** Dorling Kindersley; **349r,** Dorling Kindersley; **350 all,** Breck P. Kent; **351tl,** E.R. Degginger/Color Pic Inc.; **351tr,** Chip Clark; **351m,** Charles D. Winters/Photo Researchers, Inc.; **351bl,** Breck P. Kent; **351bm,** Breck P. Kent; **351br,** Breck P. Kent; **352tl,** E.R. Degginger/Color Pic Inc.; **352tr,** Ken Lucas/Visuals Unlimited; **352ml,** E.R. Degginger/Color Pic, Inc.; **352bl,** E. R. Degginger/Color Pic, Inc.; **352bm,** Dorling Kindersley/Colin Keates; **352br,** Breck P. Kent/Animals Animals/Earth Scenes; **353,** Russ Lappa; **354t,** Richard Haynes; **354b,** Breck P. Kent/Animals Animals/Earth Scenes; **355,** Kevin Downey; **356,** Jane Burton/Bruce Coleman, Inc.; **357t,** Ken Lucas/Visuals Unlimited; **357b,** Dorling Kindersley/Colin Keates; **358t,** Dan Fornari/WHOI; **358b,** Cary S. Wolinsky/IPN/Aurora Photos; **359bl,** Peter Ryan/Science Photo Library/Photo Researchers, Inc.; **359br,** Dudley Foster/WHOI; **360,** © 1986 The Field Museum/Ron Testa; **361,** Art Resource, NY; **362l,** C. M. Dixon; **362m,** Scala/Art Resource, NY; **362r,** C. M. Dixon; **363t,** The Granger Collection, NY; **363b,** Mark Mainz/Getty Images, Inc.; **365,** Bettmann/Corbis; **367b,** Richard Haynes; **367t,** Getty Images, Inc.; **368,** Russ Lappa; **370,** Breck P. Kent.

Chapter 11
Pages 372–373, Corbis; **373 inset,** Richard Haynes; **374t,** Breck P. Kent; **374m,** Breck P. Kent; **374b,** Jonathan Blair/Corbis; **375tl,** E.R. Degginger/Color Pic, Inc.; **375tm,** Breck P. Kent; **375tr,** Barry Runk/Grant Heilman Photography, Inc.; **375ml,** Breck P. Kent; **375mr,** E.R. Degginger/Color Pic, Inc.; **375b,** Jonathan Blair/Corbis; **376tl,** E.R. Degginger/Color Pic, Inc.; **376tm,** Breck P. Kent; **376tr,** Breck P. Kent; **376ml,** Breck P. Kent; **376mr,** Breck P. Kent; **376bl,** Jeff Scovil; **376br,** Breck P. Kent; **378t,** Doug Martin/Photo Researchers, Inc.; **378b,** Barry Runk/Grant Heilman Photography, Inc.; **379 all,** Breck P. Kent; **380,** Jan Hinsch/SPL/Photo Researchers, Inc.; **381,** Michele & Tom Grimm/Getty Images, Inc.; **382,** Tom Lazar/Animals Animals/Earth Scenes; **384l,** Runk/Schoenberger/ Grant Heilman Photography, Inc.; **384ml,** Jeff Scovil; **384mr,** North Museum/ Franklin and Marshall College/Grant Heilman Photography, Inc.; **384r,** Charles R. Belinky/Photo Researchers, Inc.; **385b,** Mark Newman/Photo Researchers, Inc.; **385t,** Alain Choisnet/Getty Images, Inc.; **385,** E.R. Degginger/Color Pic, Inc.; **386,** Tom Sobolik; **387t,** Ted Clutter/Photo Researchers, Inc.; **387b,** Dave Fleetham/Tom Stack & Associates; **388t,** Stuart Westmorland/Corbis; **388b,** Jean-Marc Trucher/Stone/Getty Images, Inc.; **389,** Richard Thom/Visuals Unlimited; **391tl,** Barry Runk/Grant Heilman Photography, Inc.; **391tm,** Jeff Scovil; **391tr,** Runk/ Schoenberger/Grant Heilman Photography, Inc.; **391bl,** Andrew J. Martinez/Photo Researchers, Inc.; **391bm,** Barry Runk/Grant Heilman Photography, Inc.; **391br,** Breck P. Kent; **392,** Catherine Karnow/Corbis; **393,** Richard Haynes; **394t,** Jeff Scovil; **394m,** Jeff Scovil; **394b,** Breck P. Kent; **395tl,** Francois Gohier/Photo Researchers, Inc.; **395tr,** David J. Wrobel/Visuals Unlimited; **395bl,** Breck P. Kent; **395br,** N.R. Rowan/Stock Boston; **396,** Breck P. Kent; **397 all,** Russ Lappa; **398,** Richard Haynes; **400tl,** Andrew J. Martinez/Photo Researchers, Inc.; **400tr,** Breck P. Kent; **400b,** E.R. Degginger/Color Pic, Inc.

Chapter 12
Pages 402–403, Image courtesy of NASA Landsat Project Science Office and USGS EROS Data Center; **404,** National Museum of American History/Smithsonian Institution; **406,** Tom Bean; **407l,** David Muench; **407r,** Tom Bean; **409,** Russ Lappa; **411,** Jim Wark/Airphoto; **412l,** The Granger Collection; **412m,** Bodleian Library, Oxford, U.K.; **412r,** Royal Geographical Society, London, UK/Bridgeman Art Library; **413l,** British Library, London/Bridgeman Art Library, London/Superstock, Inc.; **413m,** The Granger Collection; **413r,** The Granger Collection; **417,** Richard Haynes; **419t,** Russ Lappa; **419b,** Geographix; **420l,** Library of Congress; **420r,** U.S. Geological Survey; **422t,** © Boeing, all rights reserved; **422b,** Forest Johnson/Masterfile Corporation; **422–423,** Index Stock Imagery; **423,** Richard Haynes; **424t,** Richard Haynes; **424b,** Mitch Wojnarowicz/The Image Works; **425l,** Elliot Cohen/Janelco; **426,** U.S. Geological Survey; **428,** Robert Rathe/Stock Boston; **429,** Richard Haynes; **430,** British Library, London/Bridgeman Art Library, London/Superstock, Inc.; **432,** U.S. Geological Survey.

Chapter 13
Pages 434–435, Frozen Images/The Image Works; **435r,** Richard Haynes; **436,** Richard Haynes; **437t,** Jerry D. Greer; **437b,** Ron Watts/Corbis; **438t,** Susan Rayfield/Photo Researchers, Inc.; **438m,** Breck P. Kent/Animals Animals/Earth Scenes; **438b,** E.R. Degginger/Photo Researchers, Inc.; **439l,** John Sohlden/Visuals Unlimited; **439r,** Jim Steinberg/Animals Animals/Earth Scenes; **441,** Mike Mazzaschi/Stock Boston; **443all,** T.C. Meierding; **445,** Richard Haynes; **446t,** Richard Haynes; **446–447b,** Tom Bean; **452,** J.M. Labat/Jacana/Photo Researchers, Inc.; **453,** Richard Haynes; **454t,** Richard Haynes; **454b,** Tom Bean; **455t,** Corbis; **455b,** Grant Heilman Photography, Inc.; **456,** AP/Wide World Photos; **457,** Larry Lefever/Grant Heilman Photography, Inc.

Chapter 14
Pages 462–463, Ron Watts/Corbis; **463r,** Richard Haynes; **464,** AP/Wide World Photos; **466l,** Martin Miller/Visuals Unlimited; **466r,** Thomas G. Rampton/Grant Heilman Photography, Inc.; **467,** Steven Holt/Stockpix.com; **468,** Richard Haynes; **469,** Richard Haynes; **470–471,** Walter Bibikow/The Viesti Collection; **472,** Jim Wark/Airphoto; **473,** Dorling Kindersley; **474,** Tom Bean; **475t,** Martin Miller; **475b,** NASA/SADO/Tom Stack & Associates, Inc.; **479,** Dorling Kindersley; **479 inset,** Laurence Parent; **480,** Russ Lappa; **481,** Richard Haynes; **482–483b,** David Sailors/Corbis; **483t,** Alex Wong/Getty Images, Inc.; **484t,** Richard Haynes; **484b,** Eliot Cohen; **485,** Michael Quinton/Minden Pictures; **487,** Corbis; **489t,** Richard Haynes; **489b,** Marc Muench/Muench Photography, Inc.; **490,** Dorling Kindersley; **494t,** Richard Haynes; **494b,** Corbis; **495,** Dick Roberts/Visuals Unlimited; **498,** F. Stuart Westmoreland/Photo Researchers, Inc.; **499t,** Richard Haynes; **499b,** Jess Stock/Getty Images, Inc.; **500,** Tom Bean.

Chapter 15
Pages 506–507, Ron Sanford/Corbis; **507 inset,** Index Stock Imagery, Inc.; **508t,** Richard Haynes; **508–509b,** Aaron Chang/Corbis; **514l,** Robert Gill; Papilio/Corbis; **514r,** Jim Wark/Airphoto; **515,** Jim Wark/Airphoto; **516,** Gene Ahrens/Bruce Coleman, Inc.; **517,** Gene Ahrens/Bruce Coleman, Inc.; **518,** Fred Bruemmer/DRK Photo; **519,** Maher Attar/Corbis Sygma; **520–521,** Peter M. Fisher/Corbis; **522,** Alon Reininger/Corbis; **523b,** Norbert Wu; **523t,** Dave Fleetham/Seapics; **528,** Richard Haynes; **529,** Mark Thayer; **530,** Russ Lappa; **532,** Raven/Explorer/Photo Researchers, Inc.; **533,** Jeffrey Greenberg/Visuals Unlimited; **535,** Andrew J. Martinez; **537,** Richard Haynes; **538l,** Fred Bruemmer/DRK Photo; **538r,** Peter M. Fisher/Corbis.

Chapter 16
Pages 542–543, Detlev Van Ravenswaay/Photo Researchers, Inc.; **543 inset,** Richard Haynes; **544,** David Malin/Anglo-Australian Observatory; **545,** The Granger Collection, NY; **546bl,** Science Photo Library/Photo Researchers, Inc.; **546bm,** Photo Researchers, Inc.; **546br,** James A. Sugar/Corbis; **546t,** Bettmann/Corbis; **547l,** Explorer-Keystone-France/Gamma Press USA; **547m,** The Art Archive/Royal Society; **547r,** Corbis Bettmann; **550,** Richard Haynes; **550–551,** SOHO/ESA and NASA; **552,** Dr. Fred Espenak/Science Photo Library/Photo Researchers, Inc.; **553bl,** National Solar Observatory; **553br,** AURA/STScI/NASA; **553t,** SOHO/ESA and NASA; **554,** Ron Sanford/Getty Images, Inc.; **556–557,** Paul & Linda Marie Ambrose/Getty Images, Inc.; **562b,** NASA; **562t,** Julian Baum/Dorling Kindersley; **563b,** NASA; **563tl,** NASA; **563tr,** JPL/NASA; **564,** David Anderson/NASA/Photo Researchers, Inc.; **565b,** Hubble Heritage Team/NASA; **565t,** NASA; **566–567,** JPL/NASA; **567 inset,** U.S. Geological Survey; **567b,** Pat Rawlings/NASA; **568–569t,** NASA; **569 inset,** Pat Rawlings/NASA; **570,** NASA; **572l,** NASA/SPL/Photo Researchers, Inc.; **572r,** Martin Cropper/Dorling Kindersley; **573b,** David Seal/JPL/CalTech/NASA; **573ml,** JPL/NASA; **573mr,** Corbis; **573tl,** Reuters NewMedia Inc./Corbis; **573tr,** NASA; **574l,** NASA and The Hubble Heritage Team; **574r,** AFP/Corbis; **575b,** Kenneth Seidelmann, U.S. Naval Observatory/NASA; **575t,** Dorling Kindersley/Jet Propulsion Lab; **576l,** Julian Baum/Dorling Kindersley; **576r,** NASA; **577l,** Dorling Kindersley; **577r,** Lynette Cook/Photo Researchers, Inc.; **578,** Richard Haynes; **579,** Richard Haynes; **580t,** Richard Haynes; **580-581,** Jerry Lodriguss /Photo Researchers, Inc.; **581 inset,** Dorling Kindersley; **582,** NEAR Project/NLR/JHUAPL/ Goddard SVS/NASA; **583,** Frank Zullo /Photo Researchers, Inc.; **584,** NASA and The Hubble Heritage Team.

Chapter 17
Pages 588–589, Loke Tan; **589r,** Richard Haynes; **590t,** Richard Haynes; **590b,** Florence Museo delle Scienze/AKG London; **592 all,** Andy Crawford/Dorling Kindersley; **593l,** VLA/NRAO/ Smithsonian Astrophysical Observatory; **593ml,** W. M. Keck Observatory/Smithsonian Astrophysical Observatory; **593mr,** Jeff Hester and Paul Scowen/Smithsonian Astrophysical Observatory; **593r,** Marshall Space Flight Center/NASA; **594l,** Yerkes Observatory Photography; **594r,** Courtesy of the NAIC - Arecibo Observatory, a facility of the NSF; **595t,** NASA; **595bl,** David Nunuk/Science Photo Library/Photo Researchers, Inc.; **595br,** JPL/NASA; **596,** NASA; **597,** Richard Haynes; **598t,** Richard Haynes; **598b,** Dorling Kindersley; **601,** Mark Thiessen/Corbis; **605,** Luke Dodd/Science Photo Library/Photo Researchers, Inc.; **608,** Ariel Skelley/Corbis; **609,** Anglo-Australian Observatory/Royal Observatory Edinburgh; **609 inset,** AURA/STScI/NASA; **614,** Frank Zullo/Photo Researchers, Inc.; **614 all,** Celestial Image Co./Science Photo Library/Photo Researchers, Inc.; **615t,** David Malin/Anglo-Australian Observatory; **615b,** Celestial Image Co./Science Photo Library/Photo Researchers, Inc.; **616t,** David Malin/Anglo-Australian Observatory; **616m,** David Malin/Anglo-Australian Observatory; **616b,** Royal Observatory, Edinburgh/AATB/Science Photo Library/Photo Researchers, Inc.; **618l,** Dorling Kindersley; **618m,** NASA; **618r,** SOHO/ESA and NASA; **619l,** R. Corradi (Isaac Newton Group) and D. R. Gonçalves (Instituto de Astrofísica de Canarias); **619m,** Bill & Sally Fletcher/Tom Stack & Associates, Inc.; **619r,** Celestial Image Co./Science Photo Library/Photo Researchers, Inc.; **620,** NASA; **624,** American Institute of Physics; **625,** Jean-Paul Kneib/Observatoire Midi-Pyrénées, France/Caltech/ESA/NASA; **626,** Richard Haynes; **628,** NASA; **630t,** NASA; **630b,** JPL/NASA; **630–631b,** JPL/NASA; **631t,** NASA; **632,** JPL/NASA; **633,** NASA, **634t,** Pat Rawlings/NASA; **634–635b,** NASA/JPL/Cornell; **635t,** Pat Rawlings/NASA.

Chapter 18
Pages 636–637, Steve Bloom; **637 inset,** Richard Haynes; **638b,** LWA-Dann Tardif/Corbis; **638t,** Richard Haynes; **639,** James A. Sugar/Corbis; **640b,** Patrick J. LaCroix/Getty Images, Inc.; **640t,** S. Stammer/Photo Researchers; **641 all,** Richard Haynes; **642b,** Herman Eisenbeiss /Photo Researchers, Inc.; **642t,** Breck Kent/Earth Scenes; **644b,** Hubert Camille/Getty Images, Inc.; **644t,** Richard Haynes; **645l,** Breck P. Kent/Earth Scenes; **645m,** Chuck O'Rear/Corbis; **645r,** Leslie Harris/Index Stock; **646 both,** Richard Haynes; **647 both,** Dorling Kindersley/Science Museum; **648,** Tony Freeman/PhotoEdit; **649,** Charles D. Winters/Photo Researchers; **650,** Russ Lappa; **651,** Carl & Ann Purcell/Corbis; **652b,** MVR Photo; **652t,** Richard Hutchings/Corbis; **653 both,** Richard Haynes; **654,** Richard Haynes; **656 all,** Dorling Kindersley; **657,** Eye Ubiquitous/Corbis; **662,** Russ Lappa; **663,** Richard Haynes; **664b,** Eye Ubiquitous/Corbis; **664t,** S. Stammer/Photo Researchers, Inc.

Chapter 19
Pages 668–669, Greg Elms/Lonely Planet Images; **669 inset,** Richard Haynes; **670 both,** 1998, The Art Institute of Chicago; **672l,** Royalty-Free/Corbis; **672r,** Russ Lappa; **673l,** Dorling Kindersley; **673m,** Dorling Kindersley; **673r,** Frank Cezus/FPG International; **675,** courtesy of the National Institute of Science and Technology; **676b,** Richard Haynes; **676t,** Russ Lappa; **677bl,** Richard Megna/Fundamental Photographs; **677br,** Richard Megna/Fundamental Photographs; **677m,** Robert Mathena/Fundamental Photographs; **677t,** Philip Coblentz/Alamy Images; **679,** Photodisc/Getty Images, Inc.; **683,** Richard Megna/Fundamental Photos; **684,** Richard Haynes; **685b,** Cameron Davidson/Getty Images, Inc.; **685m,** Jeffrey L. Rotman/Corbis; **685t,** Dorling Kindersley; **686l,** Richard Megna/Fundamental Photographs; **686m,** Dorling Kindersley; **686r,** Eyewire/Getty Images, Inc.; **687,** Jeff Greenberg/PhotoEdit; **689b,** Richard Haynes; **689ml,** Christie's Images; **689mr,** Russ Lappa; **689t,** Richard Haynes; **690,** NASA/Johnson Space Center; **691l,** Stephen Marks/Getty Images, Inc.; **691r,** David Parker/Photo Researchers, Inc.; **692b,** Russ Lappa; **692t,** Richard Haynes; **693 both,** Richard Haynes; **694,** Kathy Bushue/Getty Images, Inc.; **695l,** Lawrence Migdale/Science Source/Photo Researchers; **695r,** Dennis McDonald/PhotoEdit; **695t,** Bettmann/Corbis; **696b,** Charles D. Winters/Photo Researchers; **696t,** Grant Heilman Photography, Inc.; **697 inset,** Michael Newman/PhotoEdit; **697l,** David Porter/Index Stock; **697r,** Joseph Devenney/Getty Images, Inc.; **698l,** Novovitch/Liaison International; **698r,** Frank Greenaway/Dorling Kindersley; **699l,** Mary Kate Denny/PhotoEdit; **699r,** Richard Megna/Fundamental Photographs; **700b,** A & L Sinibaldi/Getty Images, Inc.; **700t,** Michael Dalton/Fundamental Photographs; **701,** Andrew Syred/SPL/Photo Researchers; **703,** Grant V. Faint/Getty Images, Inc.; **704–705,** NASA; **705,** Celestron International; **706,** J.P. Harrington & K.J. Borkowski/NASA; **707,** NC: Science VU/ESO/Visuals Unlimited; **708,** Richard Megna/Fundamental Photographs.

Chapter 20
Pages 712–713, Paul Chesley/Getty Images, Inc.; **713 inset,** Jon Chomitz; **714,** John Terence Turner/FPG International; **715,** Russ Lappa; **716l,** Joe McDonald/Corbis; **716m,** Royalty-Free/Corbis; **716r,** Larry Ulrich/DRK Photo; **717,** Superstock; **718l,** Corbis-Bettmann; **718m,** Chris Rogers/Corbis; **718r,** Terry Wild Studio/Uniphoto; **719l,** David Young-Wolfe/PhotoEdit; **719m,** Jeffry W. Myers/The Stock Market; **719r,** Courtesy of Dow Corporation; **720l,** Ariel Skelley/Corbis; **720r,** David Stoecklein/Corbis; **721,** Fred Habegger/Grant Heilman Photography; **722,** Daemmrich/Uniphoto; **723,** Richard Haynes; **724,** Richard Haynes; **725b,** Richard Megna/Fundamental Photographers; **725t,** 2004 Richard Megna/Fundamental Photographers; **726b,** Photodisc; **726t,** Russ Lappa; **727l,** Diana Calder/The Stock Market; **727r,** Royalty-Free/Corbis; **729l,** Marc Pokempner/TSI; **729m,** Richard Haynes; **729l,** Dorling Kindersley; **729t,** William Hopkins; **730,** Chris Sorensen; **731,** M. Borchi White Star/Photo Researchers; **732l,** Dan McCoy/Rainbow; **732r,** Jacky Chapman/Alamy Images; **733,** James L. Amos/Peter Arnold; **734,** Ted Horowitz/The Stock Market; **736bl,** Photodisc/Getty Images, Inc.; **736br,** Robert Patrick/Corbis Sygma; **736t,** Superstock; **740b,** Colin Keates/Dorling Kindersley; **740t,** Steve Gorton/Dorling Kindersley; **740–741,** Bob Burch/Index Stock Imagery; **741b,** The British Museum/Dorling Kindersley; **741m,** Kim Jae-Hwan/AFP/Corbis; **741t,** Rosenfeld Imaged Ltd/Rainbow; **742–743,** Ali Murat Atay/Atlas Geographic; **743,** Index Stock Imagery; **744,** Winfield I. Parks/National Geographic Image Collection; **745b,** C.M. Dixon; **745t,** Royalty-Free/Corbis.

Page 792, Tony Freeman/PhotoEdit; **793b,** Russ Lappa; **793m,** Richard Haynes; **793t,** Russ Lappa; **794,** Richard Haynes; **796,** Richard Haynes; **798,** Morton Beebe/Corbis; **799,** Catherine Karnow/Corbis; **801b,** Richard Haynes; **801t,** Dorling Kindersley.